1. **NCTM Standards** As the correlation on pages T19-T20 shows, strict attention was paid to the *NCTM Standards* in developing this program. Also see the Scope and Sequence chart on pages T21-T23.

2. **Applications/Connections** Because the ability to grasp concepts and skills is enhanced when they are tied to applications, nearly every lesson opens with an application that connects the content to the students' real world. See page 95. Other features that relate to this issue are the *chapter openers* (pages 42-43), *When am I ever going to use this?* (page 26), *Did you Know?* (page 5), *Teen Scene* (page 15), and the *Extended Projects Handbook* (pages 572-581).

   Connections to *algebra* (page 44), *geometry* (page 73), *statistics* (page 133), *probability* (page 233), and *measurement* (page 325) also enhance learning, as well as increase the students' interest.

3. **Problem Solving** The ongoing attention to problem solving is evidenced by the inclusion of *Problem Solving and Applications* in every set of exercises (exercises 40-43 on page 94). *Critical Thinking* exercises add to this focus on problem solving (exercise 42 on page 94), as do the *Data Search* exercises (exercise 11 on page 16). The *Problem-Solving Strategy* lessons give students the opportunity to build a repertoire of strategies (pages 109-110). The *Decision Making* lessons add another dimension as they connect the mathematics to the students' real-life experiences as consumers (pages 162-163).

4. **Mathematics Labs** These optional hands-on activities give students the opportunity to discover mathematical concepts by working cooperatively with a partner or a group. Some serve as a preview of the lesson that follows (pages 60-61) others act as a lesson follow-up (pages 139-140). The *Mini-Labs* also afford students this opportunity within lessons (page 92).

5. **Algebra/Geometry** Because algebraic concepts and skills are introduced early and are reinforced and extended throughout the three courses, students will be better prepared for first-year algebra (page 44). Similarly, the integration of geometry will help to prepare students for high school geometry (page 73).

6. **Review** To maintain prior-taught skills and concepts, a *Mixed Review* is included in each set of exercises, and each of these problems is referenced to the related lesson (exercises 37-41 on page 108). The *Look Back* feature also relates to review, as it guides students to the related help on previously-learned concepts (page 114).

7. **Technology** To help prepare students to function in a high-tech environment, instruction on the role of the calculator and computer as problem-solving tools is integrated throughout (pages 128-129, 145, and exercise 36 on page 214). Graphing Calculator and Spreadsheet activities in the *Technology Activities* strengthen this focus (pages 658-664).

8. **Teacher Support** The Teacher's Wraparound Edition makes it easy for you to organize, present and enhance the content. The extensive set of resource materials helps you increase each student's chance for success. See pages 10-15 in the brochure that follows.

Teacher's Wraparound Edition

MATHEMATICS

Applications and Connections

Course 3

GLENCOE

McGraw-Hill

New York, New York   Columbus, Ohio   Mission Hills, California   Peoria, Illinois

Send all inquiries to:
Glencoe/McGraw-Hill
936 Eastwind Drive
Westerville, Ohio 43081

ISBN: 0-02-824625-X (Student Edition)
ISBN: 0-02-824628-4 (Teacher's Wraparound Edition)

4 5 6 7 8 9 10   VH/LP   03 02 01 00 99 98 97 96

Dear Students, Teachers, and Parents,

Mathematics students are special! That's why we've written a mathematics program designed especially for students your age. The layout will hold your interest and the exciting content will show you why you need to study mathematics every day.

As you page through Mathematics: Applications and Connections, you'll notice that the mathematics content is presented in a variety of relevant and interesting ways. You'll see the many connections made among mathematical topics and note how mathematics naturally fits into other subject areas and with technology.

You will note that content for each lesson is clearly labeled up front. And you'll appreciate the lesson format that introduces each new concept with an interesting application followed by clear examples.

As you read the text and complete the activities, you will also become aware of how frequently mathematics is used in real-world situations that relate directly to your life. If you don't already realize the importance of mathematics in your life, you soon will!

Sincerely, The Authors

Kay McClain

Linda Dritsas

David D'Salern

Patricia Frey-Mason

Beatrice Moore-Harris

Jack M. Ott

Ron Pelfrey

Barbara L. Smith

Patricia S. Wilson

William Collins teaches mathematics at James Lick High School in San Jose, California. He has served as the Mathematics Department Chairperson at James Lick and Andrew Hill High Schools. He received his B.A. from Herbert H. Lehman College and is a Masters candidate at California State University, Hayward. Mr. Collins has been a consultant for the National Assessment Governing Board. He is a member of the National Council of Teachers of Mathematics and is active in several professional mathematics organizations at the state level. Mr. Collins is currently a mentor teacher for the College Board's EQUITY 2000 Consortium in San Jose, California.

Linda Dritsas is the Mathematics Coordinator for the Fresno Unified School District in Fresno, California. She also taught at California State University at Fresno for two years. Ms. Dritsas received her B.A. and M.A. (Education) from California State University at Fresno. Ms. Dritsas has published numerous mathematics workbooks and other supplementary materials. She has been the Central Section President of the California Mathematics Council and is a member of the National Council of Teachers of Mathematics and the Association for Supervision and Curriculum Development.

Patricia Frey-Mason is the Mathematics Department Chairperson at the Buffalo Academy for Visual and Performing Arts in Buffalo, New York. She received her B.A. from D'Youville College in Buffalo, New York, and her M.Ed. from the State University of New York at Buffalo. Ms. Frey-Mason has published several articles in mathematics journals. She is a member of the National Council of Teachers of Mathematics and is active in other professional mathematics organizations at the state, national, and international levels. Ms. Frey-Mason was named a 1991 Woodrow Wilson Middle School Mathematics Master Teacher.

Arthur C. Howard is Consultant for Secondary Mathematics at the Aldine School District in Houston, Texas. He received his B.S. and M.Ed. from the University of Houston. Mr. Howard has taught in grades 7–12 and in college. He is Master Teacher in the Rice University School Mathematics Project in Houston. Mr. Howard is also active in numerous professional organizations at the national and state levels, including the National Council of Teachers of Mathematics. His publications include curriculum materials and articles for newspapers, books, and *The Mathematics Teacher*.

Kay McClain received her B.A. from Auburn University and her Educational Specialist degree from the University of Montevallo. She is currently working on a Ph.D. at Vanderbilt University. While a teacher at Mountain Brook Middle School in Birmingham, Ms. McClain received a Presidential Award for Excellence in the Teaching of Mathematics. She is a Woodrow Wilson fellow and an active member of the National Council of Teachers of Mathematics.

David D. Molina is a professor at Trinity University in San Antonio, Texas. He received his M.A. and Ph.D. in Mathematics Education from the University of Texas at Austin. Dr. Molina has been a speaker both at national and international mathematics conferences. He has been a presenter for the National Council of Teachers of Mathematics, as well as a conductor of workshops and in services for other professional mathematics organizations and school systems.

Beatrice Moore-Harris is the EQUITY 2000 Project Administrator and former Mathematics Curriculum Specialist for K-8 in the Fort Worth Independent School District in Fort Worth, Texas. She is also a consultant for the National Council of Teachers of Mathematics. Ms. Moore-Harris received her B.A. from Prairie View A & M University in Prairie View, Texas. She has also done graduate work there and at Texas Southern University in Houston, Texas, and Tarleton State University in Stephenville, Texas. Ms. Moore-Harris is active in many state and national mathematics organizations. She also serves on the Editorial Board of NCTM's *Mathematics and the Middle Grades* journal.

Ronald S. Pelfrey is the Mathematics Coordinator for the Fayette County Public Schools in Lexington, Kentucky. He has taught mathematics in Fayette County Public Schools, with the Peace Corps in Ethiopia, and at the University of Kentucky in Lexington, Kentucky. Dr. Pelfrey received his B.S., M.A., and Ed.D. from the University of Kentucky. He is also the author of several publications about mathematics curriculum. He is an active speaker with the National Council of Teachers of Mathematics and is involved with other local, state, and national mathematics organizations.

Barbara Smith is the Mathematics Supervisor for Grades K-12 at the Unionville-Chadds Ford School District in Unionville, Pennsylvania. Prior to being a supervisor, she taught mathematics for thirteen years at the middle school level and three years at the high school level. Ms. Smith received her B.S. from Grove City College in Grove City, Pennsylvania and her M.Ed. from the University of Pittsburgh in Pittsburgh, Pennsylvania. Ms. Smith has held offices in several state and local organizations, has been a speaker at national and state conferences, and is a member of the National Council of Teachers of Mathematics.

Jack Ott is a Professor of Mathematics Education at the University of South Carolina in Columbia, South Carolina. He has also been a consultant for numerous schools in South Carolina as well as the South Carolina State Department of Education and the National Science Foundation. Dr. Ott received his A.B. from Indiana Wesleyan University, his M.A. from Ball State University, and his Ph.D. from The Ohio State University. Dr. Ott has written articles for *The Mathematics Teacher* and *The Arithmetic Teacher* and has been a speaker at national and state mathematics conferences.

Jack Price has been active in mathematics education for over 40 years, 38 of those in grades K-12. He is currently the Co-Director of the Center for Science and Mathematics Education at California State Polytechnic University at Pomona, California, where he teaches mathematics and methods courses for preservice teachers and consults with school districts on curriculum change. Dr. Price received his B.A. from Eastern Michigan University, and has a Doctorate in Mathematics Education from Wayne State University. He is president of the National Council of Teachers of Mathematics and is an author of numerous mathematics instructional materials.

Patricia S. Wilson is an Associate Professor of Mathematics Education at the University of Georgia in Athens, Georgia. Dr. Wilson received her B.S. from Ohio University and her M.A. and Ph.D. from The Ohio State University. She has received the Excellence in Teaching Award from the College of Education at the University of Georgia and is a published author in several mathematics education journals. Dr. Wilson has taught middle school mathematics and is currently teaching middle school mathematics methods courses. She is on the Editorial Board of the *Journal for Research in Mathematics Education,* published by the National Council of Teachers of Mathematics.

Elaine Ivey
Mathematics Teacher
Adams Junior High School
Tampa, Florida

Donna Jamell
Mathematics Teacher
Ramsey Junior High School
Fort Smith, Arkansas

Augustus M. Jones
Mathematics Teacher
Tuckahoe Middle School
Richmond, Virginia

Marie Kasperson
Mathematics Teacher
Grafton Middle School
Grafton, Massachusetts

Larry Kennedy
Mathematics Teacher
Kimmons Junior High School
Fort Smith, Arkansas

Patricia Killingsworth
Math Specialist
Carver Math/Science Magnet
  School
Little Rock, Arkansas

Al Lachat
Mathematics Department
  Chairperson
Neshaminy School District
Feasterville, Pennsylvania

Kent Luetke-Stahlman
Resource Scholar Mathematics
J. A. Rogers Academy of Liberal
  Arts & Sciences
Kansas City, Missouri

Dr. Gerald E. Martau
Deputy Superintendent
Lakewood City Schools
Lakewood, Ohio

Nelson J. Maylone
Assistant Principal
Maltby Middle School
Brighton, Michigan

Irma A. Mayo
Mathematics Department
  Chairperson
Mosby Middle School
Richmond, Virginia

Daniel Meadows
Mathematics Consultant
Stark County Local School
  System
Canton, Ohio

Dianne E. Meier
Mathematics Supervisor
Bradford Area School District
Bradford, Pennsylvania

Rosemary Mosier
Mathematics Teacher
Brick Church Middle School
Nashville, Tennessee

Judith Narvesen
Mathematics Resource Teacher
Irving A. Robbins Middle School
Farmington, Connecticut

Raymond A. Nichols
Mathematics Teacher
Ormond Beach Middle School
Ormond Beach, Florida

William J. Padamonsky
Director of Education
Hollidaysburg Area School
  District
Hollidaysburg, Pennsylvania

Delores Pickett
Instructional Supervisor
Vera Kilpatrick Elementary
  School
Texarkana, Arkansas

Thomas W. Ridings
Team Leader
Gilbert Junior High School
Gilbert, Arizona

Sally W. Roth
Mathematics Teacher
Francis Scott Key Intermediate
  School
Springfield, Virginia

Dr. Alice W. Ryan
Assistant Professor of Education
Dowling College
Oakdale, New York

Fred R. Stewart
Supervisor of
  Mathematics/Science
Neshaminy School District
Langhorne, Pennsylvania

Terri J. Stillman
Mathematics Department
  Chairperson
Boca Raton Middle School
Boca Raton, Florida

Marty Terzieff
Secondary Math Curriculum
  Chairperson
Mead Junior High School
Mead, Washington

Tom Vogel
Mathematics Teacher
Capital High School
Charleston, West Virginia

Joanne Wilkie
Mathematics Teacher
Hosford Middle School
Portland, Oregon

Larry Williams
Mathematics Teacher
Eastwood 8th Grade School
Tuscaloosa, Alabama

Deborah Wilson
Mathematics Teacher
Rawlinson Road Middle School
Rock Hill, South Carolina

Francine Yallof
Mathematics Teacher
East Middle School
Brentwood, New York

Table of Contents

High Interest Features

Did You Know?
5, 23, 29, 51, 73, 77

Save Planet Earth
14

Teen Scene
15, 67

When Am I Ever Going To Use This?
26, 62

Cultural Kaleidoscope
53

Journal Entry
7, 10, 37, 56, 64, 76

Mini-Labs
45, 51, 54, 67, 74, 77

Chapter

3

Integers

Go to Ch. 11 — 17

Chapter

4

High Interest Features

Did You Know?
89, 102, 106, 109, 136,
139, 153

Teen Scene
91, 133

Mini-Labs
92, 98, 102, 137, 142

Save Planet Earth
105

When Am I Ever Going to Use This?
113, 155

Cultural Kaleidoscope
144

Journal Entry
105, 108, 116, 138, 148,
158

Statistics and Data Analysis

Applications and Connections

Have you ever asked yourself this question?

"When am I ever going to use this stuff?"

It may be sooner than you think! Here's two of the many ways this textbook will help you answer that question.

Applications

You'll find mathematics in all of the subjects you study in school and in your life outside of school. In Lesson 3-5 on page 98, subtracting integers is related to geography. In Example 2 on page 345, solving proportions is applied to fitness.

These and other applications provide you with fascinating information that connects math to the real world and other school subjects and gives you a reason to learn math.

On pages 665–668, you will find a **Data Bank.** You'll have the opportunity to use the up-to-date information in it to answer questions throughout the book.

The **Extended Projects Handbook** consists of interesting long-term projects that involve issues in the world around you.

Five **Decision Making** features further enable you to connect math to your real-life experience as a consumer.

Fastest Speeds of Various Animals
(in miles per hour)

cheetah
70 mph

pronghorn antelope
61 mph

wildeb
50

qua

ion
ph

jazelle
0 mph

Connections

You'll discover that various areas of mathematics are very much interrelated. For example, Lesson 8-7 on page 325 connects measurement with distance on the coordinate plane. Connections to algebra, geometry, statistics, measurement, probability, and number theory help show the power of mathematics.

Connections to algebra, geometry, statistics, measurement, probability, and number theory help show the power of mathematics.

The **Mathematics Labs** and **Mini-Labs** also help you connect what you've learned before to new concepts. You'll use counters, measuring tapes, algebra tiles, and many other objects to help you discover these concepts.

Chapter 5

Investigations in Geometry

Chapter 6

Patterns and Number Sense

High Interest Features

Teen Scene
176, 230

Mini-Labs
177, 184, 188, 192, 194,
198, 233, 236, 246

Did You Know?
191, 192, 224, 227

**When Am I Ever Going
To Use This?**
196, 233

Save Planet Earth
223

Journal Entry
179, 186, 200, 220, 232,
238

Chapter 7

Rational Numbers

Chapter 8

Real Numbers

High Interest Features

Did You Know?
259, 262, 272, 300, 325

Teen Scene
277, 316

Mini-Labs
278, 284, 325, 328, 329

Cultural Kaleidoscope
287

When Am I Ever Going To Use This?
288, 324

Save Planet Earth
302

Journal Entry
258, 261, 281, 302, 309, 331

Chapter

9

Applications with Proportion

a₁ - Measurement
① +Prob Solve...
②
③
⑪-7
6   9 Rat/Ratios
7   10 %'s
13
H

Chapter

10

Applications with Percent

Geo 5, 11
7,
12

9- Geo Trig
8 Pythag + Trig

High Interest Features

Teen Scene
344, 400

**When Am I Ever Going
To Use This?**
347, 389

Did You Know?
353, 361, 369, 381, 412

Mini-Labs
359, 362, 385, 388, 406

Cultural Kaleidoscope
363

Journal Entry
358, 360, 371, 390, 396,
408

Technology

Labs, examples, computer-connection problems, and other features help you become an expert in using computers and calculators as problem-solving tools. You'll also learn how to read data bases, use spreadsheets, and use BASIC and LOGO programs. On many pages, **Calculator Hints** and printed keystrokes illustrate how to use a calculator.

Here are some highlights.

TELEVISION TECHNOLOGY GOES HOME
Percentage of American households with TV technology.

The **Technology Activities** allow you to use a graphing calculator and spreadsheets as tools for learning and doing mathematics.

Chapter 11

Algebra: Functions and Graphs

Chapter 12

Area and Volume

High Interest Features

Did You Know?
422, 442, 470, 475, 486, 487

Teen Scene
425, 464

When Am I Ever Going To Use This?
439, 492

Save Planet Earth
441

Cultural Kaleidoscope
473

Journal Entry
427, 434, 457, 473, 477, 485

Mini-Labs
432, 436, 446, 451, 454, 475, 478

Chapter 13

Discrete Math and Probability

Chapter 14

Algebra: Investigations with Polynomials

High Interest Features

Did You Know?
504, 531, 550

Teen Scene
512, 546

Save Planet Earth
549

When Am I Ever Going To Use This?
564

Journal Entry
506, 514, 524, 545, 555, 562

Mini-Labs
507, 512, 515, 522, 528, 547, 550, 553, 558, 560

Setting The Scene

To help chart their journeys, wise travelers consult a map before they begin. Just as maps lead travelers to their destinations, the script on the next five pages points out the ways that you use the mathematics in this text in your daily lives.

Narrator:
Dia and Theresa have just received the newest issue of Fashion Teen magazine and are flipping through it.

Dia:
Wow! Look at this outfit!

Theresa:
Yeah, I love those colors. Turn the page; maybe that designer has more outfits on the next page.

Dia:
No, there's nothing but this gross cigarette ad.

Theresa:
I know. I'm sick of that ad—it's all over the place.

Dia:
I thought it was illegal to advertise cigarettes in magazines.

Theresa:
I think it's only illegal to advertise cigarettes on TV.

Dia:
Well, it should be illegal, especially for magazines that teens read. I think it's a nasty habit.

Narrator:
The girls are joined by their friend Dylan.

Dylan:
Hey!
What's up?

Theresa:
Oh, we were just flipping through this magazine. Can you believe it's got cigarette ads in it?!

Dia:
Smoking is so uncool.

OVERVIEW

Objective Use statistics and problem solving to make a convincing argument for not having cigarette ads in teen magazines.

Summary

Students read a script that involves three students who are looking through a teen magazine and run across a cigarette ad. They decide to research the health effects of smoking and write a letter to the editor of the magazine. This script demonstrates how mathematics can be useful for communicating one's opinion and how mathematical communication is important in everyday life.

Time Required

2 days

Materials Needed

calculators

Key Terms

bar graph
circle graph
data
percentages

TEACHING NOTES

Select four students to take the roles in the toolkit script: Narrator, Dia, Theresa, and Dylan. Have these students read the script. Stop the class on page xix and have your students work in groups to make a case against advertising smoking in magazines. You may want to have the groups share their ideas before you continue the reading of the script.

WRITING PROMPTS

When the students have finished reading through the script, you may want to have your students write to the following prompts.
- *How do you use mathematics to communicate an opinion or position on an important matter?*
- *What problem-solving strategies and/or mathematical tools did the characters in the script use?*

Dylan:

Hey, in science class today, we saw a video about the effects of smoking. I'll tell you one thing—I'll never smoke.

Dia:

Somebody should do something about all of these cigarette advertisements geared to teens.

Theresa:

Maybe that somebody should be us.

Dylan:

What do you mean? What can we do?

Dia:

We should at least write a letter to the editor and complain.

Dylan:

Who's gonna listen to us?

Theresa:

I've got an idea. We could get facts from the American Lung Association and use them in our letter.

Dia:

That's a great idea!

Dylan:

Okay. I'll go down to the American Lung Association and see what kind of information they have.

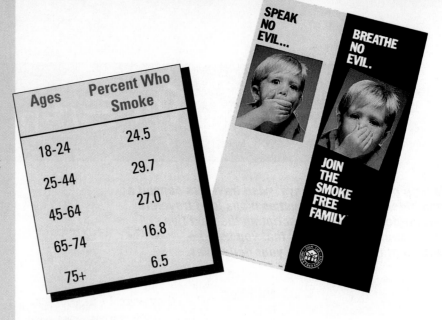

Ages	Percent Who Smoke
18-24	24.5
25-44	29.7
45-64	27.0
65-74	16.8
75+	6.5

Narrator:

Dylan searched the library at the American Lung Association and found lots of brochures that contained useful information. He wrote down the following data.

1.3 million out of 45.8 million people quit smoking each year, while 13 million people try to quit, but fail.

90% of all adults who smoke started by the age of 21, and half of them had become regular smokers by their 18th birthday.

For people ages 12-18, 15.7% have smoked in the last month, and 11.5% have smoked in the last week. For people over age 18, 25.5% are current smokers.

Over 1 billion packs of cigarettes are sold to teenagers each year. A million teenagers take up smoking each year.

434,000 Americans die prematurely each year from diseases caused by smoking. That's 20% of all deaths annually.

Cigarette companies spend over $3 billion on advertising each year. It is illegal to advertise tobacco products on TV or radio.

Stop the Script...

What does this information tell you? How can you use it to make a case against advertising cigarette smoking in magazines?

Narrator:
The students get together to discuss Dylan's findings.

Dia:
Look at all this stuff! I don't know where to start.

Dylan:
Well, we should definitely show that most people start smoking as teenagers.

Theresa:
Okay, it says that 90% of smokers start before they're 21 and half of those start before they're 18. Since $\frac{1}{2}$ of 90% is 45%, that means that 45% of smokers started when they were 17 or younger. Another 45% started when they were 18 to 20. Only 10% started when they were 21 or older.

Dia:
Right. It also says that 45.8 million people now smoke. 45% of 45.8 million is—wait, let me get my calculator—20.6 million. That's how many people started when they were in middle or high school. Only 4.6 million started as adults.

Dylan:
Why don't we make a bar graph of the data? Graphs make a big impact.

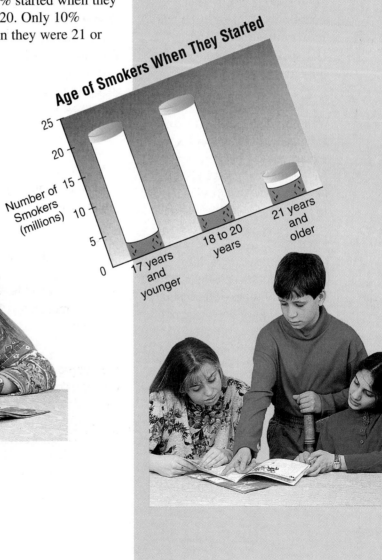

Age of Smokers When They Started

xix

Dia:

We should also show how hard it is to stop smoking.

Dylan:

The information says that 14.3 (13 + 1.3) million people try to quit each year, but only 1.3 million actually do.

Theresa:

So what percent of those who try actually quit?

Dia:

1,300,000 divided by 14,300,000 is 0.091. That means only 9.1% of those who try to quit, succeed. And only 31% of smokers even try to quit.

Dylan:

Wait a minute. Only 9.1% of 31% of the people who smoke actually quit. That means only 9.1% times 31%, or 2.8%, of all smokers quit each year. That's awful!

Theresa:

I'll make a circle graph by multiplying the percentages by 360°: 2.8% times 360° is about 10° and 31% of 360° is about 112°.

Narrator:

The friends agree that Dia should write the letter. After they all read it and make several suggestions, Dia types the letter, and they all sign it. (The final version is shown on the following page.) The students send the letter to the magazine, and it appears in the next issue in the Letters to the Editor. Underneath it is the editor's note shown below.

Editorial Note: These thoughtful readers make an excellent point. We at **Fashion Teen** are concerned with the health of our readership. Therefore, starting with our next issue, we will no longer advertise tobacco products in our magazine.

This concludes Setting the Scene. Throughout this text, you will encounter new ways to make mathematics real to you. From time to time, read through this script to remind yourself how relevant mathematics can be in your life.

Smokers and Quitting

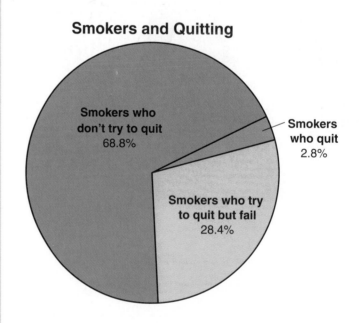

Smokers who don't try to quit
68.8%

Smokers who quit
2.8%

Smokers who try to quit but fail
28.4%

Dear Fashion Teen Editor:

We really enjoy reading your magazine and seeing the great fashions. However, in your last issue, we were troubled by your ads. As we see it, you allow tobacco advertisers to promote smoking to your readers.

As you know, the majority of your readers are teenagers. We feel that this is very irresponsible on your part. Hundreds of studies show that smoking causes premature death. In fact, 434,000 Americans die each year from diseases related to smoking. That is 20% of all deaths annually.

More people will continue to die premature deaths if cigarette companies are allowed to advertise to teenagers. In fact, most smokers start as teenagers. The graph below illustrates this fact.

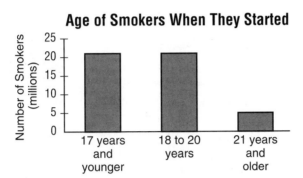

Each year, over 1 billion packs of cigarettes are sold to teenagers. One million teenagers take up smoking each year. Once a person has started to smoke, it is very difficult for that person to quit.

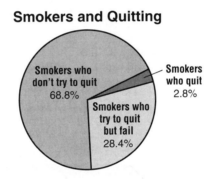

Cigarette companies spend over $3 billion on advertising each year. It is already illegal to advertise on TV or radio. We believe that Fashion Teen should take a similar position and ban all tobacco advertisements from your magazine.

Sincerely,

Dia Arroyo   *Theresa Jones*   *Dylan Rubini*

Dia Arroyo, Theresa Jones, and Dylan Rubini

MATHEMATICS
Applications and Connections

TEACHER'S HANDBOOK

NEW DIRECTIONS IN MIDDLE SCHOOL MATHEMATICS.

Middle school teachers can testify to the fact that students in this age group are a unique bunch: They are energetic and enthusiastic, yet easily bored. They may behave as children one day and as young adults the next. These students want and need structure and security. They yearn for independence from parents, yet desire their protection. Each day they struggle to find their place in their peer groups, in their schools and communities, and in the world.

Decisions made by middle school students about what and how they study can dramatically affect their futures. Our research with middle school students revealed two not-so-surprising facts:

- **Most middle school students do not believe that mathematics has much to do with their everyday lives.**

- **Most middle school students see little or no connection between mathematics and other subjects they study.**

To convince them otherwise, an effective middle school mathematics program for the 1990s must embrace the concepts of understanding, problem solving, and conjecturing about mathematical concepts in an active classroom environment that capitalizes upon the innate enthusiasm of students in this age group.

> "To show middle school students how mathematics relates to other subjects and to show its importance in their everyday lives, we must carefully and purposefully broaden their knowledge of mathematics."
>
> **Pat Wilson, Author**

We at Glencoe are firmly convinced that our program, *Mathematics: Applications and Connections*, makes it easier for teachers to help their students develop a positive attitude about mathematics. Each lesson reflects the following major goals.

ENGAGE STUDENTS IN MATHEMATICS.
Students must be convinced that mathematics belongs to them and is not solely the property of the teacher or the textbook. Our program accomplishes this by providing historical and cultural perspectives to mathematics, using multiple representations for concepts, allowing students to make decisions, and avoiding trivial, unrealistic contexts for presenting mathematics. It provides challenging tasks supported by interesting, relevant information that enables students to be active participants in mathematics.

HELP STUDENTS EXPAND AND APPLY THEIR MATHEMATICAL SKILLS.
Students must be taught to integrate the compartmentalized pieces of mathematics they learned in elementary school. For mathematics to be meaningful to them, they must learn to organize information, interpret data, communicate quantitatively, make conjectures, and solve problems. Our program helps students apply their mathematics and see it and technology as useful tools in their lives.

PREPARE STUDENTS FOR FURTHER STUDY IN MATHEMATICS.
To succeed now and in the future, all students must learn to generalize (algebra), think spatially (geometry), and reason probabilistically (probability, statistics). *Mathematics: Applications and Connections* is designed to prepare all students for the study of higher mathematics, by making sure they possess understanding as well as proficiency.

You will see that *Mathematics: Applications and Connections* meets these three goals and captures the essence of the NCTM Standards. The program provides the tools teachers need to help middle school students see, understand, and appreciate the connection between mathematics and real life. In every lesson, students at all levels repeatedly receive this message: "Math is for everyone . . . You can do it . . . You'll use it every day."

BRIDGING

from Elementary Mathematics to High School Mathematics

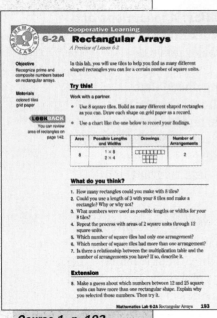

Course 1, p. 193

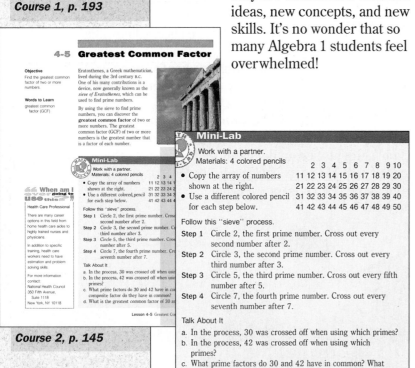

Course 2, p. 145

An examination of the mathematics textbooks for grades 6-8 of any K-8 elementary program shows that the vast majority of content focuses on review of previously-learned skills, ideas, and concepts. In fact, research shows that only about 35% of the material in the books is "new" content. Unfortunately, when these same students enter Algebra 1 class, the opposite is true. About 90% of the content is new. Suddenly—and with little warning and less preparation—they are bombarded with new ideas, new concepts, and new skills. It's no wonder that so many Algebra 1 students feel overwhelmed!

Glencoe's Middle School Mathematics program provides a more in-depth and integrated preparation for Algebra 1 and Geometry than a K-8 elementary program.

Mathematics: Applications and Connections prepares all students for success in Algebra 1 and Geometry. How? By introducing a variety of new concepts not found in traditional K-8 math curricula, and by integrating them appropriately into all three programs. For example, integers are introduced in Chapter 12 of Course 1, in Chapter 7 of Course 2, and in Chapter 3 of Course 3. Because algebra and geometry are introduced early in all three courses—and because both are reinforced throughout middle school— students are much better prepared to take these courses in high school.

Mathematics Labs and Mini-Labs help students discover concepts on their own.

Research shows that learning is more meaningful when students discover new concepts on their own. **Mathematics Labs** in ***Mathematics: Applications and Connections*** give students hands-on experience, with a partner or group, in discovering mathematics concepts for themselves.

Students may also participate in shorter **Mini-Labs** in which they investigate mathematical concepts within a lesson.

THE GAP

The **Overhead Manipulative Resources** includes transparencies and translucent objects such as counters, a geoboard, and a safety compass that can be used by the teacher or students to demonstrate concepts. A complete Teacher's Guide, correlated to the Mathematics Labs and Mini-Labs, provides suggestions for demonstrations using these resources.

The **Middle School Mathematics Manipulative Kit** offers the tools students need to work through the Mathematics Labs and Mini-Labs. A Teacher's Guide provides a correlation to all student editions.

experiences— regardless of the age of the student or the subject matter. It has also been proven that students master difficult learning tasks more readily when cooperative strategies are used.

Group Activity Cards featuring interesting problems, puzzles, and games, and more detailed cooperative learning activities are important components of ***Mathematics: Applications and Connections.***

Effective cooperative learning groups share these characteristics:

1. Students must perceive that they "sink or swim together."

2. Students are responsible for everyone else in the group, as well as themselves, in learning the assigned material.

3. Students must see that they all have the same goal, that they need to divide up the tasks and share the responsibility equally, and that one evaluation or reward will apply to all members of the group.

Keep in mind that cooperative learning does not just "happen." The first few days may be tumultuous as students learn the rules. Be patient and keep at it!

> "**Hands-on, experiential learning in which students take an active role and assume responsibility for their own learning is an integral part of the instructional practices of this program.**"
>
> **Beatrice Moore-Harris, Author**

Middle School Mathematics Manipulative Kit

Cooperative learning groups help students with academic achievement, self-esteem, and socialization

Studies show that cooperative learning experiences are more effective than competitive or individual learning

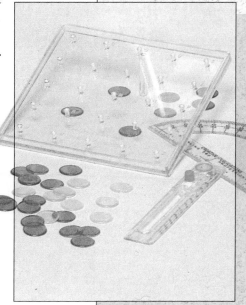

Overhead Manipulative Resources

MOTIVATING
MIDDLE SCHOOL STUDENTS

"Why do I have to study this?"
"When are we ever going to use it?"

As a middle school mathematics teacher, you have probably heard these questions from your students many times. Although they may be couched as complaints, the questions are certainly legitimate.

We at Glencoe realize that effective programs that really motivate middle school students must have more than strong content—although solid content is certainly important. The curriculum must also be interesting and must demonstrate the usefulness of mathematics in a way that relates to students' interests.

Because it highlights issues and situations that are of interest to middle school students, *Mathematics: Applications and Connections* does just that. Rather than simply present content-specific material, the program involves students in problems and situations that are current and real—and that demonstrate a practical purpose for mathematics.

For example, in Course 1, Lesson 6-5, real data about M & M's, is used to illustrate simplifying fractions. In Course 2, Lesson 1-3, students use estimation to find the number of pictures artists drew each day to create the first Mickey Mouse cartoon. And in Course 3, Lesson 10-7, students make a circle graph based on attendance statistics at four major theme parks.

> ## "THE CURRICULUM MUST GO BEYOND THE BASICS — TO BE RELEVANT, IT MUST BE OF INTEREST TO STUDENTS AND EMPHASIZE THE USEFULNESS OF MATHEMATICS."
> ### RON PELFREY, AUTHOR

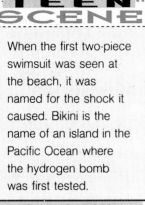
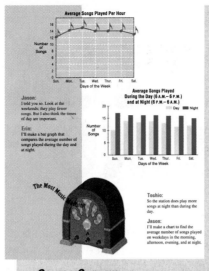

Course 2, p. xx

Mathematics: Applications and Connections is clearly a student-centered text.

At the beginning of each course, students are invited to act out a script called **Setting the Scene**. Students are placed in a real-life situation that requires the use of mathematics and makes it real to them. For example, in Course 2, students estimate how many songs a radio station plays in a month in order to win a contest.

Teen Scene provides tidbits of information to capture students' interest.

When Am I Ever Going To Use This? helps you answer that age-old question.

Save Planet Earth features environmental issues that focus on how students can make a difference.

Save Planet Earth

Start Your Own Club Students are making a significant contribution to saving our planet. Clintion Hill was a sixth-grade student when he organized an environmental activists' club at his school in New Hope, Minnesota. His enthusiasm and concern about the deteriorating environment motivated other students to become involved and help save the planet.

After Clinton's death in 1989, his parents, William and Tessa Hill, established a club called Kids for Saving Earth (KSE). Today there are over 3,600 KSE clubs in schools around the country.

How You Can Help
- Start a KSE Club in your school. For more information and a monthly newsletter, write to KSE Clubs, P.O. Box 47247, Plymouth, Minnesota 55447-0247.
- Organize and implement a recycling program in your school.

Course 1, p. 513

DEVELOPING PROBLEM SOLVING

According to the NCTM Standards, "Problem solving is the process by which students experience the power and usefulness of mathematics in the world around them. It is also a method of inquiry and application . . . to provide a consistent context for learning and applying mathematics. Problem situations can establish a 'need to know' and foster the motivation for the development of concepts." In response to the Standards, the authors of *Mathematics: Applications and Connections* made problem solving the central theme of their program. Here's how:

The first chapter of all courses is titled "Tools for Problem Solving."

Problem-Solving Strategy lessons present opportunities to solve nonroutine problems.

Frequent **Problem-Solving Hints** suggest using problem-solving strategies to investigate and understand mathematical content and apply strategies to new problem situations.

Applications opening nearly every lesson provide students with fascinating information that connects mathematics to the real world and give students a reason to learn mathematics.

Problem Solving examples give students the opportunity to study completely worked-out application problems in real-life fields, such as marketing and the environment.

Connection examples integrate one area of mathematics, such as geometry, with another, such as algebra.

Critical Thinking exercises give students practice in developing and applying higher-order thinking skills.

Mathematics becomes a vital force in the lives of middle school students as their eyes are opened to the relationship between mathematics and sports, shopping and other teen interests. They "take ownership" of their skills by writing their own problems and presenting class projects connected to real life.

(Lesson 7-3)

Problem Solving
and
Applications

42. **Personal Finance** Rosa opened a checking account with a balance of $150. She wrote a check for $87.

  a. Write an addition sentence to represent this situation.

  b. How much money remained in the account?

43. **Space Travel** During a space shuttle launch, a maneuver is scheduled to begin at T minus 75 seconds, which is 75 seconds before liftoff. The maneuver lasts 2 minutes. At what time will this maneuver be complete?

44. **Critical Thinking** Jack made up a game of darts using the target at the right. Each person throws three darts. The score is the sum of the numbers in the regions that the darts hit. If all the darts hit the target, list all possible scores.

266   Chapter 7 Integers

> "Problem solving is an integral component of this program. It requires students to think critically, examine new concepts, and then extend or generalize what they already know."
>
> Linda Dritsas, Author

MATHEMATICS: APPLICATIONS AND CONNECTIONS LINKS PRACTICAL PROBLEM SOLVING TO STUDENTS' REAL-LIFE INTERESTS

Specific features of the program that foster problem solving include:

Problem Solving and Applications exercises in each lesson directly link mathematics to real-world fields like engineering, and to art, history, science, and other subjects.

Five **Decision Making** lessons in each of Courses 1-3 provide students with opportunities to connect mathematics to their real-life experience as consumers and citizens.

The **Extended Projects Handbook** provides opportunities for your students to work together on intriguing long-term projects.

A **Data Bank** in the back of each text provides up-to-date information and statistics. Students refer to it to answer **Data Search** questions that appear throughout the student edition.

Course 1, p. 244

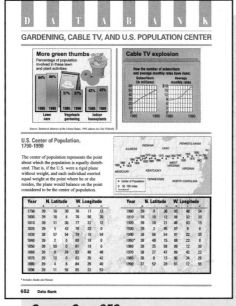

Course 2, p. 652

Course 3, p. 576

INCORPORATING TECHNOLOGY INTO YOUR CLASSROOM

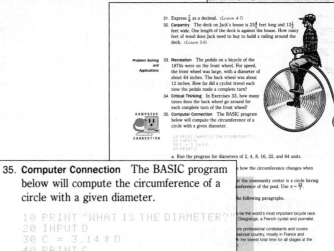

31. Express $\frac{7}{8}$ as a decimal. *(Lesson 4-7)*

32. **Carpentry** The deck on Jack's house is $25\frac{4}{5}$ feet long and $12\frac{1}{2}$ feet wide. One length of the deck is against the house. How many feet of wood does Jack need to buy to build a railing around the deck. *(Lesson 5-6)*

Problem Solving and Applications

33. **Recreation** The pedals on a bicycle of the 1870s were on the front wheel. For speed, the front wheel was large, with a diameter of about 64 inches. The back wheel was about 12 inches. How far did a cyclist travel each time the pedals made a complete turn?

34. **Critical Thinking** In Exercises 33, how many times does the back wheel go around for each complete turn of the front wheel?

COMPUTER CONNECTION

35. **Computer Connection** The BASIC program below will compute the circumference of a circle with a given diameter.

```
10 PRINT "WHAT IS THE DIAMETER?"
20 INPUT D
30 C = 3.14 * D
40 PRINT C
```

a. Run the program for diameters of 2, 4, 8, 16, 32, and 64 units.

35. **Computer Connection** The BASIC program below will compute the circumference of a circle with a given diameter.

```
10 PRINT "WHAT IS THE DIAMETER?"
20 INPUT D
30 C = 3.14 * D
40 PRINT C
```

b. The diameter of a bicycle wheel is 28 inches. How far will you travel after 1 complete turn of the wheel?

200   Chapter 5 Applications with Fractions

Course 2, p. 200

According to figures from the U.S. government, by the year 2000, seven out of ten jobs will be related to computers, electronics, and high technology. Clearly, technology is changing the workplace and the home at an increasingly rapid pace. Without technical mathematical skills, today's students will have little or no chance of finding good jobs.

Using technology in your classroom can open up many ideas and opportunities. It is up to you to decide how to present and use technology in your classroom. Many of the standard teaching techniques, such as using cooperative groups, are appropriate but there are also new ways of teaching that are appropriate when using technology in your classroom. For example, you can assign lab partners in each class. Each pair of students would then work together whenever technology is used. This can also be used if you have a limited supply of equipment.

Mathematics: Applications and Connections provides many different ways for your students to prepare to function in a high-tech environment. Practice with computers, calculators, and spreadsheets is designed to enhance — not replace — students' practice with pencil-and-paper exercises, estimation, mental math, and other important tried-and-true techniques.

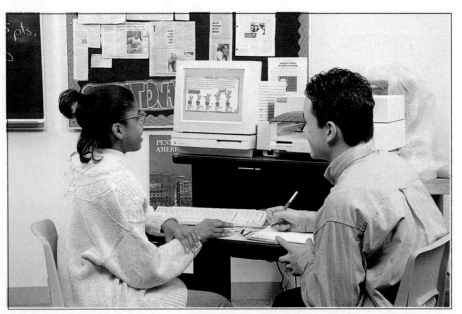

Computer Connection exercises increase students' proficiency in using computers to solve problems.

The Mathematics Lab shown at the right highlights the use of **Spreadsheets** as a problem-solving tool.

Frequent **Calculator Hints** and printed keystrokes illustrate for students how to use a calculator.

Five or six **Technology Activities** are provided in each text to give students the opportunity to work with graphing calculators and more spreadsheets. References to these activities are made throughout the student edition.

The **Interactive Mathematics Tools** multimedia software, available in Macintosh format, helps students gain mathematical power through highly interactive activities that combine video, sound, animation, graphics, and text.

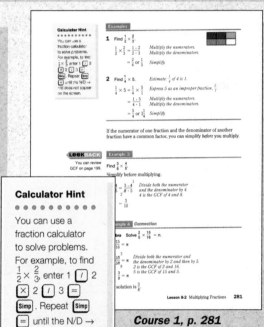

Course 3, pp. 30-31

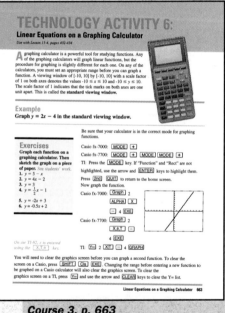

Course 3, p. 663

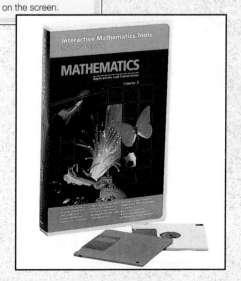

Course 1, p. 281

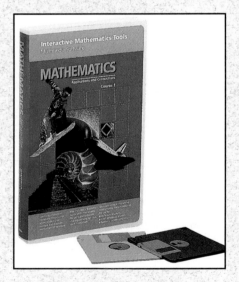

Interactive Mathematics Tools

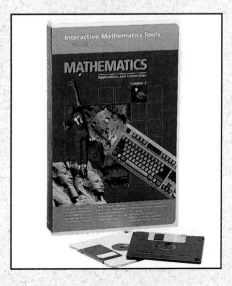

In **Mathematics: Applications and Connections**, assessment goes far beyond requiring students to exhibit simple recall of facts and algorithms. In addition, they are expected to organize information, apply previously-learned information to new situations, explain why something is true, and make conjectures based on gathered evidence.

The following program features and components help students to assess themselves and guide teachers in assessment.

OPEN-ENDED PROBLEMS Most real-world problems do not have a single correct solution. Instead, there are usually many appropriate options. To help prepare students to become smart citizens, wise consumers, and good decision-makers, the text presents a variety of open-ended problems that require students to work cooperatively, think critically, and propose multiple feasible solutions to problems. The **Decision-Making** features help teachers to assess students' reasoning skills and evaluate their abilities to work effectively in groups.

JOURNALS Besides direct observation, another effective assessment method is to regularly read students' daily journals in which they are required to record and reflect upon what they have learned. **Journal Entries** throughout the student editions provide students with prompts for journal writing.

PORTFOLIOS Another way to assess students' understanding is to periodically review their portfolios. The portfolios should contain work that is representative of their growth as a learner. **Portfolio Suggestions** appear as appropriate throughout the student editions.

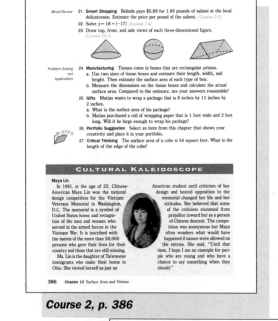

Mixed Review
21. **Smart Shopping** Belinda pays $5.89 for 1.89 pounds of salami at the local delicatessen. Estimate the price per pound of the salami. *(Lesson 2-3)*
22. Solve $y = 18 + (-17)$ *(Lesson 7-4)*
23. Draw top, front, and side views of each three-dimensional figure. *(Lesson 10-1)*

Problem Solving and Applications
24. **Manufacturing** Tissues come in boxes that are rectangular prisms.
   a. Use two sizes of tissue boxes and estimate their length, width, and height. Then estimate the surface area of each type of box.
   b. Measure the dimensions on the tissue boxes and calculate the actual surface area. Compared to the estimate, are your answers reasonable?
25. **Gifts** Matias wants to wrap a package that is 8 inches by 11 inches by 2 inches.
   a. What is the surface area of his package?
   b. Matias purchased a roll of wrapping paper that is 1 foot wide and 2 feet long. Will it be large enough to wrap his package?
26. **Portfolio Suggestion** Select an item from this chapter that shows your creativity and place it in your portfolio.
27. **Critical Thinking** The surface area of a cube is 54 square feet. What is the length of the edge of the cube?

CULTURAL KALEIDOSCOPE

Maya Lin
In 1981, at the age of 22, Chinese-American Maya Lin won the national design competition for the Vietnam Veterans Memorial in Washington, D.C. The memorial is a symbol of United States honor and recognition of the men and women who served in the armed forces in the Vietnam War. It is inscribed with the names of the more than 58,000 persons who gave their lives for their country and those that are still missing.
Ms. Lin is the daughter of Taiwanese immigrants who make their home in Ohio. She viewed herself as just an American student until criticism of her design and heated opposition to the memorial changed her life and her attitudes. She believed that some of the criticism stemmed from prejudice toward her as a person of Chinese descent. The competition was anonymous but Maya often wonders what would have happened if names were allowed on the entries. She said, "Until that time, I hope I am an example for people who are young and who have a chance to say something when they should."

386   Chapter 10 Surface Area and Volume

Course 2, p. 386

Exercises

Independent Practice
Draw a number line from -10 to 10. Graph each integer on the number line.
16. -1   17. 4   18. -7
19. -9   20. 2   21. 8

Write an integer to describe each situation.
22. a gain of 10 yards   23. 3 feet below sea level
24. positive twelve   25. 2 degrees above zero

Write the opposite of each integer.
26. -3   27. 32   28. 1   29. -21
30. 16   31. 13   32. -87   33. -53

Mixed Review
34. **Geometry** Find the volume of a rectangular prism that is 12 meters long, 8.6 meters wide, and 5 meters high.
35. Write *seven hundredths* as a decimal.
36. **Algebra** Solve the equation $\frac{11}{12} - x = \frac{5}{12}$.
37. **Geometry** Name the polygon at the right by the number of sides.

Problem Solving and Applications
38. **Economics** In 1990, about one million laptop and notebook computers were sold. In 1991, about two million of these computers were sold. Use an integer to show the increase in units sold from 1990 to 1991.

39. **Weather** The chart at the right shows the January record low temperatures for some cities in the United States. Use the chart to answer each question.
   a. What city has the lowest record low temperature?
   b. What city has the highest record low temperature?

Record Low Temperatures	
Weather	Jan.
AK Juneau	-22
AR Little Rock	-4
CA San Diego	29
CO Denver	-25
CT Hartford	-26

40. **Critical Thinking** Compare a number line to a thermometer. How are they alike? How are they different?

41. **Journal Entry** Make a time line of the 20th century. Let 0 represent this year. Mark as negative integers the years that represent events important to you that happened before this year. Mark as positive integers the years for important events you expect to happen in the future. Describe the event represented by each integer.

422   Chapter 12 Investigations with Integers

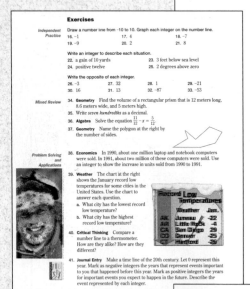

Course 1, p. 422

26. **Portfolio Suggestion** Select an item from this chapter that shows your creativity and place it in your portfolio.
27. **Critical Thinking** The surface area of a cube is 54 square feet. What is the length of the edge of the cube?

41. **Journal Entry** Make a time line of the 20th century. Let 0 represent this year. Mark as negative integers the years that represent events important to you that happened before this year. Mark as positive integers the years for important events you expect to happen in the future. Describe the event represented by each integer.

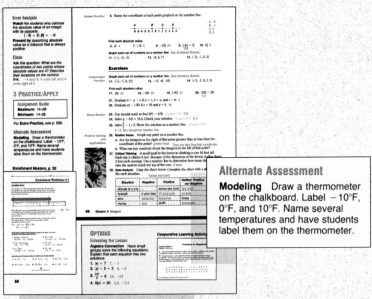

Course 3, p. 88

Alternate Assessment

Modeling Draw a thermometer on the chalkboard. Label −10°F, 0°F, and 10°F. Name several temperatures and have students label them on the thermometer.

DAILY ASSESSMENT The Teacher's Wraparound Edition contains an alternate assessment option for most lessons. Students' understanding can be evaluated through writing, modeling, or speaking activities. These provide methods for providing immediate feedback as well as motivation for students who are usually most eager to show what they know.

PERFORMANCE ASSESSMENT To determine what students know and what they can apply, they should be presented with authentic problem-solving situations. The **Performance Assessment Booklets** contain student assessment items for each chapter, as well as scoring rubrics.

Alternative Assessment in the Mathematics Classroom, one of the booklets in Glencoe's Mathematics Professional Series, contains further information and activities to help you implement other types of evaluation strategies.

Performance Assessment Booklets

Alternative Assessment in the Mathematics Classroom

Integrating the 3 R's
Reading, Writing, and 'Rithmetic

Besides being articulate speakers and fluent writers, today's and tomorrow's citizens must be able to interpret data, express mathematical ideas verbally and in writing, organize information in tables, and draw graphs and diagrams. ***Mathematics: Applications and Connections*** provides abundant opportunities for students to develop and integrate their communication skills through modeling, speaking, writing, and showing what they have learned.

Every exercise set begins with **Communicating Mathematics**. These in-class exercises help develop students' understanding through writing, talking, modeling, drawing, and so on.

Checking for Understanding

Communicating Mathematics

Read and study the lesson to answer each question.

1. **Show** two methods to solve $x = -15 + 23$.
2. **Tell** how you know the sign of the sum of two integers with different signs.
3. **Tell** how you know whether to add or subtract the absolute values to find the sum of two integers. Give examples.
4. **Write** the addition sentence shown by each model.

a.

b.
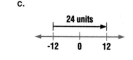

c.

24 units

-12   0   12

Course 3, p. 93

Journal Entries throughout the text give students a chance to reflect upon and record their understanding of the mathematical content.

Portfolio Suggestions offer ways for students to organize representative work samples that can be used for assessment and to show their growth.

26. **Journal Entry**   Collect data by measuring the playing surface of a court or playing field at your school. Make and label a scale drawing of it. What is its area?

Course 2, p. 245

23. **Portfolio Suggestion**   Select an item from this chapter that you feel shows your best work and place it in your portfolio. Explain why you selected it.

Course 1, p. 176

"The ability to read, listen, think creatively, and communicate about problem situations, mathematical representations, and the validation of solutions will help students to develop and deepen their understanding of mathematics."

- NCTM Curriculum and Evaluation Standards, 1989

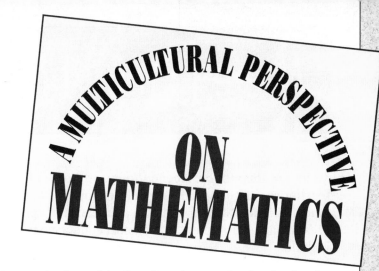

A MULTICULTURAL PERSPECTIVE ON MATHEMATICS

T̲he United States has become an increasingly multicultural society, and schools clearly reflect our country's diversity. There is a growing emphasis on educating students to understand, respect, and appreciate the differences among the many cultures that contribute to the wonderful diversity of our country and the world.

In **Mathematics: Applications and Connections**, students learn that mathematics has been shaped by the contributions of many cultures. From the ancient Egyptians, who used the "Pythagorean" theorem 1,500 years before Pythagoras, to the ancient Chinese, who calculated the value of π to ten places 1,200 years before the Europeans, the history of mathematics was molded—and continues to be developed— by persons of many cultures.

The multicultural focus of **Mathematics: Applications and Connections** helps to educate students about these important multicultural issues: that there is strength in diversity; that it is important to respect the rights of all persons and groups; and that social justice and equal opportunity must be made available to all people.

Numerous lessons, examples, and exercises contain applications that highlight multicultural experiences in mathematics.

Cultural Kaleidoscopes introduce students to persons from various cultures in the past and present who have been successful in their careers.

Multicultural Activity Masters contains one multicultural activity for each chapter in each course.

Each *Teacher's Wraparound Edition* contains suggestions in the interleaf as well as with individual lessons for incorporating a multicultural perspective in the classroom.

13-1 Counting Outcomes

Objective

Count outcomes using a tree diagram or the Fundamental Principle of Counting.

Words to Learn

outcome
tree diagram
Fundamental Principle of Counting

The games you played in Mathematics Lab 13-1A involved counting outcomes by listing them. In this lesson you will learn two other ways to count outcomes.

The Hopi Indians invented a game of chance called Totolospi. This game was played with three cane dice, a counting board inscribed on stone, and a counter for each player. Each cane die can land round side up (R) or flat side up (F). In Totolospi for two players, each player places a counter on the nearest circle. The moves of the game are determined by tossing the three cane dice.

Course 3, p. 504

Problem Solving

Practice

Strategies

Look for a pattern.
Solve a simpler problem.
Act it out.
Guess and check.
Draw a diagram.
Make a chart.
Work backward.

Solve. Use any strategy.

6. Find the number of line segments determined by six points on a line.

7. Gloria made enough money with her computer graphics to buy a new printer. She told Al and Sue who each let two of their computer network friends know ten minutes later. If the news spread like this every ten minutes, how many people knew by the end of the hour?

8. Complete the pattern 100, 98, 94, _?_ , 80, _?_ .

9. You plant 10 hyacinths in exactly 5 rows. There are 4 bulbs in each row. Draw a diagram of your garden.

10. This pattern is known as Pascal's Triangle. Find the pattern and complete the 6th and 7th rows.

```
1st row              1
2nd row            1   1
3rd row          1   2   1
4th row        1   3   3   1
5th row      1   4   6   4   1
```

11. A college student sent home this letter. If each letter stands for one digit 0-9, how much money did he ask for?

    SEND
    + MORE
    MONEY

12. Complete the chart on page 274.

13. **Data Search** Refer to page 651. If the actual temperature is 15 degrees Fahrenheit, how much colder does it feel when the wind increases from 5 mph to 10 mph?

CULTURAL KALEIDOSCOPE

Pat Neblett

If children are our future, Pat Neblett wants to make sure that they know and understand different cultures. With $2,000, the former real estate agent founded Tuesday's Child Books in 1988 from her Randolph, Massachusetts home. She began selling African-American books through direct mail catalogs. Now most of her business comes from sales to schools. The titles have expanded to include children's books about Asians,

Hispanics, Native Americans, and minority groups in the United States. Neblett carries more than 300 titles. She reads each book herself to ensure that the content positively reinforces a child's self-worth.

Sales have increased from $7,000 in her first year to a projected $25,000 in 1991. She plans to open her own retail store if her business continues to grow.

276   Chapter 7 Integers

Course 2, p. 276

Meeting Individual Needs

Mathematics: Applications and Connections provides outstanding teacher resources specifically tailored for middle school teachers and students. The program offers an abundance of options and suggestions for creating an environment that is most conducive to learning. They include:

Meeting Needs of Middle School Students provides ways to prepare students for later mathematics courses, to maintain their interest and curiosity, and to tailor material to meet their developmental stages and personal concerns.

Limited English Proficiency features methods to reach and teach students for whom English is a secondary language.

Gifted and Talented Needs suggests ways to keep these students motivated and challenged.

Team Teaching offers suggestions on how to integrate mathematics with other disciplines.

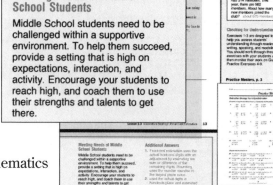

Meeting Needs of Middle School Students

Middle School students need to be challenged within a supportive environment. To help them succeed, provide a setting that is high on expectations, interaction, and activity. Encourage your students to reach high, and coach them to use their strengths and talents to get there.

Course 1, p. 13

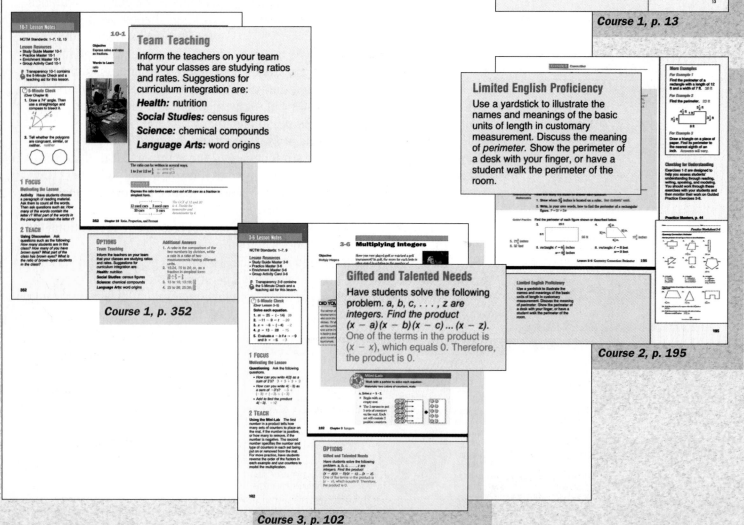

Team Teaching

Inform the teachers on your team that your classes are studying ratios and rates. Suggestions for curriculum integration are:

Health: nutrition
Social Studies: census figures
Science: chemical compounds
Language Arts: word origins

Course 1, p. 352

Limited English Proficiency

Use a yardstick to illustrate the names and meanings of the basic units of length in customary measurement. Discuss the meaning of *perimeter*. Show the perimeter of a desk with your finger, or have a student walk the perimeter of the room.

Course 2, p. 195

Gifted and Talented Needs

Have students solve the following problem. *a, b, c, . . . , z* are integers. Find the product $(x - a)(x - b)(x - c) \dots (x - z)$. One of the terms in the product is $(x - x)$, which equals 0. Therefore, the product is 0.

Course 3, p. 102

When children enter 6th grade, for a variety of reasons, it may become difficult for parents to remain on top of what's going on at school. The curricula grow more specialized, the typical middle school child becomes more independent of his or her parents, and multiple teachers replace the sole or primary teacher of the elementary school years.

When parents do have the opportunity to meet with teachers, they often ask what they can do to motivate their children. Here are some ideas to share with parents. Developed by Reginald Clark of the Academy for Educational Development in Washington, D.C., they are designed to foster positive attitudes and boost learning.

- Share the fact that there is an inverse correlation between excessive TV viewing and high achievement in school.
- Suggest that they discuss school, education, careers, life skills, etiquette, rules, and expectations with their children.
- Explain that it's important for them tell stories, recount experiences, and share problem-solving strategies with their children.
- Stress the importance of seeing to it that their children complete homework assignments.
- Urge them to provide time, space, and materials, needed for homework, reading, and hobbies.
- Remind them how important it is to listen to their children read and/or to read to their children.

FOSTERING COMMUNITY INVOLVEMENT

If your school does not have a formal community information program, suggest that one be established. Send photos and press releases to your local newspaper to inform the community about the exciting things your students are learning.

Have a "math career day" and invite local business people to describe to students how they use math in their jobs.

Set up a "shadow day" in which students spend a half-day "shadowing" people in the community who use math in their careers.

Find out about—or implement your own—math fairs and competitions that give your students a chance to shine in the "outside world."

Involving Parents and the Community in the Mathematics Classroom, one of the booklets in Glencoe's Mathematics Professional Series, presents additional suggestions on how parents and the community can be active participants in supporting mathematics instruction.

INVOLVING PARENTS AND THE COMMUNITY

CLASSROOM RESOURCES APPROPRIATE FOR FAMILIES

Some of the Teacher's Classroom Resources that accompany *Mathematics: Applications and Connections* are appropriate for parents and children to use together.

Study Guide Masters offer a brief explanation, examples, and exercises of the main concept in each lesson.

Enrichment Masters provide stimulating and thought-provoking puzzles, games, and extensions.

Multicultural Activity Masters present a cross-cultural spectrum of multicultural settings as a basis for problem solving.

Applications and Interdisciplinary Activity Masters accent the relationships among mathematics, the real world, and other disciplines.

Involving Parents and the Community in the Mathematics Classroom

Interactive Mathematics:
Activities and Investigations

Interactive Mathematics: Activities and Investigations offers an innovative, alternative approach to teaching and learning middle school mathematics. Each of the 18 units that make up this comprehensive, activity-based program may be used as an alternative or supplement to chapters in **Mathematics: Applications and Connections.** The title and mathematical focus of each of the **Interactive Mathematics: Activities and Investigations** units are as follows:

Unit	Title	Mathematical Focus
1	From the Beginning	Building Math Power
2	A Million to One	Number Sense
3	Just the Right Size	Scale Drawings and Proportional Reasoning
4	Through the Looking Glass	Spatial Visualization
5	Get a Clue	Logical Reasoning
6	The Road Not Taken	Graph Theory and Networks
7	Take It from the Top	Building Math Power
8	Data Sense	Statistics and Data Analysis
9	Don't Fence Me In	Area and Perimeter
10	Against the Odds	Probability
11	Cycles	Algebra Patterns
12	Treasure Island	Geometry and Measurement
13	Start Your Engines	Building Math Power
14	Run for Cover	Surface Area and Volume
15	On the Move	Graphing and Functions
16	Growing Pains	Linear and Exponential Growth
17	Infinite Windows	Fractals and Chaos Theory
18	Quality Control	Applied Data Analysis

The following correlation shows which units can be used with each chapter in **Mathematics: Applications and Connections.** Units of **Interactive Mathematics: Activities and Investigations (IMAI)** also are referenced as appropriate in the chapter interleaf pages of the Teacher's Wraparound Editions of **Mathematics: Applications and Connections (MAC).**

MAC Course 1 Chapter Number	IMAI Unit Numbers
1	1, 5
2	8
3	2
4	9
5	2, 7
6	2, 3
7	11
8	3, 10
9	4, 12
10	10
11	14
12	3, 11
13	11
14	10

MAC Course 2 Chapter Number	IMAI Unit Numbers
1	7
2	2, 7
3	8, 18
4	16
5	9, 10
6	8, 15
7	8, 15
8	12
9	9
10	4, 14
11	3, 7
12	16
13	6, 10
14	16

MAC Course 3 Chapter Number	IMAI Unit Numbers
1	13
2	8, 15
3	15
4	8, 18
5	4
6	17
7	9, 16
8	17, 18
9	16
10	13, 16
11	15, 16
12	14
13	6, 10, 17
14	5, 16

Mathematics: Applications and Connections is an integrated, three-year Middle School Mathematics Program.

Mathematics: Applications and Connections thoroughly integrates all thirteen curriculum standards outlined in the NCTM Standards. The standards listed below are for grades 5-8. See page 65 of the Standards.

STANDARD 1: *Mathematics as Problem Solving*
Course 1   (Chapters 1–14)
4-37, 44-71, 78-107, 116-121, 124-151, 160-162, 165-166, 168-183, 190-223, 232-264, 274-291, 293-303, 310-341, 350-379, 386-413, 420-451, 460-489, 496-521
Course 2   (Chapters 1–14)
4-41, 48-83, 90-119, 128-167, 174-213, 220-245, 254-289, 296-329, 336-367, 376-404, 410-447, 454-483, 492-525, 532-555
Course 3   (Chapters 1–14)
4-37, 44-79, 86-119, 128-167, 174-205, 212-247, 256-293, 304-335, 338-371, 380-415, 422-457, 464-493, 502-535, 542-565

STANDARD 2: *Mathematics as Communication*
Course 1   (Chapters 1–14)
4-37, 44-71, 78-107, 116-121, 124-151, 160-183, 190-223, 232-264, 274-303, 310-341, 350-379, 386-413, 420-451, 460-489, 496-521
Course 2   (Chapters 1–14)
4-41, 48-83, 90-119, 128-167, 174-213, 220-245, 254-289, 296-329, 336-367, 376-404, 410-447, 454-483, 492-525, 532-555
Course 3   (Chapters 1–14)
4-37, 44-79, 86-119, 128-167, 174-200, 202-205, 212-247, 256-293, 304-335, 338-371, 380-415, 422-457, 464-493, 502-535, 542-565

STANDARD 3: *Mathematics as Reasoning*
Course 1   (Chapters 1–14)
4-37, 44-71, 78-107, 116-121, 124-151, 160-183, 190-223, 232-264, 274-291, 293-303, 310-341, 350-379, 386-413, 420-451, 460-489, 496-521
Course 2   (Chapters 1–14)
4-41, 48-83, 90-119, 128-167, 174-213, 220-245, 254-289, 296-329, 336-367, 376-404, 410-447, 454-483, 492-525, 532-555
Course 3   (Chapters 1–14)
4-37, 44-79, 86-119, 128-167, 174-205, 212-247, 256-293, 304-335, 338-371, 380-415, 422-457, 464-493, 502-535, 542-565

STANDARD 4: *Mathematical Connections*
Course 1   (Chapters 1–14)
4-37, 44-71, 78-107, 116-121, 126-133, 135-151, 160-183, 190-192, 194-201, 204-223, 232-248, 250-264, 274-277, 280-291, 293-303, 310-317, 321-323, 326-329, 331-339, 352-357, 359-379, 386-402, 404-413, 420-425, 427-445, 448-451, 462-465, 467-470, 473-477, 480-489, 496-521
Course 2   (Chapters 1–14)
4-41, 48-83, 90-119, 128-167, 174-213, 220-245, 254-289, 296-329, 336-367, 376-404, 410-447, 454-483, 492-525, 532-555
Course 3   (Chapters 1–14)
4-37, 44-79, 86-119, 128-167, 174-179, 181-205, 212-247, 256-293, 304-335, 338-371, 380-415, 422-457, 464-493, 502-535, 542-565

STANDARD 5: *Number and Number Relationships*
Course 1   (Chapters 1–14)
25-26, 30-31, 35-37, 47-52, 57-71, 78-107, 116-121, 124-131, 134-144, 149-151, 160-183, 190-192, 194-196, 199-223, 232-243, 246-248, 250-264, 274-303, 310-323, 326-329, 331-339, 350-358, 361-379, 388-402, 404-413, 420-445, 448-451, 460-489, 498-501, 506-517, 519-521
Course 2   (Chapters 1–14)
4-41, 48-83, 90-95, 99-119, 128-167, 174-213, 220-245, 254-289, 296-300, 306, 311-316, 319-323, 336-367, 381-404, 410-447, 454-483, 492-525, 532-555
Course 3   (Chapters 1–14)
4-14, 17-37, 51-72, 86-94, 98-119, 128-138, 141-161, 164-167, 212-247, 256-258, 262-267, 270-277, 284-290, 304-309, 317-335, 338-360, 364-371, 380-397, 400-415, 425-434, 446-449, 451-457, 464-467, 491-493, 519-520

STANDARD 6: *Number Systems and Number Theory*
Course 1   (Chapters 1–14)
27-29, 32-34, 44-46, 50-56, 61-63, 78-107, 116-121, 124-131, 134-144, 146-151, 160-173, 177-183, 190-192, 194-223, 232-243, 246-248, 250-264, 274-303, 310-323, 326-329, 331-339, 352-358, 361-379, 388-402, 404-413, 420-445, 448-451, 460-489, 498-501, 506-517, 519-521
Course 2   (Chapters 1–14)
4-41, 48-83, 90-95, 99-119, 128-167, 174-213, 220-245, 254-289, 296-300, 306, 311-316, 319-323, 336-367, 381-404, 410-447, 454-483, 492-525, 532-555
Course 3   (Chapters 2, 3, 6–8)
77-79, 95-105, 212-217, 219-240, 259-261, 304-306, 310-313

STANDARD 7: *Computation and Estimation*
Course 1   (Chapters 1–14)
4-37, 47-51, 53-67, 94-107, 116-121, 124-137, 139-144, 149-151, 160-173, 177-183, 190-192, 194-201, 204-206, 221-223, 232-248, 250-264, 274-303, 310-323, 326-329, 331-339, 352-379, 386-402, 404-413, 420-445, 448-451, 460-489, 496-504, 506-517, 519-521

Course 2   (Chapters 1–14)
4-26, 28-41, 54-69, 71-83, 90-95, 99-100, 104-112, 116-119, 129-167, 174-188, 191-213, 220-222, 225-231, 233-240, 243-245, 263-266, 268-276, 278-289, 319-323, 336-342, 344-367, 381-404, 411-420, 422-447, 454-483, 497-515, 517-520, 522-525, 532-534, 536-554

Course 3   (Chapters 1–14)
4-37, 44-79, 86-119, 128-135, 145-167, 176-179, 181-190, 192-200, 212-217, 219-244, 256-275, 278-293, 304-335, 338-371, 380-402, 406-415, 422-430, 432-457, 464-469, 475-493, 504-530, 533-535, 543-563

STANDARD 8: *Patterns and Functions*
Course 1   (Chapters 1–14)
15-17, 50-51, 57-71, 116-121, 129-131, 139-151, 163-164, 190-196, 221-223, 287-291, 293-296, 331-333, 340-341, 359-363, 371-373, 391-397, 411-413, 426, 435-451, 462-465, 478-489, 496-517, 519-521

Course 2   (Chapters 4, 7, 14)
129-144, 274-276, 278-280, 287-289, 547-550

Course 3   (Chapters 1–14)
30-34, 44-47, 60-66, 139-144, 149-150, 155-158, 159-161, 164-167, 181-182, 191-195, 202-205, 212-214, 218-223, 230-232, 236-240, 256-258, 270-277, 282-283, 307-309, 314-326, 332-335, 350-352, 361-371, 391-392, 422-457, 515-520

STANDARD 9: *Algebra*
Course 1   (Chapters 1–14)
22-24, 27-29, 32-34, 53-71, 106-107, 116-121, 126-131, 135-137, 139-144, 146-151, 160-162, 171-173, 177-181, 190-192, 194-196, 207-212, 219-220, 250-252, 257-260, 280-286, 289-291, 293-302, 326-329, 355-357, 361-363, 368-370, 374-379, 388-397, 404-413, 420-445, 448-451, 460-475, 478-489, 498-501

Course 2   (Chapters 1–14)
27-41, 58-59, 61-63, 132-139, 204-206, 220-237, 241-245, 259-261, 263-266, 268-271, 278-289, 297-300, 306, 313-316, 321-323, 383-386, 394-397, 402-404, 417-420, 422-429, 465-468, 476-483, 497-499, 535-554

Course 3   (Chapters 1–14)
44-56, 60-79, 86-119, 176-179, 183-190, 197-200, 215-217, 221-232, 236-238, 256-267, 270-275, 278-281, 284-293, 310-316, 319-322, 332-335, 344-349, 353-363, 365-371, 380-390, 400-402, 406-415, 422-438, 442-457, 464-467, 487-490, 542-563

STANDARD 10: *Statistics*
Course 1   (Chapters 1–14)
4-7, 9-11, 20-21, 27-29, 32-34, 53-71, 87-90, 94-97, 103-107, 116-121, 126-133, 135-141, 146-148, 168-170, 194-196, 199-201, 204-206, 216-223, 244-245, 249-252, 257-260, 274-277, 289-291, 297-299, 314-317, 364-365, 368-379, 398-399, 420-425, 431-434, 440-445, 476-477, 483-489, 496-501, 506-509, 518-521

Course 2   (Chapters 3–14)
90-119, 164-167, 220-222, 233-235, 281-282, 313-316, 319-320, 444-447, 462-464, 469-473, 506-509, 543-554

Course 3   (Chapters 1–14)
30-31, 62-64, 86-88, 128-161, 164-167, 181-182, 239-244, 338-341, 344-349, 393-396, 403-405, 431, 439-441, 533-535

STANDARD 11: *Probability*
Course 1   (Chapters 1–4, 12, 14)
32-34, 57-63, 87-90, 124-125, 132-133, 420-422, 496-521

Course 2   (Chapters 4, 5, 9, 13)
157-160, 201-203, 363-367, 492-505, 510-513, 517-520, 522-525

Course 3   (Chapters 6, 12, 13)
233-235, 464-467, 502-509, 512-518, 521-532

STANDARD 12: *Geometry*
Course 1   (Chapters 4–14)
32-34, 85-93, 106-107, 135-137, 139-151, 160-162, 171-173, 190-193, 199-201, 210-212, 232-243, 246-248, 253-256, 274-279, 284-291, 310-341, 350-363, 371-373, 377-379, 386-413, 420-422, 431-434, 440-451, 467-470, 483-489, 506-517, 519-521

Course 2   (Chapters 5–14)
32-35, 38-41, 51-53, 194-200, 241-245, 296-318, 321-329, 338-367, 376-386, 389-404, 411-413, 422-425, 469-473, 476-478, 536-539, 551-555

Course 3   (Chapters 2–14)
8-14, 26-28, 35-37, 54-56, 73-76, 106-110, 117-119, 174-205, 218, 224-226, 230-235, 272-275, 278-290, 304-306, 308-309, 317-335, 342-343, 353-371, 391-396, 403-405, 425-427, 432-438, 442-457, 464-490, 542

STANDARD 13: *Measurement*
Course 1   (Chapters 1–14)
4-11, 18-19, 32-34, 79-86, 91-97, 100-102, 106-107, 119-121, 126-128, 139-151, 160-162, 171-176, 190-192, 199-201, 207-218, 232-243, 246-248, 253-256, 261-264, 274-291, 300-303, 310-323, 326-329, 337-339, 352-357, 359-363, 371-373, 377-379, 386-402, 404-413, 420-422, 435-437, 443-445, 448-451, 467-470, 487-489, 506-517

Course 2   (Chapters 2–14)
78-80, 142-144, 238-240, 344-367, 398-401, 417-420, 422-425, 433-435, 454-456

Course 3   (Chapters 1–14)
22-29, 77-79, 86-88, 91-101, 117-119, 174-180, 183-191, 196, 201, 227-229, 245-247, 256-258, 278-287, 342-343, 356-371, 393-397, 403-405, 470-473, 478-481, 486, 491-493

SCOPE AND SEQUENCE

Communication, cooperative learning, connections among disciplines, applications, calculator, computer, and the use of manipulatives are integrated throughout the mathematical content as appropriate.

	Course	1	2	3
Problem Solving				
Develop a plan				
Strategies				
Guess and Check				
Classifying Information				
Use a Graph				
Make a Table				
Determine Reasonable Answers				
Use a Formula				
Solve a Simpler Problem				
Choose the Method of Computation				
Make a List				
Eliminate Possibilities				
Find a Pattern				
Use Logical Reasoning				
Draw a Diagram				
Make a Model				
Work Backward				
Use an Equation				
Act It Out				
Use the Pythagorean Theorem				
Use a Venn Diagram				
Factor Polynomials				
Analyzing and Making Decisions				
Finding and classifying information				
Interpreting data				
Making predictions based on data				

	Course	1	2	3
Estimation and Mental Math				
Estimation				
Rounding whole numbers				
Rounding decimals				
Strategies for estimating				
rounding				
front-end				
patterns				
compatible numbers				
choosing the computation method				
capture-recapture				
use fractions, decimals, & percents interchangeably				
Estimating with whole numbers				
sums & differences				
products & quotients				
Estimating with decimals				
sums & differences				
products & quotients				

	Course	1	2	3
Estimation and Mental Math (cont.)				
Estimating with fractions				
sums & differences				
products & quotients				
Estimating percent				
Estimating with Geometry				
angle measures				
area, volume				
Estimating square roots				
Mental Math				
Strategies				
using properties				
patterns				
compatible numbers				
compensation				
choosing the computation method				
Solving equations mentally				

	Course	1	2	3
Decimals				
Understanding the concept				
Reading & writing				
Decimal place value				
Comparing and ordering				
Rounding				
Relating decimals & fractions				
Relating decimals, ratios, & percents				
Operations with Decimals				
Adding & subtracting				
Multiplying: by a whole number				
two decimals				
Dividing: by a whole number				
by powers of 10				
by a decimal				
with zeros in the quotient				
Estimating sums & differences				
Estimating products & quotients				
Scientific notation				
Terminating, repeating				

	Course	1	2	3
Number Theory				
Reading and writing whole numbers				
Place value of whole numbers				
Place value of decimals				
Compare & order whole numbers				
Compare & order decimals				
Compare & order fractions				
Compare & order integers				
Compare & order rationals				

Introduce

Develop

Reinforce/Integrate

Communication, cooperative learning, connections among disciplines, applications, calculator, computer, and the use of manipulatives are integrated throughout the mathematical content as appropriate.

Course	1	2	3
Number Theory (cont.)			
Compare & order irrationals			
Rounding whole numbers			
Rounding decimals			
Rounding fractions			
Positive exponents			
Negative exponents			
Greatest Common Factor (GCF)			
Least Common Multiple (LCM)			
Divisibility rules			
Prime and composite numbers			
Prime factorization			
Relative primes			
Scientific notation			
Square roots			
Relating fractions and decimals			
Fractions			
Fraction concepts			
Writing mixed numbers as fractions			
Mixed numbers and improper fractions			
Equivalent fractions			
Comparing & order fractions			
Simplifying fractions			
LCD			
Rounding & estimating fractions			
Operations with fractions			
Adding & subtracting			
Subtracting with renaming			
Multiplying & dividing			
Estimating sums & differences			
Estimating products & quotients			
Relating fractions & decimals			
Geometry			
Lines			
Constructions			
congruent lines			
perpendicular lines			
parallel lines			
segment bisectors			
Angles			
classify and measure angles			
sum of angle measures			
constructions			
congruent angles			
angle bisectors			
Tesselations			
Identify polygons			
Classify triangles and quadrilaterals			

Course	1	2	3
Geometry (cont.)			
Construct polygons			
Symmetry			
Identify congruent figures & similar figures			
Corresponding parts of similar polygons			
Translations, reflections, & rotations			
Identify & draw three-dimensional figures			
Relationships in a right triangle			
Pythagorean Theorem			
Measurement			
Metric System			
use units of length, capacity, & mass			
change units within the metric system			
Customary System			
use customary units of measurement			
convert within the customary system			
Precision and significant digits			
Measuring perimeter/circumference			
Measuring area			
of irregular figures			
of rectangles			
of parallelograms			
of triangles			
by connecting algebra & geometry			
of circles			
of a trapezoid			
Measuring surface area			
of rectangular prisms			
of triangular prisms			
of cylinders			
of spheres			
Measuring volume			
of rectangular prisms			
of cylinders			
of pyramids and circular cones			
of spheres			
Relating surface area & volume			
Probability			
Making predictions using a sample			
Conducting Experiments			
simple event			
independent events			
dependent events			
using area models			
experimental probability			
tree diagrams			
Fundamental Principle of Counting			
permutations & combinations			

Legend:
- ▨ Introduce
- ▨ Develop
- ☐ Reinforce/Integrate

Communication, cooperative learning, connections among disciplines, applications, calculator, computer, and the use of manipulatives are integrated throughout the mathematical content as appropriate.

Statistics

	Course 1	2	3
Recording & interpreting data			
organizing data into a table	■	■	
constructing graphs	■	■	
constructing line plots	■	■	
constructing stem-and-leaf plots		■	
constructing histograms			■
constructing box-and-whisker plots			■
constructing scatter plots			■
Interpret data			
mean, median, & mode	■	■	■
range & quartiles		■	■
misleading graphs & statistics	■	■	■
making predictions from statistics	■	■	■

Ratio, Proportion, & Percent

	Course 1	2	3
Ratio			
Understanding concept of ratio	■	■	
Reading and writing ratios	■	■	
Equal ratios	■	■	
The Golden Ratio			■
Proportion			
Understanding concept of proportion	■	■	
Solving proportions	■	■	
Scale drawings	■	■	
Similar figures	■	■	■
Dilations			■
Indirect measurement		■	■
Tangent, sine, & cosine ratios			■
Percent			
Understanding the concept of percent	■	■	
Writing fractions & decimals for percent	■	■	
Finding percent of a number	■	■	
Percents greater than 100%, less than 1%		■	
Percent one number is of another		■	
Finding number when percent is known		■	
Estimating percents	■	■	
Discount		■	
Sales tax		■	
Simple interest		■	
Percent of change		■	

Algebra

	Course 1	2	3
Properties			
of whole numbers	■	■	
of rational numbers			■
Integers			
Read & write integers	■	■	
Graphing integers on the number line	■	■	

Algebra (cont.)

	Course 1	2	3
Absolute value		■	■
Compare and order integers	■	■	
Add & subtract integers	■	■	
Multiply & divide integers	■	■	
Rational numbers			
Identify and simplify rational numbers			■
Scientific notation		■	■
Rational numbers as decimals		■	
Compare and order rational numbers		■	
Solve equations with rational number solutions		■	
Real Numbers			
Identify & classify real numbers		■	
Negative exponents		■	■
Square roots		■	
Irrational numbers			■
Density property			■
Patterns, Functions, Expressions, & Equations			
Recognize and extend sequences	■	■	■
Fibonacci Sequence			■
Pascal's Triangle			■
Function tables	■	■	■
Linear functions			■
Order of operations	■	■	■
Evaluate algebraic expressions	■	■	■
Solve two-step equations	■	■	
Solve equations			
with integer solutions	■	■	
with two variables			■
Write algebraic expressions from verbal phrases	■	■	■
Identify and solve inequalities		■	■
Graphing			
Points on a coordinate plane	■	■	
Functions			■
Equations			■
Transformations on a coordinate plane	■	■	
Irrational numbers on a number line			■
Linear functions			■
Quadratic functions			■
To solve systems of equations			■
Slope			■
Polynomials			
Represent & simplify polynomials			■
Add, subtract, & multiply polynomials			■
Factor polynomials			■
Multiply binomials			■

Legend:
■ Introduce
■ Develop
■ Reinforce/Integrate

BIBLIOGRAPHY

Publications

Azzolino, Agnes, *How to Use Writing to Teach Mathematics*, Keyport, NJ: Mathematical Concepts, 1987.

California State Department of Education Task Force on Middle Grade Education, *Caught in the Middle*, California State Department of Education, Sacramento, CA, 1987.

Carnegie Council on Adolescent Development, *Turning Points*, Washington, DC, 1989.

Cuevas, Gilbert J., *Mathematics Learning in English as a Second Language*, Journal for Research in Mathematics Education, XV (March 1984) 134-144.

Farrell, Margaret A., ed., *Imaginative Ideas for the Teacher of Mathematics, Grades K-12: Ranucci's Reservoir*, Reston, VA: NCTM, 1988.

Jamski, William D., ed., *Mathematical Challenges for the Middle Grades*, Reston, VA: NCTM, 1990.

Johnson, David W. and Roger T. Johnson, *Cooperation and Competition, Theory and Research*, Edina, MN: Interaction Book Co., 1989.

Kagan, Spencer, *Cooperative Learning, Resources for Teachers*, Laguna Niguel, CA: Resources for Teachers, 1989.

Mathematical Sciences Education Board and National Research Council, *Everybody Counts: A Report to the Nation on the Future of Mathematics Education*, Washington, DC: National Academy Press, 1989.

National Council of Teachers of Mathematics, *Curriculum and Evaluation Standards for School Mathematics*, Reston, VA: NCTM, 1989.

_____, *Mathematics for the Middle Grades (5-9), 1982 Yearbook*, Reston, Va:NCTM, 1982.

_____, *Professional Standards for Teaching Mathematics*, Reston, VA: NCTM, 1991.

Paulos, John A., *Innumeracy: Mathematical Illiteracy and Its Consequences*, New York, NY: 1988.

Skolnick, Joan, Carol Langbort, and Lucille Day, *How to Encourage Girls in Math and Science: Strategies for Parents and Educators*, Englewood Cliffs, NJ: Prentice Hall, 1982

Slavin, Robert, *Cooperative Learning, Student Teams, 2nd ed.*, Washington, DC: National Education Association, 1987.

Thompson, Robert G., *Practical BASIC for Teachers*, Columbus, OH: Merrill, 1985.

Thornton, Carol Z., et al., *Teaching Mathematics to Children with Special Needs*, Menlo Park, CA: Addison-Wesley, 1983.

Trafton, Paul R., and Albert P. Shulte, ed., *New Directions for Elementary School Mathematics*: 1989 Yearbook, Reston, VA: NCTM, 1989.

William T. Grant Foundation Commission on Work, Family and Citizenship, *The Forgotten Half: Pathways to Success for America's Youth and Young Families*, Washington, DC: 1988.

Computer Software

Coordinate Math, (Apple II), MECC

Data Models, (Macintosh), Wings for Learning/Sunburst

How the West Was One + Three x Four, (Apple II, Macintosh, IBM/Tandy), Wings for Learning/Sunburst

Keep Your Balance, (Apple II), Wings for Learning/Sunburst

Math Tutor: Fractions Part I, Fractions Part II, (Apple II, IBM/Tandy), Scholastic Inc.

Tobbs Learns Algebra, (Apple II), Wings for Learning/Sunburst

Films/Videotapes

Algebra for Everyone, Reston, VA: NCTM, 1991.

Guinness World Records Math Filmstrips: Problem Solving with Addition, Subtraction, Multiplication, and Division, Chicago, IL: Society for Visual Education, 1985.

Mathematics: Making the Connection, Reston, VA: NCTM, 1991.

Statistics: Understanding Mean, Median, and Mode, Bloomington, IN: Agency for Instructional Technology, 1987.

The Theory of Pythagoras, Reston, VA: NCTM, 1988.

Volume and Capacity, Los Angeles, CA: Oxford Films, 1974.

Addresses of Software Companies

Gamco Industries, P.O. Box 1862C9, Big Spring, TX 79721-1911, 800/351-1404

IBM, 4111 Northside Pwky NW, P.O. Box 2150, Atlanta, GA 30055, 800/IBM-2468

MECC, 6160 Summit Drive North, Minneapolis, MN 55430-4003, 800/685-MECC

Scholastic Inc., P.O. Box 7502, Jefferson City, MO 65102, 800/541-5513

Wings for Learning/Sunburst, 101 Castleton Street, Pleasantville, NY 10570, 800/338-3457

COURSE PLANNING GUIDES

The charts below give suggested time schedules for three Options: I, II, and III, and for two types of grading periods, 6-week and 9-week.

Option I covers Chapters 1-12. It allows extra time for longer lessons and for reteaching and review. Option II covers Chapters 1-13. Option III covers Chapters 1-14. This option is intended for students who master concepts quickly and retain skills well. Generally, one day is allotted for each lesson, Chapter Study Guide and Review, and Chapter Test.

Note that the total days suggested is 165 days which is considerably less than the number of days most school districts are in session. This is to allow the teacher flexibility in planning due to shortened class periods because of outside activities, bad weather days, or any other similar circumstances.

Course Planning Guide 6-Week Grading Period

Grading Period	Option I Chapter	Days	Option II Chapter	Days	Option III Chapter	Days
1	1	13	1	12	1	12
	2	14	2	13	2	12
			3	3	3	4
			(Lessons 3-1 to 3-3)		(Lessons 3-1 to 3-4)	
2	3	14	3	10	3	8
	4	15	(Lesson 3-4 to end)		(Lesson 3-5 to end)	
			4	14	4	13
			5	4	5	6
			(Lessons 5-1A to 5-3)		(Lessons 5-1A to 5-5)	
3	5	13	5	8	5	5
	6	14	(Lesson 5-4 to end)		(Lesson 5-6A to end)	
			6	13	6	13
			7	6	7	9
			(Lessons 7-1 to 7-5)		(Lessons 7-1 to 7-8)	
4	7	14	7	7	7	4
	8	13	(Lesson 7-6 to end)		(Lesson 7-9 to end)	
			8	12	8	11
			9	8	9	12
			(Lessons 9-1 to 9-7)			
5	9	14	9	5	10	12
	10	14	(Lesson 9-8 to end)		11	13
			10	13	12	3
			11	9	(Lessons 12-1 to 12-3B)	
			(Lessons 11-1 to 11-8B)			
6	11	14	11	4	12	8
	12	13	(Lesson 11-9 to end)		(Lesson 12-4 to end)	
			12	12	13	11
			13	12	14	9
Total Days		165		165		165

Course Planning Guide 9-Week Grading Period

Grading Period	Option I Chapter	Days	Option II Chapter	Days	Option III Chapter	Days
1	1	13	1	12	1	12
	2	14	2	13	2	12
	3	14	3	13	3	12
			4	4	4	5
			(Lessons 4-1A to 4-3B)		(Lessons 4-1 to 4-4)	
2	4	15	4	10	4	8
	5	13	(Lesson 4-4 to end)		(Lesson 4-5 to end)	
	6	14	5	12	5	11
			6	13	6	13
			7	6	7	9
			(Lessons 7-1 to 7-5)		(Lesson 7-1 to 7-8)	
3	7	14	7	7	7	4
	8	13	(Lesson 7-6 to end)		(Lesson 7-9 to end)	
	9	14	8	12	8	11
			9	13	9	12
			10	9	10	12
			(Lessons 10-1 to 10-8)		11	3
					(Lessons 11-1 to 11-3)	
4	10	14	10	4	11	10
	11	14	(Lesson 10-9 to end)		(Lesson 11-4A to end)	
	12	13	11	13	12	11
			12	12	13	11
			13	12	14	9
Total Days		165		165		165

1 Tools for Problem Solving

Previewing the Chapter

This chapter provides a solid foundation for problem solving throughout the text. It begins with a detailed look at the four-step problem-solving plan. In the **problem-solving strategy** lessons, students learn how to integrate specific strategies into the plan. Three of these, *determine reasonable answers*, *eliminate possibilities*, and *guess and check*, are general strategies applicable to a wide variety of problems. For applying these strategies, the chapter includes two additional topics, measurement (both metric and customary) and exponents.

Lesson	Lesson Objectives	NCTM Standards	State/Local Objectives
1-1	Solve problems using the four-step plan.	1–5, 7	
1-2	Compute mentally using compensation and properties of numbers.	1–5, 7, 12	
1-3	Estimate answers by using different strategies.	1–5, 7, 12	
1-4	Determine whether answers to problems are reasonable.	1–5, 7	
1-5	Solve problems by using estimation to eliminate possibilities.	1–5, 7	
Decision Making	Analyze data and make a decision.	1–4, 7	
1-6A	Measure items using a nonstandard unit of measure.	1–4, 7, 13	
1-6	Use metric units of measurement.	1–5, 7, 13	
1-7	Use customary units of measurement.	1–5, 7, 12, 13	
1-7B	Explore the origin of the mile unit of measure.	1–4, 7, 13	
1-8A	Explore the use of a computer spreadsheet.	1–4, 7, 8	
1-8	Solve problems by using guess and check.	1–5, 7, 8	
1-9	Use powers and exponents in expressions.	1–5, 7, 12	

Organizing the Chapter

LESSON PLANNING GUIDE

> *A complete, 1-page lesson plan is provided for each lesson in the Lesson Plans Masters Booklet.*

| Lesson | Materials/ Manipulatives | Extra Practice (Student Edition) | Blackline Masters Booklets | | | | | | | | | |
			Study Guide	Practice	Enrichment	Evaluation	Technology	Lab Manual	Multicultural Activities	Application and Interdisciplinary Activities	Transparencies	Group Activity Cards
1-1			p. 1	p. 1	p. 1				p. 1		1-1	1-1
1-2		p. 584	p. 2	p. 2	p. 2		p. 15				1-2	1-2
1-3		p. 584	p. 3	p. 3	p. 3						1-3	1-3
1-4			p. 4	p. 4	p. 4						1-4	1-4
1-5			p. 5	p. 5	p. 5	Quiz A, p. 7					1-5	1-5
1-6A	string, marker/ pen, scissors							p. 38				
1-6	encyclopedia	p. 584	p. 6	p. 6	p. 6					p. 1	1-6	1-6
1-7	dictionary or encyclopedia	p. 585	p. 7	p. 7	p. 7					p. 15	1-7	1-7
1-7B	yardstick							p. 39				
1-8A	calculator							p. 40				
1-8			p. 8	p. 8	p. 8						1-8	1-8
1-9	calculator	p. 585	p. 9	p. 9	p. 9	Quiz B, p. 7	p. 1				1-9	1-9
Study Guide and Review			Multiple Choice Test, Forms 1A and 1B, pp. 1–4 Free Response Test, Forms 2A and 2B, pp. 5–6 Cumulative Review, p. 8 (free response)									
Test			Cumulative Test, p. 9 (multiple choice)									

Pacing Guide: Option I (Chapters 1–12) - 13 days; Option II (Chapters 1–13) - 12 days; Option III (Chapters 1–14) - 12 days
You may wish to refer to the complete **Course Planning Guides** on page T25.

OTHER CHAPTER RESOURCES

Student Edition
Chapter Opener, pp. 2–3
Save Planet Earth, p. 14
Mid-Chapter Review, p. 19
Decision Making, pp. 20–21
Portfolio Suggestion, p. 28

 Manipulatives
Overhead Manipulative Resources
Middle School Mathematics Manipulative Kit

 Software/Technology
Interactive Mathematics Tools (Macintosh)
Test and Review Generator (IBM, Apple, Macintosh)
Teacher's Guide for Software Resources

Other Supplements
Transparency 1–0
Performance Assessment, pp. 1–2
Glencoe Mathematics Professional Series
Lesson Plans, pp. 1–12

INTERDISCIPLINARY BULLETIN BOARD

Geology Connection

Objective   Construct scale models and express measurements in customary and metric units.

How To Use It   Ask students to research and display additional information about the Mt. St. Helens eruption, expressing measurements in both customary and metric units. Have them draw or construct scale drawings or models of the volcano before and after the eruption.

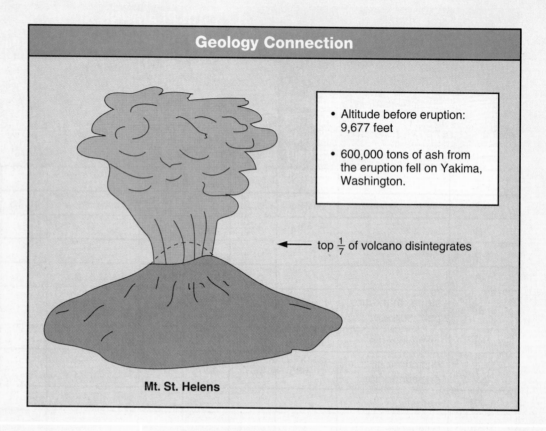

Geology Connection

- Altitude before eruption: 9,677 feet

- 600,000 tons of ash from the eruption fell on Yakima, Washington.

← top $\frac{1}{7}$ of volcano disintegrates

Mt. St. Helens

APPLICATIONS AND CONNECTIONS

Applications	Lesson	Example	Exercise
Entertainment	1-1	2	
Chemistry	1-1		5
Photography	1-1		6
Engineering	1-1		7
Transportation	1-1		8
Money	1-1		9
Smart Shopping	1-1		10
Fitness	1-1		11
Inventory	1-3		31
Arts and Crafts	1-3		34
Smart Shopping	1-4	X	
Archeology	1-6		32
Research	1-6		33d
Construction	1-7	3	
Ecology	1-7		28
Design	1-7		29
Save Planet Earth	1-7		32
Research	Lab 1-7B		4
Inventory	1-8	X	
Automobiles	1-9		32
Connections			
Geometry	1-2		34
Technology	1-3	4	
Geometry	1-3		33
Geometry	1-7		31
Geometry	1-9		30
Number Sense	1-9		33

TEAM ACTIVITIES

Multicultural Experiences

Outside Field Trips   Seek experiences that show problem-solving in a real-world setting. A visit to a small business can help students see how business people are coping with the problem of competition.

A visit to a city or state environmental agency can demonstrate how citizens are attempting to solve the problems of pollution and waste disposal.

In-Class Speakers   Invite a detective or trial attorney to discuss how logic is used to solve problems in criminal cases.

A research scientist can discuss the solving of problems in his or her field of study.

SUPPLEMENTARY BLACKLINE MASTER BOOKLETS

Some of the blackline masters for enhancing this chapter are shown below.

RECOMMENDED OUTSIDE RESOURCES

Books/Periodicals

Ecker, Michael W., *Getting Started in Problem Solving and Math Contest,* New York, NY: Franklin Watts, 1987.

Schoen, Harold and Marilyn Aweng, *Estimation and Mental Computations,* 1986 Yearbook, NCTM, 1986.

Films/Videotapes/Videodiscs

Length and Distance, Los Angeles, CA: Oxford Films, 1974.

Powers of Ten, Santa Monica, CA: Pyramid Film, 1968.

Problem Solving in Mathematics, Mount Kisco, NY: Pathescope Educational Media, 1983.

Software

Hot Dog Stand, (Macintosh, IBM/Tandy), Wings for Learning/Sunburst

Estimation Strategies, (Apple II), MECC

For addresses of companies handling software, please refer to page T24.

INTER·ACTIVE Mathematics — Glencoe's *Interactive Mathematics: Activities and Investigations* consists of 18 units that may be used as alternatives or supplemental material for *Mathematics: Applications and Connections.* The suggested unit for this chapter is Unit 13, *Start Your Engines.* See page T18 for more information.

Application and Interdisciplinary Activity Masters, pp. 1, 15

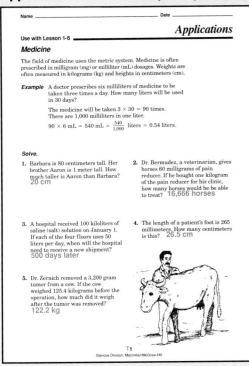

Name _____ Date _____

Applications

Use with Lesson 1-6

Medicine

The field of medicine uses the metric system. Medicine is often prescribed in milligram (mg) or milliliter (mL) dosages. Weights are often measured in kilograms (kg) and heights in centimeters (cm).

Example A doctor prescribes six milliliters of medicine to be taken three times a day. How many liters will be used in 30 days?

The medicine will be taken $3 \times 30 = 90$ times. There are 1,000 milliliters in one liter.

$90 \times 6 \text{ mL} = 540 \text{ mL} = \frac{540}{1,000}$ liters = 0.54 liters.

Solve.

1. Barbara is 80 centimeters tall. Her brother Aaron is 1 meter tall. How much taller is Aaron than Barbara? 20 cm

2. Dr. Bermudez, a veterinarian, gives horses 60 milligrams of pain reducer. If he bought one kilogram of the pain reducer for his clinic, how many horses would he be able to treat? 16,666 horses

3. A hospital received 100 kiloliters of saline (salt) solution on January 1. If each of the four floors uses 50 liters per day, when will the hospital need to receive a new shipment? 500 days later

4. The length of a patient's foot is 265 millimeters. How many centimeters is this? 26.5 cm

5. Dr. Zernich removed a 3,200 gram tumor from a cow. If the cow weighed 125.4 kilograms before the operation, how much did it weigh after the tumor was removed? 122.2 kg

T1
Glencoe Division, Macmillan/McGraw-Hill

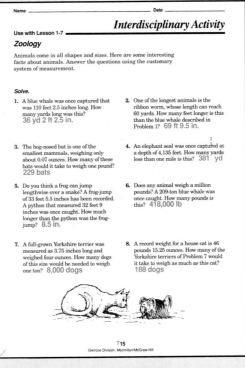

Name _____ Date _____

Interdisciplinary Activity

Use with Lesson 1-7

Zoology

Animals come in all shapes and sizes. Here are some interesting facts about animals. Answer the questions using the customary system of measurement.

Solve.

1. A blue whale was once captured that was 110 feet 2.5 inches long. How many yards long was this? 36 yd 2 ft 2.5 in.

2. One of the longest animals is the ribbon worm, whose length can reach 60 yards. How many feet longer is this than the blue whale described in Problem 1? 69 ft 9.5 in.

3. The hog-nosed bat is one of the smallest mammals, weighing only about 0.07 ounces. How many of these bats would it take to weigh one pound? 229 bats

4. An elephant seal was once captured at a depth of 4,135 feet. How many yards less than one mile is this? 381 yd

5. Do you think a frog can jump lengthwise over a snake? A frog-jump of 33 feet 5.5 inches has been recorded. A python that measured 32 feet 9 inches was once caught. How much longer than the python was the frog-jump? 8.5 in.

6. Does any animal weigh a million pounds? A 209-ton blue whale was once caught. How many pounds is this? 418,000 lb

7. A full-grown Yorkshire terrier was measured as 3.75 inches long and weighed four ounces. How many dogs of this size would be needed to weigh one ton? 8,000 dogs

8. A record weight for a house cat is 46 pounds 15.25 ounces. How many of the Yorkshire terriers of Problem 7 would it take to weigh as much as this cat? 188 dogs

T15
Glencoe Division, Macmillan/McGraw-Hill

Multicultural Activity Masters, p. 1

Name _____ Date _____

Multicultural Activity

Use with Lesson 1-1

Games and Sports

Many of the games and sports we enjoy in the United States today have come to us from other countries. Some were being played hundreds of years before Columbus arrived in America.

On this page, you will have a chance to practice your problem-solving skills. Do you read information carefully? Can you use logical reasoning to draw conclusions from given information? If you do, you should be able to match each description below with the name of the correct game or sport from the list at the right. Good luck!

Games and Sports from Many Cultures
bocci
bowling
chess
handball
jai alai
judo
lacrosse
polo

1. This sport originated in India. There its name was *pula,* after the willow tree root from which the ball was carved. polo

2. When this game originated in Ireland, it was called "fives" because you used all five fingers to hit the ball against the wall. handball

3. This game began as a religious rite in ancient Germany. It was originally played with ten clubs and a rounded rock. bowling

4. This sport originated in Italy. The first authentic balls for the sport were made from willow tree roots by a man named Luigi Boccharini. bocci

5. This game originated in India or China in the sixth century, and it has been played throughout the world. The Chinese called it *chong ki,* but, in the Old English language, its name was *check.* chess

6. This sport originated with the Basque people, who live in a region of the mountains that border Spain and France. Its name is a phrase which means *merry festival* in the Basque language. jai alai

7. The name of this sport means "the gentle way." It is a means of self-defense derived from an ancient Japanese form of combat called *ju-jitsu.* judo

8. This sport originated centuries ago with the Native American peoples. Its modern name comes from the French word for the shape of the stick that the players use. lacrosse

Source: The Ethnic Almanac by Stephanie Bernardo, New York, Doubleday & Company, Inc., 1981.

T1
Glencoe Division, Macmillan/McGraw-Hill

Technology Masters, p. 1

Name _____ Date _____

Calculator Activity

Use with Lesson 1-9

The Power Key

The power key on many calculators makes it easier to evaluate expressions with exponents. It is usually labeled y^x or x^y.

Example 1 Evaluate 5^4.

ENTER: 5 y^x 4 $=$

DISPLAY: 5   5   4   625

Therefore, $5^4 = 625$

Example 2 Evaluate $2^5 \cdot 4^3$.

ENTER: 2 y^x 5 $\times$ 4 y^x 3 $=$

DISPLAY: 2   2   5   32   4   4   3   2048

Therefore, $2^5 \cdot 4^3 = 2,048.$

Evaluate each expression.

1. 3^8 — 6,561
2. 52^4 — 7,311,616
3. $2 \cdot 6^3$ — 432
4. $4^3 \cdot 2^7$ — 8,192
5. $3 \cdot 2^5 \cdot 4^5$ — 98,304
6. $5^3 \cdot 4^2 \cdot 2^5$ — 64,000
7. $5^4 - 3^3$ — 598
8. $2 \cdot 4^3 + 3^4$ — 209
9. $3 \cdot 5^3 + 4 \cdot 2^7$ — 887
10. $5 \cdot 2^3 - 3 \cdot 2^3$ — 16
11. $(4+5)^2 + 6^3 \cdot 2^5$ — 6,993
12. $(3^5 - 2^5) \cdot 5^5$ — 659,375
13. **CHALLENGE** $10 \cdot 7^3 + 6 \cdot 2^3 \cdot 3^4 - 5 \cdot 4^3$ — 6,998

T1
Glencoe Division, Macmillan/McGraw-Hill

This two-page introduction to the chapter provides a visual, relevant way to engage students in the mathematics of the chapter. Questions are included that help students see the need to learn the mathematics in the chapter. Data in charts and graphs provide statistical information that students can analyze and interpret at this point as well as later in the chapter. The Chapter Project provides an activity that applies the mathematics of the chapter.

MAKING MATHEMATICS RELEVANT

Spotlight on Athletes

Professional athletes are among the most visible and highest-paid people in America. Million dollar salaries are common in basketball, baseball, and football. The public pays these salaries through ticket purchases and by buying products sold by sponsors of television and radio broadcasts. Nearly 200 million candy bars, earning a typical 5¢ profit each, must be sold to pay Kirby Puckett's salary for three years.

Sports generate huge amounts of data which are compiled and published as statistics. Ask students to give examples of their favorite sports statistics and records.

Using the Timeline

Ask the following questions.

* *Which event occurred closest to the year of your birth? your parents' births? your grandparents' births?*

* *Fifty-five years before the first CD, Babe Ruth became the first baseball player to hit 60 home runs. What athletic achievement occurred 5 years later?* Babe Zaharias set 4 track-and-field world records in 3 hours.

2

Chapter

1

Tools for Problem Solving

Spotlight on Athletes

Have You Ever Wondered . . .

* About how much money Kirby Puckett earns per game since he signed a three-year, $9 million deal with the Minnesota Twins?

* How many different ways can a baseball manager arrange the batting order of the nine starting players on the team?

World Swimming Records
(as of July 1991)

Event	Record Holders	Country	Time
50-meter freestyle	Tom Jager	USA	0:21.81
	Yang Wenyi	China	0:24.98
100-meter breaststroke	Adrian Moorhouse	Great Britain	1:01.49
	Silke Hoerner	Germany	1:07.91
200-meter butterfly	Michael Gross	Germany	1:56.24
	Mary T. Meagher	USA	2:05.96
200-meter backstroke	Igor Polianskiy	USSR	1:58.14
	Betsy Mitchell	USA	2:08.60
400-meter medley	Tamas Darnyi	Hungary	4:15.42
	Petra Schneider	Germany	4:36.10

1932   *1942*   *1957*

1930   **1940**   **1950**   **1960**

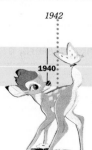

Babe Zaharias sets 4 track-and-field world records in 3 hours.

Althea Gibson becomes the first African-American woman tennis player to be ranked number one in the world.

2

"Have You Ever Wondered?" Answers

* He earns about $18,000 per game.

* There are 362,880 different arrangements.

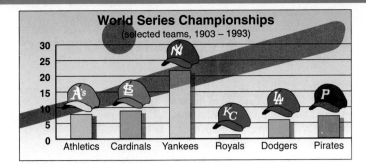

World Series Championships
(selected teams, 1903 – 1993)

Athletics | Cardinals | Yankees | Royals | Dodgers | Pirates

Chapter Project

Athletes
Work with a partner.

1. Choose a prominent athlete that plays a professional team sport near where you live. Write a short biography about his or her life.

2. Collect statistics about your athlete's career over several seasons. In how many games did he or she play? How much money did he or she earn? How many points did he or she score?

3. Suppose you and your partner will represent this player in contract negotiations. Display your findings graphically in such a way that will highlight your client's contribution to the team.

1971   1977   1982   1989   1991

1970   1980   1990

*Michael Chang wins
French Open.*

*Pelé retires after scoring
1,281 goals in 1,363
soccer games.*

*Nolan Ryan pitches his
seventh no-hitter.*

Looking Ahead

In this chapter, you will see how mathematics can be used to answer the questions about estimating player salaries and solving problems. The major objectives of this chapter are to:

- solve problems using the four-step plan

- compute mentally using properties

- estimate sums and differences of whole numbers and decimals

- solve problems by using guess and check

3

DATA ANALYSIS
Have students study the table of world swimming records. Ask the following questions.

- *At her record pace, how long would it take Yang Wenyi to swim 200 meters?* 99.92 seconds

- *What is Michael Gross's record speed in meters/second?* about 1.72 meters/second

Data Search
A question related to these data is provided in Lesson 1-7, page 28, Exercise 33.

CHAPTER PROJECT
Encourage students to select players who do not always gain media attention or those who have made major contributions which are not widely publicized. Suggest *Sports Illustrated for Kids, Sports Illustrated,* almanacs, and biographies as sources of information. Emphasize the importance of organizing data by suggesting that students record their information in a chart.

Have students display their graphs and analyze the data. Encourage them to be creative in their presentation. Discuss the factors that might affect an athlete's performance from season to season.

Allow several days to complete the project.

Chapter Opener Transparency

Transparency 1-0 is available in the Transparency Package. It provides another full-color, motivating activity that you can use to capture students' interest.

NCTM Standards: 1–5, 7

Lesson Resources
- Study Guide Master 1-1
- Practice Master 1-1
- Enrichment Master 1-1
- Multicultural Activity, p. 1
- Group Activity Card 1-1

 Transparency 1-1 contains the 5-Minute Check and a teaching aid for this lesson.

⏱ 5-Minute Check

1. Solve 70 × 20. 1,400
2. Solve 1,426 + 93.4 + 375.8. 1,895.2
3. How much greater is 5,000 than the sum of 856 and 2,063? 2,081
4. Solve 5,008 ÷ 16. 313
5. A $75 jacket was marked down $25.05 for clearance. Find the sale price. $49.95

---

1 FOCUS

Motivating the Lesson

Questioning Have students read the opening paragraph of the lesson. Ask this question: *An old joke defines a camel as a horse designed by a committee. Why do you think committees sometime fail to achieve their goals?* They lack a well-thoughtout plan.

2 TEACH

Using Models Have students estimate the number of pennies needed to cover their desktops without overlap. Have them describe their estimation methods. Sample answers: Count the number of pennies across the top of the desk and the number down one side, and multiply; divide the area of the desktop by the area of one penny.

1-1 A Plan for Problem Solving

Objective
Solve problems using the four-step plan.

The committee for the Fort Couch Middle School's fall dance has decided to decorate the ceiling of the multi-purpose room by covering it with balloons. Their sponsor agreed, but said she needed to know how many balloons they needed. If the room is 40 feet by 60 feet, what is the least number of balloons they will need?

The committee needed to come up with a plan to solve this problem. In mathematics, we have a plan to solve problems that involves four steps. The four steps are *Explore, Plan, Solve,* and *Examine.*

1. **Explore** Determine what information is given in the problem and what you need to find. Do you have all the information you need to solve the problem? Is there too much information?

2. **Plan** Make an estimate of what you think the answer should be. Then select a strategy for solving the problem. There may be any number of ideas or strategies that you can use.

3. **Solve** Solve the problem by carrying out your plan. If your plan doesn't work, try another, and maybe even another.

4. **Examine** Examine your answer carefully. See if it fits the facts given in the problem. Compare it to your estimate. If the answer is not reasonable, make a new plan. You may also want to check your answer by solving the problem again in a different way.

Example 1 *Problem Solving*

Let's try our plan on the opening problem.

Explore *What do we know?*
We know that the room is 40 feet by 60 feet.
We know that the entire ceiling is to be covered.

What are we trying to find out?
We need to find out the least number of balloons it will take to cover the ceiling. But to do that, we need to know how much space each balloon will cover.

OPTIONS

Team Teaching

Inform the other teachers on your team that your classes are using a four-step problem-solving plan. Share the plan with them. Ask them to use it occasionally to solve problems in their discipline. For example, science teachers can apply it to physics problems and health teachers to public health problems.

Plan   The committee guessed they needed about 2,000 balloons. Let's make a drawing. If you knew how many balloons fit in one row across the room and how many rows you had, you could find the total number of balloons needed.

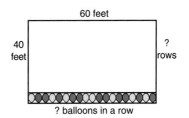

60 feet

40 feet

? rows

? balloons in a row

Solve   Suppose an inflated balloon is 1 foot across. Then 60 balloons would fit in a row across the length of the room. Since the room is 40 feet wide, there would be 40 rows. Multiply to find how many balloons there would be.

$$40 \times 60 = 2,400$$

The committee will need at least 2,400 balloons to cover the ceiling of the room for the fall dance.

Examine   The committee's estimate of 2,000 was close. The answer 2,400 assumes that the balloons are in rows and columns. It would be difficult to keep that many balloons in that pattern. The committee may want to get slightly more than 2,400 to account for this and other unforeseen problems. The committee decides to tell their sponsor that they will need 2,500 balloons.

Now let's try another problem using a different strategy but the same four steps of problem solving.

Example 2   *Problem Solving*

Entertainment   A feature film lasts two hours ten minutes. There are 15 minutes between showings of the film and 10 minutes of previews before each showing. The previews for the first showing start at 5:00 P.M. If your curfew on the weekend is 11:00 P.M. and it takes 15 minutes to go home after the film, can you attend the second showing of the film?

Explore   We know that the previews for the first show start at 5:00 and last 10 minutes. The film is two hours ten minutes long. There is a 15-minute intermission after the first show, and there are more previews before the second showing.

We need to know what time the second showing ends so we will know if that leaves enough time to get home by 11:00.

More Examples

For Example 1

The dance committee has designed a 25-foot by 30-foot dancing area. If 16 square feet are allowed for each couple, what is the maximum number of couples the area will accommodate?
46 couples

For Example 2

Mr. Argyle must attend a meeting in Centralia at 10 A.M. He plans to get up at 7:00 A.M., spend one hour and fifteen minutes getting ready, and 40 minutes eating breakfast. He expects the drive to the meeting to take 35 minutes. Can he visit his sister on the way for 20 minutes and be on time for the meeting?
Yes, with 10 minutes to spare

Checking for Understanding

Exercises 1-3 are designed to help you assess students' understanding through reading, writing, speaking, and modeling. You should work through these exercises with your students and then monitor their work on Guided Practice Exercises 4-5.

Close

Have students write a paragraph explaining the purpose of each of the four steps in the problem-solving plan.

Reteaching Activity

Using Cooperative Groups   Have groups devise a different method for solving the balloon problem. Specify that their method require reading to understand, planning, solving, and checking their solution, precisely the four steps described in the lesson.

Study Guide Masters, p. 1

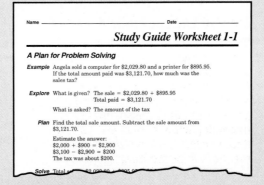

Name _____   Date _____

Study Guide Worksheet 1-1

A Plan for Problem Solving

Example   Angela sold a computer for $2,029.80 and a printer for $895.95. If the total amount paid was $3,121.70, how much was the sales tax?

Explore   What is given?   The sale = $2,029.80 + $895.95
Total paid = $3,121.70

What is asked?   The amount of the tax

Plan   Find the total sale amount. Subtract the sale amount from $3,121.70.

Estimate the answer:
$2,000 + $900 = $2,900
$3,100 − $2,900 = $200
The tax was about $200.

Solve   Total

Assignment Guide
Maximum: 6-14
Minimum: 6-13

Alternate Assessment

Writing Have pairs of students make up their own word problem. Pairs should then exchange problems, solve the problem they receive using the four-step plan, and explain their solution to the students who wrote the problem.

Additional Answer

1. Explore–Identify what information is given and what you need to find.
Plan–Estimate the answer and then select a strategy for solving.
Solve–Carry out the plan and solve.
Examine–Compare the answer to the estimate and determine if it is reasonable. If not, make a new plan.

Practice Masters, p. 1

Name _____ Date _____

Practice Worksheet 1-1

A Plan for Problem Solving

Use the four-step plan to solve each problem.

1. **Carpentry** Geraldo has dowel pieces measuring 10 inches and 11 inches long. He places a number of the pieces end-to-end. They form a line 76 inches long. How many pieces of each size dowel does he have? **six 11-inch, one 10-inch**

2. **Office** Jane's office contains 12 file cabinets. Three cabinets have 4 drawers, all the other cabinets have 5 drawers. Jane is typing new labels for each file cabinet drawer. How many labels will she need? **57 labels**

3. **Money** Bob has a stack of $1 bills, Ian has some $5 bills, and Kim has more than one $10 bill. Each person has the same amount of money. What is the least amount each one has? **$20**

4. **Clock Maker** Angeliki is sticking adhesive digits on the faces of some cuckoo clocks. She has separate compartments of 0s, 1s, 2s, and so on. If she completes 7 clock faces, how many individual digits does she use? **105 digits**

5. **Swimming** Joni walks once around the edge of the swimming pool. The rectangular-shaped pool is 60 feet long. If Joni walks a total of 176 feet, how wide is the pool? **28 feet**

6. **Transportation** The Elm Street bus passes Jamie's house every 20 minutes, and the Park bus passes every half hour. Both buses pass the house together at 1:10 P.M. When is the next time the buses pass together? **2:10 P.M.**

7. **Multiplication** Jake is thinking of a number which, when multiplied times itself gives a product of 729. What is Jake's number? **27**

8. **Artist's Studio** Eric uses molten pewter to make dragon-shaped keychain ornaments. Each dragon weighs 2 ounces. How many dragons can Eric make if he uses 1.5 pounds of molten pewter? (16 ounces = 1 pound) **12 dragons**

9. **School Repairs** Ken is replacing the ceiling tiles in the school hallway. The hallway is 60 feet long and 8 feet wide. Each ceiling tile is 4 feet long and 2 feet wide. How many tiles does Ken need to complete the job? **60 tiles**

10. **Dance Studio** Helene is recording a practice tape for her dance students. She will include rumbas, waltzes and one samba. Each rumba is 3 minutes long; each waltz, 4 minutes; and the samba, 2 minutes long. The tape will contain 30 minutes of music. If Helene wants to record at least 2 waltzes, how many songs of each type will she include in the collection? **4 waltzes, 4 rumbas, 1 samba**

T1
Glencoe Division, Macmillan/McGraw-Hill

Plan Estimate how long it will take. The two showings of the film last a little more than 4 hours. Intermissions and previews are less than 1 hour. The total should be about 5 hours. From 5:00 to 11:00 is 6 hours, so you should be able to attend the second showing. Let's make a chart to solve this problem.

Solve The chart should list each event, how long it takes, and the time it is completed.

Event	How long does it take?	When is it over?
Start time	—	5:00
Previews	10 minutes	5:00 + 0:10 = 5:10
1st showing	2 hours 10 minutes	5:10 + 2:10 = 7:20
Intermission	15 minutes	7:20 + 0:15 = 7:35
Previews	10 minutes	7:35 + 0:10 = 7:45
2nd showing	2 hours 10 minutes	7:45 + 2:10 = 9:55

The show is over at 9:55. You can attend the second showing and still be home before your curfew of 11:00.

Examine *Does your answer seem reasonable?*
The first showing including previews is about $2\frac{1}{2}$ hours. The intermission and the second showing plus previews is about $2\frac{1}{2}$ hours. At most, the total is about 5 hours. Five hours after 5:00 would be 10:00. That gives you an hour to get home by 11:00.

Checking for Understanding

Communicating Mathematics

Read and study the lesson to answer each question.

1. **Write** what each step in the four steps of problem solving means. **See margin.**

2. **Tell** what to do when your plan doesn't work. **Make a new plan.**

3. **Show** how you can use the information in your local newspaper to determine whether you can see the second evening showing of a movie and still make it home before your curfew. **See students' work.**

Guided Practice

4. Look at Example 2. What time does the third showing end? **12:30 A.M.**

5. a. beaker + sodium chloride = 84.8 grams; beaker = 63.3 grams
b. Subtract the two masses.
c. 21.5 grams

5. **Chemistry** A chemist pours sodium chloride (salt) into a beaker. If the beaker plus the sodium chloride have a mass of 84.8 grams and the beaker itself has a mass of 63.3 grams, what is the mass of the sodium chloride that was poured into the beaker? **21.5 grams**
   a. Write the *Explore* step. What do you know?
   b. Write the *Plan* step. What strategy will you use?
   c. *Solve* the problem using your plan. What is the answer?
   d. *Examine* your solution. Is it reasonable? **yes**

6 **Chapter 1** Tools for Problem Solving

OPTIONS

Limited English Proficiency

The reading required in this lesson may become overwhelming. Have students concentrate on the four steps. Illustrate the plan with a simple numerical problem rather than with the more complex examples shown.

Exercises

Problem Solving and Applications

Use the four-step plan to solve each problem.

6. **Photography** The photography class needs to enlarge a 15-centimeter by 25-centimeter picture so that the shorter side is 30 centimeters long. How long will the longer side be after the enlargement? **50 centimeters**

7. **Engineering** Geothermal energy is heat from inside the earth. Underground temperatures generally increase 9°C for every 300 feet of depth. For the ground temperature to rise 90°C, how deep would you have to dig? **3,000 feet**

8. **Transportation** A DC-11 jumbo jet carries 342 passengers with 36 in first class seating and the rest in coach class seating. A first class ticket to fly from Los Angeles to Chicago costs $750, and a coach class ticket costs $450. What will be the ticket sales for the airline if the flight is full? **$164,700**

9. **Money** Maya has only nickels in her pocket. Kim has only dimes in hers. Kareem has only quarters in his. Marta approached them for a donation for the Heart Association drive. What is the least each could donate so that each one gives the same amount? **50¢**

10. **Smart Shopping** At the school bookstore, a ball point pen costs 28¢ and a small tablet costs 23¢. What could you buy and spend exactly 74¢?

    2 tablets and 1 pen

11. **Fitness** Jonna walks along a path around the lake at Triangle Park. One trip around the lake is 4,700 feet. The lengths to two parts of the path are shown. What is the length of the third part? **2,000 feet**

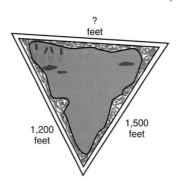

? feet

1,200 feet

1,500 feet

12. **Critical Thinking** Refer to the middle school dance problem at the beginning of the lesson. Joel and Sara decided to estimate the number of balloons needed by finding how many were needed to fill a smaller space. They used cardboard and the corner of a room to make a space 6 feet by 4 feet. They found that 28 balloons cover this space. How could they use this information to solve the problem? **Multiply 28 by 100.**

13. **Make a Model** Suppose you had 100 sugar cubes. What would be the largest cube you could build with the sugar cubes? *Remember that in a cube, all of the sides are the same length.* **4 by 4 by 4**

14. **Journal Entry** In this course, you will be required to keep a journal. Write two or three sentences in your journal that describe what you expect to learn in this course. **See students' work.**

Extending the Lesson

Community Connection Read your local newspaper to learn about a problem facing your community. If possible, speak to someone involved with the problem. Then outline a plan for addressing the problem, describing how you could incorporate the four-step plan into your idea.

Cooperative Learning Activity

Use groups of 4.

As Easy as Pi **1·1**

➡ Solve the following problem.

People have been fascinated by the number π (the circumference of a circle divided by the length of its diameter) for about 4,000 years.

Most of the time, we use 3.14 as the value of π, but if we wanted to be as accurate as possible, we would write π with 16,777,216 places after the decimal!

How long would it take to write π with 16,777,216 decimal places? How many sheets of notebook paper would be needed?

Compare your results with those of other groups.

Glencoe Mathematics: Applications and Connections, Course 3

NCTM Standards: 1–5, 7, 12

Lesson Resources
- Study Guide Master 1-2
- Practice Master 1-2
- Enrichment Master 1-2
- Technology Master, p. 15
- Group Activity Card 1-2

 Transparency 1-2 contains the 5-Minute Check and a teaching aid for this lesson.

🕐 5-Minute Check
(Over Lesson 1-1)

Use the four-step plan to solve this problem.

A car rents for $28 per day plus $0.09 per mile. Mrs. Kent rented a car for three days and drove 560 miles. Find the rental charge. $134.40

1 FOCUS

Motivating the Lesson

Questioning Have students read the opening paragraph of the lesson. Ask the following questions.

- *Find the sums 1 + 100, 2 + 99, 3 + 98, 49 + 52, and 50 + 51.* 101; 101; 101; 101; 101

- *Why does the product 50 × 101 give the sum of the numbers 1 to 100?* because there are 50 pairs of addends whose sum is 101 when adding the numbers 1 through 100

- *What was Gauss' answer?* 5,050

2 TEACH

Using Calculators Have students add 491 + 385, 492 + 384, and 493 + 383. 876; 876; 876 Have them compare the pairs of addends and then ask this question: *Why are the sums equal?* For consecutive pairs, an increase of 1 in the first addend is balanced by a decrease of 1 in the second addend.

8

Objective
Compute mentally using compensation and properties of numbers.

Words to Learn
compensation
commutative
associative
distributive

Carl Friedrich Gauss (1777–1855), a famous mathematician, entered his first class of arithmetic at age 10. One day, the teacher asked the students to find the sum of the numbers 1 through 100. Young Gauss amazed his teacher by writing the correct answer immediately. Gauss used a mental math strategy to find the sum.

Mental math strategies help you compute an answer quickly and easily when a calculator or pencil and paper are not handy. They can also help to cut calculation time when you are working with pencil and paper. Unlike estimation, mental math allows you to find an exact answer.

One mental math strategy is **compensation.** In compensation, you change a problem so it is easy to solve mentally. Then you make an adjustment to compensate for the change you made.

There are many ways to compensate in finding an answer. A number line and basic facts can show you how compensation works.

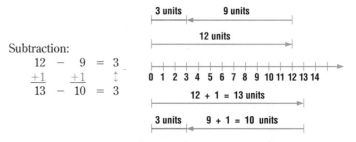

The total distance, 13, must stay the same. So if you add units to one number, you must subtract units from the other number.

The distance 3, representing the difference of the numbers, must stay the same. If you add units to one number, you must add units to the other also.

OPTIONS

Reteaching Activity

Using Models Use compensation to add 8 + 5 using toothpicks:

8 + 5 | | | | | | | | ⌒| | |
10 + 3 | | | | | | | | | | | | | |

Increasing the group of 8 by 2 decreases the group of 5 by 2. The number of toothpicks is unchanged, so the sum is 13.

Study Guide Masters, p. 2

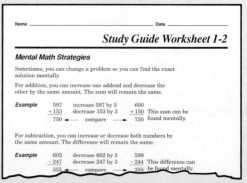

Name _____ Date _____

Study Guide Worksheet 1-2

Mental Math Strategies

Sometimes, you can change a problem so you can find the exact solution mentally.

For addition, you can increase one addend and decrease the other by the same amount. The sum will remain the same.

Example　597　increase 597 by 3　600
　　　+ 153　decrease 153 by 3　+ 150　This sum can be
　　　750　　compare　　750　found mentally.

For subtraction, you can increase or decrease both numbers by the same amount. The difference will remain the same.

Example　602　decrease 602 by 3　599
　　　− 247　decrease 247 by 3　− 244　This difference can
　　　355　　compare　　355　be found mentally.

1 Find 298 + 147.

$$298 \quad +2 \to \quad 300$$
$$\underline{+147} \quad -2 \to \quad \underline{+145}$$
$$445$$

2 Find $5.00 − $1.43.

$$\$5.00 \quad -0.01 \to \quad \$4.99$$
$$\underline{-1.43} \quad -0.01 \to \quad \underline{-1.42}$$
$$\$3.57$$

You may remember some properties of numbers from your previous mathematics courses that you can also use to do mental math. These are the **commutative, associative,** and **distributive** properties for addition and multiplication.

The symbol · means to multiply. 6 · 3 means 6 × 3.

Property	Arithmetic	Algebra
Commutative	$1 + 2 = 2 + 1$ $3 \cdot 2 = 2 \cdot 3$	$a + b = b + a$ $a \cdot b = b \cdot a$
Associative	$3 + (4 + 10) = (3 + 4) + 10$ $5 \cdot (2 \cdot 12) = (5 \cdot 2) \cdot 12$	$a + (b + c) = (a + b) + c$ $a \cdot (b \cdot c) = (a \cdot b) \cdot c$
Distributive	$6 \cdot (5 + 7) = (6 \cdot 5) + (6 \cdot 7)$	$a \cdot (b + c) = a \cdot b + a \cdot c$

Examples

3 Find $5 \cdot 27 \cdot 2$.

It is easier to multiply by 10. Use the commutative property.

$$5 \cdot 27 \cdot 2 = 5 \cdot 2 \cdot 27$$
$$= 10 \cdot 27$$
$$= 270$$

4 Find $(7 \cdot 25) \cdot 4$.

It is easier to multiply by 100. Regroup the numbers by using the associative property.

$$(7 \cdot 25) \cdot 4 = 7 \cdot (25 \cdot 4)$$
$$= 7 \cdot 100$$
$$= 700$$

5 Find $7 \cdot 15$.

Use the distributive property to rewrite 15 as the sum 10 + 5.

$$7 \cdot 15 = 7 \cdot (10 + 5)$$
$$= (7 \cdot 10) + (7 \cdot 5)$$
$$= 70 + 35 \text{ or } 105$$

Checking for Understanding

Communicating Mathematics

Read and study the lesson to answer each question.

1. **Tell** how you could compensate to add $1.98 and $3.98. **See margin.**
2. **Write** the expression 25 + 80 + 75 so it is easier to add mentally. **25 + 75 + 80**
3. **Show** several examples of how compensation and mental math involve changes that result in numbers ending in 0. **Answers will vary.**

Lesson 1-2 Mental Math Strategies **9**

Additional Answer

1. Add $0.02 to $1.98 and subtract $0.02 from $3.98.

Teaching Tip In Example 4, point out that the distributive property cannot be used since the operation in the parentheses is multiplication, not addition.

More Examples

For Example 1
Find 695 + 227. 922

For Example 2
Find 300 − 89. 211

For Example 3
Find 2 · 19 · 5. 190

For Example 4
Find (50 · 9) · 2. 900

For Example 5
Find 7 · 23. 161

Checking for Understanding

Exercises 1–3 are designed to help you assess students' understanding through reading, writing, speaking, and modeling. You should work through these exercises with your students and then monitor their work on Guided Practice Exercises 4–12.

Practice Masters, p. 2

Name _____ Date _____

Practice Worksheet 1-2

Mental Math Strategies
Use mental math to find each answer.

1. 6(15) 90
2. 51 + 99 150
3. 5 × 24 120
4. 5(17 + 3) 100
5. 97 + 33 130
6. 43 + 36 + 57 136
7. 693 + 307 1,000
8. 2 × (63 × 5) 630
9. (4 × 8) × 5 160
10. (4 × 8) × 25 800
11. 5 × (17 × 4) 340
12. 6 × $3.50 $21
13. 805 − 295 510
14. $1.95 + $4.95 $6.90
15. (367 + 230) + 70 667
16. 589 + 813 1,402
17. 752 − 217 535
18. 26 + 46 + 34 106
19. 12 · 5 · 4 240
20. 68 + 70 + 72 210
21. 802 − 112 690
22. 10(37 + 13) 500
23. (9 × 5) × 6 270
24. 552 − 48 504
25. 99 + 101 + 103 303
26. (15 · 5) · 4 300
27. 15 · 8 + 15 · 2 150
28. 208 − 49 159
29. 21(64 + 36) 2,100
30. 125 × (8 × 4) 4,000
31. 2.8(4) + 2.8(6) 28
32. 5($3.35) + 5($6.65) $50
33. 9(0.01) + 0.01 0.1

T2
Glencoe Division, Macmillan/McGraw-Hill

9

Close

Have students describe problems where compensation is an appropriate mental-math strategy, and problems where using the commutative, associative, and distributive properties make the computation easier.

3 PRACTICE/APPLY

Assignment Guide
Maximum: 13–36
Minimum: 13–29 odd, 31–35

For **Extra Practice,** see p. 584.

Alternate Assessment

Writing Have students write three mental-math problems, one solvable using compensation, one using the commutative or associative property, and one using the distributive property.

Enrichment Masters, p. 2

Guided Practice Tell how you would use mental math to find each answer. Then find the answer. **For mental math procedures, see Solutions Manual.**

4. $15 + 37 + 15$ **67**   5. $47 + 98$ **145**   6. $700 - 23$ **677**
7. $(23 + 17) \cdot 8$ **320**   8. $83 + 48 + 17$ **148**   9. $20 \cdot 93 \cdot 50$ **93,000**
10. $7 \cdot 35$ **245**   11. $43 \cdot 50 \cdot 2$ **4,300**   12. $57 + 69 + 43$ **169**

Exercises

Independent Practice Use mental math to find each answer.

13. $65 + 73 + 15$ **153**   14. $(13 \cdot 25) \cdot 4$ **1,300**   15. $9 \cdot 15$ **135**
16. $600 - 243$ **357**   17. $53(90 + 10)$ **5,300**   18. $37 + 29 + 3$ **69**
19. $498 + 329$ **827**   20. $740 + 987 + 60$ **1,787**   21. $5(15 + 5)$ **100**
22. $(21 \times 2) \times 50$ **2,100**   23. $14 \cdot 4 \cdot 25$ **1,400**   24. $69 + 93 + 31$ **193**
25. $43 + 29 + 7$ **79**   26. $702 - 598$ **104**   27. $(623 + 420) + 80$ **1,123**

28. Find $(423 \times 50) \times 2$. Tell how you found the answer. **$423 \cdot (50 \cdot 2) = 42,300$**

29. Suppose ■ $= 12 \cdot 25$. Use mental math to find the missing number. **300**

30. Suppose $a = 14 \times (7 + 10 + 13)$. If a represents the answer to the problem, find a. **420**

Mixed Review 31. **Communication** The cost of a long distance phone call is 15¢ for the first 5 minutes and 10¢ for each additional minute. If Laura makes a 30-minute long distance phone call, how much will it cost? *(Lesson 1-1)* **$2.65**

32. **Production** A furniture company produces 15 rocking chairs in one hour. How long will it take to produce 45 chairs? *(Lesson 1-1)* **3 hours**

33. **Hobbies** Romo likes to collect baseball cards. Every week he buys 20 baseball cards and sells 16 of them. How many baseball cards will he have after 7 weeks? *(Lesson 1-1)* **28 cards**

Problem Solving and Applications 34. **Geometry** Three sides of a four-sided figure are 51 inches, 49 inches, and 38 inches long. How long is the fourth side if the sum of the lengths of all the sides is 200 inches? **62 inches**

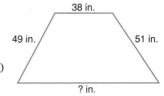

35. **Critical Thinking** José was given 30 capsules by the doctor to help him recover from strep throat. He was to take two capsules with every meal for the first two days and then one capsule with each meal until they are all taken. If he starts the medication with breakfast on Monday and eats three meals a day, on what day and with which meal did he take the last capsule? **the following Monday at dinner**

36. **Journal Entry** Find the definition of *compensate* in a dictionary. Write one or two sentences to explain how the definition describes the compensation strategy. **See students' work.**

10 **Chapter 1** Tools for Problem Solving

OPTIONS

Extending the Lesson

Combining Strategies Compare each of the following with the product $20 \cdot 7 \cdot 50 = 7,000$. Then mentally compute the number which would replace the ■.

1. $10 \cdot 7 \cdot$ ■ $= 7,000$ **100**
2. $5 \cdot 7 \cdot$ ■ $= 7,000$ **200**
3. ■ $\cdot 7 \cdot 25 = 7,000$ **40**
4. ■ $\cdot 14 \cdot 25 = 7,000$ **20**

Cooperative Learning Activity

Winner Takes All **1-2**

Number of players: 2
Materials: Index cards

↓ Copy onto cards the expressions listed on the back of this card. Decide which partner will be the dealer.

→ The dealer shuffles the cards and deals an equal number to himself or herself and to his or her partner. Both partners place a card face up. The partner whose card has the higher value takes both cards and places them in a separate pile. When a player has used all of the cards in his or her original pile, he or she shuffles the cards in the second pile and uses them. The game continues in this manner until one partner has all of the cards.

Glencoe Mathematics: Applications and Connections, Course 3

10

1-3 Estimation Strategies

Objective
Estimate answers by using different strategies.

Words to Learn
rounding
front-end
compatible numbers
clustering

Whatever happened to the gum wrapper you threw in the wastebasket the other day? Chances are it ended up in a landfill somewhere. Experts estimate that Americans throw away about 160 million tons of garbage each year. How do they get this estimate? It's not by weighing each family's garbage each week. They estimate the total by using amounts from sample days in different parts of the country.

Depending on the situation, an estimate is often good enough and an exact answer is not needed. For example, a quick estimate can also help you check whether a total on a calculator or automatic cash register is reasonable.

In this lesson, we will show four different ways you can estimate. They are by **rounding,** by **front-end estimation,** by using **compatible numbers,** and by **clustering.** The following examples will show how each type can be used.

Example 1

Estimate 6,337 + 2,875.

Use rounding.

$$
\begin{array}{rcr}
6{,}337 & \to & 6{,}000 \\
+\,2{,}875 & \to & +\,3{,}000 \\
\hline
& & 9{,}000
\end{array}
$$

One estimate for
6,337 + 2,875 is 9,000.

Use front-end estimation.

Add the left column of digits. Then add the next column of digits.

$$
\begin{array}{rcr}
6{,}337 & & 6{,}3\,37 \\
+\,2{,}875 & \to & +\,2{,}8\,75 \\
\hline
8\,000 & & 1100
\end{array}
$$

Add.
9,100

Another estimate for
6,337 + 2,875 is 9,100.

Lesson 1-3 Estimation Strategies **11**

1-3 Lesson Notes

NCTM Standards: 1–5, 7, 12

Lesson Resources
• Study Guide Master 1-3
• Practice Master 1-3
• Enrichment Master 1-3
• Group Activity Card 1-3

Transparency 1-3 contains the 5-Minute Check and a teaching aid for this lesson.

5-Minute Check
(Over Lesson 1-2)

Use mental math to find each answer.

1. 267 + 396   663
2. 800 − 337   463
3. (49 · 20) · 5   4,900
4. 250 · 13 · 4   13,000

5. Velma worked for 6 hours at a wage of $5.95 per hour. Use mental math to find her total earnings.
$35.70

1 FOCUS

Motivating the Lesson

Questioning   Have students read the opening paragraph of the lesson. Ask this question: *How could you estimate the amount each American throws away annually?*   Divide the estimated amount that all Americans throw away by the U. S. population.

2 TEACH

Using Calculators   Students will be curious to know how close the estimates in the examples are to the actual answers. Have them use their calculators to compute the actual answers. Stress that the purpose of estimating is not so much to come as close as possible to the actual answer, but to generate a number that can easily be used to test the reasonableness of a computed answer.

Teaching Tip In Example 3, point out that compatible numbers are only used when dividing.

More Examples

For Example 1

Estimate 2,788 + 6,810. rounding: 10,000; front-end: 9,500

For Example 2

Estimate 369.1 − 46.5. rounding: 320; front-end: 323

For Example 3

Estimate 2,437 ÷ 38.   60

For Example 4

When Corey added 4,821 + 5,416 + 4,733 + 5,291 on his calculator, he obtained the sum 15,386. Is this answer reasonable?   No; estimate by clustering: 20,000

Checking for Understanding

Exercises 1-3 are designed to help you assess students' understanding through reading, writing, speaking, and modeling. You should work through these exercises with your students and then monitor their work on Guided Practice Exercises 4-12.

Error Analysis

Watch for students who combine front-end-estimation sums incorrectly.

$$
\begin{array}{r}
6,\ 337 \\
+\ 2,\ 875 \\
\hline
8,\ 000
\end{array}
\qquad
\begin{array}{r}
6,\ 3 \\
2,\ 8\ 75 \\
\hline
11\ 00
\end{array}
$$

$$8 + 11 = 19,000$$

Prevent by pointing out the difference in place values.

Examples

2 Estimate 118.1 − 57.5.

Use rounding.

$$
\begin{array}{rcr}
118.1 & \rightarrow & 120 \\
-\ 57.5 & \rightarrow & -\ 60 \\
\hline
& & 60
\end{array}
$$

One estimate for 118.1 − 57.5 is 60.

Use front-end estimation.

$$
\begin{array}{rcr}
118.1 & & 118.1 \\
-\ 57.5 & \rightarrow & -\ 57.5 \\
\hline
60.0 & & 1.0
\end{array}
$$

Add.

61

Another estimate for 118.1 − 57.5 is 61.

3 Estimate 4,321 ÷ 73.

Use compatible numbers. Round the divisor to 70. Replace 4,321 with 4,200. By estimating 4,321 as 4,200, the division becomes easier. That is, 42 is divisible by 7.

$$4,321 \div 70 \quad \rightarrow \quad 4,200 \div 70 = 60$$

An estimate for 4,321 ÷ 73 is 60.

When using a calculator, it is easy to hit a wrong key. This is especially true if there are a lot of numbers to enter or if the numbers are large. You should use estimation to check your work.

Example 4   *Problem Solving*

Technology Jesse uses his calculator to find the sum of 7,129 + 6,859 + 7,523 + 6,792 + 6,928. How can he tell if the answer 35231 showing on the calculator is reasonable?

> **Estimation Hint**
> • • • • • • • • • •
> Clustering works best with numbers that all round to approximately the same number.

Use clustering. Each of the numbers in Jesse's problem is very close to 7,000. You can estimate the sum of these five numbers by multiplying 5 and 7,000.

$$5 \times 7,000 = 35,000$$

The estimate of 35,000 is very close to his answer of 35,231. The calculator answer is reasonable and is probably correct.

Some estimation methods work better in certain situations than in others. Occasionally you may want to combine different estimation methods. The purpose of estimation is to give you a guide for easily determining a number that is close to the actual number.

OPTIONS

Reteaching Activity

Using Communication Successful estimation requires a sense of which numbers are close to others. Foster this skill by stating numbers and asking students to name three numbers ending in zeros that are close to the given number. Example: 2,347; Sample answers: 2,000, 2,500, 2,300

Study Guide Masters, p. 3

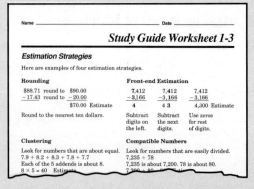

Name _____   Date _____

Study Guide Worksheet 1-3

Estimation Strategies

Here are examples of four estimation strategies.

Rounding

$88.71 round to $90.00
−17.43 round to −20.00
            $70.00 Estimate

Round to the nearest ten dollars.

Front-end Estimation

7,412	7,412	7,412
−3,166	−3,166	−3,166
4	**4 3**	4,300 Estimate

Subtract digits on the left. / Subtract the next digits. / Use zeros for rest of digits.

Clustering

Look for numbers that are about equal.
7.9 + 8.2 + 8.3 + 7.8 + 7.7
Each of the 5 addends is about 8.
8 × 5 = 40   Estimate

Compatible Numbers

Look for numbers that are easily divided.
7,235 ÷ 78
7,235 is about 7,200. 78 is about 80.
7,200 ÷ 80

Checking for Understanding

Communicating Mathematics

Read and study the lesson to answer each question. For answers to Exercises 1–3, see margin.

1. **Write** two reasons for using estimation.
2. **Tell** what to do if you have several numbers to add and clustering does not work.
3. **Show** how front-end estimation differs from rounding.

Guided Practice

Round each number to its greatest place value.

4. 5,432 **5,000**   5. 723.9 **700**   6. 0.08547 **0.09**

Tell which method you would use to estimate each answer. Explain why you chose that method. Then estimate. For answers to Exercises 7–12, see margin.

7. $628 + 547 + 432$
8. $4,423 - 2,983$
9. $5,231 - 4,108$
10. $\$12.99 - \$4.33$
11. $5.593 \div 0.74$
12. $2.3 + 2.5 + 2.8 + 2.4$

Exercises   13. 9,000; 8,900 14. 14; 13.3

Independent Practice

Estimate first by rounding and then by front-end estimation.

13. $5,293 + 3,733$
14. $6.59 + 4.65 + 2.28$
15. $0.7829 - 0.5392$ **0.3, 0.25**
16. $7,623 - 5,450$ **3,000; 2,200**

Estimate by using compatible numbers.

17. $3,593 \div 62$ **60**
18. $7.347 \div 0.79$ **9**

Estimate each sum by clustering.

19. $5,473 + 4,987 + 5,129 + 4,873$ **20,000**
20. $\$2.10 + \$1.89 + \$2.15 + \$1.98 + \$2.09$ **$10.00**

Estimate. Use an appropriate strategy.

21. $576 - 395$ **200**
22. $5.247 - 3.258$ **2**
23. $3,500 \div 62$ **60**
24. $527 + 915 + 467$ **1,890**
25. $82.43 + 79.28 + 37.41$ **198**
26. $\$5.99 + \$6.94 + \$7.15$ **$20.00**

Mixed Review

27. **Inventory** A restaurant serves 240 cups of coffee each day. If 1 pound of coffee is used to make 40 cups, how many pounds will the restaurant need in a week? *(Lesson 1-1)* **42 pounds**
28. Ted weighs 119 pounds. If Ted's weight plus Tisha's weight is 215 pounds, how much does Tisha weigh? *(Lesson 1-1)* **96 pounds**
29. Use mental math to find $21(9 + 6)$. *(Lesson 1-2)* **315**
30. Use mental math to find $534 + 88$. *(Lesson 1-2)* **622**

Lesson 1-3 Estimation Strategies   **13**

Writing Have students work in groups of four. Each of the four students selects a different estimation method and writes a problem to illustrate that method. Students then exchange problems and solve. The activity should be done four times with students choosing a different method each time.

Additional Answer

32. a.

$$3,000 + 400 = 3,400$$

b. Subtract 1 from the digit in the first answer if you have to borrow to get the second answer.

c. about 2,700

Enrichment Masters, p. 3

Name _____ Date _____

Enrichment Worksheet 1-3

Rep-Tiles

A *rep-tile* is a figure that can be divided into smaller copies of itself. Here are the rules for making rep-tiles.

Rule 1 Each small copy must be similar to the large figure. Two similar figures have the same shape.

Rule 2 All the small copies must be congruent to each other. Two congruent figures have the same shape and the same size.

Trace four copies of each figure on a separate sheet of paper. Arrange the copies to make a rep-tile. Then record your answers on these shapes.

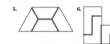
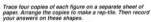
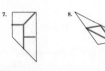
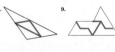

T 3
Glencoe Division, Macmillan/McGraw-Hill

---

31. Inventory Mark works in the bookstore during his free period. He learned that a ream of paper has 500 sheets. At the end of the month, he counted 423 reams of paper left. Approximately how many sheets of paper is this? **about 200,000 sheets of paper**

32. See margin.

32. Critical Thinking Sam wanted to use front-end estimation to estimate 8,325 − 4,986. He says the process presented in Example 2 doesn't work.

 a. How could Sam change the process to use the front-end method to estimate this difference?

 b. Write a rule for your method of front-end estimation.

 c. Try your rule in estimating 5,300 − 2,654.

33. a. about 2,500 feet of fence

33. Geometry Mrs. Hawks owns a farm next to the school. She donated the use of a large five-sided field to the school's agriculture program.

 a. If the field has sides that are 524 feet, 498 feet, 519 feet, 502 feet, and 486 feet long, about how much fence must they order to enclose the field?

 b. What factors must you consider when buying fence to enclose a given area? **Answers will vary.**

34. Arts and Crafts At an arts festival, the Art Club set up a booth to sell their ceramic pots. Mr. Wilburn selected pots that were priced at $5.98, $7.25, $3.25, $8.75, $9.85, $2.50, and $7.25. He has $50 in his wallet. How could he use estimation to see if he can pay cash or if he has to write a check? **Round each price to the nearest 50¢.**

Save Planet Earth

Recycling Newspapers Americans use 50 million tons of paper each year. This means we consume more than 850 million trees. It is estimated that the average American uses about 420 pounds of paper each year.

How You Can Help

● Don't throw away newspapers with the trash anymore. Select a spot in your home, stack them, tie them together, and weigh them for one week. If one tree produces 120 pounds of paper, how many trees would you save by recycling?

● Find a recycling program in your neighborhood.

If everyone in this country recycled even one-tenth of their newspapers, we would save about 25 million trees every year.

OPTIONS

Extending the Lesson

Save Planet Earth Tell students to look in the yellow pages for recycling programs in their neighborhoods. There are curbside recycling programs or receptacles at certain supermarkets.

Cooperative Learning Activity

Dare to Compare **1-3**

Use groups of 2.
Materials: Reference books

➡ Try to be the first pair to answer the questions below. Use rounding, front-end estimation, clustering, and compatible numbers.

1. What five states *together* have a land area that is about the same as the land area of Alaska?
2. What five states *together* have a population that is about the same as the population of California?
3. Which is greater—the combined population of the ten most populous states or the combined population of the remaining forty states?

Compare your work with the work of other pairs.

Glencoe Mathematics: Applications and Connections, Course 3

1-4 Determine Reasonable Answers

Objective

Determine whether answers to problems are reasonable.

You are going to paint one wall and a door of the school rec room with two coats of paint. The wall is 19 feet by 9 feet, and the door is 3 feet by 7 feet. At the store, you find that a gallon will cover about 400 ft² and a quart will cover about 100 ft², when using two coats. Which size should you buy?

$$1 \text{ ft}^2 = 1 \text{ sq ft } = 1 \text{ ft} \boxed{} 1 \text{ ft}$$
$$\begin{array}{c} 1 \text{ ft} \\ 1 \text{ ft} \end{array}$$

Explore You know that the areas to be painted are 19 feet by 9 feet and 3 feet by 7 feet. You know that a gallon will cover about 400 ft² and a quart will cover about 100 ft².

You want to find out which size is more reasonable to buy.

Plan Estimate to find the total area. Then see which size has enough paint for that area.

Solve The area of the door is 7 × 3 or 21 ft², which rounds to 20 ft². The area of the wall is about 10 × 20 or 200 ft². The total area is about 20 + 200 or 220 ft².

A quart will not be enough to cover this area.

Examine The total area to be painted is more than a quart will cover. It makes sense to buy the gallon.

Wearing eye shadow began in ancient times. The Egyptians painted their eyelids to shield their eyes from the sun.

Example

Smart Shopping You spend $5.55 plus $0.44 tax at the store for makeup and pay with a $10 bill. Would it be more reasonable to expect about $3.00 or $4.00 in change?

You can estimate how much change you should receive.
$5.55 rounds to $5.60 and $0.44 rounds to $0.40, so you spent about $5.60 + $0.40, or $6.00. Since $10.00 − $6.00 = $4.00, it is more reasonable to expect about $4.00 in change.

Lesson 1-4 Problem-Solving Strategy: Determine Reasonable Answers **15**

OPTIONS

Reteaching Activity

Using Applications Have students cut out grocery, furniture, or other sale ads from the local newspaper and create their own problems like Guided Practice Exercise 5. Have them exchange problems with other students and solve.

---

1 FOCUS

Motivating the Lesson

Activity Ask students to estimate the dimensions of one wall of the classroom, and then to estimate its area.

2 TEACH

More Examples

For the Example

Mei spent $7.56 plus $0.38 tax for food. She paid with a $10 bill. Is it more reasonable to expect about $1.00 or $2.00 in change?
about $2.00

Close

Ask the following question. *How can you use estimation to decide whether a given answer is reasonable?* Estimate the answer and compare the estimate with the given answer.

3 PRACTICE/APPLY

Assignment Guide
Maximum: 6–11
Minimum: 6–11

Enrichment Masters, p. 4

Name _____ Date _____

Enrichment Worksheet 1-4

Reasonable Questions

On this page you are to match the beginning of a problem with a logical conclusion. Notice that the final sentence in every problem is a question.

Write a number on each blank to match the beginning of each problem to its question. Then find the answer.

Beginning	Question	Answers
1. A mechanic earns $200 a day. Her expenses average $167.50 per day.	5 How much was collected for the frames?	1. $32.50
2. Kelsey paid $75 for a pair of boots and $55 for a hat.	4 How much money was lost?	2. $130
3. The average amount of rain in Cincinnati in the summer months is 13.7 in. In the winter it is 11.15 in.	1 How much can she save?	3. 2.55 in.
4. A family bought a farm for $586,700, built a house for $185,000 and then sold the property for $725,000.	2 How much did she pay for both?	4. $46,700
5. A shop owner sold 25 picture frames at $22.45 each.	6 How much will the adult earn while the teenager earns $72?	5. $561.25
6. An adult earns $16 an hour while a teenager earns $9 an hour.	7 How many sheets are there in 2.5 quires?	6. $128
7. There are 24 sheets of paper in a quire.	8 How far apart will they be in 8 hours?	7. 60
8. Two people start at the same time from the same point and travel in the same direction. One person travels at 52 mph and the other at 39 mph.	3 How much more rain falls in the summer months?	8. 104 mi

T4
Glencoe Division, Macmillan/McGraw-Hill

Checking for Understanding

Communicating Mathematics

Read and study the lesson to answer each question.

1. **Write** another way to estimate the amount of change in the Example. How does this estimate affect the answer to the problem? **See margin.**

2. **Tell** why it is good to round up when estimating the area of a wall that needs to be painted. **This ensures that there will be more than enough paint.**

Guided Practice

Solve by determining reasonable answers.

3. When Vic divided 45,109.5 by 1,479 the calculator showed 305. Is this answer reasonable? **No. 45,000 ÷ 1,500 is 30, not 300.**

4. **200 crates**

4. An orange grower harvested 1,260 pounds of oranges from one grove, 874 pounds from another, and 602 pounds from another. What is a reasonable number of crates to have on hand if each crate holds 14 pounds of oranges?

5. You need to buy 3 cans of cat food at 39¢ each, 5 pounds of tomatoes at 89¢ a pound, and a quart of milk at 75¢. Do you need to take $5.00 or $10.00 with you? **$10.00**

Margin answer:
1. $5.55 is about $5.50; $0.44 is about $0.50. The total is about $6. So your change is about $4.

Problem Solving

Practice

Solve. Use any strategy.

6. The space shuttle can carry about 65,000 pounds of cargo. A compact car weighs about 2,450 pounds. What is a reasonable number of compact cars that could be carried on the space shuttle? **26 cars**

Strategies
• • • • • • •
Look for a pattern.
Solve a simpler problem.
Act it out.
Guess and check.
Draw a diagram.
Make a chart.
Work backward.

7. On your 14th birthday, your aunt says you can have twice your age in dollars each year for 5 years or you can have $32 each year for 5 years. Which way do you get more money overall? **They are the same.**

8. If 610,184 people attended 8 Denver Bronco home games during the 1990 football season, which is a reasonable estimate for the number of people that attended each game: 7,500 or 75,000? **75,000 people**

9. As part of your exercise program, you decide to do 5 more sit-ups each day. If you start with 5 sit-ups, how many sit-ups will you do on the 10th day? **50 sit-ups**

10. Yesterday, you noted that the mileage on the family car read 60,094.8 miles. Today it read 60,099.1 miles. Was the car driven about 4 or 40 miles? **4 miles**

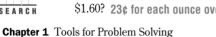
DATA SEARCH

11. **Data Search** Refer to page 665. What is the pattern in the rates for first class postage? Would a 7-ounce letter cost more or less than $1.60? **23¢ for each ounce over 1 ounce; more**

OPTIONS

Extending the Lesson

Using Connections In each case, tell whether you should overestimate or underestimate.

1. Estimating the cost of a meal to decide if you have enough money
   overestimate

2. Estimating the amount of air in your scuba-diving tank to decide how long you can stay underwater underestimate

Cooperative Learning Activity

Don't Be Unreasonable 1-4

Number of players: 2
Materials: Index cards, spinners

♦ Copy onto cards the amounts shown on the back of this card, one per card. Shuffle the cards and divide them evenly. Label the sections of a spinner $10, $15, $25, $50, $75, $100, $200, $500.

➥ Each partner places a card face up. Then one partner spins the spinner. Each partner writes the number of items you could buy at the price shown on the card with the amount of money shown on the spinner. Check the reasonableness of each other's answers. Continue in this way, taking turns at the spinner, until all of the cards have been played. Try to "purchase" more items than your partner by the end of the game.

Glencoe Mathematics: Applications and Connections, Course 3

1-5 Eliminate Possibilities

Objective
Solve problems by using estimation to eliminate possibilities.

Three after-school jobs are posted on the bulletin board. The first job pays $4.25 per hour for 15 hours of work each week. The second job pays $10.95 a day for 3 hours, 5 days each week. The third job pays $59.75 for 15 hours total each week. If you want to apply only for the job that pays the most, which should you choose?

Explore You know that each job is for 15 hours a week. One job pays $4.25 per hour; one pays $10.95 per day; and one pays $59.75 per week.

You want to compare the amount each pays, so you will know which job to apply for.

Plan First, estimate how much each job pays a week by multiplying the hours or days by the amount of pay. Then you can eliminate the lowest paying job or jobs.

Solve $4.25 can be rounded to $4.00. Since this is the amount for an hour, multiply by 15 to find the amount for the week.

$$\$4.00 \times 15 = \$60.00$$

$10.95 can be rounded to $11.00. Since this is the amount for a day, multiply by 5 to find the amount for the week.

$$\$11.00 \times 5 = \$55.00$$

$59.75 can be rounded to $60.00. This is the amount for a week.

The job that pays $10.95 a day can be eliminated, since it pays the lowest. Since $4.25 is a little more than $4.00, that job will actually pay more than $60.00 a week. Since $59.75 is less than $60.00, that job can also be eliminated. So, you should apply for the job that pays $4.25 per hour.

Examine You can check your answer by using a calculator to find the actual pay.

Lesson 1-5 Problem-Solving Strategy: Eliminate Possibilities **17**

OPTIONS

Reteaching Activity

Using Discussion Choose three students and, without informing the other students, designate one a pilot, one an actor, and the other a teacher. Have the remaining students guess who has which profession by asking questions designed to eliminate possibilities. The questions must be answerable by *yes* or *no* only.

Study Guide Masters, p. 5

Name _____ Date _____

Study Guide Worksheet 1-5

Problem-Solving Strategy: Eliminate Possibilities

Example At a rock concert, 2,143 sweatshirts were sold at $18.75 each. The receipts for the sale of the sweatshirts were:
a. $4,018   **b.** $40,181.25   **c.** $401,812.50

Explore What do you know?
2,143 sweatshirts were sold.
Each sweatshirt cost $18.75.

What do you need to find?
The sales receipts

Plan Round to estimate the sales receipts.
Then eliminate possibilities.

Solve Round 2,143 to 2,000.
Round $18.75 to $20.
Use mental math to multiply: $20 × 2,000

17

2 TEACH

Using Logical Reasoning

Explain that eliminating possibilities is a strategy for solving problems *indirectly*. It is used when you know that one of several possible answers must be the correct one. If you can logically eliminate all but one possible answer, that answer must be the correct one.

Checking for Understanding

Exercises 1–2 are designed to help you assess students' understanding through reading, writing, speaking, and modeling. You should work through these exercises with your students and then monitor their work on Guided Practice Exercises 3–5.

Practice Masters, p. 5

Suppose you have the following division problem on a multiple-choice test. How can you eliminate possibilities to choose the correct answer?

$$16,340 \div 19 =$$
a. 80   b. 860   c. 8,600

You can estimate the quotient by rounding to compatible numbers. 16,340 can be rounded to 16,000 and 19 can be rounded to 20. $16,000 \div 20 = 800$.

Choice **a** can be eliminated because 80 is too small to be the correct answer.
Choice **c** can be eliminated because 8,600 is too great to be the correct answer.
The correct answer must be choice **b**.
Check by multiplying. $860 \times 19 = 16,340$.
1. Estimate what the answer should be, then eliminate the choices that are not close to your estimate.

Checking for Understanding

Communicating Mathematics

Read and study the lesson to answer each question.

1. **Tell** how to use the eliminate possibilities strategy to solve a multiple-choice problem like the one in the example.

2. **Explain** why, in the introductory problem, you might want to choose one of the other jobs. distance from home, conflict of time, and so on

Guided Practice

Solve by eliminating possibilities.

3. Last month's gas meter reading was 16,800 ft³. This month the reading is 17,900 ft³. The number of cubic feet (ft³) of gas used was about: b
   a. 100   b. 1,000   c. 10,000

4. Sheila uses her calculator to divide 685,300 by 86.3. She should expect the result to be about: c
   a. 80   b. 800   c. 8,000

5. The Meadowlands Arena seats 20,039 people. If all tickets sell for $12.75 each, the gross receipts for a sell-out would be: b
   a. $2,554,972   b. $255,497.25   c. $25,549.72

Problem Solving

Practice

Solve using any strategy.

6. A speeding bullet travels at about 886.4 mi/h, and a rocket in orbit travels about 17,500 mi/h. The rocket travels about how many times faster than a speeding bullet? a
   a. 20   b. 25   c. 200   d. 2,000

18   Chapter 1 Tools for Problem Solving

OPTIONS

Gifted and Talented Needs

Have students research how matrices can be used to solve logic problems. Possibilities are allowed or ruled out by marking "1" or "0" in each cell of a matrix until only one cell remains. Students may enjoy trying to unravel Lewis Carroll's logic problems in his book *Symbolic Logic*.

7. Maria's house number has four digits and is divisible by 3. The second digit is the square of the first digit. The last two digits are the square of the second digit. What is her house number? **Sample answers: 1101, 3981**

Strategies
• • • • • • •
Look for a pattern.
Solve a simpler problem.
Act it out.
Guess and check.
Draw a diagram.
Make a chart.
Work backward.

8. Basil is painting a border of stars along three walls of his room. Each star measures 0.25 meters wide and the walls are 3.6 meters, 2.7 meters, and 3.3 meters long. About how many stars will he have to paint? **b**
   a. 4   b. 40   c. 400

9. Robin has five different colors of ribbons. She uses three colors for each hairbow she is making. How many different color combinations for the bows are there? **10**

10. Is the average of 342.7, 54.3, 119.45, 909.8, 17.6, and 81.75 about 25, 100, or 250? **250**

11. The human heart beats an average of 72 times in one minute. In one year, the number of times a human heart beats is about: **a**
    a. 37,800,000   b. 378,000   c. 37,800

Assessment: Mid-Chapter Review

1. **Trucking**   A service station along I-64 in Lynchburg, Virginia, charges $1.39 a gallon for diesel fuel and $1.10 a quart for oil. If a truck driver bought 38 gallons of diesel fuel and 2 quarts of oil, how much did she pay? *(Lesson 1-1)* **$55.02**

Use mental math to find each answer. *(Lesson 1-2)*

2. 12 + 35 + 18 **65**   3. $2.99 + $4.98 **$7.97**   4. 6(25 + 5) **180**

Estimate. Use an appropriate strategy. *(Lesson 1-3)*

5. 6.99 + 7.12 + 6.88 + 7.05 **28**   6. 6,245 ÷ 81 **80**

7. 8,101 − 7,002 **1,000**   8. 8.987 × 11 **99**

9. **Geography**   The population of North America is 278,000,000 and its area is 7,466,890 mi^2. Which is a reasonable estimate for the population density (number of people per unit) of this continent, 370 people or 37 people per square mile? *(Lesson 1-4)* **37**

10. **Recycling**   The recycling center pays 5¢ for every two aluminum cans turned in. If a group of students brought in 1,200 cans, how much money would they get back? *(Lesson 1-5)* **c**
    a. $3   b. $6   c. $30   d. $300

Extending the Lesson

Using Cooperative Groups   Ada, Bob, Cal, and Dot live in Austin, Boise, Chicago, and Phoenix, though not in that order. Have small groups use these clues to decide who lives in each city: Ada's brother lives in Phoenix; Bob's city has 7 letters in its name; Cal's city is not a state capital; Dot's state borders on Mexico.   Ada, Boise; Bob, Phoenix; Cal, Chicago; Dot, Austin

Cooperative Learning Activity

Use groups of 2.

On the Road Again 1-5

➡ The driving distances between certain U.S. cities are shown in the table on the back of this card. Use the table to solve the following problems. (Hint: You can estimate sums to eliminate possibilities.) Try to be the first pair to solve all of the problems.

1. A truck driver is based in Indianapolis. His route to another city shown in the table takes him through a third city shown in the table. He travels 1,204 miles one way. Name the other two cities on the driver's route.

2. A sales representative leaves her home in Pittsburgh and travels halfway to her destination in one of the other cities shown in the table before she realizes that she has forgotten her sample case. So she turns around, drives back home, picks up her case, and starts out again. By the time the sales representative gets back home from the other city, she has driven 864 miles. Where did she go?

Glencoe Mathematics: Applications and Connections, Course 3

Close

Tell students that they have been given three possible answers to a problem, one of which is correct. Have them write a few sentences describing how they could decide which answer is correct without actually solving the problem.

3 PRACTICE/APPLY

Assignment Guide
Maximum: 6–11
Minimum: 6–11
All: Mid-Chapter Review

Alternate Assessment

Modeling   Show students three cards of different colors, then cover each card with a book. Have students demonstrate how to determine the color of the card under a specific book without actually looking under that book.

Enrichment Masters, p. 5

Name _____   Date _____

Enrichment Worksheet 1-5

Quantitative Comparisons

An unusual type of problem is found on some standardized multiple-choice tests. This problem type is called the *quantitative comparison.*

Here are the directions for the quantitative comparison questions as they appear on one well-known test.

Questions 8–27 each consist of two quantities, one in Column A and one in Column B. You are to compare the two quantities and on the answer sheet, blacken space
   A if the quantity in Column A is greater;
   B if the quantity in Column B is greater;
   C if the two quantities are equal;
   D if the relationship cannot be determined from the information given.

Write the correct letter to the left of each problem number.

		Column A	Column B
C	1.	20,000 campaign posters at 35¢ each	$7,000 for the campaign posters
B	2.	$120,000,000	A quarter of a billion dollars
A	3.	0.002 + 3	0.003 + 2
D	4.	The population of County X if there are 100 people per square mile	The population of County Y if there are 50 people per square mile
A	5.	6.5	$\frac{58}{9}$
B	6.	The greatest possible product of two even numbers less than 10	The greatest possible product of two odd numbers less than 10

T5
Glencoe Division, Macmillan/McGraw-Hill

DECISION MAKING

NCTM Standards: 1–4, 7

Objective Analyze data and make a decision.

1 FOCUS

Introducing the Situation

Use the following questions to stimulate discussion.

- *What factors do you take into consideration when you make a purchase?* Sample answers: price; quality; availability

- *Is the most expensive item always the best? Explain.* No; a manufacturer may use high price as a substitute for quality.

- *When deciding which product to buy, which do you think is the better choice, the one closest in price to the amount you wish to spend or the one most closely satisfying your needs?* probably the latter

2 TEACH

Using Cooperative Groups
Urge students to study the charts carefully before attempting to answer the questions. Stress that there is no one "right" decision. Any decision which satisfies the group's needs is a sound decision.

Analyzing the Data

Point out that all the prices for the computers fall in the $1,000–$1,999.99 range in the extended-warranties chart.

Answers

1. Yes, there are two types of color monitors.
2. Yes, shipping is extra. No information is available on taxes.
3. 1 year: $119.88, 2 year: $179.98

Buying a Personal Computer

Situation

Your computer club just completed its fund-raising drive and now has $2,082 in its treasury. You have agreed to buy a new PC (personal computer). The question is, can you afford a 16MHz system with a hard drive and a color monitor? Heather brought in a catalog from a national supplier of discounted computers to help the group make a decision.

Hidden Data

Cost of extended warranty: Do you want more than one year of protections?
Cost of shipping: Do you know the cost of shipping, which will be included in your final bill?
Cost of partial payment: If you consider this option, you will want to figure the additional charges.
State tax: Will you have to pay state tax for your state or the state from which you are ordering?

Analyzing the Data

1. **Is there** more than one option for a system with 16MHz, a hard drive, and a color monitor?
2. **Does the cost** of shipping and tax, if any, increase the total cost over your spending limit?
3. **How much** is the cost for an extended warranty?

Outstanding $avings

ON OUR NEW LINE OF COMPUTER SYSTEMS

12 MHz Computer with 40 mb Hard Drive, 3¼" Floppy, and Mono Amber or Mono Rite Monitor.
$1049.88
w/80 mb Drive.....1259.88
w/124 mb Drive...1399.88

12 MHz with 800 X 600 Super Rite Color Monitor.
$1279.88
w/80 mb Drive.....1489.88
w/124 mb Drive...1629.88
For 1024 X 786 SuperRite Color Monitor, add $150

16 MHz Computer with 40 mb Hard Drive, 3¼" Floppy, and Mono Amber or Mono Rite Monitor.
$1099.88
w/80 mb Drive.....1309.88
w/124 mb Drive...1449.88

16 MHz with 800 X 600 Super Rite Color Monitor.
$1329.88
w/80 mb Drive.....1539.88
w/124 mb Drive...1679.88
For 1024 X 786 SuperRite Color Monitor, add $150

All items shipped in two cartons. Shipping weight 74 lbs. Shipping extra.

ZZ Computer Sales   1-800-555-5656

20

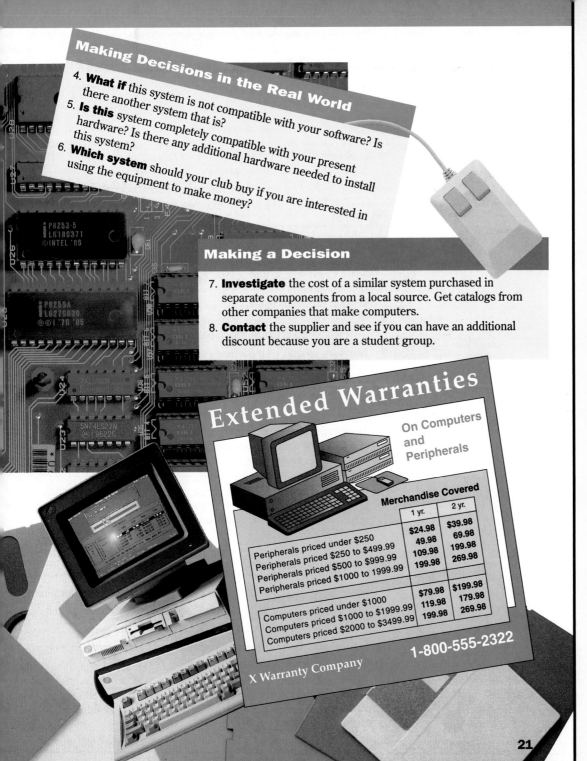

Making Decisions in the Real World

4. **What if** this system is not compatible with your software? Is there another system that is?
5. **Is this** system completely compatible with your present hardware? Is there any additional hardware needed to install this system?
6. **Which system** should your club buy if you are interested in using the equipment to make money?

Making a Decision

7. **Investigate** the cost of a similar system purchased in separate components from a local source. Get catalogs from other companies that make computers.
8. **Contact** the supplier and see if you can have an additional discount because you are a student group.

Extended Warranties

On Computers and Peripherals

Merchandise Covered	1 yr.	2 yr.
Peripherals priced under $250	$24.98	$39.98
Peripherals priced $250 to $499.99	49.98	69.98
Peripherals priced $500 to $999.99	109.98	199.98
Peripherals priced $1000 to 1999.99	199.98	269.98
Computers priced under $1000	$79.98	$199.98
Computers priced $1000 to $1999.99	119.98	179.98
Computers priced $2000 to $3499.99	199.98	269.98

X Warranty Company

1-800-555-2322

21

Checking for Understanding

Ask students to explain the purpose of an extended warranty.

3 PRACTICE/APPLY

Making a Decision

Each group should prepare a written report on its findings. The report should include answers to each question in the lesson, state the final decision made by the group, and outline the group's reasons behind that decision.

Making Decisions in the Real World

Students can collect pertinent information from newspaper ads and phone calls or visits to retailers. You may wish to have them include their findings in their class reports, comparing mail-order and local costs.

NCTM Standards: 1–4, 7, 13

Management Tips

For Students The piece of string needed by each pair of students should be 4 feet long.

For the Overhead Projector *Overhead Manipulative Resources* provides appropriate materials for teacher or student demonstration of the activities in this Mathematics Lab.

1 FOCUS

Introducing the Lab

Ask students to name some measuring units with which they are familiar. After students have read the opening paragraph about a cubit, ask them to suggest some nonstandard units of their own.

2 TEACH

Using Communication

Students may be concerned about the imprecision of their measurements. Use their concerns to drive home the point that units like "wrists" are imprecise since they cannot be defined in relation to established standard units.

3 PRACTICE/APPLY

Using Logical Reasoning In Exercise 3, point out the advantages of crawling short wrists but being paid in long ones.

Close

Have students write a few sentences explaining how they might use an orange as a nonstandard unit of weight.

1-6A Using Nonstandard Units

A Preview of Lesson 1-6

Objective
Measure items using a nonstandard unit of measure.

Materials
string
marker/pen
scissors

"What's a cubit?" someone asked while reading a story about Cleopatra. Cubits are no longer used today, but were commonly used in the countries located in what is now southwestern Asia over 2,000 years ago. The cubit was the measure along the forearm from the elbow to the end of the longest finger. How precise is this measure?

Try this!

Work with a partner.

- Wrap a piece of string around your wrist. Cut it so that it is as long as the distance around your wrist. This will be your unit of measure.
- Take another long piece of string. This will be your measuring tape.
- Measure around your partner's head using your measuring tape. How many "wrists" would it take to go around your partner's head? Estimate to the nearest $\frac{1}{4}$ wrist. Record your measure.
- Have your partner measure your head and find how many "wrists" around it is. Record your measure.
- Take turns measuring and recording the wrist measures for the distance around your knee, the length of your arm, and the distance around your neck.

What do you think?

2. If your partner's wrist is larger, the measurements will be less.
3. the smaller one; the larger one; Yes; you would want to crawl a shorter distance but have a longer roll of $1 bills.

1. Accumulate the data for the class and find an "average" size for the head, knee, and arm to the nearest $\frac{1}{4}$ wrist. Does this measure tell you how long something really is? No

2. Measure your partner's wrist. Describe how your data would be different if you had used that measure.

3. Suppose you had to crawl 1,000 wrists down the hallway. Whose wrist would you choose? Suppose you received a roll of $1 bills 100 wrists long. Whose wrist would you choose? Are these different wrists? Explain your answer.

22 **Chapter 1** Tools for Problem Solving

OPTIONS

Lab Manual You may wish to make copies of the blackline master on p. 38 of the *Lab Manual* for students to use as a recording sheet.

Lab Manual, p. 38

Name _____ Date _____

Mathematics Lab Worksheet

Use with page 22 _____

Using Nonstandard Units

Try this!

Complete. Answers will vary.

The number of "wrists" needed to go

around your partner's head _____

around your head _____

around your knee _____

the length of your arm _____

around your neck _____

1-6 The Metric System

Objective
Use metric units of measurement.

Words to Learn
metric system
meter
liter
gram

A baseball bat is a little less than a meter long. A nickel has a mass of about 5 grams. A quart of milk is a little less than a liter.

At Laddie Creek and Dead Indian Creek, sites in southern Montana, anthropologists have found arrowheads that date from 4000 B.C. to A.D. 500. The average arrowhead has a length of 35 millimeters, a width of 18 millimeters, and a neck width of 13 millimeters. The *millimeter* (mm) is a unit of length in the **metric system.**

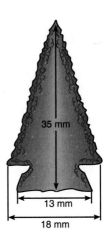

The metric system was created by French scientists in the late 18th century as a standard of measurement. The United States is the only large nation of the world that does not commonly use the metric system. The metric system is a decimal system. That means it is based on 10.

The standard unit of length in the metric system is the **meter** (m). The standard unit of capacity is the **liter** (L), and the standard unit of mass is the **gram** (g).

There are other measurements of length, capacity, and mass in the metric system, but they are all defined using the basic units (meter, liter, gram) and a prefix.

Prefix	Symbol	Meaning	Example
kilo-	k	1,000	1 km = 1,000 m
hecto-	h	100	1 hL = 100 L
deka-	da	10	1 dag = 10 g
deci-	d	0.1	1 dg = 0.1 g
centi-	c	0.01	1 cm = 0.01 m
milli-	m	0.001	1 mL = 0.001 L

The diagram below shows how you change from one unit to another by multiplying or dividing by 10.

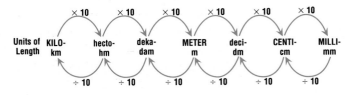

Lesson 1-6 Measurement Connection: The Metric System **23**

OPTIONS

Reteaching Activity

Using Communication Have students look up the meanings of the six metric prefixes in a dictionary and describe their findings in a letter to a classmate. If they discover other words with the same prefixes, they should define the words and tell how the prefixes relate to their meanings.

Study Guide Masters, p. 6

Name _____ Date _____

Study Guide Worksheet 1-6

Measurement: The Metric System

The metric system is a base 10 system. The meter is the basic unit of length. The liter is the basic unit of capacity. The gram is the basic unit of mass.

Prefix	Meaning	Length	Capacity	Mass
kilo-	1,000	kilometer (km)	kiloliter (kL)	kilogram (kg)
hecto-	100	hectometer (hm)	hectoliter (hL)	hectogram (hg)
deka-	10	dekameter (dam)	dekaliter (daL)	dekagram (dag)
	1	meter (m)	liter (L)	gram (g)
deci-	0.1	decimeter (dm)	deciliter (dL)	decigram (dg)
centi-	0.01	centimeter (cm)	centiliter (cL)	centigram (cg)

Checking for Understanding

Exercises 1-3 are designed to help you assess students' understanding through reading, writing, speaking, and modeling. You should work through these exercises with your students and then monitor their work on Guided Practice Exercises 4-15.

Additional Answers

1. because grams are smaller than kilograms
2. Move the decimal point two places to the right since there are two zeros in 100.

Study the patterns shown below.

- When you multiply by 10, 100, and 1,000 you can determine the answer by moving the decimal point right as many places as there are zeros in the multiplier.

  $1 \cdot 6.54 = 6.54$

  $10 \cdot 6.54 = 65.4$

  $100 \cdot 6.54 = 654.$

  $1,000 \cdot 6.54 = 6,540.$

- When you divide by 10, 100, and 1,000 you move the decimal point left as many places as you have zeros in the divisor.

  $78 \div 1 = 78$

  $78 \div 10 = 7.8$

  $78 \div 100 = 0.78$

  $78 \div 1,000 = 0.078$

This is very helpful in changing from one metric unit to another.

Mental Math Hint

If you are changing from one type of unit to a heavier, longer, or larger one, divide. If you are changing from one type of unit to a lighter, shorter, or smaller one, multiply.

Examples

1 5 g = _?_ mg

Since a gram is heavier than a milligram, you multiply. There are 1,000 mg in a gram, so multiply mentally by 1,000.

5.000 → 5,000

5 g = 5,000 mg

2 59 cm = _?_ m

A centimeter is shorter than a meter, so divide. There are 100 cm in a meter. Divide mentally.

59. → 0.59

59 cm = 0.59 m

3 1.5 L = _?_ mL

A liter is more than a milliliter, so multiply by 1,000.

1.500 → 1,500

1.5 L = 1,500 mL

4 1,035 cm = _?_ km

You can use two steps.

1,035 cm = _?_ m = _?_ km

1,035 cm = 10.35 m   *1,035*

10.35 m = 0.01035 km   *010.35*

1,035 cm = 0.01035 km

Checking for Understanding   For answers to Exercises 1–2, see margin.

Communicating Mathematics

Read and study the lesson to answer each question.

1. **Tell** why we divide when changing from grams to kilograms.
2. **Write** how to move the decimal point when multiplying by 100.
3. **Show** how many times longer a kilometer is than a centimeter by using the diagram on page 23. **A kilometer is 100,000 times longer than a centimeter.**

OPTIONS

Limited English Proficiency

Encourage students by explaining that in this lesson they are on an equal footing with others in the class, for all students must learn the Latin and Greek prefixes. Students from countries that use the metric system may enjoy explaining the system to others in the class.

Interactive Mathematics Tools

This multimedia software provides an interactive lesson that is tied directly to Lesson 1-6. Students will explore conversions in the metric system.

Tell which metric unit you would probably use to measure each item.

4. length of a book **centimeter**

5. contents of a soda can **milliliter**

6. a load of bricks **kilogram**

7. distance between cities **kilometer**

8. water in a swimming pool **kiloliter**

9. width of the letter A **millimeter**

Tell whether you multiply or divide and what number you use.
Then complete each sentence. **See Solutions Manual.**

10. $10 \text{ g} = \underline{\ ?\ } \text{ mg}$

11. $1{,}000 \text{ km} = \underline{\ ?\ } \text{ m}$

12. $4.39 \text{ mL} = \underline{\ ?\ } \text{ L}$

13. $1.5 \text{ mL} = \underline{\ ?\ } \text{ L}$

14. $5.93 \text{ g} = \underline{\ ?\ } \text{ kg}$

15. $7.89 \text{ m} = \underline{\ ?\ } \text{ km}$

Exercises

Complete each sentence.

16. $3.54 \text{ m} = \underline{\ ?\ } \text{ mm}$

17. $525 \text{ g} = \underline{\ ?\ } \text{ kg}$ **0.525**

18. $4.23 \text{ L} = \underline{\ ?\ } \text{ mL}$ **4,230**

19. $\underline{\ ?\ } \text{ m} = 1.37 \text{ km}$

20. $\underline{\ ?\ } \text{ mg} = 5.23 \text{ g}$

21. $9.24 \text{ kL} = \underline{\ ?\ } \text{ L}$

22. $\underline{\ ?\ } \text{ L} = 2{,}354 \text{ mL}$ **2.354**

23. $0.924 \text{ m} = \underline{\ ?\ } \text{ cm}$ **92.4**

24. $427 \text{ m} = \underline{\ ?\ } \text{ km}$ **0.427**

16. 3,540
19. 1,370
20. 5,230
21. 9,240

25. The width of the tail of a microorganism is 0.00723 cm wide. How many millimeters is this? **0.0723 millimeters**

26. How many grams are in 0.875 kilograms? **875 grams**

27. A mayonnaise jar holds 0.947 liters. How many milliliters does it hold? **947 milliliters**

28. 4 goldfish   29. 378; distributive property

28. **Smart Shopping**   Lora wants to buy some goldfish that cost 59¢ each. How many fish can she afford to buy with her $2.50 allowance? *(Lesson 1-1)*

29. Use mental math to find $9 \cdot 42$. Tell what method you used. *(Lesson 1-2)*

30. Estimate $7{,}103 - 2{,}980$ by rounding. *(Lesson 1-3)* **4,000**

31. Estimate $2.381 \div 0.39$ by using compatible numbers. *(Lesson 1-3)* **6**

32. Yes; the dimensions of the box are 38 millimeters by 200 millimeters.

32. **Archeology**   Look at the drawing of the arrowhead on page 23. Would it fit in a box 3.8 cm by 0.20 m? Why or why not?

33. **Critical Thinking**   Some basic metric units also are closely related. One milliliter of water at 4°C has a mass of 1 gram and a volume of 1 cubic centimeter (cm³). A 520-gram metal bar is placed in a beaker full of water. When immersed, 260 grams of water spills out.

a. How many milliliters of water spilled out? **260 milliliters**

b. The volume of water that spilled out equals the volume of the bar. What is the volume of the bar in cubic centimeters? **260 cm³**

c. *Density* is defined as mass divided by volume. What would be the density of the bar in grams per cubic centimeter? **2 g/cm³**

d. See students' work.

d. **Research**   Use the encyclopedia to find information about Archimedes. How does his work relate to this problem?

Extending the Lesson

Writing Math   List these additional metric prefixes:

mega = one million
giga = one billion
micro = one-millionth
nano = one-billionth

Have students write problems involving conversions between these new units and those used in the lesson.

Cooperative Learning Activity

To Spin or Not to Spin 1-6

Number of players: 2
Materials: Index cards, spinner

✱ Copy onto cards the measurements shown on the back of this card. Shuffle the cards. Label the sections of a spinner "kilo-," "hecto-," "deka-," "deci-," "centi-," and "milli-."

↳ In turn, each partner selects a card and then decides whether or not to spin the spinner. The spinner tells how to change the unit of measure. For example, a spin of "kilo-" would change 4 meters (4 m) to 4 kilometers. When all of the cards have been selected, partners convert all units of length back to meters, all units of mass back to grams, and all units of capacity back to liters. After determining the total length, mass, and capacity, partners compare their totals. The winner has the greater total for at least two types of measure.

Glencoe Mathematics: Applications and Connections, Course 3

Guide students to summarize the lesson by asking the following questions.

• *When would you divide to change from one metric unit to another?* when changing from a smaller unit to a larger unit

• *When would you multiply?* when changing from a larger unit to a smaller unit

3 PRACTICE/APPLY

Assignment Guide
Maximum: 16–33
Minimum: 16–32

For **Extra Practice,** see p. 584.

Alternate Assessment

Modeling   Display several common objects which are measured in metric units, such as a roll of 35 mm film for a camera. Have students write each measurement using three different units.

Enrichment Masters, p. 6

Name _____   Date _____

Enrichment Worksheet 1-6

Two Views of Measurement

The puzzle on this page is called an *acrostic*. To solve the puzzle, work back and forth between the paragraph and the puzzle box. For example, the letter N should be written on Line 20 in the paragraph, and also in Box 20 below.

An Engineer Talks About Measurement:

$\underset{20\ 37\ 18\ 49}{\text{N O N E}}$ of us use $\underset{7\ 11\ 22\ 29\ 47\ 4\ 50\ 43\ 8}{\text{C U S T O M A R Y}}$

units much any more. Metric units of $\underset{24\ 44\ 40\ 41\ 45\ 3\ 39}{\text{M E A S U R E}}$ are so

much $\underset{36\ 34\ 9\ 31\ 26}{\text{N I C E R.}}$ Even in a $\underset{12\ 42\ 23\ 30}{\text{R U S H}}$ you are less

likely to $\underset{33\ 51\ 32}{\text{E R R}}$ in placing the decimal $\underset{46\ 2\ 25\ 48\ 27\ 35}{\text{P O I N T S.}}$

$\underset{10\ 1}{\text{O F}}$ course, you need to know the prefixes; for example, a $\underset{19\ 5\ 16\ 13}{\text{D E K A}-}$

$\underset{38\ 21\ 52\ 15\ 6}{\text{M E T E R}}$ is ten times as $\underset{28\ 17\ 14\ 53}{\text{H I G H}}$ as a meter.

From a Poem by Laurence Binyon:

T6
Glencoe Division, Macmillan/McGraw-Hill

Lesson Resources
- Study Guide Master 1-7
- Practice Master 1-7
- Enrichment Master 1-7
- Interdisciplinary Master, p. 15
- Group Activity Card 1-7

 Transparency 1-7 contains the 5-Minute Check and a teaching aid for this lesson.

⏱ 5-Minute Check
(Over Lesson 1-6)

Complete each sentence.

1. 8 km = __?__ m   8,000
2. 350 mL = __?__ L   0.35
3. 0.5 m = __?__ cm   50
4. 10 mm = __?__ cm   1
5. 60,000 mg = __?__ kg   0.06

---

1 FOCUS

Motivating the Lesson

Activity   Show the lengths 1 inch, 1 foot, and 1 yard. Have students estimate the dimensions of their desktops and of the room using each unit. Ask which unit is best for each measurement.

2 TEACH

Using Manipulatives   Provide rulers or yardsticks, measuring cups, and scales to groups of students. Have each group measure the length and weight of several objects, and the capacity of various containers. Have them express each measure using two different units.

Reteaching Activity

Using Manipulatives   Provide two instruments each for measuring length, capacity, and weight (for example, length: a 1-foot ruler and a yardstick). Have students measure lengths, capacities, and weights using the instruments and then compare measurements.

1-7 The Customary System

Objective
Use customary units of measurement.

Words to Learn
customary system

 **When am I ever going to use this?**

In 1992, the EPA estimated there were about 1,200 hazardous waste sites in the United States. Scientists are often called to assist in the detoxification of these sites.

A college degree in engineering or science is usually required to be a specialist in this field.

To obtain more information, contact: EPA, 401 M. St. SW, Washington, DC 20460.

In 1990, the Environmental Protection Agency (EPA) announced that the four most polluting states released 1,730 million pounds of toxic chemicals into the environment. Pounds are units of weight in the **customary system.**

The customary system developed from a series of nonstandard measurements. The unit of length, the foot, evolved from the length of a king's foot. The inch was the length of 3 barleycorns laid end to end. The basic unit of weight is a pound, and the basic unit of capacity is the quart.

Changing from one unit to another in the customary system is not as easy as in the metric system. The customary system is *not* a decimal system. The following chart lists some common units and their equivalents.

Length:	12 inches (in.) = 1 foot (ft)
	3 ft = 1 yard (yd)
	5,280 ft = 1 mile (mi)
Capacity:	8 fluid ounces (oz) = 1 cup (c)
	2 c = 1 pint (pt)
	2 pt = 1 quart (qt)
	4 qt = 1 gallon (gal)
Weight:	16 dry ounces (oz) = 1 pound (lb)
	2,000 lb = 1 ton (T)

Changing from one unit to another in the customary system may involve more than one step. The rules about when to multiply and when to divide are like those you used with the metric system. The actual computation may not be as easy since the metric system is based on multiples of ten and the customary system is not.

Example 1

18 ft = __?__ yd

A foot is shorter than a yard, so divide. There are 3 feet in every yard, so divide by 3.

$$18 \div 3 = 6 \quad \rightarrow \quad 18 \text{ ft} = 6 \text{ yd}$$

 **Interactive Mathematics Tools**

This multimedia software provides an interactive lesson that is tied directly to Lesson 1-7. Students will explore conversions in the customary system.

Study Guide Masters, p. 7

Name _____   Date _____

Study Guide Worksheet 1-7

Measurement: The Customary System

The chart shows some customary units and equivalents.

Length	Capacity	Weight
12 inches (in.) = 1 foot (ft)	8 fluid ounces (oz) = 1 cup (c)	16 dry ounces (oz) = 1 pound (lb)
3 ft = 1 yard (yd)	2 c = 1 pint (pt)	2,000 lb = 1 ton (T)
5,280 ft = 1 mile (mi)	2 pt = 1 quart (qt)	
	4 qt = 1 gallon (gal)	

Multiply to change a larger unit to a smaller unit.
Divide to change a smaller unit to a larger unit.

Examples

Example 2

How many ounces are in 105 pounds?

A pound is heavier than an ounce, so multiply.
There are 16 ounces in each pound.

105 ☒ 16 ☐ 1680

There are 1680 ounces in 105 pounds.

Sometimes you may need to use more than one measurement to complete a problem.

Example 3 *Problem Solving*

Problem-Solving Hint
• • • • • • • • • •
Drawing a diagram may help you solve the problem.

Construction The highway department is putting a railing along a highway that edges a ravine. The railing is attached to posts placed a yard apart. If the railing is 4 miles long, how many posts do they need?

One post is needed to start with and then we need to know how many yards there are in 4 miles. We know that there are 5,280 feet in a mile. To find the number of yards, divide by 3. There are 1,760 yards in each mile.

Now, draw a diagram.

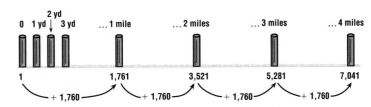

The highway department needs 7,041 posts.

Checking for Understanding

1. It is easier to change from one unit to another.

Communicating Mathematics

Read and study the lesson to answer each question.

1. **Tell** one advantage the metric system has over the customary system.
2. **Write** how you would change 6 cups to gallons. See margin.
3. **Show** another way to solve the problem in Example 3. Answers will vary.

Guided Practice

Tell whether you multiply or divide and by what number to complete each sentence. Then complete. For answers to Exercises 4–9, see margin.

4. 3 lb = __?__ oz
5. 6,000 lb = __?__ T
6. 24 c = __?__ qt
7. $2\frac{1}{2}$ yd = __?__ in.
8. 8,000 ft = __?__ mi
9. 10 gal = __?__ pt

Lesson 1-7 Measurement Connection: The Customary System **27**

More Examples

For Example 1

8 pt = __?__ qt   4

For Example 2

How many pounds are in 6 tons?   12,000 lb

For Example 3

A rectangular garden measures 8 yards by 6 yards. Starting at one corner, posts are placed at 2-foot intervals around the garden. How many posts are needed?   42 posts

Checking for Understanding

Exercises 1-3 are designed to help you assess students' understanding through reading, writing, speaking, and modeling. You should work through these exercises with your students and then monitor their work on Guided Practice Exercises 4-9.

Practice Masters, p. 7

Name _____ Date _____

Practice Worksheet 1-7

Measurement: The Customary System

Tell whether you multiply or divide and what number you use to complete each sentence. Then complete.

1. 36 in. = ___ ft
   div. by 12; 3
2. 12 qt = ___ gal
   div. by 4; 3
3. 2 lb = ___ oz
   mult. by 16; 32
4. 6 pt = ___ c
   mult. by 2; 12
5. 3,000 lb = ___ T
   div. by 2,000; 1.5
6. 6 gal = ___ qt
   mult. by 4; 24
7. 6 yd = ___ ft
   mult. by 3; 18
8. 12 pt = ___ qt
   div. by 2; 6
9. 28 oz = ___ c
   div. by 8; 3.5
10. 3 mi = ___ ft
    mult. by 5,280; 15,840
11. 18 ft = ___ yd
    div. by 3; 6
12. 72 in. = ___ ft
    div. by 12; 6
13. 32 qt = ___ gal
    div. by 4; 8
14. 4 ft = ___ in.
    mult. by 12; 48
15. 12 ft = ___ in.
    mult. by 12; 144
16. 63 ft = ___ yd
    div. by 3; 21

Complete each sentence.

17. 10,560 ft = ___ mi   2
18. ___ lb = 48 oz   3
19. 21 ft = ___ yd   7
20. 72 in. = ___ ft   6
21. ___ c = 32 oz   4
22. ___ pt = 6 c   3
23. ___ qt = 4 gal   16
24. ___ pt = 3 qt   6
25. 5,000 lb = ___ T   2.5
26. 16 oz = ___ c   1
27. 3 yd = ___ in.   108
28. 8 gal = ___ qt   32
29. ___ ft = 2 mi   10,560
30. 84 in. = ___ ft   7
31. 12 yd = ___ ft   36
32. 20 qt = ___ gal   5
33. ___ oz = 3 c   24
34. 128 oz = ___ lb   8

T7
Glencoe Division, Macmillan/McGraw-Hill

Bell Ringer

A light-year is the distance that light travels in one year. Light travels about 186,000 miles per second. Find the length of a light-year in miles. Assume that there are 365 days in a year.
about 5,900,000,000,000 miles

Additional Answers

2. 6 cups = 3 pints;
   3 pints = 1.5 quarts;
   1.5 quarts = $\frac{3}{8}$ or 0.375 gallons
4. multiply by 16; 48
5. divide by 2,000; 3
6. divide by 4; 6
7. multiply by 36; 90
8. divide by 5,280; $1\frac{17}{33}$ or $1.\overline{51}$
9. multiply by 8; 80

Close

Have students use a yardstick, a cup, quart, or gallon container, and a one-pound weight to model examples of length, capacity, and weight in the customary system.

3 PRACTICE/APPLY

Assignment Guide
Maximum: 10–33
Minimum: 10–29, 31, 32

For **Extra Practice,** see p. 585.

Alternate Assessment

Writing Have students work with a partner to write six problems, two each relating to length, capacity, and weight in the customary system. In each category, one problem should involve converting from a smaller unit to a larger unit and one should involve converting from a larger unit to a smaller one.

Enrichment Masters, p. 7

Name _____ Date _____

Enrichment Worksheet 1-7

Latitude and Longitude

Look at a globe and you will see lines running around it. The vertical lines, meeting at the poles, are the lines of *longitude*. Longitude is measured in degrees east or west of the *prime meridian*.

The prime meridian passes through Greenwich, London, which is a suburb of London, England.

The horizontal lines running parallel to the equator are the lines of *latitude*. Latitude is measured in degrees north or south of the equator.

Use an atlas or a globe to find the latitude and longitude of each of the following places.

1. Chicago, IL
   42°N, 88°W
2. La Paz, Bolivia
   17°S, 68°W
3. Paris, France
   49°N, 3°E

4. Niagara Falls, NY
   43°N, 79°W
5. Your city or town
   Answers vary.
6. Your state capital
   Answers vary.

Find the city, country, or ocean that is near each point.

7. 40°S, 0°
   Atlantic Ocean
8. 35°N, 140°E
   Kyoto, Japan
9. 39°N, 77°W
   Washington, D.C.

10. 36°N, 106°W
    Santa Fe, NM
11. 21°N, 156°W
    Pacific Ocean
12. 40°S, 175°E
    New Zealand

Describe the location of each of the following.

13. The North Pole
    90°N
14. The South Pole
    90°S
15. The International
    Dateline
    180°W or 180°E

T7
Glencoe Division, Macmillan/McGraw-Hill

Exercises

Independent Practice

Complete each sentence.

10. 12 ft = __?__ yd 4
11. 5 mi = __?__ ft 26,400
12. 2.5 gal = __?__ qt 10
13. 3.5 lb = __?__ oz 56
14. 2 T = __?__ lb 4,000
15. 7 c = __?__ pt 3.5
16. __?__ gal = 20 qt 5
17. $3\frac{1}{2}$ ft = __?__ in. 42
18. 2 gal = __?__ oz 256

19. How many gallons are there in 32 ounces of orange juice? $\frac{1}{4}$ gallons
20. How many feet are in 15 inches? $1\frac{1}{4}$ feet
21. An inchworm travels 4 yards. How many inches is that? 144 inches
22. How many feet are in $7\frac{1}{2}$ yards? $22\frac{1}{2}$ feet

23. Sample answer: Subtract 5 from both numbers and subtract the new numbers; 251.

Mixed Review

23. Tell how you could use compensation to find 404 − 153. *(Lesson 1-2)*
24. Estimate 4,521 − 3,158 using front-end estimation. *(Lesson 1-3)* 1,400
25. How many centimeters are in 2.79 meters? *(Lesson 1-6)* 279 centimeters
26. A coffee mug safely holds 375 milliliters. How many coffee mugs could you safely fill with 12 liters of coffee? *(Lesson 1-6)* 32 coffee mugs

27. No, weight and capacity are not the same.

Problem Solving and Applications

27. **Critical Thinking** Marva filled a one-cup measuring cup with sand. She said it weighed eight ounces. Is she right? Explain your answer.

28. **Ecology** Every ton of recycled office paper saves about 17 trees. Glencoe Publishing's office in Westerville, Ohio, recycled 8,000 pounds of paper in 1991. How many trees did this save? 68 trees

29. **Design** Martina designed a new cheerleader uniform that requires $3\frac{1}{2}$ yards of material. All 10 cheerleaders wear the same design. How long is the piece of cloth needed to make all their uniforms if it is measured in feet? 105 feet

30. **Portfolio Suggestion** A portfolio contains representative samples of your work collected over a period of time. Begin your portfolio by selecting an item that shows something you learned in this chapter. See students' work.

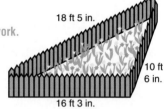
18 ft 5 in.
10 ft 6 in.
16 ft 3 in.

31. **Geometry** The fence around a triangular flower garden in front of the school has sides of 16 ft 3 in., 18 ft 5 in., and 10 ft 6 in. Approximately how many feet long is the fence? about 45 feet

32. **Save Planet Earth** In a lifetime, the average person will throw away 600 times his or her adult weight in trash. Suppose a person weighs 150 pounds. How many tons of trash will that person leave behind? 45 tons

DATA SEARCH

33. **Data Search** Refer to pages 2 and 3. How much faster is the record in the men's 200-meter butterfly than the women's record? 9.72 sec faster

28   **Chapter 1** Tools for Problem Solving

OPTIONS

Extending the Lesson

Literature Connection Nineteenth century French author Jules Verne's *Twenty-Thousand Leagues Under the Sea* is one of the most famous science fiction novels ever written. Find out how long a league is in miles and then rewrite the title using miles. 3 miles; *Sixty Thousand Miles Under the Sea*

Cooperative Learning Activity

Are You a "Has-Bean"? **1-7**

Use groups of 4.
Materials: Rulers, yardsticks, measuring cup, dried beans

➤ Each group uses 1 cup of dried beans to answer the following questions.

1. Suppose you have 1 cup of beans. Now suppose these beans are laid end to end in a line. What is your estimate for the length of this line?
2. Suppose you have a 5-gallon bucket filled with dried beans. About how long would a line made with this many beans be?

Glencoe Mathematics: Applications and Connections, Course 3

Cooperative Learning

1-7B Customary Measures

A Follow-Up of Lesson 1-7

Objective
Explore the origin of the mile unit of measure.

Materials
yardstick

The word "mile" comes from the Latin *mille passus,* which means 1,000 paces. The distance the Roman legions could travel in 1,000 paces became the standard length now known as a mile.

Try this!

Work in groups of two.

● A pace is the distance walked from the heel of one foot to the heel of the same foot when it hits the ground.

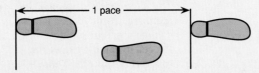

1 pace

Walk one pace. Have your partner measure the length of your pace in feet. Record the measurement. Have your partner walk one pace. Then measure the length of your partner's pace. Record this measurement.

● Repeat walking paces and measuring two more times. Record your measurements.

● Find the average pace for you and your partner.

	Trial 1	Trial 2	Trial 3	Average
Your Pace				
Your Partner's Pace				
Class Average				

What do you think?   For Exercises 1–4, see students' work.

1. Compare your group's average to the class average. Are they similar?
2. If you multiplied your average pace by 1,000, how close does it come to 5,280 feet?
3. Why do you think that the paces of the Roman legions would be nearly the same every time?

Extension

4. **Research**   Investigate the origins of other customary units of measure.

Mathematics Lab 1-7B Customary Measures   **29**

Mathematics Lab 1-7B

NCTM Standards: 1–4, 7, 13

Management Tips

For Students   Spread groups around the room so that each group has plenty of room to make its measurements.

For the Overhead Projector
Overhead Manipulative Resources provides appropriate materials for teacher or student demonstration of the activities in this Mathematics Lab.

1 FOCUS

Introducing the Lab

Ask students to estimate how long it takes the fastest human to run a mile and how long it takes an average person to walk a mile.
a little less than 4 minutes; about 15 minutes

2 TEACH

Using Alternatives   Have some groups calculate their average paces by measuring the length of 10 paces and dividing by 10. Ask students to compare and contrast the methods.

3 PRACTICE/APPLY

Using Problem Solving   At its maximum, the Roman army consisted of 175 legions. How many soldiers were in the army?   700,000 to 1,050,000

Close

Have students write a few sentences describing how units of measure originate and become standardized.

OPTIONS

Lab Manual   You may wish to make copies of the blackline master on p. 39 of the *Lab Manual* for students to use as a recording sheet.

Lab Manual, p. 39

Name _____ Date _____

Mathematics Lab Worksheet

Use with page 29 _____

Customary Measures

Try this! Answers will vary.

	Trial 1	Trial 2	Trial 3	Average
Your Pace				
Your Partner's Pace				
Class Average				

What do you think? Answers will vary.

Management Tips

For Students Have students stop after completing Activity One. Discuss the activity, then introduce the operation symbols used by the computer before having students begin work on Activity Two.

For the Overhead Projector
Overhead Manipulative Resources provides appropriate materials for teacher or student demonstration of the activities in this Mathematics Lab.

1 FOCUS

Introducing the Lab

Have students read the first paragraph of the lab. Then ask this question: *Why is the last available column of a spreadsheet named IV?* The first 26 columns are named A through Z. Columns 27 through 52 are named AA through AZ, columns 53 through 78 are named BA through BZ, and so on until column 256 which is named IV.

Objective
Explore the use of a computer spreadsheet.

Materials
calculators

Computer **spreadsheets** are important tools for organizing and analyzing data for problem solving. A spreadsheet is made of rows and columns. The columns are identified by letters and the rows are identified by numbers. Most spreadsheets have up to 2,048 rows available, numbered 1 through 2,048. There are 256 columns available. After column Z, the columns are named AA, AB, AC, and so on, through IV. However, only eight columns can be seen at a time on the computer screen.

The basic unit of a spreadsheet is called a **cell.** A cell may contain numbers, words (called labels), or a formula. Each cell is named by the column and row that describes its location, or **address.** The cell D2 is the cell in column D and row 2. *Cell D2 in the spreadsheet below contains the number 1,650.*

	A	B	C	D	E	F	G	H
1		JAN.	FEB.	MARCH	APRIL	MAY	JUNE	JULY
2	REVENUE	2,500	5,000	1,650	10,000	3,100	8,200	12,500
3	EXPENSES	700	1,200	225	3,550	1,800	2,300	5,600
4	PROFIT	1,800	3,800	1,425	6,450	1,300	5,900	6,900
5								
6								
7								

Activity One

Work with a partner. Use the spreadsheet shown above.

- Locate cell E3. What is printed in this cell? **3,550**
- Give the address of all cells that contain labels. **B1, C1, D1, E1, F1, G1, H1, A2, A3, A4**
- Locate cell B2, B3, and B4. What is the relationship among the numbers in these cells? **B2 − B3 = B4**

What do you think? 1. **E3 contains the expenses incurred in April.**

1. Write a sentence to fully describe the information in cell E3.
2. What type of information is stored in cells A2 through A4? **Labels**
3. Does the relationship that you found for B2, B3, and B4 hold true for C2, C3, and C4? Is it true for all columns? **yes, yes**

When cells are related, a formula can be used to generate this relationship. In the spreadsheet on the previous page, in every column the same pattern can be observed.

$$\text{row } 4 = \text{row } 2 - \text{row } 3$$

Instead of subtracting each time, you can use a formula to calculate the difference. The formula uses the cell names and symbols for the operations.

| + (add) | − (subtract) | * (multiply) |
| / (divide) | ^ (exponent) | |

When you type the formula C2 − C3 into cell C4, the cell will not show the formula, but the result of the subtraction. When you move the cursor to a cell, the formula in that cell appears at the bottom of the screen along with the cell address.

Activity Two

	A	B	C	D	E	F	G	H
1	CONCERT TICKETS	NUMBER SOLD	TICKET PRICE	TOTAL SALES				
2	FLOOR SEATS	150	$25	$3,750				
3	BALCONY	210	$20					
4	MEZZANINE	300	$15					
5								
6	TOTAL SEATS		TOTAL SALES					

- Locate B2, C2, and D2. How are these cells related? B2 * C2 = D2
- Suppose the value in B2 changed to 175. How would the value in D2 change? $4,375

What do you think?

4. B2 * C2, B3 * C3, B4 * C4
5. B2 + B3 + B4
6. D2 + D3 + D4
7. D3 = $4,200, D4 = $4,500, D6 = $12,450
8. B6 = B2 + B3 + B4 + B5, D6 = D2 + D3 + D4 + D5

4. Write spreadsheet formulas for cells D2, D3, and D4.
5. Write a formula for cell B6 to find the total number of seats sold.
6. Write a formula for finding the total sales for all seats.
7. Find the values that would appear in the cells of the spreadsheet.
8. Suppose the information *Standing Room Only, 100, $10* was inserted in cells A5, B5, and C5, respectively. How would the formulas in B6 and D6 change to include this information?

Application

9. Answers may include: budgets, tax information
10. See students' work.

9. Describe possible uses of spreadsheets at home and at school.
10. Create your own spreadsheet. Explain what each row and column represent and how you use formulas to save calculation time.

Mathematics Lab 1-8A Spreadsheets **31**

1-8 Guess and Check

Lesson Resources
- Study Guide Master 1-8
- Practice Master 1-8
- Enrichment Master 1-8
- Group Activity Card 1-8

 Transparency 1-8 contains the 5-Minute Check and a teaching aid for this lesson.

⏱ 5-Minute Check
(Over Lesson 1-7)

Complete each sentence.
1. 21 ft = ___?___ yd   7
2. 3 qt = ___?___ c   12
3. 3.5 T = ___?___ lb   7,000
4. 4.5 yd = ___?___ in.   162

1 FOCUS

Motivating the Lesson

Questioning Ask students to solve this problem: *Jackie borrowed 7 books from the library. The next day she returned all but 2 of the books. How many did she keep?* 2

2 TEACH

Using Models Use a stack of 10 books to illustrate how to check the first guess. Then show how a diagram can be used to represent the books, and use it to check the second guess. Have students try to check the third guess mentally.

More Examples

For the Example

A football team scored 36 points on a total of 8 touchdowns and field goals. A touchdown (plus the extra point) counts for 7 points and a field goal counts for 3 points. How many touchdowns and how many field goals did the team score?

3 touchdowns, 5 field goals

Objective
Solve problems by using guess and check.

Judith noticed the due dates for the library books she returned. All but four books were due yesterday. All but four books are due today. All but four books are due tomorrow. How many books did Judith return?

Explore What do you know?
All but 4 books were due yesterday.
All but 4 books are due today.
All but 4 books are due tomorrow.

You want to find out how many books Judith returned.

Plan Guess the number of books Judith returned. Then check this number against the due date statements. If the guess doesn't check out, you can use what you learn to make a better guess.

Solve **First guess:** Judith returned 10 books.
Check:

- *All but 4 were due yesterday.*
  Make a sketch and label it. Use Ys for books due yesterday.

  All but 4 due yesterday means 6 were due yesterday.

- *All but 4 are due today.*
  The 6 books labeled for yesterday contradicts this statement. Revise your guess downward to 8 books.

Second guess: 8 books
Check:

- *All but 4 were due yesterday.*

- *All but 4 are due today.*
  Use Ds for books due today.

- *All but 4 are due tomorrow.*
  No more books to label contradicts this statement. Revise your guess downward to 6 books.

OPTIONS

Reteaching Activity

Using Cooperative Groups One of three players secretly chooses a number from 1 to 100. A second player makes successive guesses (the first player says "high" or "low" after each guess) until finding the number. The third player counts the guesses, the total being the guesser's score. Switch roles and play again.

Study Guide Masters, p. 8

Name _____ Date _____

Study Guide Worksheet 1-8

Problem-Solving Strategy: Guess and Check

Example Leslie has 6 times as much money as Inazo. If Inazo had $1.20 more, Leslie would have 2 times as much money as Inazo. How much money does each person have?

Explore What do you know?
Leslie has 6 times as much money as Inazo.
If Inazo had $1.20 more, Leslie would have 2 times as much money as Inazo.
What do you want to know?
How much money each person has

Plan Guess how much money Inazo has. Multiply by 6 to find how much Leslie has. Then add $1.20 to your guess. Check to see if 2 times that amount equals the amount Leslie has.

Solve Guess that Inazo has $0.40. $0.40 × 6 = ...

Third guess: 6 books
Check:

- *All but 4 were due yesterday.*

- *All but 4 are due today.*

- *All but 4 are due tomorrow.*
  Use Ms for books due tomorrow.

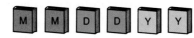

Judith returned 6 books.

Examine Out of 6 books, if exactly 2 of them are due on separate days, then all but 4 are due on each day. You have not tested all numbers. But with fewer books, you run out of books to label. With more books, you have too many books to label.

Example

Inventory Terry's job at the cafeteria includes ordering supplies. Twelve-ounce cups come in cases of 1,600, and 16-ounce cups come in cases of 1,200. Terry ordered 7,200 cups in full cases. How many of each case were ordered?

Use a table to show what you know and what you are trying to find out. You should leave a place for guesses.

About how many 12-oz cases? (Guess.)	How many 12-oz cups is that? (Multiply by 1,600.)	How many 16-oz cups are still needed? (Subtract.)	How many 16-oz cases is that? (Divide by 1,200).
1	1,600	7,200 − 1,600 = 5,600	4.7 cases
2	3,200	7,200 − 3,200 = 4,000	3.3 cases
3	4,800	7,200 − 4,800 = 2,400	2 full cases

Terry ordered 3 cases of the 12-ounce cups and 2 cases of the 16-ounce cups.

You can check by referring to the problem. Two 16-ounce cases at 1,200 cups per case is 2,400 cups. Three 12-ounce cases at 1,600 cups per case is 4,800 cups. Together, 2,400 plus 4,800 is 7,200, a check.

Lesson 1-8 Problem-Solving Strategy: Guess and Check **33**

Interactive Mathematics Tools

This multimedia software provides an interactive lesson that is tied directly to Lesson 1–8. Students will use changeable histograms to explore data.

Checking for Understanding

Exercises 1-3 are designed to help you assess students' understanding through reading, writing, speaking, and modeling. You should work through these exercises with your students and then monitor their work on Guided Practice Exercises 4-8.

Close

Tell students that a certain 3-digit house number consists of three consecutive numbers with a sum of 21. Ask them to describe how they could determine the house number. Guess a 3-digit number and add the digits. If the sum is greater than 21, guess a smaller number; if it is less than 21, guess a greater number. Continue guessing and checking until you find the answer, 678 or 876.

Practice Masters, p. 8

Name _____ Date _____

Practice Worksheet 1-8

Problem-Solving Strategy: Guess and Check

Solve. Use the guess-and-check strategy.

1. A number plus half the number is 33. Find the number. 22

2. The square of a number is 324. Find the number. 18

3. Six more than a number is 3 times the number. Find the number. 3

4. Find the greatest number whose name is spelled using three letters. ten

5. Find the least number divisible by 1, 2, 3, 4 and 6. 12

6. Find the least number divisible by 2, 5, and 9. 90

Solve. Use any strategy.

7. Some students and teachers went on a field trip. Of the 56 people, 5 were teachers. Of the students, 26 were boys. How many girls were on the field trip? 25 girls

8. Gene has 3-pound blocks and 5-pound blocks. He stacks some of each type into a pile weighing 19 pounds. How many of each type does he use? 3 @ 3-pounds; 2 @ 5-pounds

9. John fishes every third day, Mary every fourth day, and David every fifth day. Today, Thursday, they all fish together. What is the next day of the week when they all meet to fish together? Monday

10. If David weighed 10 pounds less than he does, he would weigh 8 pounds more than twice Kate's weight. David weighs 164 pounds. What is Kate's weight? 73 pounds

11. Juan has a mixture of pennies and dimes worth $2.28. He has between 39 and 56 pennies. How many dimes does Juan have? 18 dimes

12. Heather is 10 years older than Laura. In 6 years, Heather will be twice as old as Laura. How old will Laura be then? 10 years old

T8
Glencoe Division, Macmillan/McGraw-Hill

Alternate Assessment

Modeling Give students a collection of play dimes and quarters. Ask them to use the guess-and-check strategy to find 7 coins whose total worth is $1.00.
5 dimes, 2 quarters

Additional Answers

1. Estimation can help you be more accurate in your guesses.
2. Check your guess by comparing it to all conditions of the problem. If it does not meet every condition, then you must guess again.

Enrichment Masters, p. 8

Name _____ Date _____

Enrichment Worksheet 1-8

Math Problems From 1886

The "story" problems on this page were published in a math textbook in 1886. You may need to consult an encyclopedia to find some of the answers. But, try using logical reasoning and estimation first!

Match each problem to a solution plan and then to an answer. Write a problem number on each blank.

Problem	Solution Plan	Answer
1. From a cask containing 42 gallons of water, 1 gal 3 qt leak out daily. In what time will the cask be emptied?	**3** Change 1 quart to gills. Divide the result by the fractional sum, in gills, of the water and the alcohol.	**2** 0.1875 mi
2. What decimal part of a mile is the depth of a bay which when sounded was found to be 165 fathoms deep?	**5** Change the amount to barrels. (1 barrel = 196 lb) Then multiply by the price per barrel.	**4** $36.26
3. If 3/4 of a gill of water is mixed with 1 quart alcohol, what part of the mixture will be alcohol?	**1** Change the quantities to either gallons or quarts. Then divide the larger by the smaller.	**6** $172.80
4. What is the cost of 5 cwt 18 lb iron at $140 a ton?	**2** Divide 165 by the number of fathoms in a mile.	**3** 32/35
5. At $6.25 per barrel, how much should be paid for 4,704 lb flour?	**6** Change one pound to pennyweights. Multiply by 0.8 and then by 0.9.	**7** $74.70
6. Find the cost of 4/5 of a pound of gold at 90¢ per pennyweight.	**7** Change the amount to bushels. Then multiply by the cost per bushel.	**1** 24 days
7. What is the cost of 5,229 lb of shelled corn at 80¢ per bushel?	**4** Change 5 cwt 18 lb to some fraction of a ton. Then multiply by the cost per ton.	**5** $150

T8
Glencoe Division, Macmillan/McGraw-Hill

Communicating Mathematics

Read and study the lesson to answer each question.

1. **Tell** why it is important to use estimation with the guess-and-check strategy.
2. How do you know if your guess doesn't work?
3. Make a table that can be used to solve the problem in the lesson about Judith and the returned library books. **See students' work.**

Guided Practice

Use the guess-and-check strategy to find the number.

4. The sum of the number and its double is 21. **7**
5. The product of the number and itself is 196. **14**
6. One hundred more than the number is twice the number. **100**
7. The quotient of the number and itself is always 1. **all but 0**
8. The product of the number and its next two consecutive whole numbers is 60. **3**

Problem Solving

Practice

Solve using any strategy.

9. José's mother is five times as old as José. Five years from now she will be just three times as old. How old is José now? **5 years old**

Strategies
● ● ● ● ● ● ●
Look for a pattern.
Solve a simpler problem.
Act it out.
Guess and check.
Draw a diagram.
Make a chart.
Work backward.

a. Dallas/Ft. Worth
b. Denver

10. In 1991, stamps for postcards cost $0.19. Stamps for first class letters cost $0.29. Louise used both to write to 11 friends. If she spent $2.59 for stamps, how many postcards and how many letters did she send? **6 postcards, 5 letters**
11. Forty-two inches of molding are needed to frame a picture. If molding sells for $5.80 a foot, how much will the molding cost to frame the picture? **$20.30**
12. The graph below shows the busiest airports in the United States, categorized by number of passengers in 1990.

    a. Which airport has 12.5 million more flyers than Phoenix?
    b. Which airport has nearly half as many flyers as Atlanta?
    c. If this list was divided into east and west by using the Mississippi River as the dividing line, which group would have the most passengers? **east side**

BUSIEST AIRPORTS IN 1990

People flying (millions)

Chicago O'Hare	25.6
Dallas/Fort Worth	22.8
Atlanta	22.6
Los Angeles	18.1
San Francisco	13.3
Denver	11.9
NY - La Guardia	10.5
Phoenix	10.3
Detroit	9.8
Newark	9.8

OPTIONS

Extending the Lesson

Using Cooperative Groups An *automorphic* number is a number whose square ends with the number itself. The number 25 is automorphic because 25 × 25 = 6<u>25</u>. Have small groups use their calculators and the guess-and-check strategy to find all the automorphic numbers less than 25.

Cooperative Learning Activity

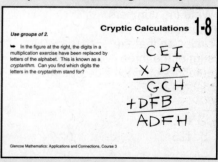

Cryptic Calculations **1-8**

Use groups of 2.

➡ In the figure at the right, the digits in a multiplication exercise have been replaced by letters of the alphabet. This is known as a *cryptarithm*. Can you find which digits the letters in the cryptarithm stand for?

```
    C E I
  X  D A
  -------
  G C H
+ D F B
-------
A D F H
```

Glencoe Mathematics: Applications and Connections, Course 3

1-9 Powers and Exponents

Objective

Use powers and exponents in expressions.

Words to Learn

factor
exponent
power
base
evaluate

Every person has 2 biological parents. Each of their parents has 2 parents, so every person has $2 \cdot 2$ or 4 grandparents. Each grandparent had 2 parents, so every person has $2 \cdot (2 \cdot 2)$ or 8 great grandparents. How many great-great grandparents does every person have?

Generation	Family Tree	Number
Person		1
Parents		$1 \cdot 2$ or 2
Grandparents		$2 \cdot 2$ or 4
Great Grandparents		$2 \cdot 2 \cdot 2$ or 8
Great-Great Grandparents	?	?

Study the pattern in the number column of the table. The next value would be $2 \cdot 2 \cdot 2 \cdot 2$ or 16. Each person has 16 great-great grandparents.

When two or more numbers are multiplied, these numbers are called **factors** of the product. When the same factor is repeated, you may use an **exponent** to simplify the notation.

$$16 = 2 \cdot 2 \cdot 2 \cdot 2 \to 2^4 \qquad \textit{4 is the exponent.}$$

An expression like 2^4 is called a **power** and is read *2 to the fourth power.* The 2 in this expression is called the **base.** The base names the factor being repeated.

Powers are often used to write a product in a shorter form. For example, $3 \cdot 4 \cdot 4 \cdot 3 \cdot 4 \cdot 3 \cdot 3 \cdot 3$ can be written as $4^3 \cdot 3^5$.

Examples

1 Write $5 \cdot 5 \cdot 5 \cdot 5 \cdot 5 \cdot 5$ using exponents.

There are six factors of 5.
$5 \cdot 5 \cdot 5 \cdot 5 \cdot 5 \cdot 5 = 5^6$

2 Write $3 \cdot 3 \cdot 5 \cdot 5 \cdot 6 \cdot 6 \cdot 6$ using exponents.

There are two factors of 3, two factors of 5, and three factors of 6.
$3 \cdot 3 \cdot 5 \cdot 5 \cdot 6 \cdot 6 \cdot 6 = 3^2 \cdot 5^2 \cdot 6^3$

Lesson 1-9 Algebra Connection: Powers and Exponents **35**

1-9 Lesson Notes

NCTM Standards: 1–5, 7, 12

Lesson Resources
• Study Guide Master 1-9
• Practice Master 1-9
• Enrichment Master 1-9
• Evaluation Master, Quiz B, p. 7
• Technology Master, p. 1
• Group Activity Card 1-9

 Transparency 1-9 contains the 5-Minute Check and a teaching aid for this lesson.

5-Minute Check
(Over Lesson 1-8)

Solve using the guess-and-check strategy.

1. The sum of two numbers is 6. Their product is 9. Find the numbers. 3, 3

2. Bonnie has some nickels and dimes, 6 coins in all. If the coins are worth $0.40, how many of each does she have?
   4 nickels, 2 dimes

1 FOCUS

Motivating the Lesson

Situational Problem Going back 5 generations, every person has 32 great-great-great grandparents. *How can the number 32 be written as a power of 2?*

2 TEACH

Using Applications Give this example to illustrate how quickly numbers grow exponentially.

If a $\frac{1}{500}$-inch-thick piece of paper was folded in half 20 times, the resulting folded paper would be $\left(\frac{1}{500} \cdot 2^{20}\right)$ inches, or about 175 feet, thick. (Point out that folding the paper 20 times is, of course, impossible to do.)
Have students use a calculator to verify this statement.

OPTIONS

Reteaching Activity

Using Problem Solving Pose the following problem. *How many times must you multiply each first number by itself to obtain the second number?*

a. 3; 81   4
b. 2; 64   6
c. 5; 125   3
d. 4; 1,024   5
e. 13; 169   2
f. 7; 2,401   4

Study Guide Masters, p. 9

Name _____ Date _____

Study Guide Worksheet 1-9

Algebra: Powers and Exponents

A power can be used to show a number multiplied by itself.

Example $3 \times 3 \times 3 \times 3$ can be written 3^4. It is read, "3 to the fourth power."

The exponent, 4, tells how many times the base, 3, is used as a factor.   Base → 3^4 ← Exponent

Example   Write $2 \times 2 \times 3 \times 2 \times 3$ using exponents.

2 is used as a factor 4 times. 3 is used as a factor 2 times.
$2 \times 2 \times 3 \times 2 \times 3 = 2^4 \times 3^2$

Multiply to find the value of expressions with exponents.

Example Find the value of 3^4.   *Example* Find the value of $2^4 \times 3^2$.
$3^4 = 3 \times 3 \times 3 \times 3 = 81$ $2^4 \times 3^2 = 2 \times 2 \times 2 \times 2 \times 3 \times 3$

35

You can use your calculator to find the values of powers.
Use the $\boxed{y^x}$ key to **evaluate,** or find the value of, a power.
Here's how to evaluate the expression $4^3 \cdot 3^5$.

4 $\boxed{y^x}$ 3 $\boxed{\times}$ 3 $\boxed{y^x}$ 5 $\boxed{=}$ `15552`

$4^3 \cdot 3^5 = 15,552$ *You can find the product of*
$4 \cdot 4 \cdot 4 \cdot 3 \cdot 3 \cdot 3 \cdot 3 \cdot 3$ to check this answer.

Examples

3 Find 8^3.

Use paper and pencil.
$8^3 = 8 \cdot 8 \cdot 8$
$\quad = 64 \cdot 8$
$\quad = 512$

Use a calculator.
8 $\boxed{y^x}$ 3 $\boxed{=}$ `512`

4 Find $2^3 \cdot 3^4$.

Use paper and pencil.
$2^3 \cdot 3^4$
$\quad = \underbrace{2 \cdot 2 \cdot 2} \cdot \underbrace{3 \cdot 3 \cdot 3 \cdot 3}$
$\quad = \quad 8 \quad \cdot \quad 81$
$\quad = 648$

Use a calculator.
2 $\boxed{y^x}$ 3 $\boxed{\times}$ 3 $\boxed{y^x}$ 4 $\boxed{=}$ `648`

Checking for Understanding

Communicating Mathematics

Read and study the lesson to answer each question.

1. **Tell** which is the base and which is the exponent in 10^5. base: 10; exponent: 5
2. **Write** the expression *5 to the fourth power* using exponents. 5^4
3. **Show** how you can use paper and pencil to verify the calculator example at the top of this page. See margin.
4. **Show** that 3^2 and 2^3 are not equal. $3^2 = 3 \cdot 3 = 9$; $2^3 = 2 \cdot 2 \cdot 2 = 8$; $9 \neq 8$

Guided Practice

Write each product using exponents.

5. $5 \cdot 5 \cdot 5$ 5^3
6. $10 \cdot 10 \cdot 10 \cdot 10$ 10^4
7. $8 \cdot 8 \cdot 8 \cdot 8 \cdot 8$ 8^5

Evaluate each expression.

8. 5^3 125
9. 7^2 49
10. $3^2 \cdot 4^2$ 144
11. $5 \cdot 6^3 \cdot 10^3$ 1,080,000

Exercises

Independent Practice

Write each product using exponents.

12. $3 \cdot 3 \cdot 5 \cdot 5 \cdot 5$ $3^2 \cdot 5^3$
13. $6 \cdot 6 \cdot 7 \cdot 6 \cdot 7$ $6^3 \cdot 7^2$
14. $2 \cdot 3 \cdot 5 \cdot 3 \cdot 2$ $2^2 \cdot 3^2 \cdot 5$

36   **Chapter 1** Tools for Problem Solving

OPTIONS

Gifted and Talented Needs

Have students research the binary system to learn how any whole number can be written as the sum of powers of 2. They can extend their study to electronics to learn how this principle is applied in switching design.

Evaluate each expression.

15. 5^4 625   16. 4^3 64   17. 2^5 32   18. 1^{40} 1

19. $2^2 \cdot 7^2$ 196   20. $5^2 \cdot 8^2 \cdot 3^3$ 43,200 21. 100^3 1,000,000 22. 56^4 9,834,496

Use your calculator to evaluate each expression.

23. $6^2 - 2^2$ 32   24. $2 \cdot 2^3 \cdot 3^2$ 144   25. $2 \cdot 3^2 + 9 \cdot 6^2$ 342

Mixed Review   26. Estimate $10.19 + $9.89 + $10.09 + $9.99 by clustering. *(Lesson 1-3)* **$40**

27. How many kilograms are in 5,734 grams? *(Lesson 1-6)* **5.734 kilograms**

28. How many pints are in 6 cups? *(Lesson 1-7)* **3 pints**

29. **Smart Shopping**   Which is the better purchase price, 39 ounces of flour for $2.70 or 2.5 pounds of flour for $2.70? *(Lesson 1-7)* **2.5 pounds for $2.70**

Problem Solving and Applications   30. **Geometry**   To find the volume of a cube, you multiply the length times the width times the depth of the box. Suppose a cube is 30 cm long, 30 cm wide, and 30 cm tall.

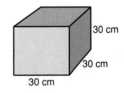
30 cm
30 cm
30 cm

a. Write an expression for the volume using exponents. **30^3**

b. Find the volume of the cube. **27,000 cm³**

31. **Critical Thinking**   Complete each sentence with the correct base or exponent.

a. $27 = 3^{\blacksquare}$ 3   b. $36 = \blacksquare^2$ 6   c. $16 = \blacksquare^2$ or $\blacksquare^4 = 4; 2$

32. **Automobiles**   The formula to determine the horsepower for a 4-cylinder car can be found by evaluating the expression $6^2 \cdot 4 \div 2.5$. Use your calculator to find the horsepower rounded to the nearest 10. **60**

33. **Number Sense**   If $2^{10} = 1,024$, find 2^{11} mentally. **2,048**

34. **Journal Entry**   Write how you could state the equivalent values in the metric system by using exponents, such as 1 km $= 10^{\blacksquare}$ m. **3; See students' work.**

35. **Mathematics and Astronomy**   Read the following paragraph.

Some scientists believe that our solar system was formed when a cloud of gas condensed to form the sun. Parts of the cloud formed small bodies called planetoids. The planetoids crashed into each other, breaking up into smaller pieces and attaching themselves to larger ones.

a. The average distance from the sun to Uranus is 2.87×10^9 km. Write this distance in standard form.
   2,870,000,000

b. The average distance from Venus to the sun is 67,200,000 mi. Between which powers of 10 is the distance? **10^7 and 10^8**

Lesson 1-9 Algebra Connection: Powers and Exponents   **37**

Extending the Lesson

Mathematics and Astronomy
Encourage students to use the power key on their calculators to complete computations involving large numbers.

Cooperative Learning Activity

Fidgety Digits 1-9

Number of players: 2
Materials: Index cards, spinner

♦ Copy onto cards the expressions shown on the back of this card, including the circles. Shuffle the cards and place them face down in a pile. Label the sections of a spinner "0," "1," "2," "4," and "5."

➥ In turn, each partner selects a card. Each partner must decide whether to write the value of the expression as shown on the card or to spin the spinner first, replacing all the circled numbers with the number spun. When all of the cards have been selected, each partner finds the sum of the values he or she has written. The partner with the greater sum wins.

Glencoe Mathematics: Applications and Connections, Course 3

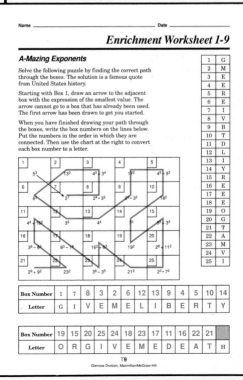

Error Analysis

Watch for students who multiply base times exponent to evaluate an exponential expression.
$$2^5 = 2 \times 5 = 10$$

Prevent by stressing that an exponent tells how many times to multiply the base by itself.
$$2^5 = 2 \cdot 2 \cdot 2 \cdot 2 \cdot 2 = 32$$

Close

Have students explain the difference between 3^4 and 3×4. 3^4 is 3 multiplied by itself four times ($3 \cdot 3 \cdot 3 \cdot 3$). 3×4 is 3 multiplied by 4.

3 PRACTICE/APPLY

Assignment Guide
Maximum: 12–35
Minimum: 13–25 odd, 26–33

For **Extra Practice**, see p. 585.

Alternate Assessment

Speaking   Name several exponential expressions, having students state each expression as a product. Name several products and have students state each as an exponential expression.

Enrichment Masters, p. 9

37

The Chapter Study Guide and Review begins with a section on Communicating Mathematics. This includes questions that review the new terms and concepts that were introduced in the chapter.

Then, the Skills and Concepts presented in the chapter are reviewed using a side-by-side format. Encourage students to refer to the Objectives and Examples on the left as they complete the Review Exercises on the right.

The Chapter Study Guide and Review ends with problems that review Applications and Problem Solving.

Chapter

Study Guide and Review

Study Guide and Review

Communicating Mathematics

Choose the correct term to complete each sentence.

1. The (quart, liter) is a unit of capacity in the metric system.
2. The (ounce, gram) is a unit of weight in the customary system.
3. $2 + 3 = 3 + 2$ is an example of the (commutative, associative) property of addition.
4. In the expression 5^3, the (base, exponent) is 3.
5. Estimating $219.8 - 78.2$ by computing $220 - 80$ is an example of (clustering, rounding).
6. Give one advantage that the metric system has over the customary system. based on 10

Self Assessment

Objectives and Examples	Review Exercises
Upon completing this chapter, you should be able to:	*Use these exercises to review and prepare for the chapter test.*

● solve problems using the four-step plan *(Lesson 1-1)*

The four steps are:

● **Explore** What do I know? What do I need to find out?
● **Plan** How will I go about solving this?
● **Solve** Carry out your plan. Does it work? Do you need another plan?
● **Examine** Does your answer seem reasonable? If not, find another.

Use the four-step plan to solve each problem.

7. **Time** The distance between John's house and Bill's house is 90 feet. If it takes John 3 seconds to walk 10 feet, how long will it take him to walk to Bill's house? 27 seconds
8. **Construction** The concrete slab for a floor is 47 feet long, 50 feet wide, and 2 feet deep. If the volume of the concrete is measured in cubic feet and is found by multiplying the length, width, and height, find the volume of the concrete used in the slab. 4,700 ft³

● compute mentally using compensation *(Lesson 1-2)*

Find $300 - 128$.

$$\begin{array}{rcl} 300 - 1 & \to & 299 \\ 128 - 1 & \to & -127 \\ \hline & & 172 \end{array}$$

Use compensation to find each answer.

9. $57 + 88$ 145
10. $600 - 461$ 139
11. $398 + 119$ 517
12. $402 - 237$ 165
13. $\$2.97 + \$4.59$ $7.56
14. $903 - 584$ 319

Classroom Vignette

"I combine the estimation strategies and the measurement connections in this chapter by giving students the opportunity to use rulers to measure lengths. If a student has trouble interpreting a unit on the ruler, I remind them that they are measuring distance and that I will accept a reasonable estimate."

Loy Koeller, Teacher
Mohawk Alternative Middle School, Columbus, OH

Objectives and Examples

- compute mentally using the commutative, associative, and distributive properties *(Lesson 1-2)*

  Find $25 + 47 + 25$.
  $$25 + 47 + 25 = 25 + 25 + 47$$
  $$= 50 + 47$$
  $$= 97$$

- estimate answers by using different strategies *(Lesson 1-3)*

  Four ways to estimate are by rounding, by front-end estimation, by using compatible numbers, and by clustering.

- use metric units of measurement *(Lesson 1-6)*

  $2.81 \text{ m} = \underline{\ ?\ } \text{ mm}$

  A meter is longer than a millimeter, so multiply.

  $1 \text{ m} = 1,000 \text{ mm}$, so multiply by 1,000.

  $2.810 = 2,810$

  $2.81 \text{ m} = 2,810 \text{ mm}$

- use customary units of measurement *(Lesson 1-7)*

  $12 \text{ qt} = \underline{\ ?\ } \text{ gal}$

  A quart is less than a gallon, so divide.

  $4 \text{ qt} = 1 \text{ gal}$, so divide by 4.

  $12 \div 4 = 3$

  $12 \text{ qt} = 3 \text{ gal}$

- use powers and exponents in expressions *(Lesson 1-9)*

  Find $5^2 \cdot 2^3$.

  $$5^2 \cdot 2^3 = \underline{5 \cdot 5} \cdot \underline{2 \cdot 2 \cdot 2}$$
  $$= \ \ 25 \ \ \cdot \ \ \ 8$$
  $$= 200$$

Review Exercises

Use the commutative, associative, and distributive properties to find each answer.

15. $7 \cdot 12$ 84   **16.** $8(10 + 40)$ 400

17. $34 + 49 + 66$ **18.** $(19 \cdot 4) \cdot 25$

19. $5 \cdot 34 \cdot 20$ 3,400   **20.** $18(47 + 53)$

17. 149   18. 1,900   1,800

Estimate. Use an appropriate strategy.

21. $2,794 \div 68$ 40

22. $628 + 482 + 817$ 1,900

23. $5,128 + 4,984 + 5,021 + 4,898$ 20,000

24. $9.872 - 5.344$ 4.500

Complete each sentence.

25. $3.4 \text{ m} = \underline{\ ?\ } \text{ km}$ 0.0034

26. $2.71 \text{ L} = \underline{\ ?\ } \text{ mL}$ 2,710

27. $620 \text{ g} = \underline{\ ?\ } \text{ kg}$ 0.620

28. $0.748 \text{ m} = \underline{\ ?\ } \text{ cm}$ 74.8

29. $\underline{\ ?\ } \text{ L} = 8.62 \text{ mL}$ 0.00862

30. $\underline{\ ?\ } \text{ mg} = 4.25 \text{ g}$ 4,250

Complete each sentence.

31. $\underline{\ ?\ } \text{ ft} = 54 \text{ in.}$ 4.5

32. $2.5 \text{ T} = \underline{\ ?\ } \text{ lb}$ 5,000

33. $15 \text{ ft} = \underline{\ ?\ } \text{ yd}$ 5

34. $6 \text{ pt} = \underline{\ ?\ } \text{ c}$ 12

35. $\underline{\ ?\ } \text{ oz} = 4 \text{ lb}$ 64

36. $22 \text{ gal} = \underline{\ ?\ } \text{ qt}$ 88

Write each product as an expression using exponents.

37. $3 \cdot 3 \cdot 8 \cdot 8 \cdot 8$ **38.** $4 \cdot 6 \cdot 4 \cdot 4 \cdot 6 \cdot 7$
       $3^2 \cdot 8^3$ $7 \cdot 6^2 \cdot 4^3$

Find the value of each expression.

39. 2^4 16   **40.** $3^2 \cdot 4^3$ 576 **41.** $5^3 \cdot 100^2$

                            1,250,000

Chapter 1 Study Guide and Review   **39**

You may wish to use a Chapter Test from the Evaluation Masters booklet as an additional chapter review. The two free-response forms are shown below. One of the two multiple-choice forms is shown on the next page.

Evaluation Masters, pp. 5–6

Name _____ Date _____

Form 2A _____ *Chapter 1 Test*

Estimate. Use an appropriate strategy.

1. $4.66 + 2.49 + 7.15$ 2. $1,898 \div 38$

3. $9,708 - 2,396$ 4. $4,621 + 2,975$

5. $2.902 + 3.122 + 2.783 + 3.016$

6. Estimate the quotient of 5,389 and 92.

7. Use mental math to find $(775 + 629) + 25$. Tell how you found the answer.

8. Explain how you would use mental math to find $803 - 497$.

Complete.

9. $0.781 \text{ kg} = \underline{?} \text{ g}$ 10. $16.5 \text{ ft} = \underline{?} \text{ yd}$

11. $\underline{?} \text{ lb} = 40 \text{ oz}$ 12. $\underline{?} \text{ L} = 3,900 \text{ mL}$

13. $75 \text{ cm} = \underline{?} \text{ m}$ 14. $2.5 \text{ yd} = \underline{?} \text{ in.}$

15. Rah's recipe makes 4 cups of dip. How many pints is this?

16. How many pints are in 2 gallons of juice?

Write each product using exponents.

17. $5 \cdot 5 \cdot 5 \cdot 8 \cdot 8$ 18. $2 \cdot 3 \cdot 7 \cdot 3 \cdot 2 \cdot 3$

Evaluate each expression.

19. $5^3 \cdot 4^2$ 20. $2^{10} \cdot 1^{11}$

21. $6^2 \cdot 8 \cdot 3^4$ 22. 64^3

Use the four-step plan to solve each problem.

23. Rachel works 5 hours as a landscaper and earns $54.25. If she works 8 hours, how much does she earn?

24. One space shuttle can carry about 65,000 pounds of cargo, and a bicycle weighs about 42 pounds. What is the greatest number of bicycles that could be carried on the shuttle?

25. You have four different colors of stained glass, and you want to use two colors for each project you are going to design. How many different color combinations can you use?

BONUS How many numbers are in the sequence 0, 4, 8 ... 100?

1. 14.1
2. 50
3. 7,400
4. 7,500
5. 12
6. 60
7. 1,429; (775 + 25) + 629.
8. 306; (803 + 3) − (497 + 3)
9. 781
10. 5.5
11. 2.5
12. 3.9
13. 0.75
14. 90
15. 2 pints
16. 16 pints
17. $5^3 \cdot 8^2$
18. $2^2 \cdot 3^3 \cdot 7$
19. 2,000
20. 1,024
21. 23,328
22. 262,144
23. $86.80
24. 1,547 bicycles
25. 6 combinations
26

5
Glencoe Division, Macmillan/McGraw-Hill

Name _____ Date _____

Form 2B _____ *Chapter 1 Test*

Estimate. Use an appropriate strategy.

1. $8.25 + 1.39 + 6.44$ 2. $2,943 \div 62$

3. $8,618 - 3,427$ 4. $5,808 + 3,279$

5. $4.221 + 4.057 + 3.801 + 4.191$

6. Estimate the quotient 6,296 ÷ 68.

7. Use mental math to find $5 \cdot 39 \cdot 2$. Tell how you found the answer.

8. Explain how you would use mental math to find $900 - 649$.

Complete.

9. $375 \text{ mL} = \underline{?} \text{ L}$ 10. $\underline{?} \text{ in.} = 1.5 \text{ yd}$

11. $1234 \text{ mm} = \underline{?} \text{ m}$ 12. $\underline{?} \text{ g} = 12 \text{ kg}$

13. $2.5 \text{ lb} = \underline{?} \text{ oz}$ 14. $16 \text{ yd} = \underline{?} \text{ ft}$

15. Jen's recipe makes 8 cups of salsa. How many quarts is this?

16. How many pounds are in 1.5 tons of gravel?

Write each product using exponents.

17. $9 \cdot 9 \cdot 4 \cdot 4 \cdot 4$ 18. $5 \cdot 6 \cdot 10 \cdot 6 \cdot 5 \cdot 6$

Evaluate each expression.

19. $3^4 \cdot 5^2$ 20. $2^7 \cdot 1^{17}$

21. $7^2 \cdot 9 \cdot 4^3$ 22. 45^3

Use the four-step plan to solve each problem.

23. A chemist pours a solution into a beaker. If the beaker plus the solution have a mass of 90.2 grams and the beaker itself has a mass of 61.8 grams, what is the mass of the solution?

24. As part of your exercise program, you decide to do 2 more pull-ups each day. If you start with 6 pull-ups, how many days will it take you to do 22 pull-ups in one day?

25. The number of a house address has 3 digits. The number is divisible by 2, 3, 6, and 7. The third digit is the square of the first digit. The sum of the first and third digits is the second digit. What is the number?

BONUS How many odd whole numbers are less than 100?

1. 15.9
2. 50
3. 5,200
4. 9,000
5. 16
6. 90
7. 390; (5 · 2) · 39
8. 251; (900 + 51) − (649 + 51)
9. 0.375
10. 54
11. 1.234
12. 12,000
13. 40
14. 48
15. 2 quarts
16. 3,000
17. $4^3 \cdot 9^2$
18. $5^2 \cdot 6^3 \cdot 10$
19. 2,025
20. 128
21. 28,224
22. 91,125
23. 28.4 g
24. 9 days
25. 462
50

6
Glencoe Division, Macmillan/McGraw-Hill

Applications and Problem Solving

42. **Consumer Math** At a restaurant, entrees cost from $8.95 to $15.95; appetizers cost from $2.25 to $5.95; a salad costs $2.75; and soup costs $1.95. A full meal includes soup, salad, appetizer, and an entree. Without tax and tip, would a couple expect to pay more or less than $30 for a full meal at this restaurant? *(Lesson 1-4)* **more than $30**

43. **Astronomy** When Venus is closest to Earth, it is about 25 million miles away. Radio waves, like light waves, travel through space at about 186,272 miles per second. Would it take about 0.225, 2.25, or 22.25 minutes to send a radio signal from Earth to Venus? *(Lesson 1-5)* **2.25 minutes**

44. Melba has 15 coins, consisting of quarters and dimes. Their total value is $3. How many of each coin does she have? *(Lesson 1-8)* **10 quarters, 5 dimes**

45. **Sports** During a football game, Steve had four punt returns that were 11 yards, 23 yards, 19 yards, and 32 yards long. Approximately how many total yards did Steve gain on punt returns during that game? *(Lesson 1-3)* **80 yd**

46. **Mail** Lisa mailed three packages. The first one weighed 186 grams, the second one weighed 198,000 milligrams, and the third one weighed 0.221 kilograms. What was the total weight of all three packages in grams? *(Lesson 1-6)* **605 grams**

Curriculum Connection Projects

● **Science** Find the steps of the scientific process from a science book. Write a short paper comparing it to the four-step plan for problem solving in math.

● **Consumer Math** From a trip to the mall or from a catalog, select five complete outfits. Record the price of each item. Estimate the total cost of each outfit, the whole wardrobe, and the amount left over from $500.

● **Physical Education** From research on the 1992 Summer Olympics, make a five-column table with the following headings: Event, Kilometers, Meters, Centimeters, and Millimeters. Record distances from five running events and five field events. Convert each to the missing metric measurements on your paper.

Read More About It

Mamioka. *Who's Hu.*
Raskin, Ellen. *The Westing Game.*
Smullyan, Raymond. *The Lady or the Tiger? And Other Logic Puzzles.*

40   **Chapter 1** Study Guide and Review

1 Test

Estimate. Use an appropriate strategy.

1. $8.25 + 3.59 + 5.76$ **17.4**   2. $2,948 \div 49$ **60**   3. $7,548 - 4,139$ **3,400**
4. $5,842 + 3,112$ **8,900**   5. $2.015 + 1.893 + 2.121 + 1.902$ **8**
6. Estimate the product of 489 and 19. **10,000**
7. Use mental math to find $(650 + 793) + 50$. Tell how you found the answer. $(650 + 50) + 793 = 1,493$
8. Explain how you would use mental math to find $500 - 232$. **See Solutions Manual.**

Complete each sentence.   **0.735**
9. ___?___ ft = 5 yd **15**   10. ___?___ kg = 735 g   11. 8.2 L = ___?___ mL **8,200**
12. 3.5 lb = ___?___ oz **56**   13. ___?___ cm = 0.52 m **52** 14. 4.21 km = ___?___ m **4,210**
15. Josh's recipe makes 9 cups of lemonade. How many pints is this? **4.5 pt**
16. How many quarts are in 6 gallons of oil? **24 qt**

Write each product using exponents.
17. $6 \cdot 6 \cdot 6 \cdot 7 \cdot 7$ **$6^3 \cdot 7^2$**   18. $3 \cdot 4 \cdot 8 \cdot 4 \cdot 3 \cdot 4$ **$8 \cdot 3^2 \cdot 4^3$**

Evaluate each expression.
19. $2^3 \cdot 4^2$ **128**   20. $2^2 \cdot 5^2 \cdot 4^3$ **6,400**

Use the four-step plan to solve each problem.

21. **Music**   Michelle wants to listen to 5 compact discs. Two compact discs are 51 minutes long each and the other three compact discs are 46 minutes long each. How long will it take Michelle to listen to all 5 compact discs? **240 min or 4 h**

22. **Earning Money**   Maria and Emilio shovel driveways in the winter for $5.00 each. If Emilio can shovel 5 driveways per hour and Maria can shovel 3 driveways per hour, how long will it take them to earn a total of $80? **2 hours**

23. Mrs. Martinez bought a house for $44,800 in 1974. She sold it in 1991 for 3.25 times more. Did the value of the house increase to $1,456,000 or $145,600? **$145,600**

24. Mr. Higgins' credit card purchases for this month are $129.47 and $169.72. His previous balance was $2,147.91 on which he had to pay $33.83 in finance charges. He also made a payment of $150. His new balance should be about: **b**
    a. $2,500   b. $2,300   c. $230   d. $200

25. Four pears cost $2.18. Three cans of apple juice cost $3.29. About how much money do you need to buy one of each? **about $1.50**

Bonus   Suppose x represents a number. Find the value of x so that $x^3 = 64$. **4**

Using the Chapter Test

This page may be used as a chapter test or another chapter review.

Evaluation Masters, pp. 1–2

Name _____ Date _____

Form 1A _____   *Chapter 1 Test*

Use mental math to find each answer for Exercises 1–4.

1. $4 \cdot (25 \cdot 15)$
   A. 150   B. 1,500   C. 1,200   D. 120   1. __B__
2. $47 + 28 + 3$
   A. 79   B. 88   C. 69   D. 78   2. __D__
3. $700 - 357$
   A. 243   B. 343   C. 443   D. 334   3. __B__
4. $630 + 878 + 70$
   A. 1,578   B. 1,478   C. 1,678   D. 1,587   4. __A__
5. Estimate $2.49 + 7.15 + 4.86$.
   A. 13.3   B. 14.0   C. 14.3   D. 15.3   5. __C__
6. Estimate $5,948 \div 21$.
   A. 300   B. 250   C. 200   D. 350   6. __A__
7. Estimate $219.2 - 58.6$.
   A. 170   B. 180   C. 150   D. 160   7. __D__
8. Estimate $5,973 + 5,988 + 6,139 + 5,783$.
   A. 24,000   B. 25,000   C. 22,000   D. 23,000   8. __A__
9. 2.64 m = ___?___ mm
   A. 0.0264   B. 264   C. 2,640   D. 26.4   9. __C__
10. 315 g = ___?___ kg
    A. 0.315   B. 3.15   C. 31.5   D. 315,000   10. __A__
11. ___?___ cm = 0.429 m
    A. 4.29   B. 429   C. 42.9   D. 0.00429   11. __C__
12. 4.5 lb = ___?___ oz
    A. 72   B. 64   C. 70   D. 75   12. __A__
13. ___?___ gal = 24 qt
    A. 8   B. 4   C. 6   D. 3   13. __C__
14. $4\frac{1}{2}$ ft = ___?___ in.
    A. 45   B. 54   C. 162   D. 36   14. __B__
15. An inchworm travels 5 yards. How many feet is that?
    A. 40   B. 10   C. 60   D. 15   15. __D__
16. A bottle holds 0.275 liters. How many milliliters does it hold?
    A. 2.75   B. 275   C. 2,750   D. 27.5   16. __B__

1
Glencoe Division, Macmillan/McGraw-Hill

Name _____ Date _____

Chapter 1 Test, Form 1A (continued)

17. Write $3 \cdot 4 \cdot 6 \cdot 4 \cdot 3 \cdot 3$ using exponents.
    A. $3^2 \cdot 4^3 \cdot 6$ B. $3^2 \cdot 4^2 \cdot 6^2$ C. $3^3 \cdot 4^3 \cdot 6$ D. $3^3 \cdot 4^2 \cdot 6$ 17. __D__
18. Write $2 \cdot 2 \cdot 2 \cdot 2 \cdot 5 \cdot 5$ using exponents.
    A. $2^4 \cdot 5^2$ B. $2^3 \cdot 5^4$ C. 10^6 D. $2^4 \cdot 5^4$ 18. __A__
19. Find the value of $2^4 \cdot 4^2$.
    A. 128   B. 256   C. 64   D. 262,144   19. __B__
20. Find the value of $2^3 \cdot 5^2 \cdot 1^3 \cdot 3^3$.
    A. 5,400   B. 27,000   C. 2,160   D. 720   20. __A__
21. At the school store, a pen costs 49¢ and a pad of paper costs 99¢. What could you buy and spend exactly $3.45?   21. __A__
    A. 3 pens, 2 pads   B. 2 pens, 3 pads
    C. 1 pen, 3 pads   D. 3 pens, 1 pad
22. Meg shows Colleen $3 from her purse and says, "This is one fourth the money left in my purse." In the beginning, how much did Meg have in her purse?   22. __D__
    A. $10   B. $1   C. $12   D. $15
23. You need to buy 3 cartons of juice at $1.99 each, 4 packages of crackers at $1.59 each, and 5 jars of olives at $0.99 each. How much do you need to bring with you?   23. __B__
    A. $5   B. $20   C. $15   D. $10
24. Find $18,560 \div 29$ without doing the long division. Use the eliminate possibilities strategy to find the quotient.   24. __D__
    A. 60   B. 6,400   C. 600   D. 640
25. A basketball team made 26 baskets to score 55 points. Three of the baskets were 1-point shots, and six of the baskets were 3-point shots. How many 2-point shots were made?   25. __B__
    A. 20   B. 17   C. 15   D. 12

BONUS If x represents a number, find the value of x so that $x^5 = 243$.   __C__
    A. 4   B. 2   C. 3   D. 1

2
Glencoe Division, Macmillan/McGraw-Hill

Test and Review Generator software is provided in Apple, IBM, and Macintosh versions. You may use this software to create your own tests or worksheets, based on the needs of your students.

The **Performance Assessment Booklet** provides an alternate assessment for evaluating student progress. An assessment for this chapter can be found on pages 1–2.

2 An Introduction to Algebra

Previewing the Chapter

This chapter introduces students to the fundamentals of algebra, focusing on writing and solving equations for word problems. Students learn the meaning of a variable and how to use variables to write algebraic expressions. Methods for solving addition, subtraction, multiplication, division, and two-step equations, and for solving inequalities are developed. In the **problem-solving strategy** lessons, students learn to solve problems by working backward and by using an equation. Finally, students apply the methods shown in the chapter to problems involving the perimeter and area of rectangles, squares, and parallelograms.

Lesson	Lesson Objectives	NCTM Standards	State/Local Objectives
2-1	Evaluate numerical and algebraic expressions by using the order of operations.	1–4, 6–9	
2-2	Identify and solve equations.	1–4, 7, 9	
2-3	Solve equations using the subtraction and addition property of equality.	1–6, 9, 12	
2-4	Solve equations using the division and multiplication property of equality.	1–7, 9, 12	
2-5	Solve problems by working backward.	1–7	
2-6A	Write algebraic expressions and equations from verbal problems.	1–4, 7–9	
2-6	Write algebraic expressions and equations from verbal phrases and sentences.	1–5	
2-7A	Use function machines to find output from a given input and then to find input from a given output.	1–4, 7–9	
2-7	Solve two-step equations.	1–6, 9	
2-8	Solve problems by using an equation.	1–5, 7, 9	
2-9	Find the perimeters and areas of rectangles, squares, and parallelograms.	1–4, 7, 9, 12, 13	
2-10	Identify and solve inequalities.	1–4, 6, 7, 9, 13	

Organizing the Chapter

A complete, 1-page lesson plan is provided for each lesson in the Lesson Plans Masters Booklet.

LESSON PLANNING GUIDE

Lesson	Materials/ Manipulatives	Extra Practice (Student Edition)	Blackline Masters Booklets										
			Study Guide	Practice	Enrichment	Evaluation	Technology	Lab Manual	Multicultural Activities	Application and Interdisciplinary Activities	Transparencies	Group Activity Cards
2-1	calculator	p. 585	p. 10	p. 10	p. 10		p. 2			p. 2	2-1	2-1
2-2		p. 586	p. 11	p. 11	p. 11						2-2	2-2
2-3	counters, cups, mats	p. 586	p. 12	p. 12	p. 12						2-3	2-3
2-4	cups, counters, mats	p. 586	p. 13	p. 13	p. 13					p. 16	2-4	2-4
2-5			p. 14	p. 14	p. 14	Quiz A, p. 16					2-5	2-5
2-6A	counters, sheets of paper							p. 41				
2-6		p. 587	p. 15	p. 15	p. 15						2-6	2-6
2-7A								p. 42				
2-7	cups, counters, mats, calculators	p. 587	p. 16	p. 16	p. 16				p. 2		2-7	2-7
2-8	calculator		p. 17	p. 17	p. 17						2-8	2-8
2-9	graph paper, scissors	p. 587	p. 18	p. 18	p. 18			p. 43			2-9	2-9
2-10	calculator, measuring tape or yardstick	p. 588	p. 19	p. 19	p. 19	Quiz B, p. 16	p. 16				2-10	2-10
Study Guide and Review			Multiple Choice Test, Forms 1A and 1B, pp. 10–13 Free Response Test, Forms 2A and 2B, pp. 14–15 Cumulative Review, p. 17 (free response)									
Test			Cumulative Test, p. 18 (multiple choice)									

Pacing Guide: Option I (Chapters 1–12) - 14 days; Option II (Chapters 1–13) - 13 days; Option III (Chapters 1–14) - 12 days
You may wish to refer to the complete **Course Planning Guides** on page T25.

OTHER CHAPTER RESOURCES

Student Edition
Chapter Opener, pp. 42–43
Cultural Kaleidoscope, p. 53
Mid-Chapter Review, p. 59
Portfolio Suggestions, pp. 59, 79

 Manipulatives
Overhead Manipulative Resources
Middle School Mathematics Manipulative Kit

Software/Technology
Interactive Mathematics Tools (Macintosh)
Test and Review Generator (IBM, Apple, Macintosh)
Teacher's Guide for Software Resources

Other Supplements
Transparency 2–0
Performance Assessment, pp. 3–4
Glencoe Mathematics Professional Series
Lesson Plans, pp. 13–24

INTERDISCIPLINARY BULLETIN BOARD

Economics Connection

Objective Find the unit value of paintings and stamps.

How To Use It Have students research the values and dimensions of five rare stamps and five famous paintings. *Scott's Standard Postage Stamp Catalog* can be used to find stamp values, and newspaper and magazine accounts of art auctions can be used to find the purchase prices of paintings. Have students calculate the area of each painting and stamp, and the value per square inch. Then have them decide whether stamps or paintings are more valuable.

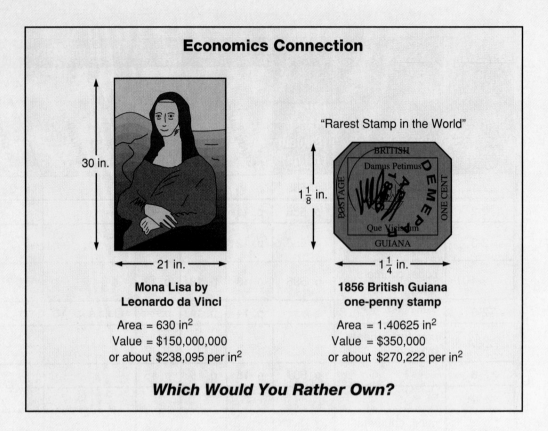

Economics Connection

30 in.

21 in.

Mona Lisa by Leonardo da Vinci

Area = 630 in^2

Value = $150,000,000

or about $238,095 per in^2

"Rarest Stamp in the World"

$1\frac{1}{8}$ in.

$1\frac{1}{4}$ in.

1856 British Guiana one-penny stamp

Area = 1.40625 in^2

Value = $350,000

or about $270,222 per in^2

Which Would You Rather Own?

APPLICATIONS AND CONNECTIONS

Applications	Lesson	Example	Exercise
Nutrition	2-1		39
Smart Shopping	2-2	2	
Lawn Care	2-2		27
Advertising	2-2		29
Weather	2-2		30
Space Science	2-4		27
Auto Mechanics	2-4		28
Sales	2-7		29
Keyboarding	2-7		31
Medicine	2-7		32
Construction	2-9	1	
Home Maintenance	2-9		18
Shipping	2-9		20
Nutrition	2-10		31
Football	2-10		32
Connections			
Number Patterns	2-1		41
Computer	2-1		42
Geometry	2-3		31
Geometry	2-4	2	
Statistics	2-6		30
Calculator	2-10		33
Measurement	2-10		34

TEAM ACTIVITIES

Multicultural Experiences

Outside Field Trips Look for trips that will demonstrate how people use variables in formulas to solve problems. A visit to a building site can allow a contractor to explain how formulas are used in construction.

A visit to a newspaper can show how advertising fees are assessed.

In-Class Speakers Invite a loan officer from a bank to discuss formulas used in calculating interest payments.

An insurance agent can discuss how actuarial formulas are used to determine insurance rates.

SUPPLEMENTARY BLACKLINE MASTER BOOKLETS

Some of the blackline masters for enhancing this chapter are shown below.

Application and Interdisciplinary Activity Masters, pp. 2, 16

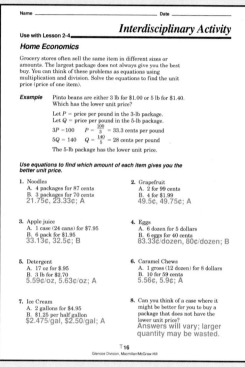

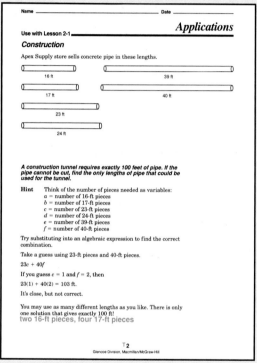

Multicultural Activity Masters, p. 2

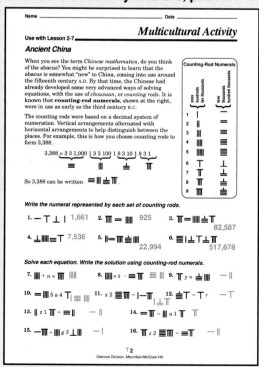

Technology Masters, p. 16

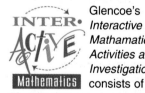

RECOMMENDED OUTSIDE RESOURCES

Books/Periodicals

California State Department of Education Task Force on Middle Grade Education, *Caught in the Middle,* California State Department of Education, Sacramento, CA, 1987.

National Council of Teachers of Mathematics, *The Ideas of Algebra, K–12, 1988 Yearbook,* Reston, VA: NCTM, 1988.

Films/Videotapes/Videodiscs

Equations in Algebra, Chicago, IL: International Film Bureau, Inc., 1963.

Graphing Inequalities, Silver Burdett, 1970.

The Story of Pi, Reston, VA: NCTM, 1989.

Software

The Super Factory, (Apple II, IBM/Tandy), Wings for Learning/Sunburst

Algebra I Homework Tutor, (Macintosh), Missing Link Software

For addresses of companies handling software, please refer to page T24.

INTER·ACTIVE Mathematics — Glencoe's *Interactive Mathamatics: Activities and Investigations* consists of 18 units that may be used as alternatives or supplemental material for *Mathematics: Applications and Connections.* The suggested units for this chapter are Unit 8, *Data Sense,* and Unit 15, *On the Move.* See page T18 for more information.

This two-page introduction to the chapter provides a visual, relevant way to engage students in the mathematics of the chapter. Questions are included that help students see the need to learn the mathematics in the chapter. Data in charts and graphs provide statistical information that students can analyze and interpret at this point as well as later in the chapter. The Chapter Project provides an activity that applies the mathematics of the chapter.

MAKING MATHEMATICS RELEVANT

Spotlight on the Human Body

There are about one billion cells in the average human body. A typical adult male's body contains about 125 pounds of water, 6 quarts of blood, and enough carbon to make black lead for 9,000 pencils.

Ask the following questions.

- *Estimate these average figures: body temperature; heart rate; breathing rate.* 98.6°F; ≈72 beats/min; ≈16 respirations/min

- *Of what importance is mathematics to the study of the human body?* Sample answer: It helps individuals better understand good health practices and researchers to analyze disease.

Using the Timeline

Ask the following questions.

- *Penicillin, an antibiotic, was discovered 54 years before the first artificial heart was created. What year was penicillin discovered?* 1928

- *How long before the discovery of radium did Mendeleev organize his periodic table of elements?* 29 years

Chapter

2

An Introduction to Algebra

Spotlight on the Human Body

Have You Ever Wondered....

- How many high school students actually see themselves as thinner or heavier than they are?

- What chemical elements make up the weight of the human body?

The Elements in a 150-pound Individual

Element	Weight (lb)	Element	Weight (lb)
Oxygen	97.5	Sodium	0.165
Carbon	27.0	Magnesium	0.06
Hydrogen	15.0	Iron	0.006
Nitrogen	4.5	Cobalt	0.00024
Calcium	3.0	Copper	0.00023
Phosphorus	1.8	Manganese	0.00020
Potassium	0.3		
Sulfur	0.3	+ other elements in minute
Chlorine	0.3	quantities

1789

1851 1869

1898

1800   1825   1875   1900

Antoine Lavoisier publishes the first list of chemical elements

Dmitri Mendeleev arranges the chemical elements in order in the periodic table

Radium is discovered by Marie and Pierre Curie because of its radioactivity

42

"Have You Ever Wondered?" Answers

- Seven percent of females and 17 percent of males perceive themselves to weigh less than their true weight, while 34 percent of females and 15 percent of males perceive themselves to weigh more than their true weight.

- Students can read from the chart the elements that make up the weight of the human body.

Chapter Project

The Human Body

Work in a group.

1. Fill a jar with different candies or coins.

2. Weigh the full jar.

3. What are the individual weights of each of the groups of candies or coins? What is the weight of the jar?

4. Calculate what percent of the human body each element represents by dividing each element's weight by the total body weight. Then change the decimal to a percent.

5. Create at least two more examples like the jar. Make a chart showing your data.

BODY IMAGES
Body weight perceptions of high school students.

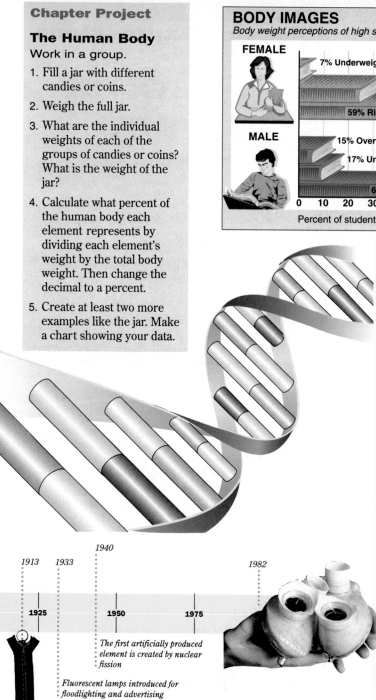

FEMALE

7% Underweight
34% Overweight
59% Right weight

MALE

15% Overweight
17% Underweight
68% Right weight

0 10 20 30 40 50 60 70

Percent of students surveyed

Looking Ahead

In this chapter, you will see how mathematics can be used to answer the questions about weight and the elements. The major objectives of the chapter are to:

- evaluate numerical and algebraic expressions
- identify and solve equations
- evaluate expressions using the order of operations
- write and solve two-step expressions and equations
- identify and solve inequalities

1913   1933   *1940*   *1982*
1925   1950   1975

The first artificially produced element is created by nuclear fission

Fluorescent lamps introduced for floodlighting and advertising

43

DATA ANALYSIS

Have students study the table of elements that comprise the human body. Then ask the following questions.

- *About how much carbon would you expect to find in a 300-pound individual?*
  about 54 pounds

- *Which element is about ten times as abundant as iron in humans? about one-fifth as abundant as hydrogen?*
  magnesium; calcium

Data Search

A question related to these data is provided in Lesson 2-2, page 50, Exercise 31.

CHAPTER PROJECT

The purpose of this project is for students to see how they can divide a quantity into its constituent parts. Whatever objects they use, urge them to use no more than four or five groups.

In the last part, students are asked to draw a parallel between a jar filled with objects and other similar examples. Accept all reasonable suggestions.

In their charts, students will have an opportunity to work with simple equations that can be manipulated to show the relationships among the weights of the objects.

Allow several days to complete the project.

Chapter Opener Transparency

Transparency 2-0 is available in the Transparency Package. It provides another full-color, motivating activity that you can use to capture students' interest.

NCTM Standards: 1–4, 6–9

Lesson Resources
- Study Guide Master 2-1
- Practice Master 2-1
- Enrichment Master 2-1
- Technology Master, p. 2
- Application Master, p. 2
- Group Activity Card 2-1

 Transparency 2-1 contains the 5-Minute Check and a teaching aid for this lesson.

🕐 5-Minute Check
(Over Chapter 1)

1. Use mental math to find $(25 \cdot 7) \cdot 4.$ 700

2. Estimate $7{,}164 \div 92$ by using compatible numbers.   80

3. Estimate $8.74 + 6.82 + 4.19$ first by rounding and then by front-end estimation.   20; 19.6

Complete each sentence.

4. $0.65 \text{ km} = \underline{} \text{ m}$ 650

5. $72 \text{ in.} = \underline{} \text{ yd}$ 2

6. Write $7 \cdot 7 \cdot 7 \cdot 2 \cdot 2 \cdot 2 \cdot 2$ using exponents.
   $7^3 \cdot 2^4$

1 FOCUS

Motivating the Lesson

Situational Problem   Marci said that $4 + 3 \times 2$ equals 14. Laurel said the expression equals 10. *How did each girl get her answer?* Lead students to see that Marci added 4 and 3, then multiplied the sum by 2, and that Laurel multiplied 3 and 2, then added 4 to the product.

2 TEACH

Teaching Tip   Before Example 1, use a simple example to show students that the order of operation rules are indeed necessary. For example, $10 - 6 - 2$ equals 2 if $10 - 6$ is evaluated first, but it equals 6 if $6 - 2$ is evaluated first.

2-1 Variables and Expressions

Objective
Evaluate numerical and algebraic expressions by using the order of operations.

Words to Learn
numerical expression
substitute
evaluate
order of operations
variable
algebraic expression

Did you know that when you see an infant on television or in a movie, the infant is often played by not one baby but by a set of identical twins? One twin can be substituted for the other during a filming sequence. In this way, production can go on, and it appears to be the same baby in each scene.

In mathematics, we also use substitution. Consider the **numerical expression** $5 + 6$. It has a value of 11. However, the expression $x + 4$ does not have a value until a value for x is given. Suppose you let $x = 12$. You can **substitute,** or put 12 in place of x in the expression. It becomes the numerical expression $12 + 4$, which has a value of 16. Therefore, if $x = 12$, then $x + 4 = 16$.

In order to **evaluate,** or find the value of, a numerical expression, we need to follow an **order of operations.** That is, you need to know which operation to do first when there is more than one operation in the expression. The following rules are used when evaluating numerical expressions.

Grouping symbols include:
- *parentheses ()*
- *brackets [].*
- *fractions bars, as in $\dfrac{6+4}{2}$, which means $(6 + 4) \div 2$.*

Order of Operations	1. Do all operations within grouping symbols first; start with the innermost grouping symbols.
	2. Do all powers before other operations.
	3. Next, do all multiplication and division in order from left to right.
	4. Then, do all addition and subtraction in order from left to right.

Example 1

Evaluate $(4 + 8) \div 3 \times 5 + (2^2 + 9)$.

Do operations in the parentheses first. You may have to follow the order of operations to do this step.

$$
\begin{aligned}
(4 + 8) \div 3 \times 5 + (2^2 + 9) &= 12 \div 3 \times 5 + 13 && \quad 2^2 + 9 = 4 + 9 \text{ or } 13 \\
&= 4 \times 5 + 13 && \quad 12 \div 3 = 4 \\
&= 20 + 13 \text{ or } 33 && \quad 4 \times 5 = 20
\end{aligned}
$$

OPTIONS

Bell Ringer

Using each of the numbers 1, 2, 3, and 4 once in each expression, write expressions equal to the whole numbers from 1 to 5. You can use grouping symbols and the operations addition, subtraction, multiplication, and division.
Example: $4 \times 3 \div 2 + 1 = 7$
Sample answers: $(4 + 2) \div 3 - 1 = 1,\ 4 + 2 - 3 - 1 = 2,$
$2 \times 3 - 4 + 1 = 3,\ 4 \div 2 + 3 - 1 = 4,\ 4 + 3 - 2 \div 1 = 5$

b. One calculator follows the order of operations. The other performs operations as they are entered.

Mini-Lab

Work with a partner.

Materials: calculator

Does your calculator follow the order of operations automatically?

- Enter this expression in your calculator.

  2 $+$ 3 $\times$ 4 $-$ 6 $\div$ 2 $=$

- Evaluate this expression using pencil and paper and the order of operations.

Talk About It

a. Are the answers the same? **See students' work.**

b. If the answers are not the same, why are they different?

Most scientific calculators follow the order of operations. Arithmetic calculators do not.

Algebra is a language of symbols. In algebra, we use letters, called **variables,** to represent unknown quantities. In the expression $x + 4$, x is a variable. Expressions that contain variables are called **algebraic expressions.** In order to evaluate algebraic expressions, you must know how to read algebraic expressions.

$3a$	means	$3 \times a$	*$3a$, $3 \times a$, $3 \cdot a$, and $3(a)$ all are ways to write the product of 3 and a.*
ab	means	$a \times b$	
$5 \cdot 6d$	means	$5 \times 6 \times d$	
$3xy^2$	means	$3 \times x \times y \times y$	
$a[b(cd)]$	means	$a \times (b \times c \times d)$	
$\dfrac{t}{3b}$	means	$t \div (3 \times b)$	

Example 2

Evaluate $x + y - 4$ if $x = 7$ and $y = 3$.

First, use substitution. Replace each variable in the expression with its value. Then use the order of operations.

$$
\begin{aligned}
x + y - 4 &= 7 + 3 - 4 \qquad \textit{Replace x with 7 and y with 3.}\\
&= 10 - 4\\
&= 6 \qquad\qquad\quad \textit{Check your answer mentally.}
\end{aligned}
$$

Lesson 2-1 Variables and Expressions   **45**

Using the Mini-Lab Write the expression $2 + 3 \times 4 - 6 \div 2$ on the chalkboard. Ask a volunteer to enclose in parentheses the operations that should be performed first according to the order of operations. $2 + (3 \times 4) - (6 \div 2)$ Explain that a scientific calculator follows the order of operations. An arithmetic calculator simply performs operations as they are entered into the calculator.

More Examples

For Example 1

Evaluate $(60 - 20) \div 4 + 3^2 \times 5$. 55

For Example 2

Evaluate $m + p \cdot 3$ if $m = 5$ and $p = 2$. 11

For Example 3

Evaluate $4x - 2y$ if $x = 8$ and $y = 6$. 20

For Example 4

Evaluate $\dfrac{h + k^2}{3h}$ if $h = 2$ and $k = 4$. 3

Checking for Understanding

Exercises 1-4 are designed to help you assess students' understanding through reading, writing, speaking, and modeling. You should work through these exercises with your students and then monitor their work on Guided Practice Exercises 5-16.

Close

Have students write four sentences explaining how to evaluate $5 + 18 \div (7 - 4)^2$. Each sentence should have this form: *First (or Next) I would evaluate _____ because _____.*

Reteaching Activity

Using Cooperative Groups

Prepare the set of seven cards shown below for each group.

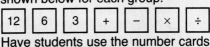

Have students use the number cards in the order 12, 6, 3, along with two operation cards to form an expression having each value below.

1. 6 $12 \div 6 \times 3$

2. 10 $12 - 6 \div 3$

Study Guide Masters, p. 10

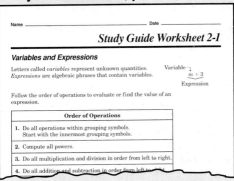

45

Assignment Guide
Maximum: 17–42
Minimum: 17–24, 25–33 odd, 34–40

For **Extra Practice,** see p. 585.

Alternate Assessment

Writing Have students work in pairs to write and evaluate numerical expressions which involve at least three operations.

Additional Answers

2. Numerical expressions contain only numbers and algebraic expressions contain numbers and variables.

3. $(4 + 3)^2 - 5 \cdot 6 = 7^2 - 30$
$= 49 - 30$
$= 19$

5. multiplication
6. multiplication
7. division
8. addition in parentheses
9. power in parentheses
10. subtraction in parentheses

Practice Masters, p. 10

Name _____ Date _____

Practice Worksheet 2-1

Variables and Expressions

Tell which operation should be done first. Then evaluate each expression.

1. $30 - 2 \cdot 3$
mult.; 24

2. $(6 - 4)^2$
sub.; 4

3. $3(4) + 4(5)$
mult.; 32

4. $2 + 3 + 4 \div 2$
div.; 7

5. $3 \cdot (4 + 5)$
add.; 27

6. $6 \div 2 + 3 \cdot 2$
div.; 9

7. $(3 + 2^2) \cdot 2$
power; 14

8. $(2 + 3)^2 \cdot 3$
add.; 75

9. $(4 + 3)^3$
add.; 343

10. $4(5) + 8 \div 4$
mult.; 22

11. $6 \cdot 12 \div 3$
mult.; 24

12. $(1 + 2) \cdot (3 + 4)$
add.; 21

Evaluate each expression.

13. $\frac{3 \cdot 2 + 6}{4} + 2(18 - 3)$ 33

14. $\frac{60 - 4^2}{4} + 2 \cdot 4$ 19

15. $30 - 3[4(4 - 2)]$ 6

16. $[(6 + 3)5] \div 3$ 15

17. $2(2 + 2) + 2(2^2 + 2)$ 20

18. $(40 - 3) \cdot (8 - 5)$ 111

19. $50 + 2[(8 - 3)2]$ 70

20. $[10 - (9 - 6)^2] - 1$ 0

Evaluate each expression if a = 5, b = 6, c = 4, and d = 3.

21. $3a - 3d$ 6

22. $5a + 6b - c$ 57

23. $10b - c - d$ 53

24. $2ab + cd$ 72

25. $2(ab + c) + d$ 71

26. $(6a \div 2)d$ 45

27. $4b + 3cd$ 60

28. $(3a + 4d) \cdot c$ 108

29. $(3a + 2c) \cdot dc$ 276

30. $10b \div c + b$ 21

31. abc^2 480

32. $a(bc)^2$ 2,880

T 10
Glencoe Division, Macmillan/McGraw-Hill

46

Examples

3 Evaluate $2a + 3b$ if $a = 4$ and $b = 12$.

$2a + 3b = 2(4) + 3(12)$ *Replace a with 4 and b with 12.*
$= 8 + 36$ *Do multiplication before addition.*
$= 44$ *Add.*

4 Evaluate $\dfrac{y^2}{3x}$ if $y = 6$ and $x = 3$.

The bar, which means division, is also a grouping symbol. Evaluate the expressions in the numerator and denominator separately before dividing.

$\dfrac{y^2}{3x} = \dfrac{6^2}{3 \cdot 3}$ *Replace y with 6 and x with 3.*

$= \dfrac{36}{9}$ *Evaluate the numerator and the denominator separately.*

$= 36 \div 9$ or 4   *Then divide.*

Checking for Understanding

Communicating Mathematics

Read and study the lesson to answer each question.

$6 \cdot x; 6(x); 6x$

1. **Write** three expressions that all mean *the product of 6 and the variable x.*

2. **Tell** what the difference is between a numerical expression and an algebraic expression. **See margin.**

4. The parenthesis changes the order of operations.

3. **Show** how to evaluate the expression $(4 + 3)^2 - 5 \cdot 6$. **See margin.**

4. **Tell** why the expressions $2 \cdot 5 + 3$ and $2 \cdot (5 + 3)$ have different values, even though they have the same numbers and operations.

For operations to Exercises 5-10, see margin.

Guided Practice

Tell which operation should be done first. Then evaluate each expression.

5. $21 + 2 \cdot 9$ 39
6. $3(5) + 4 \div 2$ 17
7. $18 \div 3 - 5$ 1
8. $(3 + 7) \div 2$ 5
9. $5 \cdot (6 + 3^2)$ 75
10. $(9 - 7)^3 - \dfrac{12}{3 \cdot 2}$ 6

Evaluate each expression if $a = 7$, $b = 6$, $c = 4$, and $d = 3$.

11. $3a + 4b - 2d$ 39
12. $abc \div 21$ 8
13. $(3b + 2c) \cdot d$ 78
14. $3b + (2c \cdot d)$ 42
15. cd^2 36
16. $(cd)^2$ 144

Exercises

Independent Practice

Evaluate each expression.

17. $3 \cdot (19 - 4) + \dfrac{23 - 7}{2}$ 53

18. $4^2 - 3 \cdot 4 + (6 - 6)$ 4

19. $(7^2 + 1) \div 5$ 10

20. $\dfrac{21}{3^2 - 2}$ 3

21. $[4 + (7 - 3)^2] + 2$ 22

22. $[7 - (8 - 6)^2] - 1$ 2

23. $[(4 + 3)\, 2] \div 7$ 2

24. $17 - 2[8 - (17 - 14)]$ 7

46   **Chapter 2** An Introduction to Algebra

OPTIONS

Gifted and Talented Needs

Have students research complex operations and write a report. These complex operations can be combinations of two or more different operations. For example, let the symbol $\odot$ represent the complex operation "divide the sum by 3."

$12 \odot 15 = (12 + 15) \div 3$
$= 27 \div 3 = 9$

Interactive Mathematics Tools

This multimedia software provides an interactive lesson that is tied directly to Lesson 2-1. Students will explore the order of operations.

25. Evaluate $7a - 3 + 2c$ if $a = 12$ and $c = 10$. **101**

26. Find the value of the expression $a^2 + b^2 - c^3$ if $a = 10$, $b = 5$, and $c = 4$. **61**

27. If $y = 36$, $x = 25$, and $w = 20$, find the value of $\frac{xy}{w} - (x + w)$. **0**

Copy each arithmetic sentence. Use your calculator to find out where to place the grouping symbols so that the sentence is true. You may need to use more than one set of grouping symbols. **For answers to Exercises 28-33, see margin.**

28. $5^2 + 4 \cdot 3 = 37$

29. $72 \div 6 + 3 = 8$

30. $46 + 4 - 36 \div 4 + 5 = 46$

31. $7 + 4^2 \div 2 + 6 = 9$

32. $3 \cdot 8 - 5 + 1 = 6$

33. $4 + 8 - 7 - 5 = 10$

Mixed Review

34. **Number Sense**   Carlos and Juanita want to share in the cost of a 45¢ candy bar. He has dimes. She has nickels. If each put in the same number of coins, what is that number? *(Lesson 1-1)* **3**

35. Estimate $328 + 671 + 459$. *(Lesson 1-3)* **1,500**

36. 1,725 meters
37. 4,000 pounds

36. How many meters are in 1.725 kilometers? *(Lesson 1-6)*

37. How many pounds of corn are in a bin that holds 2 tons? *(Lesson 1-7)*

38. Find the value of $2^3 \cdot 6^2$. *(Lesson 1-9)* **288**

Problem Solving and Applications

39. **Nutrition**   You can use the expression $\frac{C}{8p}$ to determine how many grams of protein you should eat each day if your total calorie intake is C and there are p calories in each gram of protein. Find how many grams of protein you should eat if your calorie intake in a day is 2,176 and a gram of protein has 4 calories. **68 grams of protein**

40. Sample answer: M = 48, A = 4, T = 6, H = 2

40. **Critical Thinking**   The variables M, A, T, and H represent the numbers 2, 4, 6, and 48, but not necessarily in that order. Use the sentence $M \div (A \cdot T) = H$ to determine the value of each variable.

41. $(4 \cdot 7 - 3)$ $(6 - 5 + 2 + 1)$

41. **Number Patterns**   Use each of the numbers 1, 2, 3, 4, 5, 6, and 7 exactly once and any of the four operations to find an expression that equals 100.

COMPUTER CONNECTION

42. **Computer Connection**   In the BASIC computer language, LET statements assign values to variables. BASIC uses the symbol * for multiplication and the symbol ∕ for division. Find the value of A for each statement if $X = 4$ and $Y = 12$.

   a. LET A = 5*X **20**   b. LET A = 2*Y **24**   c. LET A = X∕2 **2**

   d. LET A = Y∕3 **4**   e. LET A = Y∕X **3**   f. LET A = X*Y **48**

Lesson 2-1 Variables and Expressions   **47**

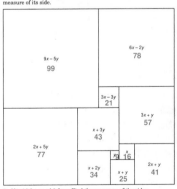

Extending the Lesson

Algebra Connection   Have students complete each table below.

x	1	2	3
$x + 5$	6	7	8

x	1	2	3
$2x + 1$	3	5	7

After studying the patterns, have students find an algebraic expression that produces each group of numbers below for $x = 1, 2, 3, 4, 5$.

1. 6, 9, 12, 15, 18   **$3x + 3$**

2. 7, 12, 17, 22, 27   **$5x + 2$**

Cooperative Learning Activity

Which Will It b? 2-1

Use groups of 2.
Materials: Index cards, spinners

▪ Copy onto cards the expressions shown on the back of this card. Shuffle the cards and place them face down in a pile. Label the sections of one spinner "3," "4," "6," and "9." Label the sections of a second spinner "2," "5," "7," and "8." Each partner must decide which spinner stands for the variable *a* and which stands for *b*. In other words, one partner's *a* spinner will be the other partner's *b* spinner.

➡ One partner selects a card while the other spins the two spinners. Each partner then evaluates the expression. Trading tasks each round, continue in the same manner until no cards remain.

Compare your results for each expression.

Glencoe Mathematics: Applications and Connections, Course 3

Additional Answers

28. No grouping symbols are needed.

29. $72 \div (6 + 3) = 8$

30. No grouping symbols are needed.

31. $7 + 4^2 \div (2 + 6) = 9$

32. $3[8 - (5 + 1)] = 6$

33. $4 + 8 - (7 - 5) = 10$

Enrichment Masters, p. 10

Name _____   Date _____

Enrichment Worksheet 2-1

Squared Rectangles

This "squared" rectangle has been cut up into squares of different sizes. The expression inside each square equals the measure of its side.

$9x - 5y$ 99	$6x - 2y$ 78
$3x - 3y$ 21	
$x + 3y$ 43	$3x + y$ 57
$2x + 5y$ 77	

yg x 16 $x + 2y$ 34 $x + y$ 25 $2x + y$ 41

1. Use 16 for x and 9 for y. Find the measures of the sides of all the squares.   **See diagram above.**

2. Find the measures of the sides of the entire rectangle. **177 by 176**

3. Another squared rectangle is made of squares with sides that measure 2, 5, 7, 9, 16, 25, 28, 33, and 36. Sketch the rectangle on a separate sheet of paper. Use $x = 2$ and $y = 5$ to write an algebraic expression for the measure of the side of each square.
   $x, y, x + y, 2x + y, 3x + 2y, 5x + 3y,$
   $4x + 4y, 4x + 5y, 8x + 4y$

T10
Glencoe Division, Macmillan/McGraw-Hill

NCTM Standards: 1–4, 7, 9

Lesson Resources
- Study Guide Master 2-2
- Practice Master 2-2
- Enrichment Master 2-2
- Group Activity Card 2-2

 Transparency 2-2 contains the 5-Minute Check and a teaching aid for this lesson.

🕐 5-Minute Check
(Over Lesson 2-1)

Tell which operation should be done first.
1. $5 + 20 \div 4$ division
2. $9 \times (8 + 4)^2$ addition

Evaluate each expression.
3. $20 - 6 \div 2$ 17
4. $[10 - (9 - 7)^2] - 5$ 1

1 FOCUS

Motivating the Lesson

Questioning   Ask students to tell whether each statement is true or false.
- Together, a 13-pound weight and a 7-pound weight weigh 20 pounds.
- Together, a bowling ball and a 7-pound weight weigh 23 pounds.

The first statement is true. We cannot determine whether the second is true or false until we know the weight of the ball.

2 TEACH

Using Calculators   Students can use a calculator to test values from the replacement set in the given equation. For example, to test values for x in $177 + x = 315$, students should first store 177 in memory. They can then enter a value from the replacement set, add the stored value by recalling it from memory, and see if the sum is 315.

2-2 Equations

Objective
Identify and solve equations.

Words to Learn
equation
open sentence
solution
replacement set

In 1917, the United States had just 7,000 miles of concrete roads. The growing popularity of the automobile called for more concrete roads to be built. By 1927, a network of 50,000 miles of roads had been built. Today there are over 4 million miles of paved highways in the United States.

Suppose you wanted to know how many miles of concrete roads were constructed between 1917 and 1927. This situation can be represented by a mathematical sentence called an **equation.** If r stands for the miles of roads built between 1917 and 1927, the equation that solves this problem would be $50,000 - 7,000 = r$.

An equation that contains a variable is an **open sentence.** When numbers are used to replace the variable, the sentence may be either true or false.

Problem Solving Hint

• • • • • • • • • •

Use the guess-and-check strategy.

Equation:	$50,000 - 7,000 = r$
Replace r with 42,000. →	$50,000 - 7,000 = 42,000$ This sentence is false.
Replace r with 43,000. →	$50,000 - 7,000 = 43,000$ This sentence is true.

The value for the variable that makes the sentence true is called the **solution** of the equation. In the equation $50,000 - 7,000 = r$, 43,000 is the solution of the equation. The process of finding the solution is called *solving the equation.*

Some equations do not have the variable alone on one side of the equals sign. For example, let's look at the equation $86 + a = 94$.

Example 1

Suppose the value of a can be selected from the set {12, 10, 8}. Find the solution of $86 + a = 94$.

Try each value from the set to see which is a solution.

The $\stackrel{?}{=}$ symbol means that you question whether the equation is true or false.

Try 12.
$86 + a = 94$
$86 + 12 \stackrel{?}{=} 94$ *Replace a with 12.*
$98 = 94$ *False*

12 is *not* a solution.

Try 10.
$86 + a = 94$
$86 + 10 \stackrel{?}{=} 94$ *Replace a with 10.*
$96 = 94$ *False*

10 is *not* a solution.

OPTIONS

Reteaching Activity

Using Manipulatives   Have students work in groups of three. Three number cubes are needed. Each student, in turn, rolls the cubes and tries to make an equation using the numbers. For example, the numbers 2, 3, and 6 can be used to make the equation $2 \times 3 = 6$. One point is scored for each equation.

Study Guide Masters, p. 11

Name _____   Date _____

Study Guide Worksheet 2-2

Equations

An equation is a mathematical sentence that contains an equal sign.

Example   Laura can build a model in 2 days. How many models can Laura build in 10 days?
Let m = the number of models.

The problem may be represented by this equation:
$m = 10 \div 2$

Divide to solve the equation. $10 \div 2 = 5$ $m = 5$
Laura can build 5 models in 10 days.

A set of numbers from which the values of the variable may be chosen is called a replacement set.

Try 8.

$86 + a = 94$

$86 + 8 \stackrel{?}{=} 94$ *Replace a with 8.*

     $94 = 94$ *True*

8 is a solution of $86 + a = 94$.

Whenever you are given a set of numbers from which to choose the value of the variable, the set of numbers is called the **replacement set** for the equation.

Example 2 *Problem Solving*

Smart Shopping Lamar had $4.93 to buy stamps. What is the greatest number of 29¢ stamps he can buy? Use the replacement set {15, 16, 17, 18}.

Let s represent the number of stamps.
Then the equation $0.29s = 4.93$ represents this situation.

Let's estimate first.   Round 29¢ to 30¢.
                           $30¢ \times 16 = \$4.80$
                           $30¢ \times 17 = \$5.10$

Both are close to $4.93. Try 16 first.

    $0.29s = 4.93$
$0.29 \cdot 16 \stackrel{?}{=} 4.93$ *Replace s with 16.*
    $4.64 = 4.93$ *False*   16 is *not* a solution.

Now try 17. $0.29 s = 4.93$
               $0.29 \cdot 17 \stackrel{?}{=} 4.93$ *Replace s with 17.*
               $4.93 = 4.93$ *True*

17 is a solution. Lamar can buy 17 stamps for $4.93.

Checking for Understanding

Communicating Mathematics

Read and study the lesson to answer each question.

1. **Tell** which symbol is always in an equation. $=$

2. **Tell** how you would solve the equation $15 \cdot 6 = w$. **Multiply 15 and 6.**

3. **Write** the definition of a replacement set. How is the solution related to this set? **A replacement set is the given set of numbers from which to choose the correct value of the variable. The solution is a part of this set.**

Guided Practice   Find the solution for each equation from the given replacement set.

4. $x = 14 + 38$, {52, 42, 24} **52**
5. $\$1.30 - c = \$0.50$, {$0.80, $1.80, $5.30} **$0.80**
6. $3m = 48$, {14, 16, 19} **16**
7. $\dfrac{792}{w} = 8$, {44, 54, 99} **99**

Solve each equation.

8. $5y = 100$ **20**
9. $34 + 16 = x$ **50**
10. $\$2.99 - \$1.25 = p$ **$1.74**

Lesson 2-2 Equations   **49**

Team Teaching

Ask the other teachers on your team how they relate formulas and equations when they use formulas in their disciplines. Inquire if and how they use the terms *variable, replacement set,* and *solution.*

Close

Have students summarize the lesson by asking the following questions.

- *What is an open sentence?* An equation having a variable.

- *How can you tell if a value from the replacement set is a solution of an equation?* Try the value in the equation. If a true sentence results, the value is a solution.

3 PRACTICE/APPLY

Assignment Guide

Maximum: 11–31
Minimum: 11–21 odd, 23–29

For **Extra Practice,** see p. 586.

Alternate Assessment

Writing Have students work in pairs to write equations that have solutions which can be found in the replacement set {23, 24, 25, 26}.

Enrichment Masters, p. 11

50

Exercises

Independent Practice

11. Solve $y + 45 = 60$ if the replacement set is {10, 15, 20, 25}. **15**

12. Solve $4x = 124$ if the replacement set is {29, 31, 33, 35}. **31**

13. Solve $p = \$5 - \$2.33$ if the replacement set is {\$3.33, \$2.77, \$2.67}. **\$2.67**

14. Solve $\frac{456}{y} = 76$ if the replacement set is {4, 6, 7, 9}. **6**

Solve each equation.

15. $\$4.50 + \$1.56 = y$ **\$6.06**   16. $6 \cdot 34 = z$ **204**

17. $\frac{98}{14} = q$ **7**   18. $t + 8 = 18$ **10**

19. $d - 7 = 24$ **31**   20. $2y = 24$ **12**

21. $42 = 6m$ **7**   22. $\frac{42}{g} = 4 + 3$ **6**

Mixed Review

23. Use mental math to find $2 \cdot (50 \cdot 78)$. *(Lesson 1-2)* **7,800**

24. Estimate $9,728 - 6,284$. Use an appropriate strategy. *(Lesson 1-3)* about **3,500**

25. Write $5 \cdot 5 \cdot 8 \cdot 8 \cdot 8$ using exponents. *(Lesson 1-9)* $5^2 \cdot 8^3$

26. Evaluate $\frac{45 - 9}{3^2 + 3}$. *(Lesson 2-1)* **3**

Problem Solving and Applications

27. **Lawn Care** The Green Grow company determines how much fertilizer to use on a lawn by finding its area. They use the formula $A = lw$ where A is the area, l is the length of the lawn, and w is the width of the lawn. What is the area of the front lawn if its length is 120 feet and its width is 90 feet? **10,800 square feet**

28. **Critical Thinking** Suppose the replacement set for an equation contains the whole numbers less than 10.

    a. Write the replacement set. **{0, 1, 2, 3, 4, 5, 6, 7, 8, 9}**

    b. Use this set to find the solution of $3x + 5 = 14$. **3**

29. **Advertising** The *Lancaster Gazette* charges \$5.50 per column inch (ci) for its employment ads. The People Line agency for temporary employment wants to put four ads in the Sunday paper. The ads are 6.5 ci, 5 ci, 3.5 ci, and 3 ci long. What would be the total cost for running the four ads? **\$99**

30. **Weather** The formula $C = \frac{5(F - 32)}{9}$ relates degrees Celsius (*C*) and degrees Fahrenheit (*F*). Tell how you would use the order of operations to find a solution for *C* if $F = 32$. **See Solutions Manual; C = 0.**

31. **Data Search** Refer to pages 42 and 43. Suppose a person's body contained the exact amounts of all the chemical elements listed in the chart except for potassium and calcium. The person's body has only half as much calcium as listed, but twice as much potassium. Will the person weigh more or less than 150 pounds? **less than 150 pounds**

DATA SEARCH

50 **Chapter 2** An Introduction to Algebra

OPTIONS

Extending the Lesson

Solving Puzzles In the puzzle below, the sum of the solutions in each row, column, and diagonal equals the length (in miles) of one of the longest stretches of straight highway in North America. **45 mi**

$x + 6 = 19$	$2p = 46$	$n - 5 = 4$
$4y = 44$	$5 = k \div 3$	$20 - m = 1$
$h + 4 = 25$	$e = 28 \div 4$	$25 = d + 8$

Cooperative Learning Activity

Gone Fishing 2-2

Number of players: 2
Materials: index cards

Copy onto cards the numbers and equations shown on the back of this card. Then decide which partner will be the dealer.

Play a game of "Go Fish." The dealer shuffles the cards, deals five cards to each partner, and places the remaining cards face down in a pile.

Each partner removes any pairs from his or her hand. (A pair is an equation and its solution.) In turn, partners try to make additional pairs by asking each other questions about the cards they are holding. If you guess a card in your partner's hand, take the card, remove the pair from your hand, and ask another question. If you do not guess correctly, take another card from the pile. If you can make a pair with this card, remove the pair from your hand. The partner who makes the most pairs is the winner.

Glencoe Mathematics: Applications and Connections, Course 3

2-3 Solving Subtraction and Addition Equations

Objective
Solve equations using the subtraction and addition property of equality.

Words to Learn
addition property
subtraction property
inverse operation

In 1988, there were 280,000 foster children living in foster homes. By the early 1990s, the number of foster children increased to 370,000. How many more foster children were there in the early 1990s than there were in 1988?

Suppose we let f represent the increase in foster children. The equation $280,000 + f = 370,000$ can be used to solve this problem. *You will solve this problem in Exercise 3.*

In Lesson 2-2, you learned to find a solution for an equation by using a replacement set. Sometimes the replacement set is not given or it contains too many numbers to try all of them. Two properties of algebra can help us solve equations when no replacement set is given.

Addition Property of Equality	**In words:** If you add the same number to each side of an equation, then the two sides remain equal.
	Arithmetic $\quad\quad$ **Algebra** $\\ 5 = 5 \quad\quad\quad a = b \\ 5 + 2 = 5 + 2 \quad a + c = b + c \\ 7 = 7$
Subtraction Property of Equality	**In words:** If you subtract the same number from each side of an equation, then the two sides remain equal. $\\$ **Arithmetic** $\quad\quad$ **Algebra** $\\ 5 = 5 \quad\quad\quad a = b \\ 5 - 2 = 5 - 2 \quad a - c = b - c \\ 3 = 3$

Let's see how these properties can be used to solve an equation like $x + 5 = 8$.

Mini-Lab

Work with a partner to solve $x + 5 = 8$.

Materials: counters, cups, mats

- Let a cup represent x. Put a cup and 5 counters on one side of the mat and 8 counters on the other side. These two quantities are equal.
  Our goal is to get the cup by itself on one side of the mat.

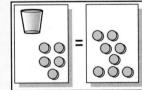

OPTIONS

Reteaching Activity

Using Cooperative Groups Have students work in groups of four. The first student writes an equation, the second writes the step involving the inverse operation, the third completes the solution, and the fourth checks the solution. Perform the activity four times, with each student performing each role once.

Study Guide Masters, p. 12

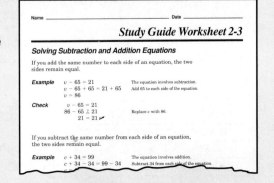

Name _____ Date _____

Study Guide Worksheet 2-3

Solving Subtraction and Addition Equations

If you add the same number to each side of an equation, the two sides remain equal.

Example $\quad v - 65 = 21$ $\quad\quad$ The equation involves subtraction.
$\quad\quad\quad v - 65 + 65 = 21 + 65 \quad$ Add 65 to each side of the equation.
$\quad\quad\quad v = 86$

Check $\quad\quad v - 65 = 21$
$\quad\quad\quad 86 - 65 \overset{?}{=} 21 \quad\quad$ Replace v with 86.
$\quad\quad\quad\quad 21 = 21$ ✔

If you subtract the same number from each side of an equation, the two sides remain equal.

Example $\quad c + 34 = 99$ $\quad\quad$ The equation involves addition.
$\quad\quad\quad c + 34 - 34 = 99 - 34 \quad$ Subtract 34 from each side of the equation.

NCTM Standards: 1–6, 9, 12

Lesson Resources
- Study Guide Master 2-3
- Practice Master 2-3
- Enrichment Master 2-3
- Group Activity Card 2-3

 Transparency 2-3 contains the 5-Minute Check and a teaching aid for this lesson.

> **5-Minute Check**
> (Over Lesson 2-2)
> 1. Solve $x + 27 = 41$ if the replacement set is {12, 14, 16}. **14**
>
> **Solve each equation.**
> 2. $33 + 47 = k$ **80**
> 3. $4x = 20$ **5**
> 4. $\$7.75 - \$2.38 = k$
> $\$5.37$

1 FOCUS

Motivating the Lesson

Activity Place equal weights on each pan of a two-pan balance. Add weight to one pan and ask students what can be done to bring the scale back into balance. Add the same weight to the other pan.

Beginning again with equal weights on each pan, remove weight from one pan and ask what can be done to bring the scale back into balance. Remove the same weight from the other pan.

2 TEACH

Using the Mini-Lab After modeling the equation with the cup and counters, ask students why the goal is to get the cup by itself on one side of the mat. The cup represents x and we want to find the value of x. Ask students why the same number of counters must be removed from each side of the mat. To keep both sides of the equation in balance

52

- Take 5 counters away from each side. What you have left is the value of the cup, which is also the value of x.

Talk About It

a. 3
b. Subtraction property

a. What is the value of x (the cup)?
b. Which property lets you take counters away from each side?
c. In the equation $x + 5 = 8$, 5 is added to x. To solve it, you subtract 5. Suppose you were solving the equation $y - 3 = 8$. What operation would you use with 3 to find y?   **addition**

To solve an equation in which a number is added or subtracted to the variable, you must use the opposite, or **inverse**, operation. Remember, it is always wise to check your solution.

Examples

1 Solve $y - 34 = 15$.

34 is subtracted from y. To solve, add 34 to each side.

Solve the equation.	*Check the solution.*
$y - 34 = 15$	Replace y with 49.
$y - 34 + 34 = 15 + 34$	$y - 34 = 15$
$y = 49$	$49 - 34 \stackrel{?}{=} 15$ *Is the sentence true?*
	$15 = 15$ ✓

The solution is 49.

2 Solve $w + \$4.35 = \$7.23$.

$4.35 is added to w. To solve, subtract $4.35 from each side.

$w + 4.35 = 7.23$	**Check:** $w + \$4.35 = \$7.23$
$w + 4.35 - 4.35 = 7.23 - 4.35$	$\$2.88 + \$4.35 \stackrel{?}{=} \$7.23$
$w = 2.88$	$\$7.23 = \$7.23$ ✓

The solution is $2.88.

Checking for Understanding

Communicating Mathematics

Read and study the lesson to answer each question.

1. **Tell** what is meant when we say addition and subtraction are inverse operations.   They "undo" each other.

2. **Write** in your own words how the addition and subtraction properties of equality are used in solving equations.   See margin.

3. **Show** how to solve the equation presented at the beginning of the lesson. What was the increase in foster children?   90,000; for steps, see Solutions Manual.

52   **Chapter 2** An Introduction to Algebra

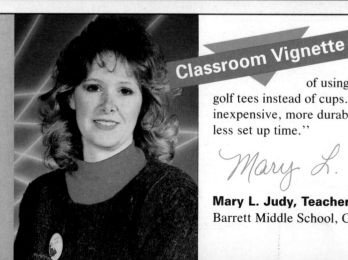

Classroom Vignette

"You may want to use bingo chips as counters instead of using paper models. I also use golf tees instead of cups. Both manipulatives are inexpensive, more durable, easy to store, and take less set up time."

Mary L. Judy

Mary L. Judy, Teacher
Barrett Middle School, Columbus, OH

4. **Model** the equation $x + 1 = 6$ by using cups and counters. Then solve it. 5

Solve each equation. Check your solution.

5. $15 + x = 21$ 6
6. $40 + n = 70$ 30
7. $p - 82 = 142$ 224
8. $y = 34 + 89$ 123
9. $r - 14 = 19$ 33
10. $81 - 56 = z$ 25
11. $24 = x - 5$ 29
12. $m + 1.2 = 1.5$ 0.3
13. $19 = 13 + s$ 6

Exercises

Independent Practice

Solve each equation. Check your solution.

14. $m + 30 = 110$ 80
15. $173 = x + 83$ 90
16. $2.34 + 1.22 = p$ 3.56
17. $s - 5.8 = 14.3$ 20.1
18. $14 + r = 23$ 9
19. $p - 72 = 182$ 254
20. $125 - 52 = q$ 73
21. $0.5 + x = 2.72$ 2.22
22. $24 = r - 18$ 42
23. $x + 1.4 = 11.2$ 9.8
24. $w = 312 + 120$ 432
25. $6.01 - 3.12 = t$ 2.89

Mixed Review

26. Use mental math to find $800 - 356$. *(Lesson 1-2)* 444
27. How many milligrams are in 4.28 grams of aspirin? *(Lesson 1-6)* 4,280 mg
28. How many gallons of juice are in 10 quarts? *(Lesson 1-7)* $2\frac{1}{2}$ gallons
29. Solve $x - 32 = 20$ if the replacement set is {47, 52, 57, 63}. *(Lesson 2-2)* 52

Problem Solving and Applications

30. **Critical Thinking** Find the solution to the equation $x + 3 = x + 7 - 4$. Explain how you arrived at your solution. All real numbers; see students' work.

31. **Geometry** Let the measure of angle $A = a$ and the measure of angle $B = b$. Angle A and angle B are complementary if $a + b = 90°$. Suppose angle A has a measure of $30°$. Use the equation to find the measure of angle B. 60°

CULTURAL KALEIDOSCOPE

Blandina Cardenas Ramirez

Blandina Cardenas Ramirez could speak and read Spanish and English before she entered school. Education continued to be of primary importance. Although she graduated from college with a degree in journalism, she continued her education after going to work for the government and received her Doctorate in Education.

She was involved with programs in Texas where she developed and directed a center concerned with multicultural education and equal educational opportunities for all children. In 1977, back in Washington, President Jimmy Carter appointed her Commissioner of the Administration for Children, Youth and Families in the Department of Health, Education and Welfare.

Lesson 2-3 Solving Subtraction and Addition Equations **53**

Interactive Mathematics Tools

This multimedia software provides an interactive lesson that is tied directly to Lesson 2-3. Students will use cups and counters to explore addition and subtraction equations.

Cooperative Learning Activity

Weighty Matters 2-3

Use groups of 2.
Materials: Counters, balance, index cards

Find the weight *in counters* of three small classroom objects—for example, a piece of chalk. Weigh one object at a time. Place the object on one pan. Then place counters one at a time on the other pan until the pans balance. Next, add counters to or take them from the first pan. Add to or take from the other pan the same number of counters.

On a card, write an equation that describes what you have done. Use a different variable to describe each object. For example, if your object weighed 45 counters and you added 3 more counters, you could write $x + 3 = 48$.

Trade cards with another pair and use counters and the balance to guess the object represented by each variable.

Glencoe Mathematics: Applications and Connections, Course 3

---

3 PRACTICE/APPLY

Assignment Guide
Maximum: 14–31
Minimum: 14–31

For **Extra Practice,** see p. 586.

Alternate Assessment

Modeling Have students use cups and counters as in the Mini-Lab to solve these equations.

1. $x + 4 = 9$ 5
2. $x - 2 = 7$ 9

Enrichment Masters, p. 12

Name _____ Date _____

Enrichment Worksheet 2-3

Geometric Equations

Equations are often used to solve geometric problems. To work the problems on this page, you will need to use these facts:

Angles are *complementary* if their measures add to 90°. If their measures add to 180°, they are *supplementary*. The total number of degrees in a circle is 360°; in a triangle, the total is 180°. A straight angle measures 180°.

Match each equation in the chart at the bottom of the page with a figure that could be used to solve for the missing angle measurement. Then solve for that measurement.

A. B. C.

D. E. F.

Equation	Letter of Figure	Angle Measurement
$35° + 20° + x = 180°$	C	125°
$90° - x = 15°$	E	75°
$x + 72° = 180°$	A	108°
$360° = x + 150° + 90°$	B	120°
$2(45°) + x = 180°$	D	90°
$30° + x + 15° = 90°$	F	45°

T12
Glencoe Division, Macmillan/McGraw-Hill

NCTM Standards: 1–7, 9, 12

Lesson Resources
- Study Guide Master 2-4
- Practice Master 2-4
- Enrichment Master 2-4
- Interdisciplinary Master, p. 16
- Group Activity Card 2-4

 Transparency 2-4 contains the 5-Minute Check and a teaching aid for this lesson.

🕐 5-Minute Check
(Over Lesson 2-3)

Solve each equation. Check your solution.

1. $98 + x = 131$ 33
2. $3.6 + 4.9 = k$ 8.5
3. $3.6 = h - 12.7$ 16.3
4. $m - 254 = 76$ 330
5. $y = 37 - 15.3$ 21.7

1 FOCUS

Motivating the Lesson

Questioning Ask students to describe the difference between the equations $4 + x = 20$ and $4x = 20$.   The first equation states that the sum of 4 and a number is 20. The second equation states that the product of 4 and a number is 20.

2 TEACH

Using the Mini-Lab Remind students that their goal is to find the value of $1y$ (1 cup). They accomplish this goal by dividing the counters into 3 equal groups. Ask students to describe how to change the activity in order to solve $4y = 12$.   Use 4 cups and divide the counters into 4 equal groups.

2-4 Solving Division and Multiplication Equations

Objective
Solve equations using the division and multiplication property of equality.

Words to Learn
division property
multiplication property

In $d = rt$, $d = $ total distance, $r = $ rate, and $t = $ time.

To work off the number of calories you consume when you eat a Burger King Whopper® with cheese, you would have to ride your bicycle at a rate of 13 miles per hour for a total of 31 miles. How much time would it take you to do this?

The formula $d = rt$ can be used to solve this problem. Substitute 31 for d and 13 for r. The formula becomes the equation $31 = 13t$.   *You will solve this equation in Exercise 2.*

In the last lesson, you learned that equations could be solved by using the inverse operation. This holds true for multiplication and division equations too. The Mini-Lab below shows how this works.

Mini-Lab

Work with a partner. Use models to solve $3y = 12$.

Materials: cups, counters, mats

- Let each cup represent $1y$. So $3y$ means 3 cups. Put 3 cups on one mat. On the other mat, put 12 counters.

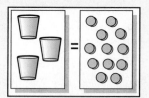

- Arrange the counters into 3 equal groups to correspond to the 3 cups.

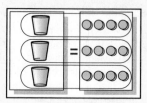

Talk About It

c. Division; separating into equal groups suggests division.

a. What number of counters matches with each cup? 4
b. If $3y = 12$, what is the value of y? 4
c. What operation does your model suggest? Explain.

OPTIONS

Reteaching Activity

Using Manipulatives Give 12 counters to each student. Direct students to solve each of the following equations by dividing their counters into equal groups.

1. $2x = 12$ 6 in each group; $x = 6$
2. $3x = 12$ 4 in each group; $x = 4$
3. $6x = 12$ 2 in each group; $x = 2$

Study Guide Masters, p. 13

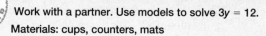

Name _____ Date _____

Study Guide Worksheet 2-4

Solving Division and Multiplication Equations

You can use inverse operations to solve multiplication and division equations.

If you multiply each side of an equation by the same number, the two sides remain equal.

Example $y \div 6 = 7$ The equation involves division.
$y \div 6 \times 6 = 7 \times 6$ Multiply each side of the equation by 6.
$y = 42$

Check $y \div 6 = 7$
$42 \div 6 \stackrel{?}{=} 7$ Replace y with 42.
$7 = 7$ ✓

If you divide each side of an equation by the same number (not 0), the two sides remain equal.

In the Mini-Lab, you solved the multiplication equation $3y = 12$ by separating the counters into three equal groups. You would get the same result if you divided each side of the equation by 3.

This division property is another property of algebra that you can use to solve equations. There is also a multiplication property.

Multiplication Property of Equality	**In words:** If you multiply each side of an equation by the same number, then the two sides remain equal.
	Arithmetic $\qquad$ **Algebra**
	$6 = 6 \qquad\qquad a = b$
	$6 \cdot 2 = 6 \cdot 2 \qquad ac = bc$
	$12 = 12$
Division Property of Equality	**In words:** If you divide each side of an equation by the same number (except 0), then the two sides remain equal.
	Arithmetic $\qquad$ **Algebra**
	$6 = 6 \qquad\qquad a = b$
	$\dfrac{6}{2} = \dfrac{6}{2} \qquad \dfrac{a}{c} = \dfrac{a}{c}, c \neq 0$
	$3 = 3$

Estimation Hint

● ● ● ● ● ● ● ● ● ●

Any number, except 0, divided by itself is 1. Since the equation equals a number greater than 1, the value of *p* must be greater than 4.

Example 1

Solve $\dfrac{p}{4} = 2$.

$\dfrac{p}{4} = 2$

$\dfrac{p}{4} \cdot 4 = 2 \cdot 4$ *Multiply to undo division by 4.*

$p = 8$

The solution is 8.

Check: $\dfrac{p}{4} = 2$

$\dfrac{8}{4} \overset{?}{=} 2$

$2 = 2$ ✔

Example 2 *Connection*

Geometry   In an equilateral triangle, all sides have the same length. If the sum of the lengths of three sides of an equilateral triangle is 36.435 meters, what is the length of one side of that triangle?

This problem can be solved with the equation $3s = 36.435$.

$3s = 36.435$ *Divide to undo multiplication by 3.*

36.435 3 = 12.145

Each side of the equilateral triangle is 12.145 meters long.

Lesson 2-4 Solving Division and Multiplication Equations   **55**

Limited English Proficiency

Provide students with additional practice using the Mini-Lab materials. Give them several simple equations and allow them an unrestricted amount of time to solve the equations. Be sure students understand the terms *addition*, *subtraction*, *multiplication*, and *division*, and that they understand the effects of inverse operations.

$x + 5 - 5 = x \qquad y \cdot 3 \div 3 = y$

Interactive Mathematics Tools

This multimedia software provides an interactive lesson that is tied directly to Lesson 2–4. Students will use cups and counters to explore multiplication and division equations.

Teaching Tip   Before Example 1, stress that the goal when solving an equation is to isolate the variable on one side of the equation by using inverse operations to eliminate numbers that appear with the variable.

More Examples

For Example 1

Solve $\dfrac{x}{7} = 3$.   21

For Example 2

The sum of the measures of the interior angles of a pentagon is 540°. The five angles all have the same measure. Solve the equation $5x = 540$ to find the measure of each angle. 108°

Checking for Understanding

Exercises 1-3 are designed to help you assess students' understanding through reading, writing, speaking, and modeling. You should work through these exercises with your students and then monitor their work on Guided Practice Exercises 4-12.

Practice Masters, p. 13

Name _____ Date _____

Practice Worksheet 2-4

Solving Division and Multiplication Equations

Solve each equation. Check your solution.

1. $12x = 36$	2. $8y = 96$	3. $48 = 6y$
3	12	8
4. $54 = 9w$	5. $a \div 3 = 15$	6. $b \div 7 = 21$
6	45	147
7. $16y = 144$	8. $14b = 168$	9. $19z = 171$
9	12	9
10. $\dfrac{a}{12} = 16$	11. $\dfrac{c}{9} = 21$	12. $\dfrac{x}{6} = 12$
192	189	72
13. $21d = 147$	14. $125 \div 5 = a$	15. $63f = 945$
7	25	15
16. $\dfrac{h}{0.3} = 19$	17. $\dfrac{k}{2.7} = 21$	18. $\dfrac{m}{18} = 39$
5.7	56.7	702
19. $8.34x = 25.02$	20. $1.2y = 2.76$	21. $3.4t = 8.5$
3	2.3	2.5
22. $y = 17 \cdot 3$	23. $2.6v = 9.62$	24. $18t = 3.6$
51	3.7	0.2
25. $\dfrac{x}{1.8} = 72$	26. $\dfrac{n}{5} = 16.4$	27. $5.25a = 21$
129.6	82	4
28. $\dfrac{x}{1.5} = 24$	29. $6p = 17.94$	30. $\dfrac{10}{1.6} = m$
36	2.99	6.25

T 13
Glencoe Division, Macmillan/McGraw-Hill

Error Analysis

Watch for students who use the wrong operation when applying the inverse.

Prevent by reviewing inverse operations and by having students check their solutions.

Close

Have students give examples of equations they would solve using the Multiplication Property of Equality or the Division Property of Equality. Have them describe how they would solve each equation.

3 PRACTICE/APPLY

Assignment Guide
Maximum: 13–29
Minimum: 13–28

For **Extra Practice,** see p. 586.

Alternate Assessment

Modeling Have students use cups and counters as in the Mini-Lab to solve the following equations.

1. $6x = 12$ 2   **2.** $2x = 10$ 5

Enrichment Masters, p. 13

Name _____ Date _____

Enrichment Worksheet 2-4

Division by Zero?

Some interesting things happen when you try to divide by zero. For example, look at these two equations.

$\frac{0}{0} = x$ $\frac{0}{0} = y$

Because multiplication "undoes" division, you can write two equivalent equations for the ones above.

$0 \cdot x = 5$ $0 \cdot y = 0$

There is no number that will make the left equation true. This equation has no solution. For the right equation, *every* number will make it true. The solution set for this equation is "all numbers."

Because division by zero leads to impossible situations, it is not a "legal" step in solving a problem. People say that division by zero is undefined, or not possible, or simply not allowed.

Explain what is wrong with each of these "proofs."

1. Step 1 $0 \cdot 1 = 0$ and $0 \cdot 2 = 0$
   Step 2   Therefore, $\frac{0}{0} = 1$ and $\frac{0}{0} = 2$.   Step 2 involves
   Step 3   Therefore, $1 = 2$.   division by zero.
   But, $1 = 2$ is a contradiction.

2. Step 1   Assume $a \neq b$.
   Step 2 $0 \cdot a = 0$ and $0 \cdot b = 0$
   Step 3   Therefore, $\frac{0}{0} = a$ and $\frac{0}{0} = b$.   Step 3 involves
   Step 4   Therefore, $a = b$.   division by zero.
   But, $a = b$ contradicts $a \neq b$.

Describe the solution set for each equation.

3. $4x = 0$ $x = 0$ **4.** $x \cdot 0 = 0$ **5.** $x \cdot 0 = x$ $x = 0$
                          all numbers
6. $\frac{0}{x} = 0$ $x \neq 0$ **7.** $\frac{0}{x} = x$ **8.** $\frac{0}{x} = \frac{0}{y}$ $x \neq 0,$
                          no solutions $y \neq 0$

T13
Glencoe Division, Macmillan/McGraw-Hill

56

Checking for Understanding

Communicating Mathematics
Read and study the lesson to answer each question.

1. Tell how solving equations that involve multiplication or division is similar to solving equations that involve addition or subtraction. **See below.**

2. Show how to use a calculator to solve the equation for the opening problem. Round to the nearest tenth. **2.4**

3. Write the equation shown by the model at the right. Then find the solution. $4x = 12$; $x = 3$

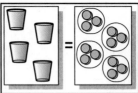

1. In both types of equations, the goal is to solve the equation by undoing the operation while maintaining an equality.

Guided Practice   Solve each equation. Check your solution.

4. $16x = 48$ 3   **5.** $24 = 6p$ 4   **6.** $q = \frac{240}{30}$ 8

7. $\frac{s}{7} = 18$ 126   **8.** $23 \cdot 4 = w$ 92   **9.** $9 = \frac{c}{60}$ 540

10. $18.4 = 0.2q$ 92   **11.** $\frac{p}{0.6} = 3.6$ 2.16   **12.** $243 \div 6 = t$ 40.5

Exercises

Independent Practice   Solve each equation. Check your solution.

13. $3m = 183$ 61   **14.** $\frac{f}{7} = 56$ 392   **15.** $14 \cdot 25 = w$ 350

16. $102 = 17p$ 6   **17.** $1.4t = 3.22$ 2.3   **18.** $2.45 \div 5 = q$ 0.49

19. $8 = \frac{s}{25}$ 200   **20.** $\frac{d}{0.11} = 5$ 0.55   **21.** $\$5.44 = \$0.34b$ 16

22. The product of 8 and a number r is 480. Find the number. 60

Mixed Review
23. Estimate $5,412 \div 58$ by using compatible numbers. *(Lesson 1-3)* about 90

24. Evaluate $(17 - 8) \div 3 + 5^2$. *(Lesson 2-1)* 28

25. Solve $y - 28 = 65$. Check your solution. *(Lesson 2-3)* 93

Problem Solving and Applications
26. Critical Thinking If n is greater than 0, which is greater, $\frac{1}{n}$ or $\frac{n}{1}$? Give examples to support your answer. $\frac{n}{1}$; $\frac{1}{3} < \frac{3}{1}$, $\frac{1}{15} < \frac{15}{1}$

27. Space Science Outer space is becoming a giant junkyard. There are more than 7,000 items trackable by radar floating around the earth. Only about 5% of them are working spacecraft. Let j represent the number of items. Use the equation $0.05j = W$ to find W, the number of working spacecraft, if $j = 7,000$. 350 items

28. Auto Mechanics Larry thinks his car needs a tune-up. He uses the formula $m = rg$, where m = total miles driven, r = miles per gallon, and g = total gallons of gas used. If he drove 2,450 miles on 112 gallons, how many miles per gallon did his car get? 21.875 miles/gallon

29. Journal Entry How is solving a division or multiplication equation similar to solving an addition or subtration equation? Do you have a method for remembering the steps to solve each type? **See students' work.**

OPTIONS

Extending the Lesson

Using Cooperative Groups Have small groups discuss the equation $2x - 3 = 7$ and devise a method they can use to solve the equation. Encourage them to check their solution to verify their method.
Add 3, then divide by 2; $x = 5$.
Then have the groups generalize their methods and use them to solve other equations.

Cooperative Learning Activity

Stationery Equations **2-4**

Use groups of 4.
Materials: Balance, beans, envelopes

● Work in pairs. Each pair secretly places an equal number of beans in each of several envelopes and then seals the envelopes.

➡ Decide which pair will go first. The first pair places its sealed envelopes on one pan of the balance. The second pair places the same number of *empty* envelopes on the other pan. The second pair then tries to guess the number of beans in each envelope by placing an equal number of beans in each envelope until the pans balance.

Write an equation that describes what you have done. Trade roles and repeat the activity.

Glencoe Mathematics: Applications and Connections, Course 3

2-5 Work Backward

Objective
Solve problems by working backward.

Toshi, Joe, and Al are talking. Along comes Jorge, who places a sticker on each of their foreheads. "What are you doing?" Toshi asks. "I'm playing the spot game," Jorge replies. "At most, two of you have a red spot on your foreheads. If you know that you have a red spot, you can't tell. But if you know that you don't have a red spot, you win." Toshi sees that Al has a red spot, but Joe has a blue spot. Does Toshi have a red spot on his forehead?

Explore   *What do you know?*
One or two of the boys has a red spot on his forehead. If Toshi knows that he has a red spot, he can't tell. If Toshi knows that he doesn't have a red spot, he wins.

What are you trying to find?
You are trying to find out if Toshi has a red spot on his forehead.

Plan   Work backward by thinking about what the boys are seeing and thinking.

Solve   Joe sees at least one red spot, Al's. He's hesitating because there can be two red spots, and he's not sure what color the spot is that's on his forehead. That means that he is not seeing two red spots. Aha! Toshi knows that he doesn't have a red spot. Joe's hesitation is his clue.

Examine   Al is quiet. If he doesn't see any red spots, he knows that he has one, but can't tell. If he sees one red spot, he's wondering if there are two.

Joe sees Al's red spot. If he sees a red spot on Toshi's forehead, then he knows that he doesn't have a red spot, since there are at most two.

Lesson 2-5   Problem-Solving Strategy: Work Backward   **57**

2-5 Lesson Notes

NCTM Standards: 1–7

Lesson Resources
• Study Guide Master 2-5
• Practice Master 2-5
• Enrichment Master 2-5
• Evaluation Master, Quiz A, p. 16
• Group Activity Card 2-5

Transparency 2-5 contains the 5-Minute Check and a teaching aid for this lesson.

⏱ 5-Minute Check
(Over Lesson 2-4)
Solve each equation. Check your solution.

1. $\frac{x}{3} = 6$ 18

2. $91 = 13k$ 7

3. $2.4(1.8) = w$ 4.32

4. $\$8.46h = \$54.99$ 6.5

5. The quotient when the number e is divided by 18 is 8. Find the number.
   144

1 FOCUS

Motivating the Lesson

Questioning   Ask students how they would solve this problem: *The price of 6 lemons is $1.45 including $0.07 tax. Find the cost of 1 lemon.*   Subtract $0.07 from $1.45 and divide by 6; the cost is $0.23.

2 TEACH

Using Models   Have three students take the roles of Toshi, Joe, and Al. Have students describe what each boy sees and his reasoning as he tries to unravel the puzzle.

OPTIONS

Reteaching Activity

Using Cooperative Groups
Recite this example: *If I add 3 to my number, then divide by 6, the answer is 2. Guess my number.*   9
One student states a problem involving two operations, like the example. The student who correctly guesses the number scores one point. Each member of the group takes a turn making up a problem.

Study Guide Masters, p. 14

Name _____   Date _____

Study Guide Worksheet 2-5

Problem-Solving Strategy: Work Backward

Example   Lola is thinking of a number. If she subtracts 6 from the number and then takes the square root, the result is 9. What is Lola's number?

Explore   What do you know?
You know that if you subtract 6 from the number and then take the square root, the result is 9.
What do you want to find?
You want to find the number.

Plan   Work backward.
Start with 9.   Square 9 to reverse   Add 6 to reverse
   taking the square root.   subtracting 6.

Solve   9 $9^2 = 81$ $81 + 6 = 87$

Checking for Understanding

Exercises 1-3 are designed to help you assess students' understanding through reading, writing, speaking, and modeling. You should work through these exercises with your students and then monitor their work on Guided Practice Exercises 4-6.

Error Analysis

Watch for students who undo operations in the wrong order.

Prevent by having them write out the sequence of operations in the problem, then work backwards, undoing operations one by one.

Practice Masters, p. 14

Name _____ Date _____

Practice Worksheet 2-5

Problem-Solving Strategy: Work Backward

Solve by working backward.

1. Bob says, "I am thinking of a number. If I decrease it by 19, and then add 40, I get 48." What is Bob's number? 27

2. I have a number. I divide it by 3. I square the result. I now have 441. What was my original number? 63

3. David pours 5 gallons of water into a tank of water. Then Carlos adds 8 gallons more to the tank. The tank now contains 32 gallons of water. How many gallons were in the tank before David added water? 19 gallons

Solve using any strategy.

4. Shawn puts a fence around the perimeter of a rectangular garden. He uses 136 feet of fencing. The garden is 40 feet long. How wide is the garden? 28 feet

5. Of the 485 people who paid to attend the eighth-grade play, 121 were adults. The rest were students. An adult ticket cost $5.00. The total ticket sales amounted to $1,060. What was the cost of a student ticket? $1.25

6. A model PL-3 shortwave radio costs $12 more than twice the cost of the model PL-1 radio. The PL-3 radio costs $191.98. What is the cost of the PL-1 radio? $89.99

7. Tiersa has a number that she multiplies by 8, takes one-fourth of the product, divides the result by 2, and arrives at 12. What is her number? 12

8. Lin removes half of a full sheet of stamps. Jackie uses 8 more stamps, and Maria takes half the remaining stamps. There are 5 stamps left. How many stamps are in a full sheet of stamps? 36 stamps

9. A large bottle of soy sauce costs $1.29 less than 3 times the cost of a small bottle of soy sauce. The large bottle costs $5.88. How much does a small bottle cost? $2.39

10. Take a number, multiply it by 8, subtract 8, divide by 12, and double the quotient. The result is 20. What is the number? 16

T 14
Glencoe Division, Macmillan/McGraw-Hill

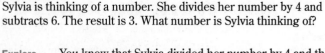

Example

Sylvia is thinking of a number. She divides her number by 4 and subtracts 6. The result is 3. What number is Sylvia thinking of?

Explore You know that Sylvia divided her number by 4 and then subtracted 6. You know that the result was 3. You want to find Sylvia's number.

Plan Work backward by reversing the operations.

Sylvia's number	Find the number.
↓	↓
Divide by 4.	Start with 3.
↓	↓
Subtract 6.	Add 6.
↓	↓
The result is 3.	Multiply by 4.

Solve Start with 3. Add 6. Multiply by 4. Sylvia's number is 36.

Examine Work forward in order to check.

$$(36 \div 4) - 6 = 3$$

This verifies that Sylvia was thinking of 36.

Checking for Understanding

Communicating Mathematics

Read and study the lesson to answer each question. **You begin with the answer.**

1. **Tell** where you begin when you are solving a problem by working backward.

2. **Explain** how you solve a problem by working backward. **Reverse the order.**

3. **Show** the order that you would need to use to solve this problem by working backward. Start with 25. Multiply by 4, divide by 10, and add 14. Then double. **divide by 2, subtract 14, multiply by 10, divide by 4**

Guided Practice

Solve by working backward.

4. Jan says, "I am thinking of a number. If I increase it by 11, and then subtract 10, I get 2." What is Jan's number? **1**

5. You are thinking of a number. You divide it by 20. Then you add 34 and divide the result by 13. Finally you triple the number. The result is 9. What was your number? **100**

6. I have a number. I halve it. I multiply the result by itself. I now have 9,801. What was my original number? **198**

OPTIONS

Bell Ringer

One more than half of the students in Yolanda's homeroom left for a pep rally. Half of the remaining students, plus 1, left for student council. Then half of those remaining, plus 1, left for choir practice, leaving only Yolanda. How many students are in her homeroom? 22

Problem Solving

Solve using any strategy.

7. Robert picked out a pair of trousers. When he saw the price, he said, "These are a third as much as I paid for my new suit last month!" The trousers cost $45.50. How much did his suit cost? **$136.50**

8. Paul is thinking of a number. He divides by 11, takes a third of the quotient, divides the result by 10, and arrives at 13. What is Paul's number? **4,290**

9. Forty-four students take the bus to Grand Lapere. Each student pays $1.20. How much did the driver collect? **$52.80**

10. Mrs. Lachinsky's class bought food for the Adopt-a-Family program. They spent $127.68. The 19 students divided the cost equally. How much did each student contribute? **$6.72**

11. Mr. Jacobs signed an installment contract to pay $400 a month for 5 years for a new car. The car's actual price is $15,900. How much extra is Mr. Jacobs paying for spreading the payments over 5 years? **$8,100**

12. **Portfolio Suggestion**   Select one of the assignments from this chapter that you found especially challenging. Place it in your portfolio. **See students' work.**

Assessment: Mid-Chapter Review

Evaluate each expression. *(Lesson 2-1)*

1. $2 + 3 \cdot 5 + 3^3 - 4$ **40**

2. $6 \cdot (6 + 3 - 2) \div (12 - \frac{24}{3})$ **10.5**

3. Evaluate $2a + b^2 - 5c + abd$ if $a = 2, b = 3, c = 0,$ and $d = 1$. *(Lesson 2-1)* **19**

4. Solve $x - 51 = 91$ if the replacement set is $\{40, 101, 141, 142, 151\}$.
   (Lesson 2-2) **142**

5. **Geometry**   The sum of the lengths of the sides of the pentagon at the right is 38 meters. Find the value of x, if x is the missing length of one side. *(Lesson 2-2)* **9 m**

Solve each equation. Check your solution. *(Lessons 2-3 and 2-4)*

6. $45 + x = 140$ **95**

7. $y - 8.9 = 10.2$ **19.1**

8. $3w = 45.6$ **15.2**

9. $50 = \frac{p}{3}$ **150**

10. Rosa is tall. Add 30 centimeters to her height and take a third of the sum. Now you have half of Alice's height. Alice is 140 centimeters tall. How tall is Rosa? *(Lesson 2-5)* **180 cm**

Lesson 2-5   Problem-Solving Strategy: Work Backward   **59**

Extending the Lesson

Science Connection   Have students read about the geology of the Grand Canyon. Then ask them to explain why a geologist hiking down into the canyon might regard the trip as "walking backward" in time.

Cooperative Learning Activity

Use groups of 2.
Materials: Spinners, counters

You've Got It Backward 2-5

▪ Each partner copies onto a separate sheet of paper the figure shown on the back of this card. Make sure that a counter will fit in each square. Label equal sections of two spinners "Up," "Down," "Left," "Right."

➡ Each partner secretly thinks of a number between 0 and 100. Place a counter on the shaded square. This counter represents the number you chose.

Each partner spins a spinner and moves his or her counter one square in the direction indicated on the spinner. Evaluate the expression in the square for your number and write the value on a sheet of paper. Write ① in the square to indicate your first move. Repeat the above, using the previous value you found and writing the number of each move in the appropriate square, until you move outside the square. Write the last value you found on the appropriate blank. Trade cards with your partner. Work backward to determine his or her original number.

Glencoe Mathematics: Applications and Connections, Course 3

NCTM Standards: 1–4, 7, 9

Management Tips

For Students   Each group of students will need 4 green, 12 red, and 6 yellow counters. Appoint "counter counters" to check that all counters are returned at the end of the lab. HINT: Assemble the counters in sandwich bags with a twist-tie for convenient management.

For the Overhead Projector
Overhead Manipulative Resources provides appropriate materials for teacher or student demonstration of the activities in this Mathematics Lab.

1 FOCUS

Introducing the Lab

Ask students to give a definition of a model.   Sample answer: a representation of an object   Point out that many real-life situations can be modeled. This allows the situations to be analyzed so that the problems they present can be solved.

Cooperative Learning

2-6A Writing Expressions and Equations

A Preview of Lesson 2-6

Objective
Write algebraic expressions and equations from verbal problems.

Materials
red, green, and yellow counters
sheets of paper

The History Club at school is assembling bags of canned goods to give to needy families in the neighborhood. They have cans of soup, vegetables, and fruit to distribute. Joey asked, "How do we know which cans to put in each bag?" Mr. Boyarski, their sponsor, told them he wrote clues about the contents of each bag on the outside of the bag.

Joey picked up the first bag and was puzzled. The clues on the bag read as follows.

> There are cans of soup, vegetables, and fruit in this bag. There is one more can of soup than vegetables. There are 9 cans in all. There are 2 cans of vegetables.

Try this!

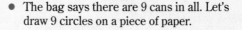

Problem Solving Hint

• • • • • • • • • • •

Use the work backward strategy. Begin with the total and work backward to find the answer.

Let's help Joey out by using a model.

● The bag says there are 9 cans in all. Let's draw 9 circles on a piece of paper.

● Let each color of counter represent a different type of can. Suppose red is soup, green is vegetable, and yellow is fruit.

● What clues do we have?
The bag says there are 2 vegetables. Put green counters on 2 of the circles.

● What other clues do we have?
It says that there is one more soup than vegetable. So, if there are 2 vegetables, there must be 3 soups. Put red counters on 3 of the circles.

● The rest of the circles represent cans of fruit since there are 9 cans in all. *How many yellow counters will you use?* **4**

Your Turn

Here are some of the clues on bags to be filled by other students. Use a model to figure out how many of each type of can is to be placed in each bag. Each bag contains at least one of each type of can.

Bag A   There are 6 vegetables.
There are 14 cans in this bag.
There is one less can of fruit
than there are of vegetables.
6 vegetables, 5 fruits, 3 soups

Bag B   There are 8 cans in this bag.
Two are fruits. There are 2
more soups than fruits.
2 fruits, 4 soups, 2 vegetables

Bag C   There are 2 vegetables.
There are 3 times as many
fruits as vegetables. There
are 10 cans in all.
2 vegetables, 6 fruits, 2 soups

Bag D   There are 19 cans in this bag,
3 of which are fruit. There
are 4 times as many soups as
fruits. **3 fruits, 12 soups,
4 vegetables**

What do you think?

1. How many fruit cans went in the bag Joey was preparing? **4 cans**

2. When making a model, how do you know how many circles to draw for each bag? **The total number of cans is written on each bag.**

3. Which clues do you look for first when figuring out each bag's contents? **Look for clues that give definite amounts.**

Extension

4. Look at Joey's bag. We can write an expression to name each clue. Study the following equations.

   There are cans of soup, vegetables, and fruit in this bag.

   Let S = soup, V = vegetables, and F = fruit.

   There is one more soup than vegetable. $S = V + 1$
   There are 9 cans in all. $S + V + F = 9$
   There are 2 vegetables. $V = 2$

   Do your values for S, V, and F make these sentences true? Explain your answer. **See students' work.**

5. Bag A: V = 6, S + V + F = 14, F = V − 1
   Bag B: S + V + F = 8, F = 2, S = 2 + F
   Bag C: V = 2, F = 3V, S + V + F = 10
   Bag D: S + V + F = 19, F = 3, 4F = S

5. Write equations for each step for bags A, B, C, and D listed in the *Your Turn* section. Check your solutions with your equations.

Mathematics Lab 2-6A Writing Expression and Equations   **61**

NCTM Standards: 1–5, 9

Lesson Resources
- Study Guide Master 2-6
- Practice Master 2-6
- Enrichment Master 2-6
- Group Activity Card 2-6

 Transparency 2-6 contains the 5-Minute Check and a teaching aid for this lesson.

🕐 5-Minute Check
(Over Lesson 2-5)

Solve by working backward.

1. Donna gave 17 of her baseball cards to her brother. The rest she divided evenly among herself and 5 friends. Her share was 29 cards. How many cards did she have at the beginning? **191**

2. Mrs. Washington wants to arrive home from a trip at 3 P.M. The trip will take 5 hours driving and she plans to take two 45-minute rest stops. What time should she begin driving? **8:30 A.M.**

1 FOCUS

Motivating the Lesson

Questioning Have students read the opening paragraph of the lesson. Ask for volunteers to state a number in English and then to translate it into another language, identifying the language used. If you have LEP students, ask them to count in their native language.

2 TEACH

Using Charts Copy the chart below on the chalkboard.

Operation	Phrase
+	
−	
×	
÷	

For each operation, ask students to supply verbal phrases that indicate the operation.

2-6 Writing Expressions and Equations

Objective

Write algebraic expressions and equations from verbal phrases and sentences.

The United Nations was established on October 24, 1945, shortly after World War II. Today the UN is composed of 159 nations, representing dozens of languages. When in official session, only six languages—Arabic, Chinese, English, French, Russian, and Spanish—are offered by translators. The delegates wear earphones to listen to the translation they choose while skilled interpreters translate the words as they are spoken.

In mathematics, we often act as interpreters, translating words and ideas into mathematical expressions and equations. There are many words and phrases that suggest arithmetic operations. Here are some examples of translated phrases. Any variable can be used to represent a number.

> **"When am I ever going to use this?"**
>
> Today, the total number of animal collections in the world exceeds 1,000.
>
> Zoo design and architecture must meet two conflicting needs, those of the animals and those of the visitors.
>
> A college degree and mathematical skills in measurement, design, drafting, and estimation are essential for this nonstandard form of architecture.
>
> For more information, contact the zoological society in your area.

Verbal Phrase	Algebraic Expression
8 more than a number	$n + 8$
a number decreased by 10	$x - 10$
the sum of twice a number and 4	$2y + 4$
a number separated into 5 groups	$\dfrac{n}{5}$

Examples

Write each sentence or phrase as an algebraic expression.

1 One year, the number of zoos in the United States increased by 3. Let z represent the number of zoos before the increase.
The word *increased* means the U.S. added to the number of zoos.
The algebraic expression is $z + 3$.

2 three less than four times the number of eggs required for a chocolate cake

Let c represent the number of eggs required for a chocolate cake.
Four times means multiply by 4.   → $4 \cdot c$ or $4c$
Three less means subtract 3.   → $4c - 3$

The algebraic expression is $4c - 3$.

OPTIONS

Reteaching Activity

Using Cooperative Groups In a group of three, one student writes an algebraic expression. A second student translates the expression into a verbal phrase. The third student, who has not seen the first student's expression, translates the phrase into an algebraic expression. The students then compare the original and final expressions.

Study Guide Masters, p. 15

Name _____ Date _____

Study Guide Worksheet 2-6

Writing Expressions and Equations

The table show phrases written as mathematical expressions.

Phrase	Expression	Phrase	Expression
8 more than a number the sum of 8 and a number x plus 8 x increased by 8	$x + 8$	7 subtracted from a number h minus 7 7 less than a number a number decreased by 7	$h - 7$

Phrase	Expression	Phrase	Expression
3 multiplied by n 3 times a number the product of n and 3	$3n$	a number divided by 5 the quotient of t divided by 5 divide a number by 5	$\dfrac{t}{5}$

Write each phrase as an algebraic expression. Variables may vary.

1. 12 more than a number $p + 12$

Verbal sentences may be translated into equations. The equation can often be used to solve a problem.

Verbal sentence	Algebraic Equation
Three is five more than a number.	$3 = n + 5$
Four times a number is one hundred.	$4n = 100$

Example 3

Jesse has $5 more than twice the amount Rosa has. Jesse has $15. Write an equation to represent this problem.

Let r = the amount Rosa has.

twice the amount Rosa has	→	$2r$
$5 more than that	→	$2r + 5$
Jesse's amount, $15, equals this.	→	$15 = 2r + 5$

Checking for Understanding

Communicating Mathematics

Read and study the lesson to answer each question.

1. **Write** two different verbal phrases that could be represented by the algebraic expression $y + 7$. **7 more than y; y increased by 7**
2. **Tell** what the expression $t - 5$ represents if t is the scheduled blastoff time of a space shuttle flight. **5 time units until blastoff**
3. **Tell** what word usually occurs in verbal sentences that can be written as equations. **is**

Guided Practice

Write each phrase or sentence as an algebraic expression or equation.

4. 17 more than p $p + 17$
5. the quotient of x and 3 $\frac{x}{3}$
6. the product of 6 and r $6r$
7. 4 less than m $m - 4$
8. three more than twice the total number of turtles t $2t + 3$
9. Six less m is 25. $6 - m = 25$
10. The difference between 8 and the quotient of a and 4 is 19. $8 - \frac{a}{4} = 19$
11. How many apples are there in each bag if you separate 37 apples into each of five bags and there are 2 apples left? $5x + 2 = 37$

Exercises

Independent Practice

Write each phrase or sentence as an algebraic expression or equation.

12. the sum of p and 4 $p + 4$
13. 18 less n $18 - n$
14. the sum of 9 and five times y $5y + 9$
15. the difference between 24 and twice a number $24 - 2x$
16. five dollars more than Leroy made $d + \$5$
17. her salary plus a $200 bonus $s + \$200$

Lesson 2-6 Writing Expressions and Equations   **63**

More Examples

For Example 1

Tony gained 15 pounds. Let t represent Tony's original weight. Write an algebraic expression for his new weight. $t + 15$

For Example 2

Manuel's age is 6 more than half Brett's age. Let b represent Brett's age. Write an algebraic expression for Manuel's age. $\frac{1}{2}b + 6$

For Example 3

Meg scored 11 points. That was 4 points less than 3 times the number of points Sumi scored. Let s represent Sumi's score. Write an equation to represent this problem. $11 = 3s - 4$

Checking for Understanding

Exercises 1-3 are designed to help you assess students' understanding through reading, writing, speaking, and modeling. You should work through these exercises with your students and then monitor their work on Guided Practice Exercises 4-11.

Practice Masters, p. 15

Name _____   Date _____

Practice Worksheet 2-6

Writing Expressions and Equations

Write each phrase or sentence as an algebraic expression or equation.

1. 8 more than x $x + 8$
2. 12 less than b $b - 12$
3. the product of 6 and y $6y$
4. the quotient of a and 4 $\frac{a}{4}$
5. the sum of 9 and c $9 + c$
6. the difference of q and 12 $q - 12$
7. 7 times d $7d$
8. 20 less n $20 - n$
9. 6 less than x is 18. $x - 6 = 18$
10. 4 more than y is 17. $y + 4 = 17$
11. The product of a and 7 is 21. $7a = 21$
12. The sum of 1 and w is 12. $1 + w = 12$
13. the sum of 8 and 6 times y $8 + 6y$
14. eight dollars less than Joni earned $j - 8$
15. Pak's salary minus a $223 deduction $p - 223$
16. twice as many flowers as Susan picked $2s$
17. 6 less than the product of 8 and c is 58. $8c - 6 = 58$
18. The cost of the tea plus 10 cents tax is $2.09. $c + 0.10 = 2.09$
19. 8 more than the number of meals served on Tuesday $T + 8$
20. 18 less than the number of gameboard squares is 126. $s - 18 = 126$
21. 63 is 1 more than twice the number of miles Timothy drove. $63 = 2m + 1$
22. The sum of 9 and the quotient of x and 7 is 11. $9 + \frac{x}{7} = 11$
23. 12 less than twice the number of cows is 36. $2c - 12 = 36$
24. 17 inches less than 3 times Maria's height is 169 inches. $3m - 17 = 169$
25. 5 more than the number of paper clips divided into 4 groups $\frac{n}{4} + 5$
26. $18 more than 3 times Tony's wages $3t + 18$
27. 8 less than the number of apples divided into 5 groups is 32. $\frac{a}{5} - 8 = 32$

T15
Glencoe Division, Macmillan/McGraw-Hill

63

Close

Guide students to summarize the lesson by asking them to describe the steps they would follow to translate the following sentence into an equation. *Four more than k is the product of 3 and 7.*

1. Translate "four more than *k*" to *k* + 4.
2. Translate "is" to =.
3. Translate "the product of 3 and 7" to 3 · 7.
4. Thus, the sentence translates to *k* + 4 = 3 · 7.

3 PRACTICE/APPLY

Alternate Assessment

Speaking   Write an algebraic expression or equation on the chalkboard. Have students state its translation into a verbal phrase or sentence.

Enrichment Masters, p. 15

Name _____ Date _____

Enrichment Worksheet 2-6

Age Problems

Problems that involve a person's age can often be solved more easily by arranging the information in a chart. Here is an example.

Ten years from now Sid will be three times as old as he is today. How old is Sid now?

The information in the chart helps you answer the question in the problem. Answer: 5 years

Age Now	*x*
Age in 10 Years	*x* + 10
Equation	*x* + 10 = 3*x*
Solution	*x* = 5

Complete the chart for each problem.

1. Twenty years ago Horace was one-fifth as old as he is now. How old is he now?

Age Now	*x*
Age 20 Years Ago	*x* − 20
Equation	$\frac{1}{5}x = x - 20$
Solution	*x* = 25
Answer	25 years

2. In 9 years, Judith will be four times as old as she is now. How old will she be then?

Age Now	*x* − 9
Age in 9 Years	*x*
Equation	*x* = 4(*x* − 9)
Solution	*x* = 12
Answer	12 years

3. Fifteen years from now Tonio will be two and a half times as old as he is now. How old is Tonio today?

Age Now	*x*
Age in 15 Years	*x* + 15
Equation	2.5*x* = *x* + 15
Solution	*x* = 10
Answer	10 years

4. Six years ago Eleanor was one-third as old as she is today. How old was she six years ago?

Age Now	*x* + 6
Age 6 Years Ago	*x*
Equation	$x = \frac{1}{3}(x + 6)$
Solution	*x* = 3
Answer	3 years

T15
Glencoe Division, Macmillan/McGraw-Hill

64

Write each phrase or sentence as an algebraic expression or equation.

18. three times as many hits as the Pirates   **3*h***

19. Two less than the quotient of 24 and *x* is 2. $\frac{24}{x} - 2 = 2$

20. the product of 5 and *x* decreased by their sum   **5*x* − (5 + *x*)**

21. six more than two times the number of pizzas ordered yesterday   **2*p* + 6**

22. The product of a number and 5 is 45.   **5*x* = 45**

23. Steve inventoried the paper left in the bookstore. There were 14 less than 3 cases of packages of paper. Steve reported there were 46 packages of paper.   **3*c* − 14 = 46**

24. Six less than the number of students divided into three groups is 47. $\frac{x}{3} - 6 = 47$

25. Use mental math to find 64 + 28 + 6.   *(Lesson 1-2)*   **98**

26. How many liters are in 34.7 milliliters of water?   *(Lesson 1-6)*   **0.0347 liters**

27. How many ounces are in $3\frac{1}{2}$ pounds?   *(Lesson 1-7)*   **56 ounces**

28. Solve *t* − 9 = 23. Check your solution.   *(Lesson 2-2)*   **32**

29. Solve 35 = 5*m*. Check your solution.   *(Lesson 2-4)*   **7**

30. **Statistics**   Use the information below to answer each question.

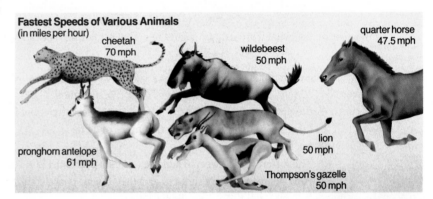

Fastest Speeds of Various Animals (in miles per hour)
cheetah 70 mph
wildebeest 50 mph
quarter horse 47.5 mph
pronghorn antelope 61 mph
lion 50 mph
Thompson's gazelle 50 mph

  a. If *s* represents the fastest speed of a cheetah, which animal's speed can be represented by *s* − 9?   **pronghorn antelope**

  b. If *x* represents the speed of the lion, which other animals have speeds that can be represented by *x*?   **wildebeest and Thompson's gazelle**

  c. If *w* represents the speed of the wildebeest, write an expression that represents the speed of the pronghorn antelope.   **w + 11**

31. **Critical Thinking**   How would you write an algebraic equation to represent 5 times the sum of twice *x* and 4 less 5 is 2 more than 15?
   5 (2*x* + 4) − 5 = 15 + 2

32. **Journal Entry**   Write what the sentence *B* = *P* + 12 means if *B* represents Bob's test score and *P* represents Paulo's test score.
   Bob scored 12 points higher on the test than Paulo.

OPTIONS

Extending the Lesson

Current Events Connection   Have students search newspapers for stories containing numerical information. Students should determine the relevant portions of the stories, choose appropriate variables, and translate newspaper phrases or sentences into algebraic expressions or equations.

Cooperative Learning Activity

Four in a Row 2-6

Use groups of 3 or more.
Materials: Index cards, counters, spinners

◆ On a sheet of paper, each group member draws a grid like the one shown at the right. Make the squares as large as possible. Write the expressions on the back of this card in the squares. No two group members' game cards should be exactly alike. Copy onto cards the phrases on the back of this card.

➠ One group member reads each phrase. All group members then place a counter on the matching algebraic expression. Try to be the first to cover four squares in a row, including diagonally.

Glencoe Mathematics: Applications and Connections, Course 3

2-7A Function Input and Output

A Preview of Lesson 2-7

Objective
Use function machines to find output from a given input and then to find input from a given output.

Today you can put flour, yeast, eggs, and other ingredients into a machine and 4 hours later, you get a loaf of bread. The machine performs all the functions of mixing, kneading, rising, and baking to complete the process of bread making.

In mathematics, we have **functions** that work like machines. You **input** a number and the **output** is the function of the number. If the number is represented by x, the function of the number is represented by $f(x)$. *This is read "f of x."*

Activity One

Look at the function machine below. You put a number into the top of the machine and at each stage an operation is performed. Then the result moves onto the next stage.

- What number is being used as input? 3

- What is the first operation? multiplication
  What is the result after the first operation is performed? 12

- Move this result to the next stage.

- What is the second operation? addition
  What is the result after this operation? 14

- What is your final output? 14

```
INPUT: X=3
   |
 × 4
   |
 + 2
   |
OUTPUT: F(X)= ?
```

What do you think?

1. Write the complete process performed by the function machine from input to output. Multiply 3 by 4. Add 2 to the product.

2. Each stage of this function machine represents a mathematical expression. If the input is represented by x, write an algebraic equation that summarizes what the function machine does. $f(x) = 4x + 2$

3. Suppose you were given the output and had to determine the input. How do you think you would go about finding the input? by working backward

---

NCTM Standards: 1–4, 7–9

Management Tips

For Students Before discussing the *Try This!* on page 66, students should review inverse operations in Lesson 2-3. Have students review the work-backward strategy presented in Lesson 2-5 before completing Exercises 6–8.

For the Overhead Projector *Overhead Manipulative Resources* provides appropriate materials for teacher or student demonstration of the activities in this Mathematics Lab.

1 FOCUS

Introducing the Lab

Have students read the opening paragraph of the lab and then ask the following questions.

- *What goes into the machine?* flour, yeast, eggs, and other ingredients

- *What are the machine's functions?* mixing, kneading, raising, baking

- *What comes out of the machine?* a loaf of bread

Using Communication Stress the idea that a function is a "machine" that operates on numbers. Draw a copy of the function machine shown on page 65 on the chalkboard or overhead projector. Using the $x = 3$ in the first box, discuss each operation performed by the machine, writing the result of the operation beside the appropriate box. You may wish to repeat the activity with other values of x.

3 PRACTICE/APPLY

Using Analogies Point out to students that the arithmetic operations of a function machine are like the operations of mixing and baking bread—they take numbers (ingredients), act on them, and turn them into something new.

Close

Draw a function machine on the chalkboard. State the number to be input and have students describe each step as the number is "processed" by the machine.

Activity Two

One day a comet passed very close to Earth and all the function machines went berserk. Everything started working backwards. The conveyor belt reversed. The machines started sucking up the outputs and spewing out inputs from the tops of the machines.

- Look at the function machine at the right. What was the output when the machine worked normally? 24

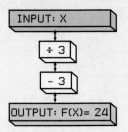

- When the machine went berserk, it performed the inverse of each operation. Describe what happens in each chamber of the berserk machine. add 3; multiply by 3
- What number was the input for the machine to get an output of 24? 81

What do you think?

4. The process used the opposite operation and worked on the output first.

4. Write about the process the berserk machine followed after the comet passed Earth. Compare this to the process the machine followed when it worked properly.

5. This machine could be the model of an equation.
   a. Write the equation represented if the input is x and the output is 24. $\frac{x}{3} - 3 = 24$
   b. What is the solution to the equation? 81

Find the missing input or output for each function machine.

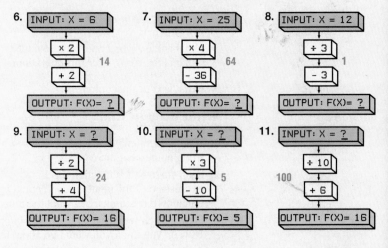

OPTIONS

Lab Manual You may wish to make copies of the blackline master on p. 42 of the *Lab Manual* for students to use as a recording sheet.

Lab Manual, p. 42

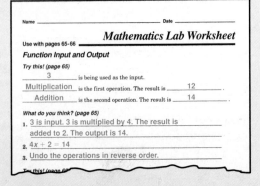

2-7 Solving Two-Step Equations

Objective
Solve two-step equations.

When you wrap a present, you put the paper on first and then you add the ribbon. To open a present you usually do the opposite—take the ribbon off first and then the paper.

You can solve an equation in a similar way. Look at the equation $4 + 2x = 8$. In this equation, the x is first multiplied by 2 and then 4 is added.

To solve the equation, you work backwards using the reverse of the order of operations. That is, you subtract 4 from each side of the equation and then divide each side by 2.

Mini-Lab

Work with a partner. Solve $4 + 2x = 8$ using models.
Materials: cups, counters, mats.

- Put 2 cups and 4 counters on one side of the mat. Put 8 counters on the other side of the mat. The two sides of the mat represent equal quantities.

- Take 4 counters from each side.

- Separate the remaining counters into 2 groups to correspond to the 2 cups.

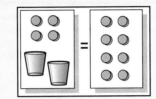

Talk About It

a. What operation is represented by removing 4 counters from each mat? **subtraction**

b. What operation is represented by separating the remaining counters into groups? **division**

c. How many counters correspond to each cup? **2**

d. What is the solution to $4 + 2x = 8$? **2**

Lesson 2-7 Solving Two-Step Equations **67**

OPTIONS

Reteaching Activity

Using Models Use these 6 cards to model the equation $3p + 4 = 13$.

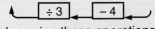

Write the appropriate inverse operations on the blank cards.

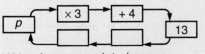

Solve using these operations.
$p = 3$

Study Guide Masters, p. 16

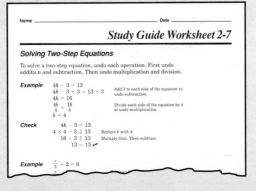

Name _____ Date _____

Study Guide Worksheet 2-7

Solving Two-Step Equations

To solve a two-step equation, undo each operation. First undo addition and subtraction. Then undo multiplication and division.

Example $4k - 3 = 13$
$4k - 3 + 3 = 13 + 3$ Add 3 to each side of the equation to undo subtraction.
$4k = 16$
$\frac{4k}{4} = \frac{16}{4}$ Divide each side of the equation by 4 to undo multiplication.
$k = 4$

Check $4k - 3 = 13$
$4 \times 4 - 3 \stackrel{?}{=} 13$ Replace k with 4.
$16 - 3 \stackrel{?}{=} 13$ Multiply first. Then subtract.
$13 = 13$ ✓

Example $\frac{r}{5} + 2 = 6$

NCTM Standards: 1–6, 9

Lesson Resources
- Study Guide Master 2-7
- Practice Master 2-7
- Enrichment Master 2-7
- Multicultural Activity, p. 2
- Group Activity Card 2-7

 Transparency 2-7 contains the 5-Minute Check and a teaching aid for this lesson.

⏱ 5-Minute Check
(Over Lesson 2–6)

Write each phrase or sentence as an algebraic expression or equation.

1. the sum of 6 and three times n $6 + 3n$

2. five less than e $e - 5$

3. the quotient of 5 and four more than h $\frac{5}{h + 4}$

4. The difference between m and 9 is 5. $m - 9 = 5$

5. Three more than the product of y and 7 is 12. $7y + 3 = 12$

---

1 FOCUS

Motivating the Lesson

Situational Problem Ask students to identify the error in the following solution of the equation $2x + 6 = 14$.

$$2x + 6 = 14$$
$$\frac{2x}{2} + 6 = \frac{14}{2}$$
$$x + 6 = 7$$
$$x = 1$$

2 TEACH

Using the Mini-Lab Ask students why they should not separate cups and counters into two groups in Step 1. The cups must be by themselves on one side of the mat before separating the counters into groups.

Teaching Tip   Before Example 1, write several two-step equations on the chalkboard. Ask students to state which operation they should undo first when solving each equation.

More Examples

For Example 1

Solve $5y + 9 = 24$. Check your solution.   3

For Example 2

Solve $\frac{n}{3} - 12 = 4$. Check your solution.   48

Checking for Understanding

Exercises 1–3 are designed to help you assess students' understanding through reading, writing, speaking, and modeling. You should work through these exercises with your students and then monitor their work on Guided Practice Exercises 4–9.

Additional Answers

1. Add 5 to each side.
2. Undo addition/subtraction first and then undo multiplication/division.

Practice Masters, p. 16

Name _____   Date _____

Practice Worksheet 2-7

Solving Two-Step Equations

Tell the first step you would do to solve each equation. Then solve the equation. Check your solution.

1. $8x + 3 = 35$ sub. 3; 4	**2.** $2y - 9 = 9$ add 9; 9	**3.** $6a + 12 = 42$ sub. 12; 5
4. $\frac{b}{4} - 2 = 8$ add 2; 40	**5.** $\frac{w}{2} + 5 = 10$ sub. 5; 10	**6.** $\frac{c}{7} - 3 = 0$ add 3; 21
7. $8 + 5d = 53$ sub. 8; 9	**8.** $12f - 9 = 27$ add 9; 3	**9.** $7 + 8g = 87$ sub. 7; 10
10. $6h + 3.7 = 51.7$ sub. 3.7; 8	**11.** $7z - 9.4 = 11.6$ add 9.4; 3	**12.** $4g + 0.7 = 36.7$ sub. 0.7; 9

Solve each equation. Check your solution.

13. $2y - 3 = 9$ 6	**14.** $6c + 4 = 58$ 9	**15.** $9d - 8 = 154$ 18
16. $9 + \frac{r}{5} = 15$ 30	**17.** $\frac{s}{3} - 7 = 7$ 42	**18.** $\frac{t}{6} + 12 = 24$ 72
19. $74 = 14 + 5k$ 12	**20.** $79 = 6t + 7$ 12	**21.** $51 = 4m - 13$ 16
22. $10 = 6 + \frac{t}{8}$ 32	**23.** $4 = \frac{s}{5} - 16$ 100	**24.** $\frac{u}{8} + 15 = 27$ 96
25. $6x + 1.2 = 4.2$ 0.5	**26.** $8y - 4.6 = 68.2$ 9.1	**27.** $10f - 0.5 = 22.5$ 2.3
28. $0.4m - 2.7 = 11.7$ 36	**29.** $1.2n + 3.6 = 14.4$ 9	**30.** $0.93 = 0.15 + 0.3w$ 2.6

T16
Glencoe Division, Macmillan/McGraw-Hill

Many equations can be solved algebraically in a similar manner.

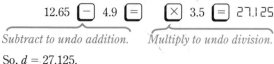

1   Solve $3k - 4 = 17$. Check your solution.

$$3k - 4 = 17$$
$$3k - 4 + 4 = 17 + 4 \qquad \text{Add to undo subtraction.}$$
$$3k = 21$$
$$\frac{3k}{3} = \frac{21}{3} \qquad \text{Divide to undo multiplication.}$$
$$k = 7$$

Check: $3k - 4 = 17$
$3(7) - 4 \overset{?}{=} 17$ *Replace k with 7.*
$21 - 4 \overset{?}{=} 17$ *Multiply before subtracting.*
$17 = 17$ ✔   *It checks. The solution is 7.*

2   Solve $\frac{d}{3.5} + 4.9 = 12.65$.

Problem Solving Hint
• • • • • • • • •
Use the work backward strategy to solve an equation.

You can use your calculator to solve this equation.

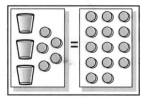

12.65 $\boxed{-}$ 4.9 $\boxed{=}$ $\boxed{\times}$ 3.5 $\boxed{=}$ 27.125

Subtract to undo addition.   *Multiply to undo division.*

So, $d = 27.125$.

Check: $\frac{d}{3.5} + 4.9 \overset{?}{=} 12.65$ if $d = 27.125$

27.125 $\boxed{\div}$ 3.5 $\boxed{+}$ 4.9 $\boxed{=}$ 12.65   *It checks.*

Checking for Understanding

For answers to Exercises 1–2, see margin. For 3–9, see Solutions Manual.

Communicating Mathematics

Read and study the lesson to answer each question.

1. **Tell** what step you would do first in solving $3e - 5 = 25$.
2. **Write** a sentence to explain how the work-backward strategy is used in solving two-step equations.
3. **Show** how to use the model to solve the equation $3x + 5 = 14$. How can you check your solution?

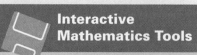

Guided Practice

Tell the first step you would do to solve each equation. Then solve the equation. Check your solution.

4. $7c + 3 = 17$
5. $8 + 3d = 17$
6. $11e - 5.3 = 5.7$
7. $\frac{b}{9} + 0.8 = 1.3$
8. $\frac{f}{4} - 3 = 4$
9. $7 + \frac{g}{2} = 8$

68   **Chapter 2** An Introduction to Algebra

OPTIONS

Multicultural Education

Many ancient civilizations developed numeration systems. But the Mayans, Native Americans of southeastern Mexico and northwestern Central America, were one of the first cultures to create and use a symbol for zero. The Mayans represented zero with a symbol which looked like a conch shell.

Interactive Mathematics Tools

This multimedia software provides an interactive lesson that is tied directly to Lesson 2–7. Students will click and drag cups and counters to explore two-step equations as in the Mini Lab.

Exercises

Independent Practice

Solve each equation. Check your solution.

10. $3x + 4 = 7$ **1**   11. $4r - 9 = 7$ **4**   12. $1.2 + 6t = 3.6$ **0.4**

13. $5 + 14s = 33$ **2**   14. $\dfrac{p}{5} - 1 = 13$ **70**   15. $\dfrac{f}{8} + 3 = 27$ **192**

Solve each equation. Check your solution.

16. $\dfrac{d}{12} - 4 = 8$ **144**   17. $2e + 5.0 = 6.0$ **0.5**   18. $3f - 15 = 6$ **7**

19. $4g + 1.7 = 2.3$ **0.15**   20. $35 = 18h - 1$ **2**   21. $0.42 = 0.17 + 0.5k$

  0.5

Write each sentence as an equation. Then solve the equation.

22. Twice a number less five is 46. $2x - 5 = 46$; **25.5**   23. $\dfrac{x}{6} - 7 = 12$; **114**

23. The quotient of a number and six, decreased by seven is twelve.

24. Suki gets \$3 more than half of Tommie's allowance. Suki gets \$5 a week. What is Tommie's allowance? $\dfrac{1}{2}T + \$3 = \$5$; **\$4**

Mixed Review

25. Estimate $3.21 + 2.95 + 3.12 + 2.89$ by clustering. *(Lesson 1-3)* **about 12**

26. Evaluate $3^3 \cdot 4^2 \cdot 1^5$. *(Lesson 1-9)* **432**

27. Solve $p + 84 = 196$. Check your solution. *(Lesson 2-3)* **112**

28. Write an algebraic expression to represent *eight less than four times the number of people in Africa.* *(Lesson 2-6)* $4x - 8$

Problem Solving and Applications

29a. $\dfrac{x}{625} = 24$

30. 9; substitute 9 into the equation for *t.*

29. **Sales** Chet Morris is a salesperson for the Beechwood Bottling Company. On Monday, he sold 625 cases of soft drinks. One case contains 24 cans. How many cans of soft drinks did he sell?
   a. Write an equation involving division that represents this situation.
   b. Solve the equation to find the total number of cans sold. **15,000 cans**

30. **Critical Thinking** Use what you have learned about two-step equations to solve the equation $\dfrac{(t + 3)}{6} + 5 = 7$. How could you show that your solution is correct?

31. **Keyboarding** Lawanda began a class to learn to type on her computer. She began at 10 words per minute. Each week she increased her speed at a steady rate. At the end of six weeks, she was typing 40 words per minute. Write an equation to find the number of words she increased per week. Then solve it.
   $10 + 6x = 40$; **5**

32. **Medicine** Dr. Poloma recommended that Anna take six tablets on the first day and then three tablets each day until the prescription ran out. The prescription contained 21 tablets. Use the equation $3d + 6 = 21$ to find how many days she will be taking pills after the first day. **5 more days**

33. **Make Up a Problem** that can be solved by using the equation $2x + 3 = 15$.
   See students' work.

Extending the Lesson

Using Models Have pairs of students use the Mini-Lab on page 67 to develop a method for solving equations where variables appear on both sides of the equation. Point out that when modeling the equations there will be cups on both sides of the mat, and that a solution is represented when cups remain on just one side.

Cooperative Learning Activity

Use groups of 2.
Materials: Balance, beans, envelopes

Balance the Beans 2-7

▶ Each partner secretly places an equal number of beans in each of several envelopes and then seals the envelopes.

▶ Decide which partner will go first. The first partner places his or her sealed envelopes plus several loose beans on one pan of the balance. The second partner places beans on the other pan until the two pans balance. Working together, both partners write an equation that describes this situation.

The second partner solves for the variable in the equation, beginning by removing the loose beans from the pan with the envelopes and an equal number from the other pan. The next step is dividing the remaining loose beans so that an equal number can be placed in the same number of envelopes as there are on the other pan.

Trade roles and repeat the activity.

Glencoe Mathematics: Applications and Connections, Course 3

Close

Have students complete the following statement by inserting the words *addition, subtraction, multiplication,* and *division*.

To solve a two-step equation, first undo the __?__ or __?__. Then undo the __?__ or __?__. The first sentence is completed using the words addition and subtraction. The second sentence is completed using the words multiplication and division.

3 PRACTICE/APPLY

Assignment Guide
Maximum: 10–33
Minimum: 11–23 odd, 25–31

For **Extra Practice,** see p. 587.

Alternate Assessment

Speaking Read the following sentence. *Three pens cost \$1.55 including \$0.08 sales tax.* Ask students to state how they would find the cost of one pen. Sample answer: Work backwards— subtract \$0.08 from \$1.55, then divide the result by 3.

Enrichment Masters, p. 16

NCTM Standards: 1–5, 7, 9

Lesson Resources
- Study Guide Master 2-8
- Practice Master 2-8
- Enrichment Master 2-8
- Group Activity Card 2-8

 Transparency 2-8 contains the 5-Minute Check and a teaching aid for this lesson.

🕐 5-Minute Check
(Over Lesson 2-7)

Solve each equation. Check your solution.

1. $6 + 4x = 38$ 8

2. $\frac{n}{9} - 3 = 2$ 45

3. $30 = 13k - 9$ 3

4. $\frac{e}{7} + 7 = 7$ 0

5. Write the following sentence as an equation. Then solve the equation. *Eight more than half a number is 15.* $\frac{x}{2} + 8 = 15; x = 14$

1 FOCUS

Motivating the Lesson

Questioning   Have students read the opening paragraph of the lesson. Then ask the following questions.

- *Of the problem-solving strategies you have studied thus far, which one seems best suited for solving this problem?*   guess and check
- *What drawbacks does this strategy present?*   There are many possible guesses which can be made and checking them all is time-consuming.

2-8 Use an Equation

Objective
Solve problems by using an equation.

Les receives $2 from his grandfather for each test he passes. If he fails a test, he pays his grandfather $3. Les has made $5 on his tests so far this year. He has passed four times as many tests as he has failed. How many tests has Les passed? How many has he failed?

Explore   What do you know?
Les has $5.
He gets $2 for passed tests.
He pays back $3 for failed tests.
He passed four times as many as he failed.

What are you trying to find out?
We want to know how many tests Les has passed and failed.

Plan   Let's use an equation.
Let f = the number of tests failed.
Then $4f$ = the number of tests passed.

Subtracting $8f - 3f$ is like subtracting 3 fruits from 8 fruits. The answer is 5 fruits. So, $8f - 3f$ is $5f$.

$$\underbrace{money\ earned}\ -\ \underbrace{money\ paid\ back}\ =\ \underbrace{money\ he\ has}$$
$$\$2 \cdot 4f\quad -\quad \$3 \cdot f\quad =\quad \$5$$

That is, $8f - 3f = 5$ or $5f = 5$.

Solve $5f = 5$

$\dfrac{5f}{5} = \dfrac{5}{5}$ *Divide each side by 5.*

$f = 1$

So, Les failed one test and passed four tests.

Examine   Passing four tests at $2 per test is $8. Failing one test at $3 is the money that Les had to pay back. Since $8 - $3 = $5, the answer checks.

OPTIONS

Reteaching Activity

Using Communication   Write several two-step equations on the chalkboard. Have students state a word problem illustrating each equation. For example, for the equation $2e + 7 = 21$ they might say, "Seven more than twice Eric's age is 21." Then have all students solve the problem.

Study Guide Masters, p. 17

Name _____ Date _____

Study Guide Worksheet 2-8

Problem-Solving Strategy: Use an Equation

Example   School T-shirts cost $14 and sweatshirts cost $24. Twice as many T-shirts as sweatshirts were sold. $2,912 was earned. How many T-shirts and how many sweatshirts were sold?

Explore   What do you know?
T-shirts cost $14. Sweatshirts cost $24. $2,912 was earned.
Twice as many T-shirts as sweatshirts were sold.

What do you want to find?
You want to find how many T-shirts and how many sweatshirts were sold.

Plan   Use an equation.
We know that the number of sweatshirts times $24 plus two times the number of sweatshirts times $14 equals $2,912.

Solve   Let s = the number of sweatshirts.
$2s$ = the number of T-shirts.
Write an equation: $24s + 14(2s) = 2$...

Example

Barbara is driving to her sister's house 425 miles away. She drove 253 miles the first day. The next morning, she drove 109 miles. How far must she drive that afternoon to reach her sister's house later that day?

Use an equation. The sum of the distances Barbara drives will equal the total distance to her sister's house.

$$253 + 109 + d = 425 \quad \textit{Let } d = \textit{the afternoon miles.}$$
$$362 + d = 425$$
$$d = 63$$

Barbara must drive 63 more miles to reach her sister's house.

Checking for Understanding

Communicating Mathematics

Read and study the lesson to answer each question.

1. **Explain** how you represent an unknown quantity in a problem in order to use it in an equation. **Represent it with a variable expression.**

2. **Show** how you would change the problem about the tests if Les paid back $2 for failing a test. $8f - 2f = 5$

3. **Explain** how the equation would change if Les failed more tests than he passed. Use the $2 rate from Exercise 2 for passing and failing. **The equation would have a negative value.**

Guided Practice

Solve by using an equation.

4. Paul bought 2 pairs of skates for $52.22 each and 2 pairs of goggles at $9.94 each. He handed the cashier $125. How much change did he get? **$0.68**

5. Three times a number minus twice the number plus one is 6. What is the number? **5**

6. Adult tickets for a play cost $5.50. Student tickets cost $5. Twice as many students as adults attended. How many tickets of each kind were sold if the total sales were $1,953? **126 adult, 252 student**

Problem Solving

Practice

Solve using any strategy.

7. The Zoological Gardens in Philadelphia is home to 15,000 species, many of them rare, in natural settings. If you could walk through the zoo for 8 hours a day and see a different species every minute, how many days would it take you to see all of the species? **31.25 days**

Bell Ringer

Have students write down the birth years of two living people they admire. Have them add the years together. To the sum, add the ages of both people today. Have students compare their results. The sum of a person's birth year and their age is the present year. Two such sums are added here, so each student's final total is twice the present year.

2 TEACH

Using Models   To help students understand the payment system set up by Les' grandfather, have them use cards labeled "$2" and "$3" to act out several different transactions between Les and his grandfather.

More Examples

For the Example

Melissa has saved $490 toward the purchase of an $825 clarinet. Her aunt gave her $75 to be used toward the purchase. Use an equation to find how much more money she must save. $490 + 75 + c = 825$; $260

Checking for Understanding

Exercises 1-3 are designed to help you assess students' understanding through reading, writing, speaking, and modeling. You should work through these exercises with your students and then monitor their work on Guided Practice Exercises 4-6.

Practice Masters, p. 17

Name _____ Date _____

Practice Worksheet 2-8

Problem-Solving Strategy: Use an Equation

Solve by using an equation.

1. Four times a number plus six times the number, minus 8, is 32. What is the number? **4**

2. There are 425 students at Dayville Elementary School. 198 of the students are girls. How many students are boys? **227 boys**

3. Mollie buys 3 magazines that cost $2.95 each and a greeting card that costs $1.50. How much change will Mollie receive if she hands the cashier a $20 bill? **$9.65**

4. Jason is driving a truck to a store 635 miles away. He drives 230 miles the first day and 294 miles the second day. How many miles must he drive the third day to reach the store? **111 miles**

5. Seven less than 12 times a number is 101. What is the number? **9**

Solve using any strategy.

6. Juanita buys 5 boxes containing 50 drinking straws each and 3 boxes containing 75 straws each. How many straws does Juanita have? **475 straws**

7. Jon had 7 quarters, 12 dimes, and 6 nickels. He gave Eric $1.55. How much money does Jon have now? **$1.70**

8. Pachee earns $5.30 per hour for her regular hours of work and one-and-one-half times as much for each hour of overtime. This week she worked her regular 40 hours and 6 hours overtime. How much did she earn? **$259.70**

9. Twelve less than 16 times a number is two less than the product of 10 and 15. What is the number? **10**

10. Mario plans to cover a wall measuring 8 feet by 10 feet with square tiles. He will need 30 tiles for the 10-foot length. How many tiles will he need to cover the entire wall? **720 tiles**

T17

Glencoe Division, Macmillan/McGraw-Hill

Tell students that the variable *n* represents the unknown quantity in a certain word problem. Ask them to explain how they can solve the problem. First write an equation relating *n* and all other relevant quantities in the problem. Then solve the equation.

3 PRACTICE/APPLY

Assignment Guide

Maximum: 7–15

Minimum: 7–14

Alternate Assessment

Writing Have students work in pairs. Each student creates several word problems that can each be solved by writing and solving an equation. The pairs then exchange problems and solve them.

Enrichment Masters, p. 17

Name _____ Date _____

Enrichment Worksheet 2-8

Matchstick Equations

The puzzles on this page involve only a box of wooden matches. Toothpicks or any other straight objects may also be used.

In each puzzle, make a true equation by moving just one matchstick.

1.

2. Find two different solutions for this puzzle. The square shape is meant to stand for zero.

3. This one uses the first three Roman numerals.

4. The solution of this puzzle involves a symbol that means "plus or minus."

T17
Glencoe Division, Macmillan/McGraw-Hill

72

Strategies

Look for a pattern.
Solve a simpler problem.
Act it out.
Guess and check.
Draw a diagram.
Make a chart.
Work backward.

8. Morita's car gets 29.5 miles per gallon. How far can the car travel on 17 gallons of fuel? **501.5 miles**

9. Seventeen times a number plus 55 is 4 more than the product of 51 and 5. What is the number? **12**

10. Melissa earns $6.25 per hour for regular hours worked and double time for overtime hours. Last week, she worked 3 hours more than her regular 35-hour week. How much did she earn? **$256.25**

11. The New Jersey shore is a 127-mile stretch of beaches, wildlife preserves, amusement parks, and boardwalks. There are more than 60 resorts available for fun-loving families. About how many resorts is that per mile of beach? **about 2**

12. Roy worked 610 hours at Grant Beach last summer for $3.90 per hour. Lyla earned $5.50 per hour in the business across the street. How much more would Roy have earned if his rate had been $5.50 per hour? **$976**

13. **Data Search** Refer to page 666.
In 1993, how did the median home price in each region compare to the median U.S. home price? **See margin.**

14. Annette is thinking of a number. She triples the number and divides the result by 3. Then she subtracts 2 from the quotient. "Now I have 10," she says. What is Annette's number? **12**

15. **Mathematics and Science** Read the following paragraph.

Gold has been used to make jewelry for thousands of years. However, the Incas used gold for everyday objects, like nails, combs, dishes, and cups. Gold was also prized by the ancient Egyptians, who recognized its beauty. Gold does not rust, tarnish, or stain. Pure gold is a soft metal that can be molded in your hands. Because of its softness, jewelers mix copper with it, to give it added strength. The mixture is measured in *karats*. Twenty-four karat gold is considered pure. Twelve-karat gold is $\frac{12}{24}$ or $\frac{1}{2}$ pure gold.

a. If there are 45 grams of gold on one pan of a balance scale, and 5.2 grams on the other, how much gold is needed to balance the scale? **39.8 grams**

b. If a piece of jewelry is $\frac{2}{3}$ gold, how would you describe it in karats? **16-karat gold**

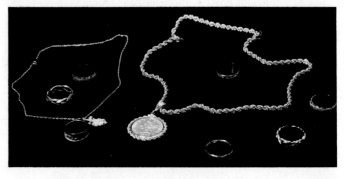

OPTIONS

Extending the Lesson

Mathematics and Science Ask students to draw a series of pictures of a balance scale and have them explain how it is similar to solving an equation with an unknown on one side of the equation. Each drawing could show a different step in solving an equation.

Cooperative Learning Activity

You Say It's Your Birthday 2-8

Use groups of 4.
Materials: Index cards

➡ You probably know that any date may be written entirely with numbers. For example, 7/4/1776 is July 4, 1776.

Write a problem on an index card in which you give clues to the month and day of your birth. Relate the number of the day to the number of the month and tell the sum of the number for day and month. For example, if you were born on March 27 (3/27), you might write, "The month is nine times greater than the day. The sum of the day and the month is 30."

Exchange cards with another group member. Use an equation to guess his or her birthday.

Glencoe Mathematics: Applications and Connections, Course 3

2-9 Perimeter and Area

Objective
Find the perimeters and areas of rectangles, squares, and parallelograms.

Words to Learn
rectangle
perimeter
square
area
parallelogram
base
height
altitude

The exterior of the John Hancock Tower in Boston, Massachusetts contains 10,334 huge 4 foot by 11 foot **rectangles** of glass. In order to calculate the sealant needed to go around each pane of glass, you need to find the **perimeter** of each rectangle.

The perimeter of a geometric figure is the sum of the measures of all of its sides. To find the perimeter of the rectangular piece of glass you can add up the lengths of all the sides or you can use an equation. The equation for the perimeter of any rectangle is $P = 2\ell + 2w$, where ℓ represents the length and w represents the width.

Example 1 *Problem Solving*

Construction Find the perimeter of each pane of glass in the John Hancock Tower.

The length of each pane is 11 feet and the width is 4 feet.

$P = 2\ell + 2w$
$P = 2(11) + 2(4)$ *Replace ℓ with 11 and w with 4.*
$P = 22 + 8$ *Multiply before adding.*
$P = 30$

The perimeter of each pane is 30 feet.

A **square** is a special rectangle in which the lengths of all the sides are equal. The values for ℓ and w in the perimeter equation are the same number. For this reason, the perimeter equation for a square is often written as $P = 4s$, where s is the length of a side. In the square shown at the right, the perimeter is 4(5) or 20 centimeters.

Squares and rectangles are special types of **parallelograms.** Each pair of opposite sides of a parallelogram are parallel and have the same length. To find the perimeter of a parallelogram, you add the lengths of the sides. The parallelogram at the right has a perimeter of 2(7) + 2(6) or 26 feet.

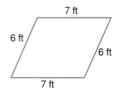

Lesson 2-9 Geometry Connection: Perimeter and Area   **73**

---

2 TEACH

Using the Mini-Lab Be sure students distinguish between the altitude and the side of a parallelogram. An altitude is drawn at right angles to each of the bases. A side does not form right angles with the bases unless the parallelogram is a rectangle.

Teaching Tip Before Example 2, point out that the orientation of a figure does not affect its classification.

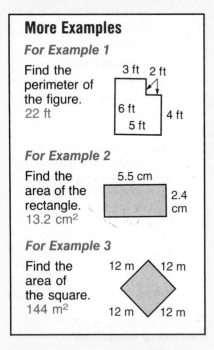

More Examples

For Example 1

Find the perimeter of the figure.
22 ft

3 ft 2 ft
6 ft 4 ft
5 ft

For Example 2

Find the area of the rectangle.
13.2 cm²

5.5 cm
2.4 cm

For Example 3

Find the area of the square.
144 m²

12 m 12 m
12 m 12 m

Checking for Understanding

Exercises 1-3 are designed to help you assess students' understanding through reading, writing, speaking, and modeling. You should work through these exercises with your students and then monitor their work on Guided Practice Exercises 4-6.

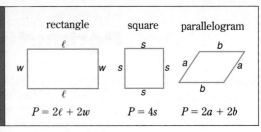

Perimeter Formulas for Rectangles, Squares, and Parallelograms	rectangle	square	parallelogram
	$P = 2\ell + 2w$	$P = 4s$	$P = 2a + 2b$

In addition to the perimeter, we often solve problems by using the **area** of a geometric figure. The area is the measure of the surface enclosed by the figure. The area of any rectangle can be found by multiplying the width and length.

Examples

Find the area of each rectangle.

2

6 in.
4 in.
4 in.
6 in.

$A = \ell w$
$A = 6 \cdot 4$
$A = 24$

The area is 24 square inches.

3

7 m 7 m
7 m 7 m

$A = s \cdot s \text{ or } s^2$
$A = 7 \cdot 7$
$A = 49$

The area is 49 square meters.

The formula for the area of a parallelogram is *not* the product of the sides. However, it is related to the formula for the area of a rectangle.

Mini-Lab

Work with a partner.

Materials: graph paper, scissors

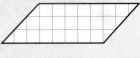

- Copy the parallelogram at the right on a piece of graph paper. Cut out the parallelogram.

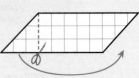

- Make a cut along the dashed line. Move the parts so that they form a rectangle.

OPTIONS

Reteaching Activity

Using Common Objects Have students find several rectangular objects in the classroom, such as textbook covers and posters. Then have them use rulers to measure the dimensions of each object in order to compute its perimeter and area.

Study Guide Masters, p. 18

Name _____ Date _____

Study Guide Worksheet 2-9

Perimeter and Area

Perimeter is the distance around a figure.
Area is the measure of the inside of the figure in square units.

Figure	Rectangle	Square	Parallelogram
Perimeter	$P = 2l + 2w$	$P = 4s$	$P = 2a + 2b$
Area	$A = lw$	$A = s^2$	$A = bh$
Example	$l = 9\text{ m}$, $w = 4\text{ m}$	$s = 8\text{ cm}$	$a = 7\text{ ft}$, $h = 6\text{ ft}$, $b = 5\text{ ft}$
	$P = 2 \times 9 + 2 \times 4$ $P = 18 + 8 = 26\text{ m}$ $A = 9 \times 4$	$P = 4 \times 8$ $P = 32\text{ cm}$ $A = 8^2$	$P = 2 \times 7 + 2 \times 5$ $P = 14 + 10 = 24\text{ ft}$ 5×6

Talk About It

a. What is the area of the rectangle you formed? **24 square units**

b. Study the parts labeled on the figure at the right. Compare the length and width of the rectangle with the **base** and **altitude** of the parallelogram. **length = base, width = altitude**

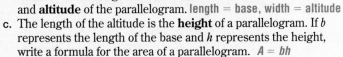

c. The length of the altitude is the **height** of a parallelogram. If *b* represents the length of the base and *h* represents the height, write a formula for the area of a parallelogram. **A = bh**

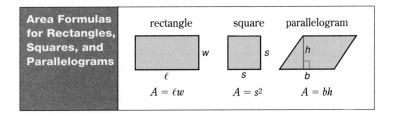

Area Formulas for Rectangles, Squares, and Parallelograms	rectangle	square	parallelogram
	$A = \ell w$	$A = s^2$	$A = bh$

Checking for Understanding

Communicating Mathematics

Read and study the lesson to answer each question. **See students' work.**

1. **Draw** and label a rectangle that has a length of $2\frac{1}{2}$ inches and a width of 1 inch.

2. **Tell** how to find the perimeter and area of the rectangle you drew in Exercise 1. $P = 2(2\frac{1}{2}) + 2(1)$

3. **Write** in your own words the difference between perimeter and area.
Perimeter is the distance around, while area is the space inside (two-dimensional).

Guided Practice

Find the perimeter and area of each figure.

4.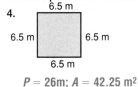
$P = 26m; A = 42.25\ m^2$

5.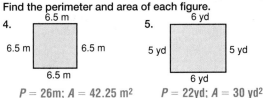
$P = 22yd; A = 30\ yd^2$

6.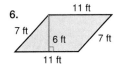
$P = 36\ ft; A = 66\ ft^2$

Exercises

Independent Practice

Find the perimeter and area of each figure.

7.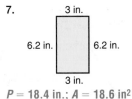
$P = 18.4\ in.; A = 18.6\ in^2$

8.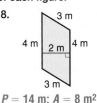
$P = 14\ m; A = 8\ m^2$

9.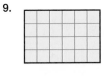
$P = 20\ units; A = 24\ units^2$

Lesson 2-9 Geometry: Perimeter and Area   **75**

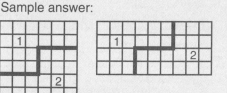
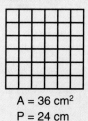
Close

Guide students to summarize the lesson by asking the following questions.

- *How can you find the perimeter of a figure?* Find the sum of the lengths of the sides.

- *How can you find the area of any parallelogram?* Find the product of the length of the base and the height.

3 PRACTICE/APPLY

Assignment Guide
Maximum: 7–22
Minimum: 7–20

For **Extra Practice,** see p. 587.

Alternate Assessment

Speaking Sketch a rectangle and a parallelogram, including the dimensions, on the chalkboard. Have students describe how they would find the perimeter and the area of each figure.

Practice Masters, p. 18

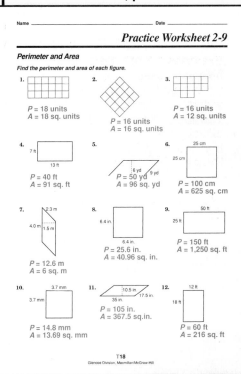

10. $P = 12$ yd
$A = 9$ yd²
11. $P = 16$ m
$A = 12.4$ m²
12. $P = 16$ units
$A = 12$ units²

10.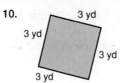

11.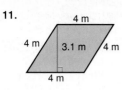

12.

13. Find the perimeter of a rectangle whose length is twice its width. Its width is 8 centimeters. **$P = 48$ cm**

14. Use an equation to find the base of a parallelogram whose height is 7 yards and whose area is 91 square yards. **$7b = 91$; 13 yards**

Mixed Review 15. How many pounds are in 6.5 tons of salt? *(Lesson 1-7)* **13,000 pounds**

16. Solve $\frac{r}{5} = 20$. Check your solution. *(Lesson 2-4)* **100**

17. Solve $12 + 5d = 72$. Check your solution. *(Lesson 2-7)* **12**

18. **$237**

Problem Solving and Applications 18. **Home Maintenance** How much will it cost to tile the floor of a room if the tiles cost $0.79 per square foot and the room is a rectangle 20 feet by 15 feet?

19. **Critical Thinking** Find the area of the shaded part in each rectangle.

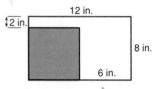

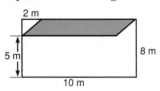

$A = 36$ in² $A = 24$ m²

20. **Shipping** The Minto Company ships candy to mail order customers. To ensure each package's safety, they place a strip of tape around the box and seal the edges. If the average box is 1 foot by 8 inches, approximately how much tape is used on each box? **40 inches of tape**

21. **Make a Drawing** Copy each of the 4-by-4 square grids below.

21b. When the darkened squares are not squares of the color on a checkerboard.

For drawings, see Solutions Manual.
a. Can the remainder of each grid be covered with 1 unit-by-2 unit rectangles without overlapping the rectangles? Draw them. **the third one**

b. Draw some other 4-by-4 grids with two darkened squares. Look for a pattern. When can the grid be covered?

22. **Journal Entry** Write a few sentences to tell two ways you can use perimeter and area at home. **See students' work.**

Name _____ Date _____

Enrichment Worksheet 2-9

Perimeters and Areas of Regular Polygons

A *polygon* is a closed two-dimensional figure whose sides are straight line segments that meet only at their endpoints. A *regular polygon* is a polygon in which all the sides are the same length and all angles have the same measure. For example, a square is a regular polygon because it has four sides of equal length. The chart gives the names and area formulas for some of the regular polygons. The variable s represents the length of one side.

Number of Sides	Name	Area Formula
3	Equilateral Triangle	$A = \frac{s^2}{4}\sqrt{3}$
4	Square	$A = s^2$
6	Regular Hexagon	$A = \frac{3s^2}{2}\sqrt{3}$
8	Regular Octagon	$A = 2s^2(\sqrt{2}+1)$

Write a perimeter formula for each figure. Let s represent the length of one side.

1. Equilateral triangle   2. Regular hexagon   3. Regular octagon
   $P = 3s$ $P = 6s$ $P = 8s$

Find the perimeter of each polygon.

4. A regular hexagon   5. An equilateral triangle
   2 centimeters on each side **12 cm**   15 inches on each side **45 in.**

Find the area of each regular polygon. Use a calculator and round each answer to one decimal place.

6. An octagon 10 yards on each side   7. A hexagon 12 meters on each side
   482.8 sq. yd   **374.1 sq. m**

8. A square with a perimeter of 28 feet   9. An equilateral triangle with a
   49 sq. ft   perimeter of 30 inches
                                              43.3 sq. in.

T18
Glencoe Division, Macmillan/McGraw-Hill

OPTIONS

Extending the Lesson
Business Connection

1. What is the total area of the six rectangles needed to make a cereal box 10 inches high, 8 inches long, and 2 inches wide? **232 in²**

2. Find the total area of a box with length ℓ, width w, and height h. **$2\ell w + 2\ell h + 2wh$**

Cooperative Learning Activity

It's All Proportional 2-9

Use groups of 2.
Materials: Centimeter grid paper

→ On grid paper, draw a rectangle that is 4 cm long and 3 cm wide. Find the perimeter and the area. Then draw a rectangle that is twice as long and twice as wide as your original rectangle. Find the perimeter and the area of the second rectangle. Finally, draw a rectangle whose length and width are three times those of the original rectangle. Find the perimeter and area of the third rectangle.

Try to be the first pair to find the perimeters and areas of rectangles that are 10, 20, and 50 times larger than your original rectangle. (Hint: Look for a pattern.)

Glencoe Mathematics: Applications and Connections, Course 3

2-10 Solving Inequalities

Objective
Identify and solve inequalities.

Words to Learn
inequality

Why is it so important to use the correct ZIP code when you mail a letter? The numbers indicate where each letter is to be sent. Mail is sorted according to the information the ZIP code provides.

geographical center   specific post office

→ 4 3 0 6 5 ←

sectional center

The first automatic sorter takes only those letters with ZIPs that begin with 0. All others go to the next sorter. That sorter takes only the 1s. For numbers greater than 1, the letters go to the next sorter, and so on.

If ℓ represents the first number of the ZIP, then $\ell > 1$ represents all letters that go to the next sorter. The sentence $\ell > 1$ is called an **inequality.** Inequalities are sentences that contain symbols like > or <. You may remember that > is read *is greater than* and < is read *is less than.*

Words: 6 is greater than 4.   **Arithmetic:** $6 > 4$
5 is less than 10. $5 < 10$

Words: $3x + 7$ is greater than 10. **Algebra:** $3x + 7 > 10$
$\frac{y}{4} - 2$ is less than 4. $\frac{y}{4} - 2 < 4$

Equations often have one solution. Unlike equations, inequalities may have many solutions. The solution can be written as a set of numbers.

Mini-Lab

Work with a partner. Solve $\frac{x}{2} - 1 > 2$.

● Draw a number line like the one shown below.

0 1 2 3 4 5 6 7 8 9 10

● Use the whole numbers 0 through 10 as your replacement set.
Color in each circle that represents a solution for $\frac{x}{2} - 1 > 2$.
a. Solutions are greater than 6.

Talk About It   b. Yes; decimal values like 6.5 and 8.75.
a. What does the number line suggest about the solution set?
b. Are there other solutions not shown on the graph? Explain.
c. Solve the equation $\frac{x}{2} - 1 = 2$. How does its solution relate to
the solution of $\frac{x}{2} - 1 > 2$? It shows where the solution set's least number is.

LOOK BACK

You can review solutions and replacement sets on page 48.

Lesson 2-10 Solving Inequalities   **77**

OPTIONS

Reteaching Activity

Using Cooperative Groups Have students work in groups of four. The first student writes a sentence containing the phrase *less than* or *more than*, the second student translates the sentence into an inequality, the third student solves the inequality, and the fourth student graphs the solution on a number line.

Study Guide Masters, p. 19

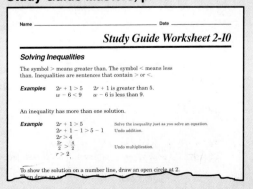

Name _____ Date _____

Study Guide Worksheet 2-10

Solving Inequalities

The symbol > means greater than. The symbol < means less than. Inequalities are sentences that contain > or <.

Examples $2r + 1 > 5$ $2r + 1$ is greater than 5.
                      $w - 6 < 9$ $w - 6$ is less than 9.

An inequality has more than one solution.

Example $2r + 1 > 5$ Solve the inequality just as you solve an equation.
                    $2r + 1 - 1 > 5 - 1$ Undo addition.
                    $2r > 4$
                    $\frac{2r}{2} > \frac{4}{2}$ Undo multiplication.
                    $r > 2$

To show the solution on a number line, draw an open circle at 2. Then draw an...

2-10 Lesson Notes

NCTM Standards: 1–4, 6, 7, 9, 13

Lesson Resources
● Study Guide Master 2-10
● Practice Master 2-10
● Enrichment Master 2-10
● Evaluation Master, Quiz B, p. 16
● Technology Master, p. 16
● Group Activity Card 2-10

Transparency 2-10 contains the 5-Minute Check and a teaching aid for this lesson.

5-Minute Check
(Over Lesson 2-9)

Find the perimeter and area of each figure.

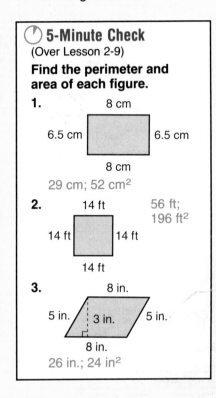

1.
8 cm
6.5 cm   6.5 cm
8 cm
29 cm; 52 cm²

2.
14 ft   56 ft; 196 ft²
14 ft   14 ft
14 ft

3.
8 in.
5 in. / 3 in. / 5 in.
8 in.
26 in.; 24 in²

1 FOCUS

Motivating the Lesson

Questioning Ask students to describe the difference between the values of *x* in these two sentences:

● *x* is the whole number 4.
● *x* is a whole number greater than 4.

In the first, 4 is the only value of *x*. In the second, *x* can be any whole number greater than 4.

77

Using the Mini-Lab To show that the solution set includes whole numbers greater than 10, have students test $x = 11$ and $x = 20$. Ask: *Suppose the symbol $<$ was used rather than $>$. Which circles on the number line would you color in?* 0, 1, 2, 3, 4, 5

More Examples

For the Example

Solve. Show the solution on a number line.

a. $2x - 9 > 1$ $x > 5$

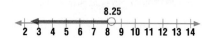

number line: 3 4 5 6 7 8 9 (open circle at 5)

b. $\frac{x}{13} + 7 < 8$ $x < 13$

number line: 9 10 11 12 13 14 15 (open circle at 13)

Checking for Understanding

Exercises 1-4 are designed to help you assess students' understanding through reading, writing, speaking, and modeling. You should work through these exercises with your students and then monitor their work on Guided Practice Exercises 5-10.

Practice Masters, p. 19

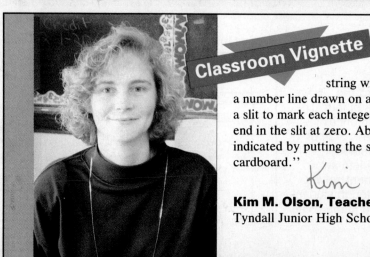

Name _____ Date _____

Practice Worksheet 2-10

Solving Inequalities

Solve each inequality. Show the solution on a number line.

1. $x + 2 > 6$ $x > 4$
2. $y + 3 < 9$ $y < 6$
3. $3 \cdot e > 12$ $e > 4$
4. $\frac{f}{4} > 2$ $f > 8$
5. $a + 12 < 18$ $a < 6$
6. $b - 2 < 6$ $b < 8$
7. $4c < 8$ $c < 2$
8. $\frac{d}{3} > 3$ $d > 9$
9. $2x + 3 > 9$ $x > 3$
10. $4y - 6 < 18$ $y < 6$
11. $\frac{t}{2} + 6 < 8$ $t < 4$

T19
Glencoe Division, Macmillan/McGraw-Hill

78

As we learned in solving equations, the guess-and-check method is not always the quickest way to solve an equation. Likewise, it is usually not the best way to solve an inequality. You can use your knowledge of solving equations to solve an inequality.

Example

Solve $4x + 17 < 50$. Show the solution on a number line.

Solve the related equation, $4x + 17 = 50$. Use your calculator. Remember to subtract to undo addition, then divide to undo multiplication.

$$4x + 17 = 50 \implies 50 \;\boxed{-}\; 17 \;\boxed{=}\; \boxed{\div}\; 4 \;\boxed{=}\; 8.25$$

The solution will either be numbers greater than 8.25 or numbers less than 8.25. Let's test a number to see which is correct.

numbers greater than 8.25	numbers less than 8.25
Try 9. $4(9) + 17 < 50$	*Try 6.* $4(6) + 17 < 50$
$36 + 17 < 50$	$24 + 17 < 50$
$53 < 50$ *false*	$41 < 50$ *true*

The numbers less than 8.25 make up the solution set. So, $x < 8.25$.

To show the solution, draw an empty circle at 8.25. Then draw a large arrow to indicate the numbers that are solutions.

The arrow shows that the numbers continue. To show numbers greater than 8.25, the arrow would go in the opposite direction.

number line: 2 3 4 5 6 7 8 9 10 11 12 13 14 (empty circle at 8.25)

Try other numbers in the set to check your solution.

Checking for Understanding

Communicating Mathematics

Read and study the lesson to anwer each question.

1. **Write** some of the numbers in the solution set if the solution set is all numbers greater than 5. {6, 7, 8, . . .}
2. **Tell** some other numbers in the solution of the inequality in Example 1. *2. Sample answers: 8, 5, 1.*
3. **Tell** how solving an equation is related to solving an inequality.
4. **Show** a number line for a solution set that is all numbers less than 8.

4. See Solutions Manual.

For number lines to Exercises 5-10, see Solutions Manual.

Guided Practice   Solve each inequality. Show the solution on a number line.

5. $6 + t > 11$ $t > 5$ 6. $a - 4 > 3$ $a > 7$ 7. $12 + d < 21$ $d < 9$

8. $3y < 15$ $y < 5$ 9. $2m - 3 > 7$ $m > 5$ 10. $\frac{p}{3} + 8 < 11$ $p < 9$

Exercises

For number lines to Exercises 11-22, see Solutions Manual.

Independent Practice   Solve each inequality. Show the solution on a number line.

11. $x - 3 < 14$ $x < 17$ 12. $y + 4 > 9$ $y > 5$ 13. $b - 9 > 6$ $b > 15$

Classroom Vignette

"To show that absolute value is distance, I use a piece of string with a knot at one end and a number line drawn on a piece of cardboard. I cut a slit to mark each integer and insert the knotted end in the slit at zero. Absolute value can be indicated by putting the string back through the cardboard."

Kim M. Olson

Kim M. Olson, Teacher
Tyndall Junior High School, Tyndall, SD

14. $2e < 16$ $e < 8$ 15. $3g < 27$ $g < 9$ 16. $\frac{s}{8} > 5$ $s > 40$

17. $2a - 5 > 9$ $a > 7$ 18. $5 + 3b < 11$ $b < 2$ 19. $5c - 8 > 7$ $c > 3$

20. $9d + 4 < 22$ $d < 2$ 21. $\frac{a}{4} + 5 > 6$ $a > 4$ 22. $\frac{c}{5} - 8 < 2$ $c < 50$

Write an inequality for each sentence. Then solve the inequality.

23. Five times a number is greater than sixty. $5x > 60$; $x > 12$

24. A number less three is less than fourteen. $x - 3 < 14$; $x < 17$

25. The sum of four times a number and five is greater than thirteen.
$4x + 5 > 13$; $x > 2$

Mixed Review   26. Use mental math to find $698 + 471$. *(Lesson 1-2)* **1,169**

27. Write an equation to represent *20 more than the number of pencils that is divided into three groups is 25.* *(Lesson 2-6)* $\frac{x}{3} + 20 = 25$

28. Solve $\frac{n}{2} + 31 = 45$. Check your solution. *(Lesson 2-7)* $n = 28$

29. **Geometry** Find the perimeter and area of a rectangle that is 2 centimeters wide and 5 centimeters long. *(Lesson 2-9)* $P = 14$ cm; $A = 10$ cm^2

Problem Solving and Applications

30. **Critical Thinking** Find the least whole number that is in the solution set of $3x - 5 > 12$.   **6**

31. **Portfolio Suggestion** Select an item from this chapter that you feel shows your best work and place it in your portfolio. Explain why you selected it. **See students' work.**

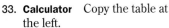

32. **Football** The graph shows which universities have had the most Heisman Trophy winners as of 1991.

32a. USC, Ohio State, Notre Dame

a. If H represents the number of Heisman trophies, name all universities that are in the solution set for $H > 3$.

b. How many winners could USC add and still have fewer than Notre Dame?   **3**

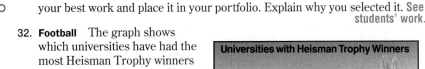

Universities with Heisman Trophy Winners

Notre Dame
Ohio State
USC
Oklahoma
Army

33. **Calculator** Copy the table at the left.

a. Use your calculator to complete the table.

b. For which values of n is each statement true?
$4^n = n^4$ $4^n < n^4$ $4^n > n^4$ $n = 2, 4$ $n = 3$ $n = 0, 1$

n	$4n$	4^n	n^4
0	0	1	0
1	4	4	1
2	8	16	16
3	12	64	81
4	16	256	256

34. **Measurement** Measure your height and the height of a classmate.

a. Write an inequality that compares these heights.   **Answers will vary.**

b. Suppose each of you grew four inches in the next year. Write an inequality that would compare your new heights.   **Answers will vary.**

Lesson 2-10 Solving Inequalities   **79**

Extending the Lesson

Combining Inequalities Find the numbers, if any, that are solutions of *both* inequalities. Use the whole numbers 0 through 10 as the replacement set.

1. $n > 5$ and $n < 9$ 6, 7, 8

2. $n < 5$ and $n > 9$ none

3. $n < 10$ and $n < 6$ 0, 1, 2, 3, 4, 5

4. $n > 4$ and $n < 4$ none

5. $n > 1$ and $n > 9$ 10

Cooperative Learning Activity

Move On **2-10**

Number of players: 2
Materials: Index cards, spinner, counters

Copy onto cards the digits 0 through 30, one digit per card. Shuffle the cards and place them face down in a pile. Label the sections of a spinner with the following inequalities: $3x - 5 > 11$, $17 + c < 25$, $4p > 16$, $\frac{s}{2} + 15 < 20$, $2f + 60 > 75$, $42 - m > 21$. On a large sheet of paper (or several sheets taped together), copy the game board below.

Both partners place a counter in the first square of a row. Decide which partner will go first. In turn, each partner selects a card and spins the spinner. You may advance one square on each turn only if the number on the card is part of the inequality's solution set.

The winner is the first partner to reach the tenth square.

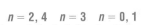

Glencoe Mathematics: Applications and Connections, Course 3

Close

Have students write a list of the similarities and differences between solving an equation and solving an inequality. Sample answer: similarities—Use inverses to undo operations and isolate the variable. differences—For an equality, a single value of the variable is the solution; for an inequality, the solution includes more than one number.

3 PRACTICE/APPLY

Assignment Guide
Maximum: 11–34
Minimum: 11–25 odd, 26–32

For **Extra Practice,** see p. 588.

Alternate Assessment

Speaking Sketch several number lines on the chalkboard, each showing the solution set of an inequality. Have students state the corresponding inequalities.

Enrichment Masters, p. 19

Name _____   Date _____

Enrichment Worksheet 2-10

A Triangle Inequality

A well known inequality in geometry relates the measures of the three sides of any triangle. Here are two different statements of this inequality.

The Triangle Inequality

The sum of the measures of any two sides of a triangle is greater than the measure of the third side.

In any $\triangle ABC$, $AB + BC > AC$.

Solve each problem.

1. Use three line segments with the measures 3, 4, and 8. Write a statement using the $<$ symbol to show that these three segments do not satisfy the triangle inequality.
$3 + 4 < 8$

2. Try to draw a triangle using the three segments in Problem 1. Describe what happens.
The two shorter lengths do not meet.

Can the three measures be used to make a triangle? Write yes or no.

3. 6 m, 2 m, 7 m   yes

4. 5 cm, 8 cm, 11 cm   yes

5. 5 in., 14 in., 7 in.   no

6. 9 cm, 5 cm, 4 cm   no

7. 10 yd, 10 yd, 10 yd   yes

8. 4 ft, 10 ft, 5 ft   no

For each triangle, describe the possible measures of side AB.

9.   10.   11.

AB is between 2 and 12, or $2 < AB < 12$. AB is between 2 and 8, or $2 < AB < 8$. AB is < 50

T19
Glencoe Division, Macmillan/McGraw-Hill

79

The Chapter Study Guide and
Review begins with a section on
Communicating Mathematics.
This includes questions that
review the new terms and
concepts that were introduced in
the chapter.

Then, the Skills and Concepts
presented in the chapter are
reviewed using a side-by-side
format. Encourage students to
refer to the Objectives and
Examples on the left as they
complete the Review Exercises
on the right.

The Chapter Study Guide and
Review ends with problems that
review Applications and Problem
Solving.

Chapter

2 Study Guide and Review

Communicating Mathematics

State whether each sentence is true or false. If false, replace the underlined word or number to make a true sentence.

1. $8 + 12$ is an <u>algebraic</u> expression. false; numerical
2. The sentence $x > 2$ is called an <u>equation</u>. false; inequality
3. In the expression $t - 9$, t is a variable. true
4. The <u>first</u> step in solving $4b + 3 = 27$ is to divide each side of the equation by 4. false; second
5. 6 is the <u>solution</u> of $x + 4 = 10$. true
6. The <u>area</u> of a rectangle is found by multiplying the width and length. true
7. Write a sentence that explains the difference between an algebraic expression and an equation. An equation contains an algebraic expression and an equal sign.

Self Assessment

Objectives and Examples	*Review Exercises*
Upon completing this chapter, you should be able to:	*Use these exercises to review and prepare for the chapter test.*

- evaluate expressions by using the order of operations *(Lesson 2-1)*
  Evaluate $3x + y$ if $x = 6$ and $y = 4$.
  $3x + y = 3(6) + 4$
  $\qquad = 18 + 4$
  $\qquad = 22$

Evaluate each expression if $a = 3$, $b = 8$, $c = 5$, and $d = 2$.

8. $cd^2 + (4b - 3)$ 49
9. $abd - 6a$ 30
10. $(2c + b) \div (ad)$ 3
11. $4a + 2c - d$ 20

- identify and solve equations *(Lesson 2-2)*
  Find the solution of $8 + m = 14$.
  Let $m = 6$. $\qquad 8 + 6 \stackrel{?}{=} 14$
  6 is the solution. $\qquad 14 = 14$ ✓

Find the solution from the replacement set for each equation.

12. $4z = 520$, $\{120, 130, 90\}$ 130
13. $x + 12 = 68$, $\{56, 46, 62\}$ 56
14. $84 - b = 47$, $\{47, 60, 37\}$ 37

- solve equations using the subtraction and addition properties of equality *(Lesson 2-3)*
  Solve $d - 24 = 18$.
  $d - 24 + 24 = 18 + 24$
  $\qquad\qquad d = 42$

Solve each equation. Check your solution.

15. $n + 50 = 80$ 30   16. $s - 12 = 61$ 73
17. $145 = a + 32$ 18. $7.2 = 3.6 + t$ 3.6
19. $r - 13 = 29$ 42   20. $1.2 = p - 2.7$ 3.9
17. 113

Objectives and Examples

- solve equations using the division and multiplication properties of equality *(Lesson 2-4)*

  Solve $3f = 42$.
  $$\frac{3f}{3} = \frac{42}{3} \quad \text{\textit{Divide to undo multipliclation.}}$$
  $$f = 14$$

- write algebraic expressions and equations *(Lesson 2-6)*

  Write an algebraic expression to represent *the sum of twice a number and 5*.

  The algebraic expression is $2n + 5$.

- solve two-step equations *(Lesson 2-7)*

  Solve $4d + 6 = 34$.
  $$4d = 28 \quad \text{\textit{Subtract 6 from each side.}}$$
  $$d = 7 \quad \text{\textit{Divide each side by 4.}}$$

- find the area and perimeter of rectangles, squares, and parallelograms *(Lesson 2-9)*

	Perimeter formula	Area formula
rectangle	$P = 2\ell + 2w$	$A = \ell w$
square	$P = 4s$	$A = s^2$
parallelogram	$P = 2a + 2b$	$A = bh$

- identify and solve inequalities *(Lesson 2-10)*

  Solve $3x - 5 > 10$.
  Solve $3x - 5 = 10$. $\rightarrow$ $x = 5$
  Test a number greater than 5.
  Try 6. $\quad 3(6) - 5 > 10$
  $$18 - 5 > 10$$
  $$13 > 10 \quad \textit{true}$$
  The solution to $3x - 5 > 10$ is all numbers greater than 5.

Review Exercises

Solve each equation. Check your solution.

21. $2.3m = 11.5$ **5**   22. $\frac{s}{6} = 45$ **270**

23. $\frac{r}{0.4} = 6.2$ **2.48**   24. $4 = \frac{d}{26}$ **104**

25. $72 = 12i$ **6**   26. $8.68 = 0.62j$ **14**

Write each phrase as an algebraic expression or equation.

27. eight less a number is 31 $8 - y = 31$

28. the product of 7 and x $7x$

29. the sum of 8 and six times u $8 + 6u$

Solve each equation. Check your solution.

30. $6f - 17 = 37$ **9**   31. $\frac{h}{5} + 20 = 31$ **55**

32. $18 = \frac{t}{2} - 6$ **48**   33. $\frac{m}{8} - 12 = 14$ **208**

34. $2k + 15 = 83$ **34**   35. $30 = 9 + 3c$ **7**

Find the perimeter and area of each figure.

36. 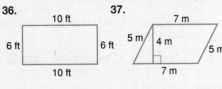   37.

$P = 32$ ft $P = 24$ m
$A = 60$ ft^2 $A = 28$ m^2

Solve each inequality. Show the solution on a number line.

38. $2r - 4 < 10$ $r < 7$

39. $4g > 24$ $g > 6$

40. $6w + 5 < 29$ $w < 4$

41. $\frac{a}{3} + 7 > 8$ $a > 3$

See margin for number lines.

Additional Answers

38.
```
 1  2  3  4  5  6  7  8
```

39.
```
 1  2  3  4  5  6  7  8
```

40.
```
 1  2  3  4  5  6  7  8
```

41.
```
 1  2  3  4  5  6  7  8
```

Evaluation Masters, pp. 14–15

Name _____ Date _____

Form 2A _____ *Chapter 2 Test*

1. Solve $7t = 133$ if the replacement set is {15, 17, 19, 21}.   **1.** ___19___

Evaluate each expression.

2. $16 \cdot 2 + 4(3 - 1)^2$ **2.** ___48___
3. $[3^4 - (25 \div 5)] + 1^2$ **3.** ___77___
4. $\frac{35 - 7}{4} + 54 \div 9$ **4.** ___13___
5. $48 \div 4 \cdot 2 - 4 + 25$ **5.** ___45___

Solve each equation.

6. $r + 18 = 41$ **6.** ___23___
7. $12s - 7 = 41$
8. $9.8 = 0.7k$ **7.** ___4___
9. $\$7.25 = \$2.95 + c$
10. $\frac{h}{11} - 3 = 2$ **8.** ___14___
11. $5 = \frac{v}{2.5}$ **9.** ___\$4.30___
12. $3x + 9 = 54$ **10.** ___55___
13. $\frac{k}{3} + 6 = 10$ **11.** ___12.5___

Write each phrase or sentence as an algebraic expression or equation.   **12.** ___15___

14. 6 decreased by three times a number   **13.** ___12___
15. The quotient of x and 9 increased by 3 is 6.   **14.** ___6 − 3n___
16. Find the value of the expression $x^2 - y^2$ if $x = 5$ and $y = 2$.   **15.** ___$\frac{x}{9} + 3 = 6$___

Find the perimeter and area of each figure.   **16.** ___21___

17.   18.   **17.** ___10.2 cm; 5.94 cm²___
(3.3 cm, 1.8 cm)   (14 in., 8 in., 6 in., 8 in.)   **18.** ___44 in.; 84 in.²___

19. Two more than twice the number of turkeys is 8. How many turkeys are there?   **19.** ___3 turkeys___

Solve each inequality. Show the solution on a number line.

20. $p - 3 < 1$ **20.** (number line 0 1 2 3 4 5 6)
21. $2h - 6 > 6$ **21.** (number line 2 3 4 5 6 7 8)
22. $\frac{c}{5} + 1 > 1$ **22.** (number line 0 1 2 3 4 5 6)
23. $9l > 27$ **23.** (number line 0 1 2 3 4 5 6)

Solve each problem.

24. Carol bought an audio tape cassette at a one-fourth off sale. The cost to Carol was $9. What was the original price of the cassette?   **24.** ___$12___
25. A number is decreased by 11, and the result is multiplied by 2. The final answer is 20. What is the number?   **25.** ___21___

BONUS Solve $1.2f - 1.5 < 2.1$.   ___f < 3___

14
Glencoe Division, Macmillan/McGraw-Hill

Name _____ Date _____

Form 2B _____ *Chapter 2 Test*

Evaluate each expression.   **1.** ___47___

1. $2(4 - 2)^2 + 13 \cdot 3$ **2.** ___44___
2. $[2^5 - (24 \div 6)] + 4^2$
3. $63 \div 7 + \frac{29 - 4}{5}$ **3.** ___14___
4. $16 \cdot 4 \div 8 - 4 + 17$ **4.** ___21___
5. Solve $8s = 176$ if the replacement set is {20, 21, 22, 23}.   **5.** ___22___

Solve each equation.

6. $7r - 8 = 6$ **6.** ___2___
7. $t + 36 = 72$
8. $0.4u = 8.8$ **7.** ___36___
9. $\$4.75 + k = \$8.45$
10. $6 = \frac{m}{5.5}$ **8.** ___22___
11. $3 = \frac{l}{6} - 3$ **9.** ___\$3.70___
12. $8c + 5 = 37$ **10.** ___33___
13. $5 + \frac{k}{2} = 10$ **11.** ___36___

Write each phrase or sentence as an algebraic expression or equation.   **12.** ___4___

14. The product of 4 and twice a number   **13.** ___10___
15. The sum of p and 5 decreased by 1 is 6.   **14.** ___4 · 2n or 8n___
16. Find the value of the expression $2ab + b^2c$ if $a = 2$, $b = 4$, and $c = 3$.   **15.** ___(p + 5) − 1 = 6___

Find the perimeter and area of each figure.   **16.** ___64___

17.   18.   **17.** ___8.6 cm; 1.92 cm²___
(2.4 cm, 1.9 cm, 0.8 cm)   (1 in., 0.5 in.)   **18.** ___3 in.; 0.5 in.²___

19. The quotient of the number of apples and 4 is 3. How many apples are there?   **19.** ___12 apples___

Solve each inequality. Show the solution on a number line.

20. $2c - 3 > 7$ **20.** (number line 2 3 4 5 6 7 8)
21. $m + 9 < 13$ **21.** (number line 0 1 2 3 4 5 6)
22. $5d > 20$ **22.** (number line 1 2 3 4 5 6 7 8)
23. $\frac{n}{8} + 6 > 6$ **23.** (number line 0 1 2 3 4 5 6 7)

Solve each problem.

24. Ramon baked brownies and gave $\frac{3}{4}$ of them to Lisa. Lisa gave back 6 brownies. Ramon ended up with 21 brownies. How many did he bake originally?   **24.** ___60 brownies___
25. The product of 5 and a number minus 6 is 2 less than the difference of 25 and 4. What is the number?   **25.** ___5___

BONUS Solve $3.1 + \frac{t}{2.3} > 6$.   ___t > 6.67___

15
Glencoe Division, Macmillan/McGraw-Hill

Applications and Problem Solving   42. cup, $5; bowl, $9

42. A cup, two saucers, and three bowls cost $38. Two bowls cost as much as one saucer and three cups. If a saucer costs $3, how much is each bowl and cup? *(Lesson 2-5)*

43. A substitute taxi driver earns time and a half for overtime driving. What is her regular rate and her overtime rate if she earns $88 for a 10-hour shift, 2 hours of which were overtime? *(Lesson 2-8)* **$8, $12**

44. **Shopping** The Spreindale Produce Market charges $1.99 a pound for red grapes. Mrs. Miller paid $5.97 for a bag of red grapes. How many pounds of grapes did she buy? *(Lesson 2-4)* **3 pounds**

45. Kimiko has four less than twice the number of necklaces that Vicki has. Kimiko has six necklaces. How many necklaces does Vicki have? *(Lesson 2-7)* **5 necklaces**

46. **Exercise** Eric lives on a block that is a square. Each side of the block is 500 feet long. If Eric jogs around the block four times, how many feet has he jogged? *(Lesson 2-9)* **8,000 feet**

Curriculum Connection Projects

- **Art** Find the value of the ten most expensive paintings in the world. Find the current exchange rates of the U.S. dollar. Write an equation that converts the value of each painting into the currency of the artist's country.

- **Consumer Awareness** Find your state's tax on a gallon of gasoline. Write an equation to find the cost to fill a car's tank as the cost per gallon changes, plus the gas tax.

- **Meteorology** A *degree day* is the difference between 64°F and the day's average temperature. Write an expression to find the degree days, if you are given the average temperatures. Find yesterday's degree day.

Read More About It

D'Ignazio, Fred. *Invent Your Own Computer Games.*
Kaufmann, John. *Fly It.*
Mitsumasa, Anno. *Socrates and the Three Little Pigs.*

82   **Chapter 2** Study Guide and Review

2 Test

1. Solve $8x = 112$ if the replacement set is {20, 16, 14, 11}. **14**

Evaluate each expression.

2. $3(6 - 4)^2 + 13 \cdot 5$ **77**

3. $[6^2 - (24 \div 8)] - 20$ **13**

4. $\dfrac{47 + 3}{5} + 48 \div 6$ **18**

Solve each equation. Check your solution.

5. $k - 20 = 55$ **75**

6. $0.4m = 9.6$ **24**

7. $\dfrac{x}{2} + 39 = 49$ **20**

8. $\$3.50 = \$1.90 + b$ **$1.60**

9. $\dfrac{n}{1.5} = 6$ **9**

10. $11 = \dfrac{a}{4} - 9$ **80**

11. Find the value of d if $d = 6.34 - 2.96$. **3.38**

12. Find the value of g if $30 + g = 61$. **31**

13. A rectangle is 14 meters wide. Find its perimeter if its length is half its width. **42 meters**

Write each phrase or sentence as an algebraic expression or equation.

14. the quotient of 6 and y, decreased by 12 $\dfrac{6}{y} - 12$

15. Eight more than five times the number of cats is 48. $8 + 5c = 48$

16. Find the value of the expression $\dfrac{xy}{z} + x^2 z$ if $x = 3, y = 6$, and $z = 9$. **83**

Find the perimeter and area of each figure.

17.
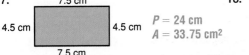
$P = 24$ cm
$A = 33.75$ cm^2

18.
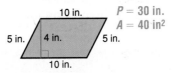
$P = 30$ in.
$A = 40$ in^2

19. Five less than three times the number of hamburgers is 31. How many hamburgers are there? **12 hamburgers**

See Solutions Manual for number lines.

Solve each inequality. Show the solution on a number line.

20. $x + 4 > 16$ $x > 12$

21. $4c - 5 < 7$ $c < 3$

22. $\dfrac{z}{3} + 8 < 10$ $z < 6$

23. $3f > 45$ $f > 15$

24. Rita has $3,193 in her savings account. She deposits $75. How much will she have in her account after the deposit? **$3,268**

25. Phil bought a CD at a one-third-off sale. The cost to Phil was $9.90. What was the original price of the CD? **$14.85**

Bonus Solve $4[(7 - 3) + 3x] = \dfrac{156}{3}$ **3**

Using the Chapter Test

This page may be used as a chapter test or another chapter review.

Evaluation Masters, pp. 10–11

Name _____ Date _____

Form 1A _____ *Chapter 2 Test*

Evaluate each expression.

1. $5^2 + 2 \cdot 3 - (4 + 2)$
 A. 75 B. 24 C. 25 D. 10 **1. C**

2. $(4^3 + 6) \div 14$
 A. 5 B. 4 C. 1 D. $1\frac{2}{7}$ **2. A**

3. $20 - 3[7 - (16 - 10)]$
 A. 23 B. 6 C. 16 D. 17 **3. D**

4. Evaluate $a^2 - b^2 + c^2 - \frac{a}{b}$ if $a = 3, b = 1$, and $c = 2$.
 A. 1 B. 11 C. 15 D. 9 **4. D**

Find the solution for each equation from the given replacement set.

5. $6k = 78$, {11, 12, 13, 14}
 A. 13 B. 14 C. 11 D. 12 **5. A**

6. $d + \$1.50 = \$3.25$, {$1.00, $1.25, $1.50, $1.75}
 A. $1.25 B. $1.75 C. $1.00 D. $1.50 **6. B**

Solve each equation.

7. $4e = 100$
 A. 400 B. 96 C. 25 D. 40 **7. C**

8. $\$6.25 - \$2.48 = u$
 A. $2.23 B. $2.77 C. $4.23 D. $3.77 **8. D**

9. $13 + z = 21$
 A. 8 B. 34 C. 7 D. 273 **9. A**

10. $36 = g - 9$
 A. 45 B. 27 C. 4 D. 324 **10. A**

11. $18 = \frac{x}{3}$
 A. 3 B. 54 C. 15 D. 6 **11. B**

12. $0.6 + 3p = 1.8$
 A. 40 B. 0.8 C. 0.4 D. 4 **12. C**

13. $\frac{n}{4} + 5 = 8$
 A. 27 B. 52 C. 12 D. 7 **13. C**

14. $42 = 5r + 17$
 A. $9\frac{4}{5}$ B. 125 C. 10 D. 5 **14. D**

10
Glencoe Division, Macmillan/McGraw-Hill

Name _____ Date _____

Chapter 2 Test, Form 1A (continued)

Write each phrase or sentence as an algebraic expression or equation.

15. the product of h and 2 increased by their sum
 A. $2h + 2$ B. $2h + 2 - h$ C. $2h - (h + 2)$ D. $2h + 2 + h$ **15. D**

16. Five less than the number of adults times two is 20.
 A. $(a + 5)2 = 20$ B. $(5 - a)2 = 20$ C. $(a - 5)2 = 20$ D. $(a - 5)20 = 2$ **16. C**

Solve each inequality.

17. $v + 5 > 12$
 A. $v < 7$ B. $v > 17$ C. $v < 17$ D. $v > 7$ **17. D**

18. $4t < 20$
 A. $t < 16$ B. $t > 80$ C. $t < 5$ D. $t > 16$ **18. C**

19. $2a - 3 > 5$
 A. $a > 4$ B. $a < 1$ C. $a > 1$ D. $2a < 8$ **19. A**

20. $\frac{m}{2} - 1 < 6$
 A. $m > 10$ B. $m < 10$ C. $m < 14$ D. $m > 14$ **20. C**

21. $6 + 3i > 15$
 A. $i > 3$ B. $i > 7$ C. $i < 7$ D. $i < 3$ **21. A**

22. Find the perimeter of the figure.
 A. 1.5 cm B. 6.2 cm C. 21 cm D. 6 cm **22. B**

23. Find the area of the figure.
 A. 24 m^2 B. 54 m^2 C. 30 m^2 D. 36 m^2 **23. D**

24. Pete says, "I am thinking of a number. If I decrease it by 12 and then add 7, I get 4." What is Pete's number?
 A. 1 B. 23 C. 9 D. 15 **24. C**

25. Maria has $565 in her savings account. She withdraws $90. How much will she have in her account after the withdrawal?
 A. $47.50 B. $475 C. $465 D. $46.50 **25. B**

BONUS Solve $2[2x - 3(2 - 1)] = 514$.
 A. 136 B. 0 C. 127 D. 130 **D**

11
Glencoe Division, Macmillan/McGraw-Hill

Chapter

3 Integers

Previewing the Chapter

In this chapter, students extend their knowledge of numbers to those that are less than zero. Integers are defined and methods for comparing and ordering them are taught. A thorough treatment of addition, subtraction, multiplication, and division of integers follows. Students learn to solve equations involving integers and to use integers on the coordinate axes. Additional applications include temperature, elevation, and stock market gains and losses. In the **problem-solving strategy** lesson, students learn to classify information.

Lesson	Lesson Objectives	NCTM Standards	State/Local Objectives
3-1	Graph integers on a number line and find absolute value.	1–7, 10, 13	
3-2	Compare and order integers.	1–7, 10	
3-3	Add integers.	1–7, 9, 10, 13	
3-4	Add more than two integers.	1–4, 6, 7, 9, 13	
3-5	Subtract integers.	1–7, 9, 13	
3-6	Multiply integers.	1–7, 9	
3-7	Divide integers.	1–7, 9, 12	
3-8	Solve problems by identifying important information.	1–5, 7, 12	
3-9A	Solve equations by using models.	1–5, 7, 9	
3-9	Solve equations with integer solutions.	1–7, 9	
3-10	Graph points on a coordinate plane.	1–5, 7, 9, 12, 13	

Organizing the Chapter

A complete, 1-page lesson plan is provided for each lesson in the Lesson Plans Masters Booklet.

LESSON PLANNING GUIDE

Lesson	Materials/ Manipulatives	Extra Practice (Student Edition)	Study Guide	Practice	Enrichment	Evaluation	Technology	Lab Manual	Multicultural Activities	Application and Interdisciplinary Activities	Transparencies	Group Activity Cards
			Blackline Masters Booklets									
3-1		p. 588	p. 20	p. 20	p. 20				p. 3		3-1	3-1
3-2		p. 588	p. 21	p. 21	p. 21						3-2	3-2
3-3	counters, mats	p. 589	p. 22	p. 22	p. 22			p. 44			3-3	3-3
3-4	calculator	p. 589	p. 23	p. 23	p. 23						3-4	3-4
3-5	counters, mats, calculator, encyclopedia	p. 589	p. 24	p. 24	p. 24	Quiz A, p. 25		p. 45		p. 17	3-5	3-5
3-6	counters, mats	p. 590	p. 25	p. 25	p. 25						3-6	3-6
3-7	counters, calculator	p. 590	p. 26	p. 26	p. 26		p. 3				3-7	3-7
3-8			p. 27	p. 27	p. 27						3-8	3-8
3-9A	counters, cups, mats							p. 46				
3-9	calculator, counters, cups, mats	p. 590	p. 28	p. 28	p. 28		p. 17				3-9	3-9
3-10		p. 591	p. 29	p. 29	p. 29	Quiz B, p. 25				p. 3	3-10	3-10
Study Guide and Review	graph paper		Multiple Choice Test, Forms 1A and 1B, pp. 19–22 Free Response Test, Forms 2A and 2B, pp. 23–24 Cumulative Review, p. 26 (free response)									
Test			Cumulative Test, p. 27 (multiple choice)									

Pacing Guide: Option I (Chapters 1–12) - 14 days; Option II (Chapters 1–13) - 13 days; Option III (Chapters 1–14) - 12 days
You may wish to refer to the complete **Course Planning Guides** on page T25.

OTHER CHAPTER RESOURCES

Student Edition
Chapter Opener, pp. 84–85
Mid-Chapter Review, p. 101
Save Planet Earth, p. 105
Portfolio Suggestion, p. 119

 Manipulatives
Overhead Manipulative Resources
Middle School Mathematics Manipulative Kit

 Software/Technology
Interactive Mathematics Tools (Macintosh)
Test and Review Generator (IBM, Apple, Macintosh)
Teacher's Guide for Software Resources

Other Supplements
Transparency 3-0
Performance Assessment, pp. 5–6
Glencoe Mathematics Professional Series Lesson Plans, pp. 25–35

INTERDISCIPLINARY BULLETIN BOARD

Anthropology Connection

Objective Construct a timeline of important dates, both B.C. and A.D., in Native American history.

How To Use It Have students research ten achievements of Native Americans and when they were accomplished. At least half should be B.C. Have students construct a timeline displaying the achievements and identifying the dates. Note similarities between B.C. and A.D. dates on the timeline and negative and positive integers on a number line.

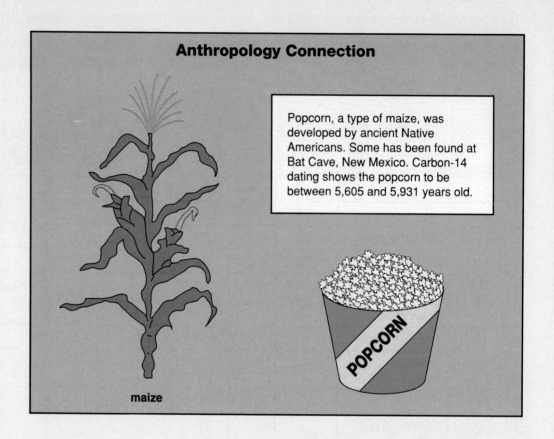

Anthropology Connection

Popcorn, a type of maize, was developed by ancient Native Americans. Some has been found at Bat Cave, New Mexico. Carbon-14 dating shows the popcorn to be between 5,605 and 5,931 years old.

maize

APPLICATIONS AND CONNECTIONS

Applications	Lesson	Example	Exercise
Data Analysis	3-1		28
Transportation	3-2		26
Sales	3-3		40
Marketing	3-3		41
Science	3-4		36
Geography	3-4		38
Accounting	3-5	3	
Geography	3-5		46
Research	3-5		47
Business	3-5		49
Health	3-6		46
Credit Cards	3-6		47
Banking	3-7		43
Business	3-7		44
Weather	3-7		46
Personal Finance	3-9	4	
Football	3-9		33
Marketing	3-9		35
Video Entertainment	3-10		41
Connections			
Number Sense	3-1		26
Computer	3-2		28
Geometry	3-10		40

TEAM ACTIVITIES

Multicultural Experiences

Outside Field Trips Take trips that illustrate the use of integers in everyday life. At a football game, students can chart positive and negative movement of the football using integers.

Visit a local weather station for students to learn about record temperatures and the wind-chill factor.

In-Class Speakers Ask a stock broker to discuss gains and losses in the stock market.

An auto mechanic can discuss temperature ranges of motor oils and antifreeze.

SUPPLEMENTARY BLACKLINE MASTER BOOKLETS

Some of the blackline masters for enhancing this chapter are shown below.

Application and Interdisciplinary Activity Masters, pp. 3, 17

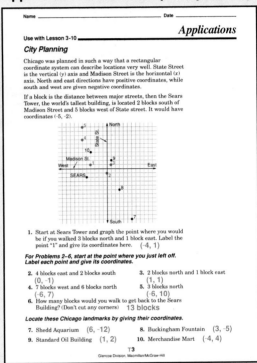

Name _____ Date _____

Applications

Use with Lesson 3-10 _____

City Planning

Chicago was planned in such a way that a rectangular coordinate system can describe locations very well. State Street is the vertical (y) axis and Madison Street is the horizontal (x) axis. North and east directions have positive coordinates, while south and west are given negative coordinates.

If a block is the distance between major streets, then the Sears Tower, the world's tallest building, is located 2 blocks south of Madison Street and 5 blocks west of State street. It would have coordinates (-5, -2).

1. Start at Sears Tower and graph the point where you would be if you walked 3 blocks north and 1 block east. Label the point "1" and give its coordinates here. (-4, 1)

For Problems 2–6, start at the point where you just left off. Label each point and give its coordinates.

2. 4 blocks east and 2 blocks south (0, -1)
3. 2 blocks north and 1 block east (1, 1)
4. 7 blocks west and 6 blocks north (-6, 7)
5. 3 blocks north (-6, 10)
6. How many blocks would you walk to get back to the Sears Building? (Don't cut any corners) 13 blocks

Locate these Chicago landmarks by giving their coordinates.

7. Shedd Aquarium (6, -12)
8. Buckingham Fountain (3, -5)
9. Standard Oil Building (1, 2)
10. Merchandise Mart (-4, 4)

T3
Glencoe Division, Macmillan/McGraw-Hill

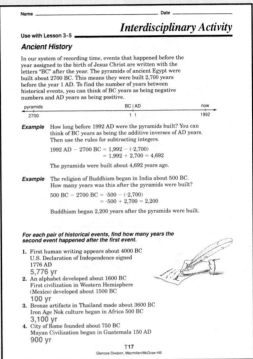

Name _____ Date _____

Interdisciplinary Activity

Use with Lesson 3-5 _____

Ancient History

In our system of recording time, events that happened before the year assigned to the birth of Jesus Christ are written with the letters "BC" after the year. The pyramids of ancient Egypt were built about 2700 BC. This means they were built 2,700 years before the year 1 AD. To find the number of years between historical events, you can think of BC years as being negative numbers and AD years as being positive.

pyramids	BC	AD	now
2700		1 1	1992

Example How long before 1992 AD were the pyramids built? You can think of BC years as being the additive inverses of AD years. Then use the rules for subtracting integers.

1992 AD − 2700 BC = 1,992 − (-2,700)
= 1,992 + 2,700 = 4,692

The pyramids were built about 4,692 years ago.

Example The religion of Buddhism began in India about 500 BC. How many years was this after the pyramids were built?

500 BC − 2700 BC = -500 − (-2,700)
= -500 + 2,700 = 2,200

Buddhism began 2,200 years after the pyramids were built.

For each pair of historical events, find how many years the second event happened after the first event.

1. First human writing appears about 4000 BC
   U.S. Declaration of Independence signed 1776 AD
   5,776 yr
2. An alphabet developed about 1600 BC
   First civilization in Western Hemisphere (Mexico) developed about 1500 BC
   100 yr
3. Bronze artifacts in Thailand made about 3600 BC
   Iron Age Nok culture began in Africa 500 BC
   3,100 yr
4. City of Rome founded about 750 BC
   Mayan Civilization began in Guatemala 150 AD
   900 yr

T17
Glencoe Division, Macmillan/McGraw-Hill

Multicultural Activity Masters, p. 3

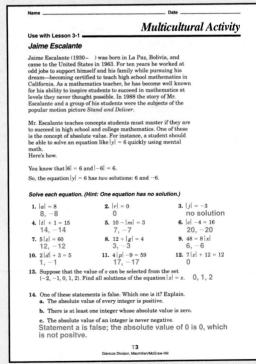

Name _____ Date _____

Multicultural Activity

Use with Lesson 3-1 _____

Jaime Escalante

Jaime Escalante (1930–) was born in La Paz, Bolivia, and came to the United States in 1963. For ten years he worked at odd jobs to support himself and his family while pursuing his dream—becoming certified to teach high school mathematics in California. As a mathematics teacher, he has become well known for his ability to inspire students to succeed in mathematics at levels they never thought possible. In 1988 the story of Mr. Escalante and a group of his students were the subjects of the popular motion picture *Stand and Deliver*.

Mr. Escalante teaches concepts students must master if they are to succeed in high school and college mathematics. One of these is the concept of absolute value. For instance, a student should be able to solve an equation like $|y| = 6$ quickly using mental math.
Here's how.

You know that $|6| = 6$ and $|-6| = 6$.

So, the equation $|y| = 6$ has *two* solutions: 6 and −6.

Solve each equation. (Hint: One equation has no solution.)

1. $|a| = 8$ 8, −8
2. $|r| = 0$ 0
3. $|j| = -3$ no solution
4. $|t| + 1 = 15$ 14, −14
5. $10 − |m| = 3$ 7, −7
6. $|c| − 4 = 16$ 20, −20
7. $5|z| = 60$ 12, −12
8. $12 ÷ |g| = 4$ 3, −3
9. $48 = 8|x|$ 6, −6
10. $2|d| + 3 = 5$ 1, −1
11. $4|p| − 9 = 59$ 17, −17
12. $7|z| + 12 = 12$ 0

13. Suppose that the value of x can be selected from the set {-2, −1, 0, 1, 2}. Find all solutions of the equation $|x| = x$. 0, 1, 2

14. One of these statements is false. Which one is it? Explain.
   a. The absolute value of every integer is positive.
   b. There is at least one integer whose absolute value is zero.
   c. The absolute value of an integer is never negative.
   Statement a is false; the absolute value of 0 is 0, which is not positive.

T3
Glencoe Division, Macmillan/McGraw-Hill

Technology Masters, p. 3

Name _____ Date _____

Calculator Activity

Use with Lesson 3-7 _____

Solving Equations

A calculator may be helpful in solving equations with integers.

Example Solve $k = \frac{850}{-10}$.

850 ÷ 10 +/- = -85
The solution is -85.

Example Solve $m = (-8) − (-12)$.

8 +/- − 12 +/- = 4
The solution is 4.

Solve each equation.

1. $k = -82 − 18$ -100
2. $\frac{48}{-4} = y$ -12
3. $-102 − (-52) = z$ -50
4. $x = (-8)(-3)(42)$ 1,008
5. $y = (-3) + (-20) + 84$ 61
6. $s = (-8)(9)(5)^2$ -1,800
7. $g = -8(14)(-3)^2$ -1,008
8. $3(-4)^2(-5) = w$ -240
9. $g = -8(14) − 10(-2)$ -92
10. $\frac{-7(2^4)}{-4} = v$ 28

Evaluate each expression if $a = -3$, $b = 5$, and $c = -8$.

11. $a − 4b − 3c$ 1
12. $(7b)(4c) + 10$ -1,110
13. $-3a^2 + 2b$ -17
14. $\frac{c^2 − b^2}{-3}$ -13
15. $a^3 + b^3 + c^3$ -414
16. $6a − 10h + 8c$ -132

17. **CHALLENGE** Evaluate $\frac{-18 − 9 + 27 − 3^3 + 45}{3 − 14 + 8}$ -6

T3
Glencoe Division, Macmillan/McGraw-Hill

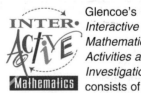

This two-page introduction to the chapter provides a visual, relevant way to engage students in the mathematics of the chapter. Questions are included that help students see the need to learn the mathematics in the chapter. Data in charts and graphs provide statistical information that students can analyze and interpret at this point as well as later in the chapter. The Chapter Project provides an activity that applies the mathematics of the chapter.

MAKING MATHEMATICS RELEVANT

Spotlight on the Telephone

The country with the most telephones per capita is Monaco (0.62 phones per person). The country with the least is Bhutan (0.00148 phones per person).

On August 18, 1975, a British man received a telephone bill for $4,386,800,000, the largest incorrect bill in history. Billing errors are rare, but point up the importance of understanding accounting procedures and analyzing monthly bills.

Ask the following question.

- *The rate for a certain telephone call is $0.63 for the first minute and $0.28 for each additional minute. What would be the cost of an 8-minute call?* $2.59

Using the Timeline

Ask the following questions.

- *In what year was the centennial (100th anniversary) of the patenting of the telephone celebrated?* 1976

- *How old were you when the first picture phone became available to the public?* The answer is the student's age in 1992.

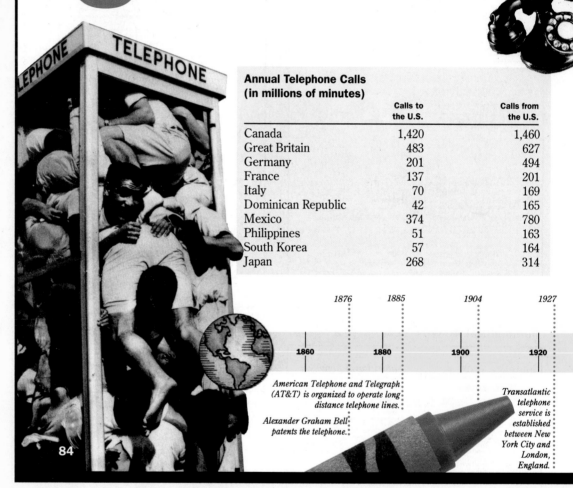

Chapter 3

Integers

Spotlight on the Telephone

Have You Ever Wondered ...

- How many telephone calls are made by all the people in the United States each day?

- How much time people in the United States spend on the telephone with people in other countries?

Annual Telephone Calls (in millions of minutes)		
	Calls to the U.S.	Calls from the U.S.
Canada	1,420	1,460
Great Britain	483	627
Germany	201	494
France	137	201
Italy	70	169
Dominican Republic	42	165
Mexico	374	780
Philippines	51	163
South Korea	57	164
Japan	268	314

1876   1885   1904   1927

1860   1880   1900   1920

American Telephone and Telegraph (AT&T) is organized to operate long distance telephone lines.

Alexander Graham Bell patents the telephone.

Transatlantic telephone service is established between New York City and London, England.

84

"Have You Ever Wondered?" Answers

- An average of 1,700 million calls were made each day in 1990.
- Over 4,537 million minutes are spent on the telephone each year with people in other countries.

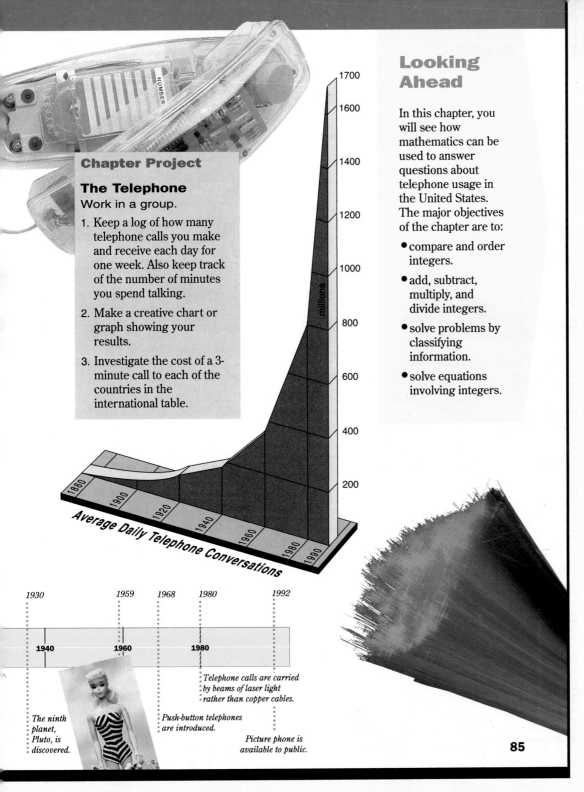

Looking Ahead

In this chapter, you will see how mathematics can be used to answer questions about telephone usage in the United States. The major objectives of the chapter are to:

- compare and order integers.
- add, subtract, multiply, and divide integers.
- solve problems by classifying information.
- solve equations involving integers.

millions

Average Daily Telephone Conversations

1880 1900 1920 1940 1960 1980 1990

1930   1959   1968   1980   1992

1940   **1960**   **1980**

The ninth planet, Pluto, is discovered.

Push-button telephones are introduced.

Telephone calls are carried by beams of laser light rather than copper cables.

Picture phone is available to public.

DATA ANALYSIS
Have students study the table of annual telephone calls. Ask the following questions.

- *Are more calls made out of the United States or into the United States?* out of the United States

- *What is the meaning of the number 70 beside Italy?* Each year 70 million minutes of telephone calls are made from Italy to the United States.

Data Search
A question related to these data is provided in Lesson 3-3, page 94, Exercise 43.

CHAPTER PROJECT

Help students prepare a chart in which they can log their telephone data. Encourage them to design creative presentations of data. One possibility is a map to show destinations and origins of the calls. If telephone bills are unavailable to the students, have them prepare a mock telephone bill. Explain that students can estimate their monthly or annual cost by multiplying their daily average by the number of days in a month or a year. With these numbers, students can calculate their portion of the telephone bill and of the nationwide data.

Allow one week to complete the project.

85

Chapter Opener Transparency

Transparency 3-0 is available in the Transparency Package. It provides another full-color, motivating activity that you can use to capture students' interest.

NCTM Standards: 1–7, 13

Lesson Resources
- Study Guide Master 3-1
- Enrichment Master 3-1
- Practice Master 3-1
- Multicultural Activity, p. 3
- Group Activity Card 3-1

 Transparency 3-1 contains the 5-Minute Check and a teaching aid for this lesson.

🕐 5-Minute Check
(Over Chapter 2)

1. Evaluate $3a^2 - (b - c)$ if $a = 2$, $b = 5$, and $c = 3$.
   10

Solve each equation or inequality.

2. $3.7p = 22.2$ 6

3. $\frac{p}{6} + 13 = 21$ 48

4. $2.4x - 4.8 < 8.4$
   $x < 5.5$

5. Find the perimeter and area of the figure.
   56 cm; 180 cm²

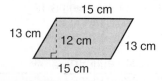

---

1 FOCUS

Motivating the Lesson

Activity   Draw a thermometer on the chalkboard—draw it long enough to record negative temperatures. Label 0°F and 80°F. Have students read the opening paragraph of the lesson. Then ask a volunteer to label −80°F on the thermometer.

2 TEACH

Using Calculators   Have students find the 🔲⁺⁄₋ key on their calculators. Demonstrate that pressing the key changes the sign of the displayed number.

Compare the ⁺⁄₋ key with the −️ key, which performs subtraction.

3-1 Integers and Absolute Value

Objective
Graph integers on a number line and find absolute value.

Words to Learn
integer
graph
coordinate
absolute value

−4 is read "negative 4." +2 or 2 is read "positive 2."

The coldest temperature recorded in the United States occurred on January 23, 1971. The Prospect Creek Camp weather station in Alaska reported a temperature of −80° F.

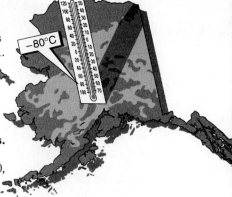

Negative numbers, like −80, are part of the set of **integers.** The set of integers can be written as {..., −4, −3, −2, −1, 0, +1, +2, +3, +4, ...}.

The ..., called ellipses, mean that the set continues without end, following the same pattern.

The positive integers are often written without the + sign. So, +2 and 2 are the same.

Integers can be graphed on a number line. On the number line, 0 is considered the starting point with the positive numbers to the right and the negative numbers to the left. Zero is neither negative nor positive.

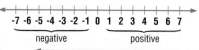

The arrows, like ..., show that the numbers continue without end.

To **graph** an integer, you locate the number and draw a dot at that point on the line. Letters are sometimes used to name points on a number line. The integer that corresponds to the letter is called the **coordinate** of the point.

Example 1

Name the coordinates of each point graphed on the number line.

The coordinate of H is −5.   The coordinate of P is 4.
The coordinate of Y is −2.   The coordinate of G is −1.

OPTIONS

Reteaching Activity

Using Cooperative Groups
Working in pairs, students take turns rolling a number cube, tossing a coin, and graphing the number (positive for heads, negative for tails) on a number line labeled from −6 to 6. If a number is already graphed, 1 point is scored. When all the numbers are graphed, the player with the low score wins.

Study Guide Masters, p. 20

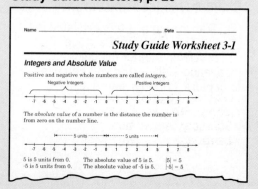

Study Guide Worksheet 3-1

Integers and Absolute Value

Positive and negative whole numbers are called *integers.*

The *absolute value* of a number is the distance the number is from zero on the number line.

5 is 5 units from 0.   The absolute value of 5 is 5. $|5| = 5$
-5 is 5 units from 0.   The absolute value of -5 is 5. $|-5| = 5$

Example 2

Graph points *M, A, T,* and *H* on a number line if *M* has coordinate 8, *A* has coordinate –3, *T* has coordinate –7, and *H* has coordinate 3.

Find each number. Draw a dot there. Write the letter above the dot.

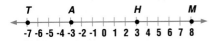

The absolute value of 0 is 0.

The **absolute value** of a number is the distance it is from 0 on the number line. We write *the absolute value of –3* as |–3|. Let's find |–3|.

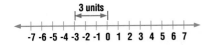

–3 is 3 units from 0. So, |–3| = 3.

Example 3

Find |6| and |–6|.

First locate each number on a number line.
Then count how many units each number is from 0.

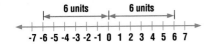

6 is 6 units from 0. So, |6| = 6.
–6 is 6 units from 0. So, |–6| = 6.

Checking for Understanding

Communicating Mathematics

Read and study the lesson to answer each question.   Sample answer: temperature.

1. **Tell** some situations in the real world where negative integers are used.

2. **Write** how you would graph –12. See margin.

3. |–4| = 4

3. **Write** an equation using absolute value that describes the value shown on the number line.

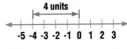

4. **Draw** a number line. Graph two points on it so that the coordinates of both points have an absolute value of 4. See margin.

Team Teaching

Inform the other teachers on your team that your classes are studying integers. Suggestions for curriculum integration are:

Health: weight gain and loss
Social Studies: elevation
Science: temperature
Language Arts: antonyms

Additional Answers

2. Draw a number line. Locate –12. Draw a dot there.

4.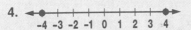

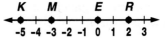
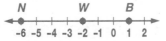
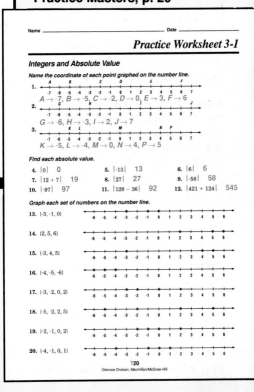

Watch for students who confuse the absolute value of an integer with its opposite.

$|-8| = 8; |8| = -8$

Prevent by describing absolute value as a distance that is always positive.

Close

Ask this question: *What are the coordinates of two points whose absolute values are 4? Describe their locations on the number line.* −4 and 4; 4 units left and 4 units right of 0

3 PRACTICE/APPLY

Assignment Guide
Maximum: 14–28
Minimum: 14–28

For **Extra Practice,** see p. 588.

Alternate Assessment

Modeling Draw a thermometer on the chalkboard. Label −10°F, 0°F, and 10°F. Name several temperatures and have students label them on the thermometer.

Enrichment Masters, p. 20

Name _____ Date _____

Enrichment Worksheet 3-1

Absolute Error

The *absolute error* of a measurement is defined to be one-half the smallest unit used in making the measurement. For example, this drawing shows the distance between the centers of the two holes in a piece of metal.

If the distance were measured to the nearest quarter of an inch, the absolute error would be one-eighth of an inch. The symbol ± means "plus or minus." This symbol is often used to report measurements.

$2\frac{3}{4}$ in. ± $\frac{1}{8}$ in.

This way of reporting measurements helps to show how accurate the measurement is. The actual measurement will lie somewhere in this interval:

$2\frac{3}{4}$ in. − $\frac{1}{8}$ in. < m < $2\frac{3}{4}$ in. + $\frac{1}{8}$ in.

$2\frac{5}{8}$ in. < m < $2\frac{7}{8}$ in.

Write each reported measurement using an interval. Use m to represent the actual measurement.

1. 25,000 ± 500 voters
   24,500 < m < 25,500
2. 15 ± 0.5 kg
   14.5 kg < m < 15.5 kg
3. 750 ± 25 customers
   725 < m < 775
4. 75 ± 5 mi
   70 mi < m < 80 mi
5. 14 ± $\frac{1}{2}$ gal
   13$\frac{1}{2}$ gal < m < 14$\frac{1}{2}$ gal
6. 7$\frac{1}{4}$ ± $\frac{1}{4}$ in.
   7 in. < m < 7$\frac{1}{2}$ in.

Name the unit of measure used to make each measurement.

7. 32 ± $\frac{1}{2}$ ft   1 ft
8. 23 ± 0.5 m   1 m
9. 5$\frac{1}{4}$ ± $\frac{1}{8}$ mi $\frac{1}{4}$ mi
10. 14 ± 0.5 cm   1 cm
11. 2$\frac{3}{8}$ ± $\frac{1}{16}$ in. $\frac{1}{8}$ in.
12. 8 ± $\frac{1}{2}$ yd   1 yd

T20
Glencoe Division, Macmillan/McGraw-Hill

88

---

5. Name the coordinate of each point graphed on the number line.

A B C D
-6 -5 -4 -3 -2 -1 0 1 2 3 4 5 6

A: −6
B: −1
C: 2
D: 5

Find each absolute value.

6. $|4|$ 4
7. $|-3|$ 3
8. $|-23|$ 23
9. $|124 + 5|$ 129
10. $|0|$ 0

Graph each set of numbers on a number line. **See Solutions Manual.**

11. $\{-1, -3, -5\}$
12. $\{4, 5, 7\}$
13. $\{-3, -1, 0, 2\}$

Exercises

Independent Practice

Graph each set of numbers on a number line. **See Solutions Manual.**

14. $\{-5, -7, 9, 12\}$
15. $\{-6, -8, -10\}$
16. $\{-3, -2, 0, 2, 3\}$

Find each absolute value.

17. $|34|$ 34
18. $|-93|$ 93
19. $|-87|$ 87
20. $|132 - 20|$ 112

21. Evaluate $b + |a - c|$ if $a = 1$, $b = 2$, and $c = 0$. 3
22. Evaluate $xy - |-30|$ if $x = 10$ and $y = 4$. 10

Mixed Review

23. Use mental math to find $297 + 478$. *(Lesson 1-2)* 775
24. Solve $q + 6.8 = 15.2$. Check your solution. *(Lesson 2-3)* 8.4
25. Solve $\frac{b}{2} - 1 > 2$. Show the solution on a number line. *(Lesson 2-10)*
   $b > 6$; See Solutions Manual for number line.

Problem Solving and Applications

26. **Number Sense** Graph any point on a number line.
   a. Are the integers to the right of that point greater than or less than the coordinate of the point? greater than They are less than that coordinate.
   b. What can you conclude about the integers to the left of that point?

27. **Critical Thinking** A small snail in the forest is climbing a tree 10 feet tall. Each day it climbs 3 feet. Because of the dampness of the forest, it slips down 2 feet each evening. Use a number line to determine how many days it will take the snail to reach the top of the tree. 8 days

28. Copy the chart below. Complete the chart with a phrase that fits each situation.

*below sea level

Situation	Negative	Positive	Neither Positive nor Negative
altitude of a city	*	above sea level	sea level
football	5 yard loss	10 yard gain	no gain
time	yesterday	tomorrow	today
money	loss	profit	breakeven

88   **Chapter 3** Integers

OPTIONS

Extending the Lesson

Algebra Connection Have small groups solve the following equations. Explain that each equation has two solutions.

1. $|x| = 7$ 7, −7
2. $|y| - 5 = 3$ 8, −8
3. $\frac{|m|}{4} = 6$ 24, −24
4. $8|p| = 20$ 2.5, −2.5

Cooperative Learning Activity

Positive or Negative? 3-1

Number of players: 2
Materials: Index cards

↓ Copy onto cards the letters shown on the number line below. Shuffle the cards and place them face down in a pile. Copy onto a sheet of paper the number line below.

→ One partner selects a card and tells the *absolute value* of the coordinate to which it corresponds. The other partner looks at the number line and then guesses the point on his or her partner's card. A correct guess is worth 1 point. Trading roles each time, continue in the same way until all of the cards have been used.

A B C D E F G H   I J K L M N O P
-8 -7 -6 -5 -4 -3 -2 -1 0 1 2 3 4 5 6 7 8

Glencoe Mathematics: Applications and Connections, Course 3

3-2 Comparing and Ordering

Objective
Compare and order integers.

What magazines do you have at your house? The list below shows five top selling magazines for 1990. The number after each magazine tells the increase (+) or decrease (−) in the circulation from the previous year.

Sports Illustrated	+94,978
People	−78,566
Seventeen	+13,853
Rolling Stone	−56,900
'Teen	+7,186

If you ordered these magazines from the greatest increase to the greatest decrease, would the order be the same as above? Which magazine would be last on your list? **No,** *People*

Think about the number line. Remember that the values increase as you go right and decrease as you go left. Let's sketch a number line for the circulation values.

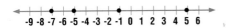

-78,566   0   -13,853
-56,900   -7,186   94,978

Which integer is graphed farthest to the right? This would be the greatest integer. **94,978** What is the least integer? **−78,566**

Let's list the numbers from greatest to least. Use the number line to confirm the order.

{94,978,   13,853,   7,186,   −56,900,   −78,566}

Any two numbers can be compared using one of three symbols.

=   *is equal to*   >   *is greater than*   <   *is less than*

Examples

Use the number line to compare integers. Replace each ● with >, <, or =.

-9 -8 -7 -6 -5 -4 -3 -2 -1 0 1 2 3 4 5 6

1 −7 ● −1
−7 is to the left of −1 on the number line.
So, −7 < −1.

2 |−5| ● 5
|−5| has a value of 5.
So, |−5| = 5.

OPTIONS

Reteaching Activity

Using Charts
Have students plot the value of MATHCO stock at the end of each day on a number line. Have them compare each day's value with the previous day's.

MATHCO Stock
Start: +20
Mon.: +3
Tue.: −6
Wed.: −2
Thu.: +5
Fri.: −9

3-2 Lesson Notes

NCTM Standards: 1–7

Lesson Resources
- Study Guide Master 3-2
- Practice Master 3-2
- Enrichment Master 3-2
- Group Activity Card 3-2

 Transparency 3-2 contains the 5-Minute Check and a teaching aid for this lesson.

⏱ 5-Minute Check
(Over Lesson 3-1)

1. Graph the set of numbers {4, 1, 0, −2, −3} on a number line.

-4 -3 -2 -1 0 1 2 3 4

Find each absolute value.

2. $|-112|$ 112   3. $|6|$ 6
4. $|72 - 59|$ 13
5. Evaluate $|x| - |y|$ if $x = -15$ and $y = 15$.   0

Practice Masters, p. 21

Name _____ Date _____

Practice Worksheet 3-2

Comparing and Ordering

Complete using >, <, or =.

1. 46 ___ 53 <
2. -19 ___ 18 <
3. 47 ___ -28 >
4. 0 ___ 13 <
5. -8 ___ 0 <
6. 0 ___ -27 >
7. -6 ___ -5 <
8. -7 ___ 7 <
9. 9 ___ -4 >
10. -46 ___ 46 <
11. 45 ___ 45 =
12. 45 ___ -45 >
13. 90 ___ -101 >
14. -10 ___ 10 <
15. |-12| ___ 12 =
16. |36| ___ |-36| =
17. |-34| ___ |-6| >
18. |0| ___ 0 =
19. |15| ___ |13| >
20. |-12| ___ |12| =
21. |-622| ___ 0 >

Order the integers in each set from least to greatest.

22. {-3, 4, -5, 6}   {-5, -3, 4, 6}
23. {-4, 4, -5, 5, 9}   {-5, -4, 4, 5, 9}
24. {-66, -98, 47, 0, 13, 28}   {-98, -66, 0, 13, 28, 47}
25. {0, 5, 8, -361, 224}   {-361, 0, 5, 8, 224}
26. {-54, -56, 55, 9, 53, 51}   {-56, -54, 9, 51, 53, 55}

Order the integers in each set from greatest to least.

27. {-3, 7, 0, -2, 8}   {8, 7, 0, -2, -3}
28. {0, 99, 16, 87, 12, -14}   {99, 87, 16, 12, 0, -14}
29. {261, -384, 275, -288}   {275, 261, -288, -384}
30. {-61, -123, -75, -126}   {-61, -75, -123, -126}

T21
Glencoe Division, Macmillan/McGraw-Hill

Study Guide Masters, p. 21

Name _____ Date _____

Study Guide Worksheet 3-2

Comparing and Ordering

To compare integers, think of a number line. The number farther to the right on the number line is greater.

-7 -6 -5 -4 -3 -2 -1 0 1 2 3 4 5 6 7

Examples

Use >, < or = to compare the integers.

1. -7 ___ 7   A negative integer is less than a positive integer.
   -7 < 7

2. -4 ___ -6   -4 is to the right of -6.
   -4 > -6

3. 2 ___ |-2| The absolute value of -2 is 2.
   2 = |-2|

Checking for Understanding

Communicating Mathematics

Read and study the lesson to answer each question.

1. **Write** two inequalities that relate −245 and 612. −245 < 612, 612 > −245

2. Always points to lesser number

2. **Tell** how you can easily remember what > and < mean.

3. **Show** how it is possible that −3 > −6, but |−3| < |−6|. Use a number line.

See Solutions Manual.

Guided Practice

Replace each ● with >, <, or =.

4. −19 ● −22 >   5. 0 ● −7 >   6. 4 ● 87 <

7. −56 ● 0 <   8. |−9| ● |−3| >   9. −459 ● −23 <

10. {−99, −7, −1, 0, 8, 34, 123}

10. Order the integers in the set {34, 0, −7, −1, 8, −99, 123} from least to greatest.

11. Order the integers in the set {78, −665, 1, 34, −99, 129, 65, −6} from greatest to least. {129, 78, 65, 34, 1, −6, −99, −665}

Exercises

Independent Practice

Replace each ● with >, <, or =.

12. −14 ● 0 <   13. −23 ● 9 <   14. −99 ● −789 >

15. 0 ● |−7| <   16. 90 ● 21 >   17. |−34| ● |−9| >

18. −632 ● −347 <   19. −56 ● 56 <   20. |214| ● |−214| =

21. Order the integers in the set {34, 0, −7, 99, −56, −9, −33} from least to greatest. {−56, −33, −9, −7, 0, 34, 99}

22. Order the integers in the set {8, −999, 12, 0, 40, −50, 93, −66} from greatest to least. {93, 40, 12, 8, 0, −50, −66, −999}

Mixed Review

23. Evaluate $(13 − 9)^2 + \dfrac{15}{21 \div 7}$. *(Lesson 2-1)* 21

24. Solve $4m − 28 = 68$. *(Lesson 2-7)* 24

25. Find $|4^2|$. *(Lesson 3-1)* 16

Problem Solving and Applications

For answers to Exercises 26 and 27, see Solutions Manual.

26. **Transportation** Use the graph at the right to answer each question.

   a. Describe the net income for each quarter of American Airlines as a gain or loss.

   b. Write a mathematical sentence to compare each quarter with the quarter that follows it.

27. **Critical Thinking** Graph all integer solutions for |x| < 5 on a number line.

COMPUTER CONNECTION

28. **Computer Connection** In BASIC, the INT(X) function finds the greatest integer that is not greater than X. INT(2.5) = 2, because 2 is the greatest integer and is not greater than 2.5. Find INT(−5.35). −6

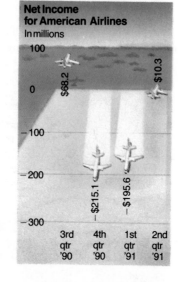

Net Income for American Airlines
In millions

3rd qtr '90	4th qtr '90	1st qtr '91	2nd qtr '91

$68.2   −$215.1   −$195.6 $10.3

90   Chapter 3 Integers

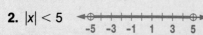

3-3 Adding Integers

Objective
Add integers.

Steve wanted to buy a new bicycle, but he did not have enough money for the 21-speed model he wanted. His parents offered him a deal. They said, "We'll lend you the money, but you must work the debt off by doing extra jobs around the house." Steve agreed. He borrowed $65 from his parents. This debt can be written as –65.

After shopping around, he realized that he needed to borrow more money from his parents. He borrowed an additional $50. This debt can be written as –50.

What is the total amount that Steve owes his parents? Let a = the total amount he owes.

$$-65 + (-50) = a$$

Addition can be represented on a number line. First graph –65. Since –50 is negative, you will move 50 units to the left.

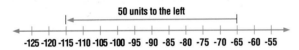

$$-65 + (-50) = a$$
$$-115 = a \qquad \text{Steve owes his parents \$115.}$$

You already know how to add two positive integers. For example, to solve $w = 45 + 30$, you simply add 45 and 30. The solution is 75. The solution for $-65 + (-50) = a$ is the same as the solution for $-(65 + 50) = a$. In each of these equations, you add the absolute value of the addends. The sum has the same sign as the integers.

Adding Integers with Same Sign	The sum of two positive integers is positive. The sum of two negative integers is negative.

NCTM Standards: 1–7, 9, 13

Lesson Resources
- Study Guide Master 3-3
- Practice Master 3-3
- Enrichment Master 3-3
- Lab Manual, p. 44
- Group Activity Card 3-3

Transparency 3-3 contains the 5-Minute Check and a teaching aid for this lesson.

5-Minute Check
(Over Lesson 3-2)

Replace ● with >, <, or =.
1. $13 ● -11$ >
2. $-4 ● -9$ >
3. $|-6| ● |-4|$ >
4. $|8| ● |-8|$ =
5. Order the integers in the set $\{18, -36, -12, 0, 12\}$ from least to greatest.
$-36, -12, 0, 12, 18$

1 FOCUS

Motivating the Lesson

Activity Label one pan of a two-pan balance "+" and the other "−." NOTE: Pan balances are available commercially; however, your school's science department may have one you could borrow. Place one penny on the "−" pan and label the pointer position -1. Adding one penny at a time, label the pointer positions for -2 through -5. Remove all pennies and then repeat the process on the "+" pan to label the pointer positions for 1 through 5. Demonstrate these sums using the balance (the pointer shows the sum): $2 + 3 = 5$, $(-2) + (-3) = -5$, $-1 + 4 = 3$, and $2 + (-5) = -3$.

OPTIONS

Gifted and Talented Needs

Have students research arithmetic operations in modular arithmetic systems. Ask them to explain the mod-12 system to the class, using a clock to illustrate mod-12 addition.

Interactive Mathematics Tools

This multimedia software provides an interactive lesson that is tied directly to Lesson 3-3. Students will click and drag cups and counters to explore operations with integers.

2 TEACH

Using the Mini-Lab Integers with the same absolute value but opposite signs are called *opposites*.

　　5 and −5 are opposites.

Point out that the sum of a number and its opposite is zero. Ask this question: *Why does a zero pair result when you pair a positive counter and a negative counter?* The counters represent opposites, −1 and 1, so their sum is zero.

Teaching Tip After completing the Mini-Lab, you may wish to present several addition problems, asking students whether the sums will be positive or negative.

More Examples

For Example 1

Solve $x = 3 + 29$. 　32

For Example 2

Solve $-9 + (-12) = k$.
−21

For Example 3

Solve $17 + (-15) = n$. 　2

For Example 4

Solve $p = -41 + 31$.
−10

Checking for Understanding

Exercises 1-4 are designed to help you assess students' understanding through reading, writing, speaking, and modeling. You should work through these exercises with your students and then monitor their work on Guided Practice Exercises 5-16.

Close

Have students write an example of each of the four types of addition problems. Have them exchange their problems with a classmate and find each sum.

Examples

1 Solve $p = 4 + 56$.
Use a number line.

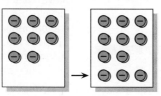

$p = 4 + 56$
$p = 60$

The solution is 60.

2 Solve $-8 + (-3) = x$.
Use counters. Put in 8 negative counters. Add 3 more negatives.

There are 11 negative counters. Therefore, $x = -11$. The solution is −11.

What do you suppose happens when you add a negative integer and a positive integer? Let's use counters to find a rule.

 Mini-Lab

Work with a partner to solve $x = 7 + (-4)$.
Materials: two colors of counters, mats

- Let one color of counter represent positive and another color represent negative. We need 7 positive counters and 4 negative counters.

- When a positive counter is paired with a negative counter, the result is called a **zero pair.** You can add or remove zero pairs without changing the value of the set. Remove all the zero pairs from the mat.

- The counters you have left represent the solution.

Talk About It
a. How many zero pairs did you find? 　4
b. What kind of counters did you have left? positive
c. What is the solution of $x = 7 + (-4)$? 　3

OPTIONS

Reteaching Activity

Using Cooperative Groups Each pair of students needs two number cubes, one with negative signs added to the numbers. Begin with a marker at 0 on a number line labeled from 10 to −10. Play alternates by rolling the cubes, stating the sum, and moving the marker accordingly. A player wins when the marker crosses the opponent's goal (10 or −10).

Study Guide Masters, p. 22

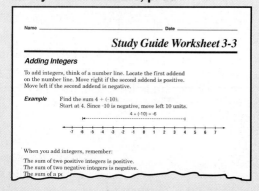

Name ＿＿＿＿＿＿＿＿＿＿ Date ＿＿＿＿

Study Guide Worksheet 3-3

Adding Integers

To add integers, think of a number line. Locate the first addend on the number line. Move right if the second addend is positive. Move left if the second addend is negative.

Example　Find the sum $4 + (-10)$.
Start at 4. Since -10 is negative, move left 10 units.

When you add integers, remember:

The sum of two positive integers is positive.
The sum of two negative integers is negative.
The sum of a po...

The results of the Mini-Lab suggest the following rule for adding two integers with different signs.

Adding Integers with Different Signs	To add integers with different signs, subtract their absolute values. The sum is: ● positive if the positive integer has the greater absolute value. ● negative if the negative integer has the greater absolute value.

Examples

3 Solve $76 + (-9) = c$.

$|76| > |-9|$, so the sum is positive.

The difference of 76 and 9 is 67, so $c = 67$.

4 Solve $a = -34 + 12$.

$|-34| > |12|$, so the sum is negative.

The difference of 34 and 12 is 22, so $a = -22$.

Checking for Understanding

Communicating Mathematics

Read and study the lesson to answer each question.

1. **Show** two methods to solve $x = -15 + 23$. See margin.

2. **Tell** how you know the sign of the sum of two integers with different signs.

3. **Tell** how you know whether to add or subtract the absolute values to find the sum of two integers. Give examples.

2. Use the sign of the integer with the greatest absolute value.

3. If the signs are the same, add. If they are different, subtract. See students' work for examples.

4. **Write** the addition sentence shown by each model.

a.

b.

c.

24 units

-12   0   12

$-7 + 3 = -4$ $5 + (-5) = 0$ $-12 + 24 = 12$

Guided Practice

Tell the sign of each sum.

5. $-45 + (-5)$ −

6. $-9 + 3$ −

7. $456 + 12$ +

8. $-32 + 40$ +

9. $12 + (-12)$ 0

10. $34 + (-60)$ −

Solve each equation.

11. $29 + (-9) = e$ 20

12. $5 + (-12) = p$ −7

13. $z = -34 + 75$ 41

14. $-41 + (-18) = w$ −59

15. $-42 + 42 = q$ 0

16. $f = 63 + 45$ 108

Lesson 3-3 Adding Integers   **93**

40a.

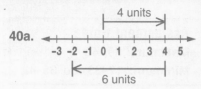

4 units

6 units

-3 -2 -1 0 1 2 3 4 5

42. She added all the positive numbers and then all the negative numbers. Then she subtracted when adding the two sums.

Enrichment Masters, p. 22

Name _____ Date _____

Enrichment Worksheet 3-3

So, What's So Funny?

To solve this acrostic, work back and forth between the clues and the puzzle box.

1. Any number with a positive sign is $\underset{33}{H}\ \underset{19}{I}\ \underset{42}{G}\ \underset{2}{H}\ \underset{3}{E}\ \underset{40}{R}$ than zero.

2. $\underset{8}{N}\ \underset{10}{O}\ \underset{26}{N}\ \underset{23}{E}$ and $\underset{27}{N}\ \underset{6}{O}\ \underset{7}{U}\ \underset{36}{G}\ \underset{16}{H}\ \underset{21}{T}$ both mean zero.

3. The absolute value of an integer never has a negative $\underset{37}{S}\ \underset{34}{I}\ \underset{4}{G}\ \underset{35}{N}$.

4. A number line does not have a definite $\underset{30}{S}\ \underset{31}{T}\ \underset{18}{A}\ \underset{5}{R}\ \underset{32}{T}$.

5. A statement or solution you are not sure of might be called $\underset{28}{I}\ \underset{12}{F}\ \underset{24}{F}\ \underset{14}{Y}$.

6. Rules for integer computation always $\underset{22}{H}\ \underset{41}{O}\ \underset{13}{L}\ \underset{9}{D}\ \underset{1}{T}\ \underset{20}{R}\ \underset{25}{U}\ \underset{17}{E}$.

7. To evaluate -3 + 4 · (-2), you should add $\underset{38}{A}\ \underset{39}{F}\ \underset{15}{T}\ \underset{29}{E}\ \underset{11}{R}$ you multiply.

Of all the funny things that live, in woodland, marsh, or bog,
That creep

1 T	2 H	3 E		4 G	5 R	6 O	7 U	8 N	9 D		10 O	11 R
12 F	13 L	14 Y		15 T	16 H	17 E		18 A	19 I	20 R		
21 T	22 H	23 E		24 F	25 U	26 N	27 N	28 I	29 E	30 S	31 T	
32 T	33 H	34 I	35 N	36 G	37 S		38 A		39 F	40 R	41 O	42 G

T 22
Glencoe Division, Macmillan/McGraw-Hill

Exercises

Solve each equation.

17. $-54 + 21 = y$ −33

18. $-456 + (-23) = j$ −479

19. $z = 60 + 12$ 72

20. $35 + (-32) = m$ 3

21. $n = -98 + (-32)$ −130

22. $s = -34 + 56$ 22

23. $r = -19 + (-37)$ −56

24. $r = -319 + (-100)$ −419

25. $56 + (-2) = b$ 54

26. $-60 + 30 = v$ −30

27. $409 + 309 = a$ 718

28. $c = 76 + (-45)$ 31

Evaluate each expression if $r = 5$, $t = -5$, and $w = -3$.

29. $r + 45$ 50

30. $w + (-7)$ −10

31. $t + w$ −8

32. $-9 + t$ −14

33. $-2 + w$ −5

34. $(r + t) + w$ −3

Mixed Review

35. Jamal put 4 pounds of sunflower seeds in his bird feeder on Sunday. On Friday, the bird feeder was empty, so Jamal put 4 more pounds of seed in it. The following Sunday, the seeds were half gone. How many pounds of sunflower seeds were consumed by the birds that week? *(Lesson 1-1)*   **6 pounds**

36. Write $4 \cdot 4 \cdot 6 \cdot 6 \cdot 6$ using exponents. *(Lesson 1-9)* $4^2 \cdot 6^3$

37. Solve $6x = 42$. Check your solution. *(Lesson 2-4)* 7

38. José has four times as many coins as Rebecca. Write an algebraic expression to represent José's coins. *(Lesson 2-6)* **4x**

39. Replace ● with >, <, or = in -114 ● -97. *(Lesson 3-2)* <

Problem Solving and Applications

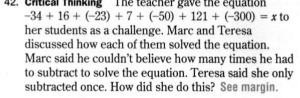

40. Sales Madeline is selling candy for the band. Her strategy is to work one side of the street and then work the other side of the street. She begins at Avenue H and Meadow Street. She travels east on Meadow Street for 4 blocks. Then she crosses the street and goes 6 blocks west.
a. Draw a diagram to find Madeline's location now. **See margin.**
b. Write an equation to show Madeline's path. $x = 4 + (-6)$
c. How far is she from her original starting point? **2 blocks west**

41. Marketing The Foot Locker® bought a certain brand of tennis shoe for $38.98 wholesale. They increased the price by $25 to make a profit. The shoes did not sell well. So to reduce inventory, the store is having a half-off sale. What will be the profit on each pair of shoes? Explain your answer.

41. $6.99 loss; The selling price is less than the wholesale price.

42. Critical Thinking The teacher gave the equation $-34 + 16 + (-23) + 7 + (-50) + 121 + (-300) = x$ to her students as a challenge. Marc and Teresa discussed how each of them solved the equation. Marc said he couldn't believe how many times he had to subtract to solve the equation. Teresa said she only subtracted once. How did she do this? **See margin.**

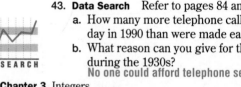

43. Data Search Refer to pages 84 and 85.   43a. about 1,200
a. How many more telephone calls were made each day in 1990 than were made each day in 1970?
b. What reason can you give for the dip in the graph during the 1930s?
No one could afford telephone service during the depression.

DATA SEARCH

OPTIONS

Extending the Lesson

Current Events Connection Have students collect examples of integer addition in newspapers and magazines. Articles on business, sports, or weather are good stories to examine.

Cooperative Learning Activity

It Evens Out **3-3**

Number of players: 2
Materials: Counters, spinners

◆ Label the sections of one spinner with the integers 1 through 6. Label the sections of a second spinner with the integers −1 through −6. Decide which color of counters will represent positive integers and which color will represent negative integers. One partner takes twenty counters of one color, and the other partner takes twenty counters of the other color.

➥ The partner with the counters that represent positive integers spins the positive integer spinner; the partner with the counters that represent negative integers spins the negative integer spinner. Both partners then place between them the number of counters indicated on their spinners. Zero pairs are removed from play. Leftover counters are returned to the partner with that color. Before the next round, partners write an equation that describes their actions and solve for the variable. Play continues until one partner runs out of counters.

Glencoe Mathematics: Applications and Connections, Course 3

3-4 More About Adding Integers

Objective

Add more than two integers.

What is your favorite television show? *The Cosby Show* has been a favorite show of TV viewers since its creation in 1984. In November of 1985, about 32 of every 100 viewers watched *The Cosby Show.* By 1986, the number rose by 2 viewers per hundred. By 1990, the number dropped by 11 viewers per hundred. What was the number of viewers (per hundred) that watched *The Cosby Show* in 1990?

The number of viewers can be found using a sum of integers. Let v = the number of viewers per hundred in 1990.

$v = 32 + 2 + (-11)$
$v = (32 + 2) + (-11)$ *Use the associative property to group the first two addends.*

$v = 34 + (-11)$
$v = 23$

About 23 viewers per hundred watched *The Cosby Show* in 1990.

LOOK BACK

You can review the commutative property and associative property on page 9.

The equation above was solved by using the associative property to group the first two addends. The commutative property can also be used when working with integers.

Each of the following examples is solved one way and checked by using these properties in another way.

Example 1

Solve $r = 12 + (-3) + 7$.

Use the associative property to group the first two addends.

$r = [12 + (-3)] + 7$
$r = (9) + 7$
$r = 16$

Use the associative property to group the last two addends.

Check: $r = 12 + [(-3) + 7]$
$r = 12 + (4)$
$r = 16$ ✔

Lesson 3-4 More About Adding Integers   **95**

NCTM Standards: 1–4, 6, 7, 9, 13

Lesson Resources
• Study Guide Master 3-4
• Practice Master 3-4
• Enrichment Master 3-4
• Group Activity Card 3-4

Transparency 3-4 contains the 5-Minute Check and a teaching aid for this lesson.

⏱ 5-Minute Check
(Over Lesson 3-3)
Solve each equation.

1. $-53 + (-71) = k$
   -124

2. $13 + (-21) = n$ -8

3. $x = 270 + 130$ 400

4. $h = -37 + 48$ 11

5. Evaluate $-15 + w$ if $w = 14$. -1

1 FOCUS

Motivating the Lesson

Questioning   Ask students to suggest an easy way to add 9 + 437 + 91 mentally.   Since 9 + 91 = 100, then 9 + 437 + 91 = 100 + 437 = 537 *Which properties were used?* commutative and associative

2 TEACH

Using Logical Reasoning
Discuss the *Cosby Show* sum. Then ask the following questions.

• *What other pairs of numbers might you have added first?* $32 + (-11)$ or $2 + (-11)$

• *Find each of these sums.*   21; -9

• *Add the remaining addend. What are these sums?*   23; 23

• *Did the order in which the addends were added affect the sum?*   no

---

OPTIONS

Reteaching Activity

Banking Connection   Write a beginning checking account balance on the chalkboard. Below it list a series of deposits (+) and withdrawals (−). Have students compute the final account balance. Encourage them to use the associative property to group deposits and withdrawals in order to minimize their work.

Study Guide Masters, p. 23

Name _____ Date _____

Study Guide Worksheet 3-4

More About Adding Integers

You can use the associative property and the commutative property to help add integers.

Associative Property: Addends may be grouped in any way. The sum will remain the same.

Example   Group the first two addends.   Group the second two addends.

   Solve $m = -4 + (-6) + 9$ **Check** $m = -4 + (-6) + 9$
        $m = [-4 + (-6)] + 9$ $m = -4 + [(-6) + 9]$
        $m = -10 + 9$ $m = -4 + 3$
        $m = -1$ $m = -1$

Commutative Property: Integers may be added in any order. The sum will remain the same.

Checking for Understanding

Exercises 1-3 are designed to help you assess students' understanding through reading, writing, speaking, and modeling. You should work through these exercises with your students and then monitor their work on Guided Practice Exercises 4-13.

Additional Answers

1. Use the commutative property to change the order, then use the associative property to group the first two addends.
2. Look for groupings that make the sum easier to find.
3. See students' work.

Practice Masters, p. 23

Name _____ Date _____

Practice Worksheet 3-4

More About Adding Integers

Solve each equation.

1. $a = 3 + (-7) + 12$
   8
2. $(-6) + 17 + 3 = d$
   14
3. $x = (-8) + 5 + 19$
   16
4. $z = (-3) + (-8) + (-9)$
   -20

Solve each equation. Check by solving another way.

5. $w = 35 + (-8) + 54$
   81
6. $51 + (-7) + (-17) = k$
   27
7. $27 + (-35) + 23 + (-15) = g$
   0
8. $m = (-32) + 16 + 18 + 43$
   45
9. $e = 41 + 26 + (-35) + 18$
   50
10. $n = -14 + (-18) + 19 + 16$
   3
11. $t = -63 + 18 + (-37) + 21$
   -61
12. $42 + (-43) + 45 + (-46) = d$
   -2
13. $75 + (-100) + 75 + (-50) = y$
   0
14. $m = -38 + 12 + (-10) + 15$
   -21
15. $w = -9 + (-7) + (-10) + (-6)$
   -32
16. $45 + 52 + (-32) + 55 = p$
   120

Evaluate each expression if $c = 4$, $x = -5$, and $h = 6$.

17. $x + 5 + 9 + (-7)$
   2
18. $(-12) + c + (-3)$
   -11
19. $h + c + x + (-12) + 8$
   1
20. $-6 + x + h$
   -5
21. $-12 + h + x + h$
   -5
22. $(c + c) + x$
   3

T 23
Glencoe Division, Macmillan/McGraw-Hill

Examples

2 Solve $y = -4 + 2 + (-8)$

Use the commutative property to change order.

$y = -4 + (-8) + 2$
$y = -12 + 2$
$y = -10$

Use the associative property to group the first two addends.

Check: $y = (-4 + 2) + (-8)$
$y = -2 + (-8)$
$y = -10$ ✓

3 Solve $t = -92 + 73 + (-51) + 100$.

$t = -92 + 73 + (-51) + 100$
$t = -92 + (-51) + 73 + 100$ *Use the commutative property.*
$t = [-92 + (-51)] + [73 + 100]$ *Use the associative property.*
$t = -143 + 173$
$t = 30$

Check: Use your calculator.

92 [+/-] [+] 73 [+] 51 [+/-] [+] 100 [=] 30 ✓

Checking for Understanding For answers to Exercises 1-3, see margin.

Communicating Mathematics

Read and study the lesson to answer each question.

1. **Write** a sentence to tell how you can use the associative and commutative properties to solve a problem with more than two addends.
2. **Tell** how mental math can be used to find the sum of two or more integers.
3. **Show** three ways to solve $x = -4 + 8 + 12 + (-6) + (-3) + 13$.

Guided Practice

Solve each equation.

4. $y = 21 + 3 + (-6)$ **18**
5. $(-3) + 8 + 9 = c$ **14**
6. $(-2) + 3 + (-10) + 6 = f$ **-3**
7. $d = 7 + 20 + (-5)$ **22**
8. $w = (-4) + (-3) + 4 + 3$ **0**
9. $(-8) + 4 + 12 + (-11) = r$ **-3**
10. $s = 9 + 10 + (-6) + 6$ **19**
11. $21 + 3 + (-9) = g$ **15**
12. $(-7) + 12 + 9 = q$ **14**
13. $p = (-6) + 12 + (-11) + 1$ **-4**

Exercises

Independent Practice

Solve each equation. Check by solving another way.

14. $a = 6 + 9 + (-11)$ **4**
15. $c = (-8) + 4 + 21$ **17**
16. $19 + 23 + (-8) + 12 = f$ **46**
17. $(-4) + 5 + 7 + 12 = g$ **20**
18. $w = -32 + 32 + 70$ **70**
19. $x = 5 + (-12) + 7 + 3$ **3**
20. $j = -8 + 6 + (-20)$ **-22**
21. $m = (-50) + 9 + 3 + 50$ **12**
22. $p = -13 + (-5) + 7 + (-20)$ **-31**
23. $8 + 30 + 21 + (-5) = r$ **54**

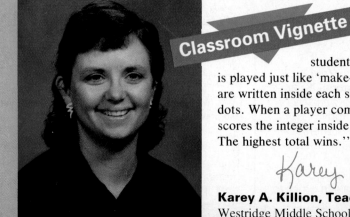

Classroom Vignette

"I reinforce adding integers by having the students play 'Gotcha'. The game is played just like 'make-a-square' except integers are written inside each square formed by a grid of dots. When a player completes a square, he or she scores the integer inside and takes another turn. The highest total wins."

Karey Killion

Karey A. Killion, Teacher
Westridge Middle School, Grand Island, NE

24. $14 + 7 + (-23) + 10 = t$ **8**

25. $v = (-30) + 5 + 12 + (-23)$ **−36**

26. $r = 4 + (-10) + 6$ **0**

27. $-21 + 17 + 10 + (-17) = z$ **−11**

Evaluate each expression if $c = 5$, $x = -4$, and $h = 6$.

28. $c + 3 + 4 + (-8)$ **4**

29. $(-6) + x + 2 + 10$ **2**

30. $(-5) + h + 1$ **2**

31. $(-5) + 16 + c + h$ **22**

Mixed Review

32. How many ounces are in 2.25 pounds of gelatin mix? *(Lesson 1-7)* **36 ounces**

33. The replacement set for $\dfrac{448}{y} = 14$ is {22, 29, 41, 32}. Find the solution. *(Lesson 2-2)* **32**

34. Solve $4s < 36$. Show the solution on a number line. *(Lesson 2-10)* $s < 9$ **See margin for number line.**

35. Solve $p = 85 + (-47)$. *(Lesson 3-3)* **38**

Problem Solving and Applications

36. Science By studying the records of earthquakes, scientists have learned that the inside of the earth is divided into three parts: the mantle, the outer core, and the inner core in that order. The outer core begins at about −1,800 miles; that is, 1,800 miles below the earth's surface. It is about 1,400 miles thick. Name an integer to tell where the inner core begins. **−3,200 miles**

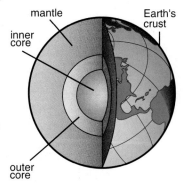

mantle
Earth's crust
inner core
outer core

37. Critical Thinking Explain how you might estimate the sum $326 + (-76) + 210 + (-330) + (-215)$. Give more than one method. **See Solutions Manual.**

38. Geography The lowest elevation on Earth is the shore of the Dead Sea. It is about 1,310 feet below sea level. If you traveled so that you gained 400 feet altitude each hour, how many hours would it take you to reach sea level? **about 3 hours**

39. Mathematics and Sports Read the following paragraph.

There are at least six kinds of football. Soccer is probably the most popular. There are 11 players on each team, and the game is played with a round ball that cannot be handled, except by the goalie. Rugby has either 13 or 15 players and is played with an oval ball that can be carried. American football has 11 players per side and is played with an oval ball that can be carried. Canadian football is similar to American football but is played with 12 players. Australian Rules is played on an oval field, and each side has 18 players. Gaelic football is like a combination of soccer and rugby and has 15 players per team.

a. Vance lost 5 yards on the first play and then gained 8 yards on the next play. Find the total number of yards gained or lost. **gained 3 yards**

b. The Bruins' offense advanced the football 15 yards. On the next play, the quarterback was sacked and lost 23 yards. Find the total number of yards gained or lost. **lost 8 yards**

Lesson 3-4 More About Adding Integers **97**

Extending the Lesson

Mathematics and Sports You may wish to draw a diagram of a football field with a number line below to illustrate the action described in the problems.

Cooperative Learning Activity

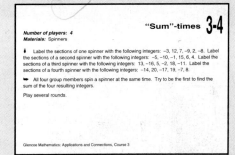

"Sum"-times **3-4**

Number of players: 4
Materials: Spinners

▸ Label the sections of one spinner with the following integers: −3, 12, 7, −9, 2, −8. Label the sections of a second spinner with the following integers: −5, −10, −1, 15, 6, 4. Label the sections of a third spinner with the following integers: 13, −16, 5, −2, 18, −11. Label the sections of a fourth spinner with the following integers: −14, 20, −17, 19, −7, 8.

▸ All four group members spin a spinner at the same time. Try to be the first to find the sum of the four resulting integers. Play several rounds.

Glencoe Mathematics: Applications and Connections, Course 3

Lesson Resources
• Study Guide Master 3-5
• Practice Master 3-5
• Enrichment Master 3-5
• Evaluation Master, Quiz A, p. 25
• Lab Manual, p. 45
• Interdisciplinary Master, p. 17
• Group Activity Card 3-5

 Transparency 3-5 contains the 5-Minute Check and a teaching aid for this lesson.

🕐 5-Minute Check
(Over Lesson 3–4)

Solve each equation. Check by solving another way.

1. $m = (-7) + 6 + 15$ 14
2. $k = -9 + (-5) + 9 + 13$ 8
3. $80 + (-50) + (-70) = w$ -40
4. $x = -8 + 14 + 9 + (-7)$ 8
5. Evaluate $15 + a + (-8) + b$ if $a = 11$ and $b = -15$.   3

1 FOCUS

Motivating the Lesson

Questioning   Ask students to read the opening paragraph of the lesson. Then ask the following question. *The altitude of K2 (a mountain in Kashmir in Asia), Earth's second highest peak, is 28,250 feet above sea level. How much higher is Mount Everest than K2?*   778 ft

---

Objective
Subtract integers.

Words to Learn
opposite
additive inverse

The highest point on Earth is Mount Everest in the Himalaya Mountains on the border of India and China. It has an altitude of 29,028 feet above sea level. The lowest verified point on Earth is in the Mariana Trench in the western Pacific Ocean. It is 35,840 below sea level. You could write these altitudes as 29,028 feet and −35,840 feet.

Suppose we want to find the difference between the altitudes of Mount Everest and the Mariana Trench. If d represents the difference, then $d = 29,028 - (-35,840)$.   *You will solve this in Exercise 2.*

Remember that we used counters to show how to add integers. You can use these counters to show subtraction, too.

🔵 Mini-Lab

Work with a partner to solve each equation.
Materials: two colors of counters, mat

a. Solve $x = -8 - (-2)$.
• Start with 8 negative counters.
• Remove 2 negative counters.

b. Solve $y = 7 - 3$.
• Start with 7 positive counters.
• Remove 3 positive counters.

c. Solve $6 - (-3) = z$.
• Start with 6 positive counters. There are no negative counters, so we can't remove 3 negatives.
• Add 3 zero pairs to the mat.
• Now remove the 3 negatives.

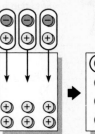

Classroom Vignette

"Students can use masking tape to create a number line on the floor. Then they walk along it to subtract integers. Starting at zero and facing the positive integers, they walk forward for positive integers, backward for negative integers, and do an about-face at the minus sign."

Janet L. Ellis

Janet Ellis, Teacher
Slippery Rock Middle School, Slippery Rock, PA

Talk About It

a. Compare the solution of $x = -8 - (-2)$ with the solution of
$x = -8 + 2$. $-6 = -6$

b. Compare the solution of $y = 7 - 3$ with the solution of
$y = 7 + (-3)$. $4 = 4$

c. Compare the solution of $6 - (-3) = z$ with the solution of
$6 + 3 = z$. $9 = 9$

In Chapter 2, you learned that adding and subtracting were opposite, or inverse, operations. Each integer also has an **opposite.** The opposite of an integer is called its **additive inverse.**

Additive Inverse	**In words:** The sum of an integer and its additive inverse is 0.

	Arithmetic	**Algebra**
	$6 + (-6) = 0$	$a + (-a) = 0$

In the Mini-Lab, you were asked to compare the result of subtracting an integer with the result of adding its inverse.

Subtraction	*Addition of the Additive Inverse*
$-8 - (-2) = -6$	$-8 + 2 = -6$
$7 - 3 = 4$	$7 + (-3) = 4$
$6 - (-3) = 9$	$6 + 3 = 9$

Adding the additive inverse of an integer produces the same result as subtracting the integer.

Subtracting Integers	To subtract an integer, add its additive inverse.

Examples

1 Solve $p = -5 - 3$.

$p = -5 - 3$
$p = -5 + (-3)$ *To subtract 3,*
$p = -8$ *add −3.*

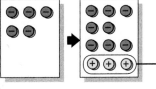

2 Solve $-34 - (-25) = s$.

$-34 - (-25) = s$
$-34 + 25 = s$ *To subtract −25, add 25.*
$-9 = s$

Lesson 3-5 Subtracting Integers **99**

2 TEACH

Using the Mini-Lab At the conclusion of the lab, ask the following questions.

• *Why wasn't it necessary to form zero pairs in parts **a** and **b**?* In part **a,** there were enough negative counters to remove 2; in part **b,** there were enough positive counters to remove 3.

• *In part **c,** why doesn't the addition of a zero pair change the value of z?* Any number plus zero equals that number.

More Examples

For Example 1
Solve $y = -8 - 9$. -17

For Example 2
Solve $-14 - (-5) = v$.
-9

For Example 3
A coal-mine elevator is located at 132 feet below ground level. It descended 256 feet, rose 195 feet, and then descended 57 feet. Find its final location. 250 feet below ground level

---

Checking for Understanding

Exercises 1-4 are designed to help you assess students' understanding through reading, writing, speaking, and modeling. You should work through these exercises with your students and then monitor their work on Guided Practice Exercises 5-17.

Close

Ask the following questions.

• *What is the additive inverse of an integer?* the integer with the same absolute value but the opposite sign

• *How do you subtract one integer from another?* You add the additive inverse of the second integer to the first integer.

Reteaching Activity

Using Charts Have students draw a chart like the one below. Give them several subtraction expressions to compute. Example: $-5 - (-2)$

Expression	Opposite of the Second Integer	Expression as an Addition	Sum
$-5 - (-2)$	$+2$	$-5 + (+2)$	-3

Study Guide Masters, p. 24

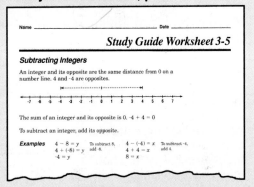

Name _____ Date _____

Study Guide Worksheet 3-5

Subtracting Integers

An integer and its opposite are the same distance from 0 on a number line. 4 and -4 are opposites.

The sum of an integer and its opposite is 0. -4 + 4 = 0

To subtract an integer, add its opposite.

Examples $4 - 8 = y$ To subtract 8, $4 - (-4) = x$ To subtract -4,
  $4 + (-8) = y$ add -8. $4 + 4 = x$ add 4.
  $-4 = y$ $8 = x$

99

Assignment Guide

Maximum: 18–49

Minimum: 19–39 odd, 41–46, 48, 49

All: Mid-Chapter Review

For **Extra Practice,** see p. 589.

Alternate Assessment

Speaking Ask students to state which of the following expressions are equivalent.

$8 - (-4)$ $8 + (-4)$
$8 + 4$ $-8 + (-4)$
$8 - (-4)$ and $8 + 4$

Additional Answers

2. $d = 29{,}028 - (-35{,}840)$
   $= 29{,}028 + 35{,}840$
   $d = 64{,}868$
4. See below.
9. $4 + 7 = y$
10. $n = -43 + (-99)$
11. $p = -23 + 2$
12. $53 + (-78) = z$
13. $y = 14 + (-14)$
14. $11 + 19 = p$
15. $x = 17 + 26$
16. $123 + 33 = n$
17. $b = -345 + (-67)$

Practice Masters, p. 24

Example 3 *Problem Solving*

Accounting The balance of credit card accounts is figured at the end of each month. The balance can be negative or positive. Additional charges are subtracted from the balance, and payments are added to the balance. Find the final balance on the spreadsheet below.

DATE	CHARGES	PAYMENTS	BALANCE
10/1			–$12.30
10/6	$56.78		
10/15	$21.20		
10/30		$75.00	

Use pencil and paper.
$-12.30 - 56.78 = -69.08$
$-69.08 - 21.20 = -90.28$
$-90.28 + 75.00 = -15.28$

Use a calculator. 12.30 [+/−] [−] 56.78 [−] 21.20 [+] 75 [=] -15.28

The final balance is –$15.28. This means the customer owes $15.28.

Checking for Understanding

Communicating Mathematics

Read and study the lesson to answer each question.

1. Sample answers:
   1, –1; –5, 5; 49, –49

1. **Write** three examples of integers and their additive inverses.
2. **Show** how you would solve the equation to find the difference between the altitudes of Mount Everest and the Mariana Trench. **See margin.**
3. **Tell** whether every integer has an additive inverse. Which integer is its own inverse? **yes; 0**
4. **Draw** a model that shows $-3 - (-5) = q$. **See margin.**

Guided Practice

Find the additive inverse of each integer.

5. 10 –10   6. –9 9   7. 30 –30   8. –29 29

For equations in Exercises 9-17, see margin.
Rewrite each equation using the additive inverse. Then solve.

9. $4 - (-7) = y$ 11   10. $n = -43 - 99$ –142   11. $p = -23 - (-2)$ –21
12. $53 - 78 = z$ –25   13. $y = 14 - 14$ 0   14. $11 - (-19) = p$ 30
15. $x = 17 - (-26)$ 43   16. $123 - (-33) = n$ 156   17. $b = -345 - 67$ –412

Exercises

Independent Practice

Solve each equation.

18. $j = 44 - (-11)$ 55   19. $4 - (-89) = u$ 93   20. $56 - (-78) = p$ 134

21. 1,313

21. $435 - (-878) = u$ 22. $k = -99 - 4$ –103   23. $w = -43 - 88$ –131

24. $x = -78 - (-98)$ 20   25. $-5 - 3 = k$ –8   26. $63 - 92 = q$ –29

29. –735

27. $m = 56 - (-22)$ 78   28. $r = -9 - (-4)$ –5   29. $-789 - (-54) = s$

30. $x = -351 - 245$ –596   31. $v = 89 - (-54)$ 143   32. $-109 - (-34) = g$
                                                               –75

Evaluate each expression if $y = -7$, $p = 9$, and $x = -10$.

33. $45 - y$ 52   34. $67 - p$ 58   35. $x - (-23)$ 13   36. $y - x$ 3

37. $x - y$ –3   38. $-240 - x$ –230   39. $y - p - x$ –6   40. $x - y - p$ –12

OPTIONS

Meeting Needs of Middle School Students

Adolescents inhabit that complex middle ground between childhood and adulthood. Striving for independence, they continue to need guidance. Let them know you have high expectations for them, but that you will support them even if they fall short of those expectations.

Additional Answer

4.

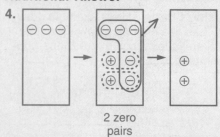

2 zero pairs

41. Find the value of 5^3. *(Lesson 1-9)* **125**

42. Evaluate $8x - 2y$ if $x = 6$ and $y = 14$. *(Lesson 1-3)* **20**

43. **Geometry** Find the area of a square if its side is 8 cm long. *(Lesson 2-9)* **64 cm²**

44. Order the set {52, –3, 128, 4, –22, 15, 0, –78} from greatest to least. *(Lesson 3-2)* **{128, 52, 15, 4, 0, –3, –22, –78}**

45. Solve $44 + 8 + (-20) + 15 = s$. Check your solution. *(Lesson 3-4)* **47**

Problem Solving and Applications

Use the graph below for Exercises 46-47.

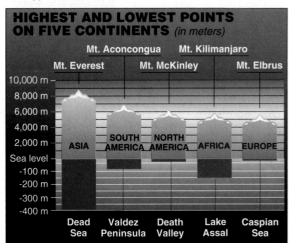

See margin.

46. **Geography** Estimate the difference between the highest and lowest points on each continent.

47. **Research** Use an encyclopedia or almanac to find the exact elevations of the highest and lowest points given in the graph.

   a. What is the actual difference between the altitudes of the highest and lowest points on each continent? **See margin.**

   b. What is the difference between the altitudes of the lowest point in Africa and the lowest point in South America? **–115 meters**

48. **Critical Thinking** Is the subtraction of integers associative? That is, does $-53 - (23 - 37) = (-53 - 23) - 37$? Explain. **no, –39 ≠ –113**

49. **Business** Accountants use the formula $P = I - E$ to find the profit *(P)* when income *(I)* and expenses *(E)* are known.
   a. Find *P* if $I = \$18,345$ and $E = \$25,000$. **–$6,655**
   b. What does this answer mean? **This is a loss.**

3   Assessment: Mid-Chapter Review

Find each absolute value. *(Lesson 3-1)*

1. $|64|$ **64**   2. $|-31|$ **31**   3. $|-4|$ **4**

4. Graph the set {4, 8, –3, 2, 0, –8, –1} on a number line. *(Lesson 3-1)* **See margin.**

5. Write the set {6, 5, –2, 0, –3, 8, –7} in order from least to greatest. *(Lesson 3-2)* **{–7, –3, –2, 0, 5, 6, 8}**

Solve each equation. *(Lessons 3-3, 3-4, and 3-5)*

6. $x = 3 + (-5)$ **–2**   7. $y = 2 + (-4) + (-6) + 8$ **0**   8. $514 - 600 = r$ **–86**

9. $90 + (-90) = p$ **0**   10. $w = 67 - (-32)$ **99**   11. $m = -89 - 25$ **–114**

Extending the Lesson

Using Manipulatives Give students a copy of the *nomograph* below. To find the difference $2 - 3$, draw a line from 3 on number line A, through 2 on number line B and read the answer, -1, where the line crosses number line C. Have students subtract other integers.

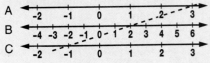

Cooperative Learning Activity

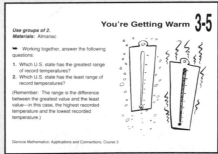

You're Getting Warm **3-5**

Use groups of 2.
Materials: Almanac

➡ Working together, answer the following questions:

1. Which U.S. state has the greatest range of record temperatures?
2. Which U.S. state has the least range of record temperatures?

(Remember: The range is the difference between the greatest value and the least value—in this case, the highest recorded temperature and the lowest recorded temperature.)

Glencoe Mathematics: Applications and Connections, Course 3

Additional Answers

46. Asia–about 9,400 m;
S. America–about 7,100 m;
N. America–about 6,200 m;
Europe–about 5,100 m;
Africa–about 6,200 m

47a. Asia: $8,848 - (-399) = 9,247$ m; S. America: $6,959 - (-40) = 6,999$ m;
N. America: $6,194 - (-86) = 6,280$ m;
Europe: $5,633 - (-28) = 5,661$ m; Africa: $5,895 - (-155) = 6,050$ m

Mid-Chapter Review

4.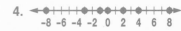

Enrichment Masters, p. 24

NCTM Standards: 1–7, 9

Lesson Resources
- Study Guide Master 3-6
- Practice Master 3-6
- Enrichment Master 3-6
- Group Activity Card 3-6

 Transparency 3-6 contains the 5-Minute Check and a teaching aid for this lesson.

⏱ 5-Minute Check
(Over Lesson 3–5)

Solve each equation.

1. $m = 25 - (-14)$ 39
2. $-11 - 9 = t$ -20
3. $x = -6 - (-4)$ -2
4. $p = 13 - 28$ -15
5. Evaluate $a - b$ if $a = -9$ and $b = -6$. -3

---

1 FOCUS

Motivating the Lesson

Questioning   Ask the following questions.

- *How can you write 4(3) as a sum of 3's?* $3 + 3 + 3 + 3$
- *How can you write 4(−3) as a sum of −3's?* $-3 + (-3) + (-3) + (-3)$
- *Add to find the product 4(−3).* -12

2 TEACH

Using the Mini-Lab   The first number in a product tells how many sets of counters to place on the mat, if the number is positive, or how many to remove, if the number is negative. The second number specifies the number and type of counters in each set being put on or removed from the mat. For more practice, have students reverse the order of the factors in each example and use counters to model the multiplication.

Objective
Multiply integers.

Have you ever played golf or watched a golf tournament? In golf, the score for each hole is often stated in relation to the number of strokes the course says is standard for that hole. *Par* means you took that number of strokes. Other scores for one hole are shown below.

eagle	−2	two strokes under par
birdie	−1	one stroke under par
par	0	even par
bogey	+1	one stroke over par
double bogey	+2	two strokes over par

DID YOU KNOW

The winner of a golf tournament is the person who took the fewest strokes. TV statisticians use the number under or over par to indicate who is leading during any given round of the tournament.

If you took 2 strokes on a par-3 hole, you would make a birdie. Add −1 to your score in relation to par.

At the 1991 Western Open, Greg Norman entered the last day of the tournament with a score of 11 under par, or −11. On the first nine holes that day, he scored 5 birdies and was even par for the other four holes. How did this affect his score?

Even par scores did not affect his score. The 5 birdies can be expressed as $5(-1)$.

$$5(-1) = (-1) + (-1) + (-1) + (-1) + (-1)$$
$$= -5$$

His score on the last day at the end of the nine holes was $-11 + (-5)$ or -16. That is, 16 under par.

Mini-Lab

Work with a partner to solve each equation.

Materials: two colors of counters, mats

a. Solve $x = 5 \cdot 2$.

- Begin with an empty mat.
- The 5 means to put 5 sets of counters on the mat. Each set will contain 2 positive counters.

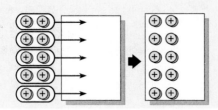

OPTIONS

Gifted and Talented Needs

Have students solve the following problem. *a, b, c, . . . , z are integers. Find the product* $(x - a)(x - b)(x - c)...(x - z)$. One of the terms in the product is $(x - x)$, which equals 0. Therefore, the product is 0.

 Interactive Mathematics Tools

This multimedia software provides an interactive lesson that is tied directly to Lesson 3–6. Students will use counters to explore multiplication with integers.

b. Solve $y = 3 \cdot (-4)$.

- Begin with an empty mat.
- The 3 means to put 3 sets on the mat. Each set will contain 4 negative counters.

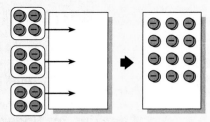

c. Solve $z = -2 \cdot (-4)$.

- Start with an empty mat.
- The −2 means to take 2 sets from the mat. Each set will contain 4 negative counters.
- Since the mat contains no counters, you must first place enough zero pairs on the mat so that it will be possible to remove 2 sets of 4 negative counters.

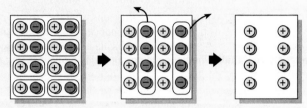

Talk About It

a. What are the values of x, y, and z? **10, −12, 8**
b. When were the products positive? **when signs were alike**
c. When were the products negative? **when signs were different**

The Mini-Lab suggests the following rule for multiplying integers.

Multiplying Integers	The product of two integers with the same sign is positive.
	The product of two integers with different signs is negative.

Examples

1 Solve $p = 5(-6)$.

The two integers have different signs. The product will be negative.

$p = 5(-6)$
$p = -30$

2 Solve $x = -7(-7)$.

The two integers have the same sign. The product will be positive.

$x = -7(-7)$
$x = 49$

Lesson 3-6 Multiplying Integers   **103**

Checking for Understanding

Exercises 1-5 are designed to help you assess students' understanding through reading, writing, speaking, and modeling. You should work through these exercises with your students and then monitor their work on Guided Practice Exercises 6-21.

Error Analysis

Watch for students who write the product of two negative integers as negative.

Prevent by reviewing the rules for multiplying integers.

Close

Have students complete each statement using the word *positive* or *negative*.

- *The product of two positive integers is* __?__.   positive
- *The product of two negative integers is* __?__.   positive
- *The product of a positive integer and a negative integer is* __?__.   negative

---

Reteaching Activity

Using Cooperative Groups Give each group of three students three number cubes of one color (positive) and three of another color (negative). Place the cubes in a paper bag. One player draws three cubes and rolls them. A second player states the sign of the product. The third player states the product and records it as a score. After five rounds, the group with the highest total wins.

Study Guide Masters, p. 25

Name _____ Date _____

Study Guide Worksheet 3-6

Multiplying Integers

The product of two positive integers is positive.

Examples $k = 4(9)$ $m = 6(7)(2)$ $j = 5(3)(5)$
$k = 36$ $m = 42(2)$ $j = 15(5)$
$m = 84$ $j = 75$

The product of two negative integers is positive.

Examples $h = (-7)(-5)$ $v = (-9)^2$ $z = (-25)(-7)$
$h = 35$ $v = -9(-9)$ $z = 175$
$v = 81$

The product of a positive integer and a negative integer is negative.

Assignment Guide
Maximum: 22–49
Minimum: 23–39 odd, 41–48

For **Extra Practice,** see p. 590.

Alternate Assessment

Writing Have students write a word problem that can be solved by multiplying 5 and −3. Have them explain how to find the product.

Additional Answers

2. $y = (7)(-9)(6)$
$y = (7)(6)(-9)$
$y = (42)(-9)$
$y = -378$

3. 6 [+/−] [x²] 36

4. See page 105.

Practice Masters, p. 25

Name _____ Date _____

Practice Worksheet 3-6

Multiplying Integers

State whether each product will be positive, negative, or zero.

1. (-3)(-6) positive	2. 5(-4) negative	3. 6(8) positive
4. (-2)(8)(-4) positive	5. (4)(0)(9) zero	6. (-3)(-4)(-5) negative

Solve each equation.

7. $a = 9(-5)$ −45	8. $h = 7(-15)$ −105	9. $n = (-7)(-12)$ 84
10. $e = (-16)(-4)$ 64	11. $(-12)(3) = j$ −36	12. $r = -14(-8)$ 112
13. $g = 14(36)$ 504	14. $k = -11(-11)$ 121	15. $s = -16(-21)$ 336
16. $b = -16(9)$ −144	17. $-14(-12) = k$ 168	18. $t = -18(0)$ 0
19. $-21(-8) = d$ 168	20. $q = -26(7)$ −182	21. $u = -33(-9)$ 297
22. $c = (-2)(8)(-90)$ 1,440	23. $m = (-18)^2$ 324	24. $8(3)(16) = w$ 384
25. $f = (-2)(8)(-5)^2$ −400	26. $p = (4)(-11)(3)$ −132	27. $x = (4)^2 \cdot (-2)^2$ 64

Evaluate each expression if $a = -2$, $b = -5$, and $c = 8$.

28. 6ab 60	29. -4bc 160	30. bc^2 -320

T25
Glencoe Division, Macmillan/McGraw-Hill

104

Examples

3 Solve $y = (7)(-9)(6)$.
Use the associative property to group the factors.
$y = [7(-9)](6)$
$y = (-63)(6)$ or −378

4 Solve $r = (-6)^2$.
The exponent says there are two factors of −6.
$r = (-6)^2$
$r = (-6)(-6)$ or 36

Checking for Understanding

Communicating Mathematics

Read and study the lesson to answer each question.

1. **Tell** why $3(-8)$ and $-8(3)$ have the same product. Multiplication is commutative.
2. **Show** another way to solve the equation in Example 3.
3. **Show** how you would use your calculator to solve the equation in Example 4.
4. **Draw** a model to show the solution for $w = (-6)(2)$.
5. **Write** a sentence that tells what the sign of y is in $y = x^2$, no matter what value of x, besides 0, you choose. y is always positive.

For answers to Exercises 2-4, see margin.

Guided Practice State whether each product will be positive, negative, or zero.

6. $7(-8)$ −
7. $98(-2)$ −
8. $(23)(-3)(-7)$ +
9. $(5)(6)(0)$ 0

Solve each equation.

10. $t = 9(-3)$ −27
11. $g = 5(-30)$ −150
12. $q = 9(-11)$ −99
13. $-3(-7) = k$ 21
14. $g = -8(-3)$ 24
15. $-12(-8) = p$ 96
16. $b = -9(12)$ −108
17. $w = 4(30)$ 120
18. $d = 6(-3)$ −18
19. $(-8)^2 = y$ 64
20. $-5(-14) = f$ 70
21. $y = 7(5)$ 35

Exercises

Independent Practice Solve each equation.

22. $p = 6(8)$ 48
23. $w = -9(7)$ −63
24. $7(-14) = y$ −98
25. $9(-9) = k$ −81
26. $r = 55(-11)$ −605
27. $w = -6(-13)$ 78
28. $-5(80)(-2) = m$ 800
29. $(-6)(7)(-12) = p$ 504
30. $u = 9(-10)(3)$ −270
31. $q = 7(23)(5)$ 805
32. $-4(-50)(-1) = j$ −200
33. $(-21)^2 = t$ 441
34. $(-8)(9)(6)^2 = k$ −2,592
35. $(3)(12)(-2) = k$ −72
36. $m = (6)^2 \cdot (-3)^2$ 324

Evaluate each expression if $a = -3$, $b = -6$, and $c = 10$.

37. $3ab$ 54
38. $-10ac$ 300
39. ab^2 −108
40. $12abc$ 2,160

Mixed Review

41. **Car Rental** Jackson Auto Rental charges $20 per day and $0.15 per mile to rent a car. Find the cost of renting a car for two days and driving 100 miles. *(Lesson 1-1)* $55

42. How many kilometers did Katra walk if she walked 39.4 meters? *(Lesson 1-6)* 0.0394 km

104 **Chapter 3** Integers

OPTIONS

Bell Ringer

Find the pair of integers whose sum and product are given.

	Sum	Product	
1.	−7	10	−2, −5
2.	11	24	3, 8
3.	−2	−24	4, −6
4.	8	−9	9, −1
5.	−5	−14	−7, 2

43. Solve $8.2 \div 0.2 = t$. Check your solution. *(Lesson 2-4)* **41**

44. Graph $\{-3, -1, 0, 2\}$ on a number line. *(Lesson 3-1)* **See margin.**

45. Solve $57 - (-26) = d$. *(Lesson 3-5)* **83**

**Problem Solving
and
Applications**

c. See
Solutions
Manual.

DATA SEARCH

48g. If n is odd,
then $(-1)^n$ is
-1. If n is even,
$(-1)^n = 1$.

46. **Health** Mr. Tu has lost an average of three pounds a week on his diet. He has dieted for 11 weeks. He weighed 268 pounds at the beginning of his diet.

   a. How much does he weigh now? **235 pounds**

   b. Mr. Tu's goal is to weigh 168 pounds. If he continues at this rate, how much longer will it take him to reach his goal? **about 23 weeks**

   c. Draw a graph to show Mr. Tu's weight loss for the first eight weeks.

47. **Data Search** Refer to page 667.
   Which state has the greatest range in record high and low temperatures?
   Which state has the least range? **Alaska; Hawaii**

48. **Critical Thinking** Find the value of each expression.

   a. $(-1)^2$ **1**   b. $(-1)^3$ **-1**   c. $(-1)^4$ **1**   d. $(-1)^5$ **-1**   e. $(-1)^6$ **1**

   f. What do you think is the value of $(-1)^{5,280}$? **1**

   g. Write a general rule for the value of $(-1)^n$, where n is a whole number.

49. **Journal Entry** How can you determine the sign of the product of two integers? Can you write a rule for determining the sign of a product based on the signs of its factors? **See student's work.**

Save Planet Earth

Aluminum Recycling The first aluminum beverage can appeared in 1963, and today it accounts for the largest single use of aluminum. In 1992, more than 92 billion beverage cans were used, and 97% of them were aluminum.

According to the Aluminum Association, Americans recycled 63 billion aluminum cans in 1992. This cuts related air pollution by 95% and uses 90% less energy than making aluminum from scratch. It is estimated that the energy saved from recycling just one aluminum can will operate a television for 3 hours.

How You Can Help

- Check the yellow pages to find out which kinds of recycling programs exist in your area. The most popular are reverse vending machines, curbside pickup, and drop-off centers with bins for recycling.

- You can also recycle aluminum foil, pie plates, and frozen food trays.

Lesson 3-6 Multiplying Integers   **105**

Extending the Lesson

Save Planet Earth Write to the Aluminum Association, 900 19th St. NW, Washington, DC 20006 to find out more about group recycling and setting up fundraising projects.

Cooperative Learning Activity

Are You Positive? 3-6

Number of players: 2
Materials: Spinners, counters

- On a large sheet of paper (or several sheets taped together), copy the game board shown below. Make sure that a counter can fit inside each square. Label the sections of one spinner with the following integers: -1, 1, 2, -2. Label the sections of a second spinner with the following integers: 0, -1, -2, -3.

- Each partner places a counter on the "Start" square. In turn, each partner spins both spinners and finds the product of the resulting numbers. For a positive product, move your counter to the right. For a negative product, move your counter to the left. Try to be the first to reach the last square on the right. If you land on or go past the last square on the left, you automatically lose.

Lose   Start   Win

Glencoe Mathematics: Applications and Connections, Course 3

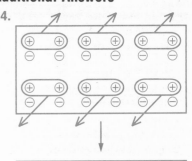

Enrichment Masters, p. 25

105

NCTM Standards: 1–7, 9, 12

Lesson Resources
- Study Guide Master 3-7
- Practice Master 3-7
- Enrichment Master 3-7
- Technology Master, p. 3
- Group Activity Card 3-7

 Transparency 3-7 contains the 5-Minute Check and a teaching aid for this lesson.

🕐 **5-Minute Check**
(Over Lesson 3-6)

Solve each equation.
1. $n = -3(12)$ -36
2. $k = -8(7)(-1)$ 56
3. $-6(-4) = p$ 24
4. $h = 2(-9)(5)$ -90
5. Evaluate m^2n if $m = -4$ and $n = -3$. -48

1 FOCUS

Motivating the Lesson

Questioning
Have students study the patterns in the equations and then write the next two equations.

$8 \div 4 =$		2
$4 \div 4 =$		1
$0 \div 4 =$		0
$-4 \div 4 =$		-1

$-8 \div 4 = -2; -12 \div 4 = -3$

2 TEACH

Using Models Use negative counters to show that $-6 \div 3 = -2$.

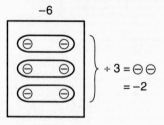

-6

$\div 3 = \ominus \ominus$
$= -2$

3-7 Dividing Integers

Objective
Divide integers.

When you watch the news, do you ever wonder what the stock market reports have to do with the economy? The greatest event in the stock market's history is probably the crash of 1929. After the stock market crash, the economy of the United States fell to an all-time low. The percent of employed people fell from 91 percent in 1930 to 75 percent in 1932. What was the average fall per year in employed people?

The change in the percent of employed people can be expressed by $75 - 91$, or -16. This occurred over 2 years. The average can be found by dividing -16 by 2.

Division of integers is related to multiplication of integers. That is, for $b \neq 0$, $a \div b = c$ if $b \cdot c = a$. Let's use this rule to solve $y = -16 \div 2$.

Write a related multiplication sentence.
$$y = -16 \div 2 \text{ if } 2y = -16$$

Think: 2 times what number equals -16?
$2 \cdot 8 = -16$ *no* $2 \cdot (-8) = -16$ ✓

So, $y = -8$. The average fall in employment was 8 percent per year.

Division is related to multiplication, so it uses the same rules of signs.

DID YOU KNOW

The greatest fall in the Dow-Jones Averages occurred on October 19, 1987. The average fell over 500 points.

Dividing Integers	The quotient of two integers with the same sign is positive.
	The quotient of two integers with different signs is negative.

Examples

1 Solve $-40 \div (-5) = z$.

$-40 \div (-5) = z$ *The signs are the same.*
$8 = z$ *The quotient is positive.*

2 Solve $v = -36 \div 9$.

$v = -36 \div 9$ *The signs are different.*
$v = -4$ *The quotient is negative.*

106   **Chapter 3** Integers

OPTIONS

Reteaching Activity

Using Connections Help students see the relationship between division and multiplication by having them solve several division problems following the format shown below.

$24 \div (-6) = \square \longrightarrow \square \cdot (-6) = 24$

The quotient tried in the first box must also be the factor in the second box.

Study Guide Masters, p. 26

Name _____ Date _____

Study Guide Worksheet 3-7

Dividing Integers

If two integers have the same sign, their quotient is positive.

Examples $m = 420 \div 7$ Both integers are positive.
$m = 60$ The quotient is positive.

$d = -90 \div (-9)$ Both integers are negative.
$d = 10$ The quotient is positive.

If two integers have different signs, their quotient is negative.

Examples $f = -25 \div 5$ The dividend is negative. The divisor is positive.
$f = -5$ The quotient is negative.

$a = \dfrac{20}{-4}$ The dividend is positive. The divisor is negative.
$a = -5$ The quotient is negative.

Remember that fractions are also a way of showing division. Another way to show $c = a \div b$ is $c = \frac{a}{b}$.

Examples

3 Solve $p = \frac{45}{9}$.

$p = \frac{45}{9}$
$p = 5$

4 Solve $\frac{81}{-9} = t$.

$\frac{81}{-9} = t$
$-9 = t$

Checking for Understanding

Communicating Mathematics

Read and study the lesson to answer each question.

1. **Write** the verbal sentence *forty-five divided by negative nine equals t* as an equation in two different ways. $45 \div (-9) = t;\ \frac{45}{-9} = t$

2. **Tell** a related multiplication sentence for $320 \div (-8) = p$. $-8p = 320$

3. **Show** how you can check a solution found by dividing.
   If $\frac{a}{b} = c$, check by seeing if $b \cdot c = a$.

Guided Practice

State whether each quotient is *positive* or *negative*.

4. $\frac{-24}{3}$ —

5. $\frac{66}{-11}$ —

6. $\frac{-145}{-11}$ +

7. $\frac{200}{-25}$ —

Solve each equation.

8. $240 \div (-60) = y$ -4

9. $365 \div (-5) = r$ -73

10. $-12 \div (-4) = h$ 3

11. $f = \frac{245}{-5}$ -49

12. $d = \frac{224}{-32}$ -7

13. $\frac{-88}{44} = t$ -2

14. $\frac{90}{10} = z$ 9

15. $-56 \div (-2) = p$ 28

16. $w = 49 \div 7$ 7

Exercises

Independent Practice

Solve each equation.

17. $\frac{62}{-2} = n$ -31

18. $\frac{700}{-100} = k$ -7

19. $m = 564 \div (-3)$ -188

20. $-26 \div (-13) = b$ 2

21. $295 \div 5 = y$ 59

22. $t = -930 \div (-30)$ 31

23. $\frac{588}{-6} = g$ -98

24. $k = \frac{-195}{65}$ -3

Evaluate each expression if $c = -9$, $r = 3$, and $t = -10$.

25. $\frac{99}{r}$ 33

26. $-\frac{99}{c}$ 11

27. $\frac{800}{t}$ -80

28. $\frac{c}{-3}$ 3

29. $t \div (-2)$ 5

30. $50 \div t$ -5

31. $342 \div c$ -38

32. $-342 \div r$ -114

33. $cr - 4$ -31

34. $rt \div (-5)$ 6

35. $5ct \div r$ 150

36. $(crt)^2 \div t$ $-7,290$

Lesson 3-7 Dividing Integers **107**

Multicultural Education

Benjamin Banneker (1731–1806) was an African-American mathematician, astronomer, and inventor. He sometimes amused himself by creating difficult problems, which he then solved. Banneker was one of three men appointed to design the city of Washington, D.C. When designer Pierre L'Enfant departed with the plans, Banneker redrew them from memory.

More Examples

For Example 1
Solve $-20 \div (-4) = m$. 5

For Example 2
Solve $p = -32 \div 8$. -4

For Example 3
Solve $x = \frac{-50}{-2}$. 25

For Example 4
Solve $\frac{18}{-3} = k$. -6

Checking for Understanding

Exercises 1-7 are designed to help you assess students' understanding through reading, writing, speaking, and modeling. You should work through these exercises with your students and then monitor their work on Guided Practice Exercises 8-16.

Error Analysis

Watch for students who use the wrong sign for the quotient.

Prevent by stressing that division of integers follows the same rules of signs as multiplication.

Practice Masters, p. 26

107

Close

Have students complete each statement using the word *positive* or *negative*.

- The quotient of two positive integers is __?__. positive
- The quotient of two negative integers is __?__. positive
- The quotient of a positive integer and a negative integer is __?__. negative

3 PRACTICE/APPLY

Maximum: 17–47
Minimum: 17–35 odd, 37–44, 46

For **Extra Practice,** see p. 590.

Alternate Assessment

Speaking Name several pairs of integers. Have students state the quotient of each pair.

Enrichment Masters, p. 26

Mixed Review

37. Use mental math to find $42 + 86 + 58$. *(Lesson 1-2)* 186
38. Solve $c + 9 = 27$. *(Lesson 2-2)* 18
39. **Geometry** Find the perimeter of a rectangle whose length is three times its width. Its width is 4 inches. *(Lesson 2-9)* 32 inches
40. Solve $z = -5 + 24 + (-8)$. Check your solution. *(Lesson 3-4)* 11
41. Solve $u = -8(10)(-12)$. *(Lesson 3-6)* 960

Problem Solving and Applications

42. **Critical Thinking** Find values for a, b, and c, so that all of the following statements are true. Sample answer: $a = -156$; $b = 13$; $c = -12$
    (1) $b > a$, $c < b$, and $a < 0$.
    (2) a has three digits.
    (3) b and c each have two digits.
    (4) c is divisible by 2 and 3.
    (5) b can only be divided by 1 and itself.
    (6) $a \div b = c$

43. **Banking** The Westminster Savings and Loan invested poorly and lost $36,048 in seven weeks. About how much did they lose on average each week? about $5,150

44. **Business** A check written by a company is recorded as a negative value on its monthly spreadsheet. The Neat Lawn Company hired several teenagers for one day to pick up the trash in a park. Each teen received the same pay. Each teen's entry on the spreadsheet was –$38.35. The total of all entries was –$345.15. Use your calculator to find out how many teens they hired to clean the park. 9 teens

45. **Make a Model** You have learned how to model addition, subtraction, and multiplication of integers using colored counters. Use colored counters to develop a model for dividing integers. See Solutions Manual.
    a. $y = -12 \div 3$ b. $x = 8 \div (-2)$ c. $-6 \div (-3) = z$

46. **Weather** The chart at the right is a record of falling temperatures every 3 hours on a November day in Roanoke, Virginia.

Time	Temperature
Midnight	60°F
3:00 A.M.	50°F
6:00 A.M.	42°F
9:00 A.M.	38°F
Noon	35°F

    a. How much did the temperature fall from each time period to the next? Write each fall as a negative temperature. –10°F; –8°F; –4°F; –3°F

    b. The average temperature fall can be calculated by finding the sum of the temperature falls and dividing by the number of time periods. What is the average temperature fall? –6.25°F

47. **Journal Entry** Write a sentence telling why the rules for signs when dividing two integers are the same as those for multiplying two integers.
    The rules are the same because division is actually multiplying by the reciprocal.

108   Chapter 3 Integers

OPTIONS

Extending the Lesson

Using Cooperative Groups Have small groups solve this problem: "Yesterday's low temperature, in degrees Fahrenheit, was very cold," said the meteorologist. "If you multiply the temperature by −4, add −4, divide by −4, and subtract −4, the result is −4." What was the temperature?

Cooperative Learning Activity

Equation Bingo 3-7

Use groups of 4.
Materials: Paper, pencils

- Each group member copies the bingo card at the right.

➡ Try to be the first to cross out all the numbers in any row, column, or diagonal. In order to cross out a number, you must get that number as the solution to one of the equations on the back of this card. Show that you have solved an equation by writing the equation number in the corner box next to the solution. The first group member to get a "bingo" must have his or her equation number verified by the other group members.

−3	7	14	−5
4	−9	3	9
−4	25	−8	−16
−7	8	−23	12

Glencoe Mathematics: Applications and Connections, Course 3

3-8 Classify Information

Objective

Solve problems by identifying important information.

The winter temperatures in Yakutsk, Yakut Republic (formerly part of the U.S.S.R.), have fallen as low as $-64°$C, and in the summer they have reached a high of $39°$C. What is the possible range of temperatures in a year?

Explore   What do you know?

- The lowest temperature is $-64°$C.
- The highest temperature is $39°$C.
- Yakutsk is in the Yakut Republic, which used to be part of the U.S.S.R.

You need to find the range of temperatures in a year.

Plan   Classify the information into what you need to know to solve the problem and what you do not need to know.

What you need to know:

- To find the range, you need to know the highest temperature and the lowest temperature.

lowest temperature	$-64°$C
highest temperature	$39°$C

What you do not need to know:

- Yakutsk is in the Yakut Republic.

There is too much information given in the problem.

Solve   To find the range, subtract the lowest temperature from the highest temperature.

Let r represent the range.

$r = 39 - (-64)$
$r = 39 + 64$ *Rewrite using the additive inverse.*
$r = 103$

The possible range of temperatures in a year is $103°$C.

Lesson 3-8   Problem-Solving Strategy: Classify Information   **109**

3-8 Lesson Notes

NCTM Standards: 1–5, 7, 12

Lesson Resources
- Study Guide Master 3-8
- Practice Master 3-8
- Enrichment Master 3-8
- Group Activity Card 3-8

 Transparency 3-8 contains the 5-Minute Check and a teaching aid for this lesson.

🕐 5-Minute Check
(Over Lesson 3-7)

Solve each equation.

1. $\frac{-42}{7} = x$ -6

2. $n = 260 \div (-20)$ -13

3. $88 \div 8 = p$ 11

4. $k = \frac{-324}{-9}$ 36

5. Evaluate $xy^2 \div 2$ if $x = -6$ and $y = -3$. -27

Practice Masters, p. 27

Name _____   Date _____

Practice Worksheet 3-8

Problem-Solving Strategy: Classify Information

Solve, if possible. Classify information in each problem by writing "not enough information" or "too much information."

1. Phien bought 3 address books that cost $4.98 each. She gave the cashier a $20 bill. What was the total cost of the books?   too much information; $14.94

2. Jimmy grew 3 inches last year and 2 inches so far this year. How tall is Jimmy now?   not enough information

3. Sheila bought 10 computer disks for $1.39 each. The disks usually sell for $1.99 each, or ten for $18. How much did she pay for the disks?   too much information; $13.90

4. Carl, a carpenter, has two tape measures. The steel tape is 8 feet long. The cloth tape is marked in metric measure at 1-centimeter intervals. How much longer is the steel tape than the cloth tape?   not enough information

Solve using any strategy.

5. Gerda pays a delivery service $18 for priority delivery, $15 for standard delivery, and $21 for Saturday delivery. How much will she save by sending a package by standard delivery instead of Saturday delivery? $6

6. Andy has two scientific calculators. The smaller one has 38 buttons, and the larger one has almost twice as many buttons. How many buttons does the larger calculator have?   not enough information

7. The difference of a number x and 12 is 18. What is the value of x?   30

8. Tim's father's age is 3 more than 10 times Tim's age. Tim is 3 years old. How old is Tim's father?   33 years old

9. Peru, in South America, has a population of approximately 20,345,000. The area of Peru is 496,222 square miles. About how many people are there per square mile?   about 41 people per square mile

10. The Ming Dynasty was established in China in 1368. It survived almost 300 years and ended more than 20 years after the pilgrim's 1620 landing in Plymouth, Massachusetts. How many years long was the Ming Dynasty?   not enough information for an exact answer; about 300 years

T 27
Glencoe Division, Macmillan/McGraw-Hill

OPTIONS

Reteaching Activity

Using Charts   Have students complete this chart for each of the Practice exercises.

What do I know?	What must I know in order to solve the problem?	Too much, not enough, or exactly enough information?

Study Guide Masters, p. 27

Name _____   Date _____

Study Guide Worksheet 3-8

Problem-Solving Strategy: Classify Information

Example   In 1961, Antonio Abertondo swam from England to France in 18 hours 50 minutes, rested 4 minutes, and swam back to England in 24 hours 16 minutes. He completed the first double crossing of the English Channel in 43 hours 10 minutes. How much less time did it take him to swim from England to France than from France to England?

Explore   What do you want to find?
How much less time it took to swim from England to France than from France to England.

What information do you need? There is too much information. To solve the problem, you need only the swimming time from England to France, 18 hours and 50 minutes, and the swimming time from France to England, 24 hours and 16 minutes.

1 FOCUS

Motivating the Lesson

Questioning Have students read the opening paragraph of the lesson. Have them compare local temperatures with those in Yakutsk.

2 TEACH

Using Connections Point out that the work-backward strategy can be used to classify information. You are working backward when you ask, "What do I need to know to answer the question?".

Close

Have students write examples of problems containing too much, too little, and just enough information.

3 PRACTICE/APPLY

Assignment Guide
Maximum: 6–11
Minimum: 6–11

Enrichment Masters, p. 27

Examine If the range is correct, you should be able to subtract the range from the highest temperature to get the lowest temperature.

$$39 - r = -64$$
$$39 - 103 \stackrel{?}{=} -64 \qquad \textit{Replace r with 103.}$$
$$39 + (-103) \stackrel{?}{=} -64 \qquad \textit{Rewrite using the additive inverse.}$$
$$-64 = -64 \checkmark \qquad \textit{The answer checks.}$$

Checking for Understanding

Communicating Mathematics

Read and study the lesson to answer each question. **Answers will vary.**

1. **Tell** how you know if a problem does not contain enough information.
2. **Write** a paragraph about a real-life situation where you did not have all the facts to solve a problem. **See students' work.**

Guided Practice

Solve, if possible. Classify information in each problem by writing *not enough information* or *too much information*.

3. Jonathan bought four compact discs. How much did he spend? **not enough information**
4. The record low temperature in Texas is −23° F. The record high temperature is 120° F. Houston averages 44.76 inches of precipitation per year. What is the range of the high and the low temperatures in Texas? **143°F, too much infor-**
5. Denver is known as the Mile High City. Its elevation is 5,283 feet. The **mation** elevation of Boise, Idaho, is 2,838 feet. About how much higher is Denver? **about 2,500 feet, too much information**

Problem Solving

Practice

Solve using any strategy.

6. The Nepalese jawa, produced in 1740, is the smallest known coin ever minted. This sliver of silver weighs in at a mere 0.014 gram. How much would a stack of 50 jawas weigh? **0.7 grams** **7. not enough information**

Strategies
• • • • • • •
Look for a pattern.
Solve a simpler problem.
Act it out.
Guess and check.
Draw a diagram.
Make a chart.
Work backward.

7. Papua, New Guinea, an independent state in the southwest Pacific, has a population of 3,221,000. How many people are there per square mile?
8. The product of 6 and a number is −36. What is the number? **−6**
9. Kimiko's second bowling score was 82 pins less than twice her first score. If her second score was 168, what was her first score? **125** **not enough infor-**
10. Find the area of a rectangular-shaped living room if its length is 15 feet. **mation**
11. Last year, Mrs. Penny spent $400 on season tickets to the Los Angeles Raiders home games. This year she bought two tickets per game at $35 each for a total of eight home games. How much did she spend this year? **$560**

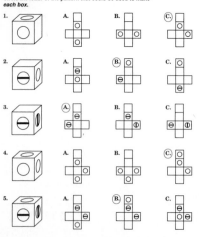

OPTIONS

Extending the Lesson

Using Cooperative Groups Have small groups solve the following problem. *For the first 9 days in December, the average low temperature in Yakutsk was − 12°C. For the next 13 days, it was 2°C. For the next 8 days, it was 9°C. The average low temperature for the month was 0°C. What was the low temperature on the 31st day?* **10°C**

Cooperative Learning Activity

Start on a Dime **3-8**

Use groups of 2.
Materials: Play money

♦ Arrange four pennies and four dimes as shown below.

→ The object of this game is to rearrange the coins so that there are four dimes followed by four pennies in the row (with all of the coins in the row touching). You are allowed four moves only. On each move you may move two touching coins to either end of the row or to a gap in the row. The value of each pair of coins you move must not exceed $0.20, and, when rearranged, the sum of the values of the coins must be $0.44.

(penny)(dime)(penny)(dime)(penny)(dime)(penny)(dime)

Glencoe Mathematics: Applications and Connections, Course 3

Cooperative Learning

3-9A Solving Equations

A Preview of Lesson 3-9

Objective

Solve equations by using models.

Materials

two colors of counters
cups
mats

You used colored counters to model integers in Lessons 3-3, 3-5, and 3-6. These can also be used to solve equations that involve integers.

Activity One

Work with a partner. Solve $x + (-5) = 8$.

- Start with an empty mat.
- Let a cup represent the unknown x value. Put a cup and 5 negative counters on one side of the mat. Place 8 positive counters on the other side.

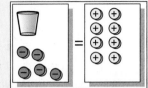

- Our goal is to get the cup by itself on one side of the mat. Then the counters on the other side will be the value of the cup, or x.

- Add 5 positive counters to each side.

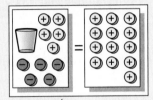

- Group the counters to form zero pairs. Then remove all zero pairs.

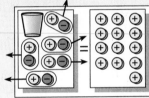

- The cup is now by itself on one side of the mat. The counters are on the other side.

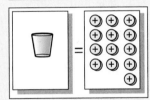

What do you think?

1. What is the solution of $x + (-5) = 8$? 13
2. How do you know what type of counter to add to each side of the mat? the opposite of what is already there

Mathematics Lab 3-9A Solving Equations **111**

NCTM Standards: 1–5, 7, 9

Management Tips

For Students To solve the equations in the lab, each pair of students will need 4 cups, 24 positive counters, and 15 negative counters. HINT: Assemble the counters in sandwich bags with a twist-tie for convenient management.

For the Overhead Projector
Overhead Manipulative Resources provides appropriate materials for teacher or student demonstration of the activities in this Mathematics Lab.

1 FOCUS

Introducing the Lab

Questioning Review equations by having students solve the following equations mentally.

1. $x + 4 = 6$ 2
2. $x - 5 = 3$ 8
3. $5x = 30$ 6
4. $\frac{x}{7} = 4$ 28

2 TEACH

Using Logical Reasoning
Before students begin Activity One, have them study the first diagram. Ask the following questions.

- *What needs to be done before the equation is solved?* The negative counters must be removed so that the cup is alone.

- *Why not just remove the negative counters?* Anything done on the left side of the mat must also be done on the right side.

3 PRACTICE/APPLY

Using Communication After students solve each equation, ask the following question. *How can you check your solution?* Substitute it in the original equation and see if a true equation results.

Close

Have students write a few sentences describing the procedure for solving the equation $2x + (-3) = 5$ using cups and counters.

Activity Two

Solve $3x - (-2) = 11$.

First rewrite the expression using the additive inverse. Then $3x - (-2) = 11$ becomes $3x + 2 = 11$.

- Begin with an empty mat.

- To represent $3x$, put 3 cups on one side of the mat. Also add 2 positive counters on that side. Put 11 positive counters on the right mat.

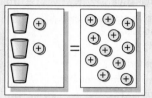

- Add 2 negative counters to each side.

- Remove any zero pairs that can be formed on each side of the mat.

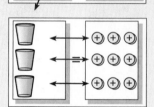

Our goal is still to get the cups alone on one side and all counters on the other side.

- Arrange the remaining counters on the right side of the mat into 3 equal groups so that they correspond to the 3 cups.

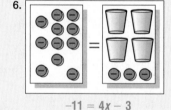

What do you think?

3. How many counters correspond to each cup? **3**

4. What is the solution of $3x - (-2) = 11$? **3**

Write an equation for each model.

5.
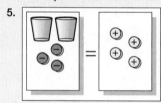
$2x - 3 = 4$

6.
$-11 = 4x - 3$

Solve these equations by using models.

7. $x + 3 = 9$ **6**   8. $x - 6 = 2$ **8**   9. $x + (-4) = 6$ **10**

10. $x + 6 = -2$ **-8**   11. $x - (-2) = 4$ **2**   12. $x - (-4) = -3$ **-7**

13. $3x = -15$ **-5**   14. $2x = 14$ **7**   15. $4x + 6 = 18$ **3**

16. $2x - 1 = 11$ **6**   17. $2x + 3 = -5$ **-4**   18. $3x - 5 = -5$ **0**

112   **Chapter 3** Integers

OPTIONS

Lab Manual You may wish to make copies of the blackline master on p. 46 of the *Lab Manual* for students to use as a recording sheet.

Lab Manual, p. 46

Name _____ Date _____

Mathematics Lab Worksheet

Use with pages 111-112

Mathematics Lab: Solving Equations

What do you think? (page 111)

1. _____ 13

2. Add the same kind of counter to each side. In this example, add 5 positive counters to form 5 zero pairs on the left side.

What do you think? (page 112)

3. 3 positive counters

4. _____ 3

Algebra Connection

3-9 Solving Equations

Objective
Solve equations with integer solutions.

When chemical reactions occur, the resulting molecules may not resemble the elements being combined. For example, oxygen and hydrogen are gases. But when they react, they can form water, a liquid.

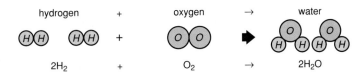

hydrogen + oxygen → water

$2H_2$ + O_2 → $2H_2O$

Chemists describe these reactions by using chemical equations. The equations are balanced. That is, they always have the same number of atoms on each side.

Equations in mathematics are also balanced. Whatever you do to one side of the equation, you must also do to the other.

You solve equations involving integers in the same way you solve equations involving whole numbers or decimals.

Examples

1 Solve $m - (-45) = 35$.

$$m - (-45) = 35$$
$$m + 45 = 35 \qquad \text{\textit{Rewrite the equation using the additive inverse.}}$$
$$m + 45 - 45 = 35 - 45 \qquad \text{\textit{Subtract 45 from each side.}}$$
$$m = -10$$

Check: $m - (-45) = 35$
$$-10 - (-45) \stackrel{?}{=} 35 \qquad \text{\textit{Replace m with -10.}}$$
$$-10 + 45 \stackrel{?}{=} 35$$
$$35 = 35 ✔$$

2 Solve $-15 = -5w$.

$$-15 = -5w$$
$$\frac{-15}{-5} = \frac{-5w}{-5} \qquad \text{\textit{Divide to undo multiplication.}}$$
$$3 = w$$

Check: $-15 = -5w$
$$-15 \stackrel{?}{=} -5(3) \qquad \text{\textit{Replace w with 3.}}$$
$$-15 = -15 ✔$$

"When am I ever going to use this?"

Suppose you are planting flowers in a garden. Read the package of seeds to see how far apart the seeds need to be planted. If you want 10 seeds in a row, use algebra to find out how long the row would be if you wanted 4 in. of extra space on each end of the row.

Lesson 3-9 Algebra Connection: Solving Equations **113**

OPTIONS

Multicultural Education

Contributions to the development of mathematics by ancient Arab mathematicians was enormous. The word *algebra* comes from *al-jabr,* a term coined by Mohammed al-Khowarizmi around 825 A.D. It means "restoring balance," a reference to the method al-Khowarizmi developed for solving equations.

NCTM Standards: 1–7, 9

Lesson Resources
- Study Guide Master 3-9
- Practice Master 3-9
- Enrichment Master 3-9
- Technology Master, p. 17
- Group Activity Card 3-9

 Transparency 3-9 contains the 5-Minute Check and a teaching aid for this lesson.

⏱ 5-Minute Check
(Over Lesson 3-8)

Classify information. Then solve, if possible.

1. Marci bought 4 pounds of ground beef for $5.16 and 3 pounds of cheese for $10.17. How much did she spend?   too much information; $15.33

2. The range of high and low temperatures in one city was 48°F. One extreme temperature was 32°F. What was the other?   not enough information

1 FOCUS

Motivating the Lesson

Questioning   Have students read the opening paragraph of the lesson. Ask the following questions.

- *What elements combine in the reaction?*   hydrogen, oxygen
- *What is formed?*   water
- *How many hydrogen atoms are on the left side of the chemical equation shown? on the right?*   4; 4
- *How many oxygen atoms are on the left side of the chemical equation? on the right?*   2; 2

113

Using Cooperative Groups
Before going over the examples, have pairs of students solve $2x + 3 = 11$ as a means of reviewing the steps involved in solving an equation algebraically.

$$2x + 3 = 11$$
$$2x + 3 - 3 = 11 - 3$$
$$2x = 8$$
$$\left(\frac{2x}{2}\right) = \left(\frac{8}{2}\right)$$
$$x = 4$$

More Examples

For Example 1

Solve $23 = x + (-16)$.   39

For Example 2

Solve $\frac{k}{-3} = -7$.   21

For Example 3

Solve $\frac{y}{-4} + (-9) = -6$.
-12

For Example 4

Mrs. Larsen is an underwater photographer. During a dive she determines that she can descend to a depth three times her present depth and still be 14 feet above her previous deepest descent of -122 feet. Find her present depth. -36 feet

---

Checking for Understanding

Exercises 1-3 are designed to help you assess students' understanding through reading, writing, speaking, and modeling. You should work through these exercises with your students and then monitor their work on Guided Practice Exercises 4-11.

Integers are also used in equations that require two steps to solve. You work backward to solve for the variable.

Example 3

LOOKBACK
You can review two-step equations on page 67.

Solve $4x - (-7) = -17$.

First rewrite the equation using the additive inverse.
Then $4x - (-7) = -17$ becomes $4x + 7 = -17$.

$$4x - (-7) = -17$$
$$4x + 7 = -17 \qquad \textit{Rewrite using the additive inverse.}$$
$$4x + 7 - 7 = -17 - 7 \qquad \textit{Subtract 7 from each side.}$$
$$4x = -24$$
$$\frac{4x}{4} = \frac{-24}{4} \qquad \textit{Divide each side by 4.}$$
$$x = -6$$

Check: Use your calculator. Replace x with -6.

4 $\boxed{\times}$ 6 $\boxed{-}$ 7 $\boxed{=}$ -17

Equations with integers can be used to represent real-life problems.

Example 4 *Problem Solving*

Personal Finance   Morty borrowed $63 from his parents to buy a video game. He promised to pay it back. Then he borrowed money two times to go to the movies. He now owes his parents $87. If he borrowed equal amounts each time he went to the movies, how much did he borrow each time?

Explore   We know his original debt is $63 and he now owes $87. He borrowed two equal amounts. We need to find out what those amounts were.

Plan   Let m represent the money he borrowed to go to the movies. Since he went twice, the amount borrowed is $2m$. Write an equation to solve this problem.

The total owed equals the sum of what he owed before and the new amount.

$$-63 + 2m = -87$$

> **Estimation Hint**
> ● ● ● ● ● ● ● ● ● ●
> The total is about $90 and he borrowed about $60 the first time. Think: $\frac{90 - 60}{2} = 15$. He borrowed about $15 each time to go to the movies.

OPTIONS

Reteaching Activity

Using Manipulatives   Have students use cups and counters to practice solving equations. Stress the similarities between cup-and-counter solutions and algebraic solutions, so that students can transfer what they learn using manipulatives to their paper-and-pencil work.

Study Guide Masters, p. 28

Name _____   Date _____

Study Guide Worksheet 3-9

Algebra: Solving Equations

Integer equations are solved like whole-number equations. For addition or subtraction equations, add or subtract the same number on both sides of the equation. Watch for signs. Use the additive inverse to simplify equations.

Examples $k + 16 = -20$ $c - (-21) = 40$
  $k + 16 - 16 = -20 - 16$ $c + 21 = 40$ Use the additive inverse.
  $k = -36$ $c + 21 - 21 = 40 - 21$
                $c = 19$

For multiplication and division equations, multiply or divide both sides of the equation by the same number.

Examples $-7t = -98$ $\frac{m}{20} = -4$
  $-7t \div (-7) = -98 \div (-7)$ $\frac{m}{20} \times 20 = -4(20)$

Solve   Use pencil and paper.

$$-63 + 2m = -87$$
$$-63 + 63 + 2m = -87 + 63 \quad \textit{Add 63 to each side.}$$
$$2m = -24$$
$$\frac{2m}{2} = \frac{-24}{2} \quad \textit{Divide each side by 2.}$$
$$m = -12$$

Use a calculator.

87 [+/-] [+] 63 [=] [÷] 2 [=] ⁻12

The solution, −12, means Morty borrowed $12 each time.

Examine   We can check our solution by adding.

amount he owed	$63
amount for first movie	$12
amount for second movie	+ $12
total borrowed	$87

This total matches the total given in the problem.

Checking for Understanding

Communicating Mathematics

Read and study the lesson to answer each question.

1. **Tell** the first step in solving $4y + 5 = -15$. Subtract 5 from each side.

2. **Show** how you could solve the equation in Example 2 by using counters, cups, and mats. See Solutions Manual.

3. **Write** a sentence to explain why it is always a good idea to check your solution to an equation. To make sure the solution is correct.

Guided Practice

Solve each equation. Check your solution.

4. $2y = -90$ −45

5. $c + 16 = -64$ −80

6. $\frac{m}{-14} = 32$ −448

7. $x - (-35) = -240$ −275

8. $36 = -12 + 8m$ 6

9. $-3y + 15 = 75$ −20

10. $\frac{t}{6} - 5 = -13$ −48

11. $2x - (-34) = 16$ −9

Exercises

Independent Practice

Solve each equation. Check your solution.

12. $2t = -98$ −49

13. $s - (-350) = 32$ −318

14. $\frac{y}{15} = 22$ 330

15. $2w + 35 = 105$ 35

16. $45 = y - 13$ 58

17. $-200 = \frac{z}{3}$ −600

18. $4p - 15 = -75$ −15

19. $-69t = -4{,}968$ 72

20. $q + (-367) = 250$ 617

21. $-30 = 42 + c$ −72

22. $5d + 120 = 300$ 36

23. $4m - 15 = 45$ 15

Lesson 3-9 Algebra Connection: Solving Equations   **115**

Bell Ringer

What kind of "bell ringers" are heard most often in the wintertime? To find out, solve the following equations on your calculator. Turn the display upside down after each calculation to read the answer.

$$\frac{x}{125} - 4{,}627 = -696$$

$$9x + 480{,}358 = 1{,}000{,}000$$

SLEIGH BELLS

32c.
$$7x = -224$$
$$8x = -512$$
$$9x = -1,152$$
$$10x = -2,560$$
$$11x = -5,632$$

Write an equation for each problem and solve.

24. The sum of two integers is −24. One of the integers is −13. What is the other integer? $x + (-13) = -24$; −11

25. The product of two integers is 35. One of the integers is −7. What is the other integer? $-7x = 35$; −5

26. Twice a number plus 7 is −21. What is the number? $2x + 7 = -21$; −14

Mixed Review 27. Estimate 4,286 + 3,716 by rounding. *(Lesson 1-3)* **8,000**

28. Solve $30 = k - 141$. Check your solution. *(Lesson 2-3)* **171**

29. Solve $9 = \dfrac{h}{4} - 6$. Check your solution. *(Lesson 2-7)* **60**

30. Solve $g = -56 - 77$. *(Lesson 3-5)* **−133**

31. Solve $f = 320 \div (-40)$. *(Lesson 3-7)* **−8**

Problem Solving and Applications 32. **Critical Thinking** Solve each equation below.
$$2x = -2 \quad -1$$
$$3x = -6 \quad -2$$
$$4x = -16 \quad -4$$
$$5x = -40 \quad -8$$
$$6x = -96 \quad -16$$

a. What pattern do you notice about the multiplier of x? **Each increases by 1x.**

b. What pattern do you notice in the solutions? **Each is twice the previous one.**

c. Use the patterns you found to write the next five equations that follow in this pattern. **See margin.**

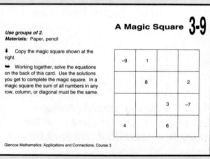

33. **Football** A football team lost 73 yards in 14 plays. Estimate the average yards lost on each play. **averaged 5 yard loss on each play**

34. **Critical Thinking** Use your calculator to solve these equations.

a. $3.1 + (-2.1) = x$ **1**   b. $4.5 - (4.5) = z$ **0**

c. $5(-2.50) = w$ **−12.5**   d. $\dfrac{-8.758}{2} = m$ **−4.379**

e. $(-3.470)(-2.11) = r$ **7.3217**   f. $\dfrac{-5.5555}{-1.1111} = p$ **5**

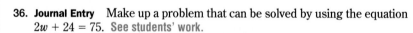

g. Write a sentence to compare solving equations with positive and negative decimals and solving equations with integers. **They are solved in the same manner.**

35. **Marketing** The profits for one day at Safety First Car Rental can be found by solving the equation $35n - 150 = P$, where n is the number of cars rented and P is the profit. On Tuesday, there were 4 cars rented.

a. Find what the profit was for that day. **−$10**

b. What does your answer mean? **There was a loss.**

36. **Journal Entry** Make up a problem that can be solved by using the equation $2w + 24 = 75$. **See students' work.**

OPTIONS

Extending the Lesson

Using Connections Have students research chemical equations and report their findings to the class. They can learn the basic techniques from a high school chemistry text. They should describe the similarities between algebra and chemistry equations, and explain how the concept of balancing is critical to both.

Cooperative Learning Activity

A Magic Square 3-9

Use groups of 2.
Materials: Paper, pencil

▸ Copy the magic square shown at the right.

➥ Working together, solve the equations on the back of this card. Use the solutions you get to complete the magic square. In a magic square the sum of all numbers in any row, column, or diagonal must be the same.

−9	1		
		8	2
		3	−7
4		6	

Glencoe Mathematics: Applications and Connections, Course 3

3-10 Coordinate System

Objective

Graph points on a coordinate plane.

Words to Learn

coordinate system
origin
x-axis
y-axis
quadrant
x-coordinate
y-coordinate
ordered pair

You have probably used a map at some time in your life. Did you know that the first person to use a coordinate system on a map was a second century Chinese scientist named Chang Heng? He did this so that positions, distances, and pathways could be studied in a more scientific way.

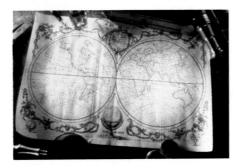

When reading maps, cities are often located by codes, such as B-3, that designate in which section of the map you can find the city. Sometimes you still have to hunt for that city because the section contains many cities.

The coordinate system is also called the coordinate plane.

In mathematics, we can locate a point more exactly by using a **coordinate system.** The coordinate system is formed by the intersection of two number lines that meet at their zero points. This point is called the **origin.** The horizontal number line is called the ***x*-axis,** and the vertical number line is called the ***y*-axis.** The two axes separate the coordinate plane into four sections called **quadrants.**

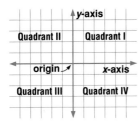

You can graph any point on the coordinate plane by using an **ordered pair** of numbers. The first number in the pair is called the ***x*-coordinate.** The second number is called the ***y*-coordinate.** The coordinates are your directions to find the point.

Example 1

Graph the point whose coordinates are (–6, 3).

Begin at the origin. The *x*-coordinate is –6. This tells you to go 6 units left of the origin.

The *y*-coordinate is 3. This tells you to go up 3 units.

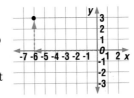

Draw a dot. You have now graphed the point whose coordinates are (–6, 3).

Lesson 3-10 Coordinate System **117**

Study Guide Masters, p. 29

Name _____ Date _____

Study Guide Worksheet 3-10

Coordinate System

You can graph a point on the coordinate plane using an ordered pair of numbers.

(x, y)

x-coordinate ⎺⎺⎺ ⎺⎺⎺ y-coordinate

Example Graph (-3, 2) on the grid below.

Begin at the origin. The x-coordinate is -3. Move 3 units to the left on the x-axis, the horizontal axis.

The y-coordinate is 2. Move 2 units up along the y-axis, the vertical axis. Draw a point to show (-3, 2).

Coordinate System

Quadrant II | Quadrant I
Origin
Quadrant III | Quadrant IV

3-10 Lesson Notes

NCTM Standards: 1–5, 7, 9, 12, 13

Lesson Resources
• Study Guide Master 3-10
• Practice Master 3-10
• Enrichment Master 3-10
• Evaluation Master, Quiz B, p. 25
• Application Master, p. 3
• Group Activity Card 3-10

Transparency 3-10 contains the 5-Minute Check and a teaching aid for this lesson.

⏱ 5-Minute Check
(Over Lesson 3-9)

Solve each equation. Check your solution.

1. $-3k = -24$ 8
2. $17 = p + (-13)$ 30
3. $\frac{x}{-2} + 7 = -2$ 18
4. $8w - (-32) = -8$ −5

1 FOCUS

Motivating the Lesson

Activity Pass out state or city maps to groups of students. State pairs of coordinates and have students use their maps to determine what is located at each pair. Then name several places on the map and have students state the coordinates that correspond to each place.

2 TEACH

Using Connections Ask the following question.

• *Where on the coordinate system can you find number lines?* the *x*-axis and the *y*-axis

• *Compare graphing a point on a number line and graphing a point on a coordinate system.*
A point graphed on a number line has one coordinate and the point lies on the number line. A point graphed on a coordinate system has two coordinates, and the point may or may not lie on one or both of the axes.

117

For Example 1

Graph the point whose coordinates are (0, −2).

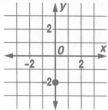

For Example 2

A point lies 4 units to the left of the *y*-axis and 3 units above the *x*-axis. Name the ordered pair for the point. (−4, 3)

Checking for Understanding

Exercises 1-4 are designed to help you assess students' understanding through reading, writing, speaking, and modeling. You should work through these exercises with your students and then monitor their work on Guided Practice Exercises 5-16.

Practice Masters, p. 29

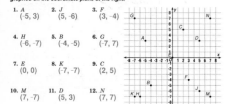

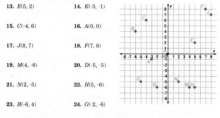

T-29
Glencoe Division, Macmillan/McGraw-Hill

118

Sometimes points are named by using letters. The symbol $B(3, 4)$ means point B has an *x*-coordinate of 3 and a *y*-coordinate of 4.

Example 2

Name the ordered pair for point *C*.

Go right on the *x*-axis to find the *x*-coordinate of point *C*. The *x*-coordinate is 5.

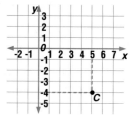

Go down along the *y*-axis to find the *y*-coordinate. The *y*-coordinate is −4.

The ordered pair for point *C* is (5, −4).

Checking for Understanding

Communicating Mathematics

Read and study the lesson to answer each question.

1. **Draw** a coordinate system and label the origin, *x*-axis, *y*-axis, and each of the quadrants. **See students' work.**

2. **Tell** the coordinates of the origin. **(0, 0)**

3. From (0,0), go 5 units right, then 7 units down.

3. **Tell** in your own words how to graph the point whose coordinates are (5, −7).

4. **Write** a sentence to tell what the symbol $E(6, 10)$ means. **Point *E* has the coordinates (6, 10).**

Guided Practice

Name the ordered pair for the coordinates of each point graphed on the coordinate plane at the right.

5. *P* (−3, 5)

6. *Q* (3, 4)

7. *R* (5, 0)

8. *S* (3, −4)

9. *T* (−3, −3)

10. *U* (−5, 2)

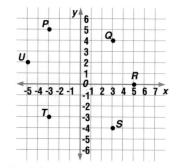

For answers to Exercises 11-16, see Solutions Manual.
Graph each point on the same coordinate plane.

11. $A(-3, -9)$ 12. $B(-4, 3)$ 13. $C(5, 0)$

14. $D(9, -7)$ 15. $E(7, 7)$ 16. $F(0, 0)$

118   **Chapter 3** Integers

OPTIONS

Bell Ringer

In a coordinate plane, the points $A(-3, 2)$, $B(5, 1)$, and $C(2, -4)$ are three of the four corners of a parallelogram. Find the coordinates of three other points that could be the fourth corner of the parallelogram. (−6, −3), (0, 7), or (10, −5)

Additional Answer

40.

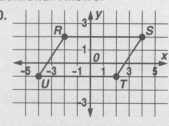

parallelogram

Exercises

Independent Practice

Name the ordered pair for the coordinates of each point graphed on the coordinate plane at the right.

17. $R\,(-2, 3)$ 18. $L\,(-4, 3)$ 19. $K\,(-3, -1)$

20. $M\,(-1, 0)$ 21. $C\,(-3, -3)$ 22. $X\,(1, -3)$

23. $J\,(3, -2)$ 24. $B\,(1, 1)$ 25. $T\,(3, 3)$

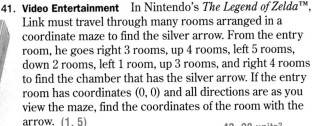

Graph each point on the same coordinate plane.

For Exercises 26–33, see Solutions Manual.

26. $J(1, 0)$ 27. $I(4, -7)$

28. $H(0, 7)$ 29. $G(-10, -3)$

30. $F(-4, -7)$ 31. $E(7, -8)$

32. $D(-6, 0)$ 33. $C(9, 9)$

Mixed Review

34. **Number Sense** The product of 9 and a number r is 54. Find the number. *(Lesson 2-4)* **6**

35. **Number Sense** Write an inequality for *Four times a number is less than 20.* Then solve the inequality. *(Lesson 2-10)* $4x < 20; x < 5$

36. Solve $-7(-31) = w.$ *(Lesson 3-6)* **217**

37. Solve $\dfrac{-108}{12} = a.$ *(Lesson 3-7)* **−9**

38. Solve $-2y + 15 = 55.$ *(Lesson 3-9)* **−20**

Problem Solving and Applications

39. **Critical Thinking** Without graphing, tell in which quadrant each point lies.
   a. $C(4, 5)$ **I**   b. $F(-1, -4)$ **III**   c. $R(-3, 2)$ **II**
   d. $W(3, -10)$ **IV**   e. $S(-4, -12)$ **III**   f. $Z(800, 400)$ **I**

40. **Geometry** Graph the points $R(-2, 2)$, $S(4, 2)$, $T(2, -1)$, and $U(-4, -1)$ on the same coordinate plane. Draw line segments from R to S, S to T, T to U, and U to R. What shape is formed? **See margin.**

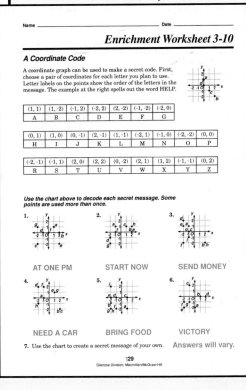

41. **Video Entertainment** In Nintendo's *The Legend of Zelda*™, Link must travel through many rooms arranged in a coordinate maze to find the silver arrow. From the entry room, he goes right 3 rooms, up 4 rooms, left 5 rooms, down 2 rooms, left 1 room, up 3 rooms, and right 4 rooms to find the chamber that has the silver arrow. If the entry room has coordinates $(0, 0)$ and all directions are as you view the maze, find the coordinates of the room with the arrow. **(1, 5)**

42. 28 units²

42. **Critical Thinking** Graph the points $A(6, 1)$, $B(6, -3)$, $C(-1, -3)$, and $D(-1, 1)$. Connect the points with line segments and find the area of the rectangle formed.

43. **Portfolio Suggestion** Review the items in your portfolio. Make a table of contents of the items, noting why each item was chosen. Replace any items that are no longer appropriate. **See students' work.**

Extending the Lesson

Using Connections Have students research the lines of latitude and longitude shown on maps of the Earth's surface. Ask them to compare and contrast latitude and longitude with the coordinate system. Have them find the latitude and longitude of their city.

Cooperative Learning Activity

Hit or Miss 3-10

Number of players: 4
Materials: Grid paper, pencil

Each group member copies onto grid paper two coordinate planes identical to the one at the right. Each group member draws a design on one of his or her coordinate planes by shading at least four squares. Each shaded square must share a side with another shaded square.

In turn, three group members try to guess the fourth's design by calling out coordinates of points. Each group of three is allowed a maximum of twenty-five guesses. Try to guess the fourth group member's design from his or her responses—"hit" if the coordinate names a point contained by the design and "miss" if it does not. (Each threesome uses one of the blank coordinate grids to plot "hits" and "misses.")

Glencoe Mathematics: Applications and Connections, Course 3

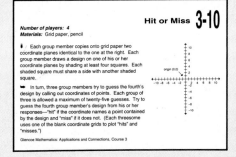

origin (0,0)

Error Analysis

Watch for students who read or graph the coordinates of points in reverse order.

Prevent by stressing the phrase "*x* before *y*," that is, relate the coordinates of a point to the *x*-axis first, and then to the *y*-axis.

Close

Tell students that a dart is found sticking in a coordinate grid. Ask them to describe how they would find the coordinates of the point where the dart is located.

3 PRACTICE/APPLY

Assignment Guide
Maximum: 17–43
Minimum: 17–33 odd, 34–42

For **Extra Practice,** see p. 591.

Alternate Assessment

Speaking State the ordered pair for a point located on a coordinate plane. Have students describe how they would graph the point.

Enrichment Masters, p. 29

Name _____ Date _____

Enrichment Worksheet 3-10

A Coordinate Code

A coordinate graph can be used to make a secret code. First, choose a pair of coordinates for each letter you plan to use. Letter labels on the points show the order of the letters in the message. The example at the right spells out the word HELP.

(1, 1)	(1, -2)	(-1, 2)	(-2, 2)	(2, -2)	(-1, 1)	(-2, 0)
A	B	C	D	E	F	G

(0, 1)	(1, 0)	(0, -1)	(2, 1)	(1, -1)	(-2, 1)	(-1, 0)	(-2, -2)
H	I	J	K	L	M	N	O	P

(-2, -1)	(-1, -1)	(2, 0)	(2, 2)	(0, -2)	(2, 1)	(1, 2)	(-1, -1)	(0, 2)
R	S	T	U	V	W	X	Y	Z

Use the chart above to decode each secret message. Some points are used more than once.

1.   2.   3.

AT ONE PM   START NOW   SEND MONEY

4.   5.   6.

NEED A CAR   BRING FOOD   VICTORY

7. Use the chart to create a secret message of your own. **Answers will vary.**

T29
Glencoe Division, Macmillan/McGraw-Hill

The Chapter Study Guide and Review begins with a section on Communicating Mathematics. This includes questions that review the new terms and concepts that were introduced in the chapter.

Then, the Skills and Concepts presented in the chapter are reviewed using a side-by-side format. Encourage students to refer to the Objectives and Examples on the left as they complete the Review Exercises on the right.

The Chapter Study Guide and Review ends with problems that review Applications and Problem Solving.

Additional Answers

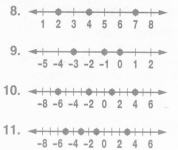

8.
1 2 3 4 5 6 7 8

9.
-5 -4 -3 -2 -1 0 1 2

10.
-8 -6 -4 -2 0 2 4 6

11.
-8 -6 -4 -2 0 2 4 6

Study Guide and Review

Chapter

3 Study Guide and Review

Communicating Mathematics

Choose the letter of the correct word or words to complete each sentence.

1. The ___?___ of a number is the distance it is from zero on a number line. e
2. To subtract an integer, add its ___?___ . f
3. The product of two integers with the same sign is ___?___ . a
4. The quotient of two integers with different signs is ___?___ . b
5. The two axes separate the coordinate plane into four ___?___ . g
6. The ___?___ is the first number in an ordered pair. c

a.	positive
b.	negative
c.	x-coordinate
d.	y-coordinate
e.	absolute value
f.	additive inverse
g.	quadrants

7. Write a sentence that explains why the additive inverse of zero is zero. **The only number you can add to 0 to get 0 is 0.**

Self Assessment

Objectives and Examples	Review Exercises
Upon completing this chapter, you should be able to:	*Use these exercises to review and prepare for the chapter test.*

• graph integers on a number line and find absolute value *(Lesson 3-1)*

Graph −2 and 1.

Find each number on a number line. Draw a dot there.

-3 -2 -1 0 1 2

Graph each set of numbers on a number line. **See margin.**

8. {2, 4, 7}
9. {−3, −1, 0}
10. {−6, −2, 1, 4}
11. {−5, −3, −1, 3}

• compare and order integers *(Lesson 3-2)*

Replace ● with >, <, or = in −6 ● −11.

−6 is to the right of −11 on a number line, so −6 > −11.

Replace each ● with >, <, or =.

12. −29 ● −345 >
13. |−481| ● 481 =
14. −15 ● 1 <
15. −8 ● |−8| <

• add integers *(Lesson 3-3)*

Solve −15 + (−25) = d.

|−15| + |−25| = 15 + 25 or 40

So, d = −40.

Solve each equation.

16. 128 + (−75) = z 53
17. −64 + (−218) = j −282
18. m = −47 + 29 −18

Objectives and Examples

- **add more than two integers**
  (Lesson 3-4)

  Solve $s = 32 + (-18) + 6$.

  $s = [32 + (-18)] + 6$

  $s = 14 + 6$

  $s = 20$

- **subtract integers** *(Lesson 3-5)*

  Solve $c = -20 - 12$.

  $c = -20 - 12$

  $c = -20 + (-12)$

  $c = -32$

- **multiply integers** *(Lesson 3-6)*

  Solve $t = (-8)(4)(6)$.

  $t = [(-8)(4)](6)$

  $t = (-32)(6)$

  $t = -192$

- **divide integers** *(Lesson 3-7)*

  Solve $a = -42 \div (-7)$.

  $a = -42 \div (-7)$

  $a = 6$

- **solve equations with integer solutions**
  (Lesson 3-9)

  Solve $y - (-40) = 275$.

  $y - (-40) = 275$

  $y + 40 = 275$

  $y + 40 - 40 = 275 - 40$

  $y = 235$

- **graph points on a coordinate plane**
  (Lesson 3-10)

  Graph the point whose coordinates are $(4, -2)$.

  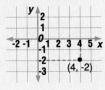

Review Exercises

Solve. Check by solving another way.

19. $21 + 15 + (-7) + 3 = k$ **32**
20. $-16 + 38 + (-25) + 1 = x$ **-2**
21. $v = -54 + 81 + 54$ **81**
22. $29 + (-60) + 11 + (-5) = p$ **-25**

Solve each equation.

23. $46 - (-62) = b$ **108**
24. $y = -59 - 33$ **-92**
25. $j = -86 - (-96)$ **10**
26. $-17 - 28 = n$ **-45**

Solve each equation.

27. $u = -8(12)$ **-96**
28. $w = -5(-20)$ **100**
29. $(-10)(-2)(4) = q$ **80**
30. $(25)(-3)(1) = g$ **-75**

Solve each equation.

31. $\frac{-66}{6} = c$ **-11**   32. $\frac{-280}{-7} = h$ **40**

33. $z = \frac{160}{5}$ **32**   34. $b = \frac{360}{-24}$ **-15**

Solve each equation.

35. $-3s = -54$ **18**
36. $3p - (-18) = 63$ **15**
37. $28 + m = -94$ **-122**
38. $\frac{r}{4} - 13 = -15$ **-8**

Graph each point on the same coordinate plane.

39. $A(-2, 8)$ **For graphs, see margin.**
40. $B(-4, -1)$
41. $C(5, 7)$
42. $D(3, -6)$

Chapter 3 Study Guide and Review   **121**

Additional Answers

39–42.

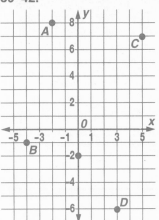

Evaluation Masters, pp. 23–24

Name _____ Date _____

Form 2A _____ *Chapter 3 Test*

Simplify.

1. |-25| 2. |7|

Replace each ___ with >, <, or =.

3. 13 ___ -13   4. |-19| ___ |19|

5. Order the set {-169, 4, 30, -338, -57, 15, 144} from least to greatest.

Solve each equation.

6. 126 ÷ (-18) = a   7. r = -462 + 58

8. x = -25(5)   9. 6m = -132

10. $\frac{c}{7}$ = -11   11. l = (-8)(-15)(2)

12. 4e - 14 = -26   13. -100 = 25 + 5u

14. w = -12 + 60 + (-75) + 9

15. Graph the set {2, -5, -2, 0, 1} on a number line.

16. State whether the product (-6)(-3)(5)(9)(-2)(-10) is positive or negative.

Evaluate each expression if d = -3, n = 6, and t = -9.

17. 5nd²   18. 3dt ÷ t²   19. -7t - 12

20. The difference of a number and -6, minus 15, is 21. What is the number?

Name the ordered pair for the coordinates of each point shown on the graph.

21. Q   22. M

23. P   24. N

25. Find the perimeter of a rectangular-shaped garden if its width is 20 yards. The garden has 30 rows of corn.

BONUS Find two integers x and y so that x < y, x + y = -4, and x - y = -14.

1.	25
2.	7
3.	>
4.	=
5.	338, 169, 57, 4, 15, 30, 144
6.	-7
7.	-404
8.	-125
9.	-22
10.	-77
11.	240
12.	-3
13.	-25
14.	-18
15.	————
16.	positive
17.	270
18.	1
19.	51
20.	30
21.	(2, -2)
22.	(3, 1)
23.	(-2, -3)
24.	(-1, 3)
25.	not enough information

x = -9, y = 5

23

Glencoe Division, Macmillan/McGraw-Hill

Name _____ Date _____

Form 2B _____ *Chapter 3 Test*

Simplify.

1. |9| 2. |-9|

Replace each ___ with >, <, or =.

3. |-20| ___ 20   4. 0 ___ -2

5. Order the set {29, -313, 40, -142, 0, -55, 142} from greatest to least.

Solve each equation.

6. 125 = -5t   7. x = -112 + 79

8. 224 ÷ (-14) = y   9. -13 = $\frac{n}{4}$

10. (-3)(12)(-8) = h   11. l = (-37)(-6)

12. 3p + 21 = -24   13. -33 = 5z - 3

14. -19 + 42 + (-66) + 3 = j

15. Graph the set {2, 0, -1, -4, 3} on a number line.

16. State whether the product (-1)(-3)(4)(9)(-10)(5) is positive or negative.

Evaluate each expression if r = 4, s = -8, and t = -2.

17. -2rt²   18. 3rs ÷ t   19. -6s - 25

20. The sum of a number and -8, plus 12, is -16. What is the number?

Name the ordered pair for the coordinates of each point shown on the graph.

21. B   22. A

23. D   24. C

25. Find the area of a piece of land in the shape of a parallelogram. It has a fence around its perimeter. Its base is 50 feet.

BONUS The product of one-half and a number, minus 6, is -6. What is the number?

1.	9
2.	9
3.	=
4.	>
5.	142, 40, 29, 0, -55, -142, -313
6.	-25
7.	-33
8.	-16
9.	-52
10.	288
11.	222
12.	-15
13.	-6
14.	-40
15.	————
16.	negative
17.	-32
18.	48
19.	23
20.	-20
21.	(-3, 3)
22.	(3, 0)
23.	(1, -2)
24.	(-2, -4)
25.	not enough information

0

24

Glencoe Division, Macmillan/McGraw-Hill

Applications and Problem Solving

43. **Chess** The Chess Club at Wiley Middle School is holding a chess tournament in which each player earns +1 for a win, -1 point for a loss, and 0 for a draw. The chart at the right shows the records of five of the players.

    a. Determine each player's total points. **See chart.**

    b. Graph the total scores on a number line. Let the first letter of each player's name be the letter for each coordinate. *(Lesson 3-1)* **See margin.**

	Player	Wins	Losses
6	Niko	6	0
-2	Chuck	2	4
-4	Rachel	1	5
2	Trenna	4	2
0	Amanda	3	3

44. **Games** Mr. Walter invents board games. In his new game *INTEGO,* you draw cards to determine how far you go on the board. Each card has an integer on it. Positive integers tell you to go forward that many spaces. Negative integers tell you to go back that many spaces. On three turns, a player drew +2, -6, and +8. Describe where the player finally landed in respect to his starting position. *(Lesson 3-4)* **4 spaces forward**

45. **Education** Carmen received her graded test back during math class. The test had five sections. In each section, Carmen received a score of -3, which meant a loss of 3 points. How many points did Carmen lose on the test? *(Lesson 3-6)* **15 points**

46. **Zoology** The heaviest domestic dog is the St. Bernard, which weighs up to 220 pounds. How much more does a St. Bernard weigh than the smallest domestic dog? *(Lesson 3-8)* **Not enough information given**

47. **Number Theory** When you add 5 to a certain number, then subtract -10, multiply by -4, and divide by 6, you get 12. What is the number? *(Lesson 3-7)* **-33**

Curriculum Connection Projects

- **History** Write a short report on mathematician Rene Descartes and the Cartesian coordinate system.

- **Graphic Arts** Draw a straight-line figure, such as a house, on a coordinate plane. Label the coordinates of each corner. Multiply each *x*- and *y*-coordinate by 2. Draw the new figure.

Read More About It

Arthur, Lee, Elizabeth James, and Judith B. Taylor. *Sportsmath: How It Works.*
Cresswell, Helen. *Absolute Zero.*
Mango, Karin N. *Mapmaking.*

122 **Chapter 3** Study Guide and Review

Additional Answer

43b.

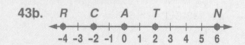

R C A T N
-4 -3 -2 -1 0 1 2 3 4 5 6

3 Test

1. Find the absolute value of −9. **9**

Replace each ● with >, <, or =.

2. 3 ● −20 **>**

3. |−44| ● 44 **=**

4. −837 ● −164 **<**

5. |−51| ● |−14| **>**

6. Order the numbers in the set {−6, −179, 20, 134, −67, 5, −348} from least to greatest.
{−348, −179, −67, −6, 5, 20, 134}

Solve each equation.

7. $r = -582 + 68$ **−514**

8. $p = -4(-16)$ **64**

9. $m = -112 \div 16$ **−7**

10. $-231 - 128 = d$ **−359**

11. $(8)(-10)(3) = h$ **−240**

12. $3g - 14 = -50$ **−12**

13. $3t = 48 - (-72)$ **40**

14. $-8 + 21 + (-12) + 15 = s$ **16**

15. Graph the set {5, −2, −4, 0, 3} on a number line. **See Solutions Manual.**

16. State whether the product $(-7)(-5)(-9)(-1)(-4)$ will be positive or negative. **negative**

Evaluate each expression if $c = -4$, $m = 5$, and $t = -10$.

17. $3mc^2$ **240**

18. $2ct \div m$ **16**

19. $-6c - 60$ **−36**

20. Write an equation to represent the sum of a number divided by −4, plus 20, is 26. Then solve. $\frac{n}{-4} + 20 = 26$, **−24**

Name the ordered pair for the coordinates of each point shown on the graph at the right.

21. R **(3, 4)**

22. E **(−2, −3)**

23. H **(2, −2)**

24. M **(−1, 3)**

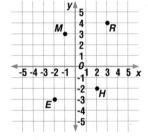

25. **Weather** Schools were closed in the district due to a winter storm. The temperature dropped 24° F over a four-hour period. If the temperature dropped at an even rate, how many degrees did the temperature fall each hour? **6 degrees**

Bonus Find two integers x and y so that $x > y$, $xy = -12$, and $x \div y = -3$. **$x = 6$, $y = -2$**

Test and Review Generator software is provided in Apple, IBM, and Macintosh versions. You may use this software to create your own tests or worksheets, based on the needs of your students.

The **Performance Assessment Booklet** provides an alternate assessment for evaluating student progress. An assessment for this chapter can be found on pages 5-6.

The Academic Skills Test may be used to help students prepare for standardized tests. The test items are written in the same style as those in state proficiency tests. The test items cover skills and concepts presented up to this point in the text.

These pages can be used as an overnight assignment. After students have completed the pages, discuss how each problem can be solved, or provide copies of the solutions from the *Solutions Manual*.

Academic Skills Test

Chapter

3
Standard Format, Chapters 1-3
Academic Skills Test

Directions: Choose the best answer. Write A, B, C, or D.

1. Maria bought 3 blouses for $108. If each blouse cost the same amount, how much did each blouse cost?
   C

   A. $30.24   B. $32.40
   C. $36.00   D. $54.00

2. $(3 \times 8) + (17 \times 8)$ is equivalent to
   C

   A. 20×16
   B. $3(8 + 17)$
   C. 20×8
   D. $8(3 \times 17)$

3. John bought a stereo that cost $532.16. He paid for the stereo in 12 equal payments. Estimate: the amount of each payment was between
   C

   A. $10 and $20
   B. $25 and $35
   C. $40 and $50
   D. $55 and $65

4. Which is a reasonable estimate of the number of meals you will eat in 10 years? (Assume 3 meals a day.)
   C

   A. 300   B. 1,000
   C. 10,000   D. 30,000

5. $14.5 \text{ cm} =$
   A

   A. 0.145 m   B. 1.45 m
   C. 145 m   D. 1,450 m

6. The product of a number and itself is 576. What is the number?
   A

   A. 24   B. 30
   C. 144   D. 288

7. How is the product $4 \cdot 4 \cdot 4$ expressed using exponents?
   B

   A. $4 \cdot 3$ B. 4^3
   C. 3^4 D. 4^4

8. If $a = 6$ and $b = 3$, what is the value of ab?
   C

   A. 216   B. 63
   C. 18   D. 2

9. Which equation is equivalent to $x + 5 = 12$?
   B

   A. $x = 12$
   B. $x + 5 - 5 = 12 - 5$
   C. $x + 10 = 24$
   D. $x + 5 - 5 = 12 + 5$

10. A certain number is divided by 4 and then 5 is subtracted from the result. The final answer is 25. What is the number?
    D

    A. 5   B. 80
    C. 100   D. 120

11. What is the solution of the inequality $12 > t + 8$?
    A

    A. $t < 4$ B. $t < 12$
    C. $t > 12$ D. $t > 20$

12. Which equation represents *three more than twice a number equals 14?*
A

    A. $2x + 3 = 14$
    B. $2x = 14 + 3$
    C. $2(x + 3) = 14$
    D. $3 + x + 2 = 14$

13. What is the perimeter of the rectangle shown at the right?
C

10 cm
14.5 cm

    A. 24.5 cm
    B. 34.5 cm
    C. 49 cm
    D. 145 cm

14. Which integers are graphed on the number line below?
C

-5   0   5

    A. $\{-5, -2\}$
    B. $\{-5, -4, -3, ...\}$
    C. $\{-5, -2, 0, 1\}$
    D. $\{-5, 0, 5\}$

15. Which symbol replaces the ● to make a true sentence?
A
          -4.5 ● $|-5.2|$

    A. $<$ **B.** $>$
    C. $=$ **D.** none of these

16. $56 + (-32) =$
C
    A. -88 **B.** -24
    C. 24 **D.** 88

17. $20 \cdot (-9) =$
A
    A. -180 **B.** -18
    C. 18 **D.** 180

18. $-64 \div 8 =$
B
    A. -12 **B.** -8
    C. 8 **D.** 12

Test-Taking Tip

Most standardized tests have a time limit, so you must budget your time carefully. Some questions will be much easier than others. If you cannot answer a question within a few minutes, go on to the next one. If there is still time left when you get to the end of the test, go back and work the questions that you skipped.

You can prepare for taking standardized tests by working through practice tests like this one. The more you work with questions in a format similar to the actual test, the better you become at test taking. Do not wait until the night before taking a test to review. Allow yourself plenty of time to review the basic skills and formulas that are tested.

19. If $\frac{c}{-3} = 6$, what is the value of *c?*
A
    A. -18 **B.** -2
    C. 2 **D.** 18

20. Which point is in the second quadrant?
A
    A. K
    B. L
    C. M
    D. N

4 Statistics and Data Analysis

Previewing the Chapter

In this chapter, students learn to organize, display, and interpret data. The first lesson of the chapter is a **problem-solving strategy** lesson on using tables to tally data and compile a frequency table. Students then learn five methods for displaying data: histograms, line plots, stem-and-leaf plots, box-and-whisker plots, and scatter plots. Lessons on measures of central tendency, measures of variation, and misleading statistics focus on analyzing data. The emphasis throughout the chapter is on analyzing statistics and on how best to visually show that analysis.

Lesson	Lesson Objectives	NCTM Standards	State/Local Objectives
4-1A	Explore the use of a computer data base.	1–4, 7, 10	
4-1	Solve problems by organizing data into a table.	1–5, 7, 8, 10	
4-2	Construct and interpret histograms.	1–5, 7–11	
4-3	Construct and interpret line plots.	1–5, 8–10	
4-3B	Use maps to display United States statistical data.	1–4, 8, 10	
4-4	Construct and interpret stem-and-leaf plots.	1–5, 8–10	
4-5	Find the mean, median, and mode of a set of data.	1–5, 7, 9, 10	
4-5B	Discover how to use statistics to predict similar situations in the future.	1–5, 8, 10	
4-6	Find the range and quartiles of a set of data.	1–5, 7, 10	
4-7	Construct and interpret box-and-whisker plots.	1–5, 7, 8, 10	
4-8	Construct and interpret scatter plots.	1–5, 8–10	
Decision Making	Analyze data and make a decision.	1–4, 7	
4-9	Recognize when graphs and statistics are misleading.	1–5, 8–10	

Organizing the Chapter

A complete, 1-page lesson plan is provided for each lesson in the Lesson Plans Masters Booklet.

LESSON PLANNING GUIDE

Lesson	Materials/ Manipulatives	Extra Practice (Student Edition)	Study Guide	Practice	Enrichment	Evaluation	Technology	Lab Manual	Multicultural Activities	Application and Interdisciplinary Activities	Transparencies	Group Activity Cards
						Blackline Masters Booklets						
4-1A								p. 47				
4-1			p. 30	p. 30	p. 30		p. 18				4-1	4-1
4-2		p. 591	p. 31	p. 31	p. 31			p. 4			4-2	4-2
4-3	a linear measuring device	p. 591	p. 32	p. 32	p. 32						4-3	4-3
4-3B	colored pencils, outline map of United States							p. 48				
4-4	encyclopedia	p. 592	p. 33	p. 33	p. 33						4-4	4-4
4-5	calculator	p. 592	p. 34	p. 34	p. 34	Quiz A, p. 34				p. 4	4-5	4-5
4-5B								p. 49				
4-6		p. 592	p. 35	p. 35	p. 35		p. 4				4-6	4-6
4-7		p. 593	p. 36	p. 36	p. 36						4-7	4-7
4-8		p. 593	p. 37	p. 37	p. 37					p. 18	4-8	4-8
4-9			p. 38	p. 38	p. 38	Quiz B, p. 34					4-9	4-9
Study Guide and Review			Multiple Choice Test, Forms 1A and 1B, pp. 28–31 Free Response Test, Forms 2A and 2B, pp. 32–33 Cumulative Review, p. 35 (free response)									
Test			Cumulative Test, p. 36 (multiple choice)									

Pacing Guide: Option I (Chapters 1–12) - 15 days; Option II (Chapters 1–13) - 14 days; Option III (Chapters 1–14) - 13 days
You may wish to refer to the complete **Course Planning Guides** on page T25.

OTHER CHAPTER RESOURCES

Student Edition
Chapter Opener,
  pp. 126–127
Cultural Kaleidoscope, p. 144
Mid-Chapter Review, p. 148
Portfolio Suggestions,
  pp. 144, 161
Mid-Chapter Review, p. 148
Decision Making,
  pp. 162–163

 Manipulatives
Overhead Manipulative
  Resources
Middle School Mathematics
  Manipulative Kit

 Software/Technology
Interactive Mathematics
  Tools (Macintosh)
Test and Review Generator
  (IBM, Apple, Macintosh)
Teacher's Guide for
  Software Resources

Other Supplements
Transparency 4–0
Performance Assessment,
  pp. 7–8
Glencoe Mathematics
  Professional Series
Lesson Plans, pp. 36–47

INTERDISCIPLINARY BULLETIN BOARD

Business Connection

Objective   Find examples of misleading claims.

How To Use It   Have students collect examples of print ads that mislead or make questionable claims. Have them display the ads, circle the misleading sections, and write their reasons for questioning the claims.

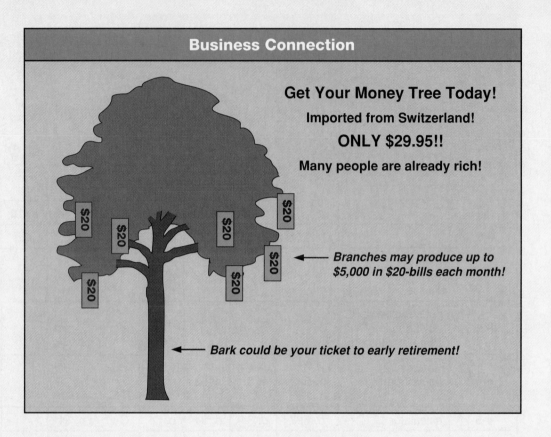

Business Connection

Get Your Money Tree Today!

Imported from Switzerland!

ONLY $29.95!!

Many people are already rich!

← *Branches may produce up to $5,000 in $20-bills each month!*

← *Bark could be your ticket to early retirement!*

APPLICATIONS AND CONNECTIONS

Applications	Lesson	Example	Exercise
Customer Service	4-1	2	
Government	4-2		14
Literature	4-3		10
Farming	Lab 4-3B		7
Sports	4-4		18
Research	4-4		19
Radio	4-5	1	
Hobbies	4-5		22
Decision Making	4-6		26
Consumer Math	4-7		32
School	4-7		35
Finance	4-8		23
Agriculture	4-8		25
Health	4-9		16
Sports	4-9		18
Connections			
Data Analysis	4-6		28

TEAM ACTIVITIES

Multicultural Experiences

Outside Field Trips   Government agencies often conduct surveys on a variety of topics. On the site of a traffic survey, students can learn how workers collect data on highway use.

A visit to a social services office can give students an opportunity to see how data on human services needs are compiled and analyzed.

In-Class Speakers   Invite a member of your congressperson's staff to discuss political polling methods with students.

An employee of an advertising agency can discuss how attitudes on consumer products are determined.

SUPPLEMENTARY BLACKLINE MASTER BOOKLETS

Some of the blackline masters for enhancing this chapter are shown below.

Application and Interdisciplinary Activity Masters, pp. 4, 18

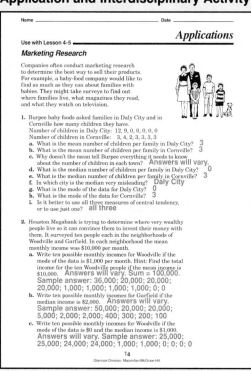

Name _____ Date _____

Applications

Use with Lesson 4-5

Marketing Research

Companies often conduct marketing research to determine the best way to sell their products. For example, a baby-food company would like to find as much as they can about families with babies. They might take surveys to find out where families live, what magazines they read, and what they watch on television.

1. Burpee baby foods asked families in Daly City and in Cornville how many children they have.
Number of children in Daly City: 12, 9, 0, 0, 0, 0, 0
Number of children in Cornville: 3, 4, 2, 3, 3, 3, 3
   a. What is the mean number of children per family in Daly City? **3**
   b. What is the mean number of children per family in Cornville? **3**
   c. Why doesn't the mean tell Burpee everything it needs to know about the number of children in each town? **Answers will vary.**
   d. What is the median number of children per family in Daly City? **0**
   e. What is the median number of children per family in Cornville? **3**
   f. In which city is the median very misleading? **Daly City**
   g. What is the mode of the data for Daly City? **0**
   h. What is the mode of the data for Cornville? **3**
   i. Is it better to use all three measures of central tendency, or to use just one? **all three**

2. Houston Megabank is trying to determine where very wealthy people live so it can convince them to invest their money with them. It surveyed ten people each in the neighborhoods of Woodville and Garfield. In each neighborhood the mean monthly income was $10,000 per month.
   a. Write ten possible monthly incomes for Woodville if the mode of the data is $1,000 per month. Hint: Find the total income for the ten Woodville people if the mean income is $10,000. **Answers will vary. Sum = 100,000.**
   Sample answer: 36,000; 20,000; 20,000; 20,000; 1,000; 1,000; 1,000; 1,000; 0; 0
   b. Write ten possible monthly incomes for Garfield if the median income is $2,000. **Answers will vary.**
   Sample answer: 50,000; 20,000; 20,000; 5,000; 2,000; 2,000; 400; 300; 200; 100
   c. Write ten possible monthly incomes for Woodville if the mode of the data is $0 and the median income is $1,000. **Answers will vary. Sample answer: 25,000; 25,000; 24,000; 24,000; 1,000; 1,000; 0; 0; 0; 0**

T4

Glencoe Division, Macmillan/McGraw-Hill

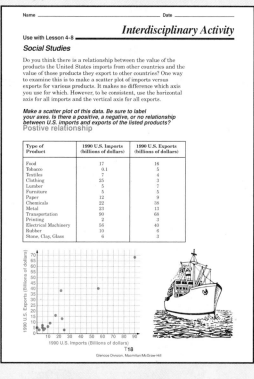

Name _____ Date _____

Interdisciplinary Activity

Use with Lesson 4-8

Social Studies

Do you think there is a relationship between the value of the products the United States imports from other countries and the value of those products they export to other countries? One way to examine this is to make a scatter plot of imports versus exports for various products. It makes no difference which axis you use for which. However, to be consistent, use the horizontal axis for all imports and the vertical axis for all exports.

Make a scatter plot of this data. Be sure to label your axes. Is there a positive, a negative, or no relationship between U.S. imports and exports of the listed products?
Postive relationship

Type of Product	1990 U.S. Imports (billions of dollars)	1990 U.S. Exports (billions of dollars)
Food	17	16
Tobacco	0.1	5
Textiles	7	4
Clothing	25	3
Lumber	5	7
Furniture	5	5
Paper	12	9
Chemicals	22	38
Metal	23	13
Transportation	90	68
Printing	2	3
Electrical Machinery	56	40
Rubber	10	6
Stone, Clay, Glass	6	3

T18

Glencoe Division, Macmillan/McGraw-Hill

Multicultural Activity Masters, p. 4

Name _____ Date _____

Multicultural Activity

Use with Lesson 4-2

African Americans in History

In February, 1989, *Ebony* magazine published this list of fifty African Americans who made significant contributions to American history and culture.

The 50 Most Important Figures in Black American History

Robert S. Abbott (1870–1940)	James Weldon Johnson (1871–1938)
Richard Allen (1760–1831)	Ernest E. Just (1883–1941)
Louis Armstrong (1900–1971)	Joe Louis (1914–1981)
Ella Baker (1903–1986)	Martin Luther King, Jr. (1929–1968)
James Baldwin (1924–1987)	Malcolm X (1925–1965)
Benjamin Banneker (1736–1806)	Benjamin E. Mays (1894–1984)
Ida B. Wells-Barnett (1862–1931)	Jesse Owens (1913–1980)
Mary McLeod Bethune (1875–1955)	Adam Clayton Powell, Jr. (1908–1972)
Ralph J. Bunche (1904–1971)	A. Philip Randolph (1889–1979)
George Washington Carver (1861?–1943)	Paul Robeson (1898–1976)
Martin R. Delany (1812–1885)	Jackie Robinson (1919–1972)
Frederick Douglass (1817–1895)	Mary Church Terrell (1863–1954)
Charles R. Drew (1904–1950)	Howard Thurman (1900–1981)
W. E. B. Du Bois (1868–1963)	William Monroe Trotter (1872–1934)
Paul Laurence Dunbar (1872–1906)	Sojourner Truth (1797?–1883)
Edward Kennedy Ellington (1899–1974)	Harriet Tubman (1821?–1913)
Marcus Garvey (1887–1940)	Henry McNeal Turner (1834–1915)
Prince Hall (1735?–1807)	Nat Turner (1800–1831)
Fannie Lou Hamer (1917–1977)	David Walker (1785–1830)
W. C. Handy (1873–1958)	Madame C. J. Walker (1867–1919)
Frances E. W. Harper (1825–1911)	Booker T. Washington (1856–1915)
Charles H. Houston (1895–1950)	Phillis Wheatley (1753?–1784)
Langston Hughes (1902–1967)	Daniel Hale Williams (1856–1931)
Zora Neale Hurston (1901?–1960)	Carter G. Woodson (1875–1950)
Jack Johnson (1878–1946)	Richard Wright (1908–1960)

1. On a separate sheet of paper, construct a histogram that displays the years of birth for these fifty people. Organize the data in twenty-year intervals, such as 1841–1860 and 1861–1880. If there is a question mark next to a person's year of birth, use that year as your data.

2. Refer to the histogram you constructed in Exercise 1. In which interval were most of these people born? In which interval were the fewest born? **1861–1880; 1761–1780**
Check students' histograms. Frequencies are as follows.
1721–1740: 2; 1741–1760: 2; 1761–1780: 0; 1781–1800: 3; 1801–1820: 2; 1821–1840: 3; 1841–1860: 2; 1861–1880: 13; 1881–1900: 9; 1901–1920: 11; 1921–1940: 3;

T4

Glencoe Division, Macmillan/McGraw-Hill

Technology Masters, p. 18

Name _____ Date _____

Computer Activity

Use with Lesson 4-1

Frequency Tables

Run this BASIC program below to see a frequency table of data you enter in any order. The computer displays your data in numerical order.

```
TYPE NEW
10    INPUT "HOW MANY DATA VALUES WILL YOU ENTER"; N
20    PRINT "INPUT EACH NUMBER. PRESS ENTER AFTER"
25    PRINT "EACH ONE"
30    DIM A(N), B(N)
40    FOR J = 1 TO N
50    INPUT A(J)
60    NEXT J
70    FOR K = 1 TO N
80    FOR J = 1 TO N-1
90    IF A(J) < A(J + 1) THEN 130
100   T = A(J)
110   A(J) = A(J + 1)
120   A(J + 1) = T
130   NEXT J
140   NEXT K
150   FOR K = 1 TO N
160   S = 0 : B(K) = 0
170   FOR J = 1 TO N
180   IF A(K) = A(J) THEN S = S + 1
190   NEXT J
200   B(K) = S
210   NEXT K
220   PRINT
230   PRINT "NUMBER"; TAB (15); "FREQUENCY"
240   A(0) = 9999
250   FOR J = 1 TO N
260   IF A(J - 1) = A(J) THEN 280
270   PRINT A(J) ; TAB (17); B(J)
280   NEXT J
290   END
```

Show a frequency table for the data values below.

1. Number	Frequency
59	2
60	4
62	3
62.5	2
64	3
65	2

2. Number	Frequency
97	4
98	3
100	2
101	2
102	2
111	2
112	2
114	1
130	1
132	1

1. Heights of Girls' Volleyball Team (inches)
60, 62, 62, 64, 59, 62, 60, 62.5, 62.5, 64, 59, 65, 64, 65, 60, 60

2. Weights of Boys' Wrestling Team (pounds)
111, 112, 98, 97, 98, 111, 97, 101, 132, 112, 97, 102, 102, 97, 98, 100, 130, 114, 100, 101

T18

Glencoe Division, Macmillan/McGraw-Hill

RECOMMENDED OUTSIDE RESOURCES

Books/Periodicals

Grouws, Douglas A., Thomas J. Cooney, and Douglas Jones, *Effective Mathematics Teaching,* Reston, VA: NCTM, 1988.

Jaffe, A.J., and Herbert F. Spirer, *Misused Statistics: Straight Talk for Twisted Numbers,* New York, NY: Marcel Dekker, Inc., 1987.

Films/Videotapes/Videodiscs

Black Mathematicians, Montclair, NJ: Mathematical Symposium, 1989.

Teaching Mathematics Effectively, Alexandria, VA: ASCD, 1982.

Software

Microsoft Works, (Macintosh, IBM/Tandy), Microsoft Corporation

For addresses of companies handling software, please refer to page T24.

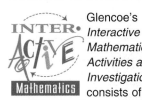

Glencoe's *Interactive Mathematics: Activities and Investigations* consists of 18 units that may be used as alternatives or supplemental material for *Mathematics: Applications and Connections.* The suggested units for this chapter are Unit 8, *Data Sense,* and Unit 18, *Quality Control.* See page T18 for more information.

Chapter

4

Statistics and Data Analysis

Spotlight on Mountain Climbing

Have You Ever Wondered...

- How many steps you would have to climb to climb as high as a mountain?

- How many laps you would have to swim in a swimming pool to equal the distance across the Atlantic Ocean?

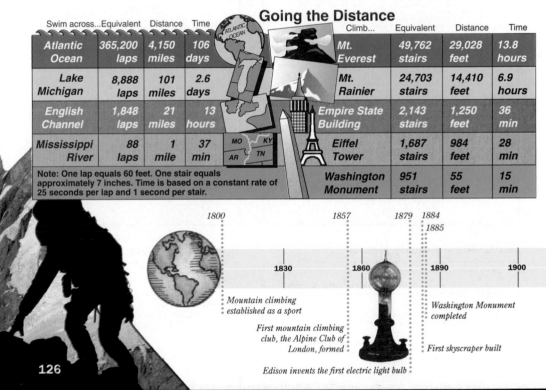

Going the Distance

Swim across...	Equivalent	Distance	Time
Atlantic Ocean	365,200 laps	4,150 miles	106 days
Lake Michigan	8,888 laps	101 miles	2.6 days
English Channel	1,848 laps	21 miles	13 hours
Mississippi River	88 laps	1 mile	37 min

Note: One lap equals 60 feet. One stair equals approximately 7 inches. Time is based on a constant rate of 25 seconds per lap and 1 second per stair.

Climb...	Equivalent	Distance	Time
Mt. Everest	49,762 stairs	29,028 feet	13.8 hours
Mt. Rainier	24,703 stairs	14,410 feet	6.9 hours
Empire State Building	2,143 stairs	1,250 feet	36 min
Eiffel Tower	1,687 stairs	984 feet	28 min
Washington Monument	951 stairs	55 feet	15 min

1800 — 1830 : Mountain climbing established as a sport

1857 — 1860 : First mountain climbing club, the Alpine Club of London, formed

Edison invents the first electric light bulb

1879 — 1890

1884 — 1885 : Washington Monument completed ; First skyscraper built

1900

126

Chapter Project

Mountain Climbing
Work in a group.

1. Guess how many steps you climb in a day and in a week. Be sure to include the steps at home, at school, on the bus, and even at the shopping mall.

2. Keep a log of how many steps you climb each day for one week. Make a graph showing your results. Compare the actual number with your initial guess.

3. If each step is 7 inches tall, how high did you climb in a week? Is this as high as any mountain? How many weeks would it take you to climb the equivalent of Mt. McKinley?

HIGHEST POINTS IN SELECTED U.S. STATES
(in feet)

State	Feet
AK: Mt. McKinley	20,320
CA: Mt. Whitney	14,494
WA: Mt. Rainier	14,410
HA: Mauna Kea	13,796
OR: Mt. Hood	11,239
TX: Guadalupe Peak	8,749
NC: Mt. Mitchell	6,684
TN: Clingmans Dome	6,643
VA: Mt. Rogers	5,729
NY: Mt. Marcy	5,344
GA: Brasstown Bald	4,784
KY: Black Mountain	4,145
PA: Mt. Davis	3,213
MI: Mt. Arvon	1,979
OH: Campbell Hill	1,550
FL: Unnamed	345

1930s
1927 *1931*
1953
1989

1930 **1960** **1990**

Gertrude Ederle is the first woman to swim English Channel

Great Depression

First people reach the top of Mt. Everest

American troops enter Panama

Looking Ahead

In this chapter, you will see how mathematics can be used to answer questions about mountain climbing. The major objectives of the chapter are to:

- make and interpret tables and plots
- measure the central tendency of a set of data
- represent information using frequency tables, histograms, line plots, stem-and-leaf plots, and box-and-whisker plots
- recognize misleading graphs and statistics

127

DATA ANALYSIS

Have students study both tables. Ask the following questions.

- *About how many times as tall as Mount Whitney is Mount McKinley?* about $1\frac{1}{2}$ times
- *What is the meaning of the number of laps and the time recorded beside Lake Michigan?* At 25 seconds per 60 feet, it would take 2.6 days to swim the 8,888 laps which is the equivalent of swimming across Lake Michigan.

Data Search

A question related to these data is provided in Lesson 4-2, page 135, Exercise 16.

CHAPTER PROJECT

Help students create an organized method for keeping track of the number of steps they climb each day. Suggest that they prepare a grid beforehand, one which is small enough to be easily carried. Warn students that their number of steps may vary significantly from day to day. Help them prepare accurate graphs of their data.

Allow ten days to complete the project.

Chapter Opener Transparency

Transparency 4-0 is available in the Transparency Package. It provides another full-color, motivating activity that you can use to capture students' interest.

NCTM Standards: 1–4, 7, 10

Management Tips

For Students Students can work on this lab alone or with a partner. All the material they will need can be found in the lesson.

For the Overhead Projector
Overhead Manipulative Resources provides appropriate materials for teacher or student demonstration of the activities in this Mathematics Lab.

1 FOCUS

Introducing the Lab

Ask students to give examples of professions that generate large amounts of data. Sample answers: science; banking; sports Choose one of these professions and discuss ways that a specific type of information in this profession might be organized to make it easier to use.

2 TEACH

Using Connections Students may be intimidated by the jargon. Use the example below to reassure them that a data base is simply a very large table.

Neighbor	Address	Phone
Baker	111 Pine	555-1204
Garcia	125 Pine	555-3765
McCall	137 Pine	555-0021

Fields: Neighbor, Address, Phone
Records: Baker 111 Pine 555–1204; Garcia 125 Pine 555–3765; McCall 137 Pine 555–0021

Additional Answers

Activity One Customer Name, Customer Number, Address, City, State, Zip Code
2. **a.** Retrieve all records under the field STATE.
   b. those in cold-weather states that receive snow

Objective
Explore the use of a computer data base.

A **data base** is a collection of information organized for quick search and retrieval by a computer. The information, or *data,* in a data base is referred to as a *file.* The file is organized into *fields* and *records.*

In Chapter 1, you learned that a spreadsheet is organized into rows and columns. In a data base, a field is a heading of a column. Each row in a data base is called a record. The data in each record is related.

The data base below contains data for a company's mailing list.

CUSTOMER NAME	CUSTOMER NUMBER	ADDRESS	CITY	ST	ZIP CODE
B & G INTERNATIONAL	152	113 E. FIFTH ST.	NEW YORK	NY	10003
WIRE & CABLE	350	1 INDUSTRIAL BLVD.	CLIFTON	NJ	07444
ABC CO.	210	15 EXECUTIVE WAY	TEANECK	NJ	07666

Activity One

- Look at the data base above. Name the fields. See margin.
- How many records are in this data base? 3

What do you think?

1. B&G International

1. With a data base, you can ask for certain records to be retrieved that have a specific characteristic. Suppose you ask the computer to retrieve all records under the field State that are in New York. What records would it retrieve?

2. The Amex Company has a mailing list of customers with 24,000 records. They do not want to send their brochures for snowboots to all their customers. See margin.

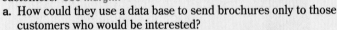

   a. How could they use a data base to send brochures only to those customers who would be interested?
   b. Which customers do you think would be interested?

Sometimes it is necessary to alter a certain part of every record in a data base. The part can be changed for each record individually, or a quicker way is to use the REPLACE command.

Activity Two

- Study the data base shown below. Identify the fields and records.

fields —

STATE CODE	SALES DISTRICT	SALESPERSON NUMBER	SALES AMOUNT	BONUS
15	2	101	500.00	50.00
18	3	200	89.95	8.99
10	1	250	1050.00	105.00
11	4	300	925.00	92.50
15	2	101	8010.00	801.00
16	2	210	3000.00	300.00
10	1	250	2500.00	250.00
10	1	250	1750.00	175.00

records —

New bonuses
55.00
9.89
115.50
101.75
881.10
330.00
275.00
192.50

- Suppose you wanted to increase everyone's bonus by 10%. This can be done by multiplying the Bonus by 1.10. Calculate the new bonus figures for each record.

What do you think?

3. Complete the command that would change the bonus values for you automatically.

   REPLACE ALL BONUS WITH BONUS* __?__ . 1.10

4. Suppose you wanted to increase everyone's bonus by 15%. Write the command that would change this. See margin.

5. Suppose you wanted to give everyone a $200 bonus in addition to their regular bonus. Write the command that would do this. See margin.

Extension

The REPLACE command can be expanded by adding a condition for the replacement. Suppose your company wanted to increase the bonus by 10%, but only for those with bonuses less than $50. The statement to do this is

REPLACE ALL BONUS WITH BONUS*1.10 FOR BONUS < 50

6. Use the data base in Activity Two. See margin.
   a. Write the command that would give all salesperson's with sales greater than $3,000 a 20% raise in their bonus.
   b. Which records would receive the 20% raise?
   c. What would be each new bonus amount?

7. Use the data base in Activity Two. See margin.
   a. Write the command that would give all salesperson's with sales less than $1,000 a 5% raise in their bonus.
   b. Which records would receive the 5% raise?
   c. What would be each new bonus amount?

Mathematics Lab 4-1A Data Base   **129**

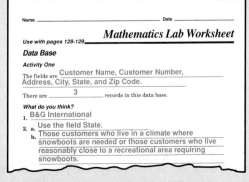

NCTM Standards: 1–5, 7, 8, 10

Lesson Resources
- Study Guide Master 4-1
- Practice Master 4-1
- Enrichment Master 4-1
- Technology Master, p. 18
- Group Activity Card 4-1

 Transparency 4-1 contains the 5-Minute Check and a teaching aid for this lesson.

⏱ 5-Minute Check
(Over Chapter 3)

Solve each equation.

1. $k = 9 + (-9)$ **0**

2. $15 + (-12) - 20 + 12 = n$ **−5**

3. $x = (-2)(-14)(5)$ **140**

4. $\frac{m}{3} - 6 = -2$ **12**

5. Graph $A(1, -2)$ on a coordinate plane.

1 FOCUS

Motivating the Lesson

Activity Tell students you are going to survey the class to find the popularity of these sports: baseball, basketball, football, tennis, soccer. Discuss ways to organize the data as the survey is taken. Then conduct the survey and ask students to interpret the results.

2 TEACH

Using Discussion Use the following question to stimulate student discussion about the radio station telephone survey. *The station is a classical music station. Based on the survey results, should the station change to a different music format? Explain your reasoning.*

Objective
Solve problems by organizing data into a table.

Words to Learn
statistics
frequency table
data analysis

In the Mathematics Lab, you learned that a data base can be used to organize data into related fields and records. A data base is a form of table.

Tables are often used in **statistics.** Statistics is the branch of mathematics that deals with collecting, organizing, and analyzing data.

One type of table used in statistics is a **frequency table.** A frequency table tells how many times each piece of data occurs in a set of information. The table below shows the results of a telephone survey done by a radio station.

Favorite Music	Tally	Frequency
Classical	卌 卌 卌 卌 卌 卌 卌 I	36
Country	卌 卌 卌 卌 卌 卌 卌 卌 卌	45
Folk	卌 卌 卌 卌 卌	25
Instrumental	卌 卌 卌 卌 卌 卌 卌 III	38
Jazz	卌 卌 卌 卌 卌 卌 卌 卌	40
Rock	卌 卌 卌 卌 卌 卌 卌 卌 卌 卌 IIII	54

The statistician made a tally mark for each response in the appropriate row.

When statisticians study the data and make conclusions from the numbers they observe, they are doing **data analysis.** Sometimes, when there is a wide range of data, statisticians will group the data into intervals.

Example 1

The scores of the Amateur Charity Miniature Golf Tournament are shown below. Make a frequency table of these scores.

25	53	70	45	32
66	72	65	33	19
56	42	85	54	39
41	81	69	60	55
48	52	67	73	89

Explore None of the scores occur more than once.
What is the highest score? **89**
What is the lowest score? **19**
What is the range of scores? **89 − 19 = 70**

OPTIONS

Reteaching Activity

Using Tables On the chalkboard write these intervals:

Jan-Apr   May-Aug   Sep-Dec

Have each student place a tally mark next to the interval containing the month in which they were born. Have students make a frequency table based on the information and explain how they did their work.

Study Guide Masters, p. 30

Name _____ Date _____

Study Guide Worksheet 4-1

Problem-Solving Strategy: Make a Table

Example Russell asked each of the people in his mountain-climbing club how many times they had been mountain climbing. The results are shown below. Make a frequency table to show the data.

5, 32, 51, 10, 6, 4, 43, 21, 15, 22, 8, 55, 40, 37, 1, 7, 32, 17

Explore The highest number is 55. The lowest number is 1. The range is 55 − 1 = 54.

Plan Use equal intervals to group the data. Tally the numbers.

Solve Select intervals of 20. Make a table with three columns. Write the intervals. Tally the data. Total the tallies.

Climbs	Tally	Frequency
0-20	卌 IIII	9

131

Plan | Since none of the scores occur more than once, let's use intervals to group the data. Decide on equal intervals, such as 10. Then tally the scores.

Solve | Make a table with three columns. Write the intervals. Tally the scores. Total the tallies.

Scores	Tally	Frequency
11-20	I	1
21-30	I	1
31-40	III	3
41-50	IIII	4
51-60	IIII I	6
61-70	IIII	5
71-80	II	2
81-90	III	3

Examine | Check to see if you have recorded each score by finding the total number of scores in the frequency column. Then count the number of scores in the original list. If these two numbers do not match, you need to tally the scores again.

Example 2 | Problem Solving

Customer Service The manager of Taco Time had to report the usual time it took the customer to be served after placing an order. She made the frequency table below. What time did she report?

Serving Time(s)	Tally	Frequency
0 - 60	II	2
61 - 120	IIII IIII	10
121 - 180	IIII IIII IIII	15
181 - 240	IIII IIII IIII III	18
241 - 300	IIII IIII I	11

Look for the time that has the most tally marks. The usual amount of time it took to serve a customer was between 181 and 240 seconds.

Checking for Understanding

Communicating Mathematics

1. The intervals overlap.
2. Sample answer: Folk is least popular and rock is most popular.

Read and study the lesson to answer each question.

1. **Tell** what is wrong with the frequency table at the right.

2. **Write** a sentence to tell what you conclude when you analyze the data in the frequency table on page 130.

Science Test Scores	Tally	Frequency
50-60	I	1
60-70	III	3
70-80	IIII I	6
80-90	IIII IIII IIII	15
90-100	IIII IIII II	12

Lesson 4-1 Problem-Solving Strategy: Make a Table **131**

Multicultural Education

Demographers use population trends to predict what the world will be like in the future. Franklin Wilson, an African-American demographer, uses a broad range of statistical methods to analyze data he collects about unemployed workers in the United States. His results are valuable for government agencies who use them to predict employment trends.

Answers to More Examples, Example 1

Temperature	Tally	Frequency
-19 — -10	III	3
-9 — 0	III	3
1 — 10	II	2
11 — 20	I	1
21 — 30	I	1

More Examples

For Example 1

The average daily temperatures for ten days in January are shown below. Make a frequency table of these temperatures.

$$-5 \quad -11 \quad 9 \quad 2 \quad -12$$
$$-8 \quad 15 \quad -13 \quad -3 \quad 23$$

For answer, see below.

For Example 2

Twenty campers hiked from their base camp to Harley Lake. What was the most frequent interval of hiking time? 41-60 minutes

Time (min)	Tally	Frequency
1-20	I	1
21-40	IIII III	8
41-60	IIII IIII	9
61-80	II	2

Checking for Understanding

Exercises 1-2 are designed to help you assess students' understanding through reading, writing, speaking, and modeling. You should work through these exercises with your students and then monitor their work on Guided Practice Exercises 3-4.

Practice Masters, p. 30

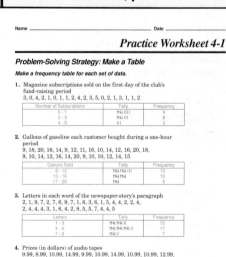

Watch for students who tally carelessly.

Prevent by having students compare the sum of the frequencies to the total number of values.

Close

Have each student create a set of data containing at least 15 values. Then have students exchange data and make frequency tables.

3 PRACTICE/APPLY

Assignment Guide
Maximum: 5–10
Minimum: 5–10

Alternate Assessment

Modeling Prepare a stack of 40 index cards numbered 1 through 40. Have students draw 10 cards, arrange them by number in intervals of 5, and determine the frequency of each interval.

Enrichment Masters, p. 30

Name _____ Date _____

Enrichment Worksheet 4-1

Relative Frequency and Circle Graphs

The *relative frequency* tells how the frequency of one item compares to the total of all the frequencies. Relative frequencies are written as fractions, decimals, or percents.

For example, in Problem 1 below, the total of all the frequencies is 50. So, the relative frequency of the grade A is 8 ÷ 50, or 0.16.

The circle at the right is divided into 20 equal parts. You can trace this circle and then use relative frequencies to make circle graphs.

Complete each chart to show the relative frequencies. Then sketch a circle graph for the data. Use decimals rounded to the nearest hundredth.

1. History Grades for 50 Students

Grade	Frequency	Relative Frequency
A	8	0.16
B	16	0.32
C	18	0.36
D	6	0.12
F	2	0.04

History Grades for 50 Students

2. Steve's Budget

Item	Amount Spent	Relative Spending
Telephone	$26	0.13
Movies	$46	0.23
Books	$24	0.12
Car	$38	0.19
Other	$66	0.33

Steve's Budget

T30
Glencoe Division, Macmillan/McGraw-Hill

132

Guided Practice   Make a frequency table for each set of data. **See Solutions Manual.**

3. To the nearest hour, how many hours did you talk on the telephone last week?

| 4 | 0 | 1 | 2 | 2 | 3 | 5 | 1 | 2 | 3 |
| 4 | 0 | 3 | 3 | 0 | 1 | 3 | 2 | 4 | 6 |

4. What was your best game in the Junior Summer Bowling League? *Bowling scores are given in terms of pins.* **See Solutions Manual.**

150	138	110	135
89	167	133	175
169	200	203	169
133	125	109	138
145	144	189	190

Problem Solving

5. See Solutions Manual.

Practice   Solve using any strategy.

Strategies
• • • • • • •
Look for a pattern.
Solve a simpler problem.
Act it out.
Guess and check.
Draw a diagram.
Make a chart.
Work backward.

5. Make a frequency table for this list of prices of popular video games.

$24.99	$16.99	$44.99	$50.50	$35.99	$32.99
$10.99	$29.99	$29.99	$43.99	$45.99	$37.99
$14.99	$18.00	$34.89	$55.80	$37.90	$40.44

a. How many games are in this list? **18**

b. To the nearest $10, which price seems most common? **$40**

6. Ninety-seven out of every 100 employees at B.Y. Chemical commute to work by car. The rest use public transportation to get to work. Approximately how many of 1,433 employees use public transportation? **about 43 employees**

7. Make a frequency table for the data. **See Solutions Manual.**

Magazine Subscriptions Sold

| 70 | 74 | 12 | 34 | 23 | 78 | 45 | 32 | 55 | 51 |
| 89 | 43 | 32 | 11 | 25 | 62 | 43 | 78 | 70 | 72 |

8. A number divided by 0.4 equals 20. Find the number. **8**

9. Make a frequency table for the data. **See Solutions Manual.**

Points Scored Each Game during Basketball Season

102	78	62	98	67
88	98	101	102	89
121	66	78	102	113
120	109	88	97	88

10. Michelle spent $56 on exactly 15 items at the grocery store. She bought nine breakfast muffins and twice as many frozen dinners as packages of vegetables. How many of each item did she buy? **9 muffins, 4 frozen dinners, 2 vegetables**

OPTIONS

Extending the Lesson

Using Cooperative Groups Have each group decide on a topic of interest, prepare a list of survey items, and conduct a survey of their classmates. Groups should make frequency tables based on their results and explain any conclusions they can reach based on their data.

Cooperative Learning Activity

That's "M-pressive" **4-1**

Use groups of 2.

The names of eight U.S. states begin with the letter M (Maine, Maryland, Massachusetts, Michigan, Minnesota, Mississippi, Missouri, and Montana). How many of the "M" states do you think the average person can name?

Ask at least fifteen people to name all of the U.S. states that begin with the letter M. Allow each person 1 minute to respond. Record the responses in a frequency table like the one shown at the right. Then write a paragraph describing your results.

State	Tally	Frequency
Maine		
Maryland		
Michigan		
Mass.		
Minn.		
Miss.		
Missouri		
Montana		

Glencoe Mathematics: Applications and Connections, Course 3

4-2 Histograms

Objective
Construct and interpret histograms.

Words to Learn
histogram

Do you spend a lot of time watching television? Some experts say the average American may spend as many as 40 hours a week watching television.

One hundred eighth graders were asked how many hours they spent watching television in a week. The frequency table at the right shows the results of this survey. A special kind of bar graph, called a **histogram,** can be used to display this data.

Hours of Television Watched by 100 Eighth Graders

Hours	Frequency
0-2	4
3-5	8
6-8	22
9-11	32
12-14	30
15-17	4

A histogram is a bar graph that displays the frequency of data that has been organized into equal intervals. Because the intervals cover all possible values of data, there are no spaces between the bars of the graph.

Example 1

Use the data from the frequency table above.
a. Construct a histogram of the data.

Draw a horizontal and vertical axis. Let the horizontal axis represent the time intervals and the vertical axis represent the frequency.

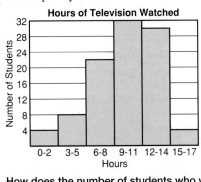

Hours of Television Watched

- *The equal intervals are shown on the horizontal axis.*
- *All bars have the same width.*
- *The frequency of the data in each interval is represented by the height of the bar.*
- *The vertical scale is often a factor of the greatest frequency.*

b. How does the number of students who watch TV 3-5 hours compare to the number of students who watch TV 0-2 hours?

Look at the bars representing 3-5 hours and 0-2 hours. The 3-5 bar is twice as tall as the 0-2 bar. Twice as many students watch TV 3-5 hours as those who watch TV 0-2 hours.

Lesson 4-2 Histograms   **133**

Interactive Mathematics Tools

This multimedia software provides an interactive lesson that is tied directly to Lesson 4-2. Students will use changeable histograms to explore data.

Study Guide Masters, p. 31

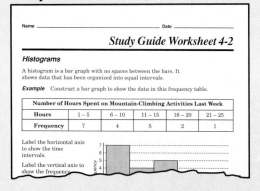

Name _____ Date _____

Study Guide Worksheet 4-2

Histograms

A histogram is a bar graph with no spaces between the bars. It shows data that has been organized into equal intervals.

Example Construct a bar graph to show the data in this frequency table.

Number of Hours Spent on Mountain-Climbing Activities Last Week				
Hours	1 – 5	6 – 10	11 – 15	16 – 20	21 – 25
Frequency	7	4	5	2	1

Label the horizontal axis to show the time intervals.

Label the vertical axis to show the frequency.

4-2 Lesson Notes

NCTM Standards: 1–5, 7–11

Lesson Resources
- Study Guide Master 4-2
- Practice Master 4-2
- Enrichment Master 4-2
- Multicultural Activity, p. 4
- Group Activity Card 4-2

Transparency 4-2 contains the 5-Minute Check and a teaching aid for this lesson.

5-Minute Check
(Over Lesson 4-1)
Make a frequency table for this list of ages of the runners in a marathon.
29 44 39 22 16 37 31
39 33 51 19 24 34 25

Age	Tally	Frequency
1–10		0
11–20	II	2
21–30	IIII	4
31–40	HHt I	6
41–50	I	1
51–60	I	1

1 FOCUS

Motivating the Lesson

Questioning Have students turn to the frequency table on page 130 and then rotate their books 90° counterclockwise. Ask them how they can use the heights of the stacks of tally marks to assess the results of the survey. The higher the stack, the more frequently that type of music was chosen.

2 TEACH

Using Questioning When posing questions about graphs, ask some questions that require students to first find values on the vertical axis and then locate the corresponding value on the horizontal axis. For the "Hours of Television Watched" graph shown in Example 1, one such question would be: *For which interval did 8 eighth-graders respond?* 3–5 hours

133

More Examples

For Example 1

a. Construct a histogram using the data below.

City Employees' Ages	
Age	**Frequency**
21–30	24
31–40	32
41–50	51
51–60	18
61–70	12

For answer, see below.

b. Which age-group interval has a frequency about half that of the age 41–50 interval?   age 21–30

For Example 2

The number of sit-ups done by 30 teenage girls in one minute is given in the chart below. Make a histogram of these data.

Sit-Ups	Number
16–20	2
21–25	5
26–30	9
31–35	12
36–40	0
41–45	2

For answer, see below.

Practice Masters, p. 31

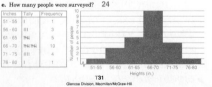

Name _____   Date _____

Practice Worksheet 4-2

Histograms

Use the histogram at the right to answer each question.

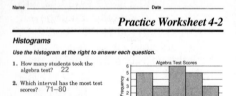

1. How many students took the algebra test?   22
2. Which interval has the most test scores?   71–80
3. Which intervals have the same number of test scores?   61–70 and 91–100; 51–60 and 81–90
4. How many more students scored 71–80 than scored 91–100?   3
5. Make a frequency table of the algebra test scores.

Scores	Frequency
51 - 60	5
61 - 70	3
71 - 80	6
81 - 90	5
91 - 100	3

6. Some people were asked their height in inches. Make a frequency table and a histogram of the following data.
68, 69, 72, 64, 74, 56, 62, 58, 69, 65, 70, 59, 71, 67, 66, 64, 73, 78, 70, 52, 61, 68, 67, 66
   a. How many heights are in the *66–70* interval?   10
   b. How many people are taller than 5 feet?   20
   c. How many people are shorter than 5 feet?   4
   d. What interval has the largest number of heights?   66–70
   e. How many people were surveyed?   24

Inches	Tally	Frequency
51 - 55	I	1
56 - 60	III	3
61 - 65	IIII	5
66 - 70	IIII IIII	10
71 - 75	IIII	4
76 - 80	I	1

T31
Glencoe Division, Macmillan/McGraw-Hill

134

Example 2

The heights (to the nearest inch) of 40 teenage boys is given in the chart below. Make a histogram of this data.

Heights	60-61	62-63	64-65	66-67	68-69	70-71	72-73	74-75
Number	5	0	3	7	10	8	5	2

Notice that the interval 62-63 has a frequency of 0. This means there will be no bar at that frequency.

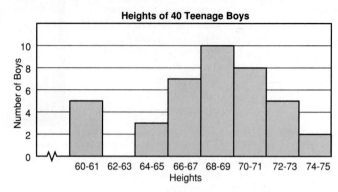

Heights of 40 Teenage Boys

The jagged line on the horizontal axis indicates that all intervals from 0 to 59 have been omitted.

Checking for Understanding

Communicating Mathematics

Read and study the lesson to answer each question.

1. **Write** a sentence to tell how a histogram and a bar graph are the same. How are they different?   Both are bar graphs, histograms show intervals.

2. **Tell** why you think histograms are used to show data with a wide range rather than bar graphs.   Sample answer: Data can be grouped in intervals so fewer bars are used.

3. It is more visual.
3. **Show** why a histogram is a more effective display than a frequency table.

4. **Tell** why there are no spaces between the bars in a histogram.   because intervals include all possible values

Guided Practice

Use the histogram at the right to answer each question.

5. See students' work.
5. Describe the data shown in this graph.

6. How large is each interval?   10 scores

7. 61-70 and 81-90
7. Which interval has the most test scores?

8. intervals from 1-40 have been omitted
8. Why is there a jagged line in the horizontal axis?

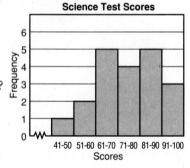

Science Test Scores

9. Make a frequency table of the same data.   See Solutions Manual.

134   **Chapter 4** Statistics and Data Analysis

**Answer to
More Examples, Example 1**

City Employees' Ages

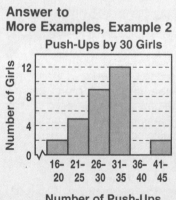

**Answer to
More Examples, Example 2**

Push-Ups by 30 Girls

Exercises

Independent Practice

10. Construct a histogram using the data in the table below. **See Solutions Manual.**

Heights of Presidents of the United States		
Height (in)	Tally	Frequency
63-65	I	1
66-68	⊮ IIII	9
69-71	⊮ ⊮ III	13
72-74	⊮ ⊮ ⊮ III	18
75-77	I	1

a. How many men have been presidents of the United States? **42**
b. What range of heights includes most of the presidents? **72-74**
c. Compared to the total, how would you describe the number of presidents that have been 6 feet or taller? $\frac{19}{42}$

11. A survey in the mall stopped people and asked how much change they had with them. Make a frequency table and histogram of the following results.

98¢   88¢   81¢   77¢   74¢   69¢   94¢   85¢   75¢   72¢
85¢   79¢   72¢   65¢   88¢   82¢   78¢   74¢   70¢   62¢
See Solutions Manual.

Mixed Review

12. **Algebra**   Solve $7 = \frac{r}{15}$. Check your solution. *(Lesson 2-4)* **105**

13. **Geometry**   Graph the points $A(-3, 2)$, $B(-3, -1)$, $C(1, -1)$, and $D(1, 2)$ on the same coordinate plane. Draw *AB, BC, CD,* and *AD*. Find the perimeter of the rectangle formed. *(Lesson 3-10)* **14 units**

Problem Solving and Applications

14b. The two tallest bars represent 31 of 49 women

15a. Can't tell; individual data is not shown.

15b. Sample answer: Leadership is associated with tallness.

DATA SEARCH

14. **Government**   As of July 1990, there were 1,273 women in the United States who held office in state legislatures. New Hampshire has 136 women in legislature. The table shows the numbers of women in the state legislatures in the other 49 states.
    a. Make a histogram of this data. **See Solutions Manual.**
    b. How does the histogram show what range of the number of women is most common?
    c. How does New Hampshire compare with the other states that have the most women in legislature? **It has more than twice the number of women.**

Women in State Legislatures	
Number of Women	Number of States
1-10	7
11-20	16
21-30	15
31-40	5
41-50	4
51-60	2

15. **Critical Thinking**   Look at the data in Exercise 10.
    a. How many presidents were exactly 6 feet tall? Explain your answer.
    b. Why do you think so many presidents were or are tall?

16. **Data Search**   Refer to pages 126 and 127.
    Use the graph of mountain heights to find which region of the United States appears to have the greatest number of high mountains. **The West**

Checking for Understanding

Exercises 1-4 are designed to help you assess students' understanding through reading, writing, speaking, and modeling. You should work through these exercises with your students and then monitor their work on Guided Practice Exercises 5-9.

Close

Ask students to list the advantages of a histogram when compared to a frequency table. Sample answer: Data are easier to compare in a histogram than in a frequency table.

3 PRACTICE/APPLY

Assignment Guide
Maximum: 10-16
Minimum: 10-15

For **Extra Practice,** see p. 591.

Alternate Assessment

Modeling   Have small groups roll two number cubes 20 times, finding the sum of each roll. Then have them make a histogram of the sums.

Enrichment Masters, p. 31

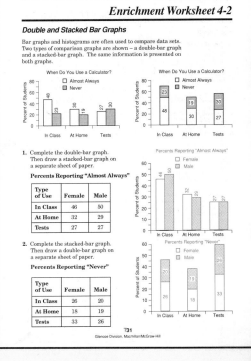

OPTIONS

Extending the Lesson

Using Cooperative Groups   Have groups roll 2 number cubes 100 times, keeping a tally of the sums. Have them make a histogram of their results. Finally, have them compare their results with the theoretical frequencies: sum of 2 − 2.8; 3 − 5.6; 4 − 8.3; 5 − 11.1; 6 − 13.9; 7 − 16.7; 8 − 13.9; 9 − 11.1; 10 − 8.3; 11 − 5.6; and 12 − 2.8.

Cooperative Learning Activity

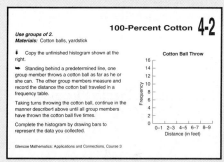

Lesson Resources
- Study Guide Master 4-3
- Practice Master 4-3
- Enrichment Master 4-3
- Group Activity Card 4-3

 Transparency 4-3 contains the 5-Minute Check and a teaching aid for this lesson.

🕐 5-Minute Check
(Over Lesson 4-2)

Sketch a histogram using this list of pulse rates.

75	83	66	72	78
68	77	87	72	65

For answer, see bottom of page 137.

1 FOCUS

Motivating the Lesson

Questioning Ask this question: *What important information about a set of values is not shown by a histogram?* Sample answers: individual values; high and low values; any significant gaps between individual values

2 TEACH

More Examples

For the Example

Construct a line plot for this inventory of men's (M) and women's (W) breathing rates (breaths/minute).

13-W	11-M	13-M	14-W
10-W	16-M	12-M	13-M
15-M	13-W	11-W	13-W

```
            W
            W
            W
      W     M
W  M  M  M  W  M  M
10 11 12 13 14 15 16
```

Breathing Rates

4-3 Line Plots

Objective
Construct and interpret line plots.

Words to Learn
line plot

In a taste test conducted by *Zillions* magazine, 44 readers judged potato chips according to texture, saltiness, potato flavor, and overall scrumptiousness. Twenty-six of the 29 brands of potato chips rated "good" or "very good."

The price of all the different brands were also studied. The price per ounce of the 26 tastiest brands are listed below along with their ratings. *V = very good, G = good*

Ratings and Cost per Ounce (¢) of Potato Chip Brands

12¢-V	21¢-G	14¢-V	25¢-G	12¢-G	18¢-V
20¢-V	17¢-G	20¢-V	21¢-G	21¢-G	23¢-V
21¢-G	24¢-G	17¢-G	21¢-V	10¢-G	28¢-G
23¢-V	21¢-G	22¢-G	13¢-V	20¢-G	24¢-G
19¢-G	25¢-G				

This data could be organized into a frequency table or shown in a histogram. Another way to display the frequency of data is by using a **line plot.** A line plot is a vertical graph of the tally marks you make in creating a frequency table.

In the line plot below, the price per ounce is shown along the horizontal axis. There is no vertical scale. Instead, each x represents a brand that is priced in that category.

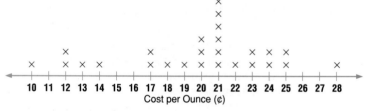

DID YOU KNOW

Each person in the United States eats an average of six pounds of potato chips per year.

From this representation, you can see that most potato chip brands are priced around 20-21¢ per ounce. Also you can see that 10¢ per ounce and 28¢ per ounce are extreme prices for chips.

You can alter this line plot to show more information. With this information, further data analysis can be done.

OPTIONS

Reteaching Activity

Using Cooperative Groups Have groups use the local newspaper to create a list of values on a topic of interest to them. Groups should then use the data to create a frequency table, a histogram, and a line plot.

Study Guide Masters, p. 32

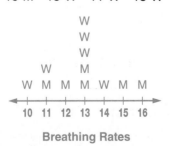

Name _____   Date _____

Study Guide Worksheet 4-3

Line Plots

Another way to organize frequency data is with a line plot.

Example A restaurant owner asked her customers to rate the food on a scale of 0 (very bad) to 10 (very good). The data below shows the results. The meal at which the customer was surveyed is also shown. B = breakfast, L = lunch.

5-B 7-L 9-L 0-B 6-B 6-L 8-B 10-L 4-B 8-L 8-B 2-B
8-L 7-B 4-B 7-L 6-B 9-L 10-L 6-B 7-B 5-B 9-L
8-L 7-L 6-B 3-B

For each customer, write the letter of the meal over the rating given.

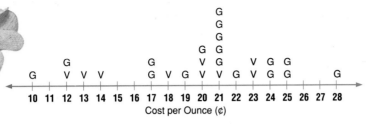

Example

Reconstruct the line plot on page 136 by replacing each x with a letter representing the quality of that brand of chip. Use V for very good and G for good. Find the best price for a chip rated very good.

Refer to the original list to find which chips are good or very good.

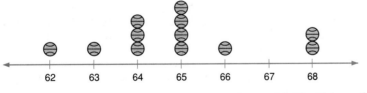

```
                                              G
                                              G
                                              G
                                   G          G
              G              G     V     G    V  G  V  G  G
      G  V  V  V        G  V  G  V  V  G  V  G  G           G
   ├──┼──┼──┼──┼──┼──┼──┼──┼──┼──┼──┼──┼──┼──┼──┼──┼──┼──┼──►
     10 11 12 13 14 15 16 17 18 19 20 21 22 23 24 25 26 27 28
                       Cost per Ounce (¢)
```

The lowest price for a chip rated very good is 12¢ per ounce.

Mini-Lab

Work in pairs.

Materials: yardstick, tape measure, or other measuring device

- Measure each other's height and record your heights on the chalkboard.
- With the help of your teacher and classmates, make a human line plot of your heights.

Talk About It
a. Which height had the most people? See students' work.
b. Which heights had more girls than boys? See students' work.

Checking for Understanding

Communicating Mathematics

Read and study the lesson to answer each question.

1. **Tell** how a line plot is like a frequency table. See margin.

2. **Show** how you could use a line plot to verify that the most common prices for brands of potato chips usually are chips rated as *good*. See students' work.

3. **Write** what the line plot below tells you about the heights of the players on the girls' basketball team. Most players are 64 or 65 inches.

Heights (in inches) of the Midway Girls' Basketball Team

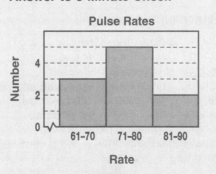

```
      ●           ●     ●     ●     ●
   ┌──┼─────┼─────┼─────┼─────┼─────┼─────┼──►
     62    63    64    65    66    67    68
```

Limited English Proficiency

In this chapter, data are graphed in several markedly different ways. LEP students may have difficulty distinguishing among the methods of displaying data. Before discussing a new method, review the previous methods. Explain new methods verbally and then give several visual examples of each. Encourage students to keep notebooks and to update and review them daily.

Answer to 5-Minute Check

Pulse Rates

```
Number
   4 ┤      ┌────┐
     │ ┌──┐ │    │
   2 ┤ │  │ │    │  ┌──┐
     │ │  │ │    │  │  │
   0 ┴─┴──┴─┴────┴──┴──┴─
       61-70  71-80  81-90
              Rate
```

Teaching Tip In the Example, ask students to name two disadvantages of the chip listed as 28¢-G. It is the most expensive chip and it is rated as only good.

Using the Mini-Lab After students have made the human line plot, group the heights in 3-inch intervals. Ask students to estimate which interval of a histogram of the heights would have the tallest bar and which would have the shortest bar.

Checking for Understanding

Exercises 1-3 are designed to help you assess students' understanding through reading, writing, speaking, and modeling. You should work through these exercises with your students and then monitor their work on Guided Practice Exercises 4-5.

Additional Answer

1. Sample answer: A line plot is a vertical graph of the tally marks made when creating a frequency table.

Practice Masters, p. 32

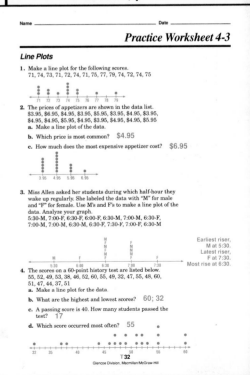

Close

Ask students to list the advantages of a line plot over a histogram.   Sample answer: A line plot is easier to construct. Every value is shown. It readily shows extreme values, clusters of values, and gaps between values.

3 PRACTICE/APPLY

Assignment Guide
Maximum: 6–12
Minimum: 6–11

For **Extra Practice,** see p. 591.

Alternate Assessment

Writing   Have students work with a partner to choose a data category, create a list of values, and draw a line plot.

Additional Answer

4.

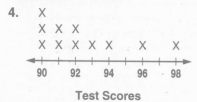

Test Scores

Enrichment Masters, p. 32

Name _____   Date _____

Enrichment Worksheet 4-3

Contour Maps

A *contour map* shows differences in elevation. The contour lines join points that all are the same distance above sea level.

To illustrate this idea, a contour map has been drawn for the block tower at the right.

Sketch a contour map for each tower. You may wish to build the towers from small cubes before you draw your maps.

1.   2.

Use the contour map at the right for these problems. The map shows the Bernal Heights section of San Francisco, California.

3. From which point, *E* or *C*, is it a steeper climb to the radio tower?
   point *E*

4. From which point, *E* or *D*, is it a steeper climb to the radio tower?
   Point *E*, since it's closer to the base.

5. Which point probably has an elevation of less than 100 feet?
   point *F*

6. Why do you think the radio tower is located where it is?
   It's the highest point in the region.

Contour Interval: 100 ft
Scale: 1 in. = 2,000 ft

T32
Glencoe Division, Macmillan/McGraw-Hill

138

---

4. Make a line plot for the following test scores..
   90, 92, 91, 94, 96, 98, 90, 91, 92, 90, 93 **See margin.**

5. The weights in kilograms of the Hendricks Middle School wrestling team are shown in the table.
   a. Make a line plot of the data. **See Solutions Manual.**
   b. Analyze the line plot. Write all conclusions you can make.
      Sample answer: most weigh 72 pounds.

Weights (in kg)			
79	79	80	75
72	72	72	72
70	75	90	68
51	65	72	
75	72	80	
68	74	62	

Exercises

6. The scores on a 50-point social studies test are given below.

45	47	38	40	41	42	50	45	47	42
34	44	41	42	39	40	33	41	45	31

   a. Make a line plot for the data. **See Solutions Manual.**
   b. What were the highest and lowest scores? **50; 31**
   c. Which score occurred the most often? **41, 42, and 45**
   d. If 35 points is considered a passing score, how many scores were passing scores? **17**

7. Mr. Cresky asked his students how many hours of sleep they got on the average each night for a week. He labeled the data with G for girls and B for boys. Use Gs and Bs to make a line plot of this data. Analyze your graph.

10-G	7.5-B	9-B	9-G	8-G	8.5-G	9.5-B	8.5-B	8.5-G
9.5-B	8-G	8-B	10-B	10-G	9.5-G	7.5-G	9-G	8.5-B

   See Solutions Manual.

8. Solve $n = -282 + 41$. *(Lesson 3-3)* **−241**

9. **Forestry**   The ranger at Crestview Nature Preserve recorded the heights of several trees in an area of the preserve. Make a histogram of this data. *(Lesson 4-2)* **See Solutions Manual.**

Height (in ft)	11-20	21-30	31-40	41-50	51-60	61-70
Number of trees	4	10	14	22	28	18

10a. See Solutions Manual.

10. **Literature**   The list at the right shows the prices paid for some early editions of books written by Mark Twain.
    a. Make a line plot of this data.
    b. If a collector went to an auction of these books with $200, how many books were within the collector's budget? **10**

Sales of Mark Twain's Books		
$150	$2,200	$160
$70	$450	$330
$110	$325	$1,600
$100	$800	$130
$60	$180	$65
$50	$420	

11. **Critical Thinking**   Use the potato chip data on page 136. **See Solutions Manual.**
    a. Select an interval and make a histogram of the data. Use different colors to divide each bar into the number of *good* brands and the number of *very good* brands.
    11b. Heights of bars and stacked letters are similar.
    b. How does your histogram compare to the line plot in the Example?

12. **Journal Entry**   Ask 15 friends how old they are in months. Make a line plot of your data. Write a few sentences about your data. **See students' work.**

OPTIONS

Extending the Lesson

Using Cooperative Groups   Give groups these definitions: *outlier:* an especially large or small value; *cluster:* an isolated group of values; *gap:* a large space between values. Have groups create a set of data containing outliers, clusters, and gaps. Have them draw a line plot of the data.

Cooperative Learning Activity

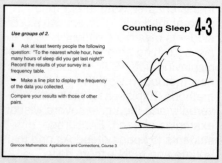

Counting Sleep **4-3**

Use groups of 2.

♦ Ask at least twenty people the following question: "To the nearest whole hour, how many hours of sleep did you get last night?" Record the results of your survey in a frequency table.

➡ Make a line plot to display the frequency of the data you collected.

Compare your results with those of other pairs.

Glencoe Mathematics: Applications and Connections, Course 3

4-3B Maps and Statistics

A Follow-Up of Lesson 4-3

Objective

Use maps to display United States statistical data.

You can pick up almost any newspaper or magazine and see a map of the United States with statistics about the individual states displayed by shading or coloring. The map below shows the percent of change in state funding of education for 1992, grades K-12. How do geographers decide how the statistics should be displayed? Why do they use maps instead of lists?

DID YOU KNOW

Gerhardus Mercator, a Flemish geographer, was the first person to use the term *atlas* for a collection of maps. He invented the Mercator map projection. He used this type of map to produce a map of Earth similar to the ones we use today.

State Funding for Grades K-12

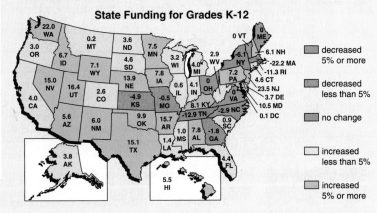

Try this!

Materials: colored pencils, outline map of the United States

State	Hispanic (Percent)	State	Hispanic (Percent)	State	Hispanic (Percent)
AL	0.6	KY	0.6	ND	0.7
AK	3.2	LA	2.2	OH	1.3
AZ	18.8	ME	0.6	OK	2.7
AR	0.8	MD	2.6	OR	4.0
CA	25.8	MA	4.8	PA	2.0
CO	12.9	MI	2.2	RI	4.6
CT	6.5	MN	1.2	SC	0.9
DE	2.4	MS	1.2	SD	0.8
DC	5.4	MO	1.2	TN	0.7
FL	12.2	MT	1.5	TX	25.5
GA	1.7	NE	2.3	UT	4.9
HI	7.3	NV	10.4	VT	0.7
ID	5.3	NH	1.0	VA	2.6
IL	7.9	NJ	9.6	WA	4.4
IN	1.8	NM	38.2	WV	0.5
IA	1.2	NY	12.3	WI	1.9
KS	3.8	NC	1.2	WY	5.7

[1990 U.S. Census, subject to update]

- The table at the left lists the 50 states and the District of Columbia with the percent of their population that is of Hispanic origin. Make a line plot of this data using the state abbreviations instead of ×s.
- Mapmakers usually like to organize the data into fewer than 7 categories. Use the ranges 0-1.99, 2-5.99, 6-11.99, 12-21.99, and 22-40 to separate the data into categories. *The intervals are selected to get a point of view across. Therefore, they are usually not equal intervals.*
- Mapmakers use colors ranging from light to dark to correspond with the ranges from least to greatest. Choose five colors of pencils. Color each state on a United States map according to its category.

Mathematics Lab 4-3B Maps and Statistics **139**

NCTM Standards: 1–4, 8, 10

Management Tips

For Students When students make their line plots in the *Try This!*, several intervals will be stacked high with state abbreviations. Students will find the plots easier to organize and read if they draw them on graph paper, using one grid square for each abbreviation.

For the Overhead Projector *Overhead Manipulative Resources* provides appropriate materials for teacher or student demonstration of the activities in this Mathematics Lab.

1 FOCUS

Introducing the Lab

Have students look at the U. S. map. Ask them to identify the percent change in educational funding for your state for 1992. Discuss possible reasons for the change.

2 TEACH

Using Estimation After students complete their U. S. map, ask these questions:

- *How would the map have changed if five equal intervals had been used?* Nearly all the data (42 items) would have been bunched in the first interval, 0–8.

- *What disadvantages would have resulted?* Almost no distinctions between states could have been drawn.

Using Communication After students complete Exercise 7, ask what conclusions they can draw about data displays created by people who try to influence your opinions? They may create false impressions. Before drawing conclusions, always insist on seeing the data on which a display is based.

Close

Have students compare and contrast the effectiveness of line plots versus maps for displaying data.

Additional Answers

1. There is a large number of states with low percentages and few states with high percentages.
5. Make large ranges for the lower percentages and small ranges for the higher percentages.

1. See margin.

5. See margin.
6. more color in the 0-3 range. That color is more dominant.

What do you think?   2. Sample answer: neater, more concise.

1. Why do you think the category ranges given were chosen?
2. Why do you think mapmakers try to use less than seven colors when making a map?
3. What areas of the country have more people of Hispanic origin than others? Why do you think this is true? CA, NM, TX, close to Mexico
4. Why is the map a more effective way to present the data than a list? more visual

Extension

5. Depending on a point of view, someone may want a map that highlights states with a small Hispanic population. How could you change the map to emphasize this point of view?
6. Make another map using the ranges 0-2, 3-5.99, 6-11.99, 12-23.99, and 24 and over. How does the appearance of this map differ from the previous one?

Application

7. **Farming** The chart below shows the percent of land that is farmland in each state and the District of Columbia.

State	Percent Farmland	State	Percent Farmland	State	Percent Farmland	State	Percent Farmland
AL	36	IL	83	MT	67	RI	11
AK	0	IN	74	NE	95	SC	33
AZ	53	IA	94	NV	15	SD	92
AR	47	KS	91	NH	9	TN	50
CA	33	KY	59	NJ	22	TX	82
CO	53	LA	33	NM	62	UT	20
CT	16	ME	8	NY	32	VT	30
DE	54	MD	43	NC	36	VA	39
DC	0	MA	14	ND	95	WA	40
FL	39	MI	31	OH	61	WV	25
GA	37	MN	57	OK	78	WI	52
HI	48	MS	46	OR	30	WY	54
ID	28	MO	70	PA	30		

7b. make large range sizes for the large percents
a. Color a map to illustrate this data. See students' work.
b. How would you change your map if you were a senator trying to get more government money for agricultural programs?
c. How would you change your map if you were an opponent of the senator in Question b and were looking for funds for urban development? make large range sizes for the small percents

140   **Chapter 4** Statistics and Data Analysis

OPTIONS

Lab Manual You may wish to make copies of the blackline master on p. 48 of the *Lab Manual* for students to use as a recording sheet.

Lab Manual, p. 48

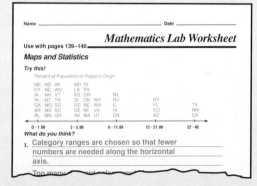

4-4 Stem-and-Leaf Plots

Objective
Construct and interpret stem-and-leaf plots.

Words to Learn
stem-and-leaf plot
stem
leaf
back-to-back stem-and-leaf plot

Growth spurts differ in boys and girls. Girls typically grow quickly around age 12, while boys grow quickly, on average, around the ages of 13 and 14.

Mrs. Jeske is the school nurse at Titusville Middle School. She measured the heights in inches of 20 students in a health class.

Height of Health Class Students (in inches)

Girls				Boys			
55	59	66	64	59	63	65	62
70	68	67	63	72	71	62	60
68	58			60	61		

This data could be presented on a line plot. Another way to organize the data is to make a **stem-and-leaf plot.**

In a stem-and-leaf plot, the greatest place value of the data can be used for the **stems,** and the next greatest place value for the **leaves.**

Follow these steps to construct a stem-and-leaf plot for the data above.

- Tens place is the greatest place value. The stems will be those digits in the tens place. Use the digits only once and list them in order from least to greatest.

  5|
  6|
  7|

- The leaves are the corresponding digits in the next greatest place value for each stem.

  Sometimes it is helpful to write the leaves first in any order and then to order them from least to greatest.

  For example, there are four numbers that have 5 in the tens place. They are 55, 59, 59 and 58. The 5, 9, 9, and 8 are the leaves for the stem 5. Always write every leaf even if it is a repeat of another leaf. Write the leaves in order from least to greatest.

  5|5899   5 is a stem.   5, 8, 9, and 9 are leaves.

- Complete the stem-and-leaf plot for all stems.

  5 | 5899
  6 | 0012233456788
  7 | 012

- Include a guide to the data.   *6|2 means 62 inches.*

Now it is easy to see that most of the students are between 60 and 68 inches tall.

Lesson 4-4 Stem-and-Leaf Plots   **141**

NCTM Standards: 1–5, 8–10

Lesson Resources
- Study Guide Master 4-4
- Practice Master 4-4
- Enrichment Master 4-4
- Group Activity Card 4-4

Transparency 4-4 contains the 5-Minute Check and a teaching aid for this lesson.

5-Minute Check
(Over Lesson 4-3)
Make a line plot for the total runs scored in 14 baseball games.

9   5   6   2   6   4   5
6   11   8   4   1   9   6

For answer, see below.

1 FOCUS

Motivating the Lesson

Questioning   Ask students to state the number of tens and the number of ones in each of the following measurements.

- **84 cm**   8 tens, 4 ones
- **6 ft**   0 tens, 6 ones
- **37 mm**   3 tens, 7 ones

2 TEACH

More Examples

For the Example

Make a back-to-back stem-and-leaf plot of the 1982–1991 National League and American League home run leader totals.

National League

37	40	36	37	37
49	39	47	40	38

American League

39	39	43	40	40
49	42	36	51	44

National		American
987776	3	699
9700	4	002349
	5	1

0|4 means 40
5|1 means 51

OPTIONS

Bell Ringer

How could you convert a stem-and-leaf plot into a histogram without using a pen or pencil?   Rotate the plot 90° so that the stems are at the bottom. The plot now resembles a histogram with stacks of leaves representing the bars.

Answer to 5-Minute Check

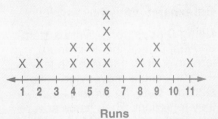

Runs

Using the Mini-Lab Be alert to the possibility that taller students may tease shorter students, especially shorter boys. Mention that height is not a measure of intelligence, athletic ability, leadership qualities, or normalcy. It is just a measure of how tall someone is.

Checking for Understanding

Exercises 1-3 are designed to help you assess students' understanding through reading, writing, speaking, and modeling. You should work through these exercises with your students and then monitor their work on Guided Practice Exercises 4-7.

Error Analysis

Watch for students who omit data when making a stem-and-leaf plot.

Prevent by having students count to see that the number of leaves and the number of data items are the same.

Close

Have students describe the kind of data that is suited for display in a stem-and-leaf plot. data with a small number of stem values, representing a range of numbers you wish to compare

Additional Answer

3. when you want to compare two sets of similar data; scores of test #1 versus scores of test #2

A **back-to-back stem-and-leaf plot** is used to compare two sets of data. In this type of plot, the leaves for one set of data are on one side of the stem and the leaves for the other set of data are on the other side of the stem. Two guides to the data are needed.

Example

Make a back-to-back stem-and-leaf plot of the heights of the health class, putting the girls' heights on one side and the boys' heights on the other.

Girls		Boys
985	5	9
887643	6	0012235
0	7	12

0|7 means 70 inches   *7|1 means 71 inches*

Notice that the greatest data are always the outermost leaves.

Mini-Lab

Work with your classmates.

Materials: the data from the Mini-Lab on page 137, four pieces of paper labeled 4, 5, 6, and 7

- Lay the numbers on the floor in a column.
- Make a human back-to-back stem-and-leaf plot with girls on one side and boys on the other.

Talk About It   a. They are the tallest for that row.

a. When everyone is in place, what can you say about the heights of the persons on the end of each row of leaves?

b. Which group appears to be taller? See students' work.

Checking for Understanding

Communicating Mathematics

Read and study the lesson to answer each question.   greatest place value

1. **Tell** what numbers you use to form the stems in a stem-and-leaf plot. of the data

2. **Write** what 80|9 means if the greatest place value is hundreds. 809

3. **Tell** when you can use a back-to-back stem-and-leaf plot. Give an example of data that you could show with one. See margin.

Guided Practice

Refer to the stem-and-leaf plot in the Example.

4. What is the height of the shortest girl? 55 inches

5. How tall is the tallest boy? 72 inches

OPTIONS

Reteaching Activity

Using Discussion Write a stem-and-leaf plot on the chalkboard, leaving spaces between the leaves. Point to various leaves and have students state the two-digit numbers they represent. Then name several two-digit numbers and have students add the leaves in the correct spaces in the plot.

Study Guide Masters, p. 33

Name _____   Date _____

Study Guide Worksheet 4-4

Stem-and-Leaf Plots

A stem-and-leaf plot may be used to organize data.

Example   The data shows the ages of boxers in heavyweight championship fights between 1980 and 1990.

Winners: 27 24 28 26 26 35 25 26 29 20 33 20 29
Losers: 30 25 26 31 29 26 35 27 29 29 33 23

The greatest place value is tens. So, the stems are tens-place digits. List them only once, in order from least to greatest.

The leaves are the ones-place digits. Write the ones-place digit for every age. Arrange the leaves in order from least to greatest.

Winners
2 | 0 0 4 5 6 6 6 7 8 9 9
3 | 3 5   3 | 5 means age 35

A back-to-back stem-and-leaf plot

6. Copy the stem-and-leaf plot on page 141. **See margin.**
   a. Replace each leaf with either G (girl) or B (boy) to correspond with the heights of girls or boys.
   b. What kind of information do you gain from this type of plot?
   c. What kind of information do you lose from this type of plot?

7. A park is giving prizes to the first 30 people through the gate on their anniversary date. In order to determine what type of prizes to get, the park asks the ages of the first 30 people through the gate on a day prior to their anniversary. The ages are 12, 11, 22, 32, 35, 45, 46, 14, 14, 16, 33, 30, 41, 7, 9, 25, 8, 51, 43, 18, 17, 19, 32, 34, 18, 22, 24, 56, 61, and 13.
   a. What numbers are used as stems in making a stem-and-leaf plot of this data? **0, 1, 2, 3, 4, 5, 6**
   b. Make a stem-and-leaf plot of these ages. **See margin.**   **7; 61**
   c. What are the ages of the youngest person and oldest person?
   d. What age group seems most representative of this group?   **teens**

Exercises

Independent Practice

State the numbers you would use for the stems in a stem-and-leaf plot of each set of data. Then make the plot. **For plots, see Solutions Manual.**   **0, 1, 2, 3, 4, 5**

8. 17, 32, 41, 34, 42, 35 **1, 2, 3, 4**
9. 9, 12, 24, 51, 33, 14, 11

10. 25, 26, 27, 28, 29   10. 294, 295, 272, 253, 280, 267

11. 7.5, 5.4, 8.6, 6.3, 7.1, 5.9 **5, 6, 7, 8**

12. The data below are test scores for Mr. Sopher's eighth-grade homeroom.

Mathematics	75	93	87	56	60	73	78	69
	83	89	94	97	65	73	87	85
Science	68	73	98	87	65	64	70	73
	72	78	81	83	68	57	63	75

12e. Mathematics; there are fewer scores in the 50-79 range than in the 80-99 range.

   a. Make a back-to-back stem-and-leaf plot for the data. **See margin.**
   b. What is the highest mathematics score? **97**
   c. What interval does each stem represent? **tens**
   d. In which interval do most of the science scores occur? **70's**
   e. In which subject did the class have better scores? Explain your answer.

13. Two companies list the ages of their employees by using a stem-and-leaf plot.

Bender Company

2	34
3	5677
4	34478899
5	1266
6	58

Flexor Company

2	2355
3	689
4	1589
5	0479
6	33489

2|2 means 22 years old.

13b. Sample answer: health care benefits expense

   a. One company can estimate the average age range of their employees more quickly than the other company. Which one? **Bender Co.**
   b. Why would a company want to find out the average age?

Lesson 4-4 Stem-and-Leaf Plots   **143**

Gifted and Talented Needs

The shape of a set of data is called the *distribution*. The "bell-shaped" distribution is the most common and most studied shape. Have students research bell-shaped (also called *normal*) distributions and find examples of common classes of data typically distributed in this way.

Additional Answer

12a.

	Math	Science
	6	5	7
	950	6	34588
	8533	7	023358
	97753	8	137
	743	9	8

3|9 means 93

9|8 means 98

143

Additional Answer

16.

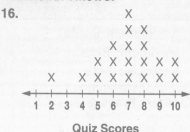

Quiz Scores

Mixed Review

14. Find |−20|. *(Lesson 3-1)* 20

15. Solve −48 ÷ 3 = *c*. *(Lesson 3-7)* −16

16. Make a line plot for these English quiz scores: **See margin.**
    7, 10, 6, 7, 5, 8, 2, 8, 6, 8, 9, 8, 7, 4, 9, 7, 6, 10, 5, and 7 *(Lesson 4-3)*

Problem Solving and Applications

17. Each shows the frequencies in regular intervals.

17. **Critical Thinking** Explain how a stem-and-leaf plot is similar to a histogram.

18. **Sports** The number of home runs hit by the league leaders in professional baseball from 1921-1990 is shown in the plot below.

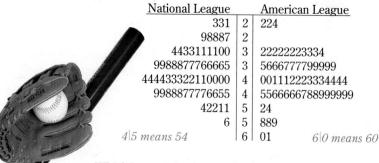

National League		American League
331	2	224
98887	2	
4433111100	3	22222223334
9988877766665	3	5666777799999
444433322110000	4	001112223334444
9988877776655	4	5566666788999999
42211	5	24
6	5	889
	6	01

4|5 means 54   *6|0 means 60*

a. Which league's leaders tend to hit more home runs? **American League**

b. Why do you think two lines were used for each stem?
   lines would be too long otherwise and this way they group better

19. **Research** Find the ages of the United States presidents at their death.

a. Make a stem-and-leaf plot of the data. **See students' work.**

b. Write a sentence to describe any patterns you notice. **See students' work.**

20. **Portfolio Suggestion** Select an item from this chapter that shows your creativity and place it in your portfolio. **See students' work.**

CULTURAL KALEIDOSCOPE

Jackie Robinson

Jackie Robinson (1919-1972) became the first African-American baseball player in modern major league history. He signed with the Brooklyn Dodgers in 1947. He played through 1956 and was both an infielder and an outfielder.

Leading the league in stolen bases, Mr. Robinson was chosen Rookie of the Year in 1947. With his help, the Dodgers won the National League Pennant that year and on September 30, 1947, he became the first African-American to compete in a World Series.

In 1949, Jackie Robinson won the batting championship with a 0.342 average and also won the Most Valuable Player award. His overall career average was 0.311. In his first year of eligibility in 1962, he was elected to the Baseball Hall of Fame.

Enrichment Masters, p. 33

Name _____ Date _____

Enrichment Worksheet 4-4

Making Pictographs

A *pictograph* uses pictures or symbols to stand for numbers of objects. When making a pictograph, it is helpful to choose a symbol that can be easily divided into fractional parts. If the data can be expressed in decimal form, a 10-part symbol is a good choice.

1. Use the data given in parentheses to complete the pictograph.

Distance From Earth
Key: Each Star = 1 Light Year

Proxima Centauri (4.2)	★ ★ ★ ★ ◊
Alpha Centauri (4.3)	★ ★ ★ ★ ◊
Barnard's Star (6.2)	★ ★ ★ ★ ★ ◊
Sirius (8.7)	★ ★ ★ ★ ★ ★ ★ ★ ☆

On a separate sheet of paper, make a pictograph for each chart.   See students' graphs.

2. Use the dot figure at the right. ✿ Each dot equals 0.1 million people.

Civilian Labor Force, by Occupation

Construction	6,224,000
Farming	4,184,000
Laborers	5,457,000
Machine Operators	8,776,000
Technicians	3,350,000
Transportation	5,079,000

3. Create a 10-part symbol of your own.

Long-Running Broadway Shows

Name	Number of Performances
Fiddler on the Roof	3,242
Hello, Dolly!	2,844
My Fair Lady	2,717
Oklahoma!	2,314
Hair	1,742
South Pacific	1,694

T33
Glencoe Division, Macmillan/McGraw-Hill

OPTIONS

Extending the Lesson

Cultural Kaleidoscope Have the class make a graph of the Brooklyn Dodgers' winning percentage in their pennant-winning seasons during Jackie Robinson's career:

1947–.610; 1949–.630; 1952–.627; 1953–.682; 1955–.641; 1956–.604

Cooperative Learning Activity

Leaf It to Me 4-4

Number of players: 2
Materials: Spinners

✿ Label equal sections of each of two spinners with the digits 0 through 9. Decide which spinner will be spinner A and which will be spinner B. For one partner, spinner A gives digits in tens place and spinner B gives units digits. For the other partner, spinner A gives units digits and spinner B gives digits in tens place.

✿ Each partner makes the "stem" portion of a stem-and-leaf plot by writing the digits 0 through 9 in a single column and drawing a vertical line to the right. Both partners then spin the spinners at the same time. Each partner records the resulting two-digit number on his or her stem-and-leaf plot. The first partner to write five leaves beside any stem wins the round. Play several rounds.

Glencoe Mathematics: Applications and Connections, Course 3

4-5

Measures of Central Tendency

Objective
Find the mean, median, and mode of a set of data.

Words to Learn
measures of central tendency
mean
median
mode

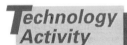

Technology Activity

You can learn how to find the mean of a set of data with a spreadsheet in Technology Activity 2 on page 659.

Calculator Hint

You can also find the sum of a group of data by using the or keys. After entering each number, press or M+. To retrieve the total, press RCL or MR.

On a test covering material from their social studies project, five members of a cooperative group received the scores listed below.

Emilio	88
Nadawi	86
Sean	85
Debbie	78
Hiroshi	88

Their teacher informed them that their project score would be the average of their group's test scores. Sean told his parents that he received an 86 on his social studies project. Nadawi told her brother that she received an 88. Hiroshi told his grandmother that he received an 85. How can all three students think they are correct?

There are three common ways to describe a set of data. These ways are called **measures of central tendency.** They are the mean, the mode, and the median.

Hiroshi chose the **mean.** Most people think of the *mean* when they use the word *average*. For the scores above, the mean is

$$(\; 88 \; + \; 86 \; + \; 85 \; + \; 78 \; + \; 88 \;) \; \div \; 5 \; = \; 85$$

The mean score is 85.
The mean is not necessarily a member of the set of data, but here, it is.

Mean	The mean of a set of data is the sum of the data divided by the number of pieces of data.

Nadawi used the score that appears most often to describe the set. This is called the **mode.**

    78   85   86   88   88

There are two 88s in this set. So, 88 is the mode.

If there was another score of 86, then 86 would also be a mode and the data would have two modes. A set of data in which no numbers appear more than once, has no mode.
If there is a mode, it is always a member of the set of data.

Mode	The mode of a set of data is the number or item that appears most often.

Lesson 4-5 Measures of Central Tendency **145**

OPTIONS

Bell Ringer

Four of the five sweaters Mrs. Cohn purchased as presents cost $49 each. The mean price of the sweaters was $56. Find the cost of the fifth sweater. $84

4-5 Lesson Notes

NCTM Standards: 1–5, 7, 9, 10

Lesson Resources
- Study Guide Master 4-5
- Practice Master 4-5
- Enrichment Master 4-5
- Evaluation Master, Quiz A, p. 34
- Application Master, p. 4
- Group Activity Card 4-5

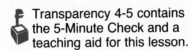 Transparency 4-5 contains the 5-Minute Check and a teaching aid for this lesson.

🕐 5-Minute Check
(Over Lesson 4-4)

Make a stem-and-leaf plot of the commuting times (in minutes) of fifteen workers.

33	23	18	30	44
28	34	17	38	28
30	18	29	23	21

Commuting Times

1	788
2	133889
3	00348
4	4

1|7 means 17

1 FOCUS

Motivating the Lesson

Situational Problem The annual salary of the president of a company was $70,000. The salaries of each of the three employees was $10,000. The president stated proudly that the average salary at the company was $25,000. Ask students if the president's claim is correct. Then ask them if this $25,000 "average salary" gives a very clear picture of all the company salaries.

2 TEACH

Using Connections To help students remember the definitions of median and mode, recite these sentences:

- The median strip runs down the middle of a highway.
- The mode is the current fashion. A fashionable item, like blue jeans, is the one that appears most often.

More Examples

For Example 1

The line plot below shows the ages of nine contestants in a senior swimming tournament. Find the mean, median, and mode of the data.

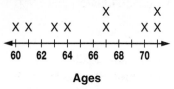

Ages

mean: 66; median: 67;
modes: 67, 71

For Example 2

Find the mean, median, and mode of the soup prices, in cents, displayed in the stem-and-leaf plot below.

```
4 | 3
5 | 258
6 | 0469      mean: 65;
7 | 158       median: 65;
8 | 9         mode: none
```

Checking for Understanding

Exercises 1-4 are designed to help you assess students' understanding through reading, writing, speaking, and modeling. You should work through these exercises with your students and then monitor their work on Guided Practice Exercises 5-8.

Error Analysis

Watch for students who divide by the wrong number when finding a mean.

Prevent by having them circle each item of data and then count the number of items marked.

Close

Have students describe a situation when the mean would be an appropriate measure of central tendency, one when the median would be appropriate, and one when the mode would be appropriate.

Sean ordered the test scores from least to greatest and chose the middle number. This is called the **median.**

78   85   86   88   88

The middle number is 86. The median score is 86.

If the number of data is even, the set has two middle numbers. In that case, the median is the mean of the two numbers. For example, in {11, 12, 15, 22, 26, and 29}, the middle numbers are 15 and 22. Their mean is $\frac{15 + 22}{2}$ or 18.5. *The median is not necessarily a member of the set of data.*

Mental Math Hint
• • • • • • • • • •
You can find the mean of pairs like 40 and 42 without dividing. Just think "what number is halfway between?"

Median	The median is the number in the middle when the data are arranged in order. When there are two middle numbers, the median is their mean.

Example 1 *Problem Solving*

Radio One advertiser claims that the average radio station plays about 44 minutes of music per hour. The line plot below shows the minutes of music per hour for 12 radio stations. Find the mean, median, and mode of the data.

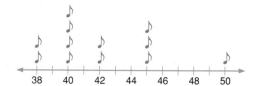

To find the mean, find the sum of the minutes and divide by 12.

$$\frac{2(38) + 4(40) + 2(42) + 3(45) + 50}{12} = \frac{505}{12} \text{ or about 42}$$

The mean is about 42 minutes.

The median is the middle number. There are 12 numbers, so the median is the mean of the 6th and 7th numbers.

$$\frac{40 + 42}{2} = 41 \qquad \text{The median is 41 minutes.}$$

The mode is the most frequent number. The mode is 40 minutes.

Since the advertiser's claim is greater than any of these measures of central tendency, you might consider the claim to be false advertising.

146   **Chapter 4** Statistics and Data Analysis

OPTIONS

Reteaching Activity

Using Cooperative Groups Have each group of three students generate a list of 10 random numbers by randomly opening their textbook and reading the page number. Then one student should explain how to find the mean of the numbers, one how to find the median, and one how to find the mode.

Study Guide Masters, p. 34

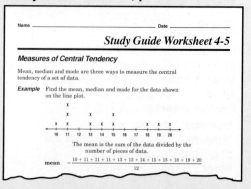

Name _____ Date _____

Study Guide Worksheet 4-5

Measures of Central Tendency

Mean, median and mode are three ways to measure the central tendency of a set of data.

Example Find the mean, median and mode for the data shown on the line plot.

The mean is the sum of the data divided by the number of pieces of data.

$$\text{mean} = \frac{10 + 11 + 11 + 11 + 13 + 13 + 14 + 15 + 15 + 18 + 19 + 20}{12}$$

To find the mean, add the heights and divide by 20.

$1273 \div 20 = 63.65$

5	5899
6	0012233456788
7	012

The mean height is 63.65 inches.

The median is the mean of the two middle numbers. Since the two middle numbers are both 63, the median height is 63 inches.

This data set has five repeated numbers, so it has five modes. They are 59, 60, 62, 63, and 68.

Checking for Understanding   1. The number that has the most x's.

Communicating Mathematics

Read and study the lesson to answer each question.

1. **Tell** how to find the mode of the data in the line plot at the right.

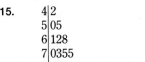

2. **Show** how to find the median of the set {17, 3, 15, 8, 5, 13, 7, 9, 12, 10}. **See margin.**

3. **Write** a sentence to tell how the mean of a set of data may differ from the median. **See margin.**

4. **Tell** which measure of central tendency in Example 1 best represents the number of minutes music is played? Explain. **median**

Guided Practice

Organize the data into either a frequency table, a line plot, or a stem-and-leaf plot. Then find the mean, median, and mode.

5. 3, 5, 7, 6, 8, 2, 9, 3, 7, 7, 8 **6; 7; 7**

6. 22, 24, 25, 26, 25, 34, 35 **27; 25; 25**

7. $49, $49, $50, $50, $52, $52 **$50; $50; $49, $50, $52**

8. 17.2, 3.5, 15.6, 8.8, 5.5, 13.1, 7, 9.6, 12.9, 10.74 **10.4; 10.17; no mode**

Exercises   10. 79.3; 79.5; 84

Independent Practice

Find the mean, median, and mode for each set of data. Round to the nearest tenth.

9. 2, 6, 4, 5, 6, 13, 5, 8, 13 **6.9; 6; 5, 6, 13**   10. 79, 84, 81, 84, 73, 75, 80, 78

11. 130, 155, 148, 184, 172 **157.8; 155; none**   12. 21, 18, 24, 21 **21; 21; 21**

13. 3.4, 1.8, 2.6, 1.8, 2.3, 3.1 **2.5; 2.5; 1.8**   14. 25.98, 30, 45.36, 25, 45.36 **34.3; 30; 45.4**

15.

4	2
5	05
6	128
7	0355
8	178

6 | 1 means 61

68.2; 70; 75

16.

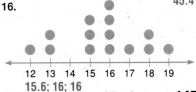

15.6; 16; 16

Lesson 4-5 Measures of Central Tendency   **147**

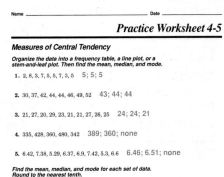

17. The growing season in Tennessee is the period from May to September. The chart at the right shows the normal rainfall for these months. **a. 3.92; 3.6; 3.7**
    a. Find the mean, mode, and median of this data.
    b. Suppose Tennessee received heavy rain in May totaling 8.2 inches. If this figure was used for May, how would the measures of central tendency be affected? **Only mean would change. It would increase.**
    c. If September is eliminated from the period, how would this affect the measures of central tendency? **Mean increases slightly; same mode; median increases slightly.**

Normal Rainfall for Tennessee	
May	4.8 in.
June	3.6 in.
July	3.9 in.
Aug.	3.6 in.
Sept.	3.7 in.

Mixed Review

18. Solve $5.17 = \frac{k}{2} + 3.68$. Check your solution. *(Lesson 2-7)* **2.98**

19. Solve $b = 65 - (-87)$. *(Lesson 3-5)* **152**

20. Twenty people attended a public speaking seminar. Make a stem-and-leaf plot of their ages: 15, 23, 42, 18, 34, 29, 56, 24, 36, 21, 43, 52, 35, 22, 16, 48, 32, 37, 26, and 45. *(Lesson 4-4)* **See margin.**

Problem Solving and Applications

21. **Critical Thinking** Mikael knows that he will have five tests this grading period and that he must have at least an 80 average to play on the school's volleyball team. His mean for the first four tests is 77. What is the least score he can get on the last test and still qualify to play volleyball? **92**

22. **Hobbies** Meagan does one cross stitch project a month. Four of her projects required 7 colors of floss, three projects required 9 colors of floss, and five projects required 10 colors of floss.
    a. Find the mean, median, and mode of the colors. **8.75; 9; 10**
    b. Which measure of central tendency is the best average? Explain. **median; The mode is an extreme and the mean is close to the median.**

23. **Journal Entry** Can you think of a time when you have heard or read about an *average*? What do you think of when you hear that word? **See students' work.**

---

4 Assessment: **Mid-Chapter Review**

The line plot shows scores on a 25-point history test.

1. Make a frequency table for the data. *(Lesson 4-1)* **See margin.**

2. Construct a histogram for the data using intervals of 3 for the scores. *(Lesson 4-2)* **See Solutions Manual.**

3. In what range do most of the scores lie in the line plot? *(Lesson 4-3)* **14-16, 17-19, 23-25**

4. Construct a stem-and-leaf plot for the data. *(Lesson 4-4)* **See margin.**

5. Would the mean, median, or mode be the best measure of central tendency to describe the "average" score? Why? *(Lesson 4-5)* **Mode; because it is most representative of the central values.**

```
                                                    ×
                               × ×                              ×
                             × × ×      × ×      × × ×
           × ×       × × × ×        × ×      × × × × ×
        +---+---+---+---+---+---+---+---+---+---+---+---+---+---+
          11 12 13 14 15 16 17 18 19 20 21 22 23 24 25
```

OPTIONS

Extending the Lesson

Using Logical Reasoning Have students solve this problem: *The median of 5 one-digit numbers is 7. The mode is 2. What are the numbers?* **2, 2, 7, 8, 9**

Cooperative Learning Activity

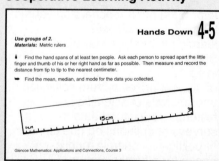

Hands Down **4-5**

Use groups of 2.
Materials: Metric rulers

▪ Find the hand spans of at least ten people. Ask each person to spread apart the little finger and thumb of his or her right hand as far as possible. Then measure and record the distance from tip to tip to the nearest centimeter.

➤ Find the mean, median, and mode for the data you collected.

Glencoe Mathematics: Applications and Connections, Course 3

Cooperative Learning

4-5B Making Predictions

A Follow-Up of Lesson 4-5

If you've ever watched *Wheel of Fortune* on television, you know that most contestants ask for the letters T, N, R, S, and E. That's because these are the four consonants that occur most often, and E is the vowel that occurs most often.

The frequency table below lists the average number of times each letter occurs in a sample of 100 letters in the English language.

● Are the letters T, N, S, R, and E good choices? yes
● What would be your next choice? A

Letter	Frequency
A	8.2
B	1.4
C	2.8
D	3.8
E	13.0
F	3.0
G	2.0
H	5.3
I	6.5
J	0.1
K	0.4
L	3.4
M	2.5

Letter	Frequency
N	7.0
O	8.0
P	2.0
Q	0.1
R	6.8
S	6.0
T	10.5
U	2.5
V	0.9
W	1.5
X	0.2
Y	2.0
Z	0.07

The coded message on the next page is a poem by Robert Frost. Each letter in the code stands for a specific letter in the English language. These types of codes are often called cryptograms.

Mathematics Lab 4-5B Making Predictions   **149**

NCTM Standards: 1–5, 8, 10

Management Tips

For Students   Students should work with a partner. Encourage them to set up a system for accurately counting the letters, since their success in decoding the poem will depend on their accuracy.

For the Overhead Projector
Overhead Manipulative Resources provides appropriate materials for teacher or student demonstration of the activities in this Mathematics Lab.

1 FOCUS

Introducing the Lab

Ask students to unscramble these letters to find the names of two U. S. presidents:

> EGGROE SHUB
> LARDON ANGREA

George Bush, Ronald Reagan

Explain that scrambling a set of letters to form an *anagram* is one way of encoding a word. This lab will introduce a more complex method.

2 TEACH

Using Communication   Point out that the frequencies shown in the tables on page 149 were found by counting a very large number of samples of the English language. In a small sampling like the Frost poem, students should expect a close correlation between the predicted and the actual frequencies but not an exact correspondence.

3 PRACTICE/APPLY

Using Discussion Ask students to suggest more complex methods that might be used to encode messages. In each case, have them describe how their code might be broken.

Close

Letter frequencies in the following message correlate with the five most frequently occurring letters in the English language.

HCX MXXC JMX HJM MXJ.

Have students decode the message, describing the method they used. ONE TEEN ATE OAT TEA.

Additional Answer

3. I have wished a bird would fly away,
   And not sing by my house all day;

   Have clapped my hands at him from the door
   When it seemed as if I could bear no more.

   The fault must partly have been in me,
   The bird was not to blame for his key.

   And of course there must be something wrong
   In wanting to silence any song.

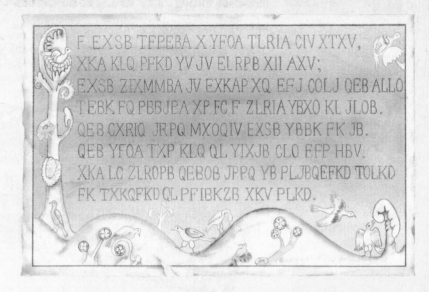

Try this!

Work with a partner to break the code.

- Make a frequency table of the number of times each letter appears in the coded message.
- Make a line plot that shows the 10 letters that occur most often in the coded message.
- Make a line plot that shows the 10 letters that occur most in the English language.
- Compare the two line plots.

What do you think?

1. Which English letter probably corresponds to the letter that occurs most often in the code? E

2. B=E, X=T, K=A, L=O, Q=N, F=R, E=I, P=S, A=H

2. Predict the English letters for the nine most frequent code letters.

3. Decode the poem. See margin.

4. about $\frac{1}{3}$ correct, others are close to frequency

4. Compare your predictions with the results of breaking the code. How well did you do?

5. The frequencies wouldn't match the normal amounts.

5. Suppose this was a poem about zippers. What effect would this have had on the frequency table for the coded letters?

150 **Chapter 4** Statistics and Data Analysis

OPTIONS

Lab Manual You may wish to make copies of the blackline master on p. 49 of the *Lab Manual* for students to use as a recording sheet.

Lab Manual, p. 49

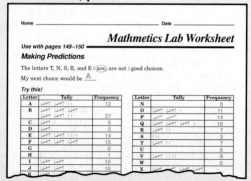

Name _____ Date _____

Mathmetics Lab Worksheet

Use with pages 149–150
Making Predictions

The letters T, N, S, and E (are) are not) good choices.

My next choice would be A

Try this!

Letter	Tally	Frequency		Letter	Tally	Frequency
A		12		N		0
B				O		11
		27		P		14
C		6		Q		16
D		5		R		7
E		14		S		3
F		15		T		7
G		0		U		0
H		1		V		9
I		10		W		0
J		10		X		
K						

4-6 Measures of Variation

Objective

Find the range and quartiles of a set of data.

Words to Learn

variation
range
quartile
interquartile range
upper quartile
lower quartile

Tai is doing research for a health project. She wants to find the amount of sugar in cereals advertised for kids.

She visited the grocery store and tallied the number of grams of sugar per serving in 27 brands of cereal. Then she displayed her results in the line plot below.

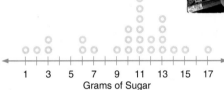

Grams of Sugar

After constructing the line plot, Tai could easily see how the data extended from a low of 1 to a high of 17. The *spread* of data is called the **variation.**

One *measure of variation* is called the **range.**

Range	The range of a set of numbers is the difference between the least and the greatest number in the set.

The range of the sugar amounts is 17 - 1 or 16.

In a large set of data, such as thousands of college entrance exam test scores, it is helpful to separate the data into four equal parts called **quartiles.** Quartiles are used in another measure of variation called the **interquartile range.**

Interquartile Range	The interquartile range is the range of the middle half of the data.

To find the interquartile range, first find the middle half of the data. The steps on the following page show how you can find the interquartile range of the data displayed in the line plot above.

Lesson 4-6 Measures of Variation   **151**

NCTM Standards: 1–5, 7, 10

Lesson Resources
• Study Guide Master 4-6
• Practice Master 4-6
• Enrichment Master 4-6
• Technology Master, p. 4
• Group Activity Card 4-6

Transparency 4-6 contains the 5-Minute Check and a teaching aid for this lesson.

5-Minute Check
(Over Lesson 4-5)

Find the mean, median, and mode for these 12 freeway speeds.

65 69 63 61 54 70
67 60 68 77 68 58
mean: 65; median: 66; mode: 68

1 FOCUS

Motivating the Lesson

Situational Problem Write these two sets of data on the chalkboard:

49, 50, 51   1, 50, 99

Ask students how they would determine which set has the greater measure of variation.

2 TEACH

Using Models Display a yardstick. Show that it "ranges" from 0 to 36, so its range is 36 inches. Explain that the range of a set of data is the distance on a number line from the least number in the set to the greatest. Have a volunteer demonstrate how to find distance on a number line.

Ask students to find the interquartile range of the yardstick. 18 inches Point out that the interquartile range is the range of the data left after the upper and lower fourths of the data have been removed.

152

More Examples

For Example 1

Find the range and interquartile range for the data in the stem-and-leaf plot below.   33; 20

```
1 | 679
2 | 01112
3 | 047
4 | 0689      1 | 6 means 16
```

For Example 2

Find the range and interquartile range for the data in the frequency table below.   3; 1

Number	Frequency
3	2
4	3
5	7
6	3

Checking for Understanding

Exercises 1-4 are designed to help you assess students' understanding through reading, writing, speaking, and modeling. You should work through these exercises with your students and then monitor their work on Guided Practice Exercises 5-11.

- Find the median of the data since the median separates the data into two halves.

1 2 3 3 6 6 7 9 10 10 10 11 11 **11** 11 11 11 11 11 12 12 13 13 13 13 13 14 15 17
                                    ↑
                                  Median

- Find the median of the upper half. This number is called the **upper quartile,** indicated by UQ.

1 2 3 3 6 6 7 9 10 10 10 11 11 **11** 11 11 11 11 11 12 12 13 13 13 13 13 14 15 17
                                    ↑   ↑
                                  Median   UQ

- Find the median of the lower half. This number is called the **lower quartile,** indicated by LQ.

1 2 3 3 6 6 7 9 10 10 10 11 11 **11** 11 11 11 11 11 12 12 13 13 13 13 13 14 15 17
              ↑   ↑   ↑
             LQ   Median   UQ

- The middle half of the data goes from 7 to 13. Subtract the lower quartile from the upper quartile.
  $13 - 7 = 6$ The interquartile range of Tai's data is 6. This means that the 13 middle amounts are between 7 and 13 grams.

Example 1

Refer to the stem-and-leaf plot of students' heights on page 141. Find the range and interquartile range of this data.

Since the stem-and-leaf plot is organized from the least data to the greatest, the range is the difference in the first and last data of the plot.

```
5 | 5899
6 | 0012233456788
7 | 012
```

$72 - 55 = 17$ The range is 17.

7 | 0 means 70

To find the interquartile range, first find the median. The median is 63. Use brackets to separate the data into two halves.

```
5 | [5899
6 | 001223] [3456788
7 | 012]
```

Now find the upper and lower quartile by finding the median of each half. Use boxes to show the location of LQ and UQ.

```
5 | [5899
6 | [00] 1223] [3456 [78] 8
7 | 012]
```

LQ is $\dfrac{60 + 60}{2}$ or 60.

UQ is $\dfrac{67 + 68}{2}$ or 67.5.

The interquartile range is $67.5 - 60$ or 7.5.

OPTIONS

Reteaching Activity

Using Manipulatives Place 19 counters side-by-side. Have a student locate the middle counter and slide it upward. Have two more students locate the middle counters of the two smaller groups and slide them downward. Explain that the interquartile range is the difference of the two lowered counters.

Study Guide Masters, p. 35

Name _____ Date _____

Study Guide Worksheet 4-6

Measures of Variation

Range and interquartile range are measures of variation in a set of data.

The range of a set of numbers is the difference between the least and the greatest numbers in the set.

For the data in the stem-and-leaf plot, the least number is 30. The greatest number is 55. The range of the data is $55 - 30$ or 25.

```
3 | 0 2 4 [6 7]
4 | 1 4 5 (8) 8 8 9
5 | [0 1] 2 3 5
```

The interquartile range is the range of the middle half of the data.

To find the interquartile range, first find the median. The circled 8 shows that the median for the data above is 48.

Then find the upper and lower quartile by finding the median of

Example 2

The frequency table at the right represents the grams of sugar per serving in 31 cereals advertised for adults. Find the range and interquartile range for this set of data.

Grams	Tally	Frequency
0	卌	5
1		0
2					3
3	卌		6
4			1
5	卌	5
6						4
7			1
8		0
9			1
10			1
11			1
12				2
13		0
14			1

The greatest value is 14 and the least value is 0. The range is $14 - 0$ or 14.

To find the interquartile range, find the median, LQ, and UQ.

0 0 0 0 0 2 2 2 3 3 3 3 3 3 4 5 5 5 5 5 6 6 6 6 7 9 10 11 12 12 14

↑ LQ   ↑ Median   ↑ UQ

The median is 5. The lower quartile is 2 and the upper quartile is 6.

The interquartile range is $6 - 2$ or 4.

Checking for Understanding

1. Measures of variation describe the dispersal of data. Measures of central tendancy describe the set as a whole.

Communicating Mathematics

Read and study the lesson to answer each question.

1. **Tell** how the measures of variation differ from the measures of central tendency.

2. **Show** how a set of data is separated into quartiles. See students' work.

3. **Find the medians of the upper half and lower half of the data.**

3. **Write** how you find the two values which determine the interquartile range.

4. **Tell** what the interquartile range means. range of the middle half of the data

Guided Practice

Find the range of each set of data.

5. 3, 4, 5, 7, 8, 8, 10 7

6. 12, 17, 16, 23, 18 11

7. 135, 170, 125, 174, 136, 145, 180, 156, 188 63

Find the median and upper and lower quartiles of each set of data.

8. 3, 4, 5, 7, 8, 8, 10 7, 8, 4

9. 12, 17, 16, 23, 18 17, 20.5, 14

10. 135, 170, 125, 174, 136, 145, 180, 156, 188 156, 177, 135.5

11. Find the interquartile range of the data in Exercise 10. 41.5

Lesson 4-6 Meaures of Variation **153**

Additional Answer

28. R − 34, IRQ − 8; The record high temperatures are similar for most of the U.S.

Exercises

Independent Practice

Use the data in the stem-and-leaf plot below.

12. What is the range? **34**

13. What is the median? **26**

14. What are the upper and lower quartiles? **30.5, 23**

15. What is the interquartile range? **7.5**

```
1 | 227
2 | 33344566889
3 | 0146
4 | 06
  4 | 0 means 40
```

The gas mileages in miles per gallon (MPG) of 4-cylinder manual transmission cars are listed at the right.

16. Organize the data into a line plot or a stem-and-leaf plot. **See Solutions Manual.**

17. What is the highest rate? **57**

18. What is the lowest rate? **24**

19. What is the range? **33**

20. What is the median? **32**

21. What are the upper and lower quartiles? **38, 29**

22. What is the interquartile range? **9**

MPG of 4-Cylinder Cars			
28	32	42	37
30	25	57	38
24	32	33	44
38	34	30	44
31	28	31	29
39	29	32	29

Mixed Review

23. Find the value of $9^2 − 2^3$. *(Lesson 1-9)* **73**

24. Solve $(−8)(12)(−10) = f$. *(Lesson 3-6)* **960**

25. Find the mean, median, and mode of the set {6, 4, 6, 12, 10, 8, 7, 12, 11, 9}. *(Lesson 4-5)* **8.5; 8.5; 6, 12**

Problem Solving and Applications

26. **Decision Making** The Remako Company is planning a sales meeting for September 20. They have narrowed their choices to Cincinnati or Baltimore. They would like to choose a location with a milder climate. The company's research department researched the temperatures for that date for the past 14 years. The results are shown below.

Cincinnati		Baltimore	
3	9 *3	9 means 39*	3	
4	2 5	4	3 5 8 9
5	3 7	5	2 6
6	0 0 0 4	6	0 0 8
7	1 3	7	4 7
8	4 6 8	8	1 4 5

a. Which city usually has a milder climate on September 20? **Neither; both average 63°.**

b. Which city do you think they will choose? Why? **Cincinnati, because the interquartile range is less.**

27. **Critical Thinking** Write two different sets of data with the same range, but with different interquartile ranges. **See students' work.**

28. **Data Search** Refer to page 667. Compare the range and the interquartile range of the record high temperatures in the U.S. What does this mean? **See margin.**

DATA SEARCH

154 **Chapter 4** Statistics and Data Analysis

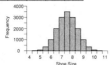

OPTIONS

Extending the Lesson

Using Cooperative Groups Have small groups each create a set of data and then find its mean. Now have them find the difference between each piece of data and the mean, listing the differences separately. Finally, have them find the mean of these differences. This value is the *mean variation*.

Cooperative Learning Activity

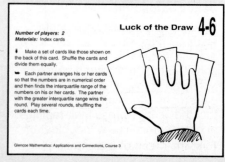

Luck of the Draw 4-6

Number of players: 2
Materials: Index cards

♦ Make a set of cards like those shown on the back of this card. Shuffle the cards and divide them equally.

➥ Each partner arranges his or her cards so that the numbers are in numerical order and then finds the interquartile range of the numbers on his or her cards. The partner with the greater interquartile range wins the round. Play several rounds, shuffling the cards each time.

Glencoe Mathematics: Applications and Connections, Course 3

4-7 Box-and-Whisker Plots

Objective
Construct and interpret box-and-whisker plots.

Words to Learn
box-and-whisker plot
outlier

So far, you have made frequency tables and stem-and-leaf plots to *display* sets of data, and you have used measures of central tendency and measures of variation to *summarize* data. Now we will combine the ideas of displaying and summarizing data. A **box-and-whisker plot** summarizes data using the median, the upper and lower quartiles, and the *extreme* (greatest and least) *values*.

Here's how to construct a box-and-whisker plot to display Tai's data on sugar content in kids' cereal on page 151.

- Use a number line. Graph points above the line for the extreme values, the median, and the quartile values.

  lower extreme: 1   upper extreme: 17
  median: 11   LQ: 7 UQ: 13

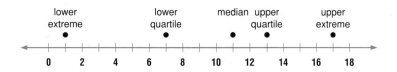

- Next, draw a *box* around the quartile values.

- Draw a vertical line through the median value.

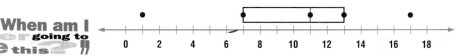

In evaluating the weekly salaries of her department, a manager can determine the median salary and the salaries in the upper and lower quartiles by using a box-and-whisker plot.

- Finally, extend *whiskers* from each quartile to the extreme data points.

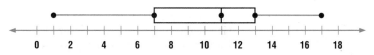

Thus, the box-and-whisker plot gives you five pieces of information about the data: lower extreme, lower quartile, median, upper quartile, and upper extreme.

NCTM Standards: 1–5, 7, 8, 10

Lesson Resources
- Study Guide Master 4-7
- Practice Master 4-7
- Enrichment Master 4-7
- Group Activity Card 4-7

 Transparency 4-7 contains the 5-Minute Check and a teaching aid for this lesson.

5-Minute Check
(Over Lesson 4-6)

Use the data in the stem-and-leaf plot.

4	248
5	01399
6	1234678
7	1123

1. What is the range?   31
2. What is the median?   62
3. What are the upper and lower quartiles?   68; 51
4. What is the interquartile range?   17

1 FOCUS

Motivating the Lesson

Questioning   Have students read the opening paragraph of the lesson. Then display an almanac table listing a large amount of data. Ask students what difficulties might arise when making a stem-and-leaf plot of the data.   The data would be hard to organize. The resulting plot would be so massive that it would be difficult to read.

2 TEACH

Using Connections   Stress that a box-and-whisker plot builds on the content of the previous lesson, displaying the measures defined there by means of the box and the whiskers. Use the drawing below to clarify the connection.

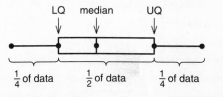

OPTIONS

Bell Ringer

Below is a box-and-whisker plot of five pieces of data.

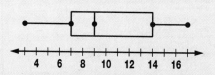

Find the mean of the data.   10

For Example 1

Draw a box-and-whisker plot for these automobile gas mileages.

31 27 12 23 45 24 39 19
48 24 20 22 29 17 34

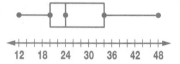

For Example 2

Draw box-and-whisker plot for the bicycle club member ages displayed in the stem-and-leaf plot.

```
1 | 0679
2 | 223578
3 | 112347
4 | 66
5 | 5        5|5 means 55
```

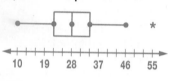

Checking for Understanding

Exercises 1-4 are designed to help you assess students' understanding through reading, writing, speaking, and modeling. You should work through these exercises with your students and then monitor their work on Guided Practice Exercises 5-16.

Error Analysis

Watch for students who find quartiles by dividing the range into four equal sections.

Prevent by stressing the quartile refers to quarters of the *number of items,* not quarters of the range.

Close

Ask students to explain how the median, quartiles, and extremes of a set of data are used to make a box-and-whisker plot.

156

Example 1

The daily high temperatures (°F) for two weeks of September in Baltimore were 43°, 45°, 48°, 49°, 52°, 56°, 60°, 60°, 68°, 74°, 77°, 81°, 84°, and 85°. Make a box-and-whisker plot of this data. How can you locate the interquartile range on the plot?

To make the plot, find the extremes, median, and quartiles.

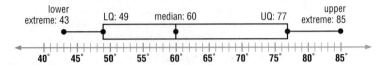

The interquartile range is the difference of the upper and lower quartiles. This is represented by the left and right sides of the box.

Sometimes the data will have such great variation that one or both of the extreme values will be far beyond the other data. Data that are more than 1.5 times the interquartile range from the upper or lower quartiles are called **outliers.**

Example 2

Draw a box-and-whisker plot for the grams of sugar per serving in cereals for adults shown below.

The median is 5; the upper quartile is 6, and the lower quartile is 2. Draw a box to show the median and the quartiles.

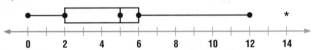

Mental Math Hint

To quickly calculate
1.5×4, think:
1.5 means $1\frac{1}{2}$.

$1 \times 4 = 4$
$\frac{1}{2} \times 4 = 2$
$4 + 2 = 6$

The interquartile range is $6 - 2$ or 4. So, data more than $1.5 \cdot 4$, or 6, from the quartiles are outliers.

Find the limits for the outliers.
Subtract 6 from the lower quartile. $\quad 2 - 6 = -4$
Add 6 to the upper quartile. $\quad 6 + 6 = 12$

So, -4 and 12 are the limits for outliers. There is one outlier in the data, 14. Plot the outlier with an asterisk. Draw the lower whisker to the lower extreme, 0, and the upper whisker to the last value that is not an outlier, 12.

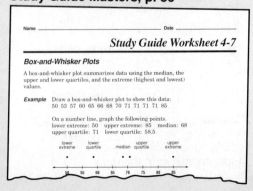

156   **Chapter 4** Statistics and Data Analysis

OPTIONS

Reteaching Activity

Using Discussion Discuss box-and-whisker plots by focusing on the five key parts of the plot. Tell students that from a mass of data, you have found the extremes 4 and 19, the quartiles 8 and 12, and the median 11. Have students draw a number line, find these five points, and draw a box-and-whisker plot.

Study Guide Masters, p. 36

Name _____ Date _____

Study Guide Worksheet 4-7

Box-and-Whisker Plots

A box-and-whisker plot summarizes data using the median, the upper and lower quartiles, and the extreme (highest and lowest) values.

Example Draw a box-and-whisker plot to show this data:
50 53 57 60 65 66 68 70 71 71 71 71 85

On a number line, graph the following points.
lower extreme: 50   upper extreme: 85   median: 68
upper quartile: 71   lower quartile: 58.5

Checking for Understanding

1. the middle half of data

Communicating Mathematics

Read and study the lesson to answer each question.

3. median, upper and lower quartiles, and upper and lower extremes

1. **Tell** what part of the data are enclosed by the box in a box-and-whisker plot.

2. **Write** which data are connected to the box by the whiskers in a box-and-whisker plot. **lower extreme, upper extreme**

3. **Write** five pieces of information you can learn from a box-and-whisker plot.

4. **Tell** how you know if a value is an outlier. **if it is more than 1.5 times the interquartile range from the quartile**

Compare the box-and-whisker plots shown below.

5. same median, same least value.

6. The top set of data is more widely dispersed than the lower one.

5. What is similar about the data in the two plots?

6. What is different about the data in the two plots?

7. Which set of data is more evenly spread over the range? Explain. **Top plot; The box is longer.**

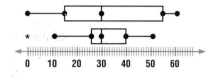

Refer to the potato chip prices on page 136.

8. Draw a box-and-whisker plot of the data. **See margin.**

9. What is the median? **21**

10. What is the upper quartile? **23**

11. What is the lower quartile? **17**

12. What is the lower extreme? **10**

13. What is the interquartile range? **6**

14. Are there any outliers? **no**

15. What are the limits on the outliers? **8 and 32**

16. Compare the box-and-whisker plot to the line plot on page 136. What similarities and differences do you see? **Answers will vary.**

Exercises

Independent Practice

The box-and-whisker plot below represents the heights in inches of the twenty students in the Fitness Club.

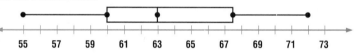

17. What is the median? **63**

18. What is the range? **17**

19. What is the upper quartile? **67.5**

20. What is the lower quartile? **60**

21. What is the interquartile range? **7.5**

22. What are the extremes? **55 and 72**

23. What are the limits on the outliers? Are there any outliers? **48.75 and 78.75; no**

24. How many students are between 60 and 63 inches tall? Explain. **See margin.**

25. How many students are less than 63 inches tall? Explain. **See margin.**

26. How does the mean of this data relate to the box-and-whisker plot if the mean is 64? **The mean falls between the median and the upper quartile.**

Lesson 4-7 Box-and-Whisker Plots **157**

Multicultural Education

In 17th century Japan, mathematics was considered an art form to be studied only by the nobility. Seki Kowa (1642–1708) promoted the idea of intellectual curiosity for all people. Although he made significant contributions to mathematical theory, Kowa is remembered in his country chiefly as the man who brought mathematics to the people.

Additional Answer

25. There is insufficient information to determine the answer. It is impossible to tell from a box-and-whisker plot what the actual members of a set of data are. For example, the set of data could have no 63's or several 63's.

Assignment Guide
Maximum: 17–36
Minimum: 17–34

For **Extra Practice,** see p. 593.

Alternate Assessment

Speaking Draw a box-and-whisker plot on the chalkboard. Have students identify the lower and upper extremes, the lower and upper quartiles, and the median.

Additional Answers

8.

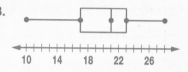

24. There is insufficient information to determine the answer. It is impossible to tell from a box-and-whisker plot what the actual members of a set of data are. For example, the set of data could have no 63's or several 63's. The same is true for 60.

Practice Masters, p. 36

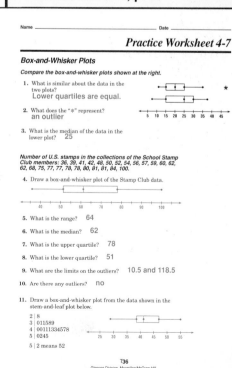

157

27. Draw a box-and-whisker plot of the ages of the residents at Piney Village given in the stem-and-leaf plot shown at the right. **See Solutions Manual.**

5	23346
6	1122233355588
7	00034447
8	5579

5 | 2 means 52 yr

Mixed Review

28. How many gallons are in 14 quarts of juice? *(Lesson 1-7)* **3.5 gallons**

29. Evaluate $4^2 + 6(12 - 8) - 15 \div 3$. *(Lesson 2-1)* **35**

30. {120, 18, 3, −24, −52, −186, −219}

30. Order the set {−219, −52, 18, 3, −24, 120, −186} from greatest to least. *(Lesson 3-2)*

31. Music The number of pages in *Rock Star Magazine* in the last nine issues is 196, 188, 184, 200, 168, 176, 192, 160, and 180. Find the median, upper quartile, and lower quartile of this data. *(Lesson 4-6)*
184, 194, 172

Problem Solving and Applications

32. Consumer Math Ten flashlight batteries were purchased from each of two different manufacturers X and Y. The batteries were tested to determine how many hours they would last. The results are given below.

X: 15.5, 14, 14, 24, 19, 16.7, 15, 11.4, 16, 15
Y: 18, 14, 15.8, 9, 12, 16, 20, 16, 13, 15

a. Make a box-and-whisker plot for each set of data. **See Solutions Manual.**
b. Based on the plots, from which manufacturer would you buy your batteries? Explain. **X; it has a better average life span.**

33. Critical Thinking Name a set of data with ten numbers whose box-and-whisker plot would have only one whisker. **See margin.**

34. Critical Thinking What information is easier to find on a box-and-whisker plot than on a stem-and-leaf plot? What information is more difficult to find? **median, quartile values; mean, mode**

35. School Before teaching a unit on Mexico, the social studies teacher had his class take a test to see how much his students already knew. Then he gave a test after teaching the unit. The results are given below. Use a box-and-whisker plot to determine whether the students' scores improved from one test to the next.
Before Unit Scores: 56, 89, 79, 70, 90, 86, 75, 68, 92, 85, 78, 87, 95, 84, 79, 80, 64, 89, 83
After Unit Scores: 87, 89, 90, 93, 95, 97, 82, 95, 100, 88, 90, 94, 99, 93, 96, 88, 93, 89, 100 **See Solutions Manual.**

36. Journal Entry Write a few sentences to tell why a box-and-whisker plot might be used to display great numbers of data. What drawbacks does a box-and-whisker plot have, if any? **All the numbers don't have to be displayed; doesn't show the frequency**

OPTIONS

Extending the Lesson

Using Cooperative Groups Have small groups give an analysis of the data represented by this box-and-whisker plot.

Sample answer: The middle half of the data is tightly clustered; the lower and upper fourths of the data are widely dispersed.

Cooperative Learning Activity

The Plot Remains the Same 4-7

Number of players: 2
Materials: Spinners, colored pencils

Label equal sections of one spinner "2" and "3." This spinner gives the digits in tens place. Label equal sections of a second spinner with the digits 0 through 9. This spinner gives the digits in ones place.

Each partner spins one of the spinners at the same time, and the resulting two-digit number is recorded on a sheet of paper. After fifteen numbers have been generated in this way, each partner constructs a box-and-whisker plot on a separate sheet of paper to describe the data.

In turn, each partner then generates fifteen additional numbers by spinning both spinners himself or herself. The partner who can add more of these additional numbers to the original data set without changing the box-and-whisker plot is the winner.

Glencoe Mathematics: Applications and Connections, Course 3

4-8 Scatter Plots

Objective
Construct and interpret scatter plots.

Words to Learn
scatter plot

You can review graphing ordered pairs on page 117.

positive relationship

negative relationship

Silvia found the results of the first state-by-state comparison of mathematics scores, measured in 1991 by the National Assessment of Educational Progress. She thinks there might be a relationship between the scores on the test and the annual average temperature for the state.

Silvia collected the temperature data for the District of Columbia and the 37 states that volunteered to report their test results. Then she formed ordered pairs in which the first number was the temperature and the second number was the score. For example, the ordered pair for North Dakota was (41, 281). After the 38 points were plotted, Silvia looked for a pattern to see if her prediction was correct.

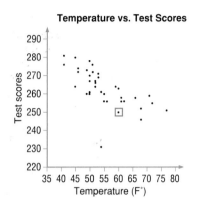

Temperature vs. Test Scores

When you graph two sets of data as ordered pairs, you form a **scatter plot.** Unlike other displays of data you have studied, scatter plots do not measure central tendencies or variations. Instead, scatter plots can suggest whether the two sets of data are truly related.

To determine if there is a pattern for the data in a scatter plot imagine a line drawn on the scatter plot where half the points are above it and half the points are below it. If the line slants upward to the right, there is a *positive* relationship. If the line slants downward to the right, there is a *negative* relationship.

Example 1

Refer to the scatter plot for test scores versus temperature.
a. **Describe the point with the box around it.**

The point with a box around it is (60, 250). It represents a temperature of 60° with a test score of 250.

b. **What type of relationship is shown by the scatter plot?**

Since the points seem to slope downward to the right, the scatter plot shows a negative relationship. That is, as the average temperature increases, the scores seem to decrease.

Lesson 4-8 Scatter Plots   **159**

OPTIONS

Reteaching Activity

Using Communication Draw and label a coordinate plane on the chalkboard. Name four points and have students plot them. Ask students to plot points showing a positive relationship. Erase these and have them plot points showing a negative relationship. Then have them plot points showing no relationship.

Study Guide Masters, p. 37

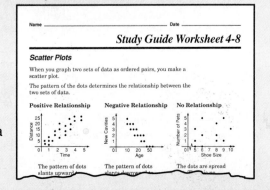

4-8 Lesson Notes

NCTM Standards: 1–5, 8–10

Lesson Resources
• Study Guide Master 4-8
• Practice Master 4-8
• Enrichment Master 4-8
• Interdisciplinary Master, p. 18
• Group Activity Card 4-8

Transparency 4-8 contains the 5-Minute Check and a teaching aid for this lesson.

5-Minute Check
(Over Lesson 4-7)
Draw a box-and-whisker plot for this list of average class sizes in 15 schools.

22 25 33 31 28 22 26 22
30 27 31 28 33 23 29

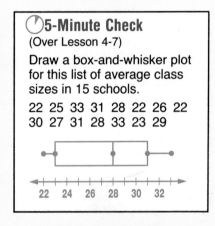

1 FOCUS

Motivating the Lesson

Situational Problem Ask students to judge whether a positive relationship exists, between each of the following items and a person's age.
• height
• number of birthday candles
• number of toes

2 TEACH

Using Connections Emphasize these aspects of scatter plots.
• They are useful for spotting relationships between two sets of data that would be difficult to see by studying the data itself.
• They do not prove that one measure *causes* the other. While such a relationship is possible, it is also possible that two sets of data may be created by a separate factor while the two sets remain totally unrelated.

159

More Examples

For Example 1

See the scatter plot at bottom of the page.

a. Describe the point with the box around it. The point is (3, 20). It represents 3 years membership and sales of 20 boxes.

b. What type of relationship is shown? positive

For Example 2

The scatter plot below compares Mike's score on his science quiz to his score on the previous week's quiz, beginning with the second quiz.

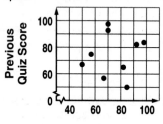

Does there appear to be a relationship between his quiz scores and his score the previous week? no

Practice Masters, p. 37

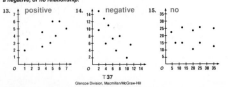

160

Example 2

The scatter plot at the right compares the week Mike took a science quiz to the quiz score. Does there appear to be any relationship between the week he took the quiz and his quiz score?

The points in the scatter plot are very spread out. There appears to be no relationship between the week Mike took the quiz and his score.

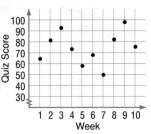

Checking for Understanding

Communicating Mathematics

Read and study the lesson to answer each question.

1. **Write** how to draw a scatter plot for two sets of data. See Solutions Manual.

2. **Tell** how the scatter plot in Example 2 would look if there was a positive relationship between when Mike took the quiz and his score. See Solutions Manual.

Guided Practice

Determine whether a scatter plot of the data below would show a positive, negative, or no relationship.

3. age of a used car and its value negative

4. heights of mothers and sons positive

5. hours of TV watched per week and test scores negative

6. income and years of school completed positive

7. height and month of birth no relationship

8. playing time and points scored in basketball positive

Determine whether each scatter plot of data shows a positive, negative, or no relationship.

9.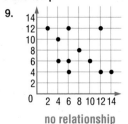
no relationship

10.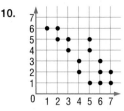
negative

11.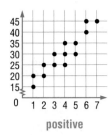
positive

Exercises

Independent Practice

Determine whether a scatter plot of the data below would show a positive, negative, or no relationship.   13. no relationship.   14. no relationship

12. height and weight positive

13. height of student and test scores

14. hair color and test scores

15. age and income positive

16. outside temperature and amount of the heating bill negative

17. miles per gallon and the weight of the car negative

Interactive Mathematics Tools

This multimedia software provides an interactive lesson that is tied directly to Lesson 4–8B. Students will use a coordinate plane to explore scatterplots and relationship lines.

More Examples, Example 1

Stationery Sales

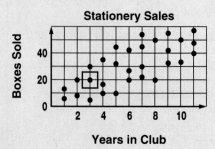

18. A scatter plot of the shots attempted and the shots made by each player in the first game of the 1991 National Basketball Association Championship series is shown at the right.

a. Describe the data represented by the C in the upper right-hand corner. **See Solutions Manual.**
b. Find the point that represents the only perfect shooter. **C(2, 2)**
c. Is there a different relationship for Los Angeles and Chicago players? **No**
d. Suppose a player attempts 14 field goals. About how many would you expect him to make? **about 6**
e. How many players made over 10 field goals? **2 players**
f. What conclusion can you make from the scatter plot? **There is a positive relationship.**

Mixed Review
19. Solve $158 = s - 36$. Check your solution. *(Lesson 2-3)* **194**

20. **See Solutions Manual.**
20. Solve $5x + 32 < 42$. Show the solution on a number line. *(Lesson 2-10)*

21. Solve $h = -28 + 15 + 6 + (-30)$. Check your solution by solving another way. *(Lesson 3-4)* **-37**

22. Draw a box-and-whisker plot for the set {36, 26, 32, 15, 44, 29, 38, 20, 11, 33, 47, 24, 42}. *(Lesson 4-7)* **See Solutions Manual.**

See Solutions Manual.

Problem Solving and Applications

23. **Finance** Make a scatter plot for the data in the table below.

Hours Worked	12	23	18	46	17	18	34	15	21	10	40	1	21
Money Earned ($)	51	82	65	199	157	68	186	75	189	42	180	5	170

a. How will you form the ordered pairs? **(hours worked, money earned)**
b. Does the data show a relationship between hours worked and money earned? If so, what type of relationship is it? **Yes; positive.**

24. **Critical Thinking** In the scatter plot of test scores and temperatures on page 159, it appears that as the temperatures got warmer the test scores got lower.

a. Why do you think the relationship might exist? **See Solutions Manual.**
b. Does this negative relationship necessarily mean that one factor caused the other? Why or why not? **No; answers may vary.**
c. What are some other factors that affect test scores? **See Solutions Manual.**
d. How many states did not report scores from the test? **13**
e. What effect might the states that did not report scores have on the scatter plot? **Sample answer: The data might show no pattern exists on the plot.**

25. **Portfolio Suggestion** Select some of your work from this chapter that shows how you used a calculator or computer. Place it in your portfolio. **See students' work.**

Lesson 4-8 Scatter Plots   **161**

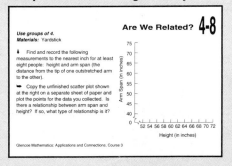

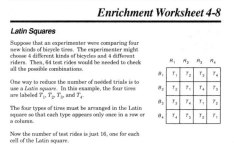
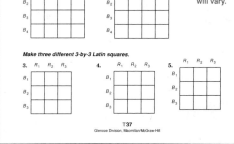

DECISION MAKING

Decision Making

NCTM Standards: 1–4, 7

Objective Analyze data and make a decision.

1 FOCUS

Introducing the Situation

Have students read the "Situation" paragraph. If any students have attended a conference, ask them to share their experiences with the class. Then ask the following question: *What is the value of attending a conference?* Sample answer: You can meet people who share your interests, and you can learn about the latest developments in the field.

2 TEACH

Using Cooperative Groups

Students should work on this activity in cooperative groups. After students read the "Hidden Data" questions, ask them to list possible travel and lodging options and to estimate the costs of each option.

Analyzing the Data

Students should explain their reasons for each answer. If some group members are unfamiliar with the duties of a newspaper editor, give a description of these duties or ask a member of the school newspaper staff to do so.

Answers

1. Wednesday and Thursday
2. yes

Planning a School Trip

Situation

As the editor of your school newspaper, you have been selected by the newspaper advisor to attend a conference. The 3-day conference will include sessions on utilizing word processing software for typesetting, graphic design, and using windows to make layout of copy more efficient. The advisor has set aside $600 from the budget for your expenses. The question is, how many days can you afford to stay and which sessions should you attend?

Hidden Data

Cost of travel: Is the conference local or will you need to travel by plane, bus, or train to get there?
Cost of lodging: Will you need to stay in a hotel?
Cancellation charges: Will you get your deposit refunded if you are unable to attend the conference?

Analyzing the Data

1. Which conference day(s) seem better suited to the newspaper editor?
2. Are any sessions offered more than once?

162

Tuesday, Januaary 28

8:30 - 10:00
• Yearbook Editor Issues
• Product Promises vs. Reality
• Photography in the Yearbook
• School Issues
• Word Processing into Type
• Multimedia

10:30 - 11:30
KEY NOTE ADDRESS AND PANEL DISCUSSION

12:00 - 1:30
• Multimedia
• What Fonts Can Do
• Developing Solutions: Case Studies
• PC or Mac?
• Software Design Principles
• Windows: What are They?

2:00 - 3:00
EXHIBITS VIEWING

3:30 - 5:00
• Training Your Staff
• Computer Editing: Is it for You?
• Microsoft Strategy Briefing
• Yearbook Advisors Tell New Trends
• Graphics: Import or use PMTs
• 4-Color Yearbook Production

Wednesday, January 29

8:30 - 10:00
• Sharpening Your Skills
• Window Presentation Sofware
• Style, Design, and Graphics
• What's Hot and What's Not in Newspapers
• Training Your Staff
• Desktop Publishing

10:30 - 12:00
• Clip Art
• Utilities for the PC
• State of the Art Publishing
• Computer Editing
• Beyond B & W Photos
• Layout and Design

12:30 - 1:30
COLUMNISTS PANEL DISCUSSION

2:00 - 3:30
Utilities for the PC
Which Pagemaking Program?
Sharpening Your Skills
Style, Design, and Graphics
Distributing Your Newspaper
Layout and Design

4:00 - 5:00
EXHIBIITS VIEWING

Thursday, January 30

8:30 - 9:30
DEVELOPER'S KEYNOTE

10:00 - 11:30
• Desktop Publishing II
• Data Bases for Circulation
• Spreadsheets in the Real World
• Computer Editing
• Developing Macros
• Logos

12:00 - 1:00
SPECIAL INTERESTS SESSION

1:30 - 3:00
• Distributing Your Newspaper
• Managing Styles
• State of the Art Publishing
• Mail-Order Software
• Developing Skills for Writers
• Computer-Shy Writers and You

3:30 - 4:30
EXHIBITS VIEWING

PROFESSIONAL SEMINARS

Making a Decision

3. **Are you able** to attend more than one day of the conference?

4. **What if** the conference is not compatible with the methods you currently use for newspaper production?

5. **Is the cost** of the full conference program less expensive than the number of days you plan to attend?

REGISTRATION

Full Conference Program *$295.00*
Conference registration includes admission to all educational sessions, fast track and keynote presentations, all conference materials, unlimited access to the exhibit hall and all special events.

Single Day Conference Program *$175.00*
Conference registration includes admission to all educational sessions, keynote presentations, conference materials, and all special events on any one of the three days. Includes unlimited access to the exhibit hall on all three days. Please be sure to indicate which day you plan to attend.

Making Decisions in the Real World

6. Investigate the seminars or conferences available to student journalists in your area. Share this information with your newspaper advisor.

163

Checking for Understanding

Ask students to write a few sentences describing what they would hope to accomplish at the conference.

3 PRACTICE/APPLY

Making a Decision

Each group should prepare a written report answering the questions in the lesson. Groups should also indicate whether they decided to attend the conference. If they have decided not to attend, they should explain why not. If they have decided to attend this conference, they should say for how long, which sessions they will attend, and how they will budget the $600.

Making Decisions in the Real World

For further information, students can write:

Society of Professional Journalists
53 West Jackson Boulevard
Suite 731
Chicago, IL   60604

American Society of Newspaper Editors
11600 Sunrise Valley Drive
Reston, VA   22091

NCTM Standards: 1–5, 8–10

Lesson Resources
- Study Guide Master 4-9
- Practice Master 4-9
- Enrichment Master 4-9
- Evaluation Master, Quiz B, p. 34
- Group Activity Card 4-9

 Transparency 4-9 contains the 5-Minute Check and a teaching aid for this lesson.

🕐 5-Minute Check
(Over Lesson 4-8)

Determine whether a scatter plot of the data below would show a positive, negative, or no relationship.

1. person's height and area code. no

2. age and total number of apples consumed
positive

3. hourly wage and number of hours needed to earn $1,000 negative

---

1 FOCUS

Motivating the Lesson

Situational Problem A toothpaste ad shows a smiling movie star and the caption reads "More beautiful people brush with Glisten." Ask students how the ad misleads. Lead students to see that the ad is vague and that it is based on vanity rather than hard facts.

2 TEACH

Using Problem Solving Tell students that the cookie survey rated Tasty Cookies at 45. Have them sketch a graph that hides the large rating difference between Tasty Cookies and Mrs. Fields.

4-9 Misleading Graphs and Statistics

Objective
Recognize when graphs and statistics are misleading.

Words to Learn
sample

An advertising agency conducted a test at the Mill Creek Mall for Mrs. Field's cookies. They prepared their finding in two different graphs.

- Do both graphs show the same information?
- Which graph might influence your choice of cookie?

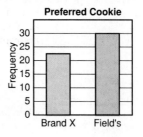 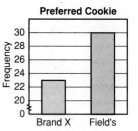

Sometimes using a different scale helps to make a graph easier to read. However, scales may also be chosen to make the data appear to support a particular point of view.

The graph at the right does not begin at 0 and has a different scale than the graph at the left. The difference in the number of votes is the same in each graph. However, the bars in the graph at the right make it appear that Mrs. Field's is the overwhelming choice.

Example 1

The graph shows the number of students in each grade that had a B average or better.

a. How many more eighth graders are on the honor roll than sixth graders?

There are 30 more eighth graders on the honor roll than sixth graders.

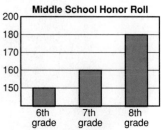

b. What impression does the height of the bars give you about comparing the number of seventh graders to the number of eighth graders?

The height of the bars make it look as if the eighth grade has twice as many on the honor roll as the seventh grade.

164 Chapter 4 Statistics and Data Analysis

OPTIONS

Bell Ringer

Draw the figure below on the chalkboard and have students read the message aloud.

STOP
LOOK AND
AND LISTEN

Additional Answers

1. using different scales and not beginning the graph at 0
2. Sample answer: What were the ages of those surveyed and where was the survey conducted.
4b. A relatively small change in the numbers, but the second house is both wider and taller.

LOOKBACK

You can review measures of central tendency on pages 145 and 146.

Statistics can also be misleading. In Lesson 4-5, you learned about three types of averages, the mean, the median, and the mode. If a cereal company was trying to publicize how many raisins they have in the raisin bran, which average do you think they would use out of the three shown below?

mean = 186 raisins

median = 184 raisins

mode = 214 raisins

They probably would use the mode, since it is the greatest number.

When a survey of 100 people is taken, the 100 responses to the survey are called a **sample.** Statisticians often use samples to represent larger groups of data. However, if the sample is not typical of all the data, the wrong conclusions could be drawn from the results of the sample.

Example 2

Alicia asked 20 adults how many times they went to the movies in the past month. Then she asked 20 of her classmates the same question. How did her choice of sample affect her results?

The results of asking 20 adults is probably a number less than the results of asking 20 classmates, since young people usually attend movies more often than adults.

Checking for Understanding

Communicating Mathematics

Read and study the lesson to answer each question.

1. **Tell** two ways that a graph might be misleading. See margin.

2. **Write** some things you might question when reading the results of a survey on your favorite radio station. See margin.

3. **Draw** a graph that is misleading and tell why it is misleading. See students' work.

Guided Practice

4. Look at the graph at the right.

a. How did the number of house sales change from December 1991 to July 1992? increased by 2,000

b. How does this change compare with the change in the sizes of the houses on the graph? See margin.

c. Is this a misleading graph? Explain. yes

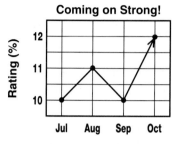
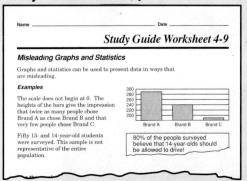

Have students make a deceptive graph or create a misleading statistic from a set of data.

3 PRACTICE/APPLY

Assignment Guide
Maximum: 6–19
Minimum: 6–17

Alternate Assessment

Modeling Display various magazine ads. Ask students to judge whether they are misleading or not. If they are, have students explain how. If not, have them tell what information is accurately conveyed.

Additional Answer

12. a.

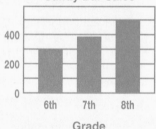

Candy Bar Sales

b. See page 167.

Practice Masters, p. 38

Practice Worksheet 4-9

Misleading Graphs and Statistics

Look at the graph at the right.

1. What is the stock's price in April?

2. What is the stock's price in July?

3. How many times as long as the "July" bar is the "April" bar?

4. Is the "April" price of the stock *twice* as much as the "July" price?

5. Is this a misleading graph? Explain.

6. John is offered a weekly salary that will be the average for the workers in his department. The seven workers in the department earn $480, $470, $480, $485, $490, $495, and $480. Which average should John use? Explain.

7. The Otis Oatmeal Company samples ten lots of oatmeal for fat content. The number of grams of fat in the samples are 1.8, 2.3, 2.2, 1.9, 2.0, 1.8, 1.7, 2.0, 1.8, and 2.1. If Otis wants to emphasize the health benefits of its low-fat cereal, which average should Otis use? Explain.

8. Soula has 11 stuffed animals, Maria has 12, and Nicole has 20 animals.
a. Draw a bar graph that is not misleading.
b. Draw a bar graph that makes it appear that Nicole has more than three times as many animals as Soula has.

38
Glencoe Division, Macmillan/McGraw-Hill

---

5. The test scores of five students on a project were Emilio 88, Nadawi 86, Dean 85, Debbie 78, and Hiroshi 88. Their actual grade will be the average of these grades. Which average do they hope the teacher will choose and why?
the mode, 88, because it's the highest

Exercises

Independent Practice

6. The two graphs below show the increases in Marty's allowance over the last six years.

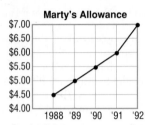

Marty's Allowance

Marty's Allowance

a. Tell if either of the graphs are misleading. left graph is misleading

b. If Marty wants an increase in his allowance, which graph would he probably show his parents? Explain your answer.
The right graph shows a smaller increase

7. The number of calories in a sample of six cookies from the Sugar-Lite company are 45, 60, 63, 75, 75, and 90. Which average would they use to promote the low calorie count in their cookies? mean

Decide whether each location given is a good place to find representative samples for the selected survey. Justify each answer. For reasons, see Solutions Manual.

8. Survey the number of books read in a month in a shopping mall yes

9. Survey the favorite kind of entertainment in a concert hall no

10. Survey the number of dogs owned in an apartment complex no

11. Survey the favorite fast food restaurant in a school no

12. See margin.

12. Roosevelt Junior High School sold candy bars to raise money for the parent-teacher association. The sixth graders sold 300 candy bars. The seventh graders sold 385 candy bars. The eighth graders sold 500 candy bars.

a. Draw a bar graph that is not misleading.

b. Draw a bar graph that makes it appear that the eighth graders sold three times as many candy bars as the sixth graders.

166 **Chapter 4** Statistics and Data Analysis

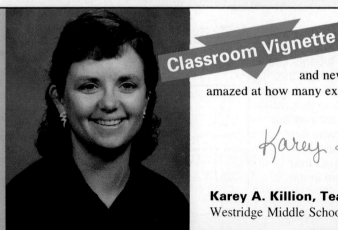

Classroom Vignette

"I ask my students to look for misleading statistics in magazines and newspapers. They were amazed at how many examples they found."

Karey A. Killion, Teacher
Westridge Middle School, Grand Island, NE

13. Use mental math to find 12 · 15.
    (Lesson 1-2) **180**

14. Solve −460 = −16*a* + 52. *(Lesson 3-9)* **32**

15. Determine whether a scatter plot of hours spent fishing and fish caught would show a positive, negative, or no relationship. Explain your answer.
    (Lesson 4-8) **No relationship; fishing is mostly chance.**

16. **Health** A magazine says "Four out of five doctors recommend Multi-Zip vitamins." **16a. fewer doctors in survey, less reliable the results   b. no**
    a. How could the number of doctors in the survey affect the truth of this ad?
    b. Dr. Mentos was part of this survey. He says that he also recommends other brands of vitamins in addition to Multi-Zip. Does the ad reflect this?
    c. How might the results of this survey be different if this survey was taken in Lincoln, Nebraska instead of Los Angeles, California?

16c. Sample answer: Multi-Zip may not be sold in Neb.

17. **Critical Thinking** Suppose your grades on the last six history tests are 74, 75, 80, 88, 90, and 94.
    a. You have been grounded because your grades have not been good. Draw a graph of your test scores to show your parents how well you have improved your grades. **See margin.**
    b. If your parents ask what your average test score is, what score might you tell them and why? **Median; it is highest.**

18. **Sports** Mr. Otashi loves soccer and wants the local cable television company to carry more stations that cover this sport. He wants to get 500 people to sign a petition to increase the cable company's soccer coverage. What would be a good way to get 500 signatures of people genuinely interested in seeing more soccer on cable television? **Go to a soccer game and ask people.**

19. **Mathematics and Food Processing** Read the following paragraphs.

> Statistical methods are used in all stages of food manufacturing. The information from samples are used as the measure of the quality of the product. Samples are also used in testing how many of the products fall below government or company standards.
>
> The rate at which samples are taken is determined by previous experience with the product. The cost of taking samples and testing is also considered. New products are often tested more frequently to make sure the characteristics desired are presented in all samples.

A manufacturer produces 1 million applesauce cups per week. They test the first 100 cups for contamination.

    a. Is this a representative sample? **No; samples should be more random.**
    b. What does the manufacturer need to consider in the evaluation of the results of this sample? **Sample answer: what is the past history of the product or is it a new product.**

Lesson 4-9 Misleading Graphs and Statistics   **167**

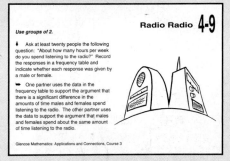
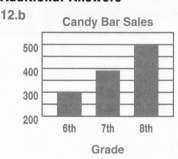
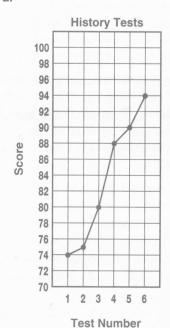
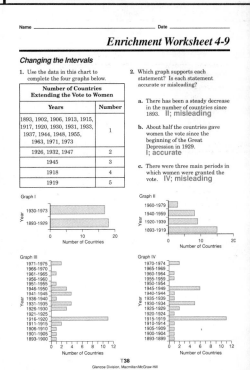

The Chapter Study Guide and Review begins with a section on Communicating Mathematics. This includes questions that review the new terms and concepts that were introduced in the chapter.

Then, the Skills and Concepts presented in the chapter are reviewed using a side-by-side format. Encourage students to refer to the Objectives and Examples on the left as they complete the Review Exercises on the right.

The Chapter Study Guide and Review ends with problems that review Applications and Problem Solving.

Additional Answers

8. median, upper and lower quartiles, and interquartile range

10.

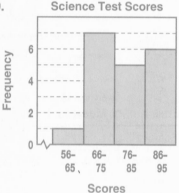

Science Test Scores

Chapter

4 Study Guide and Review

Study Guide and Review

Communicating Mathematics

Choose the correct term to complete each sentence.

2. scatter plot

stem
1. In a stem-and-leaf plot, the greatest place value of the data can be used for the (stem, leaf).
2. A (scatter plot, line plot) is a graph whose ordered pairs consist of two sets of related data.
3. A (frequency table, histogram) is a bar graph that shows the frequency of data organized in intervals. histogram
4. The (interquartile range, range) of a set of numbers is the difference between the least and greatest number in the set. range
5. Data that are more than 1.5 times the interquartile range from the quartiles are called (whiskers, outliers). outliers
6. A (mode, sample) is a small group representative of a larger group. sample
7. The (mean, median) of a set of data is the sum of the data divided by the number of pieces of data. mean

8. See margin.
8. Tell what information a box-and-whisker plot shows that a line plot does not.
9. Explain the difference between the mean and the median of a set of data.
   Mean is the average of the set and median is the middle number.

Skills and Concepts

Objectives and Examples	Review Exercises
Upon completing this chapter, you should be able to:	*Use these exercises to review and prepare for the chapter test.*

● construct and interpret histograms
(Lesson 4-2)
Construct a histogram for {1, 2, 2, 3, 4, 5, 5, 6, 6, 6, 7, 8, 9, 9, 10}

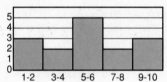

10. Construct a histogram for the following science test scores:

70, 75, 90, 83, 72, 77, 93, 80, 67, 84, 70, 68, 86, 71, 56, 87, 94, 79, 91

10. See margin.

● construct and interpret line plots
(Lesson 4-3)
Construct a line plot for the data above

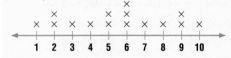

11. Construct a line plot for the following ages: See Solutions Manual.

72, 73, 68, 78, 76, 69, 65, 70, 77, 80, 74, 63, 73, 69, 66, 75, 70, 77, 75, 73

168   **Chapter 4** Study Guide and Review

Classroom Vignette

"For a final project, I have my students select their own survey question. Then they survey 50 people, organize their findings, and display the results in more than one form. Afterward, we play 'Classroom Feud'."

Dennis Newell, Teacher
Emporia Middle School, Emporia, KS

Objectives and Examples

- construct and interpret stem-and-leaf plots *(Lesson 4-4)*

Construct a stem-and-leaf plot for {13, 15, 17, 20, 21, 22, 22, 26, 29, 34, 53}

```
1 | 3 5 7
2 | 0 1 2 2 6 9
3 | 4
4 |            5|3 means 53
5 | 3
```

- find the mean, median, and mode of a set of data *(Lesson 4-5)*

Find the mean, median, and mode of {53, 53, 57, 62, 65}.

The mean is $\frac{53+53+57+62+65}{5}$ or 58.

The median is 57. The mode is 53.

- find the range and quartiles of a set of data *(Lesson 4-6)*

Find the range and quartiles of {1, 2, 2, 2, 3, 3, 4, 4, 5, 6, 6}.

The range is $6 - 1 = 5$. The median is 3. The lower quartile is 2 and the upper quartile is 5.

- construct and interpret box-and-whisker plots *(Lesson 4-7)*

Construct a box-and-whisker plot of {1, 2, 2, 2, 3, 3, 4, 4, 5, 6, 6}

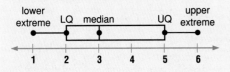

- construct and interpret scatter plots *(Lesson 4-8)*

A scatter plot is a graph of points whose ordered pairs consist of two sets of data.

Review Exercises

12. Make a stem-and-leaf plot for the following temperatures:

60, 53, 68, 72, 66, 80, 73, 51, 62, 48, 56, 84, 77, 45, 79, 65

```
4 | 5 8
5 | 1 3 6
6 | 0 2 5 6 8
7 | 2 3 7 9
8 | 0 4
        7|3 means 73
```

Find the mean, median, and mode for each set of data. Round to the nearest tenth.

13. 8.2, 6.8, 7.4, 8.5, 7.1, 8.3 *See margin.*

14. 41, 26, 35, 30, 20, 41, 21

15. 173, 132, 157, 191, 118

16. 4, 6, 11, 2, 4, 8, 12, 3

Find the range and quartiles of each set of data.

17. 149, 137, 144, 126, 151, 132, 142, 120, 166 *46, 150, 129*   **18.** *5, 5, 2*

18. 4, 3, 1, 6, 2, 6, 5, 1, 5, 3, 4, 2, 1, 3, 6

19. 25, 30, 28, 22, 24 *8, 29, 23*

Draw a box-and-whisker plot for each set of data. *See margin.*

20. 12, 15, 14, 18, 20, 17

21. 41, 36, 45, 20, 31, 54, 22, 35, 49, 23, 51, 37, 42

Determine whether a scatter plot of the data below would show a positive, negative, or no relationship.

22. height and income *no relationship*

23. temperature and snow *negative*

Additional Answers

13. 7.7, 7.8, no mode

14. 30.6, 30, 41

15. 154.2, 157, no mode

16. 6.3, 5, 4

20.

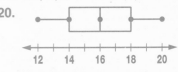

Additional Answer

21.

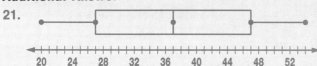

You may wish to use a Chapter Test from the Evaluation Masters booklet as an additional chapter review. The two free-response forms are shown below. One of the two multiple-choice forms is shown on the next page.

Evaluation Masters, pp. 32–33

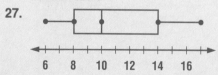

Objectives and Examples

- recognize when graphs and statistics are misleading *(Lesson 4-9)*

  Statistics can be misleading if the data comes from a sample that is not representative of the larger group. A graph can be misleading if the scale is inappropriate or parts of the scale are missing.

Review Exercises

24. Tell which graph below might be misleading and tell why. **See margin.**

Applications and Problem Solving

25. The cost of air fares from Denver to Newark are shown below.

$248	$756	$350	$298	$650	$987	$326	$211	$345
$378	$888	$458	$298	$321	$789	$667	$703	$498

a. Make a frequency table for the data. Use reasonable intervals. *(Lesson 4-1)*
b. Make a histogram of the data. *(Lesson 4-2)* **25a-b. See Solutions Manual.**

26. **Grades** In order to receive a B in Mr. Carmona's math class, the average of Ling's five test scores must be 80 or above. His test scores are 78, 85, 83, 76, and 80. Will he receive a B in Mr. Carmona's class? Explain. *(Lesson 4-5)* **yes, mean = 80.4**

27. **Wildlife** Miss Kaiser is a biologist working for the state of Ohio. She is studying fish in Leesville Lake. These are the lengths in inches of large-mouth bass that she captured and released: 12, 9, 8, 15, 7, 8, 13, 10, 6, 14, 17, 8, 14, 12, and 7. Draw a box-and-whisker plot of the data. *(Lesson 4-7)* **See margin.**

Curriculum Connection Projects

- **Automotive** Make a tally of all the first numbers of the license plates in the school parking lot, and another of all the first letters. Find the mode and median of each tally.
- **Government** Construct stem-and-leaf plots of the ages of your state representatives and the ages of your state senators.

Read More About It

McWhirter, Norris, and Ross. *Guinness Sports Record Book.*
Janeczko, Paul B. *Loads of Codes and Ciphers.*
Brooks, Bruce. *The Moves Make the Man.*

Additional Answers

Chapter Review

24. The graph on the right is misleading. It has an unequal vertical scale.

27.

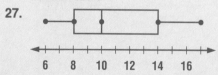

Chapter Test, p. 171

5.

History Test	
Points	**Frequency**
30–32	1
33–35	3
36–38	4
39–41	3
42–44	6
45–47	3
48–50	5

Chapter
4 Test

Use the histogram at the right to answer each question.

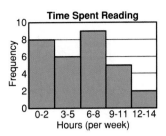

Time Spent Reading

1. For which interval is the frequency the greatest? **6-8**
2. How many people spend 3-5 hours reading per week? **6**
3. How many people were surveyed? **30**
4. How many people spend more than 5 hours per week reading? **16**

The scores on a 50-point history test are given at the right.

43	48	40	36	50
42	49	33	37	41
45	32	50	44	47
38	41	49	33	42
45	35	38	42	43

5. Make a frequency table for the data. **See Solutions Manual.**
6. Make a line plot for the data. **See Solutions Manual.**
7. Make a stem-and-leaf plot for the data. **See Solutions Manual.**
8. What is the frequency of the score that occurred most often? **3**
9. How many students received a score of 38? **2**
10. How many students received a score of 45 or above? **8**

11. What numbers would you use for stems in a stem-and-leaf plot of {319, 334, 321, 325, 312, 346, and 338}? **31, 32, 33, 34**
12. Find the mean, median, and mode for the following set of data. 30, 14, 23, 20, 12, 18, 14, 19
    18.75, 18.5, 14

The ages of the customers at Bob's Ice Cream Palace are 20, 34, 26, 40, 13, 23, 15, 41, 45, 35, 31, 12, 38, 18, 25, 48, 29.

13. What is the range? **36**
14. What is the median? **29**
15. What are the upper and lower quartiles? **39, 19**
16. What is the interquartile range? **20**
17. What are the limits on the outliers? Are there any outliers? **69, –11; no**
18. Draw a box-and-whisker plot for the data. **See Solutions Manual.**

19. Make a scatter plot for the data in the table below. Does the data show a positive or negative relationship between gasoline used and miles driven? **positive**
    For graph, see Solutions Manual.

Gas Used (gal)	12	20	15	18	10	22	19	11	17	8	13
Miles Driven	215	336	247	320	181	356	336	172	312	149	201

20. Make a frequency table for these points scored in a basketball game.
    See Solutions Manual.

    102 78 62 98 67 88 98 101 102 89
    121 66 78 102 113 120 109 88 97 98

Bonus Write six numbers whose mean, median, and mode is the same number.
Sample answer: 26, 37, 40, 40, 44, 53

Using the Chapter Test

This page may be used as a chapter test or another chapter review.

Evaluation Masters, pp. 28–29

Name _____ Date _____

Form 1A _____ *Chapter 4 Test*

Wayne's Sweater Shop conducted a survey of favorite sweater colors. The table shows the results of the color survey.

Color	Red	White	Blue	Green	Brown	Black
Frequency	15	17	18	13	9	6

1. If Wayne can buy only three colors, what should they be?
   A. blue, green, brown   B. red, white, green
   C. red, blue, green   D. red, white, blue   1. ___ D
2. Look at the histogram. How many walkers walk from 5 through 15 miles per week?
   A. 50   B. 45
   C. 40   D. 70   2. ___ B

Walking Record

Use the line plot for Exercises 3 through 5.

3. Find the mode.
   A. 70   B. 75
   C. 80   D. 90   3. ___ A
4. Find the median.
   A. 70   B. 74.1
   C. 72.5 D. 75   4. ___ C
5. Find the mean to the nearest tenth.
   A. 71.3 B. 72.5
   C. 73.1 D. 74.2   5. ___ D

Use the stem-and-leaf plot for Exercises 6 through 9.

6. Find the median.
   A. 50   B. 52
   C. 55   D. 54   6. ___ B

2	3 7
3	9
4	6 6
5	1 3 4 5
6	0 9
8	1

7. Find the lower and upper quartiles.
   A. 46, 56.5   B. 47, 57
   C. 46.5, 56   D. 42.5, 57.5   7. ___ D
8. Find the interquartile range.
   A. 15   B. 58   C. 20   D. 56   8. ___ A
9. Find any outliers.
   A. none   B. 20   C. 81   D. 20, 81   9. ___ C

Use the following test information for Exercises 10 through 12. The test scores of six students on a small-group project were Jan 78, Hui Ping 80, Len 50, Raul 83, Chevan 81, and Nat 50. Their actual grade will be the average of these grades.

10. Find the mean to nearest whole number.
    A. 60   B. 79   C. 83   D. 70   10. ___ D

28
Glencoe Division, Macmillan/McGraw-Hill

Name _____ Date _____

Chapter 4 Test, Form 1A (continued)

11. Find the mode and the median.
    A. 50, 50   B. 50, 79   C. 50, 70   D. 78, 79   11. ___ B
12. Which average do Hui Ping and Nat want the teacher to use?   12. ___ A
    A. median   B. mode   C. mean   D. their own score

Use the box-and-whisker plot for Exercises 13 through 16.

13. Find the median.
    A. 35   B. 32
    C. 23   D. 40   13. ___ B
14. Find the lower and upper quartiles.
    A. 23, 32   B. 21, 40   C. 23, 35   D. 21, 35   14. ___ C
15. Find the interquartile range.
    A. 19   B. 9   C. 8   D. 12   15. ___ D
16. Find the extremes.
    A. 23, 35   B. 21, 35   C. 21, 40   D. 23, 40   16. ___ C

Use the scatter plots below for Exercises 17 through 19. What relationship is shown by each scatter plot?

P   Q   R

17. Scatter plot P
    A. positive   B. negative   C. none   D. quartile   17. ___ B
18. Scatter plot Q
    A. positive   B. negative   C. none   D. quartile   18. ___ C
19. Scatter plot R
    A. positive   B. negative   C. none   D. quartile   19. ___ A
20. What will a scatter plot of the relationship between study time and exam scores show?   20. ___ A
    A. positive   B. negative   C. none   D. quartile

BONUS Which average is affected by very high or low values in a set of data?   ___ C
    A. median   B. mode   C. mean   D. All are affected.

29
Glencoe Division, Macmillan/McGraw-Hill

5 Investigations in Geometry

Previewing the Chapter

This chapter develops basic concepts in geometry. In the mathematics labs, students learn the classic methods of construction using a compass and a straightedge. Students study the properties of parallel lines, then look at the classification and properties of triangles and quadrilaterals. Methods of comparing and transforming geometrical figures are introduced in lessons on congruence, similarity, and symmetry. All of this material is brought together in a lesson on Escher-like drawings. In the **problem-solving strategy** lesson, students learn how to use Venn diagrams.

Lesson	Lesson Objectives	NCTM Standards	State/Local Objectives
5-1A	Define congruence in terms of angle measurement and length.	1–4, 12, 13	
5-1	Identify lines that are parallel.	1–4, 7, 9, 12, 13	
5-1B	Construct a line parallel to a given line.	1–3, 12, 13	
5-2	Use a Venn diagram to solve problems.	1–4, 7, 8, 10, 12	
5-3	Classify triangles.	1–4, 7, 9, 12, 13	
5-4	Classify quadrilaterals.	1–4, 7, 9, 12, 13	
5-5A	Construct a reflection using a geoboard.	1–4, 8, 12, 13	
5-5	Explore line symmetry and rotational symmetry.	1–4, 7, 8, 12	
5-6A	Draw an enlargement of a figure.	1–4, 7, 12, 13	
5-6	Identify congruent figures and similar figures.	1–4, 7, 9, 12	
5-6B	Construct a triangle congruent to a given triangle.	1, 3, 4, 12, 13	
5-7	Create Escher-like drawings by using translations and rotations.	1–4, 8, 12	

Organizing the Chapter

A complete, 1-page lesson plan is provided for each lesson in the *Lesson Plans Masters Booklet*.

LESSON PLANNING GUIDE

| Lesson | Materials/ Manipulatives | Extra Practice (Student Edition) | Blackline Masters Booklets | | | | | | | | | |
			Study Guide	Practice	Enrichment	Evaluation	Technology	Lab Manual	Multicultural Activities	Application and Interdisciplinary Activities	Transparencies	Group Activity Cards
5-1A	compass, inch ruler, protractor							p. 50				
5-1	colored pencils, ruler, protractor	p. 593	p. 39	p. 39	p. 39						5-1	5-1
5-1B	compass							p. 51				
5-2			p. 40	p. 40	p. 40					p. 19	5-2	5-2
5-3	scissors	p. 594	p. 41	p. 41	p. 41		p. 19				5-3	5-3
5-4	protractor	p. 594	p. 42	p. 42	p. 42	Quiz A, p. 43					5-4	5-4
5-5A	geoboard, rubber bands							p. 52				
5-5	MIRA®, tracing paper, pin	p. 594	p. 43	p. 43	p. 43				p. 5	p. 5	5-5	5-5
5-6A	graph paper, colored pencils							p. 53				
5-6	tracing paper, scissors	p. 595	p. 44	p. 44	p. 44		p. 5				5-6	5-6
5-6B	compass							p. 54				
5-7	tracing paper, scissors		p. 45	p. 45	p. 45	Quiz B, p. 43					5-7	5-7
Study Guide and Review			Multiple Choice Test, Forms 1A and 1B, pp. 37–40 Free Response Test, Forms 2A and 2B, pp. 41–42 Cumulative Review, p. 44 (free response)									
Test			Cumulative Test, p. 45 (multiple choice)									

Pacing Guide: Option I (Chapters 1–12) - 13 days; Option II (Chapters 1–13) - 12 days; Option III (Chapters 1–14) - 11 days
You may wish to refer to the complete **Course Planning Guides** on page T25.

OTHER CHAPTER RESOURCES

Student Edition
Chapter Opener, pp. 172–173
Mid-Chapter Review, p. 190
Portfolio Suggestion, p. 205

 Manipulatives
Overhead Manipulative Resources
Middle School Mathematics Manipulative Kit

 Software/Technology
Interactive Mathematics Tools (Macintosh)
Test and Review Generator (IBM, Apple, Macintosh)
Teacher's Guide for Software Resources

Other Supplements
Transparency 5-0
Performance Assessment, pp. 9–10
Glencoe Mathematics Professional Series
Lesson Plans, pp. 48–59

INTERDISCIPLINARY BULLETIN BOARD

Social Studies Connection

Objective Find geometric figures in state or national flags.

How To Use It Have students research state and national flags, looking for those with geometric figures in the design. Ask them to create displays of five such flags, identifying the figures in each, and indicating important statistics about the state or nation.

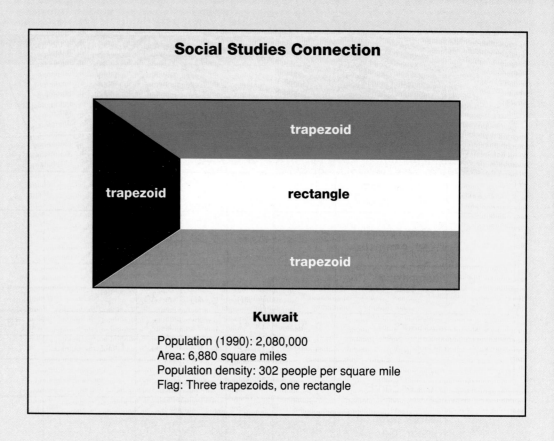

Social Studies Connection

trapezoid

trapezoid

rectangle

trapezoid

Kuwait

Population (1990): 2,080,000
Area: 6,880 square miles
Population density: 302 people per square mile
Flag: Three trapezoids, one rectangle

APPLICATIONS AND CONNECTIONS

Applications	Lesson	Example	Exercise
Engineering	5-1		23
Architecture	5-3		31
Teaching	5-4		27
Design	5-5	4	
Science	5-5		20
Typography	5-5		21
Entertainment	5-6		19
Art	5-7		18
Connections			
Algebra	5-1	3	
Algebra	5-3		24, 25
Algebra	5-4		21, 22
Algebra	5-6	4	
Computer	5-6		20

TEAM ACTIVITIES

Multicultural Experiences

Outside Field Trips Students will enjoy experiences that document real-world applications of geometry. Visit a print shop, sign shop, or advertising agency to see graphic designers at work.

At a jewelry store, students can observe symmetries and geometric patterns in gem cuttings and jewelry settings.

In-Class Speakers Invite an architect to discuss applications of geometry to building design.

A quilt-maker can show how geometric patterns are incorporated into quilt design.

SUPPLEMENTARY BLACKLINE MASTER BOOKLETS

Some of the blackline masters for enhancing this chapter are shown below.

Application and Interdisciplinary Activity Masters, pp. 5, 19

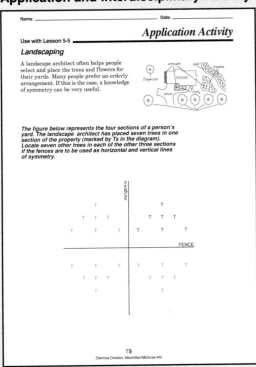

Application Activity

Use with Lesson 5-5

Landscaping

A landscape architect often helps people select and place the trees and flowers for their yards. Many people prefer an orderly arrangement. If this is the case, a knowledge of symmetry can be very useful.

The figure below represents the four sections of a person's yard. The landscape architect has placed seven trees in one section of the property (marked by Ts in the diagram). Locate seven other trees in each of the other three sections if the fences are to be used as horizontal and vertical lines of symmetry.

T5
Glencoe Division, Macmillan/McGraw-Hill

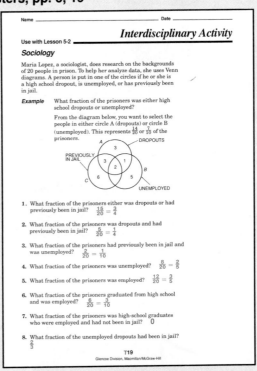

Interdisciplinary Activity

Use with Lesson 5-2

Sociology

Maria Lopez, a sociologist, does research on the backgrounds of 20 people in prison. To help her analyze data, she uses Venn diagrams. A person is put in one of the circles if he or she is a high school dropout, is unemployed, or has previously been in jail.

Example What fraction of the prisoners was either high school dropouts or unemployed?

From the diagram below, you want to select the people in either circle A (dropouts) or circle B (unemployed). This represents $\frac{14}{20}$ or $\frac{7}{10}$ of the prisoners.

1. What fraction of the prisoners either was dropouts or had previously been in jail? $\frac{15}{20} = \frac{3}{4}$

2. What fraction of the prisoners was dropouts and had previously been in jail? $\frac{5}{20} = \frac{1}{4}$

3. What fraction of the prisoners had previously been in jail and was unemployed? $\frac{2}{20} = \frac{1}{10}$

4. What fraction of the prisoners was unemployed? $\frac{8}{20} = \frac{2}{5}$

5. What fraction of the prisoners was employed? $\frac{12}{20} = \frac{3}{5}$

6. What fraction of the prisoners graduated from high school and was employed? $\frac{6}{20} = \frac{3}{10}$

7. What fraction of the prisoners was high-school graduates who were employed and had not been in jail? 0

8. What fraction of the unemployed dropouts had been in jail? $\frac{2}{3}$

T19
Glencoe Division, Macmillan/McGraw-Hill

Multicultural Activity Masters, p. 5

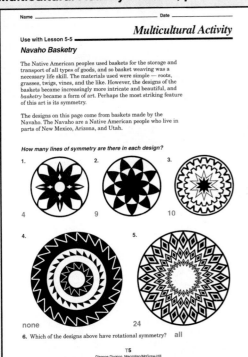

Multicultural Activity

Use with Lesson 5-5

Navaho Basketry

The Native American peoples used baskets for the storage and transport of all types of goods, and so basket weaving was a necessary life skill. The materials used were simple — roots, grasses, twigs, vines, and the like. However, the designs of the baskets became increasingly more intricate and beautiful, and *basketry* became a form of art. Perhaps the most striking feature of this art is its symmetry.

The designs on this page come from baskets made by the Navaho. The Navaho are a Native American people who live in parts of New Mexico, Arizona, and Utah.

How many lines of symmetry are there in each design?

1. 4   2. 9   3. 10

4. none   5. 24

6. Which of the designs above have rotational symmetry? all

T5
Glencoe Division, Macmillan/McGraw-Hill

Technology Masters, p. 5

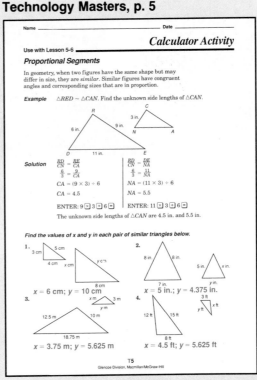

Calculator Activity

Use with Lesson 5-6

Proportional Segments

In geometry, when two figures have the same shape but may differ in size, they are *similar*. Similar figures have congruent angles and corresponding sizes that are in proportion.

Example $\triangle RED \sim \triangle CAN$. Find the unknown side lengths of $\triangle CAN$.

Solution

$\frac{RD}{CN} = \frac{RE}{CA}$

$\frac{6}{3} = \frac{9}{CA}$

$CA = (9 \times 3) \div 6$

$CA = 4.5$

ENTER: 9 $\times$ 3 $\div$ 6 $=$

$\frac{RD}{CN} = \frac{DE}{NA}$

$\frac{6}{3} = \frac{11}{NA}$

$NA = (11 \times 3) \div 6$

$NA = 5.5$

ENTER: 11 $\times$ 3 $\div$ 6 $=$

The unknown side lengths of $\triangle CAN$ are 4.5 in. and 5.5 in.

Find the values of x and y in each pair of similar triangles below.

1. $x = 6$ cm; $y = 10$ cm
2. $x = 5$ in.; $y = 4.375$ in.
3. $x = 3.75$ m; $y = 5.625$ m
4. $x = 4.5$ ft; $y = 5.625$ ft

T5
Glencoe Division, Macmillan/McGraw-Hill

RECOMMENDED OUTSIDE RESOURCES

Books/Periodicals

National Council of Teachers of Mathematics, *Learning and Teaching Geometry, K–12, 1987 Yearbook,* Reston, VA: NCTM, 1987.

Films/Videotapes/Videodiscs

Geometry—What's That? San Rafael, CA: Coronet Media, 1975.

Mathematics of the Honeycomb, Whittier, CA: Moddy Institute of Science, 1964.

Software

Creativity Unlimited, (Apple II), Wings for Learning/Sunburst

For addresses of companies handling software, please refer to page T24.

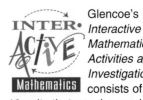

Glencoe's *Interactive Mathematics: Activities and Investigations* consists of 18 units that may be used as alternatives or supplemental material for *Mathematics: Applications and Connections.* The suggested unit for this chapter is Unit 4, *Through the Looking Glass.* See page T18 for more information.

This two-page introduction to the chapter provides a visual, relevant way to engage students in the mathematics of the chapter. Questions are included that help students see the need to learn the mathematics in the chapter. Data in charts and graphs provide statistical information that students can analyze and interpret at this point as well as later in the chapter. The Chapter Project provides an activity that applies the mathematics of the chapter.

MAKING MATHEMATICS RELEVANT

Spotlight on Rivers and Waterfalls

Rivers contain fresh water which ultimately flows into one of the oceans. There are some 55,000 cubic miles of water in the world's rivers. Much of the world's energy is generated by rivers turning the turbines in dams. Grand Coulee Dam, the largest hydroelectric plant in the United States (and third largest in the world), generates about 9 thousand megawatts (1 megawatt = 1 million watts) of electricity per hour. The reservoir of water behind Grand Coulee Dam contains nearly 12 billion cubic meters of water. Ask this question: *A man must work about 13 hours to generate a kilowatt (1,000 watts) of energy. How many days would a man have to work to generate the power produced at Grand Coulee Dam in one hour?*
4.875 million days

Chapter

Investigations in Geometry

Spotlight on Rivers and Waterfalls

Have You Ever Wondered...

- What the longest river in the world is?
- Where the tallest waterfall in the world is?

River	Outflow	Length (mi)
Amazon	Atlantic Ocean	4,000
Amur	Tatar Strait	2,744
Chang Jiang	East China Sea	3,964
Congo	Atlantic Ocean	2,718
Huang	Yellow Sea	2,903
Lena	Laptev Sea	2,734
Mississippi	Gulf of Mexico	2,340
Missouri	Mississippi River	2,540
Nile	Mediterranean Sea	4,160
Ob-Irtysh	Gulf of Ob	3,362

THE FAR SIDE BY GARY LARSON

© Chronicle Features, 1980

3-11   LARSON

"... and then the second group comes in—"row, row, row your boat"..."

172

"Have You Ever Wondered?" Answers

- The longest river in the world is the Nile River.
- The tallest waterfall in the world is in Venezuela.

Have students study the waterfall graph. Ask the following questions.

- *Which waterfall is about one-fourth the height of King George VI Falls?* Victoria Falls

- *Which two waterfalls together approximately equal the height of Giesbach Falls?* King George VI and Victoria

Data Search

A question related to these data is provided in Lesson 5-4, page 190, Exercise 29.

CHAPTER PROJECT

Encourage students to be creative when choosing materials for their models. For example, they could use marbles instead of water and halves of plastic drink containers for river beds.

Students will discover that a river travels in the same direction as the river bank and that any object in the river will be carried in the same direction. This discovery will serve as an introduction to *parallelism.* You may wish to have students build bridges across their rivers. Through research, students will find that engineers use triangular shapes to give bridges strength.

Allow one week to complete the project.

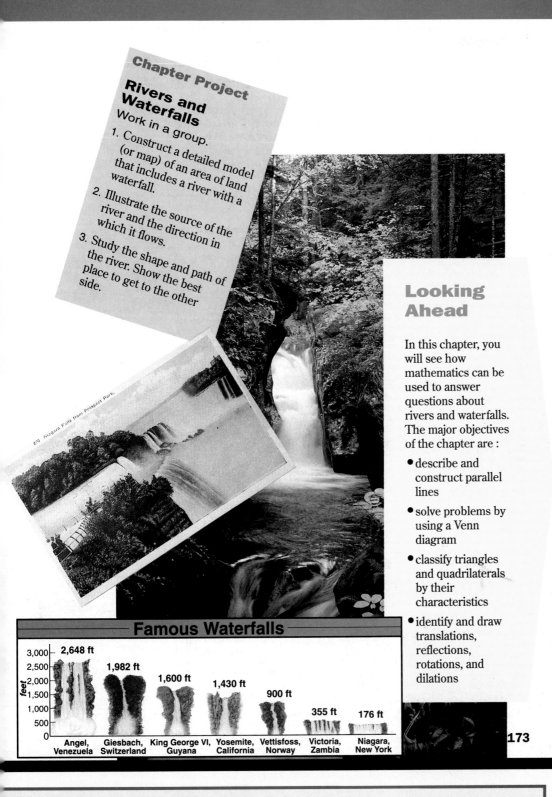

Chapter Project

Rivers and Waterfalls

Work in a group.

1. Construct a detailed model (or map) of an area of land that includes a river with a waterfall.

2. Illustrate the source of the river and the direction in which it flows.

3. Study the shape and path of the river. Show the best place to get to the other side.

Looking Ahead

In this chapter, you will see how mathematics can be used to answer questions about rivers and waterfalls. The major objectives of the chapter are :

- describe and construct parallel lines

- solve problems by using a Venn diagram

- classify triangles and quadrilaterals by their characteristics

- identify and draw translations, reflections, rotations, and dilations

Famous Waterfalls

2,648 ft — Angel, Venezuela
1,982 ft — Giesbach, Switzerland
1,600 ft — King George VI, Guyana
1,430 ft — Yosemite, California
900 ft — Vettisfoss, Norway
355 ft — Victoria, Zambia
176 ft — Niagara, New York

173

Chapter Opener Transparency

Transparency 5-0 is available in the Transparency Package. It provides another full-color, motivating activity that you can use to capture students' interest.

1 FOCUS

NCTM Standards: 1–4, 12, 13

Management Tips

For Students   Appoint materials managers to pass out and collect rulers, compasses, and protractors.

For the Overhead Projector
Overhead Manipulative Resources provides appropriate materials for teacher or student demonstration of the activities in this Mathematics Lab.

1 FOCUS

Introducing the Lab

Sketch this arrangement of three points on the chalkboard. Ask these questions:

A•   •B
   •C

- *How many line segments are needed to connect the points in all possible ways?*   3

- *How many angles will result?*   3

Sketch this arrangement of four points on the chalkboard. Repeat the questions above.

A•   •B
C•   •D

6; 16, not counting those angles measuring 180° or greater

Objective
Define congruence in terms of angle measurement and length.

Materials
straightedge (ruler)
compass
protractor

In Chapter 1, you learned two systems of measurement, the metric system and the customary system. In geometry we use both of these systems for measuring line segments.

Activity One

Work with a partner.

- Each segment below can be named by its endpoints. For example, a segment with endpoints *W* and *Z* can be named as $\overline{WZ}$ or as $\overline{ZW}$. Name each segment shown below.

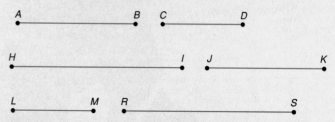

- Measure each segment to the nearest centimeter. Record your measurements.

What do you think?

1. Which segments had the same length? $\overline{AB}$, $\overline{JK}$; $\overline{CD}$, $\overline{LM}$; $\overline{HI}$, $\overline{RS}$

2. Segments with the same length are said to be *congruent*. To say *segment WZ is congruent to segment OP,* we write $\overline{WZ} \cong \overline{OP}$. Use the proper symbols to write all pairs of congruent segments shown above. $\overline{AB} \cong \overline{JK}$; $\overline{CD} \cong \overline{LM}$; $\overline{HI} \cong \overline{RS}$

Extension

3. A compass and straightedge are used to construct congruent segments. Construct a segment congruent to $\overline{AB}$ by following these steps.   **See students' work.**

   a. Draw a long line with a straightedge. Put a point on the line. Call it *F*.

   b. Open your compass to the same width as the length of $\overline{AB}$.

   c. Put the point of the compass at *F* and draw an arc to intersect the line. Label this intersection *G*. Segment *FG* should be congruent to segment *AB*, or $\overline{FG} \cong \overline{AB}$.

Angles are measured in units called *degrees*. You can use a protractor to measure an angle or to draw an angle of a given measurement.

Activity Two

Use a protractor to measure ∠ABC.

$\overrightarrow{BC}$ *means ray BC. A ray is part of a line. It has one endpoint, B, and goes on continuously in one direction from that point.*

- Trace ∠ABC on your paper and extend sides $\overrightarrow{BA}$ and $\overrightarrow{BC}$.

- Place a protractor over ∠ABC with the center point on vertex B.

- Align the horizontal line with side $\overrightarrow{BC}$.

- Locate the point on the protractor where $\overrightarrow{BA}$ intersects the edge of the protractor.

- Read the measurement from the scale that has 0° along $\overrightarrow{BC}$. To say, *the measure of angle ABC is 110 degrees,* we write $m\angle ABC = 110°$.

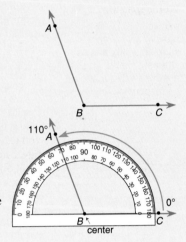

center

What do you think?

4. scale where 0° aligns with one side of angle

4. How do you know which scale to use when measuring an angle?
5. Two angles that have the same measurement are congruent. Suppose $m\angle XYZ = 110°$. Write a sentence relating ∠XYZ and ∠ABC. **∠XYZ ≅ ∠ABC**

Extension

6. You can use a protractor to draw an angle with a specific measure. Draw ∠MNO if $m\angle MNO = 45°$. **See students' work.**

   a. Draw a ray. Label the endpoint N and put point M on the ray.

   b. Align your protractor so that the center is at N and the horizontal line aligns with $\overrightarrow{MN}$.

   c. Find the scale containing 0° along $\overrightarrow{MN}$. Follow that scale until you find 45°. Label this point O.

   d. Draw $\overrightarrow{NO}$. $m\angle MNO = 45°$.

Mathematics Lab 5-1A Measurement in Geometry   **175**

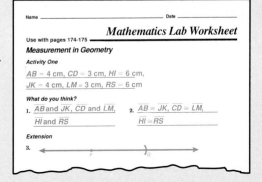

Lesson Resources
- Study Guide Master 5-1
- Practice Master 5-1
- Enrichment Master 5-1
- Group Activity Card 5-1

 Transparency 5-1 contains the 5-Minute Check and a teaching aid for this lesson.

5-Minute Check
(Over Chapter 4)

1. Make a stem-and-leaf plot for the data:

| 81 | 86 | 91 | 81 | 79 | 85 |
| 87 | 92 | 90 | 87 | 81 | 92 |

```
7 | 9
8 | 1115677
9 | 0122    9|0 means 90
```

2. Find the mean, median, and mode for the data above.   86; 86.5; 81

3. Find the range, upper quartile, and lower quartile of these data:

| 31 | 32 | 35 | 39 | 41 | 45 |
| 48 | 53 | 59 | 60 | 61 |

30; 59; 35

1 FOCUS

Motivating the Lesson

Questioning   Pick a rectangular wall in the room. State the distance between the top and bottom edges at the left end and ask students to estimate the distance at the right end.   the same   Ask why the distances are the same.   The edges are always the same distance apart.

2 TEACH

Using the Mini-Lab   Students' measurements of angles may be slightly inaccurate. Acknowledge their findings, and ask them why their measurements differ. Remind students of the meaning of supplementary angles. Ask how they can use supplementary angles to verify their measurements.

5-1 Parallel Lines

Objective

Identify lines that are parallel.

Words to Learn

parallel
transversal
supplementary angles
alternate interior angles
alternate exterior angles
corresponding angles

In the Olympics, two gymnastic events are men's parallel bars and women's uneven parallel bars. Gymnasts are judged on required moves and difficulty in their routines. The highest score they can receive is a 10.0.

Parallel bars have some of the same characteristics as **parallel lines.** That is, if you extended them indefinitely, they would never meet. In order for two lines to never meet, they must be the same distance apart. To say *line ℓ is parallel to line m,* we write $\ell \parallel m$.

Many geometric figures contain parallel segments. If the lines that would contain those segments are parallel, the segments are parallel.

> *In this book, when two lines look parallel, you can assume they are.*

Example 1

Name the parallel segments in each figure.

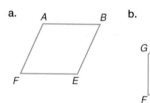

a.
$\overline{AB} \parallel \overline{FE}, \overline{AF} \parallel \overline{BE}$

b.
$\overline{FG} \parallel \overline{IJ}$

c.
none

A line that intersects two other lines is called a **transversal.** In the figure, $m \parallel n$. Line p is the transversal. Eight angles are formed when a transversal intersects two parallel lines.

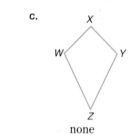
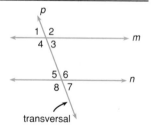

transversal

OPTIONS

Bell Ringer

A wall intersects two parallel walls. Describe the intersection.   two parallel lines (or line segments)

Mini-Lab

Work with a partner.

Materials: notebook paper, colored pencils, ruler, protractor

- Draw two parallel lines using the lines on your notebook paper. Draw any line to intersect these two lines.

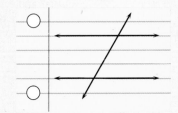

- Label the angles formed using the numbers 1 through 8. Measure each angle and record its measurement.

- Use a different colored pencil to circle the numbers of all of the angles that are congruent.

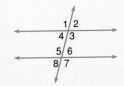

Congruent angles have the same measure.

Talk About It   For answers to Exercises a-b, see margin.

a. List the pairs of congruent angles in which one angle is formed by the transversal and one of the parallel lines and the other angle is formed by the transversal and the other parallel line.

b. Which pairs of congruent angles are on the same side of the transversal?

c. Which pairs of congruent angles are on opposite sides of the transversal? **Sample answers:** ∠3, ∠5; ∠4, ∠6; ∠2, ∠8; ∠2, ∠4

d. How do m∠2 and m∠3 relate? ∠2 and ∠3 are **supplementary angles.** Name other pairs of supplementary angles. **Sample answers:** ∠1, ∠2; ∠1, ∠4; ∠4, ∠3; ∠4, ∠5; ∠1, ∠8

If the sum of two angle measures is 180°, the angles are supplementary.

The congruent angles formed by parallel lines and a transversal have special names. Remember that the symbol ≅ means *is congruent to*.

Why do you think ∠1 and ∠5 are called corresponding angles?

Congruent Angles with Parallel Lines	If a pair of parallel lines is intersected by a transversal, these pairs of angles are congruent:

alternate interior angles:
∠4 ≅ ∠6, ∠3 ≅ ∠5

alternate exterior angles:
∠1 ≅ ∠7, ∠2 ≅ ∠8

corresponding angles:
∠1 ≅ ∠5, ∠2 ≅ ∠6, ∠3 ≅ ∠7, ∠4 ≅ ∠8.

Lesson 5-1 Parallel Lines   **177**

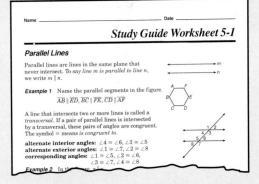

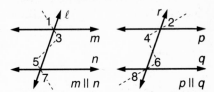

Close

Have students draw a pair of parallel lines and a transversal, numbering the angles formed 1 through 8. Then have them list all pairs of alternate interior angles, all pairs of alternate exterior angles, and then all pairs of corresponding angles.

3 PRACTICE/APPLY

Assignment Guide
Maximum: 10–25
Minimum: 11–19 odd, 20–24

For **Extra Practice,** see p. 593.

Alternate Assessment

Speaking Draw the figure at the top of page 178 on the chalkboard. Name an angle. Have students name an angle that is congruent to it and tell why they are congruent. Repeat using other angles.

Practice Masters, p. 39

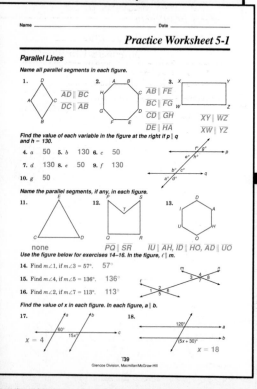

Name ____ Date ____

Practice Worksheet 5-1

Parallel Lines
Name all parallel segments in each figure.

1.   2.   3.
$\overline{AD} \parallel \overline{BC}$ $\overline{AB} \parallel \overline{FE}$
$\overline{DC} \parallel \overline{AB}$ $\overline{BC} \parallel \overline{FG}$
     $\overline{CD} \parallel \overline{GH}$ $\overline{XY} \parallel \overline{WZ}$
     $\overline{DE} \parallel \overline{HA}$ $\overline{XW} \parallel \overline{YZ}$

Find the value of each variable in the figure at the right if p ∥ q and h = 130.

4. a   50   5. b   130   6. c   50
7. d   130   8. e   50   9. f   130
10. g   50

Name the parallel segments, if any, in each figure.

11.   12.   13.
none $PQ \parallel SR$ $IU \parallel AH, ID \parallel HO, AD \parallel UO$

Use the figure below for exercises 14–16. In the figure, ℓ ∥ m.

14. Find m∠1, if m∠3 = 57°.   57°
15. Find m∠4, if m∠5 = 136°.   136°
16. Find m∠2, if m∠7 = 113°.   113°

Find the value of x in each figure. In each figure, a ∥ b.

17.   18.
x = 4   x = 18

T39
Glencoe Division, Macmillan/McGraw-Hill

178

In the figure, $m \parallel n$ and $m\angle 7 = 100°$.

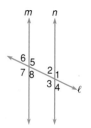

a. Find $m\angle 3$.
   $\angle 7$ and $\angle 3$ are corresponding angles. They are congruent so their measures are the same.

$$m\angle 3 = m\angle 7$$
$$m\angle 3 = 100°$$

b. Find $m\angle 5$.
   $\angle 3$ and $\angle 5$ are alternate interior angles. Their measures are the same, so $m\angle 5 = 100°$.

Algebra In the figure, $m \parallel n$. Find the value of x, if $m\angle 5 = 110°$ and $m\angle 3 = 2x + 10°$.

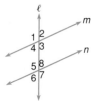

$\angle 5$ and $\angle 3$ are alternate interior angles. They are congruent, so their measures are equal. You can write an equation.

$$m\angle 5 = m\angle 3$$
$$110 = 2x + 10$$
$$110 - 10 = 2x + 10 - 10$$
$$100 = 2x$$
$$\frac{100}{2} = \frac{2x}{2}$$
$$50 = x \qquad \text{The value of } x \text{ is 50.}$$

Checking for Understanding   For answers to Exercises 1–5, see margin.

Communicating Mathematics   Read and study the lesson to answer each question.

1. **Write** a definition for parallel lines.
2. **Tell** how you think a parallelogram got its name.
3. **Show** two examples of parallel segments in your classroom.
4. **Draw** two parallel lines p and q. Then draw a transversal r. Measure one angle. Then, without measuring, put the measures of all angles on your drawing.
5. **Tell** what it means when two angles are supplementary.

Guided Practice   Name all parallel segments in each figure.

6. 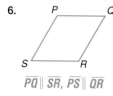   7. 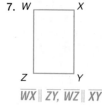   8.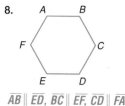

$\overline{PQ} \parallel \overline{SR}, \overline{PS} \parallel \overline{QR}$ $\overline{WX} \parallel \overline{ZY}, \overline{WZ} \parallel \overline{XY}$ $\overline{AB} \parallel \overline{ED}, \overline{BC} \parallel \overline{EF}, \overline{CD} \parallel \overline{FA}$

178   **Chapter 5** Investigations in Geometry

OPTIONS

Team Teaching

Inform the other teachers on your team that your classes are studying geometry. Ask them to draw attention to lines, angles, symmetries, and geometric shapes whenever possible. Suggestions for curriculum integration are:

Art: the Golden Rectangle
Social Studies: maps, flags

Additional Answers

1. Parallel lines are lines that are the same distance apart and never meet.
2. Opposite pairs of sides are parallel.
3. Sample answers: opposite sides of a floor tile; top and bottom edges of the chalkboard

9. Find the value of each variable in the figure at the right if $p \parallel q$ and $h = 60°$.

a. a 60   b. b 120   c. c 120   d. d 60

e. e 60   f. f 120   g. g 120

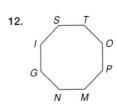

Exercises

Independent Practice

Name the parallel segments, if any, in each figure.

10.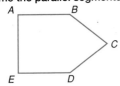

11.

12.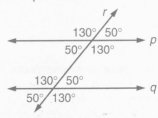

12. $\overline{ST} \parallel \overline{NM}$,
$\overline{TO} \parallel \overline{NG}$,
$\overline{OP} \parallel \overline{GI}$,
$\overline{PM} \parallel \overline{IS}$

$\overline{AB} \parallel \overline{ED}$ none

Use the figure at the right for Exercises 13-16.

13. Find $m\angle 6$, if $m\angle 2 = 35°$. **35**
14. Find $m\angle 3$, if $m\angle 5 = 77°$. **77**
15. Find $m\angle 4$, if $m\angle 8 = 122°$. **122**
16. Find $m\angle 7$, if $m\angle 1 = 68°$. **68**

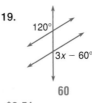

Find the value of x in each figure.

17.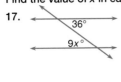

18.

19.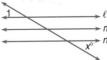

4   **38**   **60**

Mixed Review

20. Use mental math to find $5.00 - $2.49. *(Lesson 1-2)* **$2.51**
21. Find the absolute value of 10. *(Lesson 3-1)* **10**
22. **Statistics** Which average (mean, median, or mode) would best describe the height of eighth grade students at Dunbar Junior High? *(Lesson 4-8)* **mean**

Problem Solving and Applications

23. **Engineering** In Birmingham, Alabama, the city blocks are arranged like a grid. The roads running north and south are called streets and those running east and west are called avenues.
    a. What is true of all the avenues? **They are parallel.**
    b. What is true of all the streets? **They are parallel.**
    c. What is the measure of the angle formed when a street intersects an avenue? **90**

24. 30; alternate exterior angles are congruent.

24. **Critical Thinking** Find the value of x in the figure at the right if $m\angle 1 = 30°$. Explain how you found this value.

25. **Journal Entry** Write how the statement *If $\ell \parallel m$ and $m \parallel n$, then $\ell \parallel n$* has to be true.
    Two lines parallel to the same line are parallel to each other.

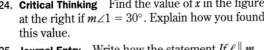

Extending the Lesson

Using Cooperative Groups Have students work in small groups to solve the following problem:
In how many points can 3 lines intersect? Draw sketches to illustrate your answer.

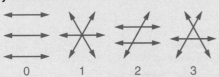

Cooperative Learning Activity

One Thing Leads to Another 5-1

Number of players: 2
Materials: Spinners

You know that certain pairs of angles are congruent when a pair of parallel lines is intersected by a transversal. Parallel lines intersected by a transversal have another interesting property: The interior angles on the same side of the transversal are **supplementary**. In other words, the interior angles on the same side of the transversal have a combined measure of 180°.

▲ Label equal sections of one spinner with the letters A through H. Label equal sections of a second spinner with the following angle measures: 84°, 120°, 60°, 30°, 110°, 45°.

➡ Each partner spins a spinner. Try to be the first to write the measure of all of the other angles in a figure like the one shown on the back of this card if the angle shown on the first spinner has the angle measure shown on the second spinner. (Note: The figure shows the locations of angles A through H *only*. The actual measures of angles A through H depend on the results of your spins.)

Glencoe Mathematics: Applications and Connections, Course 3

NCTM Standards: 1–3, 12, 13

Management Tips

For Students Remind students that in compass-and-straightedge constructions, rulers and protractors are not used to make measurements.

For the Overhead Projector
Overhead Manipulative Resources provides appropriate materials for teacher or student demonstration of the activities in this Mathematics Lab.

1 FOCUS

Introducing the Lab

Ask students to suggest ways they could draw a line on a wall of the room parallel to the base of the wall.

2 TEACH

Using Questioning Ask students to name the pair of congruent angles used to create the parallel lines. ∠TPU ≅ ∠SQR

3 PRACTICE/APPLY

Using Connections Ask students how they could continue the construction to create other lines parallel to ℓ and *m*. Repeat the construction using other points on $\overline{PQ}$.

Close

Have students describe how they could construct parallel lines using alternate exterior angles.

Cooperative Learning

5-1B Constructing Parallel Lines

A Follow-Up of Lesson 5-1

Objective
Construct a line parallel to a given line.

Materials
compass
straightedge

You can use a compass and straightedge to construct a line parallel to a given line.

Try this!

- Draw a line and label it ℓ.

- Choose any point *P*, not on ℓ.

- Draw a line through *P* that intersects ℓ. Label this point *Q*.

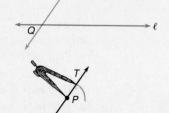

- Place your compass point at *Q* and draw a large arc. Label points *R* and *S*.

- With the same setting, place the compass point at *P* and draw a large arc. Label point *T*.

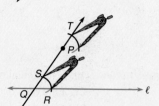

- Use your compass to measure the distance from *R* to *S*.

- With the same setting, place your compass at *T* and draw an arc to intersect the one already drawn. Label this point *U*.

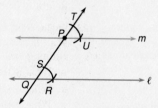

- Draw a line through *P* and *U*. Label it line *m*. By construction, ℓ ∥ *m*.

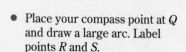

What do you think?

1. Look at your completed construction. What type of angles did you use to create your parallel lines? **corresponding angles**

2. Measure the angles in your construction. The angles you constructed may not be congruent. Explain how this could happen. **error in construction**

180 **Chapter 5** Investigations in Geometry

OPTIONS

Lab Manual You may wish to make copies of the blackline master on p. 51 of the *Lab Manual* for students to use as a recording sheet.

Lab Manual, p. 51

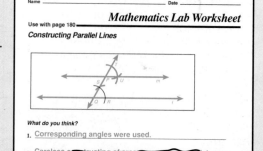

5-2 Use a Venn Diagram

Objective
Use a Venn diagram to solve problems.

Words to Learn
Venn diagram

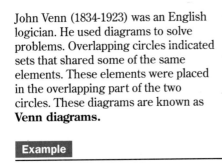

John Venn (1834-1923) was an English logician. He used diagrams to solve problems. Overlapping circles indicated sets that shared some of the same elements. These elements were placed in the overlapping part of the two circles. These diagrams are known as **Venn diagrams.**

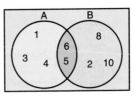

set A = {1, 3, 4, 5, 6}
set B = {2, 5, 6, 8, 10}

Example

The table below shows the states that produce over 100 million bushels of corn, wheat, or soybeans per year. Make a Venn diagram of this information and determine how many states produce over 100 million bushels of either corn or wheat.

Crop	State
corn	MI, NE, SD, WI, TX, IL, IA, IN, MN, OH
wheat	CO, KS, MT, ND, OK, WY, TX
soybeans	MO, IL, IA, IN, MN, OH

Explore
What do you know?
You know which states produce over 100 million bushels of corn, wheat, or soybeans.

What are you trying to find?
How many states produce over 100 million bushels of either corn or wheat?

Plan
Draw a Venn diagram to organize the states. Make a note of which states appear in more than one category.

Solve
Draw three intersecting circles in a rectangle to represent corn, wheat, and soybeans. List the state abbreviations in the appropriate sections. Count the number of states in both the corn circle and the wheat circle.

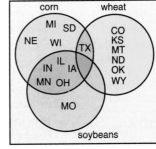

corn only	corn and soybeans	corn and wheat	wheat only		
4	+ 5	+ 1	+ 6	=	16 states

Lesson 5-2 Problem-Solving Strategy: Use a Venn Diagram **181**

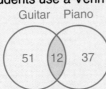
Study Guide Masters, p. 40

Name _____ Date _____

Study Guide Worksheet 5-2

Problem-Solving Strategy: Use a Venn Diagram

Example One weekend at Rosewood Middle School, 24 eighth graders attended the band concert, 35 went to the basketball game, and 40 went to the dance. Eight students attended all three events, 6 students attended the basketball game and the dance, 5 students attended the band concert and the dance, and 7 attended the band concert and the basketball game. How many students attended only one weekend event?

Explore You know how many students attended each event and each combination of events. You are trying to find the number of students who attended only one event.

Plan Draw a Venn diagram to organize the data.

Solve Draw three intersecting circles, one for each of the three events. Write the number of students who attended each combination of events in the appropriate sections. Then subtract to find the

---

5-2 Lesson Notes

NCTM Standards: 1–4, 7, 8, 10, 12

Lesson Resources
- Study Guide Master 5-2
- Practice Master 5-2
- Enrichment Master 5-2
- Interdisciplinary Master, p. 19
- Group Activity Card 5-2

Transparency 5-2 contains the 5-Minute Check and a teaching aid for this lesson.

🕐 5-Minute Check
(Over Lesson 5-1)
Use the figure.

1. If ∠3 is one of a pair of alternate interior angles, name the other. ∠7

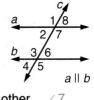
$a \parallel b$

2. If ∠8 is one of a pair of corresponding angles, name the other. ∠6

3. Find the value of *x*, if $m\angle 1 = 120°$ and $m\angle 5 = 4x + 16°$. 26

Practice Masters, p. 40

Name _____ Date _____

Practice Worksheet 5-2

Problem-Solving Strategy: Use a Venn Diagram

Solve using a Venn diagram.

1. Some pet owners were asked whether they owned a cat or a dog. Altogether, the group owned 45 dogs and 40 cats. Fourteen people said they owned both a cat and a dog. Make a Venn diagram of this information.

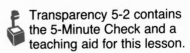
Pets
31 14 26
Dogs Cats

2. Refer to the Venn diagram at the right.
   a. How many people bought more than one type of fund? 8
   b. How many invested in Utilities and Energy funds? 3

   Mutual Fund Choices

   c. How many investors are represented? 29
   d. How many bought Utilities or Bio-Medical funds? 21
   e. How many bought Energy and Bio-Medical funds? 4
   f. What does the "1" in the center of the diagram represent?
      One investor bought all three funds.

Solve. Use any strategy.

3. In the Sports-Card Collectors' Club, 9 members collect basketball cards; 18 members, baseball cards; and 15 members, football cards. Four collect baseball and football cards; 3, baseball and basketball cards; 3 basketball and football cards; and 1 collects all three types of cards.
   a. Make a Venn diagram of this information.
   b. How many members are in the club? 33

   Baseball Football

   c. How many collect baseball or football cards? 29
   d. How many collect only basketball cards? 4
   e. How many collect only baseball cards? 12

   Basketball

4. Twenty-eight less than the result of dividing a number by 7 is 196 less than the number. What is the number? 196

5. Forty-nine small tiles cover the same area as one large tile. How many small tiles will be needed to cover a wall now covered by 96 large tiles? 4,704 small tiles

1 FOCUS

Motivating the Lesson

Questioning Have students read the opening paragraph of the lesson. Ask this question: *What would be indicated by a Venn diagram with two circles that do not overlap?* No elements belong to both sets.

2 TEACH

More Examples

For the Example

Rock   Classical

12 6 8
1 2 4
5
Jazz

a. How many people like rock or jazz? 30 people

b. How many like both classical and rock, but not jazz? 6 people

3 PRACTICE/APPLY

Assignment Guide

Maximum: 5–8

Minimum: 5–8

Enrichment Masters, p. 40

Name _____ Date _____

Enrichment Worksheet 5-2

Intersection and Union of Sets

In the drawings below, suppose A is the set of points inside the ellipse and B is the set of points inside the square. Then, the shaded areas show the union and intersection of sets A and B.

Union $A \cup B$ Intersection $A \cap B$

For example, if A = {1, 2, 3, 4} and B = {3, 4, 5, 6}, then their union and intersection are written as:

Union: $A \cup B$ = {1, 2, 3, 4, 5, 6}   Intersection: $A \cap B$ = {3, 4}

If A = {the odd numbers} and B = {the even numbers}, $A \cap B$ is a set with no members. This set is called *the empty set* and is written with the symbol Ø: $A \cap B$ = Ø. A Venn diagram for these sets would show two shapes that do not overlap.

For each problem, draw a Venn diagram for sets A and B. Then write the elements included in $A \cup B$ and $A \cap B$.

1. A = {integers between 0 and 7}
   B = {factors of 12}
   $A \cup B$ = {1, 2, 3, 4, 5, 6, 12}
   $A \cap B$ = {1, 2, 3, 4, 6}

2. A = {positive integers less than 4}
   B = {negative integers greater than -4}
   $A \cup B$ = {-3, -2, -1, 1, 2, 3}
   $A \cap B$ = Ø

3. A = {perfect squares between 0 and 30}
   B = {odd whole numbers less than 10}
   $A \cup B$ = {1, 3, 4, 5, 7, 9, 16, 25}
   $A \cap B$ = {1, 9}

4. A = {the five vowels in English}
   B = {the letters in your first name}   Answers will vary.

T40
Glencoe Division, Macmillan/McGraw-Hill

182

Examine   Compare the lists of states for corn and wheat. How many states are in each list? How many states are in both lists? Subtract the number of states in both lists from the total.

$$\begin{array}{ccccccccc} corn & + & wheat & - & both & = & ? \\ 10 & + & 7 & - & 1 & = & 16 \end{array}$$

This matches the count from the Venn diagram.

Checking for Understanding

1. It represents states that produce over 100 million bushels of all three grains.

Communicating Mathematics

Read and study the lesson to answer each question.

1. **Write** what the section in the Venn diagram where all three circles overlap represents in the Example.

2. **Tell** how many states produce over 100 million bushels of either corn or soybeans. 11 states

Guided Practice

Solve using a Venn diagram.

3. Refer to the Example.

   a. How many states produce over 100 million bushels of either wheat or soybeans? 13 states

   3b. 0 states
   b. How many states produce over 100 million bushels of all three grains?

4. The results of a supermarket survey showed that 83 customers chose wheat cereal, 83 chose rice, and 20 chose corn. Of those customers who bought two boxes, six bought corn and wheat, 10 bought rice and corn, and 12 bought rice and wheat. Four customers bought all three. Make a Venn diagram of this information. **See Solutions Manual.**

Problem Solving

Practice

Solve using any strategy.

5. Of the 30 members in a cooking club, 20 like to mix salads, 17 prefer baking desserts, and 8 like to do both.

Strategies
• • • • • • •
Look for a pattern.
Solve a simpler problem.
Act it out.
Guess and check.
Draw a diagram.
Make a chart.
Work backward.

   a. Make a Venn diagram of this information. **See Solutions Manual.**

   b. How many like to mix salads, but not bake desserts? 12 people

   c. How many do not like either baking desserts or mixing salads? 1 person

6. Luisa put some counters into a beaker holding 500 cm³ of water. The water level rose to a reading of 625 cm³. What is the volume of the counters? 125 cm³

7. A number increased by 29 is 6 less than twice the number. What is the number? 35

8. Refer to the Venn diagram at the right.

   a. How many eighth grade students are in the band and the chorus? 5 students

   8b. 25 students
   b. How many are in the band or the chorus?

   c. Are there more in the orchestra than in the band? Explain. No; There are 14 students in the band and 12 students in the orchestra.

8th Grade Activities (number of students)

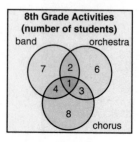

band   orchestra
7   2   6
4 1 3
8
chorus

182   Chapter 5 Investigations in Geometry

OPTIONS

Extending the Lesson

Using Cooperative Groups Have students work in small groups to solve the following problem: *A survey of 100 tourists showed that 45 had visited France, 48 China, 26 Chile, 10 Chile and China, 6 Chile and France, 8 France and China, and 5 all three countries. How many had visited China but not France or Chile?* 35

Cooperative Learning Activity

Use groups of 4.   Spellbound **5-2**
Materials: Index cards

• Copy onto cards the following words, one per card.

measurable   rhapsody   forfeit   bouquet

→ Each group member selects one card. Work in pairs. Ask twenty people to spell the two words you and your partner selected. Determine the number of people who could spell the first word only, the second word only, both words, or neither word. Record the responses in a frequency table.

Copy the Venn diagram shown on the back of this card. Write the number of responses in the appropriate place. Do not write the number of people who misspelled both words.

Trade Venn diagrams with the other pair in your group. Find the number of people who could not spell the other pair's two words.

Glencoe Mathematics: Applications and Connections, Course 3

5-3 Classifying Triangles

Objective
Classify triangles.

Words to Learn
scalene
isosceles
equilateral
acute
right
obtuse
perpendicular

Have you ever looked under the bleachers at the football field? If you look at the end of the bleachers, you will probably notice that a triangular frame was used to support them.

Triangles are named by using letters at their vertices. The triangle at the right can be named as $\triangle XYZ$. *A vertex is the point where two sides meet.*

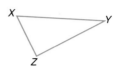

Triangles are often classified by how many congruent sides they have.

Slashes are often used to show which sides of figures are congruent.

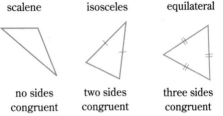

Triangles Classified by Sides	scalene	isosceles	equilateral
	no sides congruent	two sides congruent	three sides congruent

Triangles can also be classified by the type of angles they have. An angle is classified by its measure.

Acute angles have measures less than 90°.
Right angles have measures equal to 90°.
Obtuse angles have measures greater than 90°, but less than 180°.
Straight angles have measures equal to 180°.

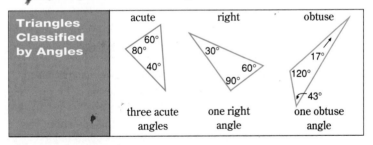

Triangles Classified by Angles	acute	right	obtuse
	three acute angles	one right angle	one obtuse angle

Mental Math Hint

Use the corner of your notebook paper to estimate whether an angle has a measure greater than 90°, equal to 90°, or less than 90°.

The ⌐ symbol in the figure at the left, indicates that an angle is a right angle. When segments meet to form right angles, they are **perpendicular.** To say $\overline{AB}$ is perpendicular to $\overline{CD}$, we write $\overline{AB} \perp \overline{CD}$.

Lesson 5-3 Classifying Triangles **183**

OPTIONS

Bell Ringer
How many triangles (of any size) are there in this figure? **27**

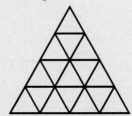

Interactive Mathematics Tools

This multimedia software provides an interactive lesson that is tied directly to Lesson 5-3. Students will use changeable triangles to explore the measures of the angles of a triangle.

5-3 Lesson Notes

NCTM Standards: 1–4, 7, 9, 12, 13

Lesson Resources
• Study Guide Master 5-3
• Practice Master 5-3
• Enrichment Master 5-3
• Technology Master, p. 19
• Group Activity Card 5-3

Transparency 5-3 contains the 5-Minute Check and a teaching aid for this lesson.

5-Minute Check
(Over Lesson 5-2)

Hobby Survey
Baseball Cards

Stamps   Coins

Use the Venn diagram to determine how many people collected the following.

1. stamps and baseball cards   11
2. stamps or coins   58
3. stamps, coins, and baseball cards   5

1 FOCUS

Motivating the Lesson

Activity   Ask students to find examples of triangles in the classroom. List these on the chalkboard. Have students describe similarities and differences among the examples.

2 TEACH

Using the Mini-Lab   Instead of tearing corners, students can fold the vertices together:

Help students to see that since the three angles form a straight angle, the sum of their measures is 180°.

183

More Examples

Classify each triangle by its sides and by its angles.

For Example 1

7 ft / 95° \ 3 ft
40°   45°
9 ft

scalene
obtuse

For Example 2

2 in.

2 in.

isosceles
right

For Example 3

3⅜ m
63°
3 m   54°
63°
3⅜ m

isosceles
acute

Teaching Tip In Example 3, point out that since the triangle has two sides congruent, it is isosceles as well as equilateral. By agreement, such a triangle is named by its more specific classification, equilateral.

Checking for Understanding

Exercises 1-5 are designed to help you assess students' understanding through reading, writing, speaking, and modeling. You should work through these exercises with your students and then monitor their work on Guided Practice Exercises 6-11.

Additional Answers

1. Equilateral triangles are isosceles triangles but isosceles triangles are not equilateral triangles.

3.

Classify each triangle by its sides and by its angles.

Equilateral triangles are also equiangular. That is, all its angles have the same measure.

1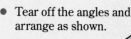
3 ft
4 ft   5 ft

scalene,
right

2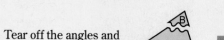
2.5 cm
120°   30°
2.5 cm   4.3 cm
30°

isosceles,
obtuse

3
2 yd   60°
2 yd
60°
60°
2 yd   60°

equilateral,
acute

  Mini-Lab

Work with a partner.
Materials: scissors, straightedge

- Draw any large triangle and cut it out. Label the angles *A*, *B*, and *C*.

- Tear off the angles and arrange as shown.

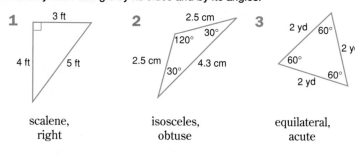

Talk About It

a. straight angle; 180°

b. Both are 180°.

c. Sum of measures of angles of a triangle is 180°.

a. When the angles were put together, what type of angle did they form? What is the measure of this type of angle?

b. Measure each of the angles and find the sum of their measures. Compare this sum to your result in question a.

c. Try this activity with another triangle. What do you think is true about the measures of the angles of *any* triangle?

Checking for Understanding

Communicating Mathematics

Read and study the lesson to answer each question.

1. **Write** what the Venn diagram at the right says about isosceles and equilateral triangles. **See margin.**

2. **Tell** how you would complete this sentence. The sum of the angle measures of a triangle is ___?___°. **180**

3. **Draw** a right isosceles triangle. **See margin.**

4. **Tell** what the symbol ⊥ means. **perpendicular to**

TRIANGLES

Scalene	Isosceles
	Equilateral

184   **Chapter 5** Investigations in Geometry

OPTIONS

Reteaching Activity

Using Cooperative Groups
Prepare six index cards with the names of the six classes of triangles. Prepare six more cards picturing examples of the six classes. Show side lengths and angle measurements as needed. Shuffle the cards, arrange them face down, and have students play "Concentration."

Study Guide Masters, p. 41

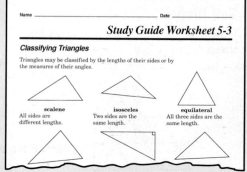

Name _____ Date _____

Study Guide Worksheet 5-3

Classifying Triangles

Triangles may be classified by the lengths of their sides or by the measures of their angles.

scalene
All sides are different lengths.

isosceles
Two sides are the same length.

equilateral
All three sides are the same length.

5. Show how you can use the results of the Mini-Lab to find the value of x in $\triangle PQR$.
   Solve $100 + 50 + x = 180$; 30.

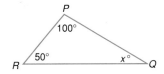
P
100°
R 50° x° Q

Classify each triangle by its sides and by its angles.

6.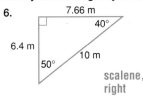
7.66 m
40°
6.4 m
10 m
50°
scalene, right

7.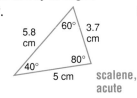
60° 3.7 cm
5.8 cm
40° 80°
5 cm
scalene, acute

8. isosceles, acute
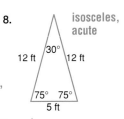
30°
12 ft 12 ft
75° 75°
5 ft

9.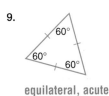
60°
60° 60°
equilateral, acute

10.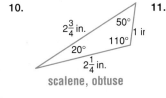
$2\frac{3}{4}$ in. 50° 1 ir
110°
20°
$2\frac{1}{4}$ in.
scalene, obtuse

11. isosceles, right

45°
45°

Exercises

Classify each triangle by its sides and by its angles.

12.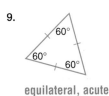
11 m 60°
60° 11 m
60°
11 m
equilateral, acute

13.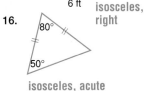
6 ft $8\frac{1}{2}$ ft
6 ft
isosceles, right

14. isosceles, obtuse
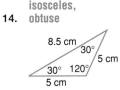
8.5 cm 30°
5 cm
30° 120°
5 cm

15.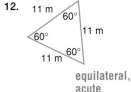
scalene, right

16.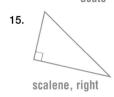
80°
50°
isosceles, acute

17.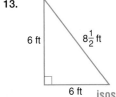
equilateral, acute

Tell if each statement is *true* or *false*. Then draw a figure to justify your answer.

18. A triangle can be isosceles and acute. true
19. A triangle can be obtuse and scalene. true
20. A right triangle can also have an obtuse angle. false
21. A triangle can contain two obtuse angles. false
22. An equilateral triangle can never be a right triangle. true
23. An equilateral triangle is also an isosceles triangle. true

For figures to Exercises 18-23, see Solutions Manual.

24. **Algebra** Find the value of x in $\triangle ABC$ if $m\angle A = 90°$, $m\angle B = 32°$, and $m\angle C = x°$. 58
25. **Algebra** Find the value of x in $\triangle XYZ$ if $m\angle X = 2x°$, $m\angle Y = 64°$, and $m\angle Z = 36°$. 40

Lesson 5-3 Classifying Triangles **185**

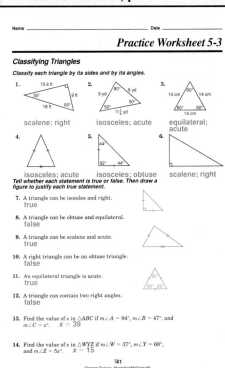

Classroom Vignette

"If a computer is available, students can use software like 'The Geometric Supposer: Triangles' or LOGO for more practice in classifying triangles. Working in pairs, one student creates a triangle while the other classifies it and justifies their answer. Then they switch roles."

Clare L. Polzin

Clare Polzin, Teacher
Red Rock Central Junior High School,
Lamberton, MN

185

186

Mixed Review

26. Solve $b - 19 = 73$. *(Lesson 2-3)* **92**

27. Solve $e = 8(-3)(-4)^2$. *(Lesson 3-6)* **−384**

28. **Statistics** Refer to the temperature box-and-whisker plot in Example 1 on page 156. What fraction of the days had temperatures above 49°? *(Lesson 4-7)* $\frac{3}{4}$ **of the days**

29. Name the parallel segments in the figure at the right. *(Lesson 5-1)* **$\overline{HI} \parallel \overline{KJ}$**

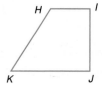

Problem Solving and Applications

30b. No; 5 + 2 is not greater than 7.
30c. See margin.

30. **Critical Thinking** Use the number of toothpicks as units to form the sides of as many triangles as possible and complete the chart.

Number of toothpicks	3	4	5	6	7	9	12
Number of triangles formed	?	?	?	?	?	?	?
Types of triangles formed	?	?	?	?	?	?	?

} See margin.

yes, for 4 units

a. Were there any numbers for which you could not build a triangle?

b. Suppose you were told the lengths of the sides of a scalene triangle were 5 meters, 2 meters, and 7 meters. Is this possible? Explain your answer.

c. Write what you can conclude about the relationship between the sum of the lengths of two sides of a triangle and the length of the third side.

31. **Architecture** Triangles are often used in structural designs.

a. Name all the types of triangles in the structure shown at the left. **See students' work.**

b. Why do you think architects use triangles in structures rather than other figures? **Triangles will not collapse as easily as other figures.**

32. **Critical Thinking** Build the figure at the right with straws. Take away four straws to leave exactly four congruent equilateral triangles. **See margin.**

33. **Journal Entry** Write all possible types of triangles if you classify them both by angles and by sides. **See margin.**

34. **Mathematics and History** Read the following paragraph.

In 2600 B.C., the Egyptians used a detailed system of geometry to build the pyramid of Snefu. The builders measured the base of the pyramid with a rope that had 12 equal sections knotted in it. It was stretched around three pegs to form sides of three, four, and five sections. This formed a right triangle.

a. The measures of complementary angles have a sum of 90°. If two angles of a triangle are complementary, what is the measure of the third angle? **90**

b. Find the area of a triangle with a 7-centimeter base and a height of 9 centimeters. Use the formula $A = \frac{1}{2}bh$. **31.5 cm²**

OPTIONS

Extending the Lesson

Mathematics and History You may wish to have students recreate what the Egyptians did by using a geoboard. In solving Exercise 1, remind students that the two angles are said to be complementary if the sum of their measures is 90°.

Cooperative Learning Activity

Try Angles 5-3

Number of players: 2
Materials: Index cards, spinners

• Copy onto cards the angle measures shown on the back of this card, one measure per card. Shuffle the cards and place them face down in a pile. Label equal sections of a spinner "Acute," "Right," and "Obtuse."

► Each partner takes five cards. One partner then spins the spinner. If possible, remove from your hand three cards containing angle measures that have a sum of 180° and that describe the type of triangle shown on the spinner. Replace cards removed from your hand with cards from the pile and award yourself 1 point. If you cannot form the type of triangle indicated on the spinner with any combination of the angle measures on the cards in your hand, you may trade some or all of your cards for cards from the pile before the next spin. Continue in the same way, taking turns at the spinner, until one partner has 10 points. (Shuffle and reuse cards that have been discarded.)

Glencoe Mathematics: Applications and Connections, Course 3

5-4 Classifying Quadrilaterals

Objective
Classify quadrilaterals.

Words to Learn
quadrilateral
rhombus
trapezoid

What characteristics do a baseball diamond, a football field, a basketball court, and a long jump pit have in common? You may have guessed that all are four-sided figures. Any four-sided figure is a **quadrilateral.**

When you say the word *cat*, different people picture different animals. Each breed of cat has its own set of characteristics. Some breeds share characteristics, or attributes. The same is true of quadrilaterals.

You are already familiar with three types of quadrilaterals.

 LOOK BACK

You can review parallelograms, rectangles, and squares on page 73.

parallelogram
  opposite sides parallel
  opposite sides congruent

rectangle
  opposite sides parallel
  opposite sides congruent
  four right angles

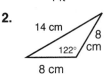

square
  opposite sides parallel
  four sides congruent
  four right angles

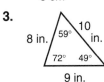

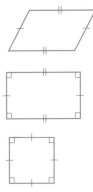

The Venn diagram relates these quadrilaterals by their attributes. It shows that rectangles and squares are types of parallelograms. A square is also a special type of rectangle.

Another type of parallelogram is a **rhombus.** A rhombus is a parallelogram that has four congruent sides. Two *rhombi* are shown at the right. A rhombus with four right angles is also a square. A quadrilateral that is not in the parallelogram family is the **trapezoid.** A trapezoid has *only one* pair of parallel sides. The other pair of sides are not parallel.

Quadrilaterals are named by the letters of their four vertices.

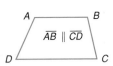

$\overline{AB} \parallel \overline{CD}$

Lesson 5-4 Classifying Quadrilaterals   **187**

OPTIONS

Bell Ringer

Make this figure using toothpicks.

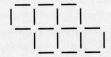

Remove two toothpicks to form exactly four squares.

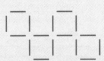

Interactive Mathematics Tools

This multimedia software provides an interactive lesson that is tied directly to Lesson 5-4. Students will use changeable quadrilaterals to explore squares and rectangles.

5-4 Lesson Notes

NCTM Standards: 1–4, 7, 9, 12, 13

Lesson Resources
• Study Guide Master 5-4
• Practice Master 5-4
• Enrichment Master 5-4
• Evaluation Master, Quiz A, p. 43
• Group Activity Card 5-4

Transparency 5-4 contains the 5-Minute Check and a teaching aid for this lesson.

5-Minute Check
(Over Lesson 5-3)

Classify each triangle by its sides and by its angles.

1.   3 ft   5 ft   4 ft   scalene right

2.   14 cm   8 cm   122°   8 cm   isosceles obtuse

3.   8 in.   10 in.   59°   72°   49°   9 in.   scalene acute

4. Find the value of *x* in △ABC if $m\angle A = 47°$, $m\angle B = x°$, and $m\angle C = 38°$.   95

1 FOCUS

Motivating the Lesson

Questioning Draw these figures on the chalkboard:

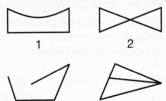

Have students explain why they are not quadrilaterals.
1: contains a curve; 2: segments intersect; 3: not closed; 4: more than two segments intersect at a vertex

187

2 TEACH

Using the Mini-Lab To show that the sum of the measures of the angles in a quadrilateral is 360°, divide the figure into two triangles by drawing one of the diagonals. Point out that the sum of the measures of the angles of the quadrilateral is the same as the sum of the measures of the angles in the two triangles, which is 180° + 180° or 360°.

More Examples

Identify all names that describe each quadrilateral.

For Example 1

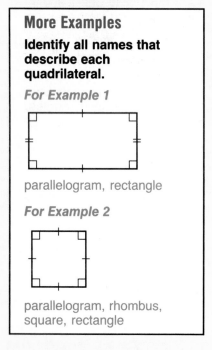

parallelogram, rectangle

For Example 2

parallelogram, rhombus, square, rectangle

Checking for Understanding

Exercises 1-4 are designed to help you assess students' understanding through reading, writing, speaking, and modeling. You should work through these exercises with your students and then monitor their work on Guided Practice Exercises 5-8.

Close

Have students write a list of the characteristics of each quadrilateral as you name them.

Additional Answers

2.

3. A parallelogram has two pairs of opposite sides parallel while a trapezoid has only one pair of opposite sides parallel.

188

Identify all names that describe each quadrilateral.

1   **2**

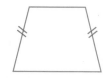

parallelogram,   trapezoid
rhombus

If the two nonparallel sides of a trapezoid are congruent, the trapezoid is called an isosceles trapezoid.

Mini-Lab

Work with a partner.

Materials: straightedge, protractor

- Draw a parallelogram. Use your protractor to measure all four angles. Record your measurements.

- Draw a trapezoid. Measure all four angles. Record your measurements.

- Draw a quadrilateral that has no sides parallel. Measure all four angles. Record your measurements.

Talk About It

a. What is the sum of the angle measures for each figure? **360°**

b. What is the sum of the angle measures in a rectangle? **360°**

c. Write a sentence to describe the sum of the angle measures in any quadrilateral. **Sum of angle measures of quadrilateral is 360°.**

Checking for Understanding

Communicating Mathematics

Read and study the lesson to answer each question.

1. **Tell** what attribute all quadrilaterals have. **4 sides**

2. **Draw** a rhombus that isn't a square. **See margin.**

3. **Tell** why a parallelogram is not a trapezoid. **See margin.**

4. **Write** the number that completes this statement.
   The sum of the angle measures of any quadrilateral is ___?___°. **360**

OPTIONS

Reteaching Activity

Using Models Have students work in pairs to find examples of quadrilaterals in the classroom. They should describe each example, measure its sides and angles, record each measurement, and identify what type of quadrilateral it is.

Study Guide Masters, p. 42

Name _____ Date _____

Study Guide Worksheet 5-4

Classifying Quadrilaterals

A quadrilateral is a figure with four sides and four angles. You can use sides and angles to classify quadrilaterals.

Parallelogram	Opposite sides are parallel. Opposite sides are congruent.	
Rectangle	Opposite sides are parallel. Opposite sides are congruent. All four angles are right angles.	
Square	Opposite sides are parallel. All four sides are congruent. All four angles are right angles.	
Rhombus	Opposite sides are parallel. All four sides are congruent.	

Guided Practice Sketch each figure on your paper. Let Q = quadrilateral, P = parallelogram, R = rectangle, S = square, RH = rhombus, and T = trapezoid. Write all letters inside the figure that describe it.

5.

Q, P, R, S, RH

6. Q, T

7. Q

8. In quadrilateral *ABCD*, *m∠A* = 90°, *m∠B* = 90°, and *m∠C* = 120°. Find *m∠D*. 60°

Exercises

Independent Practice Sketch each figure on your paper. Let Q = quadrilateral, P = parallelogram, R = rectangle, S = square, RH = rhombus, and T = trapezoid. Write all letters inside the figure that describe it.

9. Q, P

10. Q, P, R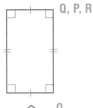

11.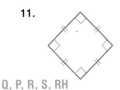

Q, P, R, S, RH

12. Q, P, RH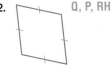

13. Q

14.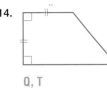

Q, T

15. rhombus, parallelogram, rectangle, square

15. Name all quadrilaterals that have both pairs of opposite sides parallel.

16. Name all quadrilaterals that have four right angles. rectangle, square

17. Name all quadrilaterals that have four congruent sides. square, rhombus

For figures to Exercises 18-20, see margin.

Tell if each statement is *true* or *false*. Then draw a figure to justify your answer.

18. Every square is a parallelogram. true

19. A rhombus is a square. false

20. A trapezoid can have only one right angle. false

21. **Algebra** In trapezoid *WXYZ*, *m∠W* = 2*a*°, *m∠X* = 40°, *m∠Y* = 110°, and *m∠Z* = 70°. Find the value of *a*. 70

22. **Algebra** In rhombus *PQRS*, *m∠P* = 60°, *m∠Q* = *x*°, *m∠R* = 60°, and *m∠S* = *x*°. Find the value of *x*. 120

Lesson 5-4 Classifying Quadrilaterals **189**

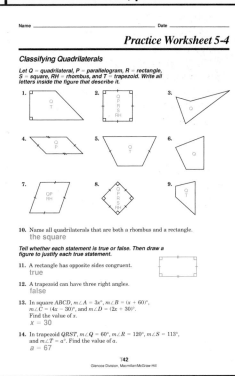

Additional Answers

26.

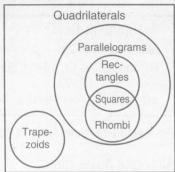

Quadrilaterals / Parallelograms / Rectangles / Squares / Rhombi / Trapezoids

27. Sample answer:

29a.

2,648 ft — 100 ft

Mid-Chapter Review

4.

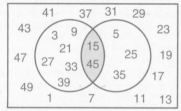

41 37 31 29
43   3 9   5   23
47 21 15 25 19
    27 33 45 35 17
49 39   7 11 13
    1

2 odd multiples of 3 and 5: 15, 45

190

---

23. Find the perimeter and area of a rectangle that has a length of 3 centimeters and a width of 5.5 centimeters. *(Lesson 2-9)* **P = 17 cm, A = 16.5 cm²**

24. Without graphing, tell in which quadrant the point M(6, −4) lies. *(Lesson 3-10)* **IV**

25. **Algebra** Find the value of x in △DEF if m∠D = 4x°, m∠E = 60°, and m∠F = 72°. *(Lesson 5-3)* **12**

26. Draw a Venn diagram to represent the relationships between all quadrilaterals. **See margin.**

27. **Teaching** A furniture company manufactures tables whose tops are shaped like trapezoids for use in the classroom. A teacher wants to arrange six of these tables so that 12 students can sit in a group. Make a sketch of how these tables could be arranged. **See margin.**

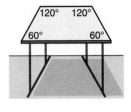
120° 120°
60°   60°

28. **Critical Thinking** A diagonal is a segment that connects any two nonconsecutive vertices. An isosceles trapezoid has two congruent diagonals. What other types of quadrilaterals have two congruent diagonals?
rectangle, square

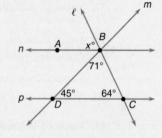
$\overline{AC} \cong \overline{BD}$

29. **Data Search** Refer to pages 172 and 173. Suppose you were 100 feet from the bottom of Angel Falls. Assume the waterfall forms a 90° angle with the river.

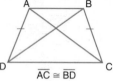
DATA SEARCH

   a. Draw the triangle formed by connecting the points representing the top of the falls, the bottom of the falls, and where you are standing. **See margin.**

   b. Would you draw a different triangle if the falls were Niagara Falls? Explain. **Yes, height would only be 176 feet instead of 2,648 feet.**

Assessment: Mid-Chapter Review

5

Use the figure for Exercises 1-3. $\overline{AB} \parallel \overline{CD}$

1. Name all parallel segments. *(Lesson 5-1)*

2. What is the value of x? *(Lesson 5-1)* **64**

3. Classify △BCD by its sides and by its angles. *(Lesson 5-3)* **scalene, acute**

4. Draw a Venn diagram to determine how many odd numbers from 1 to 50 are multiples of both 3 and 5. *(Lesson 5-2)* **See margin.**

5. Draw a rhombus that has at least one right angle. Describe your rhombus. *(Lesson 5-4)* **See students' work; square.**

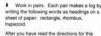
ℓ   m
B
n   A x°
71°
p   45° 64°
D   C

OPTIONS

Extending the Lesson

Social Studies Connection The Czechoslovakian flag is made up of two trapezoids and an isosceles triangle. Have students find examples of triangles and quadrilaterals on the flags of other countries. Have them sketch the flags and identify the geometric shapes.

Cooperative Learning Activity

Quad Squad 5-4

Use groups of 4.
Materials: Newspapers and magazines

◆ Work in pairs. Each pair makes a log by writing the following words as headings on a sheet of paper: rectangle, rhombus, trapezoid.

After you have read the directions for this activity, decide on a reasonable time limit, such as 5 minutes.

➡ Look around the classroom and in newspapers and magazines to find examples of things that suggest quadrilaterals. Each pair writes as many examples of each type of quadrilateral as possible in the predetermined amount of time.

Glencoe Mathematics: Applications and Connections, Course 3

Cooperative Learning

5-5A Reflections

A Preview of Lesson 5-5

NCTM Standards: 1–4, 8, 12, 13

Objective
Construct a reflection using a geoboard.

Materials
geoboards
rubber bands

When you see your reflection in a mirror, it seems that your image is as far back from the mirror as you are in front of the mirror. In mathematics, we create reflections of figures using a line instead of a mirror.

Try this!

Work with a partner.

- Place two geoboards side by side. Use a rubber band to create the figure shown.
- Let the edge where the two boards meet be the line of reflection. Vertex *A* is 2 pegs left of the line. Find a peg on the same row that is 2 pegs right of the line. Place a rubber band around this peg.
- Vertex *B* is 4 pegs left of the line. Find a peg on the same row that is 4 pegs right of the line. Stretch the rubber band to fit around this peg.
- Find the corresponding pegs for vertices *C* and *D*. Complete the figure with the rubber band. The figure on the right-hand board is the reflection of the image on the left-hand board.

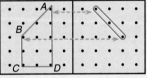

What do you think?

1. Compare the two figures. Are their corresponding sides congruent? **yes**
2. What type of quadrilateral are these figures? **trapezoid**
3. Write a sentence to explain how this reflection is like a reflection in a mirror. **See students' work.**

For answers to Exercises 4-7, see Solutions Manual.
Use side-by-side geoboards to reflect each figure.

4.

5.

6.

7. Suppose the second geoboard is placed below the first. Repeat Exercises 4-6 using this type of reflection. How do they compare with the first reflections?

DID YOU KNOW

Did You Know
Mirrors and mirror arrangements with reducing convex mirrors or concave lenses were used in the 17th and 18th centuries as drawing aids in the preparation of reproductions.

Management Tips

For Students Appoint materials managers to pass out and collect geoboards and rubber bands.

For the Overhead Projector
Overhead Manipulative Resources provides appropriate materials for teacher or student demonstration of the activities in this Mathematics Lab.

1 FOCUS

Introducing the Lab

Draw a geometric figure and its reflection on the chalkboard. Ask students to describe how the figures are alike and how they are different.

2 TEACH

Using Logical Reasoning Ask students if the figures would be reflections of each other if the geoboard on the left were placed on the right. yes

3 PRACTICE/APPLY

Using Logical Reasoning Ask students how each figure would appear to someone looking at it from the top of the geoboards.
like its reflection

Close

Have students compare and contrast a given figure and its reflection.

Mathematics Lab 5-5A Reflections **191**

OPTIONS

Lab Manual You may wish to make copies of the blackline master on p. 52 of the *Lab Manual* for students to use as a recording sheet.

Lab Manual, p. 52

Name _____ Date _____
Mathematics Lab Worksheet
Use with page 191
Reflections
What do you think?
1. yes
2. trapezoid
3. Right and left are reversed; for example,
$\overline{AD}$ is 2 units from the right edge of the geoboard, and its
corresponding side is 2 units from the left edge of
the other geoboard.

NCTM Standards: 1–4, 7, 8, 12

Lesson Resources
- Study Guide Master 5-5
- Practice Master 5-5
- Enrichment Master 5-5
- Multicultural Activity, p. 5
- Application Master, p. 5
- Group Activity Card 5-5

 Transparency 5-5 contains the 5-Minute Check and a teaching aid for this lesson.

🕐 5-Minute Check
(Over Lesson 5-4)

Identify all names that describe each quadrilateral.

1. 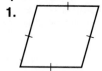 parallel-ogram, rhombus

2. parallelogram, rectangle, square, rhombus

1 FOCUS

Motivating the Lesson

Activity Give each student an equilateral triangle cut from construction paper. Ask them to find all the possible ways to fold the triangle in half so that the halves match.

3 ways:

2 TEACH

Using the Mini-Labs In the first mini-lab, give students an opportunity to get used to the MIRA's ability to reflect and transmit images simultaneously. When students have completed the second mini-lab, ask them to predict the angle of rotation of an equilateral triangle. 120°, 240°, 360°

5-5 Symmetry

Objective
Explore line symmetry and rotational symmetry.

Words to Learn
line symmetry
reflection
rotational symmetry

Yoshizawa Akira of Tokyo is one of the world's best known origamist. Origami is the Japanese art of paper folding. A 15 centimeter by 25 centimeter sheet of thin colored paper is folded to form birds, fish, and flowers without cutting or gluing.

One of the first steps in many origami figures is to fold the rectangle in half. When you do this, each point on one half of the rectangle is matched with a point on the other half. If you can fold a figure exactly in half, it is said to have **line symmetry.**

The cookie cutter at the right has line symmetry. The right half is a **reflection** of the left half and the center line is the *line of reflection*. The line of reflection is also called the *line of symmetry*. Some figures have more than one line of symmetry.

DID YOU KNOW

Origami is divided into two categories, figures used in ceremonial etiquette and objects such as birds, animals, insects, and flowers. Some figures have movable parts.

🧮 Mini-Lab

Work with a partner.
Materials: MIRA®, colored pencil

- Draw a large square on a piece of paper.
- Place the MIRA® on the square. Look at one side of the MIRA®. Notice the position of the reflection.
- Move the MIRA® until the reflection exactly matches the other half of the square you see through the pane.
- Hold the MIRA® steady. Use a colored pencil to draw along the edge of the MIRA®.

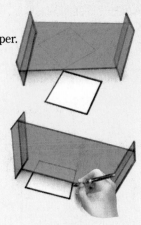

Talk About It

a. They are the same.

a. Look at the line you drew. How do the parts on each side of the line compare?
b. There are four lines of symmetry in a square. Use the MIRA® to find all of them. See margin.

OPTIONS

Bell Ringer

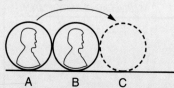

Penny A is rolled along the edge of penny B to position C. Will the figure of Lincoln be upright or upside down at C? upright

Additional Answer

Mini-Lab

b.

Trace each figure. Draw all lines of symmetry.

1   **2**    **3**

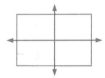      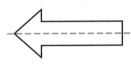

You can also use a MIRA® or paper folding to find the reflection.

Example 4 *Problem Solving*

Design   The art club is making reflection neckties to sell to raise money for art supplies. They make a pattern for each design. Create a reflection design for the figure at the right.

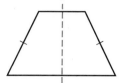

- Copy the design on tracing paper. Fold the paper along the vertical line so the figure is on the outside.

- Use another color to trace all parts you see through the paper.

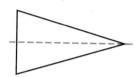

- Open the paper. The colored parts are the reflection of the original design.

When you turn your compass completely around, it forms a circle. A circle contains 360°. If a figure can be turned less than 360° about its center and it looks like the original, then the figure has **rotational symmetry**.

original   90° turn   180° turn   270° turn   360° turn

Lesson 5-5 Symmetry   **193**

More Examples

Copy the figure. Draw all lines of symmetry.

For Example 1

For Example 2

For Example 3

For Example 4

Sketch the four figures that would result by reflecting an isosceles trapezoid about each of its sides.

Teaching Tip   In Example 1, point out that the diagonals of a rectangle are not lines of symmetry. While each divides the rectangle into two congruent triangles, you cannot fold along the diagonal and have the two halves match. Have students check by folding a 3 × 5 index card along a diagonal.

Checking for Understanding

Exercises 1-3 are designed to help you assess students' understanding through reading, writing, speaking, and modeling. You should work through these exercises with your students and then monitor their work on Guided Practice Exercises 4-7.

Reteaching Activity

Using Models   Give students regular polygons cut from construction paper. Have them fold the figures to discover all possible lines of symmetry. Inform students that the point where the lines of symmetry intersect is the center point. Now have them repeat the steps of the second mini-lab using their polygons.

Study Guide Masters, p. 43

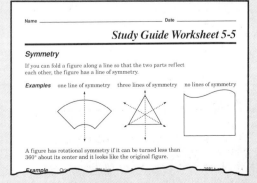

193

Close

Have students draw examples of figures having line symmetry and others having rotational symmetry.

3 PRACTICE/APPLY

Assignment Guide
Maximum: 8–22
Minimum: 8–13, 17–22

For **Extra Practice,** see p. 594.

Additional Answers

1. In line symmetry, one half of the figure is a reflection of the other half.

2. Sample answer:

4.

5.  6.

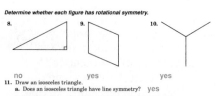

Mini-Lab

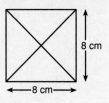

Work with a partner.
Materials: straightedge, pin, tracing paper

- Draw a square that is 8 centimeters on each side. Then draw its diagonals.

- Place a piece of tracing paper over the square and trace it.

- The point where the diagonals meet is the center point. Place a pin through the center points to hold the two figures together.

- Turn the top figure. Make a note of how many times the top matches the bottom.

Talk About It

a. How many times did the top figure match the bottom in a full turn? *Caution: Don't count the original position twice.* **4 times**

b. Divide 360° by the number of times it matched. This is the first angle of rotation. What are the other angles of rotation?

b. 90°; 180°; 270°; 360°

Checking for Understanding

Communicating Mathematics

Read and study the lesson to answer each question.

1. **Write** a sentence to tell how a reflection is related to line symmetry. See margin.
2. **Draw** a shape that has both line symmetry and rotational symmetry. See margin.
3. **Tell** how many degrees are in a full turn. 360

Guided Practice

Trace each figure. Determine if the figure has line symmetry. If so, draw the lines of reflection. For answers to Exercises 4-6, see margin.

4.   5.   6.

7. Which of the figures in Exercises 4-6 have rotational symmetry? **all of them**

Classroom Vignette

"If students have difficulty tracing, (paper too thick to see through), they can use small mirrors to establish the location of each line of symmetry."

Suetta Gladfelter

Suetta Gladfelter, Teacher
Caroline Middle School, Milford VA

Exercises

Independent Practice Trace each figure. Determine if the figure has line symmetry. If so, draw the lines of reflection. For answers to Exercises 8-10, see margin.

8.   9.    10.

Determine if each figure has rotational symmetry.

11.   12.   13.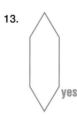

yes   yes   yes

15. rhombus, parallelogram, rectangle, square; See students' work.

14. Which of the quadrilaterals you have studied have line symmetry? Draw them. rectangle, square, rhombus, isosceles trapezoid; See students' work.

15. Which quadrilaterals have rotational symmetry? Draw them.

16. Are there any quadrilaterals that have both rotational and line symmetry? yes; rhombus, square, rectangle

Mixed Review 17. Solve $-281 - (-52) = j$. *(Lesson 3-5)* $j = -229$

18. **Statistics** Determine whether a scatter plot that related the amount of candy eaten with the number of cavities would show a positive, negative, or no relationship. *(Lesson 4-8)*

18. positive

19. **Algebra** In trapezoid *LMNO*, $m\angle L = 120°$, $m\angle M = 120°$, $m\angle N = 2x°$, and $m\angle O = 60°$. Find the value of x. *(Lesson 5-4)* 30

Problem Solving and Applications 20. **Science** List five objects in nature that have symmetry. Describe the type of symmetry they have. See students' work.

21. **Data Search** Refer to page 667. A font is the type style used in printing. Which letters of the alphabet in the Helvetica font have line symmetry? A, B, C, D, E, H, I, K, M, O, T, U, V, W, X, Y

DATA SEARCH

22. For answers to Exercises a-c, see Solutions Manual.

22. **Critical Thinking** Copy each pattern on graph paper. Shade in additional squares so that the patterns have the given lines of symmetry.

a. vertical line of symmetry

b. two diagonal lines of symmetry

c. vertical and horizontal lines of symmetry

Extending the Lesson

Using Cooperative Groups The capital letter T has a vertical line of symmetry. The capital letter D has a horizontal line of symmetry. Have students work together to find <u>words</u> that are either vertically or horizontally symmetric.

Sample answers:

--DEBBIE--

MATH (vertical)

Cooperative Learning Activity

Flip Out 5-5

Use groups of 4 or more.
Materials: Grid paper, colored pencils, spinner

♦ Label equal sections of a spinner "Above," "Below," "Left," "Right."

➡ One group member creates a figure by shading three squares in the center of a sheet of grid paper. In turn, each of the other group members spins the spinner, draws a line of reflection in the position indicated on the spinner, and draws a reflection of the previous group member's figure. No two group members should use the same color pencil. Each group member should have a chance to go first.

Glencoe Mathematics: Applications and Connections, Course 3

Alternate Assessment

Writing Have students write a few sentences describing how they would decide whether a figure had line symmetry, rotational symmetry, or neither.

Additional Answers

8.

9. no line symmetry

10.

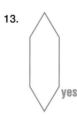

Enrichment Masters, p. 43

Name _____ Date _____

Enrichment Worksheet 5-5

Order of Rotational Symmetry

The two examples below show how to create designs with rotational symmetry. In both cases, point *P* is the center of the rotation.

Notice that the *order of rotational symmetry* is the number of times the original figure maps onto itself in a complete rotation. The first step in making the design is to divide 360° by the order of rotation.

$360° \div 8 = 45°$ Rotate 45° and trace.   Repeat 6 times.   Rotational Symmetry Order 8

$360° \div 3 = 120°$ Rotate 120° and trace.   Repeat 1 time.   Rotational Symmetry Order 3

Write the order of rotational symmetry for each design.

1. 4   2. 5   3. 9   4. 8   5. 6

Use a shape like the one shown to create a design with the given center and order of rotational symmetry.

6. Order 8   7. Order 3   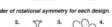   8. Order 5

9. Order 6   10. Order 4   11. Order 6

T-43

Glencoe Division, Macmillan/McGraw-Hill

NCTM Standards: 1–4, 7, 12, 13

Management Tips

For Students Have a supply of cartoons and photos available. Allow each student to choose one to enlarge.

For the Overhead Projector
Overhead Manipulative Resources provides appropriate materials for teacher or student demonstration of the activities in this Mathematics Lab.

1 FOCUS

Introducing the Lab

Have students read the first paragraph of the lesson. Ask them to name examples of other reduced or enlarged images. Sample answers: maps; scale drawings; TV screens

2 TEACH

Using Cooperative Groups
Students can split up the tasks in the first two steps but should work together on the third step.

3 PRACTICE/APPLY

Using Logical Reasoning Ask the following question: *How many times as much paint would be needed to paint the enlarged picture as compared to the amount needed for the original?*

Close

Have students describe how they could enlarge their original drawing to five times its normal size. Mark off a piece of graph paper in 5 × 5 squares and use it to draw the enlarged picture.

Cooperative Learning

5-6A Dilations

A Preview of Lesson 5-6

Objective
Draw an enlargement of a figure.

Materials
graph paper
colored pencils

When you get a picture developed, you have to specify the size you want. All the pictures come from a small piece of film, so for any size picture the image on the film must be enlarged. In mathematics, an enlargement or reduction of an image is called a **dilation**.

Try this!

Work with a partner.
- Place a piece of graph paper over a cartoon or picture you want to enlarge. Trace the picture. *It may help to put the paper against a window pane to see the picture more clearly.*
- On another piece of graph paper, use a colored pencil to draw horizontal lines every 3 squares. Then draw vertical lines every 3 squares.
- Now sketch the parts of the figure contained in each small square of your original picture onto each large square of the grid you created.

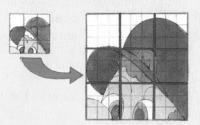

What do you think? 2. one with smaller squares

1. Measure the heights of your original figure and your enlargement. How do they compare? The enlargement is 3 times as long.
2. What type of grid do you think you would use to reduce a picture?
3. When you enlarge or reduce a figure, does the shape of the figure change? Explain. No, enlarging or reducing does not distort.
4. On graph paper, draw a rectangle that is 12 units by 6 units with these dimensions.
   a. Divide each measurement by 3. Draw the new rectangle. 4×2
   b. How does the new rectangle compare with the original in size and shape? It is $\frac{1}{9}$ as large as the original.

196   **Chapter 5** Investigations in Geometry

"When am I ever going to use this?"

A photojournalist's ability to perceive the significant in a fraction of a second and to use the camera with such speed and precision is a great creative gift. To be a good photographer, you also need to have good mathematical skills to estimate distance, calculate F-stop settings, and crop photos.

For more information, contact:
Associated Press
50 Rockefeller Plaza
New York, NY 10020

OPTIONS

Lab Manual You may wish to make copies of the blackline master on p. 53 of the *Lab Manual* for students to use as a recording sheet.

Lab Manual, p. 53

Name _____ Date _____

Mathematics Lab Worksheet

Use with page 196
Dilations

What do you think?
1. The enlargement is 3 times the original figure.
2. To reduce a picture, use a smaller grid.
3. The shape of the figure does not change, only the size is enlarged or reduced.
4. a.

5-6 Congruence and Similarity

Objective
Identify congruent figures and similar figures.

Words to Learn
congruent
similar

Have you ever looked into the back of a clock or watch? All of the gears fit finely together to keep the clock running smoothly. How can hundreds of these be made every day so that each one will work?

Each part in the clock is die cast by a computerized machine so that thousands of that part come out exactly the same size and shape. When all parts are made this way, they fit together creating a clock guaranteed to work.

In geometry, when two figures are exactly the same size and shape, we say they are **congruent.** That is, when you cut one figure out, it can fit exactly on top of the other. Congruent figures have corresponding sides and angles that are congruent.

Example 1

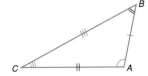
You can review congruent angles and congruent segments on pages 174-175.

Determine if △ABC is congruent to △DEF.

Compare the measures of the sides and angles.

The slashes tell us which sides are congruent.

$\overline{AB} \cong \overline{DE}$
$\overline{BC} \cong \overline{EF}$
$\overline{AC} \cong \overline{DF}$

The arcs tell us which angles are congruent.

$\angle ABC \cong \angle DEF$
$\angle BCA \cong \angle EFD$
$\angle CAB \cong \angle FDE$

All corresponding parts are congruent. So, △ABC ≅ △DEF.

Check: Trace △DEF and cut it out. Does it fit exactly on top of △ABC? *You may have to turn or flip it to get it to fit.*

You may wonder if you always have to look at both the sides and the angles to see if two figures are congruent. Wouldn't looking at one set of corresponding parts be enough?

Lesson 5-6 Congruence and Similarity **197**

For Example 1

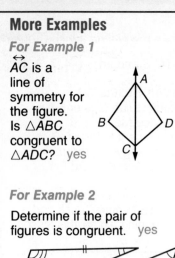

$\overleftrightarrow{AC}$ is a line of symmetry for the figure. Is $\triangle ABC$ congruent to $\triangle ADC$? yes

For Example 2

Determine if the pair of figures is congruent. yes

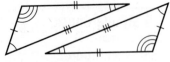

For Example 3

Determine if the pair of figures is congruent. no

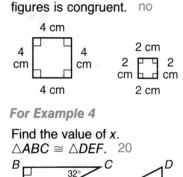

For Example 4

Find the value of x.
$\triangle ABC \cong \triangle DEF$. 20

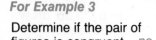

Checking for Understanding

Exercises 1–5 are designed to help you assess students' understanding through reading, writing, speaking, and modeling. You should work through these exercises with your students and then monitor their work on Guided Practice Exercises 6–9.

Error Analysis

Watch for students who write congruences incorrectly.

Prevent by pointing out that the order of the letters in a written congruence indicates the correspondences between sides and angles.

Mental Math Hint

• • • • • • • •

Which sides are corresponding? Find two pairs of congruent angles and compare the sides they include. If $\angle X \cong \angle P$ and $\angle Y \cong \angle Q$, then compare $\overline{XY}$ and $\overline{PQ}$.

Determine if each pair of figures is congruent.

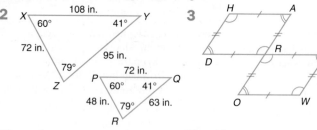

The angles are congruent. The sides are *not* congruent. The triangles are *not* congruent.

The sides are congruent. The angles are congruent. $\square HARD \cong \square WORK$
$\square$ *is the symbol for parallelogram.*

In Example 2, the triangles have the same shape, but are not congruent. Figures that have the same shape, but may differ in size are **similar** figures. To say $\triangle XYZ$ *is similar to* $\triangle PQR$, we write $\triangle XYZ \sim \triangle PQR$.

Congruent figures are also similar figures.

Congruent figures can be cut out and matched exactly. When you cut out similar triangles, other relationships can be observed.

Mini-Lab

Work with a partner.
Materials: scissors, tracing paper

• Trace each pair of figures below and cut them out.

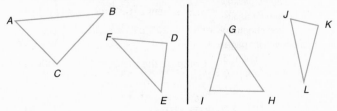

• Compare the angles in each pair of figures.
• For each pair of triangles, see if you can place one figure inside the other with an equal amount of space separating the corresponding sides in every case.

Talk About It

a. What did you find when you compared the angles?
b. If you can fit one triangle inside another with equal space separating all corresponding sides, the triangles are similar. Name the similar figures. Is this true for all figures?

a. Angles in the triangles on the left have the same measure. Those on the right have different measures.

b. $\triangle ABC \sim \triangle EFD$; no, it is only true for triangles.

OPTIONS

Reteaching Activity

Using Models Cut five pairs of congruent triangles from construction paper and mix them up. Have students find the congruent pairs and explain how they know that they have correctly matched each triangle with its partner.

Study Guide Masters, p. 44

Name _____ Date _____

Study Guide Worksheet 5-6

Congruence and Similarity

If two figures are exactly the same size and shape, they are congruent. Congruent figures have corresponding sides and corresponding angles equal.

If two figures are the same shape, they are similar. Similar figures may differ in size.

Examples Is each pair of figures congruent, similar, or neither?

You can use the relationships between the angles and sides of congruent and similar figures to find missing measures.

Example 4 *Connection*

Algebra Find the value of *x* in each pair of figures.

a. $\triangle ROB \cong \triangle STL$

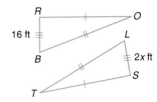

The corresponding sides are congruent.

$RB = 2x$

$16 = 2x$ $\overline{RB}$ *is 16 feet long.*

$8 = x$ *Divide each side by 2.*

b. $\square ABCD \sim \square EFGH$

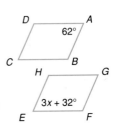

The corresponding angles are congruent, so $m\angle A = m\angle E$.

$m\angle A = m\angle E$

$62 = 3x + 32$ *Replace $m\angle A$ with 62 and $m\angle E$ with $3x + 32$.*

$30 = 3x$ *Subtract 32 from each side.*

$10 = x$ *Divide each side by 3.*

Checking for Understanding

For answers to Exercises 1-5, see margin.

Communicating Mathematics

Read and study the lesson to answer each question.

1. **Tell** what must be true for two figures to be congruent.

2. **Show** one way that you can tell if two figures are similar.

3. **Draw** two congruent parallelograms.

4. **Draw** two similar trapezoids.

5. **Write** why two congruent figures are also similar.

Guided Practice

For justifications to Exercises 6-9, see Solutions Manual.

Tell if each pair of figures is congruent, similar, or neither. Justify your answer.

6.
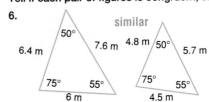
similar

7.
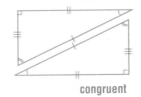
congruent

8.

neither

9.

similar

Lesson 5-6 Congruence and Similarity **199**

 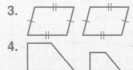
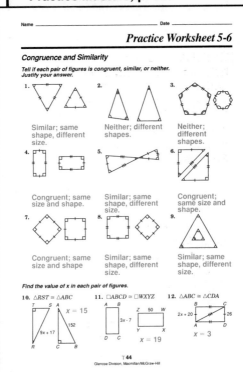
199

Exercises

For justifications to Exercises 10-13, see Solutions Manual.

Independent Practice

Tell if each pair of figures is congruent, similar, or neither. Justify your answer.

10.
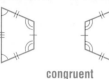
congruent

11.
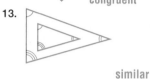
congruent

12.
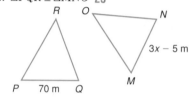
neither

13.
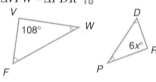
similar

Find the value of *x* in each pair of figures.

14. $\triangle PQR \cong \triangle MNO$ **25**

R   O   N

                      $3x - 5$ m

                   M

P   70 m   Q

15. $\triangle VFW \sim \triangle PDR$ **18**

V   108°   W   D
                          $6x°$ R
F   P

Mixed Review

16. Estimate $5,381 + 3,416$ first by rounding and then by front-end estimation. *(Lesson 1-3)* **8,000; 8,700**

17. Evaluate $5a^2 - (b + c)$ if $a = 3$, $b = 8$, and $c = 10$. *(Lesson 2-1)* **27**

18. Determine if the figure at the right has rotational symmetry. *(Lesson 5-5)* **yes**

Problem Solving and Applications

19. **Entertainment**   The graph shows an estimated cost of a night out for a family of four.

  a. If the charge for adults and children is the same, what is the average cost for a rock concert ticket? **$28.50**

  b. If a family of four spent about $100 on entertainment, how do you think they spent it?

19b. Family Show

20. **Critical Thinking**   In the figure at the left, $\triangle ABC$ is similar to $\triangle FGH$. Find the values of *x, y,* and *z*.

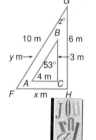

21. **Journal Entry**   Write a sentence telling some occupations that would use congruent or similar figures.

See students' work.   **20. $x = 8$; $y = 5$; $z = 53$**

200   **Chapter 5** Investigations in Geometry

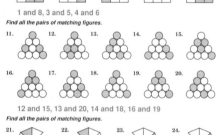
200

OPTIONS

Extending the Lesson

Using Cooperative Groups   The geoboard shown here has been divided into four congruent quadrilaterals. Have students work in small groups to find as many ways as possible to divide a geoboard into four congruent quadrilaterals.

Cooperative Learning Activity

Fits to a T(riangle) **5-6**

Number of players: 2
Materials: Tracing paper

◆ Each partner traces the figure at the right five times on a sheet of tracing paper and then draws or traces other figures all around these five. The object is to make it difficult for your partner to tell which five figures are congruent to the figure on this card.

➡ Trade sheets of tracing paper with your partner. Try to be the first to identify the five figures that are congruent to the figure on this card. (Trace the figure on this card onto a second sheet of tracing paper. If this figure fits exactly on top of one of the figures on your partner's paper, the figures are congruent.)

Glencoe Mathematics: Applications and Connections, Course 3

Cooperative Learning

5-6B Constructing Congruent Triangles

A Follow-Up of Lesson 5-6

Objective
Construct a triangle congruent to a given triangle.

Materials
compass
straightedge

Mapmakers, or cartographers, often need to copy figures from one place to another. They often use a compass and straightedge to do this.

Try this!

Work with a partner. Construct a triangle congruent to △ABC.

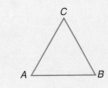

- Use a straightedge to draw a line. Put a point on the line. Label it *G*.

- Set your compass to the same width as the length of $\overline{AB}$. Put the compass point at *G*. Draw an arc to intersect the line. Call this intersection *H*.

- Set your compass to the same width as the length of $\overline{AC}$. Put the compass at *G* and draw an arc above the line.

- Set your compass to the same width as the length of $\overline{BC}$. Put the compass at *H* and draw an arc above the line to intersect the arc you just drew. Label this point *I*.

- Draw $\overline{HI}$ and $\overline{IG}$.

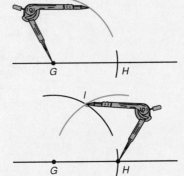

What do you think?   2. Corresponding angles are congruent.

1. How do the lengths of $\overline{AB}$, $\overline{BC}$, and $\overline{CA}$ compare to the lengths of $\overline{GH}$, $\overline{HI}$, and $\overline{IG}$? $AB \cong GH; BC \cong HI; CA \cong IG$
2. How do the corresponding angles of the two triangles compare?
3. What is the relationship of △ABC and △GHI? $\triangle ABC \cong \triangle GHI$

Mathematics Lab 5-6B Constructing Congruent Triangles **201**

Mathematics Lab 5-6B

NCTM Standards: 1, 3, 4, 12, 13

Management Tips

For Students Partners can alternate steps of the construction. They should then repeat the construction, reversing roles.

For the Overhead Projector
Overhead Manipulative Resources provides appropriate materials for teacher or student demonstration of the activities in this Mathematics Lab.

1 FOCUS

Introducing the Lab
Ask students to divide an equilateral triangle into 2, 3, and 4 congruent triangles.

2 TEACH

Using Models When students have completed the construction, have them compare their triangle with the original by overlaying the two sheets of paper and holding them up to a light source.

3 PRACTICE/APPLY

Using Logical Reasoning Help students see that two triangles must be congruent if they know that all three pairs of corresponding sides are congruent. If the corresponding sides are congruent, then the corresponding angles must also be congruent.

Close

Ask students to explain why these triangles are congruent.

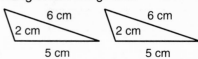

The sides of the first are congruent to the corresponding sides of the second.

OPTIONS

Lab Manual You may wish to make copies of the blackline master on p. 54 of the *Lab Manual* for students to use as a recording sheet.

Lab Manual, p. 54

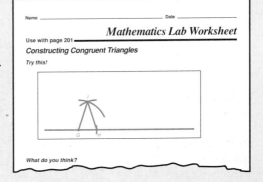

Lesson Resources
- Study Guide Master 5-7
- Practice Master 5-7
- Enrichment Master 5-7
- Evaluation Master, Quiz B, p. 43
- Group Activity Card 5-7

Transparency 5-7 contains the 5-Minute Check and a teaching aid for this lesson.

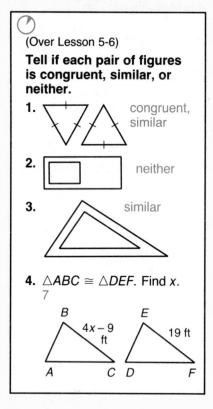

(Over Lesson 5-6)

Tell if each pair of figures is congruent, similar, or neither.

1. congruent, similar

2. neither

3. similar

4. △ABC ≅ △DEF. Find x.
7

B E
4x − 9 ft   19 ft
A   C D   F

1 FOCUS

Motivating the Lesson

Activity Sketch the rectangle below which is covered by congruent right triangles. Ask students to find other congruent figures with which a rectangle can be covered.

5-7 Transformations and M. C. Escher

Objective
Create Escher-like drawings by using translations and rotations.

Words to Learn
tessellation
transformation
translation
rotation

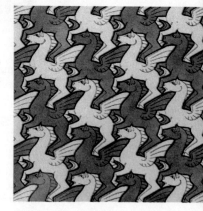

©M.C. Escher/Cordon Art—Baarn—Holland
Collection Haags Gemeentemuseum—The Hauge

Maurits Cornelis Escher (1898-1972) was a Dutch artist famous for his repetitive, interlocking patterns. His works look like paintings but were done by woodcarving and lithographs.

Escher's designs are made from variations on tiling patterns called **tessellations.** A floor covered by square tiles is an example of a tessellation of squares. By modifying these squares, you can create an Escher-like drawing.

Tessellations can be modified by using **transformations.** Transformations are movements of geometric figures. One transformation commonly used is a slide, or **translation,** of a figure.

A square can be modified by making a change on one side and then translating that change to the opposite side.

You can create more complex designs starting with square tessellations and making changes on both pairs of sides.

Example 1

Make an Escher-like drawing using the modification shown at the right.

Draw a square. Copy the pattern shown. Translate the change shown on the top side to the bottom side.

Now translate the change shown on the left side to the right side to complete the pattern unit.

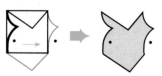

OPTIONS

Bell Ringer

A triangle was transformed using a translation, a rotation, a dilation, and a reflection. Only one of the transformations resulted in a triangle which is not congruent to the first. Which one? dilation

Repeat this pattern on a tessellation of squares. *It is sometimes helpful to complete one pattern unit, cut it out, and trace it for the other units.*

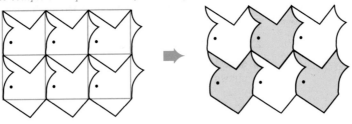

Other tessellations can be modified by using changes with a **rotation.** Rotations are transformations that involve a turn about the vertices of the base figure.

base figure	change	change one side	rotate to change another

Example 2

Make an Escher-like drawing using a tessellation of equilateral triangles and the rotation shown at the right.

This involves one rotation.
Draw an equilateral triangle.
Copy the change shown.

Rotate the triangle so you can copy the change on the side indicated.

Now repeat this pattern unit on a tessellation of equilateral triangles.

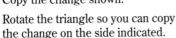

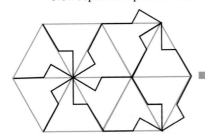 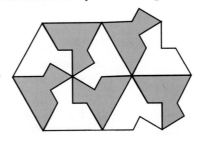

Lesson 5-7 Transformations and M.C. Escher **203**

Using Connections Show students that Escher transformations simply alter borders between figures, making them interlock like jigsaw puzzle pieces.

More Examples

For Example 1

Make an Escher-like drawing using these translations.

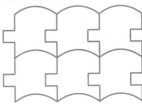

For Example 2

Make an Escher-like drawing using a tessellation of equilateral triangles and this rotation.

Checking for Understanding

Exercises 1–3 are designed to help you assess students' understanding through reading, writing, speaking, and modeling. You should work through these exercises with your students and then monitor their work on Guided Practice Exercises 4–7.

Close

Have students create their own square modifications, exchange them with other students, and create Escher-like drawings from the modifications they receive.

Reteaching Activity

Using Patterns Most students will have an easier time making tessellations with squares than with triangles. Have students begin with an array of squares. Then have them replace all the vertical segments with the same pattern. You may also choose to have them replace all the horizontal segments.

Study Guide Masters, p. 45

Name _____ Date _____

Study Guide Worksheet 5-7

Transformations and M.C. Escher

M.C. Escher (1898–1972) was a Dutch artist famous for his repetitive interlocking patterns. You can use transformations to create Escher-like patterns.

Slides and rotations are examples of transformations.

Example 1 Use slides to modify a tessellation of squares.

Tessellation of squares	Make a change on the top of the square. Slide the change to the bottom of the square.	Make a change on one side of the square. Slide the change to the other side of the square.	Repeat the pattern.

3 PRACTICE/APPLY

Alternate Assessment

Speaking Show a tessellation composed of Escher-like figures. Have students name the simple geometric figure on which it is based and describe how the figure was modified to make the tessellation.

Additional Answer

3.

Practice Masters, p. 45

Name _____ Date _____

Practice Worksheet 5-7

Transformations and M.C. Escher

Make an Escher-like drawing for each pattern described. Use a tessellation of two rows of three squares as your base.

1.

2.

3.

4. Tell whether each pattern in Exercises 1–3 involves a translation or a rotation.   Each is a translation.

Make an Escher-like drawing for each pattern described. For squares, use a tessellation of two rows of three squares as your base. For triangles, use a tessellation of two rows of five equilateral triangles as your base.

5.

6.

T45

204

Checking for Understanding

Communicating Mathematics

Read and study the lesson to answer each question.   translation, rotation

1. **Tell** two transformations that Escher used in his drawings.

2. A tessellation is a repetitive, interlocking pattern.

2. **Write** a sentence to explain what a tessellation is.

3. **Show** how you would create the unit for the pattern shown at the right. See margin.

Guided Practice

For answers to Exercises 4-6, see Solutions Manual.

Make an Escher-like drawing for each pattern described. Use a tessellation of two rows of three squares as your base.

4.

5.

6. (square with V notch and arrow)

7. Tell whether each pattern in Exercises 4-6 involves translations or rotations.   Exercise 4: translation; 5: rotation; 6: two translations

Exercises

For answers to Exercises 8-13, see Solutions Manual.

Independent Practice

Make an Escher-like drawing for each pattern described. For squares, use a tessellation of two rows of three squares as your base. For triangles, use a tessellation of two rows of five equilateral triangles as your base.

8.

9.

10.

11.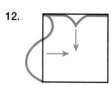

12. (square with curve and arrow)

13.

Mixed Review

14. Solve $\frac{a}{15} - 5 = 1$. *(Lesson 2-7)* 90

15. **Statistics** Refer to page 136. Make a histogram of the potato chip data. Use reasonable intervals. *(Lesson 4-2)* See Solutions Manual.

16. Tell if the pair of figures at the right are congruent, similar, or neither. *(Lesson 5-6)* congruent

204   **Chapter 5** Investigations in Geometry

OPTIONS

Meeting Needs of Middle School Students

Middle school students need to know what is expected of them. Set clear goals and objectives for students. Tell them your homework, grading, and discipline policies. Let them know how you expect them to behave and to perform academically, and apply your standards consistently.

17. **Critical Thinking** Look at the tessellation at the right.

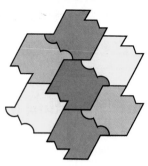

a. What type of base figure was modified to produce the pattern unit? hexagon

b. What transformation was used to create the pattern unit? rotation

c. Describe each change used to create the pattern unit. **See margin.**

Additional Answer

17c.

Rotate the two changes about the midpoint of the respective side of the regular hexagon.

18. **Art** The Escher lithograph below, entitled *Study of Regular Division of the Plane with Reptiles,* was created in 1939. Study the figures carefully.

©M.C. Escher/Cordon Art—Baarn—Holland
Collection Haags Gemeentemuseum—The Hauge

a. Trace the outside edge of one pattern unit. See students' work.

b. What geometric shape do you think was used for this tessellation?

b. hexagon

c. What transformation did this use? rotation

19. **Portfolio Suggestion** Select your favorite word problem from this chapter and place your solution to it in your portfolio. Attach a note explaining why it is your favorite. See students' work.

20. **Computer Connection** The LOGO program below will tessellate a square design to fill the computer screen. The commands that create the design unit are in blue. For answers to Exercises a-b, see Solutions Manual.

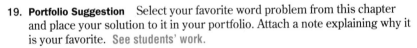

```
PU SETXY -100 100 PD HT
REPEAT 10[REPEAT 10[REPEAT 4[FD 20 RT 90]
FD 10 RT 45 REPEAT 4[FD 14.14 RT 90] LT 45 BK 10 RT 90
FD 20 LT 90] PU LT 90 FD 200 RT 90 BK 20 PD]
```

a. Sketch the pattern unit.
b. Sketch a portion of the tessellation.

Enrichment Masters, p. 45

Name _____   Date _____

Enrichment Worksheet 5-7

Compass Creations

The designs on this page can all be constructed using just a compass and straightedge. Copy the designs and color them to make symmetrical patterns. Then create two more designs of your own.

1.   2.

3.   4.

5.   6.

Check students' constructions.

T45

Extending the Lesson

Using Research Have students read more about Maurits Escher and the connections he found between mathematics and art. In addition to tessellations, Escher created impossible worlds where water runs uphill and people climb stairs forever. Have students display Escher prints, describe the apparent scenes, and attempt to explain how the artist created them.

Cooperative Learning Activity

Cover Story **5-7**

Use groups of 2.
Materials: Cardboard, rulers, scissors, colored pencils

♦ Suppose that you and your partner have been asked to create a tessellation that will appear on the front cover of your school's arts magazine. There are two requirements: Your design must be based on one of the shapes below, and it must be suitable for a cover that measures 8.5 by 11 inches.

➡ Decide what shape to base your design on and decide on a size for the basic figure. Draw the basic figure on cardboard and then cut it out. Create your design by repeatedly tracing the cardboard figure on a sheet of paper. When you have completely filled the page without overlapping any figures, shade the figures using colored pencils.

Share your work with other pairs.

Using the Chapter Study Guide and Review

The Chapter Study Guide and Review begins with a section on Communicating Mathematics. This includes questions that review the new terms and concepts that were introduced in the chapter.

Then, the Skills and Concepts presented in the chapter are reviewed using a side-by-side format. Encourage students to refer to the Objectives and Examples on the left as they complete the Review Exercises on the right.

The Chapter Study Guide and Review ends with problems that review Applications and Problem Solving.

Additional Answers

9. If a figure can be turned less than 360° about its center and it looks like the original, then the figure has rotational symmetry.

10. Sample answer:

Communicating Mathematics

Choose a word or symbol from the list at the right to correctly complete each statement.   2. rotations   4. line symmetry

1. A(n) __?__ is a line that intersects two other lines. transversal
2. __?__ are transformations that involve a turn about a given point.
3. A parallelogram that has four congruent sides is a(n) __?__. rhombus
4. A figure that can be folded exactly in half is said to have __?__.
5. __?__ angles have measures greater than 90° and less than 180°.
6. The symbol __?__ means *is parallel to*. ‖
7. The symbol __?__ means *is perpendicular to*. ⊥
8. The symbol __?__ means *is similar to*. ~
9. Tell how to determine if a figure has rotational symmetry. See margin.
10. Draw a scalene obtuse triangle. See margin.

rhombus
trapezoid
rotational
 symmetry
line symmetry
transversal
acute
obtuse
rotations
⊥
~
‖

Self Assessment

Objectives and Examples	Review Exercises

● identify lines that are parallel *(Lesson 5-1)*

Name the parallel segments in the figure.

$\overline{AB} \parallel \overline{DC}, \overline{AD} \parallel \overline{BC}$

Name the parallel segments in each figure.

11.

12.

$\overline{WX} \parallel \overline{ZY}, \overline{ZW} \parallel \overline{YX}$ $\overline{DH} \parallel \overline{NM}$

● classify triangles *(Lesson 5-3)*

Classify the triangle by its sides and by its angles.

The triangle is isosceles and acute.

Classify each triangle by its sides and by its angles.

13.   14.

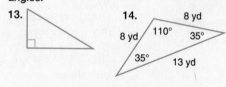

scalene, right   isosceles, obtuse

Objectives and Examples

● classify quadrilaterals *(Lesson 5-4)*

Identify all names that describe the quadrilateral.

parallelogram, rectangle

● explore line symmetry *(Lesson 5-5)*

Draw all lines of symmetry for a rectangle.

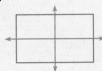

● explore rotational symmetry *(Lesson 5-5)*

A figure has rotational symmetry if it can be turned less than 360° about its center and looks like the original.

● identify congruent and similar figures *(Lesson 5-6)*

Figures that have the same size and shape are congruent.

Figures that have the same shape, but *not* the same size are similar.

● create Escher-like drawings by using translations and rotations *(Lesson 5-7)*

An example of a tessellation of squares is a floor covered by tiles. By modifying these squares, an Escher-like drawing can be made.

Review Exercises

Sketch each figure on your paper. Let Q=quadrilateral, P=parallelogram, R=rectangle, S=square, RH=rhombus, and T=trapezoid. Write all letters inside the figure that describe it. 15. Q, P, RH   16. Q, T

15.   16.

Copy each figure. Determine if the figure has line symmetry. If so, draw the lines of symmetry. See margin.

17.   18.

Determine if each figure has rotational symmetry.   19. yes   20. no

19.   20.

Tell if each pair of figures are congruent, similar, or neither.   21. similar   22. neither

21.   22.

Make an Escher-like drawing for each pattern described. Use a tessellation of two rows of three squares as your base.

23.   24.

For answers to Exercises 23-24, see Solutions Manual.

Chapter 5 Study Guide and Review   **207**

Additional Answers

17.

18.

Evaluation Masters, pp. 41–42

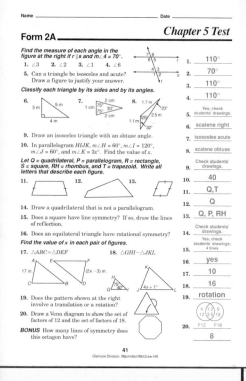

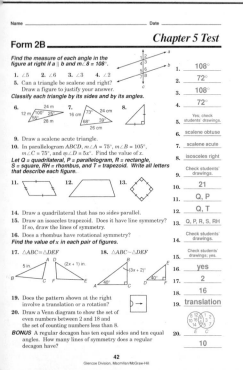

Applications and Problem Solving

25. Traffic The shape of a STOP sign is an octagon. How many pairs of edges in a STOP sign are parallel? *(Lesson 5-1)* **4 pairs**

26. A 24-foot ladder is leaning against a house. The base of the ladder is 8 feet from the house. *(Lesson 5-3)*

   a. Draw a sketch of this situation. **See margin.**

   b. What type of triangle is formed by the house, ground, and ladder? **scalene, right triangle**

27. The 48 members of the senior class voted on their choice of a class trip. They could choose Atlantic City (A), Barnegat Bay (B), or Cape May (C). They could vote for as many as all three choices. The results were displayed as the Venn diagram shown at the right. Use the diagram to find out which location received the most total votes. *(Lesson 5-2)* **Cape May (C)**

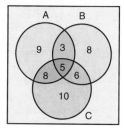

28. Hobbies Olivedale Senior Center offers different activities each quarter for their members. Twenty-one members have signed up for aerobics classes. Thirty members have signed up for healthful cooking classes. Of the members that have signed up for classes, six have signed up for both activities. *(Lesson 5-2)*

   a. Make a Venn diagram to show how many have signed up for activities at the Olivedale Senior Center. **See Solutions Manual.**

   b. What is the total number of members that have signed up for these two classes? **45 members**

Curriculum Connection Projects

- **Music and Entertainment** Find how many students in your class have a VCR, a CD player, a Walkman-type cassette player, or none of these. Draw a Venn diagram of your results. **See students' work.**

- **Language Arts** Survey the adults in your school to find how many regularly read novels, poetry, magazines, newspapers, or none of these. Draw a Venn diagram of your results. **See students' work.**

Read More About It

- DeClements, Barthe, and Greimes, Christopher, *Double Trouble*

- White, Laurence B., Jr. and Broehel, Ray, *Optical Illusions*

- Demi, *Demi's Reflective Fables*

208   Chapter 5 Study Guide and Review

Additional Answer

26a.

24 ft

8 ft

5 Test

Find the measure of each angle in the figure at the right if $m \parallel n$ and $m\angle 4 = 40°$.

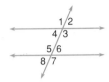

1. $\angle 1$ **140**   2. $\angle 2$ **40**   3. $\angle 3$ **140**   4. $\angle 5$ **140**

5. Can a triangle be isosceles and obtuse? Draw a figure to justify your answer. **Yes; see Solutions Manual.**

Classify each triangle by its sides and by its angles.

6.

equilateral, acute

7.
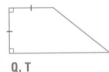
6 m 64° 4 m
38° 78°
5.75 m
scalene, acute

8.

16 in.
16° 58°
11.75 in. 106° 3.6 in.
scalene, obtuse

9. Draw an isosceles right triangle. **See Solutions Manual.**

10. In rhombus $DEFG$, $m\angle D = 66°$, $m\angle E = 114°$, $m\angle F = 66°$, and $m\angle G = 2x°$. Find the value of x. **57**

Let Q = quadrilateral, P = parallelogram, R = rectangle, S = square, RH = rhombus, and T = trapezoid. Write all letters that describe each figure.

11.

Q, P, R

12.
Q, T

13.
Q, P, R, S, RH

14. Draw a parallelogram that is not a rectangle, a square, or a rhombus. **See Solutions Manual.**

15. Does an equilateral triangle have line symmetry? If so, draw the lines of symmetry.

16. Does a rectangle have rotational symmetry? **yes**

15. Yes; See Solutions Manual.

Find the value of x for each pair of figures.

17. $\triangle ABC \cong \triangle DEF$ **16**

A
F 2x − 4 m E
C 28 m B D

18. $\triangle HMB \sim \triangle TKR$ **15**

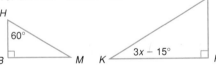
H
60°
B M K 3x − 15° R T

19. Does the pattern shown at the right involve a translation or a rotation? **rotation**

20. Draw a Venn diagram to show the set of odd numbers from 1 through 15 and the set of counting numbers from 1 through 10. **See Solutions Manual.**

See Solutions Manual.

Bonus Draw a figure that has line symmetry but not rotational symmetry.

Using the Chapter Test

This page may be used as a chapter test or another chapter review.

Study Guide and Review

Evaluation Masters, pp. 37–38

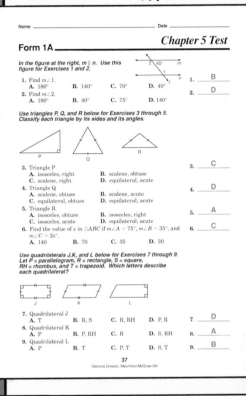

Name _____ Date _____

Form 1A _____ *Chapter 5 Test*

In the figure at the right, $m \parallel n$. Use this figure for Exercises 1 and 2.

1. Find $m\angle 1$.
   A. 180° B. 140° C. 70° D. 40° **1.** B
2. Find $m\angle 2$.
   A. 180° B. 40° C. 75° D. 140° **2.** D

Use triangles P, Q, and R below for Exercises 3 through 5. Classify each triangle by its sides and its angles.

3. Triangle P
   A. isosceles, right B. scalene, obtuse
   C. scalene, right D. equilateral, acute **3.** C
4. Triangle Q
   A. scalene, obtuse B. scalene, acute
   C. equilateral, obtuse D. equilateral, acute **4.** D
5. Triangle R
   A. isosceles, obtuse B. isosceles, right
   C. isosceles, acute D. equilateral, acute **5.** A
6. Find the value of x in $\triangle ABC$ if $m\angle A = 75°$, $m\angle B = 35°$, and $m\angle C = 2x°$.
   A. 140 B. 70 C. 35 D. 30 **6.** C

Use quadrilaterals J, K, and L below for Exercises 7 through 9. Let P = parallelogram, R = rectangle, S = square, RH = rhombus, and T = trapezoid. Which letters describe each quadrilateral?

7. Quadrilateral J
   A. T B. R, S C. R, RH D. P, R **7.** D
8. Quadrilateral K
   A. P B. P, RH C. R D. S, RH **8.** A
9. Quadrilateral L
   A. P B. T C. P, T D. S, T **9.** B

37

Glencoe Division, Macmillan/McGraw-Hill

Name _____ Date _____

Chapter 5 Test, Form 1A (continued)

10. In rhombus $PQRS$, $m\angle P = 55°$, $m\angle Q = x°$, $m\angle R = 55°$, and $m\angle S = x°$. Find the value of x.
    A. 125 B. 45 C. 115 D. 55 **10.** A
11. How many lines of symmetry does an isosceles triangle have?
    A. 6 B. 4 C. 2 D. 1 **11.** D
12. How many lines of symmetry does an equilateral triangle have?
    A. 4 B. 6 C. 3 D. 5 **12.** C
13. Which figure does *not* have rotational symmetry?
    A. square B. rectangle
    C. scalene triangle D. equilateral triangle **13.** C
14. Which figure has both rotational and line symmetry?
    A. isosceles triangle B. square
    C. trapezoid D. scalene triangle **14.** B
15. In Figure 1, what is the relationship between the figures?
    A. congruent B. similar
    C. congruent, similar D. none **15.** C
16. In Figure 2, what is the relationship between the figures?
    A. congruent B. similar
    C. congruent, similar D. none **16.** B
17. In Figure 3, what is the relationship between the figures?
    A. congruent B. similar
    C. congruent, similar D. none **17.** D
18. Suppose you want to make an Escher-like drawing using the modification shown at the right. Which of the drawings below would it be?
    A. B. C. D. **18.** A
19. Of the 25 members in the math club, 15 like to solve equations, 12 prefer geometric constructions, and 3 like to do both. How many like to solve equations, but do not like geometric constructions?
    A. 15 B. 12 C. 12 D. 13 **19.** C
20. In Exercise 19, how many do not like either solving equations or geometric constructions?
    A. 1 B. 0 C. 6 D. 9 **20.** A
BONUS If $m \parallel n$, find the value of x when $m\angle 1 = 110°$ and $m\angle 2 = (2x + 10)°$.
    A. 30 B. 40 C. 60 D. 70 A

38

Glencoe Division, Macmillan/McGraw-Hill

Test and Review Generator software is provided in Apple, IBM, and Macintosh versions. You may use this software to create your own tests or worksheets, based on the needs of your students.

The **Performance Assessment Booklet** provides an alternate assessment for evaluating student progress. An assessment for this chapter can be found on pages 9–10.

6 Patterns and Number Sense

Previewing the Chapter

This chapter develops basic ideas in number theory. Patterns are stressed. Students investigate prime factorization, greatest common factor, and least common multiple, and then apply these concepts to fraction simplification and probability. Rational numbers are introduced, their relationship to decimals is investigated, and methods of comparing and ordering them are developed. In the **problem-solving strategy** lesson, students learn to solve problems by making a list.

Lesson	Lesson Objectives	NCTM Standards	State/Local Objectives
6-1	Use divisibility rules for 2, 3, 4, 5, 6, 8, 9, and 10.	1–8	
6-2	Find the prime factorization of a composite number.	1–7, 9	
6-2B	Discover the relationship of relatively prime numbers.	1–5, 8, 12	
6-3	Solve problems by making an organized list.	1–8	
6-4	Find the greatest common factor of two or more integers.	1–9	
6-5	Identify and simplify rational numbers.	1–7, 9, 12	
6-6	Express rational numbers as decimals and terminating decimals as fractions.	1–7, 9, 13	
6-7	Express repeating decimals as fractions.	1–9, 12	
6-8	Find the probability of a simple event.	1–4, 6, 7, 11, 12	
6-9	Find the least common multiple of two or more integers.	1–9	
6-10A	Discover ways to find a rational number between two given rational numbers.	1–8, 10	
6-10	Compare and order rational numbers expressed as fractions and/or decimals.	1–5, 7, 10	
6-11	Express numbers in scientific notation.	1–5, 13	

Organizing the Chapter

A complete, 1-page lesson plan is provided for each lesson in the Lesson Plans Masters Booklet.

LESSON PLANNING GUIDE

Lesson	Materials/ Manipulatives	Extra Practice (Student Edition)	Study Guide	Practice	Enrichment	Evaluation	Technology	Lab Manual	Multicultural Activities	Application and Interdisciplinary Activities	Transparencies	Group Activity Cards
6-1	calculator	p. 595	p. 46	p. 46	p. 46					p. 6	6-1	6-1
6-2	calculator	p. 595	p. 47	p. 47	p. 47						6-2	6-2
6-2B	colored pencils, tracing paper							p. 55				
6-3			p. 48	p. 48	p. 48						6-3	6-3
6-4		p. 596	p. 49	p. 49	p. 49		p. 20				6-4	6-4
6-5		p. 596	p. 50	p. 50	p. 50						6-5	6-5
6-6	calculator	p. 596	p. 51	p. 51	p. 51	Quiz A, p. 52					6-6	6-6
6-7	calculator	p. 597	p. 52	p. 52	p. 52						6-7	6-7
6-8	dice or number cubes	p. 597	p. 53	p. 53	p. 53					p. 20	6-8	6-8
6-9	colored pencils, calculator	p. 597	p. 54	p. 54	p. 54						6-9	6-9
6-10A	inch ruler, typing paper, calculator							p. 56 p. 57				
6-10		p. 598	p. 55	p. 55	p. 55						6-10	6-10
6-11	scientific calculator	p. 598	p. 56	p. 56	p. 56	Quiz B, p. 52	p. 6		p. 6		6-11	6-11
Study Guide and Review	newspaper, atlas		Multiple Choice Test, Forms 1A and 1B, pp. 46–49 Free Response Test, Forms 2A and 2B, pp. 50–51 Cumulative Review, p. 53 (free response)									
Test			Cumulative Test, p. 54 (multiple choice)									

Blackline Masters Booklets

Pacing Guide: Option I (Chapters 1–12) - 14 days; Option II (Chapters 1–13) - 13 days; Option III (Chapters 1–14) - 13 days
You may wish to refer to the complete **Course Planning Guides** on page T25.

OTHER CHAPTER RESOURCES

Student Edition
Chapter Opener, pp. 210–211
Save Planet Earth, p. 223
Mid-Chapter Review, p. 229
Portfolio Suggestions, pp. 229, 244
Academic Skills Test, pp. 252–253

Manipulatives
Overhead Manipulative Resources
Middle School Mathematics Manipulative Kit

Software/Technology
Interactive Mathematics Tools (Macintosh)
Test and Review Generator (IBM, Apple, Macintosh)
Teacher's Guide for Software Resources

Other Supplements
Transparency 6–0
Performance Assessment, pp. 11–12
Glencoe Mathematics Professional Series
Lesson Plans, pp. 60–72

INTERDISCIPLINARY BULLETIN BOARD

Transportation Connection

Objective   Use scientific notation to write numbers relating to travel and transportation.

How To Use It   Have students research and display at least ten statistics on travel and transportation, using scientific notation. Encourage students to display data creatively and to use only statistics best expressed in scientific notation rather than standard notation.

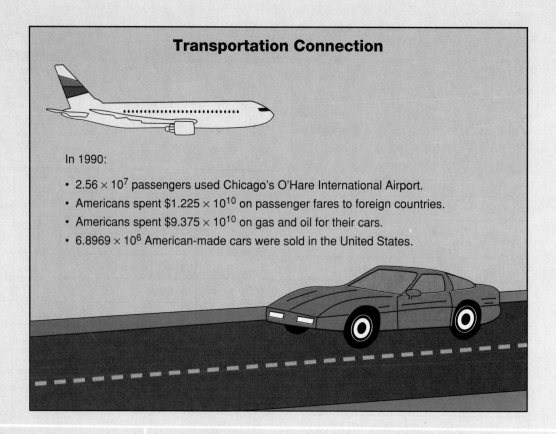

Transportation Connection

In 1990:

- 2.56×10^7 passengers used Chicago's O'Hare International Airport.
- Americans spent $\$1.225 \times 10^{10}$ on passenger fares to foreign countries.
- Americans spent $\$9.375 \times 10^{10}$ on gas and oil for their cars.
- 6.8969×10^6 American-made cars were sold in the United States.

APPLICATIONS AND CONNECTIONS

Applications	Lesson	Example	Exercise
Entertainment	6-1		34
Industrial Technology	6-4		31
Physical Fitness	6-4		32
School	6-5		35
Housing	6-5		36
Marketing	6-8		35
Packaging	6-9		36
Sports	6-10	1	
Travel	6-10		36
Smart Shopping	6-10		37
Meteorology	6-10		39
Connections			
Computer	6-1		36
Algebra	6-2	2	
Number Sense	6-2		33, 36
Algebra	6-2		35, 37
Number Sense	6-4		33
Number Sense	6-5		34
Measurement	6-6		40
Algebra	6-7	3	
Geometry	6-7		37
Number Sense	6-7		40
Geometry	6-8	X	
Number Sense	6-8		36, 37
Number Sense	6-9		37, 38
Algebra	6-9		39
Statistics	6-10	5	

TEAM ACTIVITIES

Multicultural Experiences

Outside Field Trips   Divisibility rules can be used to determine how odd-sized materials can be cut to produce the least waste. Visit a lumber yard or fabric store to see how this principle can be applied.

Visit the offices of the state lottery or companies sponsoring contests to see how prize-winning probabilities are determined.

In-Class Speakers   The f-stop on a camera is a fraction comparing the size of the lens opening to the focal length of the camera. Invite a photographer to explain this relationship to students.

A scientist can discuss applications of scientific notation.

SUPPLEMENTARY BLACKLINE MASTER BOOKLETS

Some of the blackline masters for enhancing this chapter are shown below.

Application and Interdisciplinary Activity Masters, pp. 6, 20

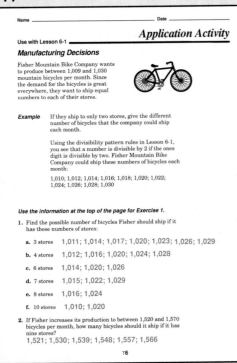

Name _____ Date _____

Use with Lesson 6-1 _____

Application Activity

Manufacturing Decisions

Fisher Mountain Bike Company wants to produce between 1,009 and 1,030 mountain bicycles per month. Since the demand for the bicycles is great everywhere, they want to ship equal numbers to each of their stores.

Example If they ship to only two stores, give the different number of bicycles that the company could ship each month.

Using the divisibility pattern rules in Lesson 6-1, you see that a number is divisible by 2 if the ones digit is divisible by two. Fisher Mountain Bike Company could ship these numbers of bicycles each month:

1,010; 1,012; 1,014; 1,016; 1,018; 1,020; 1,022; 1,024; 1,026; 1,028; 1,030

Use the information at the top of the page for Exercise 1.

1. Find the possible number of bicycles Fisher should ship if it has these numbers of stores:

   a. 3 stores   1,011; 1,014; 1,017; 1,020; 1,023; 1,026; 1,029
   b. 4 stores   1,012; 1,016; 1,020; 1,024; 1,028
   c. 6 stores   1,014; 1,020; 1,026
   d. 7 stores   1,015; 1,022; 1,029
   e. 8 stores   1,016; 1,024
   f. 10 stores   1,010; 1,020

2. If Fisher increases its production to between 1,520 and 1,570 bicycles per month, how many bicycles should it ship if it has nine stores?
   1,521; 1,530; 1,539; 1,548; 1,557; 1,566

T6

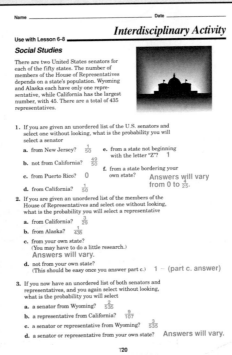

Name _____ Date _____

Use with Lesson 6-8 _____

Interdisciplinary Activity

Social Studies

There are two United States senators for each of the fifty states. The number of members of the House of Representatives depends on a state's population. Wyoming and Alaska each have only one representative, while California has the largest number, with 45. There are a total of 435 representatives.

1. If you are given an unordered list of the U.S. senators and select one without looking, what is the probability you will select a senator

   a. from New Jersey? $\frac{1}{50}$
   b. not from California? $\frac{49}{50}$
   c. from Puerto Rico? 0
   d. from California? $\frac{1}{50}$
   e. from a state not beginning with the letter "Z"? 1
   f. from a state bordering your own state?
   Answers will vary from 0 to $\frac{4}{25}$.

2. If you are given an unordered list of the members of the House of Representatives and select one without looking, what is the probability you will select a representative

   a. from California? $\frac{3}{29}$
   b. from Alaska? $\frac{1}{435}$
   c. from your own state?
   (You may have to do a little research.)
   Answers will vary.
   d. not from your own state?
   (This should be easy once you answer part c.)   1 − (part c. answer)

3. If you now have an unordered list of both senators and representatives, and you again select without looking, what is the probability you will select

   a. a senator from Wyoming? $\frac{2}{535}$
   b. a representative from California? $\frac{9}{107}$
   c. a senator or representative from Wyoming? $\frac{3}{535}$
   d. a senator or representative from your own state?   Answers will vary.

T20

Multicultural Activity Masters, p. 6

Name _____ Date _____

Use with Lesson 6-11 _____

Multicultural Activity

Ellen Ochoa

Ellen Ochoa (1957–   ) is a research engineer from San Diego, California. She graduated from San Diego State University with a bachelor's degree in physics, then went on to earn both a master's degree and doctorate in electrical engineering from Stanford University. In 1990, she became the first Hispanic American woman chosen to be an astronaut in the space shuttle program. Her dream is to someday participate in the building of a space station.

Engineers like Ms. Ochoa deal with many measurements that are extremely large or extremely small. They use scientific notation, of course, but sometimes they also express these measurements using the metric prefixes shown at the right. Here are two examples.

Metric Prefixes	
Prefix	Meaning
exa-	10^{18}
peta-	10^{15}
tera-	10^{12}
giga-	10^{9}
mega-	10^{6}
kilo-	10^{3}
no prefix	10^{0}
milli-	10^{-3}
micro-	10^{-6}
nano-	10^{-9}
pico-	10^{-12}
femto-	10^{-15}
atto-	10^{-18}

$5,200,000,000 = 5.2 \times 10^{9}$ meters
$= 5.2$ gigameters

0.0000000000089 meter $= 8.9 \times 10^{-12}$ meter
$= 8.9$ picometers

Express each measurement using one of the metric prefixes above.

1. 4×10^{-9} meter   4 nanometers
2. 6.5×10^{18} grams   6.5 exagrams
3. 4.27×10^{-15} gram   4.27 femtograms
4. 1.05×10^{6} meters   1.05 megameters

Complete.

5. 6.2×10^{16} meters $= 62 \times 10^{15}$ meters $= 62$ __petameters__
6. 3×10^{-10} gram $= 300 \times 10^{-12}$ gram $= 300$ __picograms__
7. 4.5×10^{10} grams $= \underline{45} \times 10^{9}$ grams $= 45$ gigagrams
8. 1.6×10^{-13} meter $= \underline{160} \times 10^{-15}$ meter $= 160$ femtometers

Express each measurement using one of the metric prefixes above.

9. diameter of the sun: 1,400,000,000 meters   1.4 gigameters
10. time needed for a computer to perform one calculation: 0.0000000025 second   2.5 nanoseconds

T6

Technology Masters, p. 20

Name _____ Date _____

Use with Lesson 6-4 _____

Computer Activity

Greatest Common Factor

The greatest of the factors common to two or more numbers is called the greatest common factor. The following BASIC program can be used to find the greatest common factor.

TYPE   NEW

```
10   PRINT "GIVE THE GREATEST COMMON FACTOR"
20   PRINT "FOR THE FOLLOWING SETS OF NUMBERS"
30   FOR J = 1 TO 10
40   LET A = INT(RND(1) * 200 + 1)
50   LET B = INT(RND(1) * 100 + 1)
60   LET C = INT(RND(1) * 200 + 1)
70   LET D = INT(RND(1) * 2)
80   FOR K = 1 TO A
90   IF D = 1 THEN 120
100  IF ((INT(A/K) = A/K) AND (INT (B/K) = B/K)) THEN
     F = K
110  GOTO 130
120  IF ((INT(A/K) = A/K) AND (INT (B/K) = B/K) AND
     (INT (C/K) = C/K)) THEN F = K
130  NEXT K
140  IF D = 0 THEN PRINT A; " ";B
150  IF D = 1 THEN PRINT A; " ";B;" "; C
160  INPUT G
170  IF G = F THEN PRINT "GOOD JOB!"
180  IF G <> F THEN PRINT "SORRY. THE CORRECT ANSWER IS
     ";F;"."
190  NEXT J
200  END
```

Check the results of this partial sample run.

```
GIVE THE GREATEST COMMON FACTOR
FOR THE FOLLOWING SETS OF NUMBERS
195 33 192
? 3
GOOD JOB!
32 74
? 2
GOOD JOB!
25 66 192
? 5
SORRY. THE CORRECT ANSWER IS 1.
```

T20

RECOMMENDED OUTSIDE RESOURCES

Books/Periodicals

Hiebert, James, and Merlyn Behr, *Number Concepts and Operations in the Middle Grades,* Reston, VA: NCTM, 1988.

Schulte, Albert P., ed., *Teaching Statistics and Probability,* 1981 Yearbook, NCTM, 1981.

Films/Videotapes/Videodiscs

Between Rational Numbers, Silver Burdett, 1970.

Probability, Wilmette, IL: Films Inc., 1970.

Software

Math Shop Spotlight: Fractions & Decimals, (Apple II, IBM/Tandy, Macintosh), Scholastic Inc.

For addresses of companies handling software, please refer to page T24.

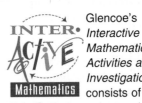

Glencoe's *Interactive Mathematics: Activities and Investigations* consists of 18 units that may be used as alternatives or supplemental material for *Mathematics: Applications and Connections.* The suggested unit for this chapter is Unit 17, *Infinite Windows.* See page T18 for more information.

MAKING MATHEMATICS RELEVANT

Spotlight on the Planets

The solar system is enormous, and mostly empty. The nine planets and other objects—comets, asteroids, moons, meteors—occupy only a tiny fraction of the total volume. The five planets nearest Earth are visible to the naked eye; but to see Uranus, Neptune, and Pluto, you need a telescope.

The planets exhibit great physical extremes:
* The volume of Jupiter is 10,000 times that of Pluto.
* Saturn has at least 22 moons.
* The surface temperature of Mercury can reach 800°F.
* The surface temperature on Pluto may be as low as −360°F. Its distance from Earth is so great that a satellite traveling 20,000 miles per hour would need about 21 years to reach Pluto.

Astronomers use mathematics to analyze optical-wave and radio-wave data received from satellites nearing the planets. The conclusions they reach have great importance to us on Earth. Facts learned about our eight sister planets are clues to the past, present, and future of the planet we live on.

6

Patterns and Number Sense

Spotlight on the Planets

Have You Ever Wondered...

* How far each of the planets is from the sun?
* How many planets the size of Earth could fit into a planet the size of Jupiter?

Average Distance from the Sun	
Planet	Miles
Mercury	3.59×10^7
Venus	6.7×10^7
Earth	9.29×10^7
Mars	1.42×10^8
Jupiter	4.83×10^8
Saturn	9.14×10^8
Uranus	1.78×10^9
Neptune	2.79×10^9
Pluto	3.68×10^9

210

"Have You Ever Wondered?" Answers

* Students can look at the chart to see how far each planet is from the sun.
* 1,403 planets the size of Earth could fit into a planet the size of Jupiter.

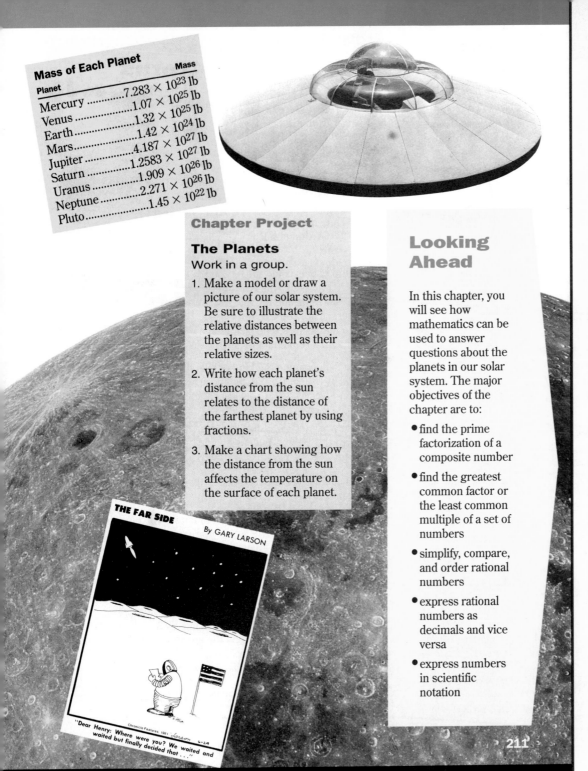

Mass of Each Planet	
Planet	Mass
Mercury	7.283×10^{23} lb
Venus	1.07×10^{25} lb
Earth	1.32×10^{24} lb
Mars	1.42×10^{27} lb
Jupiter	4.187×10^{27} lb
Saturn	1.2583×10^{26} lb
Uranus	1.909×10^{26} lb
Neptune	2.271×10^{26} lb
Pluto	1.45×10^{22} lb

Chapter Project

The Planets

Work in a group.

1. Make a model or draw a picture of our solar system. Be sure to illustrate the relative distances between the planets as well as their relative sizes.

2. Write how each planet's distance from the sun relates to the distance of the farthest planet by using fractions.

3. Make a chart showing how the distance from the sun affects the temperature on the surface of each planet.

THE FAR SIDE   BY GARY LARSON

Chronicle Features, 1981

"Dear Henry: Where were you? We waited and waited but finally decided that . . ."

Looking Ahead

In this chapter, you will see how mathematics can be used to answer questions about the planets in our solar system. The major objectives of the chapter are to:

● find the prime factorization of a composite number

● find the greatest common factor or the least common multiple of a set of numbers

● simplify, compare, and order rational numbers

● express rational numbers as decimals and vice versa

● express numbers in scientific notation

211

DATA ANALYSIS

Have students study the distances of the planets from the sun. Then ask the following questions.

- *Which planet is closest to Earth?* Venus

- *Which planet is about 10 times as far from the sun as Earth is? about one-third as far?* Saturn; Mercury

Data Search

A question related to these data is provided in Lesson 6-11, page 247, Exercise 35.

CHAPTER PROJECT

For drawings, in order to accommodate the vast differences in size and distance among the planets, students will need a roll of paper or tape for taping several sheets of paper together. Urge them to think carefully about the scales they will use. The project should give students a greater appreciation for the vastness of the solar system. Even placing the model for Mercury only 1 inch from the model of the sun will require placing the model for Pluto more than 8 feet away. If the model of Pluto is the size of a ping-pong ball, then the model of Jupiter would be more than 5 feet in diameter.

You may wish to extend the project by asking students to compare the distance from Earth to the sun to the distances between some major cities.

Allow several days to complete the project.

Chapter Opener Transparency

Transparency 6-0 is available in the Transparency Package. It provides another full-color, motivating activity that you can use to capture students' interest.

Lesson Resources
• Study Guide Master 6-1
• Practice Master 6-1
• Enrichment Master 6-1
• Application Master, p. 6
• Group Activity Card 6-1

 Transparency 6-1 contains the 5-Minute Check and a teaching aid for this lesson.

🕐 5-Minute Check
(Over Chapter 5)

1. Name the parallel segments in the figure. $\overline{MQ} \parallel \overline{NP}$

2. Classify the triangle below by its sides and by its angles. **isosceles obtuse**

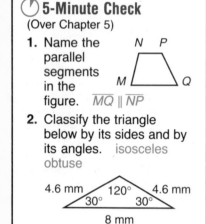

4.6 mm 120° 4.6 mm
30°   30°
8 mm

3. Draw all lines of symmetry for a rectangle.

---

1 FOCUS

Motivating the Lesson

Activity Give each student 12 counters. Ask students to find as many ways as they can to separate the counters equally into smaller groups with no counters left over. **1 group of 12, 2 groups of 6, 3 groups of 4, 4 groups of 3, 6 groups of 2, 12 groups of 1**

2 TEACH

Using Mental Math Write the number 360 on the chalkboard. Ask students if it is divisible by 2, 3, 4, 5, 6, 8, 9, or 10. It is divisible by each of the numbers.

6-1 Divisibility Patterns

Objective
Use divisibility rules for 2, 3, 4, 5, 6, 8, 9, and 10.

Words to Learn
divisible

LOOKBACK
You can review factors on page 34.

Michael DeSoto received a $40 check from his grandmother for his birthday. When he went to the bank to cash the check, the teller asked, "How would you like this?" He said, "All the bills the same." Then the teller asked, "What kind of bills do you want?"

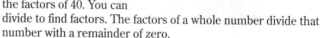

What kind of bills could the teller give Michael? This is another way of asking for all the factors of 40. You can divide to find factors. The factors of a whole number divide that number with a remainder of zero.

In order to determine the kind of bills the teller can give Michael, divide 40 by 1, 2, 5, 10, and 20. These are the possible types of bills.

$40 \div 1 = 40$ *The remainder is 0 so 1 and 40 are factors.*
$40 \div 2 = 20$ *The remainder is 0 so 2 and 20 are factors.*
$40 \div 5 = 8$ *The remainder is 0 so 5 and 8 are factors.*
$40 \div 10 = 4$ *The remainder is 0 so 10 and 4 are factors.*
$40 \div 20 = 2$ *The remainder is 0 so 20 and 2 are factors.*

Michael could receive 40 $1-bills, 20 $2-bills, 8 $5-bills, 4 $10-bills, or 2 $20-bills.

Mental Math Hint
. . . .
You can use the divisibility rule for 2 to determine whether a number is divisible by 4 and 8. Mentally divide the number by 2. If the quotient is even, the original number is divisible by 4. Divide the quotient by 2 again. If the new quotient is even, the original number is divisible by 8.

If a number is a factor of a given number, we can also say that the given number is **divisible** by the factor. For example, since 4 is a factor of 40, 40 is *divisible* by 4. The following rules will help you determine whether a number is divisible by 2, 3, 4, 5, 6, 8, 9, or 10.

A number is divisible by:
• 2 if the ones digit is divisible by 2.
• 3 if the sum of the digits is divisible by 3.
• 4 if the number formed by the last two digits is divisible by 4.
• 5 if the ones digit is 0 or 5.
• 6 if the number is divisible by 2 *and* 3.
• 8 if the number formed by the last three digits is divisible by 8.
• 9 if the sum of the digits is divisible by 9.
• 10 if the ones digit is 0.

OPTIONS

Reteaching Activity

Using Charts Have each student prepare a chart with the numbers 2, 3, 4, 5, 6, 8, 9, and 10 as the column heads. In each column have students list numbers divisible by the number heading that column. Then show that the numbers in each column satisfy the divisibility rule for the number heading the column.

Study Guide Masters, p. 46

Name _____ Date _____

Study Guide Worksheet 6-1

Divisibility Patterns

The following rules will help you determine if a number is divisible by 2, 3, 4, 5, 6, 8, 9, or 10.

A number is divisible by:
• 2 if the ones digit is divisible by 2.
• 3 if the sum of the digits is divisible by 3.
• 4 if the number formed by the last two digits is divisible by 4.
• 5 if the ones digit is 0 or 5.
• 6 if the number is divisible by 2 and 3.
• 8 if the number formed by the last three digits is divisible by 8.
• 9 if the sum of the digits is divisible by 9.
• 10 if the ones digit is 0.

Example Determine whether 2,120 is divisible by 2, 3, 4, 5, 6, 8, 9, or 10.
2: The ones digit is divisible by 2.
2,120 is divisible by 2.
3: The sum of the digits, 2 + 1 + 2 + 0 = 5, is not divisible by 3.

1 Determine whether 104 is divisible by 2, 3, 4, 5, 6, 8, 9, or 10.

2: The ones digit is divisible by 2. So 104 is divisible by 2.

3: The sum of the digits, $1 + 0 + 4 = 5$, is *not* divisible by 3. So 104 is *not* divisible by 3.

4: The number formed by the last two digits, 04, is divisible by 4. So 104 is divisible by 4.

5: The ones digit is *not* 0 or 5. So 104 is *not* divisible by 5.

6: The number is divisible by 2 but *not* by 3. So 104 is *not* divisible by 6.

8: The number formed by the last 3 digits, 104, is divisible by 8. So 104 is divisible by 8.

9: The sum of the digits, $1 + 0 + 4 = 5$, is *not* divisible by 9. So 104 is not divisible by 9.

10: The ones digit is not 0, so 104 is *not* divisible by 10.

Therefore, 104 is divisible by 2, 4, and 8, but not 3, 5, 6, 9, or 10.

2 Find two different pairs of factors of 3,267.

The sum of the digits $3 + 2 + 6 + 7$, or 18, is divisible by 3 and 9. So 3,267 is divisible by both 3 and 9.

$3{,}267 \; [\div] \; 3 \; [=] \; 1089 \qquad 3{,}267 \; [\div] \; 9 \; [=] \; 363$

Two pairs of factors of 3,267 are 3 and 1,089, and 9 and 363.

Checking for Understanding

Communicating Mathematics

Read and study the lesson to answer each question.

1. **Tell** why 7 is a factor of 42.   When 42 is divided by 7, the remainder is zero.

2. See Solutions Manual.

2. **Write** two factors of 78 that are greater than 1 and less than 78.

3. **Tell** why an odd number cannot be divisible by 6. See Solutions Manual.

4. **Write** one or two sentences to explain why a number that is divisible by 9 is also divisible by 3. See Solutions Manual.

Guided Practice

Using divisibility rules, determine whether each number is divisible by 2, 3, 4, 5, 6, 8, 9, or 10.

5. 58 2

6. 153 3, 9

7. −330
2, 3, 5, 6, 10

8. 881 none

9. 12,345
3, 5

10. Is 6 a factor of 228? yes

11. Is 5 a factor of 523? no

12. Is 231 divisible by 9? no

13. Is 432 divisible by 4? yes

14. Find two ways to write 126 as a product of two factors. See margin.

15. Find two numbers that are divisible by 2 and 3. Sample answers: 6, 12, 18

Lesson 6-1 Divisibility Patterns   **213**

More Examples

For Example 1

Determine whether 456 is divisible by 2, 3, 4, 5, 6, 8, 9, or 10.   456 is divisible by 2, 3, 4, 6, and 8, but not by 5, 9, or 10.

For Example 2

Find two different pairs of factors of 915.   3 and 305, 5 and 183

Teaching Tip   Before Example 1, remind students that even numbers are divisible by 2, but odd numbers are not.

Checking for Understanding

Exercises 1–4 are designed to help you assess students' understanding through reading, writing, speaking, and modeling. You should work through these exercises with your students and then monitor their work on Guided Practice Exercises 5–15.

Additional Answer

14. Sample answers: 2×63, 3×42, 6×21, 7×18, 9×14

Practice Masters, p. 46

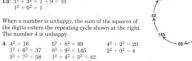

Exercises

Independent Practice

Use divisibility rules to determine if the first number is divisible by the second number. Write *yes* or *no*.

16. 7,774; 2 yes   **17.** 335; 5 yes   **18.** 991; 3 no   **19.** 902; 6 no

20. 112; 8 yes   **21.** 2,034; 9 yes   **22.** 5,142; 4 no   **23.** 10,105; 10 no

24. Sample answer: 4 · 246; 3 · 328

24. Use divisibility rules to find two different pairs of factors of 984.

25. Use divisibility rules and a calculator to find two different pairs of factors of 43,210. **Sample answers: 2 · 21,605; 5 · 8,642; 10 · 4,321**

Use mental math, paper and pencil, or a calculator to find a number that satisfies the given conditions. **Sample answers given.**

26. a number divisible by both 4 and 9 36

27. a three-digit number divisible by 3, 6, and 9 486

28. a four-digit number divisible by 4, but *not* 8 3,996

29. a five-digit number *not* divisible by 4, 5, 9, or 10 26,378

Mixed Review

30. Fund Raising Kim is participating in a walk-a-thon for the Lung Association. Jamal is sponsoring her at 10¢ for each mile she walks and Andreina is sponsoring her at 11¢ per mile. If Kim walks 9 miles, what is the total amount she will collect from Jamal and Andreina? *(Lesson 1-1)* **$1.89**

31. Solve $p = -654 - 175$. *(Lesson 3-5)* **-829**

32. probably no relationship

32. Statistics Determine whether a scatterplot of height and eye color would show a positive, negative, or no relationship. *(Lesson 4-8)*

33. Geometry Make an Escher-like drawing for the pattern shown at the right. Use a tessellation of two rows of five equilateral triangles as your base. *(Lesson 5-7)* **See Solutions Manual.**

Problem Solving and Applications

34. Entertainment There are 144 students in the school band. They need to march in a rectangular formation. List all the formations that are possible. **See Solutions Manual.**

35. Critical Thinking What is the greatest six-digit number that is *not* divisible by 4 or 9? **999,998**

COMPUTER CONNECTION

36. Computer Connection The BASIC program shown below will print the factors of a given number.

```
10   INPUT N
20   FOR D = 1 TO N
30   IF INT(N/D) = N/D THEN 50
40   GOTO 60
50   PRINT D
60   NEXT D
```

Use the program to find the number, less than 100, that has the greatest number of factors.
96, 90, 84, 72, and 60 each have 12 factors.

6-2 Prime Factorization

Objective
Find the prime factorization of a composite number.

Words to Learn
prime
composite
prime factorization
factor tree
Fundamental Theorem
of Arithmetic

Did you ever wonder how water changes to steam and then the steam seems to disappear? As water is heated, the molecules begin to move more rapidly. The molecules move farther apart forming a vapor. The vapor bubbles rise and escape into the air.

If you separate a water molecule into smaller parts, you would find 2 atoms of hydrogen and 1 atom of oxygen. These are the basic elements of water.

In mathematics, we use factoring to separate a number into smaller parts. The basic elements of a number are its factors. When a whole number *greater than 1* has *exactly* two factors, 1 and itself, it is called a **prime number.** For example, 5 is a prime number since it has two factors, 1 and 5.

Any whole number, except 0 and 1, that is not prime can be written as a product of prime numbers. When a whole number *greater than 1* has more than two factors, it is called a **composite number.** For example, 6 is a composite number since it has four factors, 1, 2, 3, and 6.

The numbers 0 and 1 are *neither* prime *nor* composite. Notice that 0 has an endless number of factors and that 1 has only one factor, itself.

To find the prime factors of any composite number, begin by expressing the number as a product of two factors. Then continue to factor until all the factors are prime. When a number is expressed as a product of factors that are all prime, the expression is called the **prime factorization** of the number.

The diagrams below each show a different way to find the prime factorization of 24. These diagrams are called **factor trees.**

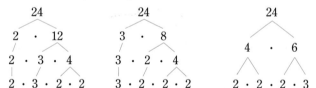

Every number has a unique set of prime factors. Notice that the bottom row of "branches" in each factor tree is the same except for the order in which the factors are written. This property of numbers is called the **Fundamental Theorem of Arithmetic.**

Lesson 6-2 Prime Factorization **215**

NCTM Standards: 1–7, 9

Lesson Resources
- Study Guide Master 6-2
- Practice Master 6-2
- Enrichment Master 6-2
- Group Activity Card 6-2

Transparency 6-2 contains the 5-Minute Check and a teaching aid for this lesson.

5-Minute Check
(Over Lesson 6-1)
Use divisibility rules to determine if the first number is divisible by the second number. Write *yes* or *no*.
1. 777; 3   yes
2. 3,605; 10   no
3. 802; 6   no
4. 5,328; 9   yes
5. 13,712; 4   yes

1 FOCUS

Motivating the Lesson

Activity   Have students use their calculators to find all whole numbers from 1 through 20 by which 1,649 is divisible.   1, 17

2 TEACH

Using Logical Reasoning   To determine whether a number is prime, you need only test for divisibility by prime numbers less than the square root of the number (the square root can be found using a calculator). For example, the number 97 need only be tested by 2, 3, 5, and 7 since $\sqrt{97} \approx 9.8$. Ask students which numbers they would use to test 147 for divisibility.   2, 3, 5, 7, and 11

OPTIONS

Reteaching Activity

Using Manipulatives   Have students use blocks or tiles to form a rectangular array using the number of blocks that you name. Point out that only one rectangular array can be formed from a prime number of blocks, and that more than one rectangular array can be formed from a composite number of blocks.

Study Guide Masters, p. 47

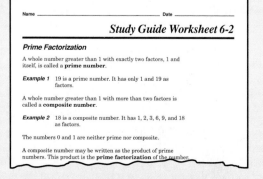

Name _____ Date _____

Study Guide Worksheet 6-2

Prime Factorization

A whole number greater than 1 with exactly two factors, 1 and itself, is called a **prime number**.

Example 1   19 is a prime number. It has only 1 and 19 as factors.

A whole number greater than 1 with more than two factors is called a **composite number**.

Example 2   18 is a composite number. It has 1, 2, 3, 6, 9, and 18 as factors.

The numbers 0 and 1 are neither prime nor composite.

A composite number may be written as the product of prime numbers. This product is the **prime factorization** of the number.

215

You can use a calculator and the divisibility rules as tools to find the prime factorization of a number.

Example 1

Find the prime factorization of 315.

Divide by prime factors until the quotient is prime.

prime factors
↓

315 $\div$ 5 $=$ 63   *The ones digit is 5. So 315 is divisible by 5.*

63 $\div$ 3 $=$ 21   *The sum of the digits, $6 + 3 = 9$, is divisible by 3. So 63 is divisible by 3.*

21 $\div$ 3 $=$ 7   *7 is a prime number.*

$315 = 3^2 \cdot 5 \cdot 7$

For centuries, mathematicians have tried to find an expression for calculating every prime number. While an expression may yield some prime numbers, none has been found to yield all prime numbers.

Example 2   Connection

Algebra   Show that the expression $n^2 - n + 41$ yields a prime number for $n = 1, 2$, and 3.

$n^2 - n + 41 = 1^2 - 1 + 41$ *Replace n with 1.*
$= 41$ *41 has only two factors, 1 and 41. 41 is a prime number.*

$n^2 - n + 41 = 2^2 - 2 + 41$ *Replace n with 2.*
$= 43$ *43 has only two factors, 1 and 43. So 43 is a prime number.*

$n^2 - n + 41 = 3^2 - 3 + 41$ *Replace n with 3.*
$= 47$ *47 has only two factors, 1 and 47. So 47 is a prime number.*

Sometimes you may need to factor a negative integer. Any negative integer may be written as the product of -1 and a whole number.

Example 3

Find the prime factorization of -140.

First, write -140 as the product $-1 \cdot 140$.

$-140 = -1 \cdot 140$
$= -1 \cdot 2 \cdot 70$ *140 is divisible by 2.*
$= -1 \cdot 2 \cdot 2 \cdot 35$ *70 is divisible by 2.*
$= -1 \cdot 2 \cdot 2 \cdot 5 \cdot 7$ *35 is divisible by 5. 7 is a prime number.*

$-140 = -1 \cdot 2^2 \cdot 5 \cdot 7$

Checking for Understanding

Communicating Mathematics

Read and study the lesson to answer each question.

1. **Tell** the difference between prime and composite numbers. See margin.
2. **Draw** two different factor trees to find the prime factorization of 60.

2. See Solutions Manual.

3. **Write** the number whose prime factorization is given by $2^3 \cdot 3^2$. 72

Guided Practice

Determine whether each number is *prime* or *composite*.

4. 52 composite   5. 13 prime   6. 29 prime   7. 51 composite

Draw a factor tree to find the prime factorization of each number.

8. 57 $3 \cdot 19$ 9. 36 $2^2 \cdot 3^2$ 10. 90 $2 \cdot 3^2 \cdot 5$ 11. 180 $2^2 \cdot 3^2 \cdot 5$

For factor trees for Exercises 8-11, see Solutions Manual.

Exercises

Independent Practice

Determine whether each number is *prime, composite,* or *neither.*

12. 23 prime   13. 93 composite   14. 77 composite   15. 68 composite

16. 1 neither   17. 453 composite   18. 43,000 composite   19. -97 prime

20. State the least prime number that is a factor of the number 48. 2

Find the prime factorization of each number.

21. 81 3^4 22. 605 $5 \cdot 11^2$ 23. 64 2^6 24. 31 $1 \cdot 31$

25. 400 $2^4 \cdot 5^2$ 26. -144 $-1 \cdot 2^4 \cdot 3^2$ 27. -2,700 $-1 \cdot 2^2 \cdot 3^3 \cdot 5^2$ 28. 20,310 $2 \cdot 3 \cdot 5 \cdot 677$

Mixed Review

29. See margin.
30. See Solutions Manual.

29. Solve $4m < 24$. Show the solution on a number line. *(Lesson 2-10)*

30. **Statistics**   Make a line plot for the data below. *(Lesson 4-3)*
    27, 22, 23, 26, 22, 20, 25, 28, 23, 20, 21, 22, 25, 23, 22

31. **Geometry**   Determine if the figure at the right has rotational symmetry. *(Lesson 5-5)* **no symmetry**

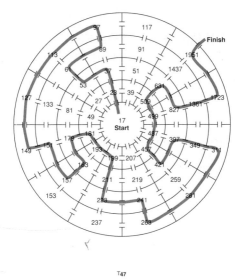

32. Use divisibility rules to determine if 672 is divisible by 3. *(Lesson 6-1)* **yes**

Problem Solving and Applications

33b. 6, 12, 18, 30; They are multiples of 6. Yes; they are even and divisible by 3.

33. **Number Sense**   Primes that differ by two are called *twin primes*. One such pair is 11 and 13. 33a. 3, 5; 5, 7; 11, 13; 17, 19; 29, 31; 41, 43; 59, 61; 71, 73
    a. Find all the twin primes less than 100.
    b. List the numbers that are between twin primes for primes greater than 3 and less than 37. What do these numbers have in common? Is this true for all twin primes? Why or why not?

34. **Critical Thinking**   Find the prime factorization of the perfect squares 9, 36, and 100. $9 = 3^2$; $36 = 2^2 \cdot 3^2$; $100 = 2^2 \cdot 5^2$
    a. What characteristics do the prime factorizations have? See margin.
    b. Is this true for all perfect squares? Explain. Yes; see margin.

35. prime

35. **Algebra**   Is the value of $3a + 4b$ prime or composite if $a = 5$ and $b = 4$?

36. **Number Sense**   Two primes that differ by one are 2 and 3. Find all such pairs of primes less than 1,000. 2, 3

37. **Algebra**   Find the least whole number, n, for which the expression $n^2 - n + 41$ is not prime. 41

Lesson 6-2 Prime Factorization   **217**

Extending the Lesson

Using Logical Reasoning   Have students answer these questions.

1. Is $3 \cdot 4 \cdot 5 + 1$ divisible by 3? 4? 5?   no; no; no
2. Is $16 \cdot 17 \cdot 18 + 1$ divisible by 16? 17? 18?   no; no; no
3. Using Exercises 1-2, describe how to find a number that is not divisible by any number from 10 to 20.   Find the product of the numbers from 10 to 20 and add 1.

Cooperative Learning Activity

Factorization Determination 6-2

Number of players: 2
Materials: Index cards, spinner

▶ Label equal sections of a spinner "54," "96," "180," "200," "210," and "312." Make two sets of cards containing the prime numbers shown on the back of this card. (The numbers in parentheses tell how many cards each partner should make for each number.) Shuffle the cards and place them face down in a pile.

➡ Each partner takes six cards from the pile. One partner then spins the spinner. Each partner determines whether he or she is holding cards that could be used to express the prime factorization of the number on the spinner. If yes, remove the cards from your hand and replace them with cards from the pile. Award yourself 1 point. If you do not have the cards showing the prime factorization, you may replace some or all of your cards with cards from the pile before the next spin. Continue in the same way until one partner has 5 points. (Shuffle and reuse cards that have been discarded.)

Close

Ask students to complete this sentence: *The prime factorization of a number is ___?___.* **an expression showing the number as a product of prime factors**

3 PRACTICE/APPLY

Assignment Guide
Maximum: 12–37
Minimum: 13–27 odd, 29–34

For **Extra Practice,** see p. 595.

Alternate Assessment

Writing   State a range of five numbers, for example, 41 through 45. Have students list the prime numbers in the range. Then have them write the prime factorizations of the composite numbers in the range.

Additional Answers

1. Prime numbers have exactly two factors, while composite numbers have more than two factors.

29. See page 216.
34. See page 216.

Enrichment Masters, p. 47

Name _____   Date _____

Enrichment Worksheet 6-2

Prime Maze

Find your way through the maze by moving to the next greatest prime number.

NCTM Standards: 1–5, 8, 12

Management Tips

For Students If nine different colors of pencils are not available, have students trace the diagram several times so that each path can be distinguished from the others.

For the Overhead Projector
Overhead Manipulative Resources provides appropriate materials for teacher or student demonstration of the activities in this Mathematics Lab.

1 FOCUS

Introducing the Lab

Ask students to solve this problem: *The girls' and boys' basketball teams both had games today. The girls play every 4 days, the boys every 5 days. When will they again play on the same day?*
in 20 days

2 TEACH

Using Logical Reasoning After students have drawn all nine paths, ask this question: *Why is the path of the ball the same (except for direction) when 1 and 9 are called?* Passing to the first person to the right is the same as passing to the ninth person to the left.

3 PRACTICE/APPLY

Using Logical Reasoning After completing Exercise 5, ask this question: *If the number of players in the drill is prime, what is the only number that will grant a water break?* 1

Close

Have students name numbers from 1 through 11 that are relatively prime with 12.

Additional Answer

2. The numbers and 10 have no common factors.

218

Objective
Discover the relationship of relatively prime numbers.

Materials
colored pencils
tracing paper

Ms. Carozza coaches the eighth grade girls' basketball team. She is also a mathematics teacher. Sometimes she uses drills at basketball practice that reinforce concepts she covered in class.

Try this!

- The figure at the right represents the members of the team standing around a circle for a passing drill. The drill starts when the player with the ball (B) calls out a number, such as 4, and passes the ball to the fourth player to her right. The person catching the ball continues the pattern by passing the ball to the fourth person to her right and so on.

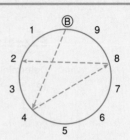

- Sometimes the player who starts the drill calls out a number that results in every player around the circle touching the ball once before it returns to her. When this happens, the team is given a water break. Use colored pencils to record the different paths the ball takes when each of the numbers 1 through 9 is called.
- Copy and complete the table at the right to determine when the team gets a water break.

Number of Players	Number Called	Water Break?
10	1	yes
10	2	no
10	3	yes
10	4	no
10	5	no
10	6	no
10	7	yes
10	8	no
10	9	yes

What do you think?

1. What numbers can be called so the team can take a break? 1, 3, 7, 9
2. Make a conjecture about the relationship between 10 and the numbers in the answer to Exercise 1. See margin.
3. Find the greatest factor common to 10 and each number in the answer to Exercise 1. 1
4. Describe the pattern that exists between the pairs of numbers you used in Exercise 3. The greatest common factor is 1.
5. When two whole numbers have 1 as their greatest common factor, the numbers are **relatively prime.** How did the coach use relatively prime numbers in the passing drill? water break when a number was relatively prime with 10

218　**Chapter 6** Patterns and Number Sense

OPTIONS

Lab Manual You may wish to make copies of the blackline master on p. 55 of the *Lab Manual* for students to use as a recording sheet.

Lab Manual, p. 55

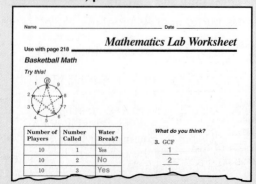

6-3 Make a List

Objective
Solve problems by making an organized list.

You know that prime numbers have exactly two factors. What numbers have exactly three factors? or four factors?

Explore *What do you know?*
Prime numbers have exactly two factors.
Composite numbers are not prime.

What are you trying to find?
The composite numbers that have exactly three factors
The composite numbers that have exactly four factors

Plan Find the factors of the numbers from 2 through 15. List them according to the number of factors each has. Describe the numbers in the 3-factor list. Then describe the numbers in the 4-factor list.

Solve

Exactly 2 Factors	Exactly 3 Factors	Exactly 4 Factors	Exactly 5 Factors
2: 1, 2	4: 1, 2, 4	6: 1, 2, 3, 6	16: 1, 2, 4, 8, 16
3: 1, 3	9: 1, 3, 9	8: 1, 2, 4, 8	
5: 1, 5		10: 1, 2, 5, 10	
7: 1, 7		14: 1, 2, 7, 14	
11: 1, 11		15: 1, 3, 5, 15	
13: 1, 13			

Study the lists for 3 and 4 factors. Look for a pattern to help describe the numbers in terms of their factors.

3-Factor List
The numbers are squares of their prime factor.

4-Factor List
Except for 8, each number is the product of its two prime factors.

Examine Determine the next number in each list to test its description.

25: 1, 5, 25   *25 is the square of its prime factor and has three factors. The description is accurate.*

21: 1, 3, 7, 21   *21 is the product of its two prime factors and has four factors. The description is accurate.*

Lesson 6-3 Problem-Solving Strategy: Make a List   **219**

---

1 FOCUS

Motivating the Lesson

Questioning Ask this question: *How could you find a number that has every whole number from 1 to 10 as a factor?* Find the product of the whole numbers from 1 to 10.

2 TEACH

Using Communication Explain that the make-a-list strategy is used to organize information into a logical framework. This allows the data to be analyzed more easily so that patterns, if they exist, can be spotted.

Close

A 2-symbol code begins with A, B, C, or D and ends with 1, 2, or 3. Have students make a list of all the possible codes. **A1, A2, A3, B1, B2, B3, C1, C2, C3, D1, D2, D3**

3 PRACTICE/APPLY

Assignment Guide
Maximum: 6–12
Minimum: 6–11

Enrichment Masters, p. 48

Enrichment Worksheet 6-3

Figurate Numbers

Numbers that can be represented by dots in geometric arrangements are called *figurate numbers*. Here are three examples.

3rd Pentagonal Number 7th Hexagonal Number 4th Star Number

Make sketches to complete this chart. Look for patterns in the numbers to help you.

	Name	1st	2nd	3rd	4th	5th
1.	Triangular	1	3	6	10	15
2.	Square	1	4	9	16	25
3.	Pentagonal	1	5	12	22	35
4.	Hexagonal	1	6	15	28	45
5.	Octagonal	1	8	21	40	65
6.	Star	1	8	21	40	65

7. How are square numbers and triangular numbers related?
   Each square number equals the sum of two consecutive triangular numbers.

8. How are the star numbers related to other types of figurate numbers?
   Same as octagonal; sum of a square number and four triangular numbers.

220

Checking for Understanding

Communicating Mathematics

Read and study the lesson to answer each question.

1. **Tell** what you can do to a prime number to get a number that will have exactly three factors. **Square it.**

2. **Show** that the description *a double or triple of a prime number* does not describe the numbers with exactly four factors. **8 is not a double or triple of a prime number.**

Guided Practice

Solve by making a list.

3. Predict a number from 50 through 150 that can be placed in each list. Use the BASIC program on page 214 to check your predictions.

3. 2 factors: 53;
   3 factors: 49;
   4 factors: 51;
   5 factors: 81

4. 6: 123, 132, 231, 213, 312, 321

4. How many three-digit numbers can be formed by the digits 1, 2, and 3 if no digit is repeated? What are the numbers?

5. Extend the list of numbers that have exactly 5 factors. Write a description of the list. **81, 625, 2,401; n^4, where n is prime**

Problem Solving

Practice

Solve using any strategy.

Strategies

• • • • • • •

Look for a pattern.
Solve a simpler problem.
Act it out.
Guess and check.
Draw a diagram.
Make a chart.
Work backward.

6. Marty and some friends are sharing a pizza. Marty starts with 9 slices of pizza. She takes the first slice, then passes the pizza around the table. Each friend takes one slice and continues to pass the pizza around the table. Marty takes the last slice. Counting Marty, how many people could be sharing the pizza? **4 or 8 people**

7. There are 108 students signed up for the basketball league. They have 18 sponsors. How many teams of 9 players can be formed? **12 teams**

8. Paper cups can be purchased in packages of 40 or 75. Alexis buys 7 packages and gets 350 cups. How many packages of 75 does she buy? **2 packages**

9. Neal is using a beaker containing water for a science experiment. He uses half of the water and gives half of the remaining amount to Juanita for her experiment. At the end of class, Neal has 225 mL left in the beaker. How much water was in the beaker originally? **900 mL**

10. Alishanee bought 15 posters to give to friends. She wants to know how many friends she can equally share them with if she keeps one for herself. How can she determine all the possibilities without making lists? **Factor 14.**

11. Mary has a basket containing 21 muffins to share with friends. She takes the first one and each friend takes one as they continue around the table. There is one muffin left when the basket returns to Mary. How many people could have shared the muffins if the basket can go around the table more than once? **20, 10, 5, 4, 2**

See students' work.

12. **Journal Entry** Write a problem that can be solved by making a list.

220 Chapter 6 Patterns and Number Sense

OPTIONS

Extending the Lesson

Counting Factors The number of factors for a number can be found by writing its prime factorization, adding 1 to each exponent, and multiplying the sums.

$40 = 2^3 \cdot 5^1$:

$(3 + 1)(1 + 1) = 4 \cdot 2 = 8$

Thus, 40 has 8 factors.

Have students find the number of factors for 72 and 50. **12, 6**

Cooperative Learning Activity

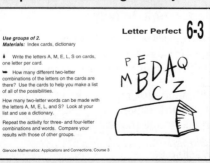

Letter Perfect **6-3**

Use groups of 2.
Materials: Index cards, dictionary

◆ Write the letters A, M, E, L, S on cards, one letter per card.

➡ How many different two-letter combinations of the letters on the cards are there? Use the cards to help you make a list of all of the possibilities.

How many two-letter words can be made with the letters A, M, E, L, and S? Look at your list and use a dictionary.

Repeat the activity for three- and four-letter combinations and words. Compare your results with those of other groups.

Glencoe Mathematics: Applications and Connections, Course 3

6-4 Greatest Common Factor

Objective

Find the greatest common factor of two or more integers.

Words to Learn

greatest common factor (GCF)

In July of 1976, Dr. Robert B. Craven of the U.S. Center for Disease Control in Atlanta began to receive calls from physicians in Pennsylvania. The doctors described a rare form of pneumonia which they had never seen before. The disease was often fatal. Upon further investigation, the Center found that all of the people struck with this disease had been in or near the Bellevue-Stratford Hotel in Philadelphia during a convention of the American Legion. This disease became known as Legionnaire's disease.

Doctors unraveled the mystery of Legionnaire's disease by looking for *common factors* in those who were ill.

Two or more numbers may also have some common factors. The greatest of the factors common to two or more numbers is called the **greatest common factor** (GCF) of the numbers. You can use prime factorization to find the GCF. Consider the prime factorization of 84 and 90 shown below.

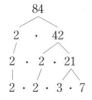

The integers 84 and 90 have 2 and 3 as common prime factors. The product of these prime factors, 2 · 3 or 6, is the GCF of 84 and 90.

Example 1

Use prime factorization to find the GCF of 84, 126, and 210.

Write each number as a product of prime factors.

$$84 = 2 \cdot 2 \cdot 3 \cdot 7$$
$$126 = 2 \cdot 3 \cdot 3 \cdot 7$$
$$210 = 2 \cdot 3 \cdot 5 \cdot 7 \quad \textit{The common prime factors are 2, 3, and 7.}$$

Thus, the GCF is 2 · 3 · 7 or 42.

Lesson 6-4 Greatest Common Factor · **221**

OPTIONS

Reteaching Activity

Using Drawings Provide schematic drawings like the one below to guide students to the GCF.

$$12 = \boxed{2} \cdot \boxed{2} \cdot 3$$
$$\qquad\quad \downarrow \quad\;\; \downarrow$$
$$18 = \qquad \boxed{2} \cdot \boxed{3} \cdot \boxed{3}$$
$$\qquad\qquad \downarrow \quad\;\; \downarrow$$
$$GCF = \quad \boxed{2} \cdot \boxed{3} \qquad = \boxed{6}$$

Study Guide Masters, p. 49

Name _____ Date _____

Study Guide Worksheet 6-4

Greatest Common Factor

The greatest of the factors common to two or more numbers is the **greatest common factor (GCF)**. You can use prime factorization to find the greatest common factor.

Example 1 Find the greatest common factor of 90 and 120.

$$90 = 3 \cdot 30 \qquad\qquad 120 = 3 \cdot 40$$
$$= 3 \cdot 15 \cdot 2 \qquad\qquad = 3 \cdot 10 \cdot 4$$
$$= 3 \cdot 5 \cdot 3 \cdot 2 \qquad\qquad = 3 \cdot 2 \cdot 5 \cdot 2 \cdot 2$$

90 and 120 have 2, 3, and 5 as common factors. The product of the common factors is the greatest common factor.

NCTM Standards: 1–9

Lesson Resources
- Study Guide Master 6-4
- Practice Master 6-4
- Enrichment Master 6-4
- Technology Master, p. 20
- Group Activity Card 6-4

 Transparency 6-4 contains the 5-Minute Check and a teaching aid for this lesson.

⏱ 5-Minute Check
(Over Lesson 6-3)

Arturo, Beth, Carl, and Diane are running for class president. Etta and Frank are running for vice-president. Using the first letter of each name, make a list of all the possible president/vice-president combinations. How many are there? AE, AF, BE, BF, CE, CF, DE, DF; 8

1 FOCUS

Motivating the Lesson

Activity Choose two students. Have the class name characteristics (factors) the students have in common. List these on the chalkboard. Try to decide on a "greatest common factor," the most important shared characteristic.

2 TEACH

Using Language Point out that the words "greatest," "common," and "factor" indicate a method for finding the GCF:
1. List all <u>factors</u> of each number.
2. Find all factors that are <u>common</u>.
3. Which common factor is the <u>greatest</u>?

Teaching Tip In the Example, have students use a calculator to find all factors of 84. Then have them test each factor to see if it is also a factor of both 126 and 210.

221

222

Another way to find the GCF is to list all the factors of each number. Then find the greatest number that is in both lists.

Example 2

Find the GCF of 24 and 60.

factors of 24: 1, 2, 3, 4, 6, 8, 12, 24
factors of 60: 1, 2, 3, 4, 5, 6, 10, 12, 15, 20, 30, 60

The *common factors* of 24 and 60, shown in blue, are 1, 2, 3, 4, 6, and 12. The greatest common factor of 24 and 60 is 12.

Checking for Understanding

Communicating Mathematics

Read and study the lesson to answer each question.

1. **Tell** how to find the GCF of two or more numbers. **See margin.**

2. **Draw** factor trees to find the prime factorization of 120 and 168. Then circle the common factors. **See Solutions Manual.**

3. **Tell** what the GCF is for the two numbers whose prime factorizations are shown at the right. **12**

4. **Write** two numbers whose GCF is 15. **Sample answer: 30, 45**

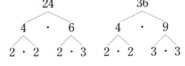

Guided Practice

Find the GCF for each set of numbers.

5. $8 = 2 \cdot 2 \cdot 2$
   $12 = 2 \cdot 2 \cdot 3$ **4**

6. $35 = 5 \cdot 7$
   $20 = 2 \cdot 2 \cdot 5$ **5**

7. $28 = 2 \cdot 2 \cdot 7$
   $70 = 2 \cdot 5 \cdot 7$ **14**

8. 60, 105 **15**

9. 9, 15, 24 **3**

10. 15, 45 **15**

11. 18, 27 **9**

12. 7, 11 **1**

13. 26, 34, 64 **2**

Exercises

Independent Practice

Find the GCF for each set of numbers.

14. 8, 34 **2**

15. 16, 24 **8**

16. 36, 27 **9**

17. 125, 100 **25**

18. 28, 56 **28**

19. 96, 108 **12**

20. 12, 18, 30 **6**

21. 10, 15, 30 **5**

22. 45, 105, 75 **15**

23. 210, 330, 150 **30**

24. 510, 714, 306 **102**

25. How do you know just by looking that two numbers will have 5 as a common factor? **if the units digits are 0 or 5**

26. What is the GCF of $3^2 \cdot 5$ and $2 \cdot 3 \cdot 5^2$? **15**

Mixed Review

27. How many liters are in 864 milliliters? *(Lesson 1-6)* **0.864 L**

28. Find the absolute value of −21. *(Lesson 3-1)* **21**

29. **Geometry** Classify the triangle at the right according to its sides and its angles. *(Lesson 5-3)* **scalene, obtuse**

30. Find the prime factorization of 56. *(Lesson 6-2)* $2^3 \cdot 7$

222 **Chapter 6** Patterns and Number Sense

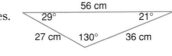

Classroom Vignette

"I introduce the division algorithm of finding the GCF after developing the concept using prime factorization. This process is an application of computer programming and allows students to develop an understanding of looping through the same steps until a result is achieved (a remainder of zero)."

Lyle D. Jensen

Lyle Jensen, Teacher
Albright Middle School, Villa Park, IL

31. **Industrial Technology** Charles wants to resurface the top of a table with ceramic tiles. The table is 30 inches long and 24 inches wide.
    a. What is the largest square tile that he can use without having to use any partial squares?
    b. How many of these tiles will Charles need?

DATA SEARCH

32. **Data Search** Refer to page 665. Suppose Venus and Earth are aligned with the sun, that is, at the same point in their orbit relative to the sun. How many years will pass before they are aligned again? **45 years**

33. **Number Sense** Write three numbers that have a GCF of 7. **Sample answer: 7, 14, 21**

34. **Critical Thinking** Let p represent a prime number.
    a. What is the GCF of $8p$ and $16p$? **8p**
    b. What is the GCF of $15p$ and $27p$? **3p**

35. **Critical Thinking** Numbers that have a GCF of 1 are **relatively prime.** Use this definition to determine if each statement is *true* or *false* and tell why.
    a. Any two prime numbers are relatively prime.
    b. If two numbers are relatively prime, one of them must be prime.
    35a. True; their only common factor is 1.
    35b. False; 4 and 9 are relatively prime but neither is prime.

Save Planet Earth

Environmentally Safe Cars Mercedes Benz's "S-Class" cars are free of asbestos and other toxic materials. They contain only recyclable plastics and have a sophisticated emissions-control system. Their air-conditioning system does not contain CFCs. None of these compounds, which can destroy the ozone, are used in the making of foam in seats and interior panels. In 1994, all of the "S" cars will be painted with a water-based paint rather than petroleum-based paint.

While the price of these cars is out of reach for most consumers, the technology will eventually make its way into less-expensive vehicles.

How You Can Help
- Write to major car manufacturers and ask them what environmentally safe technology they plan to use in their new models. Consumer pressure could convince many car manufacturers to start making environmentally safe vehicles much sooner.

Lesson 6-4 Greatest Common Factor **223**

Extending the Lesson

Save Planet Earth Ask students what is being done statewide to control the toxic materials being emitted into the air by automobiles. Discuss the possibility of implementing a nationwide emissions-testing program.

Cooperative Learning Activity

How Do You Stack Up? 6-4

Number of players: 3
Materials: Index cards

▪ Make three sets of cards containing the numbers shown on the back of this card. (The numbers in parentheses tell how many cards to make for each number.) Shuffle the cards and put them in a pile. Sit in a circle on the floor.

➡ Each group member takes five cards. These cards show the prime factors of a number. Each group member writes the product of the prime factors on a sheet of paper. Then one group member places his or her cards face up in a single row and arranges them so that the factors are in increasing order. Each of the other two group members place any cards showing the same factors face up on top of the first group member's cards. Find the product of the numbers on cards for which there is more than one card in the stack. This is the GCF of the numbers each group member wrote. Show the number you wrote to the other group members.

Repeat the procedure several times, shuffling all the cards each time.

Glencoe Mathematics: Applications and Connections, Course 3

Enrichment Masters, p. 49

Name _____ Date _____

Enrichment Worksheet 6-4

GCFs By Successive Division

Here is a different way to find the greatest common factor of two numbers. This method works well for large numbers.

Find the GCF of 848 and 1,325.

Step 1 Divide the smaller number into the larger.
$$848 \overline{)1{,}325} \quad \begin{array}{r} 1 \ R477 \\ \underline{848} \\ 477 \end{array}$$

Step 2 Divide the remainder into the divisor. Repeat this step until you get a remainder of 0.
$$477\overline{)848} \ \begin{array}{c}1 \ R371\\ \underline{477}\\371\end{array} \quad 371\overline{)477}\ \begin{array}{c}1 \ R106\\ \underline{371}\\106\end{array} \quad 106\overline{)371}\ \begin{array}{c}3 \ R53\\ \underline{318}\\53\end{array} \quad 53\overline{)106}\ \begin{array}{c}2 \ R0\\ \underline{106}\\0\end{array}$$

Step 3 The last divisor is the GCF of the two original numbers. The GCF of 848 and 1,325 is 53.

Use the method above to find the GCF for each pair of numbers.

1. 187; 578 **17**   2. 161; 943 **23**
3. 215; 1,849 **43**   4. 453; 484 **1**
5. 432; 588 **12**   6. 279; 403 **31**
7. 1,325; 3,498 **53**   8. 9,840; 1,751 **1**
9. 3,484; 5,963 **67**   10. 1,802; 106 **106**
11. 45,787; 69,875 **1**   12. 35,811; 102,070 **173**

T 49
Glencoe Division, Macmillan/McGraw-Hill

NCTM Standards: 1–7, 9, 12

Lesson Resources
- Study Guide Master 6-5
- Practice Master 6-5
- Enrichment Master 6-5
- Group Activity Card 6-5

 Transparency 6-5 contains the 5-Minute Check and a teaching aid for this lesson.

🕐 5-Minute Check
(Over Lesson 6-4)

Find the GCF of each set of numbers.

1. $16 = 2 \cdot 2 \cdot 2 \cdot 2$
   $28 = 2 \cdot 2 \cdot 7$ 4
2. 10, 14   2
3. 14, 35   7
4. 12, 18, 36   6
5. 81, 18, 9   9

1 FOCUS

Motivating the Lesson

Questioning State that the word *ratio* can be defined as "a comparison of two numbers." Ask students to guess the meaning of the word *rational.* Sample answer: capable of being expressed as a comparison of two numbers

2 TEACH

Using Cooperative Groups
When you discuss the Venn diagram, have small groups each draw a number line from −10 to 10. Have them graph each of the rational numbers except −80 shown in the Venn diagram.

Error Analysis

Watch for students whose fractions are simplified but not in simplest terms.

Prevent by having them factor the numerator and denominator of their answer to look for other common factors.

6-5 Rational Numbers

Objective
Identify and simplify rational numbers.

Words to Learn
rational number
simplest form

DID YOU KNOW
Edison's light was a glass bulb containing a carbon filament in a vacuum. It burned for $13\frac{1}{2}$ hours.

In 1879, Thomas Alva Edison invented the electric light. His light was an incandescent bulb. That is, light was produced by running electricity through a filament to produce the light. Fluorescent bulbs produce light by running current through mercury vapor.

Fluorescent bulbs save energy. They last longer and use about $\frac{1}{4}$ the energy of an incandescent bulb. A 60-watt incandescent bulb costs around $0.53, while a compact fluorescent bulb costs about $12.

The numbers $\frac{1}{4}$, 0.53, and 12 are all **rational numbers.** Rational numbers can also be negative.

Rational Numbers	Any number that can be expressed in the form $\frac{a}{b}$, where a and b are integers and $b \neq 0$, is called a rational number.

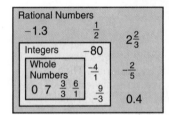

You can use a Venn diagram to show how sets within the rational numbers are related.

In the Venn diagram at the left, the smallest rectangle contains the set of *whole numbers.* The middle rectangle contains the set of *integers,* and the largest rectangle contains the set of *rational numbers.*

Notice that whole numbers and integers are included in the set of rational numbers because integers, such as 6 and −4, can be written as $\frac{6}{1}$ and $\frac{-4}{1}$.

The set of rational numbers also includes decimals because they can be written as fractions with a power of ten for the denominator. For example, −0.17 can be written as $-\frac{17}{100}$.

The number line below is separated into eighths to show the graphs of some common fractions and decimals.

0	0.125	0.25	0.375	0.5	0.625	0.75	0.875	1
$\frac{0}{8}$	$\frac{1}{8}$	$\frac{1}{4}$	$\frac{3}{8}$	$\frac{1}{2}$	$\frac{5}{8}$	$\frac{3}{4}$	$\frac{7}{8}$	$\frac{8}{8}$

OPTIONS

Reteaching Activity

Using Models Have students model a fraction by shading the appropriate sections of a rectangle. Then have them shade sections of a congruent rectangle to model the equivalent fraction in simplest form.

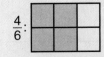

$\frac{4}{6}$: $\frac{2}{3}$:

Study Guide Masters, p. 50

Name _____ Date _____

Study Guide Worksheet 6-5

Rational Numbers

Whole numbers are numbers in the set {0, 1, 2, 3, . . .}. Integers are the whole numbers and their opposites.

Rational numbers are numbers that can be expressed in the form $\frac{a}{b}$, where a and b are integers and $b \neq 0$.

Examples $6\frac{1}{7}$ can be written as $\frac{43}{7}$.   58 can be written as $\frac{58}{1}$.

     0.65 can be written as $\frac{65}{100}$.   -79 can be written as $\frac{-79}{1}$.

     -0.7 can be written as $\frac{-7}{10}$.   0 can be written as $\frac{0}{1}$.

When a rational number is expressed as a fraction, it is commonly written in simplest form. A fraction is in simplest form when the GCF of the numerator and denominator is 1.

Example   Write $\frac{15}{24}$ in simplest form.

Mixed numbers are also included in the set of rational numbers because any mixed number can be written as an improper fraction. For example, $2\frac{2}{3}$ can be written as $\frac{8}{3}$.

Examples

Name all the sets of numbers to which each number belongs.

1 **18**   18 is a whole number and an integer. Since it can be written as $\frac{18}{1}$, it is also a rational number.

2 **−7**   −7 is an integer and a rational number. −7 can be written as $\frac{-7}{1}$ or $\frac{7}{-1}$.

3 **$-4\frac{3}{5}$**   Since $-4\frac{3}{5}$ can be written as $-\frac{23}{5}$, it is a rational number.

4 **0.261**   Since 0.261 can be written as $\frac{261}{1,000}$, it is a rational number.

When a rational number is represented as a fraction, it is commonly expressed in **simplest form**. A fraction is in simplest form when the GCF of the numerator and denominator is 1.

Example 5

Write $\frac{12}{30}$ in simplest form.

Method 1

$12 = 2 \cdot 2 \cdot 3$ *The GCF of 12*
$30 = 2 \cdot 3 \cdot 5$ *and 30 is 2 · 3 or 6.*

$\frac{12}{30} \quad \Rightarrow \quad \frac{12 \div 6}{30 \div 6} = \frac{2}{5}$

Method 2

$$\frac{12}{30} = \frac{\overset{1}{\cancel{2}} \cdot 2 \cdot \overset{1}{\cancel{3}}}{\underset{1}{\cancel{2}} \cdot \underset{1}{\cancel{3}} \cdot 5} = \frac{2}{5}$$

The slashes indicate that the numerator and denominator are divided by 2 · 3, the GCF.

Since the GCF of 2 and 5 is 1, the fraction $\frac{2}{5}$ is in simplest form.

Checking for Understanding

Communicating Mathematics

Read and study the lesson to answer each question.

1. **Tell** how you know if a number is a rational number. See margin.
2. **Write** an example of a rational number that is not an integer. $\frac{3}{4}$
3. **Tell** how you know whether a fraction is in simplest form. See margin.
4. **Write** directions telling how to express $\frac{20}{25}$ in simplest form. See margin.

Bell Ringer

Study these examples of fractions rewritten in simplest form:

$$\frac{16}{64} = \frac{1}{4} \qquad \frac{19}{95} = \frac{1}{5} \qquad \frac{26}{65} = \frac{2}{5}$$

Compare the digits in the original fraction and the simplified fraction. What is unusual about these expressions that is not true of other fractions? They can be simplified by "cancelling" like digits in the numerator and denominator.

Additional Answers

1. The number can be written in the form $\frac{a}{b}$ where *a* and *b* are integers and $b \neq 0$.
3. The GCF of the numerator and denominator is 1.
4. Divide 20 and 25 by their GCF.

More Examples

Name all the sets of numbers to which each number belongs.

For Example 1

−2.3   rationals

For Example 2

412   wholes, integers, rationals

For Example 3

$\frac{-10}{2}$ integers, rationals

For Example 4

0.55   rationals

For Example 5

Write $\frac{18}{24}$ in simplest form. $\frac{3}{4}$

Checking for Understanding

Exercises 1–4 are designed to help you assess students' understanding through reading, writing, speaking, and modeling. You should work through these exercises with your students and then monitor their work on Guided Practice Exercises 5–13.

Practice Masters, p. 50

Name _____ Date _____

Practice Worksheet 6-5

Rational Numbers

Name all the sets of numbers to which each number belongs.

1. $\frac{2}{3}$ rationals   2. -1.7 rationals   3. -3 rationals, integers

4. $\frac{200}{5}$ rationals, integers, whole numbers   5. 0 rationals, integers, whole numbers   6. $-\frac{6}{2}$ rationals, integers

7. 9 rationals, integers, whole numbers   8. $6\frac{2}{8}$ rationals   9. 4.7 rationals

Determine whether each fraction is in simplest form. If it is not in simplest form, write it in simplest form.

10. $\frac{8}{24}$ $\frac{1}{3}$ 11. $\frac{15}{60}$ $\frac{1}{4}$ 12. $\frac{27}{36}$ $\frac{3}{4}$

13. $-\frac{42}{50}$ $-\frac{21}{25}$ 14. $-\frac{32}{48}$ $-\frac{2}{3}$ 15. $-\frac{19}{47}$ in simplest form

Write each fraction in simplest form.

16. $\frac{18}{36}$ $\frac{1}{2}$ 17. $-\frac{24}{45}$ $-\frac{8}{15}$ 18. $\frac{64}{72}$ $\frac{8}{9}$

19. $\frac{18}{22}$ $\frac{9}{11}$ 20. $\frac{32}{70}$ $\frac{16}{35}$ 21. $\frac{17}{52}$ $\frac{17}{52}$

22. $\frac{15}{80}$ $\frac{3}{16}$ 23. $-\frac{68}{17}$ -4 24. $\frac{36}{104}$ $\frac{9}{26}$

25. $-\frac{24}{100}$ $-\frac{6}{25}$ 26. $\frac{18}{54}$ $\frac{1}{3}$ 27. $-\frac{30}{75}$ $-\frac{2}{5}$

28. $\frac{1,000}{2,000}$ $\frac{1}{2}$ 29. $\frac{14}{64}$ $\frac{7}{32}$ 30. $-\frac{9}{108}$ $-\frac{1}{12}$

T50
Glencoe Division, Macmillan/McGraw-Hill

Draw a number line on the chalkboard. Indicate various points on the line and ask students to say whether the coordinate of each point is a whole number, an integer, and/or a rational number.

3 PRACTICE/APPLY

Assignment Guide
Maximum: 14–36
Minimum: 14–17, 19–27 odd, 28–35

For **Extra Practice,** see p. 596.

Alternate Assessment

Modeling Provide students with a thermometer with negative temperatures indicated. Ask students to identify whole numbers, integers, and rational numbers on the thermometer.

Additional Answer

36. **a.** $\frac{3}{4}$ as many in 1970 as in 1985.
b. $\frac{6}{6.5}$ or $\frac{12}{13}$; $\frac{7}{5}$; $\frac{8}{5}$, $\frac{8.25}{4.25}$ or $\frac{33}{17}$; $\frac{8.75}{4.25}$ or $\frac{35}{17}$

Enrichment Masters, p. 50

Name _____ Date _____

Enrichment Worksheet 6-5

Rational Numbers as Ordered Pairs

If you think of a rational number as an ordered pair, it can be located on a coordinate system. The example graph shows the number $\frac{3}{2}$. The horizontal axis is used for the numerator and the vertical axis for the denominator.

Graph the rational numbers as ordered pairs.

1. $\frac{1}{2}$, $\frac{2}{4}$, $\frac{3}{6}$, $\frac{4}{8}$
2. $\frac{4}{3}$, $\frac{8}{6}$, $\frac{12}{9}$, $\frac{16}{12}$, $\frac{20}{15}$
3. $\frac{-3}{2}$, $\frac{-6}{4}$, $\frac{-9}{6}$
4. $\frac{-5}{2}$, $\frac{-10}{4}$, $\frac{5}{2}$, $\frac{10}{6}$

5. Complete this generalization: A rational number $\frac{a}{b}$ is shown on a coordinate system using the ordered pair (a, b). Using this model, equivalent rational numbers will _all lie on the same line_.

6. Show that this generalization is false: A rational number $\frac{a}{b}$ is shown on a coordinate system using the ordered pair (a, b). All ordered pairs on the same line stand for equivalent rational numbers. _Answers will vary. Possible counterexample is (0,0)._

T 50
Glencoe Division, Macmillan/McGraw-Hill

226

Name all the sets of numbers to which each number belongs.

5. $1\frac{2}{3}$ R
6. -11.6 R
7. $\frac{15}{32}$ R
8. 0 W, I, R

Determine whether each fraction is in simplest form. If it is not in simplest form, write it in simplest form.

9. $-\frac{42}{48}$ $-\frac{7}{8}$
10. $\frac{4}{5}$ simplest form
11. $\frac{8}{16}$ $\frac{1}{2}$
12. $\frac{13}{52}$ $\frac{1}{4}$
13. $-\frac{27}{49}$ simplest form

Exercises

Name all the sets of numbers to which each number belongs.

14. 1.5 R
15. $16\frac{8}{9}$ R
16. -10 I, R
17. 625 W, I, R

Write each fraction in simplest form.

18. $-\frac{2}{8}$ $-\frac{1}{4}$
19. $\frac{-3}{12}$ $-\frac{1}{4}$
20. $\frac{6}{21}$ $\frac{2}{7}$
21. $\frac{24}{54}$ $\frac{4}{9}$
22. $-\frac{5}{8}$ $-\frac{5}{8}$
23. $\frac{3}{51}$ $\frac{1}{17}$
24. $-\frac{10}{16}$ $-\frac{5}{8}$
25. $-\frac{45}{72}$ $-\frac{5}{8}$
26. $\frac{81}{99}$ $\frac{9}{11}$
27. $\frac{14}{66}$ $\frac{7}{33}$

28. Write two other names for -10. $\frac{-10}{1}$ or $\frac{10}{-1}$

29. Evaluate $3[14 - (8 - 5)^2] + 20$. *(Lesson 2-1)* **35**
30. Solve $s = -\frac{132}{11}$. *(Lesson 3-7)* **–12**
31. **Statistics** Find the interquartile range of the set {239, 226, 232, 212, 243, 216, 250}. *(Lesson 4-6)* **27**
32. Find the GCF of 36, 108, and 180. *(Lesson 6-4)* **36**

33. **Critical Thinking** Does $\frac{8}{3.2}$ name a rational number? If so, what one? If not, why not? **yes; 2.5 or $2\frac{1}{2}$**
34. **Number Sense** Both the numerator and denominator of a fraction are even. Can you tell if the fraction is in simplest form? Explain. **See Solutions Manual.**
35. **School** Vanesa correctly answered 16 of 25 history test questions. How would you describe her success as a fraction in simplest form? $\frac{16}{25}$

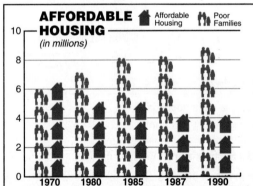

AFFORDABLE HOUSING (in millions)
Affordable Housing   Poor Families
1970 1980 1985 1987 1990

36. **Housing** The graph at the left shows the number of poor families and the number of affordable housing.
   a. How does the number of poor families in 1970 compare to the number of poor families in 1985?
   b. Suppose p represents the number of poor families and h represents the number of affordable houses. Describe the value of $\frac{p}{h}$ for each year shown on the graph.
   36a–b. See margin.

226   **Chapter 6** Patterns and Number Sense

OPTIONS

Extending the Lesson

Geometry Connection The design below illustrates the equivalence $\frac{6}{12} = \frac{1}{2}$. Have students create their own designs and exchange with other students, asking them to name the equivalent fractions modeled.

Cooperative Learning Activity

What's Your Source? **6-5**

Use groups of 4.
Materials: Newspapers, magazines

• Write the headings "Found Form," "$\frac{a}{b}$," and "Source" in a row at the top of a sheet of paper.

➡ Using newspapers and magazines, find examples of rational numbers expressed as fractions, mixed numbers, decimals, whole numbers, and integers. Write each rational number as it appears in the newspaper or magazine under the heading "Found Form," and then write the number in the form $\frac{a}{b}$ under the "$\frac{a}{b}$" heading. Finally, under the "Source" heading, write where you found each rational number.

Share your work with other groups.

Glencoe Mathematics: Applications and Connections, Course 3

Rational Numbers and Decimals

Objective

Express rational numbers as decimals and terminating decimals as fractions.

Words to Learn

terminating decimal

Scott Kuns and Richard Buchanan install glass in office buildings. Each pane of glass they installed in the 13th and 14th floors of the Beggs Building in Columbus, Ohio was $1\frac{3}{16}$ inch thick and weighed about 400 pounds each. The mixed number $1\frac{3}{16}$ is equivalent to $\frac{19}{16}$.

DID YOU KNOW

In 1952, A. Pilkington developed the float glass process, the main method of producing glass today. Molten glass is poured onto the surface of molten tin. This makes the surface of the glass very smooth. A ribbon of glass passes over rollers into a tunnel where it is cooled and cut into sheets.

It is sometimes more convenient to write rational numbers as decimals instead of fractions. One reason is that it is easier to compare decimals. It may also be more convenient to use decimals when computing with a calculator or computer.

Consider the fraction $\frac{19}{16}$. Remember that a fraction is another way of writing a division problem. So, $\frac{19}{16}$ means $19 \div 16$. Any fraction can be expressed as a decimal by dividing the numerator by the denominator.

Use a calculator.

19 $\boxed{\div}$ 16 $\boxed{=}$ 1.1875

Use pencil and paper.

$$
\begin{array}{r}
1.1875 \\
16\overline{)19.0000} \\
-16 \\
\hline
3\,0 \\
-1\,6 \\
\hline
1\,40 \\
-1\,28 \\
\hline
120 \\
-112 \\
\hline
80 \\
-80 \\
\hline
0
\end{array}
$$

Annex zeros to the numerator: 19 = 19.0000.

Mental Math Hint

• • • • • • • • • •

Here are some commonly used fraction-decimal equivalencies. It is helpful to know them by memory.

$\frac{1}{2} = 0.5$ $\frac{1}{5} = 0.2$

$\frac{1}{4} = 0.25$ $\frac{1}{10} = 0.1$

$\frac{1}{8} = 0.125$

The fraction $\frac{19}{16}$ can be expressed as the decimal 1.1875. Remember that a decimal like 1.1875 is called a **terminating decimal** because the division ends or terminates when the remainder is zero.

Lesson 6-6 Rational Numbers and Decimals **227**

NCTM Standards: 1–7, 9, 13

Lesson Resources
• Study Guide Master 6-6
• Practice Master 6-6
• Enrichment Master 6-6
• Evaluation Master, Quiz A, p. 52
• Group Activity Card 6-6

Transparency 6-6 contains the 5-Minute Check and a teaching aid for this lesson.

🕐 5-Minute Check
(Over Lesson 6-5)

Name all the sets of numbers to which each number belongs.

1. -5 integers, rationals

2. 0.37   rationals

3. $\frac{8}{2}$ wholes, integers, rationals

Write each fraction in simplest form.

4. $-\frac{9}{18}$ $-\frac{1}{2}$ **5.** $\frac{6}{10}$ $\frac{3}{5}$

1 FOCUS

Motivating the Lesson

Activity   Show a collection of 10 identical objects. Have a student remove 5 of them. Ask the following questions.

• *How can you write the fraction of objects removed?* $\frac{1}{2}$

• *How can you write the portion removed as a decimal?*   five tenths = 0.5

Write: $\frac{1}{2} = 0.5$

2 TEACH

Using Mental Math   Draw attention to the equivalents listed in the Mental Math Hint. Ask students to use them to find the following decimal equivalents mentally.

a. $\frac{3}{4}$ 0.75   **b.** $\frac{2}{5}$ 0.4

c. $\frac{7}{10}$ 0.7   **d.** $\frac{4}{5}$ 0.8

e. $\frac{3}{8}$ 0.375   **f.** $\frac{3}{10}$ 0.3

OPTIONS

Reteaching Activity

Using Cooperative Groups   One player secretly finds the decimal expression of a fraction with a denominator of 16, 32, or 64. The player states the denominator and the decimal. The other players use their calculators to find the correct numerator. The first player to find the numerator scores a point.

Study Guide Masters, p. 51

Name _____   Date _____

Study Guide Worksheet 6-6

Rational Numbers and Decimals

To change a fraction to a decimal, divide the numerator by the denominator.

Example   Express $\frac{5}{8}$ as a decimal.

Use a calculator.

5 $\boxed{\div}$ 8 $\boxed{=}$ 0.625

$\frac{5}{8} = 0.625$

The remainder is 0. 0.625 is a terminating decimal.

Use paper and pencil.

$$
\begin{array}{r}
0.625 \\
8\overline{)5.000} \\
-48 \\
\hline
20 \\
-16 \\
\hline
40 \\
-40 \\
\hline
0
\end{array}
$$

Annex zeros as needed.

$\frac{5}{8} = 0.625$

A **terminating decimal** can be written as a fraction with

227

Examples

1 Express $\frac{3}{5}$ as a decimal.

$3 \boxed{\div} 5 \boxed{=} 0.6$ So, $\frac{3}{5} = 0.6$.

2 Express $4\frac{9}{16}$ as a decimal.

$$4\frac{9}{16} = 4 + \frac{9}{16}$$

$4 \boxed{+} 9 \boxed{\div} 16 \boxed{=} 4.5625$ So, $4\frac{9}{16} = 4.5625$.

Every terminating decimal can be expressed as a fraction with a denominator of 10, 100, 1,000, and so on. Thus, terminating decimals are rational numbers.

Examples

Express each decimal as a fraction or mixed number in simplest form.

3 0.65
$$0.65 = \frac{65}{100}$$
$$= \frac{13}{20} \quad \text{\textit{Simplify. The GCF of 65 and 100 is 5.}}$$

4 -2.625
$$-2.625 = -2\frac{625}{1,000}$$
$$= -2\frac{5}{8} \quad \text{\textit{Simplify.}}$$

Checking for Understanding

Communicating Mathematics

Read and study the lesson to answer each question.

1. **Tell** how to express a fraction as a decimal. numerator $\div$ denominator

2. **Write** two examples of fractions that can be expressed as terminating decimals. Sample answers: $\frac{1}{2}$, $\frac{3}{4}$

3. **Show** why 0.37 is a rational number. $\frac{37}{100}$

4. **Write** sixteen thousandths as a decimal and then as a fraction. 0.016, $\frac{16}{1,000}$

Guided Practice

Express each fraction or mixed number as a decimal.

5. $\frac{2}{5}$ 0.4   6. $-\frac{7}{8}$ -0.875   7. $\frac{13}{4}$ 3.25   8. $-\frac{7}{20}$ -0.35   9. $3\frac{14}{25}$ 3.56

Express each decimal as a fraction or mixed number in simplest form.

10. -0.4 $-\frac{2}{5}$ 11. 0.75 $\frac{3}{4}$ 12. 0.17 $\frac{17}{100}$ 13. 3.12 $3\frac{3}{25}$ 14. -5.375 $-5\frac{3}{8}$

Exercises

Independent Practice

Express each fraction or mixed number as a decimal.   23. -0.28125 19. -5.375

15. $-\frac{4}{5}$ -0.8   16. $\frac{9}{10}$ 0.9   17. $-\frac{7}{25}$ -0.28   18. $\frac{11}{4}$ 2.75   19. $-5\frac{3}{8}$

20. $\frac{5}{16}$ 0.3125   21. $7\frac{1}{4}$ 7.25   22. $-\frac{17}{20}$ -0.85   23. $-\frac{9}{32}$ 24. $\frac{71}{40}$ 1.775

228   **Chapter 6** Patterns and Number Sense

Express each decimal as a fraction or mixed number in simplest form.

25. 0.05 $\frac{1}{20}$

26. -1.3 $-1\frac{3}{10}$

27. 0.64 $\frac{16}{25}$

28. -8.52 $-8\frac{13}{25}$

29. 3.85 $3\frac{17}{20}$

30. 4.105 $4\frac{21}{200}$

31. -0.075 $-\frac{3}{40}$

32. -20.35 $-20\frac{7}{20}$

33. When $\frac{131}{200}$ is expressed as a decimal, what kind of decimal is it? **terminating**

34. How would you use a calculator to express $9\frac{11}{15}$ as a decimal? **See margin.**

Mixed Review

35. **Algebra** Write an algebraic expression to represent *the quotient of y and 3 decreased by 15.* (*Lesson 2-6*) $\frac{y}{3} - 15$

36. Replace ● with >, <, or = in 10 ● −10. (*Lesson 3-2*) **>**

37. **Statistics** What numbers would you use as stems to make a stem-and-leaf plot of 11.4, 9.7, 10.8, 11.2, 9.5, 12.4, and 10.3? (*Lesson 4-4*) **9, 10, 11, 12**

38. Name all the sets of numbers to which −38 belongs. (*Lesson 6-5*) **I, R**

39. $\frac{1}{2}, \frac{1}{4}, \frac{1}{5}, \frac{1}{8}, \frac{1}{10}, \frac{1}{16}$

Problem Solving and Applications

39. **Critical Thinking** A unit fraction is a fraction that has one as its numerator. Determine the six greatest unit fractions that are terminating decimals.

40. **Measurement** A micrometer measured the thickness of the wall of a plastic pipe as 0.084 inches. What fraction of an inch is this? $\frac{21}{250}$

41. **Portfolio Suggestion** Select one of the assignments from this chapter that you found particularly challenging. Place it in your portfolio. **See students' work.**

6 Assessment: Mid-Chapter Review

Use divisibility rules to determine if the first number is divisible by the second number. Write *yes* or *no*. (*Lesson 6-1*)

1. 582; 6 **yes**

2. 838; 4 **no**

3. 342; 9 **yes**

4. 10,290; 5 **yes**

Find the prime factorization of each number. (*Lesson 6-2*)

5. 36 $2^2 \cdot 3^2$

6. −45 $-1 \cdot 3^2 \cdot 5$

7. 128 2^7

8. 200 $2^3 \cdot 5^2$

9. **Weather** The high temperatures during your vacation were: 31°F, 26°F, 30°F, 29°F, 28°F, 27°F, 30°F, 32°F, 31°F, 28°F, 30°F, 29°F, 26°F, 27°F. Find the mode. (*Lesson 6-3*) **30°F**

Find the GCF for each group of numbers. (*Lesson 6-4*)

10. 25, 30 **5**

11. 64, 48 **16**

12. 12, 72, 24 **12**

Express each fraction in simplest form. (*Lesson 6-5*)

13. $\frac{8}{32}$ $\frac{1}{4}$

14. $-\frac{45}{60}$ $-\frac{3}{4}$

15. $\frac{35}{175}$ $\frac{1}{5}$

16. $\frac{27}{15}$ $1\frac{4}{5}$

Express each decimal as a fraction in simplest form and each fraction as a decimal. (*Lesson 6-6*)

17. -0.8 $-\frac{4}{5}$

18. $\frac{13}{25}$ 0.52

19. $-\frac{5}{8}$ -0.625

20. 4.85 $4\frac{17}{20}$

Lesson 6-6 Rational Numbers and Decimals **229**

Extending the Lesson

Using Cooperative Groups Have small groups find the missing digits in this division problem:

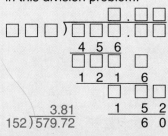

Cooperative Learning Activity

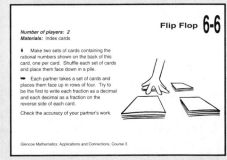

Flip Flop **6-6**

Number of players: 2
Materials: Index cards

● Make two sets of cards containing the rational numbers shown on the back of this card, one per card. Shuffle each set of cards and place them face down in a pile.

➤ Each partner takes a set of cards and places them face up in rows of four. Try to be the first to write each fraction as a decimal and each decimal as a fraction on the reverse side of each card.

Check the accuracy of your partner's work.

Glencoe Mathematics: Applications and Connections, Course 3

229

NCTM Standards: 1–9, 12

Lesson Resources
- Study Guide Master 6-7
- Practice Master 6-7
- Enrichment Master 6-7
- Group Activity Card 6-7

 Transparency 6-7 contains the 5-Minute Check and a teaching aid for this lesson.

5-Minute Check
(Over Lesson 6-6)

Express each fraction as a decimal.

1. $\frac{1}{8}$ 0.125
2. $\frac{9}{4}$ 2.25
3. $6\frac{3}{10}$ 6.3

Express each decimal as a fraction or mixed number in simplest form.

4. 0.44 $\frac{11}{25}$
5. −2.8 $-2\frac{4}{5}$

1 FOCUS

Motivating the Lesson

Activity Have students read the opening paragraph of the lesson. Have those students in the class who wear glasses or contacts raise their hands, and count them. Have students write the fraction of the class that wears glasses or contacts and compare it with the national average.

2 TEACH

Using Patterns Have students use their calculators and bar notation to express each fraction as a decimal.

a. $\frac{17}{99}$ $0.\overline{17}$
b. $\frac{41}{99}$ $0.\overline{41}$
c. $\frac{65}{99}$ $0.\overline{65}$
d. $\frac{87}{99}$ $0.\overline{87}$

Ask students to use their results to write 0.585858 . . . as a fraction.

$\frac{58}{99}$

6-7 Repeating Decimals

Objective
Express repeating decimals as fractions.

Words to Learn
repeating decimals
bar notation

How many students in your class wear glasses or contacts? Did you know that $\frac{2}{3}$ of all adults in the United States wear glasses or contacts at some time in their lives?

Calculator Hint

Most calculators round answers, but some truncate answers. *Truncate* means to cut-off at a certain place-value position, ignoring the digits that follow. How can you tell whether your calculator rounds or truncates?

When you divide 2 by 3 to find its decimal equivalent, you find that the digit 6 is repeated.

$$3\overline{)2.0000}0.6666\ldots \qquad \text{or} \qquad 2 \boxed{\div} 3 \boxed{=} 0.6666667$$

Decimals like 0.666666... are called **repeating decimals.** Since it is awkward to write all of these digits, you can use **bar notation** to show that the 6 repeats.

$$0.666666\ldots = 0.\overline{6}$$

Examples

Express each decimal using bar notation.

1   0.363636...
The digits 36 repeat.
$0.363636\ldots = 0.\overline{36}$

2   10.0456456...
The digits 456 repeat.
$10.0456456\ldots = 10.0\overline{456}$

The following examples show how to rename repeating decimals as fractions.

Example 3 Connection

TEEN SCENE

In 1938, Orbig Co., a U.S. corporation, produced the first plastic contact lenses. In the late 1970s, manufacturers began selling different-colored contact lenses for cosmetic purposes.

Algebra Express $0.\overline{2}$ as a fraction.

Let $N = 0.2$, or 0.222.... Then $10N = 2.222....$ *Multiply N by 10, because 1 digit repeats.*

Subtract $N = 0.222$ to eliminate the repeating part, 0.222....

$$\begin{array}{r} 10N = 2.222\ldots \\ -1N = 0.222\ldots \\ \hline 9N = 2 \end{array} \qquad N = 1N$$

$$N = \frac{2}{9} \qquad \text{So, } 0.\overline{2} = \frac{2}{9}.$$

Check: $2 \boxed{\div} 9 \boxed{=} 0.2222222$ ✔

OPTIONS

Reteaching Activity

Using Manipulatives Have students work in pairs using three number cubes and a calculator. One student rolls the cubes and uses the numbers to write a fraction. The numerator is the lowest number and the denominator is the sum of the other two numbers. The other student finds the decimal equivalent of the fraction.

Study Guide Masters, p. 52

Name _____ Date _____

Study Guide Worksheet 6-7

Repeating Decimals

A decimal in which a digit or group of digits repeat is called a **repeating decimal**. A repeating decimal is written with a bar over the digits that repeat.

Examples   0.58585858 . . .
The digits 58 repeat.
0.58585858 . . . = $0.\overline{58}$

3.1095095095 . . .
The digits 095 repeat.
3.1095095095 . . . = $3.1\overline{095}$

Repeating decimals can be expressed as fractions.

Example   Express $1.\overline{39}$ as a fraction.
Let $N = 1.3939$ . . .
Then $100 N = 139.3939$ . . .   Multiply by 100 because 2 digits repeat.
$100N = 139.3939$ . . .   Subtract to eliminate the repeating part

Example 4

Express $6.\overline{30}$ as a fraction.

Let $N = 6.\overline{30}$. Then $100N = 630.\overline{30}$. *Multiply N by 100, because 2 digits repeat.*

$$100N = 630.\overline{30}$$ *Subtracting eliminates the*
$$\underline{-\ N = \ \ \ 6.\overline{30}}$$ *repeating part, $0.\overline{30}$.*
$$99N = 624$$
$$N = \frac{624}{99} \text{ or } 6\frac{10}{33}$$

So, $6.\overline{30} = \frac{624}{99}$ or $6\frac{10}{33}$. **Check:** 624 ⌷÷⌷ 99 ⌷=⌷ 6.3030303 ✓

Since repeating decimals can be expressed as fractions, repeating decimals are included in the set of rational numbers.

2. Sample answers: $\frac{1}{3}, \frac{1}{6}$

3. 100 because 2 digits repeat

Checking for Understanding

Communicating Mathematics

Read and study the lesson to answer each question.

1. **Tell** how to express $2\frac{3}{11}$ as a repeating decimal. $3 \div 11 + 2$

2. **Write** two examples of fractions that can be expressed as repeating decimals.

3. **Tell** how you would choose a multiplier to express $1.\overline{13}$ as a fraction.

4. **Tell** why one of the steps in expressing a repeating decimal as a fraction involves multiplying by a power of 10. **so the repeating part can be eliminated**

Guided Practice

Write the first ten decimal places of each decimal.

5. $0.\overline{264}$ 6. $0.9\overline{2}$ 7. $0.5\overline{082}$ 8. $0.5\overline{082}$ 9. $0.2\overline{16}$

5. 0.2642642642 6. 0.9222222222 7. 0.5082508250 8. 0.5082082082 9. 0.2161616161

What multiplier, 10 or 100, would you use to express each decimal as a fraction?

10. 0.454545... **100** 11. $8.\overline{7}$ **10**   12. 10.622222... **10** 13. $-9.\overline{81}$ **100**

Exercises

Independent Practice

Express each decimal using bar notation.   16. $0.\overline{428571}$ 19. $-7.0\overline{74}$

14. 0.166666... $0.1\overline{6}$ 15. 29.272727... $29.\overline{27}$ 16. 0.42857142...

17. -2.454545... $-2.\overline{45}$ 18. 98.666666... $98.\overline{6}$ 19. -7.074747...

20. If $N = 0.\overline{894}$, what power of ten should you multiply by in order to express the decimal as a fraction? 10^3 or 1,000

21. Which number is greater, $8.\overline{32}$ or $8.\overline{31}$? $8.\overline{32}$

Bell Ringer

Arrange these decimals in order from least to greatest:

$$0.\overline{43},\ 0.43,\ 0.4\overline{3}$$

$0.43,\ 0.4\overline{3},\ 0.\overline{43}$

More Examples

For Example 1
Express 0.707070 . . . using bar notation. $0.\overline{70}$

For Example 2
Express 6.00943943 . . . using bar notation. $6.00\overline{943}$

For Example 3
Express $0.\overline{8}$ as a fraction. $\frac{8}{9}$

For Example 4
Express $1.\overline{18}$ as a fraction. $1\frac{2}{11}$

Checking for Understanding

Exercises 1–4 are designed to help you assess students' understanding through reading, writing, speaking, and modeling. You should work through these exercises with your students and then monitor their work on Guided Practice Exercises 5–13.

Practice Masters, p. 52

Close

Have students work in pairs. One student explains to the other how to express $0.\overline{4}$ as a fraction. $\frac{4}{9}$

Then the second student explains to the first student how to express $0.\overline{75}$ as a fraction. $\frac{25}{33}$

3 PRACTICE/APPLY

Assignment Guide

Maximum: 14–41
Minimum: 15–31 odd, 32–40

For **Extra Practice,** see p. 597.

Alternate Assessment

Speaking Tell students that you are thinking of a certain repeating decimal. Then tell them the number of repeating digits, 1, 2, or 3. Ask them to tell what power of 10 they would multiply N by to express the decimal as a fraction.

Enrichment Masters, p. 52

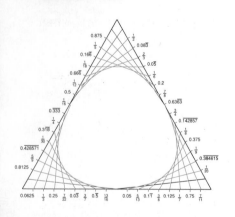

Express each repeating decimal as a fraction.

22. $0.\overline{4}$ $\frac{4}{9}$ 23. $-1.\overline{7}$ $-1\frac{7}{9}$ 24. $2.\overline{6}$ $2\frac{2}{3}$ 25. $0.\overline{54}$ $\frac{6}{11}$ 26. $-4.\overline{01}$ $-4\frac{1}{99}$

27. $2.\overline{5}$ $2\frac{5}{9}$ 28. $0.6\overline{2}$ $\frac{28}{45}$ 29. $0.\overline{24}$ $\frac{8}{33}$ 30. $7.\overline{52}$ $7\frac{52}{99}$ 31. $0.\overline{345}$ $\frac{115}{333}$

Mixed Review

32. Write $4 \cdot 4 \cdot 5 \cdot 5 \cdot 4$ using exponents. *(Lesson 1-9)* $4^3 \cdot 5^2$

33. Solve $63.45 = 4.23g$. Check your solution. *(Lesson 2-4)* 15

34. **Geometry** Find the value of x in the figure below. *(Lesson 5-1)* 25

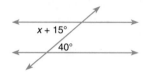

35. Draw a box-and-whisker plot of the following bowling scores: 122, 158, 163, 193, 111, 124, 194, 133, 193, 175, 166, 135, 164. What are the extremes? *(Lesson 4-7)* **See Solutions Manual.**

36. Express 8.68 as a mixed number in simplest form. *(Lesson 6-6)* $8\frac{17}{25}$

Problem Solving and Applications

37. **Geometry** In the figure at the right, what part of the perimeter is represented by the length of $\overline{AB}$? Express it as a decimal. $\frac{17}{57} \approx 0.2982456$

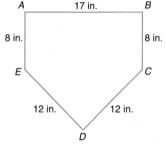

38. **Technology** A spreadsheet's display and two calculators' displays for $5 \div 9$ are listed below. How would each display the answer to $3 \div 11$?

a. 0.6 0.3

b. 0.5555556 0.2727273

c. 0.555555 0.272727

39. **Critical Thinking** List the factors of the denominators of several fractions in simplest form that can be expressed as repeating decimals. List the factors of the denominators of several fractions that can be expressed as terminating decimals. How can you tell by looking at the factors of the denominator of a fraction whether the fraction can be expressed as a repeating decimal? **See Solutions Manual.**

40. **Number Sense** Write a number that is between the pair of numbers shown in Exercise 21. **Sample answer: 8.314**

41. **Journal Entry** What concept in this chapter have you found most challenging? What do you think made it more difficult for you? **See students' work.**

OPTIONS

Extending the Lesson

Using Tables Have students study the following table.

Fraction	$\frac{5}{9}$	$\frac{74}{99}$	$\frac{415}{999}$
Decimal	$0.\overline{5}$	$0.\overline{74}$	$0.\overline{415}$

Ask them to express these decimals as fractions:

a. $0.\overline{512}$ $\frac{512}{999}$ b. $0.\overline{68}$ $\frac{68}{99}$

Cooperative Learning Activity

Bar Code 6-7

Number of players: 2
Materials: Index cards, spinners

♦ Each partner makes a set of cards containing the decimals shown on the back of this card. Each partner shuffles his or her cards and then places them face down in rows of four. Label equal sections of two spinners "T" and "R."

➡ In turn, each partner spins a spinner. If your spinner lands on "T," write each decimal in the first row of cards as a fraction in simplest form. If your spinner lands on "R," you must draw a bar over the digits to the right of the decimal point on each card in the first row and then write the repeating decimals as fractions in simplest form. (Each partner writes his or her fractions on a separate sheet of paper.) Repeat the procedure for all five rows. Try to complete each row faster than your partner. Check the accuracy of each other's work.

Glencoe Mathematics: Applications and Connections, Course 3

6-8 Simple Events

Objective
Find the probability of a simple event.

Words to Learn
outcome
random
event
probability

Mr. Cummins teaches mathematics at Lyons Township Middle School. When his class works in cooperative groups, he tosses a number cube to determine which group will demonstrate how they solved a problem. What is the chance that the number cube lands on 4?

When Mr. Cummins tosses the number cube, there are six equally-likely results or **outcomes.** The cube can show either 1, 2, 3, 4, 5, or 6. Each outcome has the same chance of occurring. When all outcomes have an *equally likely* chance of happening, we say that the outcomes happen at **random.**

An **event** is a specific outcome or type of outcome. In this case, the event is tossing a 4. **Probability** is the chance that an event will happen.

Definition of Probability	$\text{Probability} = \dfrac{\text{number of ways that an event can occur}}{\text{number of possible outcomes}}$

" When am I ever going to use this? "
Suppose you play tennis after school once a week with 5 friends. Each week, your opponent is selected by picking names from a hat. To determine the probability that you will get a particular opponent, you can make a sample space of all the possibilities.

Use the scale below when you consider the probability of an event. When it is *impossible* for an outcome to happen, its probability is 0. An outcome that is *certain* to happen has a probability of 1.

```
        impossible          50-50
                            chance                    certain
        |-----------------------|------------------------|
        0                       1                        1
                                ─
                                2
```

The probability of an outcome is written as a number from 0 to 1.

Mini-Lab

Work with a partner.
Materials: dice or number cubes

- Roll two dice 50 times and find the sum of the numbers on the dice. Record each sum as being either even or odd.
- Roll two dice 50 times and find the product of the numbers on the dice. Record each product as being either even or odd.

Talk About It

a. Same; half of the possibilities yield an even sum.
b. More likely; 3 of 4 possibilities have an even factor.

a. Would you say that an even sum is more likely or less likely to occur than an odd sum? Why?

b. Would you say that an even product is more likely or less likely to occur than an odd product? Why?

Lesson 6-8 Probability Connection: Simple Events **233**

OPTIONS

Reteaching Activity

Using Manipulatives Have pairs of students calculate the probabilities of the following outcomes when a die is tossed.

1. 6 $\frac{1}{6}$ 2. an odd number $\frac{1}{2}$

Now have students roll a die 50 times, record the results, and explain them in regard to the calculated probabilities.

Study Guide Masters, p. 53

Name _____ Date _____

Study Guide Worksheet 6-8

Probability: Simple Events

If you toss a coin, there are two possible outcomes, heads or tails. Each outcome has the same chance of occurring. The two outcomes are equally likely. A particular outcome, such as tossing a tail, or a set of outcomes is an event. Probability is the chance that an event will happen.

$\text{Probability} = \dfrac{\text{number of ways that an event can occur}}{\text{number of possible outcomes}}$

Tossing tails can occur 1 way out of 2 possible outcomes. $P(\text{tail}) = \frac{1}{2}$

The probability of an event can be written as a number from 0 to 1. If it is impossible for an event to happen, the event has a probability of 0. If an event is certain to happen, it has a probability of 1.

impossible   equal chance   certain

6-8 Lesson Notes

NCTM Standards: 1–4, 6, 7, 11, 12

Lesson Resources
- Study Guide Master 6-8
- Practice Master 6-8
- Enrichment Master 6-8
- Interdisciplinary Master, p. 20
- Group Activity Card 6-8

Transparency 6-8 contains the 5-Minute Check and a teaching aid for this lesson.

⏱ 5-Minute Check
(Over Lesson 6-7)

Express each decimal using bar notation.

1. 0.777 . . . $0.\overline{7}$
2. 1.353535 . . . $1.\overline{35}$
3. −6.9242424 . . .
   $-6.9\overline{24}$
4. Express $0.\overline{5}$ as a fraction.
   $\frac{5}{9}$

1 FOCUS

Motivating the Lesson

Questioning Ask students to rate the likelihood of each of the following events on a scale of 0 to 10 (0 = impossible, 10 = certain).
- The sun will come up tomorrow.
- The next president will be a woman.
- There is life elsewhere in the universe.
- It will rain cats and dogs today.

2 TEACH

Using the Mini-Lab Have students prepare a table for recording their results like the one shown here. One student can roll the dice while the other records the outcome. Students should switch roles so that they share the two tasks equally.

Odd	Even
ℍℍ	ℍℍ
ℍℍ	III
I	

Geometry A pin is dropped onto the square at the right. The point of the pin lands in one of the small regions.

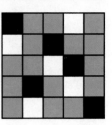

a. What is the probability that the point lands inside either a red or a black region?

$$P(\text{red or black}) = \frac{\text{red squares} + \text{black squares}}{\text{total number of squares}}$$

$$= \frac{7 + 5}{25}$$

$$= \frac{12}{25} \text{ or } 0.48$$

b. What is the probability that the point lands inside a blue region?

Since there are no blue regions, the probability is 0.

Checking for Understanding   For answers to Exercises 3-5, see margin.

Communicating Mathematics

2. The outcome is certain to happen.

Read and study the lesson to answer each question.

1. **Tell** what probability means. chance that an event will happen
2. **Tell** what it means for an outcome to have a probability of 1.
3. **Write** an example of an outcome with a probability of 1.
4. **Tell** why the probability of spinning a number divisible by three on the spinner at the right is 0.
5. **Draw** a spinner where the probability of an outcome of one is $\frac{1}{2}$.

Guided Practice

State the probability of each outcome as a fraction and a decimal.

6. A coin is tossed and shows tails. $\frac{1}{2}$ or 0.5
7. Your friend will live to be 500 years old. 0
8. A die is rolled and it shows a number divisible by three. $\frac{1}{3}$ or $0.\overline{3}$
9. A date picked at random is Tuesday. $\frac{1}{7}$ or $0.\overline{142857}$
10. This is a mathematics book. 1

A bag contains three black, seven red, four orange, and six green jelly beans. A blindfolded student draws one jelly bean. Find the probability of each outcome.

11. It is a white jelly bean. 0
12. It is a white or a green jelly bean. $\frac{3}{10}$
13. It is red. $\frac{7}{20}$
14. It is not orange. $\frac{4}{5}$
15. It is not purple. 1
16. It is black, red, or green. $\frac{4}{5}$

234   **Chapter 6** Patterns and Number Sense

Exercises

Independent
Practice

The letters of the word "commutative" are written one each on 11 identical slips of paper and shuffled in a hat. A blindfolded student draws one slip of paper. Find the probability of each outcome.

17. $P(t)$ $\frac{2}{11}$

18. $P(\text{vowel})$ $\frac{5}{11}$

19. $P(n)$ 0

20. $P(\text{not c})$ $\frac{10}{11}$

21. $P(\text{m or v})$ $\frac{3}{11}$

22. $P(\text{not m or t})$ $\frac{7}{11}$

Numbers from 1 to 49 are printed on table tennis balls, mixed by a machine, and drawn at random. One ball is drawn.

23. What is $P(\text{an even number})$? $\frac{24}{49}$

24. What is $P(\text{a two-digit number})$? $\frac{40}{49}$

25. What is $P(\text{a positive number})$? 1

26. What is $P(\text{a perfect square})$? $\frac{1}{7}$

27. What is $P(\text{a number divisible by 10})$? $\frac{4}{49}$

28. What is $P(\text{a negative number})$? 0

29. What is P (a number that is the product of four different prime numbers)? 0

Mixed Review

30. **Geometry** Find the perimeter and area of the figure at the right. *(Lesson 2-9)*
$P = 36$ in., $A = 60$ in²

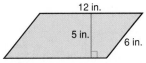

12 in.

5 in.

6 in.

31. Solve $s = -72 + 59$. *(Lesson 3-3)* -13

32. **Geometry** Tell if the pair of figures at the right are congruent, similar, or neither. *(Lesson 5-6)* **neither**

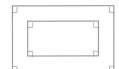

33. Express $8.\overline{72}$ as a mixed number. *(Lesson 6-7)* $8\frac{8}{11}$

Problem Solving
and
Applications

34. **Make Up a Problem** Write a problem in which the answer will be a probability of $0.\overline{3}$. See students' work.

35. **Marketing** Pricey's Drive Thru is promoting their new sausage sandwich by distributing cards with a chance to win a free sandwich, a free soft drink, or a free dessert. They want the probability of winning a sandwich to be 0.015, of winning a drink to be 0.2, and of winning a dessert to be 0.04. They will distribute 10,000 cards.

a. How many winning cards will there be for a free sandwich? **150 cards**

b. How many winning cards will there be for a free drink? **2,000 cards**

c. How many winning cards will there be for a free dessert? **400 cards**

d. How many cards will say "Better luck next time!"? **7,450 cards**

36. **Number Sense** Can a probability ever be greater than 1? Why?

37. **Number Sense** Can a probability ever be less than 0? Why? **No; the number of ways something can occur cannot be negative.**

38. **Critical Thinking** A spider lowers itself onto one of the six squares of the T-shaped figure shown and then randomly moves to an adjacent square. Out of these moves, what is the probability that the spider ends up on a red square? $\frac{3}{5}$

36. No; the number of ways an event can occur cannot exceed the number of possible outcomes.

Extending the Lesson

Using Cooperative Groups

The *odds* that an event will occur are the ratio of favorable outcomes to unfavorable outcomes. When a number cube is tossed, the probability of rolling a 2 is $\frac{1}{6}$. The odds in favor of rolling a 2 are 1:5. Have small groups create and exchange problems involving the calculation of odds.

Cooperative Learning Activity

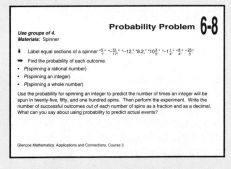

Probability Problem 6-8

Use groups of 4.
Materials: Spinner

Label equal sections of a spinner "$\frac{5}{1}$," "$-\frac{51}{17}$," "-12," "8.2," "$10\frac{3}{5}$," "$-1\frac{1}{4}$," "$\frac{8}{1}$," "$\frac{25}{3}$"

Find the probability of each outcome.
- $P(\text{spinning a rational number})$
- $P(\text{spinning an integer})$
- $P(\text{spinning a whole number})$

Use the probability for spinning an integer to predict the number of times an integer will be spun in twenty-five, fifty, and one hundred spins. Then perform the experiment. Write the number of successful outcomes out of each number of spins as a fraction and as a decimal. What can you say about using probability to predict actual events?

Glencoe Mathematics: Applications and Connections, Course 3

Close

Guide students to summarize the lesson by asking the following question. *How can you find the probability that an event will happen?* Divide the number of ways that the event can occur by the number of possible outcomes.

3 PRACTICE/APPLY

Assignment Guide

Maximum: 17–38

Minimum: 17–29 odd, 30–38

For **Extra Practice,** see p. 597.

Alternate Assessment

Modeling Have students use a deck of ten index cards numbered 1 through 10 to make up problems involving the probability of drawing certain cards. Have students explain their solutions.

Enrichment Masters, p. 53

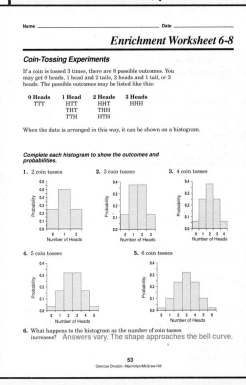

Name _____ Date _____

Enrichment Worksheet 6-8

Coin-Tossing Experiments

If a coin is tossed 3 times, there are 8 possible outcomes. You may get 0 heads, 1 head and 2 tails, 2 heads and 1 tail, or 3 heads. The possible outcomes may be listed like this:

0 Heads	1 Head	2 Heads	3 Heads
TTT	HTT	HHT	HHH
	THT	THH	
	TTH	HTH	

When the data is arranged in this way, it can be shown on a histogram.

Complete each histogram to show the outcomes and probabilities.

1. 2 coin tosses
2. 3 coin tosses
3. 4 coin tosses
4. 5 coin tosses
5. 6 coin tosses

6. What happens to the histogram as the number of coin tosses increases? Answers vary. The shape approaches the bell curve.

53

Glencoe Division, Macmillan/McGraw-Hill

NCTM Standards: 1–9

Lesson Resources
- Study Guide Master 6-9
- Practice Master 6-9
- Enrichment Master 6-9
- Group Activity Card 6-9

 Transparency 6-9 contains the 5-Minute Check and a teaching aid for this lesson.

🕐 **5-Minute Check**
(Over Lesson 6-8)

A drawer contains 3 yellow socks, 4 red socks, and 5 blue socks. One sock is drawn at random. Find the probability of each outcome.

1. P(red) $\frac{1}{3}$
2. P(red or blue) $\frac{3}{4}$
3. P(sock) 1
4. P(hat) 0

---

1 FOCUS

Motivating the Lesson

Activity Have students cut 4×6 rectangles from graph paper. Ask them to find the smallest square that can be constructed entirely of rectangles of this size. 12×12

2 TEACH

Using the Mini-Lab If colored pencils are not available, students can circle multiples of 2, draw X's through multiples of 4, and draw squares around multiples of 6.

6-9 Least Common Multiple

Objective
Find the least common multiple of two or more integers.

Words to Learn
multiple
least common
 multiple (LCM)

In the United States, a president is elected every four years. Members of the House of Representatives are elected every two years, and Senators are elected every six years. If a voter has the opportunity to vote for a president, a representative, and a senator in the same year, how long will it be until the same situation occurs again?

You can use multiples and the problem-solving strategy *make a list* to answer this question. A **multiple** of a number is the product of that number and any whole number.

Mini-Lab

Work with a partner.
Materials: colored pencils

- List the numbers from 1 to 30 on a sheet of paper. Use divisibility rules to cross out all the multiples of 2. Using a different color, cross out all the multiples of 4. Repeat the procedure with a third color to cross out all the multiples of 6.

Talk About It   b. common multiples of 2, 4, and 6
a. Which numbers were crossed out by all three colors? 12, 24
b. How would you describe these numbers?
c. What is the least number crossed out by all three colors? 12

In the Mini-Lab, you discovered some common multiples of 2, 4, and 6. The least of the nonzero common multiples of two or more numbers is called the **least common multiple (LCM)** of the numbers. The LCM of 2, 4, and 6 is 12. So, a voter will vote for all three positions in the same year 12 years from now.

Problem Solving Hint

• • • • • • • • • •

Find multiples by making a list.

Examples

1 List the first four multiples of 6.

$$\text{multiples of 6} \rightarrow \begin{array}{l} 0 \cdot 6 = 0 \\ 1 \cdot 6 = 6 \\ 2 \cdot 6 = 12 \\ 3 \cdot 6 = 18 \end{array}$$

2 List the first four multiples of x.

$$\text{multiples of } x \rightarrow \begin{array}{l} 0 \cdot x = 0 \\ 1 \cdot x = x \\ 2 \cdot x = 2x \\ 3 \cdot x = 3x \end{array}$$

OPTIONS

Reteaching Activity

Using Lists Many students will choose to list multiples when finding the LCM. Prepare charts like the one below for students. LCM = 12

	1	2	3	4	5	6
6	6	⑫	18	㉔	30	36
4	4	8	⑫	16	20	㉔

Study Guide Masters, p. 54

Name _____ Date _____

Study Guide Worksheet 6-9

Least Common Multiple

A multiple of a number is the product of that number and any whole number. The least nonzero multiple of two or more numbers is the **least common multiple (LCM)** of the numbers.

Example Find the least common multiple of 12 and 15.

multiples of 12: 0, 12, 24, 36, 48, 60, 72, 84, 96, 108, 120, 132, . . .
multiples of 15: 0, 15, 30, 45, 60, 75, 90, 105, 120, 135, . . .

60 and 120 are common multiples. The LCM is 60.

Prime factorization can also be used to find the LCM.

Example Find the least common multiple of 15, 28, and 30.

Calculator Hint

• • • • • • • • • •

You can use a calculator to find the LCM of a pair of numbers. Divide multiples of the greater number by the lesser number until you get a whole number quotient.

Example 3

Find the LCM of 6, 10, and 15.

multiples of 6: 0, 6, 12, 18, 24, 30, 36, 42, . . .
multiples of 10: 0, 10, 20, 30, 40, 50, 60, . . .
multiples of 15: 0, 15, 30, 45, 60, 75, 90, . . .

The LCM is 30.

Prime factorization can be used to find the LCM of a set of numbers. A common multiple contains *all* the prime factors of each number in the set. The LCM contains *each* factor the greatest number of times it appears in the set.

Examples

Use prime factorization to find the LCM for each set of numbers.

4 8, 20

$$8 = \boxed{2} \cdot \boxed{2} \cdot 2$$
$$20 = \boxed{2} \cdot \boxed{2} \cdot \quad 5$$

Express each common factor and all other factors.

$$\downarrow \quad \downarrow \quad \downarrow \quad \downarrow$$
$$2 \cdot 2 \cdot 2 \cdot 5$$

Multiply all the factors, using the common factors only once.

The LCM of 8 and 20 is $2^3 \cdot 5$ or 40.

5 21, 25, 9

$21 = 3 \cdot 7$ *The greatest power of 3 is 3^2.*
$25 = 5 \cdot 5$ or 5^2 *The greatest power of 5 is 5^2.*
$9 = 3 \cdot 3$ or 3^2 *The greatest power of 7 is 7^1.*

The LCM of 21, 25, and 9 is $3^2 \cdot 5^2 \cdot 7$ or 1,575.

Checking for Understanding

Communicating Mathematics

Read and study the lesson to answer each question.

1. **Tell** how to find the first six multiples of any number.

1. Multiply that number by 0, 1, 2, 3, 4, and 5.

2. **Write** a three-step procedure for finding the LCM of a set of numbers based on prime factorization. **See Solutions Manual.**

3. **Tell** what is always true about the first multiple of any number. It is zero.

4. **Tell** how to find the LCM of a set of numbers if you know the greatest power of each prime factor. multiply

Lesson 6-9 Least Common Multiple   **237**

More Examples

For Example 1
List the first four multiples of −3.   0, −3, −6, −9

For Example 2
List the first four multiples of 2n.   0, 2n, 4n, 6n

For Example 3
Find the LCM of 9, 12, and 18.   36

For Example 4
Use prime factorization to find the LCM of 21 and 27.   189

For Example 5
Use prime factorization to find the LCM of 48, 20, and 30.   240

Checking for Understanding

Exercises 1–4 are designed to help you assess students' understanding through reading, writing, speaking, and modeling. You should work through these exercises with your students and then monitor their work on Guided Practice Exercises 5–16.

Practice Masters, p. 54

Classroom Vignette

"My students find it easier to use the division method for finding the LCM."

The LCM of 24 and 36 is $2 \cdot 2 \cdot 3 \cdot 2 \cdot 3$ or $2^3 \cdot 3^2$.

$$
\begin{array}{r r}
2)\ 24 & 36 \\
2)\ 12 & 18 \\
3)\ 6 & 9 \\
2 & 3
\end{array}
$$

James L. Ruppe

James L. Ruppe, Teacher
Medina Junior High School, Medina, OH

Watch for students who confuse LCM and GCF.

Prevent by having them find both the LCM and GCF of several pairs of numbers. Point out that the LCM is a multiple, so it is <u>greater</u> than the given numbers; and the GCF is a factor, so it is <u>less</u> than the given numbers.

Close

Have students compare and contrast the two methods for finding the LCM, listing multiples and using prime factorization.

3 PRACTICE/APPLY

Assignment Guide
Maximum: 17–41
Minimum: 17–29 odd, 30–40

For **Extra Practice,** see p. 597.

Alternate Assessment

Writing Have students write a few sentences explaining how they would find the LCM of 18 and 30.

Enrichment Masters, p. 54

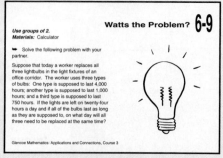

Name _____ Date _____

Enrichment Worksheet 6-9

Diophantine Equations

A *Diophantine equation* has integers for coefficients. And, there are restrictions on the possible solutions. The solutions usually are restricted to positive integers. Sometimes, negative integers are also allowed.

Solving Diophantine equations requires trial and error—and some luck!

Example Find all possible solutions for the Diophantine equation $5x + 2y = 42$. The numbers in each solution must be integers greater than 0.

$5x + 2y = 42$

First solve the equation for x: $x = \frac{42 - 2y}{5}$

The right side can be simplified: $x = 8 + \frac{2 - 2y}{5}$

Now, notice that the numerator $2 - 2y$ must be a multiple of 5. Otherwise, x will not be an integer.

Experiment with different values for y. The four possible solutions turn out to be (8, 1), (6, 6), (4, 11), and (2, 16).

Find at least one pair of positive integers that satisfies each Diophantine equation. The integers must be greater than 0.

1. $3x + 2y = 15$
   (1, 6) or (3, 3)
2. $2x + 7y = 29$
   (11, 1) or (4, 3)
3. $7x + 3y = 40$
   (4, 4) or (1, 11)
4. $3x + 4y = 22$
   (6, 1) or (2, 4)
5. $2x + 5y = 32$
   (11, 2), (6, 4), or (1, 6)
6. $7x + 5y = 118$
   (14, 4), (9, 11), or (4, 18)
7. $5x - 14y = 11$
   (5, 1), (19, 6), and others
8. $8x - 13y = 100$
   (19, 4), (32, 12), and others

Find one pair of integers that satisfies each equation. The integers may be either positive or negative, but one of them must be greater than 0.

9. $27x + 65y = 3$
   (-36, 15)
10. $45x + 144y = 36$
    (-12, 4)

54
Glencoe Division, Macmillan/McGraw-Hill

List the first six multiples of each number.

5. 5 **0, 5, 10, 15, 20, 25**
6. 18 **0, 18, 36, 54, 72, 90**
7. 20 **0, 20, 40, 60, 80, 100**
8. n **0, n, 2n, 3n, 4n, 5n**

Use lists to find the LCM for each set of numbers.

9. 1, 3, 5 **15**
10. 7, 21, 5 **105**
11. 15, 45, 60 **180**
12. 8, 28, 30 **840**

Use prime factorization to find the LCM for each set of numbers.

13. 12, 16 **48**
14. 10, 15, 20 **60**
15. 35, 25, 49 **1,225**
16. 18, 24 **72**

Exercises

Independent Practice

Find the LCM for each set of numbers.

17. 12, 15 **60**
18. 16, 88 **176**
19. 12, 35 **420**
20. 16, 24 **48**

21. 20, 50 **100**
22. 7, 12 **84**
23. 4, 8, 12 **24**
24. 10, 12, 14 **420**

25. 24, 12, 6 **24**
26. 45, 10, 6 **90**
27. 71, 17, 7 **8,449**
28. 68, 170, 4 **340**

29. Determine whether 116 is a multiple of 6. **no**

Mixed Review

30. Use mental math to find $320 + 159 + 80$. *(Lesson 1-2)* **559**

31. Solve $12 = \frac{a}{14} + 10$. Check your solution. *(Lesson 2-7)* **28**

32. Solve $r + (-125) = 483$. Check your solution. *(Lesson 3-9)* **608**

33. **Statistics** Would a pet store be a good **33. no** location to find a representative sample for a survey of number of pets owned? *(Lesson 4-9)*

34. *True* or *false:* Every square is a rhombus. Make a drawing to justify your answer. *(Lesson 5-4)* **True; see students' work.**

35. **Probability** A die is rolled. What is the probability it shows an odd number? *(Lesson 6-8)* $\frac{1}{2}$

37. when one number is a factor of the other number

Problem Solving and Applications

36. **Packaging** Brass cabinet hinges are shipped in cartons of individually boxed hinges. Each hinge box is 6 cm wide, 2 cm tall, and either 9 cm, 12 cm, or 18 cm long. A carton is long enough to hold 3 rows of boxes. **a. 36 cm**

   a. What is the shortest length a carton can be so a complete row of each length of hinge box will fit with no extra space left at the end of a row?

   b. If the carton in part **a** is 12 cm tall, how many of each kind of hinge box will the carton hold? **72, 54, 36**

37. **Number Sense** When will the LCM of two numbers be one of the numbers?

38. **Number Sense** When will the LCM of two numbers be the product of the two numbers? **when the GCF is 1**

39. **Algebra** What is the LCM of $3n$, $6n^2$, and 8? $24n^2$

40. **Critical Thinking** Find three numbers whose LCM is the product of the numbers. **Sample answer: 3, 5, 7**

41. **Journal Entry** Write a sentence or two describing how you can find the LCM of a set of numbers if you have the prime factorization of each number.

See students' work.

238   **Chapter 6** Patterns and Number Sense

OPTIONS

Extending the Lesson

Using Algebra Let m and n represent two numbers. Let g represent the GCF of the numbers. The Greek mathematician Euclid found that the LCM of m and n is given by the expression $\frac{m \cdot n}{g}$.

Use his method to find the LCM of 108 and 352. **9,504**

Cooperative Learning Activity

Watts the Problem? 6-9

Use groups of 2.
Materials: Calculator

→ Solve the following problem with your partner.

Suppose that today a worker replaces all three lightbulbs in the light fixtures of an office corridor. The worker uses three types of bulbs: One type is supposed to last 4,000 hours; another type is supposed to last 1,000 hours; and a third type is supposed to last 750 hours. If the lights are left on twenty-four hours a day and if all of the bulbs last as long as they are supposed to, on what day will all three need to be replaced at the same time?

Glencoe Mathematics: Applications and Connections, Course 3

Cooperative Learning
6-10A Density Property

A Preview of Lesson 6-10

Objective
Use customary units of measurement.

Materials
12-inch ruler
typing paper
calculator

How many numbers are there between $-1\frac{7}{8}$ and $-1\frac{3}{4}$? Would you guess a *few, many,* or *none?* The **density property** states that between any two rational numbers, no matter how close they may seem, there is at least one other rational number.

Activity One

Work with a partner.

- Near the middle of a piece of typing paper draw an eight-inch line segment parallel to the long side of the paper. Mark the ends and each one-inch interval with a vertical dash. Below the line, label the left endpoint 0, the right endpoint 2, and the middle point 1.

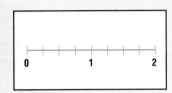

Endpoints	Midpoint	Mean
0 and 2	1	1
1 and 2	$1\frac{1}{2}$	1.5
1 and $1\frac{1}{2}$	$1\frac{1}{4}$	1.25
$1\frac{1}{2}$ and $1\frac{1}{4}$	$1\frac{3}{8}$	1.375
$1\frac{3}{8}$ and $1\frac{1}{4}$	$1\frac{5}{16}$	1.3125

- Copy and complete the *Midpoint* column of the chart at the left to find the midpoint between each pair of endpoints.

- Express the numbers in the *Endpoints* column as decimals. Find the mean of the two decimals. Record each result in the *Mean* column.

What do you think?

1. What is the relationship between the numbers in the *Midpoint* column and the numbers in the *Endpoints* column? See margin.
2. What is the relationship between the numbers in the *Midpoint* column and the numbers in the *Mean* column? same
3. Tell how you would find the midpoint between $\frac{5}{8}$ and $\frac{3}{4}$. See margin.
4. Tell how you would find a rational number between any two rational numbers. Add the two numbers together and divide by 2.

Mathematics Lab 6-10A Density Property   **239**

NCTM Standards: 1–8, 10

Management Tips

For Students Stress the importance of cooperation between partners. While one constructs the eight-inch line, the other can copy the chart. They should work together to find the midpoints and means.

For the Overhead Projector
Overhead Manipulative Resources provides appropriate materials for teacher or student demonstration of the activities in this Mathematics Lab.

1 FOCUS

Introducing the Lab

Tell students that the *density* of a substance is a measure of how tightly packed, or compact, it is. Steel is very dense; air is not. Point out that in mathematics, density refers to the closeness of the numbers in certain sets, such as the set of rational numbers. Ask the following questions: *Would you say that the number line between 0 and 100 is dense with whole numbers?* no *with multiples of 20?* no *with rational numbers?* yes

Additional Answers

1. The midpoint is the mean of the sum of the endpoints.
3. Add them together and divide by 2.

2 TEACH

Using Manipulatives
A compass can be used to find the midpoint of a line segment. Arcs of equal radius are drawn using the endpoints of the

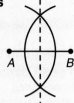

line segment as centers. The line passing through the points of intersection of the arcs passes through the midpoint of the line segment.

3 PRACTICE/APPLY

Using Cooperative Groups
After students have completed Exercises 1–8, have them create problems that require finding a number between two given fractions and between two given decimals. Have partners exchange problems and solve.

Close

Ask students to outline a procedure they could use to find a rational number between any two given rational numbers.

Additional Answer

5. The new number is between the original numbers.

Activity Two

Work with a partner.

● List any two decimals with all but the last digits the same; for example, 3.14 and 3.15. Add a digit other than 0 to the end of the lesser number.

● Repeat this procedure for four more pairs of decimals.

What do you think?

5. What is the relationship between the original numbers and the number formed by adding a digit? See margin.

6. Explain why this procedure works for finding a number between any two rational numbers. Adding a digit creates a number that is between the original numbers with zeros annexed to them.

Extension

7. List any two fractions. See students' work.

   a. Add the numerators and add the denominators to form a new fraction. For example, $\frac{3}{7}, \frac{4}{9} \rightarrow \frac{3+4}{7+9} \rightarrow \frac{7}{16}$

   b. Express the three fractions as decimals and order the decimals from least to greatest. Use a calculator.

   c. Repeat this procedure for four other pairs of fractions.

8. Describe any patterns you notice when you order the decimal representations. The new fraction is between the original fractions.

240   **Chapter 6** Patterns and Number Sense

OPTIONS

Lab Manual   You may wish to make copies of the blackline master on pp. 56-57 of the *Lab Manual* for students to use as a recording sheet.

Lab Manual, p. 56

Name _____   Date _____

Mathematics Lab Worksheet

Use with pages 239-240

Density Property

Activity One

Endpoints	Midpoint	Mean
0 and 2	1	1.0
1 and 2	$1\frac{1}{2}$	1.5
1 and $1\frac{1}{2}$	$1\frac{1}{4}$	1.25
$1\frac{1}{2}$ and $1\frac{1}{4}$	$1\frac{3}{8}$	1.375
$1\frac{3}{8}$ and $1\frac{1}{4}$	$1\frac{5}{16}$	1.3125

What do you think?

6-10 Comparing and Ordering Rational Numbers

Objective
Compare and order rational numbers expressed as fractions and/or decimals.

Words to Learn
least common denominator (LCD)

The eighth grade ensemble at Ferris Middle School was assembled in the gym to have their picture taken. The first task was to line everyone up from shortest to tallest. The teachers helped students do this by comparing one student to another to determine who was taller.

You can follow a similar procedure to compare and arrange any set of rational numbers. Sometimes a number line is used in comparing numbers. However, when numbers are very small, very large, or the difference between them is very small, a number line is not convenient.

Suppose you correctly answered 17 of 20 questions on a history test. On a science test, you answered 22 of 25 questions correctly. On which test did you do better?

To solve this problem, compare $\frac{17}{20}$ and $\frac{22}{25}$. One way to compare these fractions is to express them as decimals and then compare the decimals.

$$\frac{17}{20} \rightarrow 17 \boxed{\div} 20 \boxed{=} 0.85 \qquad \frac{22}{25} \rightarrow 22 \boxed{\div} 25 \boxed{=} 0.88$$

In the hundredths place, 5 < 8.

Since $0.85 < 0.88$, $\frac{17}{20} < \frac{22}{25}$. You did better on the science test.

Another way to compare two rational numbers is to express them as equivalent fractions with like denominators. Any common denominator may be used, but the computation may be easier if the *least common denominator* is used. The **least common denominator (LCD)** is the LCM of the denominators.

Example 1 *Problem Solving*

Sports After playing 18 basketball games, the New York Knicks had won 12 games. During the same time, the Portland Trailblazers won 13 games out of 20. Which team had the better record?

The LCM of 18 and 20 is 180.

$$\frac{12}{18} = \frac{\blacksquare}{180} \rightarrow \frac{12 \times 10}{18 \times 10} = \frac{120}{180} \qquad \frac{13}{20} = \frac{\blacksquare}{180} \rightarrow \frac{13 \times 9}{20 \times 9} = \frac{117}{180}$$

Since $\frac{120}{180} > \frac{117}{180}$, then $\frac{12}{18} > \frac{13}{20}$. The Knicks had the better record.

Lesson 6-10 Comparing and Ordering Rational Numbers **241**

OPTIONS

Limited English Proficiency

When vocabulary is difficult, students may understand concepts but have difficulty articulating their understanding. Go over the vocabulary thoroughly but give your students equal time to demonstrate their comprehension visually, through the use of number lines, Venn diagrams, and so on.

6-10 Lesson Notes

NCTM Standards: 1–5, 7, 10

Lesson Resources
• Study Guide Master 6-10
• Practice Master 6-10
• Enrichment Master 6-10
• Group Activity Card 6-10

 Transparency 6-10 contains the 5-Minute Check and a teaching aid for this lesson.

⏱ **5-Minute Check**
(Over Lesson 6-9)
List the first four multiples of each number.
1. 9   0, 9, 18, 27
2. *k*   0, *k*, 2*k*, 3*k*

Find the LCM for each set of numbers.
3. 10, 15   30
4. 4, 8   8
5. 4, 6, 9   36

1 FOCUS

Motivating the Lesson

Activity Present a collection of six pencils or drinking straws of different lengths. While disguising the difference in the lengths, have each of six volunteers draw a pencil or straw. Have the remaining students arrange the volunteers according to the lengths of the pencils or straws, from shortest to longest.

2 TEACH

Using Connections Recall for students that measurements are easier to compare when they are expressed in the same units. For example, it is easier to see that 50 inches is greater than 4 feet by expressing 4 feet as 48 inches. Similarly, rational numbers can be compared by expressing them with the same denominators or in the same decimal form.

Examples

Replace each ● with <, >, or = to make a true sentence.

2 $-\frac{1}{2}$ ● 0.12

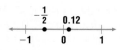

When two numbers are graphed on the same number line, the number on the left is less.

Therefore, $-\frac{1}{2} < 0.12$.

3   −0.7 ● $-\frac{5}{6}$

−0.7 ● −0.8333 ...   *Express $-\frac{5}{6}$ as a decimal.*

5 [+/−] [÷] 6 [=]   −0.8333333

In the tenths place, −7 > −8. Therefore, $-0.7 > -\frac{5}{6}$.

You have seen rational numbers compared by expressing them in the same form. When there are several numbers, it is usually easier and faster if all the numbers are decimals.

Example 4

Order 0.6, $\frac{6}{11}$, $\frac{1}{2}$, and $0.\overline{63}$ from least to greatest.

Change the fractions to decimals.

$\frac{6}{11}$ → 6 [÷] 11 [=] 0.5454546 $\frac{1}{2} = 0.5$

The order from least to greatest is $\frac{1}{2}$, $\frac{6}{11}$, 0.6, and $0.\overline{63}$.

Example 5

LOOKBACK

You can review median on page 146.

Statistics   Find the median of the set of data below.

21.4, 19, $21\frac{1}{2}$, $21\frac{3}{8}$, and 20.9

To find the median, the numbers must be in order.

$21\frac{1}{2}$ → 21.5 $21\frac{3}{8}$ → 21 [+] 3 [÷] 8 [=] 21.375

The order from least to greatest is 19, 20.9, $21\frac{3}{8}$, 21.4, and $21\frac{1}{2}$. The median is $21\frac{3}{8}$.

Checking for Understanding

Communicating Mathematics

Read and study the lesson to answer each question.

1. **Tell** two different ways to compare 0.625 and $\frac{1}{2}$. **See margin.**

2. **Draw** a 10-by-10 square on graph paper. Let the square represent 1. Use the square to explain why 0.2 > 0.09. **See Solutions Manual.**

Guided Practice

Find the LCD for each pair of fractions.

3. $\frac{1}{2}, \frac{1}{3}$ 6
4. $\frac{2}{5}, \frac{3}{8}$ 40
5. $\frac{5}{6}, \frac{7}{9}$ 18
6. $\frac{7}{25}, -\frac{3}{4}$ 100

Replace each ● with <, >, or = to make a true statement.

7. $3\frac{3}{7}$ ● $3\frac{4}{9}$ <
8. $\frac{1}{6}$ ● $0.1\overline{6}$ =
9. $-\frac{7}{2}$ ● $-\frac{3}{4}$ <
10. 1.4 ● 1.403 <
11. -1.808 ● -1.858 >
12. $10\frac{2}{5}$ ● 10.4 =
13. 5.92 ● $5\frac{23}{25}$ =

Order each set of rational numbers from least to greatest.

14. $-5, -1, 2, -12, 5$
  $-12, -5, -1, 2, 5$
15. $\frac{1}{2}, \frac{4}{5}, \frac{2}{5}, 0$ $0, \frac{2}{5}, \frac{1}{2}, \frac{4}{5}$
16. $\frac{3}{8}, 0.376, 0.367, \frac{2}{5}$
  $0.367, \frac{3}{8}, 0.376, \frac{2}{5}$

Exercises

Independent Practice

Replace each ● with <, >, or = to make a true sentence.

17. -4.6 ● -4.58 <
18. 1.5 ● -1.52 >
19. 0.88 ● $0.\overline{8}$ <
20. $\frac{5}{7}$ ● $\frac{9}{21}$ >
21. $-9\frac{2}{3}$ ● $8\frac{7}{8}$ <
22. $\frac{4}{5}$ ● $\frac{8}{10}$ =
23. $11\frac{1}{8}$ ● 11.26 <
24. 7.47 ● $7\frac{47}{100}$ =
25. -5.2 ● $5\frac{1}{5}$ <

26. Using a number line, explain why $-7.4 < -7$. **See margin.**

27. What is the LCD of $\frac{3}{8}$ and $\frac{13}{25}$? 200

28. 0.056, 0.06, 0.5, 0.56

Order each set of rational numbers from least to greatest.

28. $0.056, 0.56, 0.5, 0.06$
29. $\frac{1}{9}, \frac{1}{10}, -\frac{1}{3}, -\frac{1}{4}, -\frac{1}{3}, \frac{1}{4}, \frac{1}{10}, \frac{1}{9}$
30. $1.8, 1.07, \frac{17}{9}, \frac{18}{9}$ $1.07, 1.8, \frac{17}{9}, \frac{18}{9}$
31. $0.182, 0.182\overline{5}, 0.18\overline{2}, 0.\overline{18}$
  $0.\overline{18}, 0.182, 0.18\overline{2}, 0.1825$

Mixed Review

32. How many quarts are in $3\frac{1}{2}$ gallons? *(Lesson 1-7)* 14 quarts

33. Solve $t = -62 + 47 + (-18) + 22$. Check by solving another way. *(Lesson 3-4)* −11

34. **Statistics** Find the mean, median, and mode for the data set 14, 3, 6, 8, 11, 9, 3, 2, 7. *(Lesson 4-5)* 7, 7, 3

35. Find the LCM of 8, 15, and 12. *(Lesson 6-9)* 120

Lesson 6-10 Comparing and Ordering Rational Numbers **243**

Bell Ringer

Find the median of $\frac{1}{2}$, $-\frac{1}{2}$, and the mean of $\frac{1}{2}$ and $-\frac{1}{2}$. 0

Additional Answer

26.

-7.4 is to the left of -7 on the number line, so $-7.4 < -7$.

Close

Have students explain how they would compare two fractions, two decimals, and a fraction and a decimal.

3 PRACTICE/APPLY

Assignment Guide
Maximum: 17–40
Minimum: 17–31 odd, 32–38

For **Extra Practice,** see p. 598.

Alternate Assessment

Speaking Write a pair of fractions on the chalkboard. Have students tell which fraction is greater. Repeat with a pair of decimals and then with a fraction and a decimal.

Additional Answers

1. Express $\frac{1}{2}$ as a decimal and compare the decimals. Express 0.625 as a fraction and express both fractions as equivalent fractions with like denominators, then compare.

26. See below.

Practice Masters, p. 55

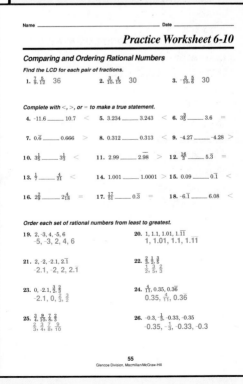

36. **Travel** Sharon has traveled 5 miles of her 16-mile trip, and Bob has traveled 21 miles of his 64-mile trip. Who has completed the greater part of their journey so far? **Bob**

37. **Portfolio Suggestion** Select an item from this chapter that you feel shows your best work and place it in your portfolio. Attach a note explaining why you selected it. **See students' work.**

38. **Critical Thinking** Are there any rational numbers between $0.\overline{4}$ and $\frac{4}{9}$? Explain. **No; because $0.\overline{4} = \frac{4}{9}$.**

39. **Meteorology** The chart below shows the Monthly Normal Precipitation in inches for several cities in the United States.

City	Feb	Mar	Apr	May	June
Asheville, NC	3.6	5.1	3.8	4.2	4.2
Burlington, VT	1.7	2.2	2.8	3.0	3.6
Columbus, OH	2.2	3.2	3.4	3.8	4.0
Honolulu, HI	2.7	3.5	1.5	1.2	0.5
Kansas City, MO	1.0	2.1	2.7	3.4	4.1
Los Angeles, CA	3.0	2.4	1.2	0.2	0.0
Phoenix, AZ	0.6	0.8	0.3	0.1	0.2
Seattle, WA	4.2	3.6	2.4	1.6	1.4
San Antonio, TX	1.9	1.3	2.7	3.7	3.0

a. What is the median rainfall for April for the cities in the table? **2.7 inches**

b. Which of the cities listed has the highest median precipitation? **Asheville, NC**

40. **Mathematics and Science** Read the following paragraphs.

Ions are atoms or groups of atoms with positive or negative electrical charges. British physicist Michael Faraday demonstrated that it takes a definite amount of charge to convert an ion of an element into an atom of the element and that the amount of charge depends on the element used.

Faraday's work was the first to imply the electrical nature of matter and the existence of subatomic particles and a fundamental unit of charge. Faraday wrote: "The atoms of matter are in some way endowed or associated with electrical powers, to which they owe their most striking qualities, and amongst them their mutual chemical affinity." Faraday did not, however, conclude that atoms cause electricity.

Which has the greater electrical charge, 3 magnesium and 1 phosphate ion or 2 aluminum and 3 oxide ions?
3 magnesium and 1 phosphate ion

Electrical Charge of Various Ions			
chloride	−1	magnesium	+2
silver	+1	phosphate	−3
oxide	−2	aluminum	+3

Enrichment Masters, p. 55

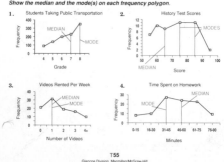

Name _____ Date _____

Enrichment Worksheet 6-10

Frequency Polygons

Histograms are often used to display frequency distributions. A *frequency polygon* can also be used. In the graphs below, a histogram is shown on the left; a frequency polygon on the right. The vertical lines drawn on the frequency polygon show the locations of the median and the mode.

Show the median and the mode(s) on each frequency polygon.

T55
Glencoe Division, Macmillan/McGraw-Hill

OPTIONS

Extending the Lesson

Mathematics and Science Tell students that they can use the [+/−] key on their calculators to complete computations with integers.

Cooperative Learning Activity

Number of players: 2	Rational Pastime	**6-10**

Materials: Index cards

Copy onto cards the rational numbers shown on the back of this card, one per card. Shuffle the cards and then divide them evenly.

Try to be the first to arrange your cards so that the rational numbers are ordered from least to greatest. Check the accuracy of your partner's work.

Glencoe Mathematics: Applications and Connections, Course 3

6-11 Scientific Notation

Objective
Express numbers in scientific notation.

Words to Learn
scientific notation

Have you ever been to a ballgame where the national anthem was being played live and also broadcast over a radio system? You could hear it on your radio sooner than you did in person. This is because radio waves travel at 3.0×10^8 meters per second (m/s) while sound waves travel slower at 3.4×10^2 m/s. The numbers 3.0×10^8 and 3.4×10^2 are written in **scientific notation.**

In standard form, the speed of radio waves is written 300,000,000 m/s. So, $3.0 \times 10^8 = 300{,}000{,}000$. Large numbers like 300,000,000 are written in scientific notation to lessen the chance of omitting a zero or misplacing the decimal point.

Notice that when a number is expressed in scientific notation, it is written as a product of a factor and a power of 10. The factor must be greater than or equal to 1 and less than 10.

Mental Math Hint
• • • • • • • • • •
Multiplying by a positive power of 10 moves the decimal point to the right the same number of places as the exponent.

Example 1

Express 7.821×10^6 in standard form.

$7.821 \times 10^6 = 7.821 \times 1{,}000{,}000 \qquad 7.821000$

$\qquad\qquad = 7{,}821{,}000 \qquad\qquad\quad$ *6 places*

Scientific notation is also used to express very small numbers. Study the patterns in the chart to see when a negative power of 10 is used.

3.45×10^1	$= 34.5$
3.45×10^0	$= 3.45$
3.45×10^{-1}	$= 0.345$
3.45×10^{-2}	$= 0.0345$
3.45×10^{-3}	$= 0.00345$

Mental Math Hint
• • • • • • • • • •
Multiplying by a negative power of 10 moves the decimal point to the left the same number of places as the absolute value of the exponent.

Example 2

Express 8.3×10^{-5} in standard form.

$8.3 \times 10^{-5} = 8.3 \times \dfrac{1}{10^5}$

$\qquad\qquad = 8.3 \times \dfrac{1}{100{,}000}$

$\qquad\qquad = 8.3 \times 0.00001 \qquad 00008.3$

$\qquad\qquad = 0.000083 \qquad\qquad$ *5 places*

Lesson 6-11 Scientific Notation　　**245**

6-11 Lesson Notes

NCTM Standards: 1–5, 13

Lesson Resources
• Study Guide Master 6-11
• Practice Master 6-11
• Enrichment Master 6-11
• Evaluation Master, Quiz B, p. 52
• Technology Master, p. 6
• Multicultural Activity, p. 6
• Group Activity Card 6-11

 Transparency 6-11 contains the 5-Minute Check and a teaching aid for this lesson.

🕐 5-Minute Check
(Over Lesson 6-10)

Replace each ● with <, >, or = to make a true sentence.

1. $\frac{1}{5}$ ● $\frac{1}{4}$　<
2. 5.2 ● -5.3　>
3. 0.4 ● 0.07　>
4. $\frac{3}{5}$ ● 0.6　=
5. Order 0.66, $0.\overline{6}$, $0.\overline{65}$, and $0.6\overline{65}$ from least to greatest.　$0.\overline{65}$, 0.66, $0.6\overline{65}$, and $0.\overline{6}$

1 FOCUS

Motivating the Lesson

Situational Problem On the chalkboard write the digit 9 followed by 23 zeros. Tell students that the Sahara Desert has been estimated to contain that many grains of sand. Ask students to suggest ways to write the number more concisely.

2 TEACH

Using the Mini-Lab Remind students that the absolute value of a number is the number's distance from zero on the number line. It is always a positive number.

After students have studied their lab results, ask them to predict how their calculators will display 345,000 in scientific notation. 3.45 05 Have them check their predictions on the calculator.

245

Checking for Understanding

Exercises 1–3 are designed to help you assess students' understanding through reading, writing, speaking, and modeling. You should work through these exercises with your students and then monitor their work on Guided Practice Exercises 4–14.

Practice Masters, p. 56

Name _____ Date _____

Practice Worksheet 6-11

Scientific Notation

Express each number in standard form.

1. 4.2×10^6 2. 3.75×10^2 3. -8.45×10^7
   4,200,000   375   -84,500,000

4. -6.32×10^{-5} 5. 8.84×10^{-7} 6. 4.125×10^5
   -0.0000632   0.000000884   412,500

7. 3.72×10^{-6} 8. -6.1×10^8 9. -3.4×10^{-3}
   0.00000372   -610,000,000   -0.0034

State where the decimal point should be placed in order to express each number in scientific notation. State the power of ten by which you should multiply. Then express each number in scientific notation.

10. 3,450,000   11. 22,846,000   12. 0.000345
    between 3 and 4;   between 2 and 2;   between 3 and 4;
    10^6; 3.45×10^6 10^7; 2.2846×10^7 10^{-4}; 3.45×10^4

13. 0.01624   14. 1,200   15. 0.00000008
    between 1 and 6;   between 1 and 2;   following the 8;
    10^{-2}; 1.624×10^{-2} 10^3; 1.2×10^3 10^{-8}; 8.0×10^{-8}

Express each number in scientific notation.

16. 4,862   17. 9,000,000   18. 0.000023
    4.862×10^3 9.0×10^6 2.3×10^{-5}

19. 0.000603   20. 42,000,000   21. 423,000
    6.03×10^{-4} 4.2×10^7 4.23×10^5

22. 1,100,000,000   23. 0.0000061   24. 0.00412
    1.1×10^9 6.1×10^{-6} 4.12×10^{-3}

25. 3,250,000   26. 32,500,000,000   27. 0.143
    3.25×10^6 3.25×10^{10} 1.43×10^1

56
Glencoe Division, Macmillan/McGraw-Hill

246

The Mini-Lab below shows how to enter a number in standard form and have the calculator express it in scientific notation.

Mini-Lab

Work with a partner.

Materials: scientific calculator

- Copy the chart below and use a calculator to express the numbers in scientific notation. Record each display as the product of the first three digits and 10 to the power of the last two digits. For example, 3.45 06 means 3.45×10^6. Record the absolute value of the exponent in the third column.

ENTER	Scientific Notation	Absolute Value of Exponent
3450 [EE] [=]	3.45×10^3	3
345 [EE] [=]	3.45×10^2	2
34.5 [EE] [=]	3.45×10^1	1
3.45 [EE] [=]	3.45×10^0	0
0.345 [EE] [=]	3.45×10^{-1}	1
0.0345 [EE] [=]	3.45×10^{-2}	2

Talk About It   They are the same.

What is the relationship between the number of places the decimal point moved and the absolute value of the exponent?

The relationship you discovered in the Mini-Lab allows you to use mental math to express any number in scientific notation.

Examples

Express each number in scientific notation.

3   12,345,000

$12,345,000 = 1.2345 \times 10^7$

The decimal point moves 7 places to the left. Divide by 10^7.

4   0.0000375

$0.0000375 = 3.75 \times 10^{-5}$

The decimal point moves 5 places to the right. Divide by 10^{-5}.

Example 5 shows how to enter a number in a calculator with too many digits to fit on the display screen in standard form.

Example 5

Enter 0.000000825 into a calculator.

First write the number in scientific notation. $0.000000825 = 8.25 \times 10^{-7}$

Then enter the number. 8.25 [EE] 7 [+/−] The display shows 8.25 −0.7.

OPTIONS

Bell Ringer

A year is officially 365 days, 6 hours, 9 minutes, and 9.5 seconds long. Express the number of seconds in a year using scientific notation.
3.15581495×10^7 seconds

Additional Answers

1. 45.6 and 0.456 are not greater than or equal to 1 and less than 10.
2. Sample answer: 4.78×10^3
3. to lessen the chance of omitting a zero or misplacing the decimal point.

31.

6 7 8 9 10 11

Checking for Understanding

Communicating Mathematics

Read and study the lesson to answer each question. For answers to Exercises 1-3, see margin.

1. **Tell** why 45.6×10^2 and 0.456×10^{-6} are not written in scientific notation.

2. **Write** an example of a number that is written in scientific notation.

3. **Tell** why very large numbers and very small numbers are written in scientific notation.

Guided Practice

Express each number in standard form.

4. 3.45×10^7 **34,500,000**   5. 8.9×10^{-5} **0.000089**   6. 3.777×10^4 **37,770**

State where the decimal point should be placed in order to express each number in scientific notation. State the power of ten by which you should multiply. Then express the number in scientific notation.

7. 12,300,000   8. 1,230,000   9. 0.000123   10. 12.3

11. 0.0056789   12. 829   13. 0.000007   14. 0.001^2

7. 1.23×10^7 8. 1.23×10^6 9. 1.23×10^{-4} 10. 1.23×10^1
11. 5.6789×10^{-3} 12. 8.29×10^2 13. 7.0×10^{-6} 14. 1.0×10^{-6}

Exercises

Independent Practice

Express each number in standard form.   15. −0.0000000999   17. 0.0000042

15. -9.99×10^{-8} 16. 4.2×10^6 **4,200,000**   17. 4.2×10^{-6}

18. 2.54×10^3 **2,540**   19. 9.6×10^{-2} **0.096**   20. 3.853×10^4 **38,530**

21. the distance to the sun, 9.3×10^7 miles **93,000,000**

Express each number in scientific notation.   24. 6.35×10^{-5}

22. 9,700,000 9.7×10^6 23. 85,420,000 8.542×10^7 24. 0.0000635

25. 0.000056 5.6×10^{-5} 26. 3,478 3.478×10^3 27. 0.0002^2 4.0×10^{-8}

28. the product of 7,000,000 and 800 5.6×10^9

29. the product of 0.00008 and 0.0009 7.2×10^{-8}

Mixed Review

30. Solve $y - 8.3 = 20.9$. Check your solution. *(Lesson 2-3)* **29.2**

31. Solve $\frac{c}{4} + 8 > 10$. Show the solution on a number line. *(Lesson 2-10)*
   $c > 8$; see margin.

32. Solve $-319 - (-98) = w$. *(Lesson 3-5)* **−221**

33. Find the LCD of $-\frac{5}{6}$ and $\frac{3}{8}$. *(Lesson 6-10)* **24**

Problem Solving and Applications

34. **Critical Thinking** The galaxy NGC1232 is over 65 million light years from the earth. A light year is 9.46×10^{12} kilometers. Use scientific notation to express the distance to the galaxy in kilometers. 6.149×10^{20} km

35. **Data Search** Refer to pages 210 and 211.
   a. Which planet is the largest? **Jupiter**
   b. How far is this planet from the Sun?
   c. How far is this planet from Earth?
   b. 4.83×10^8 miles
   c. 3.901×10^8 miles

Lesson 6-11 Scientific Notation   **247**

Close

Have students write a few sentences completing each of the following statements.

- *A number is written in standard form. To express it in scientific notation, __?__.*
  Check students' work.

- *A number is written in scientific notation. To express it in standard form, __?__.*
  Check students' work.

3 PRACTICE/APPLY

Assignment Guide
Maximum: 15–35
Minimum: 15–29 odd, 30–34

For **Extra Practice,** see p. 598.

Alternate Assessment

Writing Have each student write four numbers in standard form and four numbers in scientific notation. Students then exchange their numbers with another student, expressing the numbers they receive in the opposite form.

Enrichment Masters, p. 56

Name _____   Date _____

Enrichment Worksheet 6-11

Perfect Numbers

The *divisors* of an integer are those integers that divide the given integer and leave a remainder of 0. If the integer is excluded from the set of its divisors, the remaining set contains the *proper divisors* of that integer. For example, the divisors of 6 are 1, 2, 3, and 6; the proper divisors are 1, 2, and 3.

Positive integers can be classified into three types: perfect, abundant, or deficient. A positive integer is *perfect* if it equals the sum of its proper divisors. If the sum is greater than the integer, the integer is *abundant*. If the sum is less, the integer is *deficient*.

Example   Classify 28 as perfect, abundant, or deficient.

The proper divisors of 28 are 1, 2, 4, 7, and 14.

Since $1 + 2 + 4 + 7 + 14 = 28$, 28 is perfect.

Complete the chart to classify each number as perfect, abundant, or deficient.

	Number	Proper Divisors	Sum of Divisors	Type
1.	16	1, 2, 4, 8	15	Deficient
2.	36	1, 2, 3, 4, 6, 9, 12, 18	55	Abundant
3.	212	1, 2, 4, 53, 106	166	Deficient
4.	496	1, 2, 4, 8, 16, 31, 62, 124, 248	496	Perfect
5.	558	1, 2, 3, 6, 9, 18, 31, 62, 93, 186, 279	690	Abundant
6.	1,001	1, 7, 143	151	Deficient
7.	8,128	1, 2, 4, 8, 16, 32, 64, 127, 254, 508, 1,016, 2,032, 4,064	8,128	Perfect
8.	945	1, 3, 5, 7, 9, 15, 21, 27, 35, 45, 63, 105, 135, 189, 315	975	Abundant

T 56
Glencoe Division, Macmillan/McGraw-Hill

Extending the Lesson

Astronomy Connection

Have students use books and encyclopedia articles on astronomy to find examples of large numbers used by astronomers and to write them in both standard form and scientific notation. Students should write a brief explanation of the meaning of each number.

Cooperative Learning Activity

Use groups of 2.

Lands of Confusion **6-11**

➡ Read the following passage.

You probably know that there are differences between British English and American English. For example, in British English the word *boot* can be used to describe footwear or an automobile trunk. As the table at the right shows, the differences extend to numbers as well.

Decide which partner will use British English and which will use American English. Write each number on the back of this card in standard form. Then write the number in word form. Compare your results.

	Number of Zeroes	
Number	Brit. English	Am. English
Quadrillion	24	15
Quintillion	30	18
Sextillion	36	21
Septillion	42	24
Octillion	48	27
Nonillion	54	30
Decillion	60	33
Undecillion	66	36
Duodecillion	72	39
Tredecillion	78	42
Quattuordecillion	84	45
Quindecillion	90	48
Sexdecillion	96	51
Septendecillion	102	54

Glencoe Mathematics: Applications and Connections, Course 3

The Chapter Study Guide and Review begins with a section on Communicating Mathematics. This includes questions that review the new terms and concepts that were introduced in the chapter.

Then, the Skills and Concepts presented in the chapter are reviewed using a side-by-side format. Encourage students to refer to the Objectives and Examples on the left as they complete the Review Exercises on the right.

The Chapter Study Guide and Review ends with problems that review Applications and Problem Solving.

Additional Answer

6. Write the digits of the decimal as the numerator. Use the appropriate power of 10 (10, 100, 1,000, and so on) as the denominator. Then simplify.

Study Guide and Review

Chapter

6 Study Guide and Review

Communicating Mathematics

Choose the correct term to complete each sentence.

factors

1. The (factors, multiples) of a whole number divide that number with a remainder of zero.
2. A whole number greater than 1 that has exactly two factors is called a (composite, prime) number. prime
3. A fraction is in (bar notation, simplest form) when the GCF of the numerator and denominator is 1. simplest form
4. The least common denominator of two fractions is the (LCM, GCF) of the denominators.
5. An outcome that is certain to happen has a probability of (1, 0). 1   LCM
6. Explain how to express a terminating decimal as a fraction. See margin.

Self Assessment

Objectives and Examples	Review Exercises
Upon completing this chapter, you should be able to:	*Use these exercises to review and prepare for the chapter test.*

- use divisibility rules for 2, 3, 4, 5, 6, 8, 9, and 10 *(Lesson 6-1)*

  Determine whether 738 is divisible by 9.

  The sum of the digits, 18, is divisible by 9. So 738 is divisible by 9.

  Use divisibility rules to determine if the first number is divisible by the second number. Write *yes* or *no*.

  7. 523; 3 no   8. 1,895; 5 yes
  9. 328; 4 yes   10. 4,291; 8 no
  11. 16,542; 6 yes 12. 1,001; 10 no

- find the prime factorization of a composite number *(Lesson 6-2)*

  Factor 60 completely.

  $60 = 2 \cdot 30$
  $= 2 \cdot 2 \cdot 15$
  $= 2 \cdot 2 \cdot 3 \cdot 5$ or $2^2 \cdot 3 \cdot 5$

  Find the prime factorization of each number.

  13. 48 $2^4 \cdot 3$ 14. −56 $-1 \cdot 2^3 \cdot 7$
  15. 175 $5^2 \cdot 7$ 16. −252
  17. 33 $3 \cdot 11$ 18. −27 $-1 \cdot 3^3$
                  16. $-1 \cdot 2^2 \cdot 3^2 \cdot 7$

- find the greatest common factor of two or more numbers *(Lesson 6-4)*

  Find the GCF of 20 and 32.

  factors of 20: 1, 2, 4, 5, 10, 20
  factors of 32: 1, 2, 4, 8, 16, 32
  The GCF of 20 and 32 is 4.

  Find the GCF for each set of numbers.

  19. 18, 54 18   20. 15, 45 15
  21. 14, 28, 49 7   22. 36, 84, 108 12
  23. 120, 440, 360 40

Objectives and Examples

Review Exercises

● identify and simplify rational numbers
(*Lesson 6-5*)

Write $\frac{60}{150}$ in simplest form.

$$\frac{60}{150} = \frac{\cancel{2} \cdot 2 \cdot \cancel{3} \cdot \cancel{5}}{\cancel{2} \cdot \cancel{3} \cdot \cancel{5} \cdot 5} = \frac{2}{5}$$

Write each fraction in simplest form.

24. $-\frac{15}{18}$ $-\frac{5}{6}$ 25. $\frac{12}{16}$ $\frac{3}{4}$

26. $\frac{63}{72}$ $\frac{7}{8}$ 27. $-\frac{42}{63}$ $-\frac{2}{3}$

● express fractions as decimals
(*Lesson 6-6*)

Write $\frac{3}{11}$ as a decimal.

$$\frac{3}{11} = 3 \div 11$$
$$= 0.2727272 \text{ or } 0.\overline{27}$$

Express each fraction or mixed number as a decimal. Use bar notation if necessary.

28. $\frac{3}{8}$ 0.375   29. $\frac{4}{22}$ $0.\overline{18}$

30. $1\frac{2}{5}$ 1.4   31. $6\frac{8}{12}$ $6.\overline{6}$

● express terminating decimals as fractions   (*Lesson 6-6*)

Express 0.75 as a fraction.

$$0.75 = \frac{75}{100} = \frac{3}{4}$$

Express each decimal as a fraction or mixed number in simplest form.

32. 0.45 $\frac{9}{20}$ 33. −0.028 $-\frac{7}{250}$

34. −11.375 $-11\frac{3}{8}$ 35. 4.8125 $4\frac{13}{16}$

● express repeating decimals as fractions
(*Lesson 6-7*)

Express $2.\overline{84}$ as a fraction.
Let $N = 2.\overline{84}$. Then $100N = 284.\overline{84}$.

$$100N = 284.\overline{84}$$
$$-\ N = \ \ \ 2.\overline{84}$$
$$\overline{99N = 282}$$
$$N = \frac{282}{99} \text{ or } 2\frac{28}{33} \quad \text{So, } 2.\overline{84} = 2\frac{28}{33}.$$

Express each repeating decimal as a fraction.

36. $0.\overline{7}$ $\frac{7}{9}$

37. $-5.\overline{28}$ $-5\frac{28}{99}$

38. $-0.3\overline{18}$ $-\frac{7}{22}$

39. $6.\overline{630}$ $6\frac{70}{111}$

40. $0.\overline{48}$ $\frac{16}{33}$

41. $-0.\overline{03}$ $-\frac{1}{33}$

● find the probability of a simple event
(*Lesson 6-8*)

Probability =

$$\frac{\text{number of ways an event can occur}}{\text{number of possible outcomes}}$$

A bag contains five red, seven blue, and eight white marbles. A blindfolded student draws a marble. Find the probability of each outcome.

42. It is white. $\frac{2}{5}$ 43. It is not red. $\frac{3}{4}$

44. It is red or blue. $\frac{3}{5}$

● find the least common multiple of two or more integers   (*Lesson 6-9*)

Find the LCM of 6 and 8.
   multiples of 6: 0, 6, 12, 18, 24, . . .
   multiples of 8: 0, 8, 16, 24, 32, . . .
   The LCM of 6 and 8 is 24.

Find the LCM for each set of numbers.

45. 15, 20   60   46. 18, 24   72

47. 54, 72   216   48. 8, 20, 24   120

49. 5, 174, 30   870

Chapter 6 Study Guide and Review   **249**

You may wish to use a Chapter Test from the Evaluation Masters booklet as an additional chapter review. The two free-response forms are shown below. One of the two multiple-choice forms is shown on the next page.

Evaluation Masters, pp. 50–51

Name _____ Date _____

Form 2A _____ *Chapter 6 Test*

1. Is 6,142 divisible by 8? Why or why not?
2. Is 7,776 divisible by 9? Why or why not?

Find the prime factorization for each number.
3. 54   4. -130   5. 323

Find the GCF for each set of numbers.
6. 18, 45   7. 28, 42   8. 18, 36, 270

Write each fraction in simplest form.
9. $-\frac{20}{35}$ 10. $\frac{72}{64}$ 11. $-\frac{30}{75}$

Express each fraction as a decimal.
12. $-\frac{7}{20}$ 13. $\frac{11}{16}$ 14. $-\frac{9}{8}$

Express each decimal as a fraction or mixed number in simplest form.
15. -0.08   16. 0.65   17. -6.025
18. Express -3.074747 . . . using bar notation.

Express each repeating decimal as a fraction in simplest form.
19. $-0.\overline{7}$ 20. $2.\overline{027}$ 21. $-5.\overline{54}$

Find the LCM for each set of numbers.
22. 18, 27   23. 28, 98   24. 18, 24, 28

Replace each ● with <, >, or = to make a true sentence.
25. 1.48 ● -1.75   26. $\frac{5}{8}$ ● $\frac{6}{7}$

Order each set of rational numbers from least to greatest.
27. 0.07, 0.6, 0.67, 0.067
28. $-\frac{1}{2}, \frac{1}{3}, -\frac{1}{6}, \frac{3}{4}$

The letters of the word "factorization" are written one each on 13 identical slips of paper and shuffled in a hat. A blindfolded student draws one slip of paper. Find the probability of each outcome for Exercises 29 and 30.
29. $P(f)$ 30. $P(t \text{ or } o)$

31. Express -2.97×10^{-6} in standard form.
32. Express 0.000000563 in scientific notation.
33. A basketball league has seven teams. Each team plays each other twice. How many games will be played in the basketball league?

BONUS Find the number of positive integers that are less than 103 and are divisible by 3.

1. No
2. Yes
3. $2 \cdot 3 \cdot 3 \cdot 3$
4. $-1 \cdot 2 \cdot 5 \cdot 13$
5. $17 \cdot 19$
6. 9
7. 14
8. 9
9. $-\frac{4}{7}$
10. $\frac{9}{8}$
11. $-\frac{2}{5}$
12. -0.35
13. 0.6875
14. -1.125
15. $-\frac{2}{25}$
16. $\frac{13}{20}$
17. $-6\frac{1}{40}$
18. $-3.0\overline{74}$
19. $-\frac{7}{9}$
20. $\frac{75}{37}$
21. $-\frac{61}{11}$
22. 54
23. 196
24. 504
25. >
26. <
27. 0.067, 0.07, 0.6, 0.67
28. $-\frac{1}{2}, -\frac{1}{6}, \frac{1}{3}, \frac{3}{4}$
29. $\frac{1}{13}$
30. $\frac{2}{13}$
31. -0.00000297
32. 5.63×10^{-7}
33. 42 games

34

50

Glencoe Division, Macmillan/McGraw-Hill

Name _____ Date _____

Form 2B _____ *Chapter 6 Test*

1. Is 1,842 divisible by 3? Why or why not?
2. Is 2,894 divisible by 6? Why or why not?

Find the prime factorization for each number.
3. -90   4. 138   5. -551

Find the GCF for each set of numbers.
6. 54, 72   7. 44, 77   8. 28, 32, 96

Write each fraction in simplest form.
9. $\frac{68}{51}$ 10. $\frac{84}{108}$ 11. $-\frac{46}{115}$

Express each fraction as a decimal.
12. $-\frac{19}{25}$ 13. $\frac{17}{40}$ 14. $\frac{21}{8}$

Express each decimal as a fraction or mixed number in simplest form.
15. -0.06   16. 0.8125   17. -4.055
18. Express -5.083333 . . . using bar notation.

Express each repeating decimal as a fraction in simplest form.
19. $-1.\overline{21}$ 20. $0.0\overline{6}$ 21. $-0.6\overline{81}$

Find the LCM for each set of numbers.
22. 25, 45   23. 24, 36   24. 12, 16, 20

Replace each ● with <, >, or = to make a true statement.
25. $-\frac{9}{4}$ ● $-\frac{8}{5}$ 26. $0.\overline{8}$ ● $\frac{8}{9}$

Order each set of rational numbers from least to greatest.
27. $1.7, \frac{16}{9}, 1.06, \frac{17}{9}$
28. $0.\overline{16}, 0.1625, 0.16\overline{2}, 0.162$

The letters of the word "mathematical" are written one each on 12 identical slips of paper and shuffled in a hat. A blindfolded student draws one slip of paper. Find the probability of each outcome for Exercises 29 and 30.
29. $P(m)$ 30. $P(a \text{ or } l)$

31. Express 9.07×10^{-3} in standard form.
32. Express 0.0000716 in scientific notation.
33. A softball league has nine teams. Each team plays each other twice. How many games will be played in the softball league?

BONUS What are all of the possible digits that can be the ones digit of a prime number greater than ten?

1. Yes
2. No
3. $-2 \cdot 3 \cdot 3 \cdot 5$
4. $2 \cdot 3 \cdot 23$
5. $-19 \cdot 29$
6. 18
7. 11
8. 4
9. $\frac{4}{3}$
10. $\frac{7}{9}$
11. $-\frac{2}{5}$
12. -0.76
13. 0.425
14. 2.625
15. $-\frac{3}{50}$
16. $\frac{13}{16}$
17. $-4\frac{11}{200}$
18. $-5.08\overline{3}$
19. $-\frac{40}{33}$
20. $\frac{1}{15}$
21. $-\frac{15}{22}$
22. 225
23. 72
24. 240
25. >
26. =
27. $1.06, 1.7, \frac{16}{9}, \frac{17}{9}$
28. $0.\overline{16}, 0.162, 0.16\overline{2}, 0.1625$
29. $\frac{1}{6}$
30. $\frac{1}{3}$
31. 0.00907
32. 7.16×10^{-5}
33. 72 games

1, 3, 7, 9

51

Glencoe Division, Macmillan/McGraw-Hill

250

Objectives and Examples

- compare and order rational numbers expressed as fractions and/or decimals *(Lesson 6-10)*

  Is $0.65 < \frac{2}{3}$?

  $\frac{2}{3} = 0.\overline{66}$, and $0.65 < 0.\overline{66}$

  So, yes, $0.65 < \frac{2}{3}$.

- express numbers in scientific notation *(Lesson 6-11)*

  Express 0.000294 in scientific notation.

  $0.000294 \rightarrow 2.94 \times 10^{-4}$

  4 places

Review Exercises

Replace each ● with <, >, or = to make a true sentence.
50. -10.29 ● -10.3   >
51. $\frac{11}{15}$ ● $\frac{4}{5}$ <
52. $\frac{3}{8}$ ● 0.375   =
53. $0.\overline{4}$ ● 0.4   >

Express each number in scientific notation.
54. 5,830,000   55. 0.0000735
56. 12,500 1.25×10^4 57. 0.00068 6.8×10^{-4}
58. 95,700,000 9.57×10^7
54. 5.83×10^6 55. 7.35×10^{-5}

Applications and Problem Solving

59. Eva and Karl are saving money to attend an art show at the museum. Travel and tickets cost $31.50 in all. Eva starts with $10.15 and saves $1.60 a week. Karl starts with $8.30 and saves $1.75 a week. When will they save enough? *(Lesson 6-3)* **4th week**

60. **Science** Radio waves travel at 3.0×10^8 m/s. Sound waves travel at 3.4×10^2 m/s. Write each number in standard form and find the difference in the two speeds. *(Lesson 6-11)*
300,000,000; 340; 299,999,660

Curriculum Connection Projects

- **Geography** Consult an atlas or almanac and express the populations of ten countries in scientific notation.
- **Life Science** Take a survey of shoe sizes in your class. Find the probability of a new student having the same size as the most frequent size of your classmates.

Read More About It

Gordon, A. C. *Solve-a-Crime.*
Wells, H. G. *The Invisible Man.*
White, Lawrence B. Jr. and Ray Broekel *Math-a-Magic: Number Tricks for Magicians.*

250 **Chapter 6** Study Guide and Review

6 Test

1. Is 718 divisible by four? Why or why not? **No; the number formed by the last two digits, 18, is not divisible by four.**

Find the GCF for each set of numbers.

2. 40, 24 **8**

3. 56, 98 **14**

4. 108, 234, 30 **6**

5. 320, 16, 176 **16**

Write each fraction in simplest form.

6. $-\frac{10}{16}$ **$-\frac{5}{8}$**

7. $\frac{42}{72}$ **$\frac{7}{12}$**

8. $-\frac{18}{81}$ **$-\frac{2}{9}$**

9. $\frac{90}{21}$ **$4\frac{2}{7}$**

10. Write the prime factorization of 360. **$2^3 \cdot 3^2 \cdot 5$**

Write each decimal as a fraction or mixed number and each fraction as a decimal.

11. -3.45 **$-3\frac{9}{20}$**

12. $\frac{5}{16}$ **0.3125**

13. 0.4 **$\frac{2}{5}$**

14. $-\frac{3}{8}$ **-0.375**

15. 20.8125 **$20\frac{13}{16}$**

Express each repeating decimal as a fraction.

16. $-3.\overline{2}$ **$-3\frac{2}{9}$**

17. $0.\overline{621}$ **$\frac{23}{37}$**

18. $5.\overline{28}$ **$5\frac{28}{99}$**

The letters of the word "composite" are written one each on nine identical slips of paper and shuffled in a bag. A blindfolded student draws one slip of paper. Find the probability of each outcome.

19. $P(c)$ **$\frac{1}{9}$**

20. $P(o \text{ or } p)$ **$\frac{1}{3}$**

21. $P(\text{vowel})$ **$\frac{4}{9}$**

22. $P(\text{not } o \text{ or } t)$ **$\frac{2}{3}$**

23. Express 18.42727... using bar notation. **$18.4\overline{27}$**

24. Use prime factorization to find the LCM of 24 and 28. **168**

Find the LCM for each set of numbers.

25. 9, 21 **63**

26. 12, 15, 18 **180**

27. 81, 34, 54 **2,754**

Replace each ● with <, >, or = to make a true sentence.

28. $\frac{4}{9}$ ● $\frac{11}{27}$ **>**

29. $5\frac{31}{100}$ ● 5.31 **=**

30. -4.68 ● -4.7 **>**

31. Express 3.7×10^{-4} in standard form. **0.00037**

32. Express 58,930,000 in scientific notation. **5.893×10^7**

33. The CLV company supplies CDs, LPs, and Vs (videos) to five stores. Records show that 426 CDs, 152 LPs, and 102 Vs are in the stores. CLV delivers 509 CDs, 209 LPs, and 205 Vs. Later the stores report 453 CDs, 183 LPs, 198 Vs in stock. How much of each product was sold? **482 CDs; 178 LPs; 109 Vs**

Bonus Is it possible for three different numbers to have 1 as their GCF? If so, name three such numbers. **yes; sample answer: 3, 4, 5**

Using the Chapter Test

This page may be used as a chapter test or another chapter review.

Evaluation Masters, pp. 46–47

Name _____ Date _____

Form 1A _____ *Chapter 6 Test*

1. Which number is divisible by 6?
   A. 12,069 B. 6,310 C. 8,526 D. 225
   1. __C__

2. Which number is not divisible by 5?
   A. 564 B. 570 C. 1,285 D. 2,890
   2. __A__

3. Find the prime factorization for -60.
   A. $-3 \cdot 3 \cdot 7$ B. $2 \cdot 2 \cdot 3 \cdot 5$
   C. $-4 \cdot 3 \cdot 5$ D. $-1 \cdot 2 \cdot 2 \cdot 3 \cdot 5$
   3. __D__

4. Find the prime factorization for 429.
   A. $31 \cdot 13$ B. $29 \cdot 17$ C. $3 \cdot 143$ D. $3 \cdot 11 \cdot 13$
   4. __D__

5. Find the GCF for 20 and 30.
   A. 15 B. 10 C. 2 D. 1
   5. __B__

6. Find the GCF for 18, 36, and 45.
   A. 3 B. 6 C. 9 D. 18
   6. __C__

7. Write $-\frac{22}{33}$ in simplest form.
   A. $-\frac{5}{6}$ B. $-\frac{3}{2}$ C. $-\frac{2}{3}$ D. $-\frac{3}{4}$
   7. __C__

8. Write $\frac{49}{21}$ in simplest form.
   A. $\frac{7}{3}$ B. $\frac{4}{3}$ C. $\frac{3}{4}$ D. $\frac{14}{6}$
   8. __A__

9. Express $-\frac{17}{25}$ as a decimal.
   A. -6.8 B. -0.68 C. -0.068 D. 0.068
   9. __B__

10. Express $\frac{17}{16}$ as a decimal.
    A. 10.625 B. $1\frac{1}{16}$ C. 1.0625 D. $1.062\overline{5}$
    10. __C__

11. Express 1.1292929... using bar notation.
    A. $1.\overline{129}$ B. $1.1\overline{29}$ C. $1.\overline{129}$ D. $1.1\overline{29}$
    11. __D__

12. Express $0.\overline{5}$ as a fraction in simplest form.
    A. $\frac{5}{9}$ B. $\frac{3}{5}$ C. $\frac{9}{7}$ D. $\frac{5}{99}$
    12. __A__

13. Express $1.\overline{09}$ as a fraction in simplest form.
    A. $\frac{10}{9}$ B. $\frac{7}{11}$ C. $\frac{12}{11}$ D. $\frac{15}{11}$
    13. __C__

14. Find the LCM for 12 and 84.
    A. 84 B. 12 C. 24 D. 6
    14. __A__

15. Find the LCM for 21, 35, and 42.
    A. 7 B. 210 C. 14 D. 30,870
    15. __B__

Replace each ___ to make a true statement.

16. -0.39 ___ -0.38
    A. = B. > C. < D. +
    16. __C__

17. $\frac{7}{8}$ ___ $\frac{8}{9}$
    A. = B. > C. < D. +
    17. __C__

46

Glencoe Division, Macmillan/McGraw-Hill

Name _____ Date _____

Chapter 6 Test, Form 1A (continued)

18. Order $\frac{1}{4}$, $\frac{9}{7}$, and $\frac{4}{9}$ from least to greatest.
    A. $\frac{1}{4}$, $\frac{4}{9}$, $\frac{9}{7}$ B. $\frac{1}{4}$, $\frac{4}{9}$, $\frac{9}{7}$ C. $\frac{9}{7}$, $\frac{4}{9}$, $\frac{1}{4}$ D. $\frac{9}{7}$, $\frac{1}{4}$, $\frac{4}{9}$
    18. __A__

19. Express -0.04 as a fraction in simplest form.
    A. $-\frac{2}{5}$ B. $-\frac{1}{100}$ C. $-\frac{4}{25}$ D. $\frac{4}{100}$
    19. __C__

20. Express 2.045 as a mixed number in simplest form.
    A. $2\frac{9}{200}$ B. $2\frac{9}{20}$ C. $2\frac{99}{100}$ D. $2\frac{55}{1,000}$
    20. __A__

The letters of the word "symmetry" are written one each on 8 identical slips of paper and shuffled in a hat. A blindfolded student draws one slip of paper. Find the probability of each outcome for Exercises 21 and 22.

21. $P(m)$
    A. $\frac{1}{4}$ B. $\frac{5}{8}$ C. $\frac{7}{8}$ D. $\frac{1}{8}$
    21. __A__

22. $P(s \text{ or } y)$
    A. $\frac{3}{8}$ B. $\frac{5}{8}$ C. $\frac{7}{8}$ D. $\frac{1}{8}$
    22. __A__

23. Express 3.11×10^3 in standard form.
    A. 0.311 B. 0.0311 C. 0.00311 D. 3,110
    23. __C__

24. Express 0.000021 in scientific notation.
    A. 2.1×10^{-6} B. 21×10^{-4} C. 2.1×10^4 D. 2.1×10^{-5}
    24. __D__

25. Find the whole numbers between 20 and 60 that are divisible by both 2 and 3.
    A. 24, 32, 36, 42, 48, 54 B. 24, 30, 36, 42, 48, 54
    C. 24, 32, 36, 42, 52 D. 24, 30, 36, 42, 48
    25. __B__

BONUS Two types of patio blocks have heights of 12 centimeters and 28 centimeters. Find the least number of rows of each type that will have equal heights.
A. 7 rows of 12-cm blocks, 3 rows of 28-cm blocks
B. 7 rows of 28-cm blocks, 3 rows of 12-cm blocks
C. 7 rows of 12-cm blocks, 3 rows of 28-cm blocks
D. 3 rows of 12-cm blocks, 6 rows of 28-cm blocks
__C__

47

Glencoe Division, Macmillan/McGraw-Hill

Test and Review Generator software is provided in Apple, IBM, and Macintosh versions. You may use this software to create your own tests or worksheets, based on the needs of your students.

The **Performance Assessment Booklet** provides an alternate assessment for evaluating student progress. An assessment for this chapter can be found on pages 11–12.

The Academic Skills Test may be used to help students prepare for standardized tests. The test items are written in the same style as those in state proficiency tests. The test items cover skills and concepts presented up to this point in the text.

These pages can be used as an overnight assignment. After students have completed the pages, discuss how each problem can be solved, or provide copies of the solutions from the *Solutions Manual*.

Academic Skills Test

Chapter

6 Academic Skills Test
Standard Format, Chapters 1-6

Directions: Choose the best answer. Write A, B, C, or D.

1. To find the difference of 3.4 and 1.8, **B**

   A subtract 2 from 3.2.

   B subtract 2 from 3.6.

   C subtract 2.2 from 3.

   D subtract 1.2 from 4.

2. Three friends will equally share the cost of a $28.95 board game. Which is *not* a reasonable estimate of each person's share? **C**

   A $9.90

   B $9.65

   C $8.80

   D All are reasonable.

3. 96 yd = ___?___ ft **B**

   A 960   B 288

   C 96   D 32

4. If $b = 5$ and $c = 8$, what is the value of $b(10 - c)$? **A**

   A 10   B 42

   C 50   D 52

5. If $4.2 = \frac{x}{3}$, what is the value of x? **D**

   A 1.2   B 1.26

   C 1.4   D 12.6

6. On a math test, Lee scored 10 points less than twice the lowest score. If his score was 96, what was the lowest score? **B**

   A 86   B 53

   C 48   D 43

7. $-3 + 8 + (-3) + 1 =$ **B**

   A −15   B 3

   C 9   D 15

8. $-145 - 86 =$ **D**

   A 231   B 59

   C −59   D −231

9. An airplane descended 250 feet in 5 minutes. How can you find its average change in altitude per minute? **A**

   A Divide −250 by 5.

   B Multiply 250 by 5.

   C Subtract −25 from 250.

   D Not enough information given to solve.

10. The line plot shows the heights in inches of the Washington Middle School girls' basketball team. **D**

    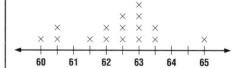

    Which sentence best describes the data?

    A The range is 6 inches.

    B Most of the players are 63 inches tall.

    C There are 8 players.

    D Most of the players are between 62 and 64 inches tall.

11. These are the daily low temperatures (°F) for two weeks in April.
36, 42, 38, 50, 48, 44, 46, 50, 52, 49, 48, 45, 46, 48
What is the median temperature? **C**

A 44° B 46°
C 47° D 48°

12. What is the interquartile range of the data in Exercise 11? **B**

A 2 B 5
C 12 D 16

13. Which figure could contain exactly one right angle? **B**

A acute triangle
B isosceles triangle
C obtuse triangle
D rectangle

14. How many lines of symmetry does a square have? **D**

A none B 1
C 2 D 4

15. How many pairs of congruent triangles are formed by the diagonals of rectangle *ABCD*? **D**

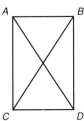

A 1 B 2
C 3 D 4

16. If △*JKL* is similar to △*QRP*, what is the value of *x*? **A**

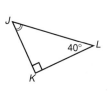 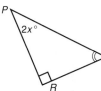

A 20 B 25
C 40 D 50

Test-Taking Tip

When you prepare for a standardized test, review basic definitions such as the ones below.

- A number is *divisible* by another number if it can be divided with 0 as a remainder. A number is divisible by each of its *factors*.

- A number is *prime* if it has exactly two factors, itself and 1. 5 is a prime number. 12 is not prime since it has factors other than itself and 1. 2, 3, 4, and 6 are also factors of 12.

17. What is the least prime factor of 54? **B**

A 1 B 2
C 3 D 6

18. The number −13.6 belongs to what set(s) of numbers? **A**

A rational numbers
B whole numbers and rational numbers
C integers and rational numbers
D none of these

19. What is the probability of the spinner landing on a prime number? **B**

A 0.25 B 0.5
C 0.75 D 1

20. A red blood cell is about 0.00075 cm long. How is this measure expressed in scientific notation? **B**

A 0.75×10^{-3}
B 7.5×10^{-4}
C 7.5×10^{-5}
D 75×10^{-5}

7 Rational Numbers

Previewing the Chapter

This chapter builds on the foundation of Chapter 6. Methods for applying all the arithmetic operations to rationals are developed. Students apply these methods to solving equations involving rational numbers. Other applications include the areas of triangles and trapezoids and the circumference of circles. In the **problem-solving strategy** lesson, students learn to solve problems by finding a pattern. They then apply the strategy to sequences, including the Fibonacci sequence.

Lesson	Lesson Objectives	NCTM Standards	State/Local Objectives
7-1	Add and subtract fractions with like denominators.	1–5, 7–9, 13	
7-2	Add and subtract fractions with unlike denominators.	1–4, 6, 7, 9	
7-3	Multiply fractions.	1–5, 7, 9	
7-4	Identify and use rational number properties.	1–5, 7, 9	
Decision Making	Analyze data and make a decision.	1–4, 7	
7-5	Solve problems by finding and extending a pattern.	1–5, 7–9	
7-6	Recognize and extend arithmetic and geometric sequences.	1–5, 7–9, 12	
7-6B	Discover the numbers that make up the Fibonacci sequence.	1–5, 8	
7-7	Find the areas of triangles and trapezoids.	1–4, 7, 9, 12, 13	
7-7B	Connect algebra and geometry to find the area of a triangle.	1–4, 7, 8, 12, 13	
7-8	Find the circumference of circles.	1–5, 7, 9, 12, 13	
7-9	Divide fractions.	1–5, 7, 9. 12	
7-10	Solve equations with rational number solutions.	1–4, 7, 9	

Organizing the Chapter

A complete, 1-page lesson plan is provided for each lesson in the Lesson Plans Masters Booklet.

LESSON PLANNING GUIDE

Lesson	Materials/ Manipulatives	Extra Practice (Student Edition)	Blackline Masters Booklets									
			Study Guide	Practice	Enrichment	Evaluation	Technology	Lab Manual	Multicultural Activities	Application and Interdisciplinary Activities	Transparencies	Group Activity Cards
7-1		p. 598	p. 57	p. 57	p. 57						7-1	7-1
7-2		p. 599	p. 58	p. 58	p. 58						7-2	7-2
7-3		p. 599	p. 59	p. 59	p. 59						7-3	7-3
7-4		p. 599	p. 60	p. 60	p. 60					p. 7	7-4	7-4
7-5			p. 61	p. 61	p. 61	Quiz A, p. 61					7-5	7-5
7-6	calculator	p. 600	p. 62	p. 62	p. 62					p. 21	7-6	7-6
7-6B	colored pencils							p. 58				
7-7	graph paper, scissors	p. 600	p. 63	p. 63	p. 63						7-7	7-7
7-7B	geoboard, rubber bands							p. 59				
7-8	calculator, tape measure, circular objects	p. 600	p. 64	p. 64	p. 64		p. 7	p. 60			7-8	7-8
7-9		p. 601	p. 65	p. 65	p. 65						7-9	7-9
7-10		p. 601	p. 66	p. 66	p. 66	Quiz B, p. 61	p. 21			p. 7	7-10	7-10
Study Guide and Review	newspaper, penny, nickel, dime, half dollar		Multiple Choice Test, Forms 1A and 1B, pp. 55–58 Free Response Test, Forms 2A and 2B, pp. 59–60 Cumulative Review, p. 62 (free response) Cumulative Test, p. 63 (multiple choice)									
Test												

Pacing Guide: Option I (Chapters 1–12) - 14 days; Option II (Chapters 1–13) - 13 days; Option III (Chapters 1–14) - 13 days
You may wish to refer to the complete **Course Planning Guides** on page T25.

OTHER CHAPTER RESOURCES

Student Edition
Chapter Opener, pp. 254–255
Decision Making, pp. 268–269
Mid-Chapter Review, p. 275
Cultural Kaleidoscope, p. 287
Portfolio Suggestion, p. 287

 Manipulatives
Overhead Manipulative Resources
Middle School Mathematics Manipulative Kit

 Software/Technology
Interactive Mathematics Tools (Macintosh)
Test and Review Generator (IBM, Apple, Macintosh)
Teacher's Guide for Software Resources

Other Supplements
Transparency 7–0
Performance Assessment, pp. 13–14
Glencoe Mathematics Professional Series Lesson Plans, pp. 73–84

INTERDISCIPLINARY BULLETIN BOARD

Zoology Connection

Objective   Express real-world facts as fractions.

How To Use It   Have students research facts on the length, weight, life span, and speed of at least ten animals. Have them display photos or drawings of the animals together with fractions comparing their vital statistics.

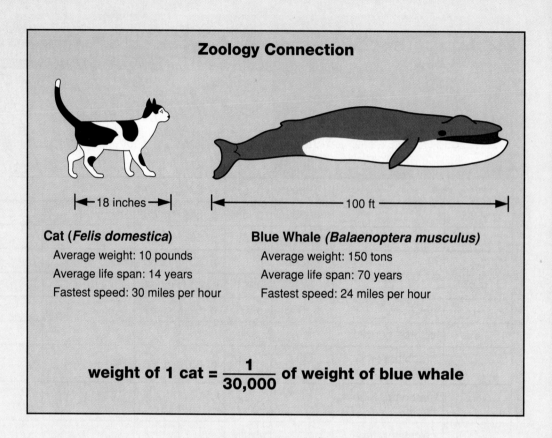

Zoology Connection

Cat (*Felis domestica*)

Average weight: 10 pounds

Average life span: 14 years

Fastest speed: 30 miles per hour

←18 inches→

Blue Whale (*Balaenoptera musculus*)

Average weight: 150 tons

Average life span: 70 years

Fastest speed: 24 miles per hour

←————— 100 ft —————→

$$\text{weight of 1 cat} = \frac{1}{30{,}000} \text{ of weight of blue whale}$$

APPLICATIONS AND CONNECTIONS

Applications	Lesson	Example	Exercise
Football	7-1		35
Carpentry	7-2		32
Publishing	7-2		34
Zoology	7-4	1	
Home Economics	7-4		38
Consumer Awareness	7-6		38
Business	7-6		39
Hydrology	7-7	1	37
Geography	7-7		39
Manufacturing	7-8		25
Astronomy	7-8		27
Sports	7-8		29
Food	7-9	1	
Advertising	7-9		32
Home Economics	7-9		33
Safe Driving	7-10		31
Connections			
Algebra	7-1	3	
Probability	7-1		37
Algebra	7-3	3	
Geometry	7-3		34
Computer	7-5		10
Algebra	7-6	5	
Geometry	7-6		42
Geometry	7-8	1	

TEAM ACTIVITIES

Multicultural Experiences

Outside Field Trips   Visit a carpentry shop for students to see how rational number operations are carried out on customary measurements.

A trip to the offices of a newspaper or magazine will allow students to learn how column inches are added to assess advertising charges.

In-Class Speakers   Ask a musician or music teacher to explain the use of fractions in music notation.

A cook can explain how to multiply or divide fractions in order to alter quantities in recipes.

SUPPLEMENTARY BLACKLINE MASTER BOOKLETS

Some of the blackline masters for enhancing this chapter are shown below.

Application and Interdisciplinary Activity Masters, pp. 7, 21

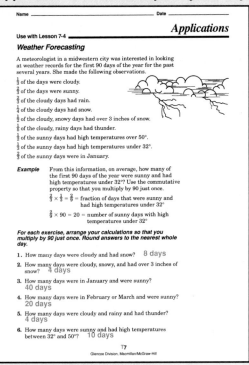

Name _____ Date _____

Applications

Use with Lesson 7-4 _____

Weather Forecasting

A meteorologist in a midwestern city was interested in looking at weather records for the first 90 days of the year for the past several years. She made the following observations.

$\frac{1}{3}$ of the days were cloudy.

$\frac{2}{3}$ of the days were sunny.

$\frac{2}{5}$ of the cloudy days had rain.

$\frac{1}{4}$ of the cloudy days had snow.

$\frac{1}{2}$ of the cloudy, snowy days had over 3 inches of snow.

$\frac{1}{6}$ of the cloudy, rainy days had thunder.

$\frac{1}{2}$ of the sunny days had high temperatures over 50°.

$\frac{1}{3}$ of the sunny days had high temperatures under 32°.

$\frac{2}{3}$ of the sunny days were in January.

Example From this information, on average, how many of the first 90 days of the year were sunny and had high temperatures under 32°? Use the commutative property so that you multiply by 90 just once.

$\frac{2}{3} \times \frac{1}{3} = \frac{2}{9}$ = fraction of days that were sunny and had high temperatures under 32°

$\frac{2}{9} \times 90 = 20$ = number of sunny days with high temperatures under 32°

For each exercise, arrange your calculations so that you multiply by 90 just once. Round answers to the nearest whole day.

1. How many days were cloudy and had snow? **8 days**

2. How many days were cloudy, snowy, and had over 3 inches of snow? **4 days**

3. How many days were in January and were sunny? **40 days**

4. How many days were in February or March and were sunny? **20 days**

5. How many days were cloudy and rainy and had thunder? **4 days**

6. How many days were sunny and had high temperatures between 32° and 50°? **10 days**

T7
Glencoe Division, Macmillan/McGraw-Hill

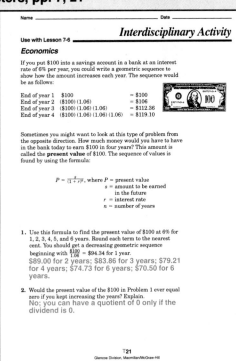

Name _____ Date _____

Interdisciplinary Activity

Use with Lesson 7-6 _____

Economics

If you put $100 into a savings account in a bank at an interest rate of 6% per year, you could write a geometric sequence to show how the amount increases each year. The sequence would be as follows:

End of year 1	$100	= $100
End of year 2	($100) (1.06)	= $106
End of year 3	($100) (1.06) (1.06)	= $112.36
End of year 4	($100) (1.06) (1.06) (1.06)	= $119.10

Sometimes you might want to look at this type of problem from the opposite direction. How much money would you have to have in the bank today to earn $100 in four years? This amount is called the **present value** of $100. The sequence of values is found by using the formula:

$$P = \frac{s}{(1 + r)^n}, \text{ where } P = \text{present value}$$
$$s = \text{amount to be earned in the future}$$
$$r = \text{interest rate}$$
$$n = \text{number of years}$$

1. Use this formula to find the present value of $100 at 6% for 1, 2, 3, 4, 5, and 6 years. Round each term to the nearest cent. You should get a decreasing geometric sequence beginning with $\frac{\$100}{1.06} = \$94.34$ for 1 year.
$89.00 for 2 years; $83.86 for 3 years; $79.21 for 4 years; $74.73 for 6 years; $70.50 for 6 years.

2. Would the present value of the $100 in Problem 1 ever equal zero if you kept increasing the years? Explain.
No; you can have a quotient of 0 only if the dividend is 0.

T21
Glencoe Division, Macmillan/McGraw-Hill

Multicultural Activity Masters, p. 7

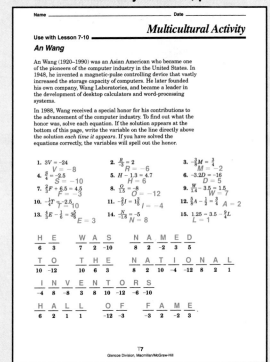

Name _____ Date _____

Multicultural Activity

Use with Lesson 7-10 _____

An Wang

An Wang (1920–1990) was an Asian American who became one of the pioneers of the computer industry in the United States. In 1948, he invented a magnetic-pulse controlling device that vastly increased the storage capacity of computers. He later founded his own company, Wang Laboratories, and became a leader in the development of desktop calculators and word-processing systems.

In 1988, Wang received a special honor for his contributions to the advancement of the computer industry. To find out what the honor was, solve each equation. If the solution appears at the bottom of this page, write the variable on the line directly above the solution *each time it appears*. If you have solved the equations correctly, the variables will spell out the honor.

1. $3V = -24$
   $V = -8$

2. $\frac{R}{-3} = 2$
   $R = -6$

3. $-\frac{3}{8}M = \frac{3}{4}$
   $M = -2$

4. $\frac{S}{4} = -2.5$
   $S = -10$

5. $H - 1.3 = 4.7$
   $H = 6$

6. $-3.2D = -16$
   $D = 5$

7. $\frac{2}{3}F + 6.5 = 4.5$
   $F = -3$

8. $\frac{O}{15} = -8$
   $O = -12$

9. $\frac{W}{14} - 3.5 = 1.5$
   $W = 7$

10. $-\frac{1}{4}T = -2.5$
    $T = 10$

11. $-\frac{2}{3}I = 1\frac{3}{3}$
    $I = -4$

12. $\frac{5}{8}A - 1\frac{1}{4} = \frac{2}{4}$
    $A = 2$

13. $\frac{4}{3}E - \frac{1}{6} = 3\frac{5}{6}$
    $E = 3$

14. $\frac{N}{-1.6} = -5$
    $N = 8$

15. $1.25 = 3.5 - \frac{9}{4}L$
    $L = 1$

H	E		W	A	S		N	A	M	E	D
6	3		7	2	-10		8	2	-2	3	5

T	O		T	H	E		N	A	T	I	O	N	A	L
10	-12		10	6	3		8	2	10	-4	-12	8	2	1

I	N	V	E	N	T	O	R	S
-4	8	-8	3	8	10	-12	-6	-10

H	A	L	L		O	F		F	A	M	E
6	2	1	1		-12	-3		-3	2	-2	3

T7
Glencoe Division, Macmillan/McGraw-Hill

Technology Masters, p. 7

Name _____ Date _____

Calculator Activity

Use with Lesson 7-8 _____

The π Key

π is a specially marked key on many calculators that makes it easier to evaluate expressions containing π.

Example Find the circumference of a bicycle tire with diameter 30 inches.

Solution $C = \pi d$

$C = \pi \times 30$

π × 30 =
The display is 94.247779.

Rounded to the nearest inch, the circumference is 94 inches.

Find the circumference of each circle described below. Round to the nearest tenth.

1. [circle, 10 m]
   62.8 m

2. [circle, 14 ft]
   44.0 ft

3. The diameter is 11 inches.
   34.6 in.

4. The radius is 0.5 centimeters.
   3.1 cm

5. The radius of the equator of the Earth is 4,000 miles.
   25,132.7 mi

6. The diameter of the rim of a can is 2.5 inches.
   7.9 in.

7. The diameter of the base of a lamp is 6 inches.
   18.8 in.

8. The radius of the base of a cone is 8 cm.
   50.3 cm

9. The diameter of an orange is 7 centimeters.
   22.0 cm

10. The diameter of an automobile headlight is 8.5 inches.
    26.7 in.

T7
Glencoe Division, Macmillan/McGraw-Hill

RECOMMENDED OUTSIDE RESOURCES

Books/Periodicals

Fuys, David, Dorothy Geddes, and Rosamond Tischler, *The van Heile Model of Thinking in Geometry Among Adolescents,* Reston, VA: NCTM, 1988.

Marcy, Steve, and Janis Marcy, *Pre-Algebra with Pizzazz,* Palo Alto, CA: Creative Publications, 1978.

Films/Videotapes/Videodiscs

Between Rational Numbers, Silver Burdett, 1970.

Dividing with Fractions—Reciprocals, Summit, NJ: 1970.

The Story of Pi, Reston, VA: NCTM, 1989.

Software

The Geometric Supposer: Triangles, (Apple II, IBM/Tandy, Macintosh), Wings for Learning/Sunburst

For addresses of companies handling software, please refer to page T24.

INTER·ACTIVE Mathematics

Glencoe's *Interactive Mathematics: Activities and Investigations* consists of 18 units that may be used as alternatives or supplemental material for *Mathematics: Applications and Connections.* The suggested units for this chapter are Unit 9, *Don't Fence Me In,* and Unit 16, *Growing Pains.* See page T18 for more information.

This two-page introduction to the chapter provides a visual, relevant way to engage students in the mathematics of the chapter. Questions are included that help students see the need to learn the mathematics in the chapter. Data in charts and graphs provide statistical information that students can analyze and interpret at this point as well as later in the chapter. The Chapter Project provides an activity that applies the mathematics of the chapter.

MAKING MATHEMATICS RELEVANT

Spotlight on Baseball

For some people, the calculating and memorizing of baseball statistics are nearly as much a part of the sport as the games themselves. Ask students to calculate the following statistics.

- *A player stole 54 bases in 60 attempts. Express the success rate as a decimal.* 0.9

- *A pitcher struck out 12 of the 32 batters he faced. Express his strikeout rate as a decimal.* 0.375

- *A player got two doubles, a triple, and a home run in one game. How many total bases is this?* 11

Using the Timeline

Ask the following questions.

- *Which baseball player was inducted into the Hall of Fame the same year that the Golden Gate Bridge was completed?* Tris Speaker

- *How many years before you were born did the first World Series take place?* The answer is the student's birth year minus 1903.

Chapter

7 Rational Numbers

Spotlight on Baseball

Have You Ever Wondered...

- How a player's batting average is figured?

- What the fraction $\frac{11}{31}$ means when it describes the number of left-handed Cy Young Award winners?

LEADING BATTERS IN BASEBALL HALL OF FAME

Player	Year Inducted	Years Played	At Bats	Hits	Batting Avg.
Ty Cobb	1936	24	11,436	4,190	.366
Rogers Hornsby	1942	23	8,173	2,930	.358
Ed Delhanty	1945	16	7,493	1,593	.346
Willie Keeler	1939	19	8,570	2,955	.345
Billy Hamilton	1961	14	6,262	2,157	.344
Ted Williams	1966	19	7,706	2,654	.344
Tris Speaker	1937	22	10,208	3,515	.344
Dan Brouthers	1945	19	6,682	2,288	.342
Jessee Burkett	1946	16	8,389	2,872	.342
Babe Ruth	1936	22	8,399	2,873	.342
Harry Heilmann	1952	17	7,787	2,660	.342
Bill Terry	1954	14	6,428	2,193	.341
George Sisler	1939	15	8,267	2,812	.340
Lou Gehrig	1939	17	8,001	2,721	.340

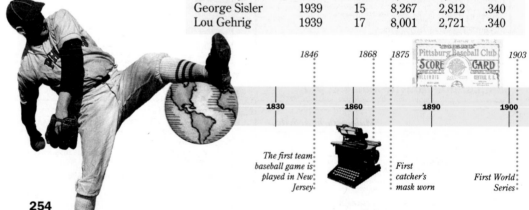

1846   1868   1875   Pittsburg Baseball Club SCORE CARD   1903

1830   1860   1890   1900

The first team baseball game is played in New Jersey.

First catcher's mask worn

First World Series

254

"Have You Ever Wondered?" Answers

- The number of hits is divided by the number of times at bat.
- Of the 31 National League Cy Young Award winners, 11 were left-handed.

Have students study the Hall of Fame table. Ask the following questions.

- *Which player averaged less than 100 hits per year during his career?* Ed Delhanty
- *What argument can you make that Tris Speaker was a better hitter than Billy Hamilton?* He sustained the same batting average for eight more years.

Data Search

A question related to these data is provided in Lesson 7-8, page 287, Exercise 30.

CHAPTER PROJECT

If you are not completing this chapter during baseball season, copy statistics from old newspapers or from almanacs; or simply have students choose athletes from the sport currently being played. Students should choose statistics that will give them plenty of opportunities to write and use rational numbers.

Encourage students to choose an interesting way to display their data, and also to use fractions in their displays.

Allow five weeks to complete the project.

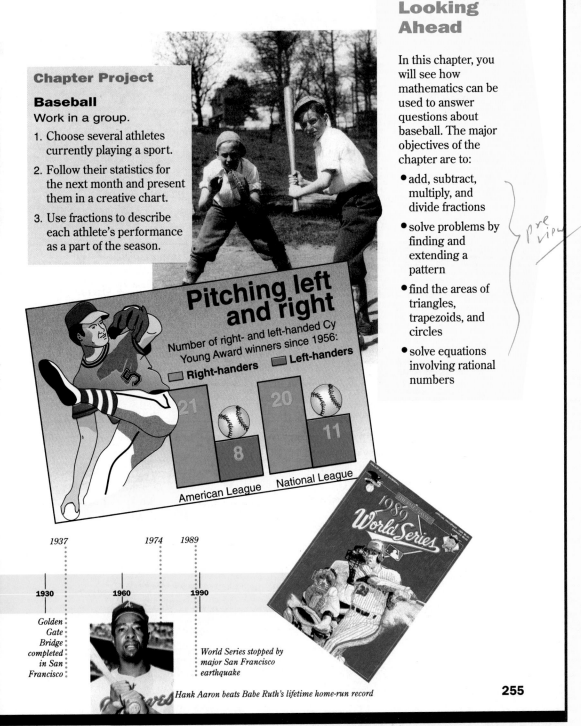

Chapter Project

Baseball

Work in a group.

1. Choose several athletes currently playing a sport.
2. Follow their statistics for the next month and present them in a creative chart.
3. Use fractions to describe each athlete's performance as a part of the season.

Pitching left and right

Number of right- and left-handed Cy Young Award winners since 1956:

☐ Right-handers   ■ Left-handers

21   8   American League

20   11   National League

Looking Ahead

In this chapter, you will see how mathematics can be used to answer questions about baseball. The major objectives of the chapter are to:

- add, subtract, multiply, and divide fractions
- solve problems by finding and extending a pattern
- find the areas of triangles, trapezoids, and circles
- solve equations involving rational numbers

preview

1937   1974   1989

1930   1960   1990

Golden Gate Bridge completed in San Francisco

World Series stopped by major San Francisco earthquake

Hank Aaron beats Babe Ruth's lifetime home-run record

255

Chapter Opener Transparency

Transparency 7-0 is available in the Transparency Package. It provides another full-color, motivating activity that you can use to capture students' interest.

Lesson Resources
- Study Guide Master 7-1
- Practice Master 7-1
- Enrichment Master 7-1
- Group Activity Card 7-1

 Transparency 7-1 contains the 5-Minute Check and a teaching aid for this lesson.

🕐 5-Minute Check
(Over Chapter 6)

1. Find the prime factorization of 180.
   $2^2 \cdot 3^2 \cdot 5$

2. Find the GCF for 36 and 84. **12**

3. Write $-\frac{12}{28}$ in simplest form. $-\frac{3}{7}$

4. Express 0.65 as a fraction in simplest form.
   $\frac{13}{20}$

5. Find the LCM for 18 and 24. **72**

1 FOCUS

Motivating the Lesson

Activity Use 1-cup and 2-cup liquid measures to illustrate fractions. Pour water in various fractions of the small cup into the large one to find sums. For example, $\frac{3}{4} + \frac{3}{4} = \frac{6}{4}$ or $1\frac{1}{2}$. Show subtraction by pouring water back into the small cup.

2 TEACH

Using Models Use quarters (money) to convince students that only the numerators are added when adding like fractions:
2 *quarters* + 3 *quarters* = 5 *quarters*, <u>not</u> 5 *eighths*.

7-1 Adding and Subtracting Like Fractions

Objective
Add and subtract fractions with like denominators.

Words to Learn
mixed number

The electric eel, found in Venezuela and Brazil, is really not an eel, but a greenish-black fish 2 to 4 feet long. The inner organs of the eel are located in the first $\frac{1}{5}$ of its body. The remaining $\frac{4}{5}$ contain the organs that produce an electric current.

Notice that the rational numbers $\frac{1}{5}$ and $\frac{4}{5}$ have like denominators. Fractions with like denominators are also called *like fractions*.

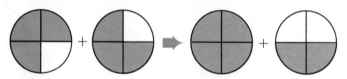

Adding Like Fractions	**In words:** To add fractions with like denominators, add the numerators.	
	Arithmetic	**Algebra**
	$\frac{2}{7} + \frac{3}{7} = \frac{5}{7}$	$\frac{a}{c} + \frac{b}{c} = \frac{a+b}{c}, c \neq 0$

LOOKBACK

You can review simplifying fractions on page 225.

Sometimes the sum of two fractions is greater than 1. When this happens, we usually write the sum as a mixed number in simplest form. A **mixed number** is the sum of a whole number and a fraction.

Example 1

John ate $\frac{3}{4}$ of a pizza and Jeanne ate $\frac{3}{4}$ of a pizza. How much pizza did they eat together?

$$\frac{3}{4} + \frac{3}{4} = \frac{6}{4} \qquad \textit{Add the numerators.}$$
$$= 1\frac{2}{4} \qquad \textit{Rename } \frac{6}{4} \textit{ as a mixed number, } 1\frac{2}{4}.$$
$$= 1\frac{1}{2} \qquad \textit{Write the mixed number in simplest form.}$$

John and Jeanne ate a total of $1\frac{1}{2}$ pizzas.

Subtracting like fractions is similar to adding them.

Interactive Mathematics Tools

This multimedia software provides an interactive lesson that is tied directly to Lesson 7-1. Students will use fraction models to add like fractions as in Example 1.

Study Guide Masters, p. 57

Name _____ Date _____

Study Guide Worksheet 7-1

Adding and Subtracting Like Fractions

To add fractions with like denominators, add the numerators.

Examples $m = \frac{7}{8} + \left(-\frac{5}{8}\right)$
$m = \frac{2}{8}$ Add the numerators.
$m = \frac{1}{4}$ Simplify.

$n = \frac{5}{6} + \frac{5}{6}$
$n = \frac{10}{6}$ Add the numerators.
$n = 1\frac{4}{6}$ Rename the improper fraction as a mixed number.
$n = 1\frac{2}{3}$ Simplify.

To subtract fractions with like denominators, subtract the numerators.

Subtracting Like Fractions	In words: To subtract fractions with like denominators, subtract the numerators.

Arithmetic	Algebra
$\dfrac{3}{5} - \dfrac{2}{5} = \dfrac{1}{5}$	$\dfrac{a}{c} - \dfrac{b}{c} = \dfrac{a - b}{c}, c \neq 0$

Rational numbers include positive and negative fractions. Use the rules for adding and subtracting integers to determine the sign of the sum or difference of two rational numbers.

Example 2

Solve $a = -\dfrac{5}{6} - \left(-\dfrac{7}{6}\right)$.

$-\dfrac{5}{6}, \dfrac{-5}{6},$ and $\dfrac{5}{-6}$ all name the same rational number.

$a = -\dfrac{5}{6} - \left(-\dfrac{7}{6}\right)$ *Since the denominators are the same, subtract the numerators.*

$a = \dfrac{-5 - (-7)}{6}$

$a = \dfrac{2}{6}$ or $\dfrac{1}{3}$ *Simplify.*

Example 3 Connection

Algebra   Simplify $3\dfrac{1}{4}x + \dfrac{3}{4}x - 2\dfrac{3}{4}x$.

$3\dfrac{1}{4}x + \dfrac{3}{4}x - 2\dfrac{3}{4}x = \left(3\dfrac{1}{4} + \dfrac{3}{4} - 2\dfrac{3}{4}\right)x$ *Distributive Property*

$= \left(3\dfrac{4}{4} - 2\dfrac{3}{4}\right)x$ *Add $3\dfrac{1}{4}$ and $\dfrac{3}{4}$.*

$= 1\dfrac{1}{4}x$

Checking for Understanding

Communicating Mathematics

Read and study the lesson to answer each question.

1. **Write** the addition sentence shown by the following model. $\dfrac{5}{6} + \dfrac{5}{6} = 1\dfrac{2}{3}$

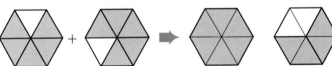

2. **Draw** a model to show the sum of $\dfrac{5}{8}$ and $\dfrac{5}{8}$. Write the sum as a mixed number.
See Solutions Manual. $1\dfrac{1}{4}$

3. **Tell** a simple rule for adding and subtracting like fractions.
Add numerators; leave same denominator.

Guided Practice

Solve each equation. Write each solution in simplest form.

4. $\dfrac{3}{8} + \dfrac{1}{8} = d$ $\dfrac{1}{2}$ 5. $\dfrac{3}{5} + -\dfrac{2}{5} = x$ $\dfrac{1}{5}$ 6. $\dfrac{36}{21} - \dfrac{8}{21} = y$ $1\dfrac{1}{3}$

7. $\dfrac{3}{16} + \dfrac{15}{16} = m$ $1\dfrac{1}{8}$ 8. $s = -\dfrac{4}{5} - \left(-\dfrac{3}{5}\right)$ $-\dfrac{1}{5}$ 9. $r = \dfrac{9}{7} - \dfrac{5}{7}$ $\dfrac{4}{7}$

Lesson 7-1 Adding and Subtracting Like Fractions   **257**

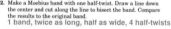

Exercises

Independent Practice   Solve each equation. Write each solution in simplest form.

10. $\frac{5}{8} + \frac{1}{8} = n$ $\frac{3}{4}$

11. $\frac{17}{9} + \left(-\frac{1}{9}\right) = y$ $1\frac{7}{9}$

12. $b = -\frac{7}{12} - \frac{5}{12}$ -1

13. $z = \frac{1}{18} - \frac{7}{18}$ $-\frac{1}{3}$

14. $5\frac{3}{4} + 2\frac{3}{4} = g$ $8\frac{1}{2}$

15. $c = \frac{21}{8} - \frac{49}{8}$ $-3\frac{1}{2}$

16. $m = -\frac{3}{5} - \left(-\frac{4}{5}\right)$ $\frac{1}{5}$

17. $-2\frac{5}{9} - \frac{5}{9} = r$ $-3\frac{1}{9}$

18. $k = -\frac{2}{3} - \frac{1}{3}$ -1

19. Find the sum of $\frac{5}{6}$ and $-\frac{1}{6}$. $\frac{2}{3}$

20. Find the sum of $-\frac{5}{12}$ and $-\frac{1}{12}$. $-\frac{1}{2}$

21. Subtract $-\frac{5}{8}$ from $-\frac{1}{8}$. $\frac{1}{2}$

22. Subtract $-2\frac{1}{2}$ from $5\frac{1}{2}$. 8

23. Find the sum of $-\frac{25}{6}$ and $\frac{7}{6}$. -3

24. Subtract $-\frac{7}{9}$ from $\frac{4}{9}$. $1\frac{2}{9}$

Evaluate each expression if $c = -\frac{3}{5}$ and $d = \frac{12}{5}$.

25. $d - c$ 3

26. $c + d$ $1\frac{4}{5}$

27. $c - d$ -3

Simplify each expression.

28. $4\frac{1}{2}y + \frac{1}{2}y - 2\frac{1}{2}y$ $2\frac{1}{2}y$

29. $-2\frac{1}{3}n + \left(-\frac{2}{3}n\right) + 4n$ n

30. $\frac{9}{5}r + \left(-\frac{1}{5}r\right) - \frac{3}{5}r$ r

Mixed Review

31. How many tons are in 7,000 pounds? *(Lesson 1-7)* $3\frac{1}{2}$ tons

32. Solve $-42 \div (-14) = p$. *(Lesson 3-7)* 3

33. **Geometry** Determine if the figure at the right has rotational symmetry. *(Lesson 5-5)* yes

34. Express 52,380,000 in scientific notation. *(Lesson 6-11)*
    5.238×10^7

Problem Solving and Applications

35. **Football** The first touchdown in a football game was made $3\frac{1}{4}$ minutes after the opening kickoff. Another $5\frac{3}{4}$ minutes passed before a field goal was made. If the clock started counting down from 15 minutes, how much time was left when the field goal was scored? 6 minutes

36. **Critical Thinking** Which is greater, $\frac{x}{1}$ or $\frac{1}{x}$? Use examples to defend your answer.
    See margin.

37. **Probability** A number cube is rolled.
    a. What is the probability of rolling a 3 or a 6? $\frac{1}{3}$
    b. What is the probability of *not* rolling a 3 or a 6? $\frac{2}{3}$
    c. Find the sum of the answers to Exercises **a** and **b**. 1

38. **Journal Entry** Write a few sentences that would explain to a younger student how to add and subtract fractions with like denominators. See students' work.

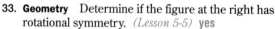

7-2 Adding and Subtracting Unlike Fractions

Objective
Add and subtract fractions with unlike denominators.

Johann Strauss, Jr. (1825-1899) is known as the Waltz King. A waltz is written in $\frac{3}{4}$ time. This means there are three beats in a measure and the quarter note gets one beat. The value of the notes can be expressed as fractions and the total value of each measure is $\frac{3}{4}$. The first few measures of *The Laughing Song* are shown below with the values of each note. What type of note must be used to finish the last measure?

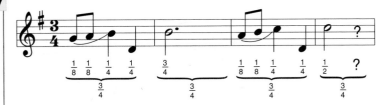

To find the missing note, subtract $\frac{1}{2}$ from $\frac{3}{4}$. The fractions do not have the same denominator, but $\frac{1}{2}$ can be renamed with a denominator of 4.

$$\frac{3}{4} - \frac{1}{2} = \frac{3}{4} - \frac{2}{4} \qquad \textit{Rename } \frac{1}{2} \textit{ as } \frac{2}{4}.$$
$$= \frac{1}{4} \qquad \textit{The difference, } \frac{1}{4}, \textit{ can be read as "one quarter."}$$

A note with a value of $\frac{1}{4}$ could be used to finish the last measure.

Adding and Subtracting Unlike Fractions	To find the sum or difference of two fractions or mixed numbers with unlike denominators, rename the fractions with a common denominator. Then add or subtract and simplify.

The least common denominator (LCD) is the least common multiple of the denominators. The LCD is helpful in renaming fractions for adding and subtracting.

Example 1

Solve $a = \frac{5}{6} + \frac{7}{9}$. Write the solution in simplest form.

$a = \frac{5}{6} + \frac{7}{9}$ $6 = 2 \cdot 3$ *and* $9 = 3^2$ *The LCM of 6 and 9 is* $2 \cdot 3^2$ *or 18.*

$a = \frac{15}{18} + \frac{14}{18}$ $\frac{5 \cdot 3}{6 \cdot 3} = \frac{15}{18}$ *and* $\frac{7 \cdot 2}{9 \cdot 2} = \frac{14}{18}$

$a = \frac{29}{18}$ *or* $1\frac{11}{18}$ *Rename* $\frac{29}{18}$ *as* $1\frac{11}{18}$.

Lesson 7-2 Adding and Subtracting Unlike Fractions   **259**

OPTIONS

Reteaching Activity

Using Models Have students use a ruler to model addition and subtraction of fractions with denominators of 2, 4, or 8. For example, to add $1\frac{1}{2} + \frac{5}{8}$, have students draw a segment $1\frac{1}{2}$ inches long, then extend the segment $\frac{5}{8}$ inch farther to the right (to a length of $2\frac{1}{8}$ inches).

Study Guide Masters, p. 58

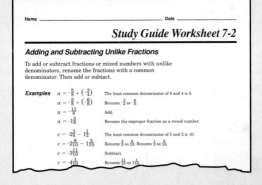

---

1 FOCUS

Motivating the Lesson

Questioning Ask students to name real-life situations that require adding and subtracting fractions. Sample answer: calculating the quantities of construction materials needed to build a house

2 TEACH

Using Connections Remind students that in the previous lesson they added and subtracted fractions with like denominators. This lesson shows how to rename fractions so they have like denominators. Then the fractions can be added and subtracted using the method shown in the previous lesson.

Teaching Tip In Example 1, point out that the LCD is the same as the LCM of the denominators.

259

More Examples

For Example 1

Solve $k = \frac{3}{8} + \frac{11}{12}$. $1\frac{7}{24}$

For Example 2

Solve $p = \frac{2}{3} - \frac{8}{9}$. $-\frac{2}{9}$

For Example 3

Solve $w = 2\frac{3}{4} + 3\frac{7}{8}$. $6\frac{5}{8}$

For Example 4

Solve $5\frac{2}{5} - 3\frac{9}{10} = r$. $1\frac{1}{2}$

Checking for Understanding

Exercises 1-2 are designed to help you assess students' understanding through reading, writing, speaking, and modeling. You should work through these exercises with your students and then monitor their work on Guided Practice Exercises 3-12.

Practice Masters, p. 58

Name _____ Date _____

Practice Worksheet 7-2

Adding and Subtracting Unlike Fractions

Complete.

1. $4\frac{3}{7} = 3\frac{?}{7}$ 10   2. $8\frac{2}{3} = 7\frac{?}{3}$ 5   3. $2\frac{4}{9} = 1\frac{?}{9}$ 13

Solve each equation. Write each solution in simplest form.

4. $a = \frac{3}{4} + \frac{7}{12}$ $1\frac{1}{3}$ 5. $r = -\frac{5}{12} + \frac{3}{8}$ $-\frac{1}{24}$ 6. $-\frac{3}{10} + \left(-\frac{2}{5}\right) = x$ $-\frac{7}{10}$

7. $2\frac{2}{3} + \left(-4\frac{1}{4}\right) = q$ $-1\frac{7}{12}$ 8. $4\frac{3}{4} - \left(-2\frac{3}{8}\right) = g$ $7\frac{1}{8}$ 9. $t = \frac{11}{12} - 1\frac{2}{3}$ $-\frac{3}{4}$

10. $-3\frac{3}{5} - \frac{9}{10} = b$ $-4\frac{1}{2}$ 11. $-2\frac{1}{6} - 3\frac{3}{4} = s$ $-5\frac{11}{20}$ 12. $-2\frac{1}{3} - \left(-4\frac{2}{3}\right) = d$ $2\frac{1}{3}$

13. $p = 8 - 3\frac{2}{3}$ $4\frac{1}{3}$ 14. $c = 3\frac{2}{3} - 8$ $-4\frac{1}{3}$ 15. $w = -10\frac{2}{3} - \left(-3\frac{1}{2}\right)$ $-6\frac{2}{3}$

16. Find the sum of $\frac{4}{9}$ and $\frac{9}{27}$. $\frac{17}{27}$ 17. What is $3\frac{2}{3}$ less than $-5\frac{1}{12}$? $-8\frac{3}{4}$

Evaluate each expression if $x = \frac{3}{8}$, $y = 2\frac{7}{12}$, and $z = -\frac{5}{8}$.

18. $x + y + z$ $2\frac{1}{8}$ 19. $x - z$ $1\frac{5}{24}$ 20. $y - (-z)$ $1\frac{3}{4}$

21. $x + z$ $-\frac{11}{24}$ 22. $y - x$ $2\frac{5}{24}$ 23. $z + (-y)$ $-3\frac{5}{12}$

T58
Glencoe Division, Macmillan/McGraw-Hill

Example 2

Solve $y = \frac{1}{4} - \left(-\frac{5}{8}\right)$.

$y = \frac{1}{4} - \left(-\frac{5}{8}\right)$

$y = \frac{2}{8} - \left(-\frac{5}{8}\right)$ *Use the LCM of 4 and 8 to rename $\frac{1}{4}$ as $\frac{2}{8}$.*

$y = \frac{2}{8} + \frac{5}{8}$ *Subtract $-\frac{5}{8}$ by adding its inverse, $\frac{5}{8}$.*

$y = \frac{2+5}{8}$ or $\frac{7}{8}$ *Add the numerators.*

To add or subtract mixed numbers with unlike denominators, first rename the fractions with a common denominator.

Examples

3   Solve $d = 3\frac{7}{8} + 5\frac{5}{24}$.   *Estimate: 4 + 5 = 9*

$d = 3\frac{7}{8} + 5\frac{5}{24}$

$d = 3\frac{21}{24} + 5\frac{5}{24}$ *Use the LCM of 8 and 24 to rename $\frac{7}{8}$ as $\frac{21}{24}$.*

$d = 8\frac{26}{24}$ *Add the whole numbers. Then add the fractions.*

$d = 9\frac{2}{24}$ or $9\frac{1}{12}$ *Simplify.*

4   Solve $5\frac{1}{3} - 3\frac{3}{4} = m$.   *Estimate: 5 − 4 = 1*

In Example 4, why is it necessary to rename $5\frac{4}{12}$ as $4\frac{16}{12}$?

$$\begin{array}{c} 5\frac{1}{3} \\ -3\frac{3}{4} \\ \hline \end{array} \Rightarrow \begin{array}{c} 5\frac{4}{12} \\ -3\frac{9}{12} \\ \hline \end{array} \Rightarrow \begin{array}{c} 4\frac{16}{12} \\ -3\frac{9}{12} \\ \hline 1\frac{7}{12} \end{array}$$

Rename $5\frac{4}{12}$ as $4\frac{16}{12}$.

So, $1\frac{7}{12} = m$.

Checking for Understanding

Communicating Mathematics

Read and study the lesson to answer each question.

1. **Tell** the first step you should take when adding and subtracting fractions with unlike denominators. **Rename fractions with common denominators.**

2. **Tell** why you might rename $3\frac{5}{8}$ as $2\frac{13}{8}$ in a subtraction problem.
Sample answer: The number being subtracted contains $\frac{6}{8}$ or $\frac{7}{8}$.

260   **Chapter 7** Rational Numbers

OPTIONS

Bell Ringer

Find the sums of these unit fractions (fractions with 1 as the numerator):

$\frac{1}{4} + \frac{1}{5}$ $\frac{9}{20}$ $\frac{1}{3} + \frac{1}{7}$ $\frac{10}{21}$ $\frac{1}{8} + \frac{1}{9}$ $\frac{17}{72}$

Study your results. Then draw a conclusion. In the sum: the denominator is the product of the denominators and the numerator is their sum.

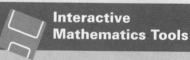

Interactive Mathematics Tools

This multimedia software provides an interactive lesson that is tied directly to Lesson 7-2. Students will use fraction models to add unlike fractions.

Complete.

3. $7\frac{2}{5} = 6\frac{\blacksquare}{5}$ 7   4. $3\frac{1}{4} = 2\frac{\blacksquare}{4}$ 5   5. $4\frac{5}{12} = 3\frac{\blacksquare}{12}$ 17   6. $9\frac{3}{8} = 8\frac{\blacksquare}{8}$ 11

Solve each equation. Write each solution in simplest form.

7. $\frac{2}{3} - \frac{3}{4} = a$ $-\frac{1}{12}$ 8. $x = \frac{1}{2} + \frac{2}{3}$ $1\frac{1}{6}$ 9. $\frac{1}{2} + \left(-\frac{7}{8}\right) = y$ $-\frac{3}{8}$

10. $h = 3\frac{1}{2} - 2\frac{2}{9}$ $1\frac{5}{18}$ 11. $5 - 3\frac{1}{3} = k$ $1\frac{2}{3}$ 12. $g = 9\frac{1}{3} - 2\frac{1}{2}$ $6\frac{5}{6}$

Exercises

Solve each equation. Write each solution in simplest form.

13. $h = \frac{1}{2} + \frac{4}{5}$ $1\frac{3}{10}$ 14. $-\frac{7}{10} + \frac{1}{5} = f$ $-\frac{1}{2}$ 15. $j = -\frac{3}{4} + \left(-\frac{1}{3}\right)$ $-1\frac{1}{12}$

16. $5\frac{1}{5} - \left(-2\frac{7}{10}\right) = z$ $7\frac{9}{10}$ 17. $w = -4\frac{1}{8} - 5\frac{1}{4}$ $-9\frac{3}{8}$ 18. $9 - 6\frac{1}{4} = x$ $2\frac{3}{4}$

19. $7\frac{3}{4} - \left(-1\frac{1}{8}\right) = y$ $8\frac{7}{8}$ 20. $t = 3\frac{2}{3} + \left(-5\frac{3}{4}\right)$ $-2\frac{1}{12}$ 21. $-8\frac{5}{9} - 2\frac{1}{6} = m$ $-10\frac{13}{18}$

22. Find the sum of $\frac{7}{6}$ and $\frac{5}{18}$. $1\frac{4}{9}$ 23. What is $2\frac{1}{2}$ less than $-8\frac{1}{5}$? $-10\frac{7}{10}$

Evaluate each expression if $a = \frac{5}{8}$, $b = 3\frac{11}{12}$, and $c = -\frac{5}{9}$.

24. $c - b$ $-4\frac{17}{36}$ 25. $a + b + c$ $3\frac{71}{72}$ 26. $a - c$ $1\frac{13}{72}$ 27. $b - (-c)$ $3\frac{13}{36}$

28. Solve $16 + n = 43$. *(Lesson 2-3)* 27

29. **Statistics** Find the median and upper and lower quartiles for the following set of data. 128, 140, 132, 146, 120 *(Lesson 4-6)* 132; 143; 124

30. Write $\frac{24}{32}$ in simplest form. *(Lesson 6-5)* $\frac{3}{4}$

31. Find the sum of $-5\frac{1}{6}$ and $2\frac{5}{6}$. *(Lesson 7-1)* $-2\frac{1}{3}$

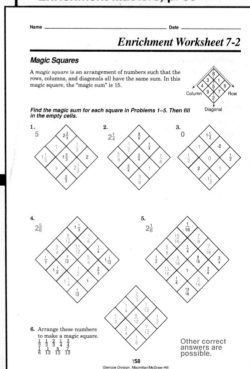

32. **Carpentry** The Cabinet Shop made a $\frac{13}{16}$ inch desktop by gluing a sheet of $\frac{1}{16}$-inch oak veneer to a sheet of $\frac{3}{4}$-inch plywood. What was the total thickness of the desktop?

33. **Critical Thinking** A drainpipe is cut in half and one-half is used. Then one-fifth of the remaining pipe is cut off and used. The piece left is 12 feet long. How long was the pipe originally? 30 feet

34. **Publishing** The width of a page of a newspaper is $13\frac{3}{4}$ inches. The left margin is $\frac{7}{16}$ inch and the right margin is $\frac{1}{2}$ inch. What is the width of the page inside the margins? $12\frac{13}{16}$ inches

35. **Journal Entry** Write a sentence or two explaining how to subtract fractions that have different denominators. See students' work.

Lesson 7-2 Adding and Subtracting Unlike Fractions **261**

Extending the Lesson

Using Cooperative Groups The ancient Egyptians expressed every fraction, except $\frac{2}{3}$, as a sum of unit fractions (fractions with numerator 1).

$$\frac{3}{4} = \frac{1}{2} + \frac{1}{4} \qquad \frac{33}{40} = \frac{1}{2} + \frac{1}{5} + \frac{1}{8}$$

Have small groups find ways to express other fractions as the sum of two or more different unit fractions.

Cooperative Learning Activity

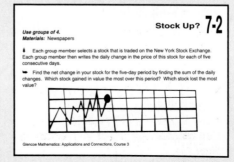

Stock Up? **7-2**

Use groups of 4.
Materials: Newspapers

• Each group member selects a stock that is traded on the New York Stock Exchange. Each group member then writes the daily change in the price of this stock for each of five consecutive days.

➥ Find the net change in your stock for the five-day period by finding the sum of the daily changes. Which stock gained in value the most over this period? Which stock lost the most value?

Glencoe Mathematics: Applications and Connections, Course 3

Name _____ Date _____

Enrichment Worksheet 7-2

Magic Squares

A *magic square* is an arrangement of numbers such that the rows, columns, and diagonals all have the same sum. In this magic square, the "magic sum" is 15.

Find the magic sum for each square in Problems 1–5. Then fill in the empty cells.

6. Arrange these numbers to make a magic square.
$\frac{1}{6}$ $\frac{1}{3}$ $\frac{5}{6}$ $\frac{4}{3}$
$\frac{1}{12}$ $\frac{7}{12}$ $\frac{2}{3}$ $\frac{3}{2}$

Other correct answers are possible.

T58
Glencoe Division, Macmillan/McGraw-Hill

261

Lesson Resources
- Study Guide Master 7-3
- Practice Master 7-3
- Enrichment Master 7-3
- Group Activity Card 7-3

 Transparency 7-3 contains the 5-Minute Check and a teaching aid for this lesson.

⏱ 5-Minute Check
(Over Lesson 7-2)

Solve each equation. Write each solution in simplest form.

1. $n = \frac{2}{3} + \frac{5}{6}$ $1\frac{1}{2}$

2. $-\frac{5}{8} + \frac{3}{4} = k$ $\frac{1}{8}$

3. $p = 2\frac{1}{5} - \left(-1\frac{3}{10}\right)$ $3\frac{1}{2}$

4. $w = 4\frac{1}{6} + \left(-5\frac{4}{9}\right)$ $-1\frac{5}{18}$

---

1 FOCUS

Motivating the Lesson

Activity   Have students fold a sheet of paper in thirds, unfold it, and shade one third using a colored pencil. Then have them fold the sheet in half in the other direction and shade one half using a different colored pencil. Ask them to write the multiplication problem illustrated by the shading; point out that the product is represented by the region shaded with both colors. $\frac{1}{3} \times \frac{1}{2} = \frac{1}{6}$

2 TEACH

Using Communication   Remind students that "of" means multiply.

$\frac{2}{5}$ of 3 feet $\rightarrow \frac{2}{5} \cdot 3$ feet

Point out that unlike addition and subtraction, multiplication of fractions does not require finding a common denominator.

7-3 Multiplying Fractions

Objective
Multiply fractions.

The length of a flag is called the *fly*, and the width is called the *hoist*. The blue rectangle in the United States flag is called the *union*. The length of the union is $\frac{2}{5}$ of the fly and the width is $\frac{7}{13}$ of the hoist. If the fly of a United States flag is 3 feet, how long is the union?

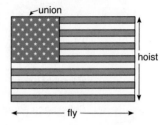

DID YOU KNOW

The largest United States flag measures 64 by 125 meters. It is kept in the White House and brought out for display each Flag Day.

The length of the union would be $\frac{2}{5}$ of 3 feet. You can multiply to find the actual length.

$\frac{2}{5} \cdot 3 = \frac{2}{5} \cdot \frac{3}{1}$ *Rewrite the whole number as a fraction.*

$\quad = \frac{2 \cdot 3}{5 \cdot 1}$ *Multiply the numerators.*
   Multiply the denominators.

$\quad = \frac{6}{5}$

$\quad = 1\frac{1}{5}$ *Rename as a mixed number.*

The width of the union is $1\frac{1}{5}$ feet.

Multiplying Fractions	**In words:** To multiply fractions, multiply the numerators and multiply the denominators.
	Arithmetic **Algebra**
	$\frac{2}{5} \cdot \frac{1}{3} = \frac{2}{15}$ $\qquad \frac{a}{b} \cdot \frac{c}{d} = \frac{ac}{bd}; b \neq 0, d \neq 0$

Example

1 Solve $m = \frac{3}{5} \cdot \frac{4}{9}$.

Method 1
Multiply first.
Then simplify.

$m = \frac{3}{5} \cdot \frac{4}{9}$

$m = \frac{3 \cdot 4}{5 \cdot 9}$ *Multiply.*

$m = \frac{12}{45}$ or $\frac{4}{15}$ *Simplify.*

Method 2
Divide common factors.
Then multiply.

$m = \frac{3}{5} \cdot \frac{4}{9}$

$m = \frac{\overset{1}{3}}{5} \cdot \frac{4}{\underset{3}{9}}$ *The GCF of 3 and 9 is 3.*
   Divide 3 and 9 by 3.

$m = \frac{1 \cdot 4}{5 \cdot 3}$ or $\frac{4}{15}$ *Multiply.*

OPTIONS

Reteaching Activity

Using Manipulatives   To model $\frac{1}{3} \cdot \frac{3}{4} = \frac{1}{4}$, draw a rectangle on a transparency overlay and shade $\frac{3}{4}$ of it. Place a new overlay on the first and shade $\frac{1}{3}$ of the previously-shaded region. Stress that this second shading is $\frac{1}{4}$ of the rectangle.

Study Guide Masters, p. 59

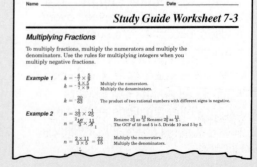

Use the rules of signs for multiplying integers when you multiply rational numbers.

 LOOKBACK

You can review exponents on page 35.

The rules for exponents that were stated for whole numbers also hold for rational numbers. For example, the expression $\left(\dfrac{2}{3}\right)^2$ means $\dfrac{2}{3} \cdot \dfrac{2}{3}$.

Example 3 *Connection*

Algebra   Evaluate $(ab)^2$ if $a = -\dfrac{1}{2}$ and $b = \dfrac{5}{6}$.

$(ab)^2 = \left(-\dfrac{1}{2} \cdot \dfrac{5}{6}\right)^2$

$(ab)^2 = \left(-\dfrac{5}{12}\right)^2$

$(ab)^2 = \left(-\dfrac{5}{12}\right)\left(-\dfrac{5}{12}\right)$

$(ab)^2 = \dfrac{25}{144}$

Checking for Understanding

Communicating Mathematics

Read and study the lesson to answer each question.

1. **Write** the product of $\dfrac{1}{3}$ and $\dfrac{3}{4}$. $\dfrac{1}{4}$

2. **Tell** how the model at the right shows the product of $\dfrac{1}{3}$ and $\dfrac{3}{4}$. See Solutions Manual.

3. **Draw** a model that shows the product of $\dfrac{3}{5}$ and $\dfrac{2}{3}$. See margin.

Team Teaching

- The area of Alaska is $\dfrac{4}{25}$ that of the entire United States.

Urge the other teachers on your team to draw attention to fractions when they appear in their subjects (such as the geography sample above), to operate with them whenever possible, and to explore their meanings and implications with students.

Interactive Mathematics Tools

This multimedia software provides an interactive lesson that is tied directly to Lesson 7-3. Students will use fraction models to multiply fractions.

More Examples

For Example 1

Solve $x = \dfrac{5}{8} \cdot \dfrac{6}{25}$. $\dfrac{3}{20}$

For Example 2

Solve $c = -2\frac{1}{4}\left(-2\frac{2}{3}\right)$.   6

For Example 3

Evaluate mn^2 if $m = -\dfrac{5}{8}$ and $n = \dfrac{2}{3}$. $-\dfrac{5}{18}$

Checking for Understanding

Exercises 1-3 are designed to help you assess students' understanding through reading, writing, speaking, and modeling. You should work through these exercises with your students and then monitor their work on Guided Practice Exercises 4-13.

Additional Answers

3.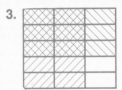

Practice Masters, p. 59

Guided Practice
Solve each equation. Write each solution in simplest form.

4. $\frac{3}{5} \cdot \frac{5}{8} = a$ $\frac{3}{8}$ 5. $\frac{5}{9} \cdot \frac{8}{15} = r$ $\frac{8}{27}$ 6. $y = \frac{4}{9} \cdot 2$ $\frac{8}{9}$

7. $-4\frac{1}{2}\left(-\frac{2}{3}\right) = j$ 3   8. $5\frac{1}{3} \cdot \frac{5}{12} = g$ $2\frac{2}{9}$ 9. $d = -2\left(\frac{3}{8}\right)$ $-\frac{3}{4}$

10. $\frac{15}{16} \cdot 3\frac{3}{5} = k$ $3\frac{3}{8}$ 11. $-2\frac{1}{4} \cdot \frac{2}{3} = h$ $-1\frac{1}{2}$ 12. $-2\frac{2}{5}\left(-1\frac{3}{4}\right) = x$ $4\frac{1}{5}$

13. Find the product of $-\frac{1}{3}$ and $2\frac{1}{4}$. $-\frac{3}{4}$

Exercises

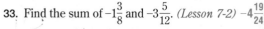

Independent Practice
Solve each equation. Write each solution in simplest form.

14. $\frac{2}{7} \cdot \frac{3}{4} = p$ $\frac{3}{14}$ 15. $-\frac{5}{12} \cdot \frac{8}{9} = n$ $-\frac{10}{27}$ 16. $\frac{1}{19}\left(-\frac{15}{16}\right) = x$ $-\frac{15}{304}$

17. $-3\frac{3}{8} \cdot -\frac{5}{6} = y$ $2\frac{13}{16}$ 18. $z = \frac{1}{6} \cdot 1\frac{3}{5}$ $\frac{4}{15}$ 19. $k = (-6)\left(2\frac{1}{4}\right)$ $-13\frac{1}{2}$

20. $-3\frac{1}{3}\left(-1\frac{1}{5}\right) = d$ 4   21. $h = 8\frac{1}{4} \cdot 3\frac{1}{3}$ $27\frac{1}{2}$ 22. $6\left(-7\frac{1}{2}\right) = m$ -45

23. $x = \left(\frac{2}{3}\right)^2$ $\frac{4}{9}$ 24. $b = \left(-\frac{8}{13}\right)^2$ $\frac{64}{169}$ 25. $5 \cdot \left(\frac{4}{5}\right)^2 = t$ $3\frac{1}{5}$

Evaluate each expression if $a = \frac{4}{5}$, $d = -3\frac{3}{4}$, $r = \frac{1}{2}$ and $p = -1\frac{1}{3}$.

26. ar $\frac{2}{5}$ 27. $2d$ $-7\frac{1}{2}$ 28. p^2 $1\frac{7}{9}$ 29. $r^2(-d)$ $\frac{15}{16}$

Mixed Review
30. Find the perimeter and area of the figure at the right. *(Lesson 2-9)* $P = 20$ cm, $A = 25$ cm²

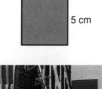

5 cm

5 cm

31. Solve $d = 56 + (-18)$. *(Lesson 3-3)* 38

32. $-\frac{1}{5}, -\frac{1}{10}, \frac{1}{8},$
$\frac{1}{3}, \frac{1}{2}$

32. Order the set of rationals $\left\{\frac{1}{2}, -\frac{1}{5}, \frac{1}{3}, \frac{1}{8}, -\frac{1}{10}\right\}$ from least to greatest. *(Lesson 6-10)*

33. Find the sum of $-1\frac{3}{8}$ and $-3\frac{5}{12}$. *(Lesson 7-2)* $-4\frac{19}{24}$

Problem Solving and Applications
34. **Geometry** In the United States flag, the fly is $1\frac{9}{10}$ times the hoist.
   a. What is the area of the flag if the hoist is 18 meters? $615\frac{3}{5}$ m²
   b. What is the area of the union if the hoist is $9\frac{1}{2}$ feet? $36\frac{1213}{1300}$ ft²

35. **Critical Thinking** How is $\left(-\frac{3}{4}\right)^2$ different from $-\left(\frac{3}{4}\right)^2$? **See margin.**

36. Greater than; for example, $\frac{2}{3} \cdot (-6) = -4, -4 > -6.$

36. **Critical Thinking** In multiplying a negative number by $\frac{2}{3}$, will the product be greater or less than the original number? Explain.

264 **Chapter 7** Rational Numbers

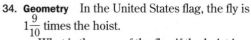
264

7-4 Properties of Rational Numbers

Objective
Identify and use rational number properties.

Words to Learn
multiplicative inverse
reciprocal

The Alaskan brown bear is one of the largest bears in the world. The average Alaskan brown bear is about $1\frac{1}{8}$ times as long as a grizzly bear. If the average grizzly bear is 8 feet long, how long is an Alaskan brown bear? *You will solve the bear problem in Example 1.*

You can use fraction properties to find the length mentally. All of the properties that were true for addition and multiplication of integers are also true for addition and multiplication of rationals.

Property	Arithmetic	Algebra
Commutative	$\frac{2}{3} + \frac{1}{2} = \frac{1}{2} + \frac{2}{3}$	$a + b = b + a$
	$\frac{1}{4} \cdot \frac{3}{5} = \frac{3}{5} \cdot \frac{1}{4}$	$a \cdot b = b \cdot a$
Associative	$\left(-\frac{1}{4} + \frac{2}{3}\right) + \frac{1}{2} = -\frac{1}{4} + \left(\frac{2}{3} + \frac{1}{2}\right)$	$(a + b) + c = a + (b + c)$
	$\left(\frac{1}{3} \cdot \frac{5}{6}\right) \cdot \frac{3}{8} = \frac{1}{3} \cdot \left(\frac{5}{6} \cdot \frac{3}{8}\right)$	$(a \cdot b) \cdot c = a \cdot (b \cdot c)$
Identity	$\frac{2}{3} + 0 = \frac{2}{3}$ $\quad$ $\frac{4}{5} \cdot 1 = \frac{4}{5}$	$a + 0 = a$ $\quad$ $a \cdot 1 = a$

In Chapter 3, you learned about the inverse property of addition. A similar property that applies to multiplication of rational numbers is called the **inverse property of multiplication.** Two numbers whose product is 1 are **multiplicative inverses,** or **reciprocals,** of each other. For example, $-\frac{4}{3}$ and $-\frac{3}{4}$ are multiplicative inverses because $-\frac{4}{3} \cdot \left(-\frac{3}{4}\right) = 1$.

Inverse Property of Multiplication	**In words:** The product of a rational number and its multiplicative inverse is 1.
	Arithmetic $\qquad$ **Algebra**
	$\frac{1}{3} \cdot \frac{3}{1} = 1$ $\qquad$ $\frac{a}{b} \cdot \frac{b}{a} = 1$, where $a, b, \neq 0$.

Lesson 7-4 Properties of Rational Numbers **265**

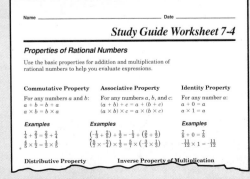

More Examples

For Example 1

A chihuahua is 6 inches tall. A German shepherd is $3\frac{2}{3}$ the height of the chihuahua. Find the height of the German shepherd.
22 inches

For Example 2

Find $9 \cdot 4\frac{5}{9}$.   41

For Example 3

Find $\frac{4}{5} \cdot 10\frac{3}{4}$. $8\frac{3}{5}$

Checking for Understanding

Exercises 1-4 are designed to help you assess students' understanding through reading, writing, speaking, and modeling. You should work through these exercises with your students and then monitor their work on Guided Practice Exercises 5-15.

Practice Masters, p. 60

266

The distributive property involves two operations, multiplication and addition.

Distributive Property	In words: The product of a number and a sum of numbers is the same as the sum of the products of the number and each addend.
	Arithmetic $\qquad$ **Algebra** $9\left(5 + \frac{1}{3}\right) = 9(5) + 9\left(\frac{1}{3}\right)$ $\qquad$ $x \cdot (y + z) = x \cdot y + x \cdot z$

You can use the multiplicative inverse property and the distributive property to find products mentally.

Example 1 *Problem Solving*

Zoology   Use the information at the beginning of the lesson to find the length of an average Alaskan brown bear.

$$1\frac{1}{8} \cdot 8 = 8 \cdot 1\frac{1}{8} \qquad \textit{Commutative property}$$
$$= 8\left(1 + \frac{1}{8}\right)$$
$$= (8 \cdot 1) + \left(8 \cdot \frac{1}{8}\right) \qquad \textit{Distributive property}$$
$$= 8 + 1 \text{ or } 9 \qquad \textit{Identity and Inverse Properties}$$

The average Alaskan brown bear is 9 feet long.

Examples

Find each product.

2 $6 \cdot 3\frac{5}{6}$

$$6 \cdot 3\frac{5}{6} = 6 \cdot \left(3 + \frac{5}{6}\right)$$
$$= (6 \cdot 3) + \left(6 \cdot \frac{5}{6}\right)$$
$$= 18 + 5 \text{ or } 23$$

3 $\frac{3}{4} \cdot 12\frac{1}{3}$

$$\frac{3}{4} \cdot 12\frac{1}{3} = \frac{3}{4}\left(12 + \frac{1}{3}\right)$$
$$= \frac{3}{4}(12) + \frac{3}{4}\left(\frac{1}{3}\right)$$
$$= 9 + \frac{1}{4} \text{ or } 9\frac{1}{4}$$

Checking for Understanding

Communicating Mathematics

Read and study the lesson to answer each question.

1. **Write** the multiplicative inverse of $\frac{5}{7}$. $\frac{7}{5}$

2. **Tell** how you would find the multiplicative inverse of $-4\frac{2}{5}$. See margin.

3. **Write** a number sentence that shows the commutative property of multiplication for rational numbers.   Sample answer: $\frac{3}{4} \cdot \frac{4}{5} = \frac{4}{5} \cdot \frac{3}{4}$

4. **Tell** what property allows you to compute $\frac{1}{3} \cdot \left(6 \cdot \frac{4}{3}\right)$ as $\left(\frac{1}{3} \cdot 6\right) \cdot \frac{4}{3}$.
   associative property of multiplication

OPTIONS

Bell Ringer

What number is the reciprocal of the reciprocal of the number k, for $k \neq 0$? k

Additional Answer

2. Change $-4\frac{2}{5}$ to an improper fraction and then find the reciprocal; $\frac{-5}{22}$.

State which pairs of numbers are multiplicative inverses. Write yes or no.

5. $8, \frac{1}{8}$ yes

6. $-\frac{6}{5}, \frac{5}{6}$ no

7. $0.75, \frac{3}{4}$ no

8. $\frac{5}{6}, 1\frac{1}{5}$ yes

Name the multiplicative inverse of each number.

9. 5 $\frac{1}{5}$

10. $-\frac{2}{3}$ $\frac{3}{2}$

11. 0.2 5

12. $2\frac{4}{5}$ $\frac{5}{14}$

Solve using mental math.

13. $m = \left(-\frac{1}{4} \cdot \frac{2}{3}\right) \cdot \frac{1}{2}$ $-\frac{1}{12}$

14. $n = \frac{1}{2} \cdot 12\frac{4}{5}$ $6\frac{2}{5}$

15. $4 \cdot 5\frac{1}{2} = k$ 22

Exercises

Name the multiplicative inverse of each of the following.

16. 10 $\frac{1}{10}$

17. $-\frac{3}{5}$ $-\frac{5}{3}$

18. 0.4 $\frac{5}{2}$

19. $2\frac{8}{9}$ $\frac{9}{26}$

20. $\frac{7}{8}$ $\frac{8}{7}$

21. -1 -1

22. $\frac{c}{d}$ $\frac{d}{c}$

23. $-x$ $-\frac{1}{x}$

24. Is $\frac{8}{9}$ the multiplicative inverse of $-1\frac{1}{8}$? Why or why not? No; the reciprocal is $1\frac{1}{8}$.

25. Is 0.3 the multiplicative inverse of $3\frac{1}{3}$? Why or why not? yes; $\frac{3}{10} \cdot \frac{10}{3} = 1$.

Evaluate each expression if $a = -\frac{1}{2}$, $b = \frac{2}{3}$, $x = -2\frac{1}{4}$, and $y = 1\frac{5}{6}$.

26. by $1\frac{2}{9}$

27. $2x$ $-4\frac{1}{2}$

28. a^2 $\frac{1}{4}$

29. $ax + \frac{1}{2}$ $1\frac{5}{8}$

30. $3b - 4a$ 4

31. $\frac{1}{2} + a$ 0

32. $b^2(y + 5)$ $3\frac{1}{27}$

33. $a + b + x$ $-2\frac{1}{12}$

34. How many millimeters are in 2.75 meters? *(Lesson 1-6)* 2,750 millimeters

35. **Statistics** What is the interquartile range of the data in the box-and-whisker plot at the right? *(Lesson 4-7)* 30

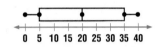

0 5 10 15 20 25 30 35 40

36. Find the GCF of 24 and 64. *(Lesson 6-4)* 8

37. Solve $-\frac{7}{16} \cdot \frac{4}{9} = j$. Write the solution in simplest form. *(Lesson 7-3)* $-\frac{7}{36}$

38. **Home Economics** Marcie wants to make enough custard to serve 16 friends. The recipe that serves 4 requires $1\frac{3}{4}$ cups of milk. How much milk will she need? 7 cups

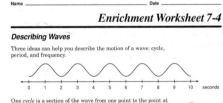

39. **Critical Thinking** Complete the table shown below.

39a. See margin
39b. They are multiplicative inverses.

n	1	2	3	4
n^2	1	4	9	16
$\frac{1}{n^2}$	1	$\frac{1}{4}$	$\frac{1}{9}$	$\frac{1}{16}$

a. What pattern do you notice as you move across each row to the right?

b. What relationship do you see between n^2 and $\frac{1}{n^2}$?

Lesson 7-4 Properties of Rational Numbers **267**

Extending the Lesson

Using Cooperative Groups Have students work together to research the reflexive, symmetric, and transitive properties of equality. Have them prepare a table like the one on page 265 with arithmetic and algebraic statements of each property.

Cooperative Learning Activity

Summing Up 7-4

Number of players: 2
Materials: Index cards

♦ Copy onto cards the rational numbers shown on the back of this card, one per card. Shuffle the cards and then divide them evenly.

▬ Each partner removes from his or her hand pairs of cards showing multiplicative inverses. Then one partner places one of his or her remaining cards face up. If the other partner has the card showing the multiplicative inverse, he or she takes both cards. Otherwise, the other partner places any card face up, and the first partner takes both cards.

Continue in the same way, taking turns playing the first card in each round, until neither partner has any cards in his or her hand. Then find the sum of the products of the pairs of cards that you removed from your hand or that you won. The winner is the partner with the greater sum.

Glencoe Mathematics: Applications and Connections, Course 3

Have students write an example of each of the properties introduced in the lesson.

3 PRACTICE/APPLY

Assignment Guide
Maximum: 16–39
Minimum: 17–33 odd, 34–39

For **Extra Practice**, see p. 599.

Alternate Assessment

Speaking Write examples of the properties of rational numbers on the chalkboard, using both arithmetic and algebraic expressions. Have students identify the properties.

Additional Answer

39a. Numbers in the n^2 row get larger; numbers in the $\frac{1}{n^2}$ row get smaller.

Enrichment Masters, p. 60

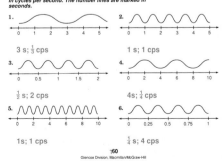

DECISION MAKING

Decision Making

NCTM Standards: 1–4, 7

Objective Analyze data and make a decision.

1 FOCUS

Introducing the Situation

Ask students to relate experiences they have had selling products to make money. Ask the following questions to stimulate discussion.

- *What risks were involved?*
- *Did unforeseen circumstances arise? How did you deal with them?*
- *How would you do things differently next time?*

2 TEACH

Using Cooperative Groups

Before groups begin work, have them write a goal for the band. Explain that their success as decision-makers will depend on how well they achieve their goal.

Checking for Understanding

Ask students to calculate how much the band will be paid if it plays at the picnic for three hours. $120

Choosing Employment

Situation

You and three other teens have formed a band called Sweet Tooth. Your band usually plays for free, but sells T-shirts and cassettes of the music after the performance to earn money. You buy the T-shirts wholesale, have them printed locally, and sell them for three times the wholesale price of one shirt. You send an original recording to a manufacturer to have duplicate tapes produced and sell them at three times the manufacturer's cost for one tape.

Suppose Sweet Tooth is offered two possible engagements for the same evening. One offer is to play at a school dance. The other offer is from the Park and Recreation Board to play at a community picnic. However, the Board wants to pay each of the band members $10 per hour instead of allowing them to sell shirts and cassettes. Which engagement should you accept?

Hidden Data

- attendance at each event: Will there be enough students at the dance to sell a lot of shirts and cassettes?
- length of performance: How long does the Board want the band to play?
- shipping costs of T-shirts and cassettes: How much extra will this add to the order?

Textile USA Wholesale T-shirts

Youth Sizes: S-M-L
1-5 shirts..............$4 ea.
6-15 shirts.............$3 ea.
over 15 shirts........$2 ea.

Adult Sizes: S-M-L-XL
1-5 shirts.............$5 ea.
6-15 shirts............$4 ea.
over 15 shirts........$3 ea.
XL sizes...............$5 ea.

Send check or money order, Visa, Mastercard, or Discover. Minimum credit card order $30. No COD's. No billings. Add 15% for delivery (Alaska and Hawaii add 30%). Next day delivery in continental United States, add 30%

AUDIO RECORDINGS, Inc.
CASSETTES OR REEL-TO-REEL HOME RECORDING REPRODUCTIONS

High Quality Low Price

1-10 tapes
5⁰⁰ ea.

11-25 tapes
4⁰⁰ ea.

26-50 tapes
3⁰⁰ ea.

over 50 tapes
2⁰⁰ ea.

$0.00-$25.00...........$5.85
$25.00-$100.00.........$8.75
over $100.00...........$10.00
Shipping:

Art on the Go

We'll print anything on cloth!

1 shirt..................$2.50 ea.
2-25 shirts.............$1.00 ea.
more than 25 shirts......50¢ ea.

268

Analyzing the Data

1. How much profit can Sweet Tooth make on each medium adult shirt?
2. Including shipping, what is the actual cost per tape if you order 15 tapes? What if you order 25 tapes?
3. What is the total cost of ordering and printing 5 youth shirts, size L, 5 adult shirts, size M, and 5 adults shirts, size, L?

"SWEET TOOTH"

sat. night only

NO REFUND $2⁰⁰

3013917

Making a Decision

4. **How many items** must you sell to beat the Park and Recreation Board's offer?
5. **If you play** at the school
   a. **How many** shirts and cassettes should you order?
   b. **How many** of each size shirt should you order?
6. **What if** you talk the board into letting you sell shirts and cassettes instead of being paid cash? Does this affect your decision?

Making Decisions in the Real World

7. Take a poll of students who have been to a recent concert. Compare the types of souvenirs offered for sale and the prices of these items.

269

Answers

1. 1 shirt: $6.75; 2–5 shirts: $8.25; 6–15 shirts: $9.40; 16–25 shirts: $10.55; over 25 shirts: $11.05
2. For 15 tapes, about $4.58 each; for 25 tapes, $4.35 each
3. 84 (5 youth @ $4 + 10 adult @ $4 = $60; add 15% shipping → $69; add printing for 15 shirts @ $1)

3 PRACTICE/APPLY

Making a Decision

Each group should prepare a written report on its findings, stating the group's decision and the reasons behind that decision. If they have decided to play at the school dance, they should detail their projections for attendance and product sales, and specify their pre-performance costs. If they will be playing at the picnic, they should state the minimum number of hours they need to play and explain how they reached that decision.

Making Decisions in the Real World

Ask students to describe unexpected circumstances that would invalidate their decision.

7-5 Find a Pattern

Lesson Resources
- Study Guide Master 7-5
- Practice Master 7-5
- Enrichment Master 7-5
- Evaluation Master, Quiz A, p. 61
- Group Activity Card 7-5

 Transparency 7-5 contains the 5-Minute Check and a teaching aid for this lesson.

🕐 5-Minute Check
(Over Lesson 7-4)

Name the multiplicative inverse of each rational number.

1. $\frac{3}{4}$ $\frac{4}{3}$ 2. $-3\frac{1}{2}$ $-\frac{2}{7}$

Evaluate each expression if $x = -1\frac{1}{3}$ and $y = 2\frac{1}{6}$.

3. xy $-2\frac{8}{9}$

4. $2x - 4y$ $-11\frac{1}{3}$

5. $x^2(y - 3)$ $-1\frac{13}{27}$

Practice Masters, p. 61

Name _____ Date _____

Practice Worksheet 7-5

Problem-Solving Strategy: Find a Pattern
Solve by finding a pattern.

1. What is the total number of rectangles in the figure below?   18

2. How many diagonals does a 6-sided polygon have?   9

3. Find the next number in the set {20, 22, 25, 29, 34, _?_ }.   40

4. Find the next number in the set {113, 106, 99, 92, _?_ }.   85

Solve using any strategy.

5. In a science experiment, Xiomara uses a 20-pound block of dry ice. The block loses one-half its weight every 15 minutes. How much will the block of dry ice weigh at the end of Xiomara's 1¼-hour experiment? **0.625 pounds**

6. Stacey challenges her friends to find the product of the number of 1s on a clock's face and the number of 2s on a clock's face without looking at a clock. What is Stacey's product?   **10**

7. Jesse is thinking of the least number that is divisible by the first four prime numbers. Find Jesse's number.   **210**

8. A record-player turntable from the 1940s spins at 78 revolutions per minute (rpm), and a modern turntable spins at 33⅓ rpm. Both turntables spin for 9 minutes. Find the difference in the number of turns they make.   **402 revolutions**

Objective
Solve problems by finding and extending a pattern.

Have you ever heard of a wayward goose winging its way to Tallahassee, Florida? It started from Akimiske Island in the Hudson Bay one sunny morning to catch up with friends 1,600 miles away. It flew halfway and stopped for a rest. It could only fly half the remaining distance each time. Did it ever get to Tallahassee?

Explore   *What do you know?*
The distance is 1,600 miles.
The goose could fly half the remaining distance on each flight.

What are you trying to find out?
Whether the goose ever gets to Tallahassee.

Plan   Visualize the trip with a model. Let the 1,600-mile journey equal 1 unit. Then each flight is a fraction of 1.

Solve   The goose traveled half the distance on its first flight. After the second flight it traveled half the distance left: $\frac{1}{2}$ of $\frac{1}{2}$, or $\frac{1}{4}$. After two flights, the goose had traveled $\frac{1}{2} + \frac{1}{4}$, or $\frac{3}{4}$, of the total distance. Copy the drawing below. Draw and label a few more flights.

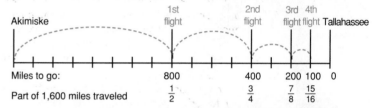

According to this pattern the goose will have 50 miles to go after the fifth flight. The distance left would continue as follows.

$$50 \cdot \frac{1}{2} = 25 \quad \rightarrow \quad 25 \cdot \frac{1}{2} = 12\frac{1}{2} \quad \rightarrow \quad 12\frac{1}{2} \cdot \frac{1}{2} = 6\frac{1}{4}$$

In theory, the goose continues to get closer, but will never travel the entire 1,600 miles. In reality, the distance will get so small that the goose will eventually travel to Tallahassee.

Examine   Let n represent the number of flights. The distance remaining can be represented by the following list.

$$\frac{1}{2}, \frac{1}{4}, \frac{1}{8}, \frac{1}{16}, \cdots \frac{1}{2^n}$$

As n increases, the distance remaining approaches 0, but it can never equal 0.

270   **Chapter 7** Rational Numbers

OPTIONS

Reteaching Activity

Using Models   Take a large square and cut it in half. Set one half aside and cut the other in half again. Continue cutting successive pieces in half, until the halves are rather small. Point out that, theoretically, the remaining piece can always be cut in half. Thus, the pieces cut off never equal the whole square.

Study Guide Masters, p. 61

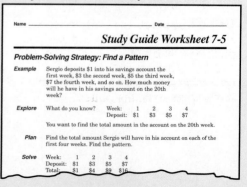

Name _____ Date _____

Study Guide Worksheet 7-5

Problem-Solving Strategy: Find a Pattern

Example   Sergio deposits $1 into his savings account the first week, $3 the second week, $5 the third week, $7 the fourth week, and so on. How much money will he have in his savings account on the 20th week?

Explore   What do you know?   Week: 1   2   3   4
                                    Deposit: $1 $3 $5 $7

You want to find the total amount in the account on the 20th week.

Plan   Find the total amount Sergio will have in his account on each of the first four weeks. Find the pattern.

Solve   Week: 1   2   3   4
          Deposit: $1 $3 $5 $7
          Total: $1 $4 $9 $16

Checking for Understanding

Communicating Mathematics

Read and study the lesson to answer each question. $\frac{1}{2^1} + \frac{1}{2^2} + \frac{1}{2^3} + \frac{1}{2^4} + \cdots + \frac{1}{2^n}$

1. **Tell** where 2^n comes from in the list of the remaining distances in the *Examine* step.

2. $\frac{255}{256}$ **Write** the distance the goose traveled after eight flights as a fraction of 1,600.

Guided Practice

Solve by finding a pattern.

3. What is the total number of rectangles in the figure below? **21**

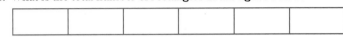

4. How many diagonals does a 7-sided polygon have? **14**

5. Find the next number in the set {100, 95, 85, 70, __?__ }. **50**

Problem Solving

Strategies
• • • • • • •
Look for a pattern.
Solve a simpler problem.
Act it out.
Guess and check.
Draw a diagram.
Make a chart.
Work backward.

Solve using any strategy.

6. Jackson Middle School's football team scored seven times for a total of 34 points. They only scored touchdowns and field goals. Only once did they succeed in getting the extra point after a touchdown. How many touchdowns did the team make? **4 touchdowns** *(handwritten: (5)   30 + 3 + 1)*

7. José was assigned some math exercises for homework. He answered half of them in study hall. After school he answered 7 more exercises. If he still has 11 exercises to do, how many exercises were assigned? **36 exercises**

8. Marla Guerrero needs to buy numbers to put on the doors of each apartment in a 48-unit apartment building. The apartments are numbered 1 through 48. How many of each digit 0, 1, 2, 3, 4, 5, 6, 7, 8, and 9 should she order? **4-0s, 15-1s, 15-2s, 15-3s, 14-4s, 5-5s, 5-6s, 5-7s, 5-8s, 4-9s**

9. **Data Search**   Refer to page 667.
How many Olympic swimming pools would fit on a soccer field? Draw a diagram to verify your answer. **6; See students' diagrams.**

10. **Computer Connection**   Suppose your science teacher wants to investigate how many times a ball will bounce, when it is dropped from a height of 25 feet. You know that each time the ball bounces, it returns to a height that is 0.40 times the previous height.

BALL BOUNCE		
	A	B
1	INITIAL HIT (FT)	25
2	BOUNCE FACTOR	0.40
3	HIT NUMBER	RETURN HT
4	0	= B1
5	= A4 + 1	= B4*B2
6	= A5 + 1	= B5*B2

Instead of performing tedious calculations, you can organize the data into a spreadsheet like the one shown at the left.

a. What value will be in cell B5? **10**

b. A different ball will return to a height that is 0.5 times the previous height. How would you modify the spreadsheet? **change cell B2 to 0.5.**

Lesson 7-5 Problem-Solving Strategy: Find a Pattern   **271**

Extending the Lesson

Using Cooperative Groups   Have students work in pairs to find several patterns that begin with the numbers 1, 2, ... They should give the rule governing each pattern and the next three numbers in the pattern.
Sample answers: 1, 2, 3, 4, 5, add 1; 1, 2, 4, 8, 16, multiply by 2

Cooperative Learning Activity

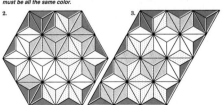

Use groups of 2.

The Dating Game **7-5**

Read the following. Then, working together, solve the problem.

➡ In 1907, Bertram Boltwood discovered that radioactive materials decay at a constant rate. This discovery made it possible to find the age of geological specimens and human artifacts.

All living things contain the radioactive material carbon 14 (C-14). After death, the amount of C-14 steadily decreases. After 5,570 years, only half of the original amount of C-14 remains. The C-14 continues to decrease by half every 5,570 years.

Using the information above, find a pattern that will tell you what part of the original amount of C-14 contained in a plant remains in its fossil after 38,990 years.

Glencoe Mathematics: Applications and Connections, Course 3

---

1 FOCUS
Motivating the Lesson

Activity   Have a student stand at a point halfway between the front and back walls of the classroom. Then have another student stand halfway between the first student and the front wall. Continue the pattern for two more students.

2 TEACH

Using Questioning   Ask students the following questions.

• *What fractions represent the total part of the flight completed after each of the first five flights?* $\frac{1}{2}, \frac{3}{4}, \frac{7}{8}, \frac{15}{16}, \frac{31}{32}$

• *How do you know the pattern never reaches 1?*   The numerator is always 1 less than the denominator.

3 PRACTICE/APPLY

Assignment Guide
Maximum: 6–10
Minimum: 6–9

Enrichment Masters, p. 61

Name _____   Date _____

Enrichment Worksheet 7-5

Three-Part Triangles

If an equilateral triangle is divided into three equal parts, the parts can be colored to create puzzle pieces. If each of the three parts is colored with one of four different colors, a set of 24 different triangles results. Reflections are considered different, but rotations are not.

1. Three of the 24 possible triangles are shown above. Color these 24 triangles to show the complete set.

The 24 triangles can be used to make many shapes. Here are two for you to try. In both problems, the border of the shape must be all the same color.

2.   3.

Many correct solutions are possible.

T61
Glencoe Division, Macmillan/McGraw-Hill

271

NCTM Standards: 1–5, 7–9, 12

Lesson Resources
- Study Guide Master 7-6
- Practice Master 7-6
- Enrichment Master 7-6
- Interdisciplinary Master, p. 21
- Group Activity Card 7-6

 Transparency 7-6 contains the 5-Minute Check and a teaching aid for this lesson.

🕐 5-Minute Check
(Over Lesson 7-5)

This table lists the number of 8th Grade graduates of Harding Junior High, 1989–92.

1989	76
1990	91
1991	106
1992	121

Assume the pattern continues.

1. Describe the pattern in the number of graduates. The number increases by 15 each year.

2. Predict the number of graduates in 1993 and 1994. 136; 151

1 FOCUS

Motivating the Lesson

Activity Arrange 15 items in a triangle as shown at the right. Ask students how each row differs from the row above. It contains one more item.

272

7-6 Sequences

Objective

Recognize and extend arithmetic and geometric sequences.

Words to Learn

sequence
term
arithmetic sequence
common difference
geometric sequence
common ratio

DID YOU KNOW

Joanne won by spelling "antipyretic," which is an agent used to reduce fever.

In 1991, Joanne Lagatta of Clintonville, Wisconsin, won the National Spelling Bee. For winning, she received $5,000. Suppose she opened a savings account with it and adds $10 to the account every month.

The chart below shows her balance after each month during the first year.

Month	0	1	2	3	4	5	6
Total Deposits	5,000	5,010	5,020	5,030	5,040	5,050	5,060

Month	7	8	9	10	11	12
Total Deposits	5,070	5,080	5,090	5,100	5,110	5,120

A list of numbers in a certain order, such as 0, 1, 2, 3, ... or 5,000, 5,010, 5,020, 5,030, ... is called a **sequence.** Each number is called a **term** of the sequence. When the difference between any two consecutive terms is the same, the sequence is called an **arithmetic sequence.** The difference is called the **common difference.**

Examples

State whether each sequence is arithmetic. Then write the next three terms of each sequence.

1 $4, 7\frac{1}{3}, 10\frac{2}{3}, 14, ...$

$$4 \quad \underset{+\,3\frac{1}{3}}{\overbrace{\qquad}} \quad 7\frac{1}{3} \quad \underset{+\,3\frac{1}{3}}{\overbrace{\qquad}} \quad 10\frac{2}{3} \quad \underset{+\,3\frac{1}{3}}{\overbrace{\qquad}} \quad 14$$

The difference between any two consecutive terms is $3\frac{1}{3}$. So, the sequence is arithmetic. Add $3\frac{1}{3}$ to the last term of the sequence, and continue adding until the next three terms are found. The next three terms are $17\frac{1}{3}, 20\frac{2}{3}$, and 24.

2 $11, 4, -2, -7, ...$

$$11 \quad \underset{-\,7}{\overbrace{\qquad}} \quad 4 \quad \underset{-\,6}{\overbrace{\qquad}} \quad -2 \quad \underset{-\,5}{\overbrace{\qquad}} \quad -7$$

Since there is no common difference, the sequence is *not* arithmetic. Add −4 to the last term of the sequence, and continue adding the next greater integer until the next three terms are found. The next three terms are −11, −14, and −16.

272 **Chapter 7** Rational Numbers

OPTIONS

Bell Ringer

What is the next letter in the following sequence?

    J, F, M, A, M, J, . . .

J, for July

💾 Interactive Mathematics Tools

This multimedia software provides an interactive lesson that is tied directly to Lesson 7-6. Students will extend arithmetic and geometric sequences.

When consecutive terms of a sequence are formed by multiplying by a constant factor, the sequence is called a **geometric sequence.** The factor is called the **common ratio.**

Examples

State whether each sequence is geometric. Then write the next three terms of each sequence.

3 2, –6, 18, –54, ...

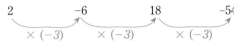

Since there is a common ratio, –3, the sequence is geometric. Multiply the last term of the sequence by –3, and continue multiplying until the next three terms are found.

The next three terms are 162, –486, and 1,458.

4 24, 12, 4, 1, ...

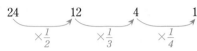

Since there is no common ratio, the sequence is *not* geometric. Multiply the last term by $\frac{1}{5}$, and continue multiplying by $\frac{1}{6}$ and then $\frac{1}{7}$ to find the next three terms. The next three terms are $\frac{1}{5}$, $\frac{1}{30}$, and $\frac{1}{210}$.

Example 5 *Connection*

Algebra The first term of a sequence is represented by a, the second term a_2, and so on up to the *n*th term, a_n. Find the twentieth term, a_{20}, in the sequence 18, 14, 10, 6, ...

This sequence is arithmetic, and the common difference is –4. To find the twentieth term, you can add –4 to 18 nineteen times, or you can use the formula $a_n = a + (n - 1)d$, where *n* is the number of the term you want to find and *d* is the common difference.

$a_n = a + (n - 1)d$
$a_{20} = 18 + (20 - 1)(-4)$ *Replace n with 20, d with –4, and a with 18.*
$a_{20} = 18 + (19)(-4)$
$a_{20} = 18 + (-76)$
$a_{20} = -58$

So, the twentieth term is –58.

Lesson 7-6 Algebra Connection: Sequences   **273**

273

Exercises 1-4 are designed to help you assess students' understanding through reading, writing, speaking, and modeling. You should work through these exercises with your students and then monitor their work on Guided Practice Exercises 5-16.

Close

Have each student write examples of an arithmetic sequence and a geometric sequence. Then have students compare and contrast the sequences.

3 PRACTICE/APPLY

Assignment Guide
Maximum: 17–42
Minimum: 17–31 odd, 33–41
All: Mid-Chapter Review

For **Extra Practice,** see p. 600.

Practice Masters, p. 62

Name _____ Date _____

Practice Worksheet 7-6

Sequences

State whether each sequence is arithmetic, geometric, or neither. Then write the next three terms of each sequence.

1. $13, 18, 23, 28, \ldots$
   arithmetic; 33, 38, 43
2. $\frac{1}{2}, \frac{1}{3}, \frac{1}{4}, \frac{1}{5}, \ldots$
   neither; $\frac{1}{6}, \frac{1}{7}, \frac{1}{8}$
3. $27, 25, 23, 21, \ldots$
   arithmetic; 19, 17, 15
4. $16, -15, 14, -13, \ldots$
   neither; 12, -11, 10
5. $3, 6, 12, 24, \ldots$
   geometric; 48, 96, 192
6. $512, 256, 128, 64, \ldots$
   geometric; 32, 16, 8
7. $1, 2, 4, 7, \ldots$
   neither; 11, 16, 22
8. $7, -7, 7, -7, \ldots$
   geometric; 7, -7, 7
9. $1, -4, 16, -64, \ldots$
   geometric; 256, -1,024, 4,096
10. $1.3, 2.6, 3.9, 5.2, \ldots$
    arithmetic; 6.5, 7.8, 9.1
11. $8, 8, 8, 8, \ldots$
    arithmetic or geometric; 8, 8, 8
12. $20, 18, 15, 13, 10, \ldots$
    neither; 8, 5, 3

Write the next three terms of each sequence.

13. $17, 34, 51, 68, \ldots$ 85, 102, 119
14. $216, 36, 6, 1, \ldots$ $\frac{1}{6}, \frac{1}{36}, \frac{1}{216}$
15. $8, 12, 18, 27, \ldots$ 40.5, 60.75, 91.125
16. $8, 0, 8, 0, \ldots$ 8, 0, 8
17. $-2, 4, -6, 8, \ldots$ -10, 12, -14
18. $17, 23, 29, 35, \ldots$ 41, 47, 53

19. The sixth term of an arithmetic sequence is 50. The common difference is -3. Find the second term of the sequence. 62

20. Name the ninth term in the sequence $17, 22, 27, \ldots$ 57

T-62
Glencoe Division, Macmillan/McGraw-Hill

Checking for Understanding

Communicating Mathematics

Read and study the lesson to answer each question.

1. **Write** an arithmetic sequence with a common difference of 4. **See margin.**
2. **Tell** how you can find the next term of a geometric sequence if you know one term and the common ratio. **Multiply the known term by the common ratio.**
3. **Tell** the sixth term of the sequence $0, 3, 6, 9, \ldots$ 15
4. **Write** the first five terms in a geometric sequence with a common ratio of 0.5. The first term is 20. 20, 10, 5, 2.5, 1.25

Guided Practice

State whether each sequence is arithmetic, geometric, or neither. Then write the next three terms of each sequence.

5. $1, 4, 9, 16, \ldots$ N; 25, 36, 49
6. $-5, 1, -\frac{1}{5}, \frac{1}{25}, \ldots$ G; $-\frac{1}{125}, \frac{1}{625}, -\frac{1}{3,125}$
7. $2, 4, 8, 16, \ldots$ G; 32, 64, 128
8. $98.6, 98.2, 97.8, \ldots$ A; 97.4, 97, 96.6
9. $9, 3, -3, -9, \ldots$ A; -15, -21, -27
10. $20, 24, 28, 32, \ldots$ A; 36, 40, 44
11. $99, 88, 77, 66, \ldots$ A; 55, 44, 33
12. $1, -3, 9, -27, \ldots$ G; 81, -243, 729
13. $1.5, 3, 4.5, 6, \ldots$ A; 7.5, 9, 10.5
14. $89, 89, 89, 89, \ldots$ A and G; 89, 89, 89
15. $-6, -4, -2, 0, \ldots$ A; 2, 4, 6
16. $-256, 128, -64, \ldots$ G; 32, -16, 8

Exercises

Independent Practice

Write the next three terms of each sequence.

17. $100, 91, 82, 73, \ldots$ 64, 55, 46
18. $25, 5, 1, \frac{1}{5}, \ldots$ $\frac{1}{25}, \frac{1}{125}, \frac{1}{625}$

20. 24.3, -72.9, 218.7

22. 124, 149, 137

19. $9, 6, 3, 0, \ldots$ -3, -6, -9
20. $0.3, -0.9, 2.7, -8.1, \ldots$
21. $1,256, -628, 314, \ldots$ -157, $78\frac{1}{2}$, $-39\frac{1}{4}$
22. $97, 85, 110, 98, 123, 111, 136, \ldots$
23. $5, 6.5, 8, 9.5, \ldots$ 11, 12.5, 14
24. $54, 60, 66, 72, \ldots$ 78, 84, 90
25. $1, 2, 5, 10, 17, \ldots$ 26, 37, 50
26. $-3, 12, -48, 192, -768; 3,072; -12,288$
27. $\frac{1}{4}, \frac{1}{12}, \frac{1}{36}, \ldots$ $\frac{1}{108}, \frac{1}{324}, \frac{1}{972}$
28. $4\frac{1}{2}, 4\frac{1}{6}, 3\frac{5}{6}, 3\frac{1}{2}, \ldots$ $3\frac{1}{6}, 2\frac{5}{6}, 2\frac{1}{2}$

29. Name the tenth term in the sequence $100, 95, 90, 85, \ldots$ 55

30. Write the first four terms in a geometric sequence with a common ratio of $\frac{3}{4}$. The first term is 16. 16, 12, 9, $6\frac{3}{4}$

31. The fifth term of an arithmetic sequence is 14. The common difference is -2. Find the first four terms. 22, 20, 18, 16

32. Name the eighth term in the sequence $16, 8, 4, \ldots$ $\frac{1}{8}$

Mixed Review

33. Use mental math to find $700 - 365$. *(Lesson 1-2)* 335
34. Solve $x = -43 - (-89)$. *(Lesson 3-5)* 46
35. **Statistics** Construct a line plot for the following English quiz scores. $21, 24, 17, 19, 16, 22, 25, 19, 18, 21, 23, 18, 24, 19, 25$. *(Lesson 4-3)* **See margin.**
36. Express $-\frac{5}{8}$ as a decimal. *(Lesson 6-6)* -0.625
37. Compute $\frac{5}{6} \cdot 3\frac{3}{7}$ mentally. *(Lesson 7-4)* $2\frac{6}{7}$

274 **Chapter 7** Rational Numbers

OPTIONS

Gifted and Talented Needs

When the terms of a sequence are added, the sum of the terms is called a *series*. Have students research sigma notation for expressing sums and the formulas for finding general terms of both arithmetic and geometric series.

Additional Answers

1. Sample answer: 1, 5, 9, 13, ...

35.

$$16 \quad 17 \quad 18 \quad 19 \quad 20 \quad 21 \quad 22 \quad 23 \quad 24 \quad 25$$

38. **Consumer Awareness** In 1992, the cost of mailing a letter first class was 29¢ for the first ounce and 23¢ for each additional ounce. How much did it cost to mail a 4-ounce letter first class? **98¢**

39. **Business** Lisa bought a car for $12,200. If it loses $\frac{1}{5}$ of its value every year, what is the value at the end of three years? **$6,246.40**

40. **Critical Thinking** Can a geometric sequence contain zero as a term? Explain. **Only if the sequence contains only zeros.**

41. **Critical Thinking** The second term of an arithmetic sequence is 6 and the sixth term is 38. **See margin.**

    a. What is the common difference? How did you find it?

    b. Explain how to find the common difference of an arithmetic sequence if you know any two terms.

42. **Geometry** Study the pattern of circles.

    a. Draw the next two figures in the sequence. **a-d. See Margin.**

    b. Write a sequence for the number of pieces in each circle.

    c. What kind of sequence does this illustrate? Explain.

    d. Write a sequence for the number of cuts across each circle.

    e. What is the relationship between the number of cuts and the number of pieces? **The number of cuts is half the number of pieces.**

---

7 Assessment: Mid-Chapter Review

3. $6\frac{3}{11}$ 5. $-10\frac{5}{24}$

Solve each equation. Write each solution in simplest form. *(Lessons 7-1, 7-2, 7-3)*

1. $n = -\frac{3}{4} + \frac{1}{4}$ $-\frac{1}{2}$
2. $\frac{7}{8} - \frac{3}{8} = m$ $\frac{1}{2}$
3. $2\frac{8}{11} + 3\frac{6}{11} = d$
4. $x = \frac{3}{4} + \frac{4}{5}$ $1\frac{11}{20}$
5. $y = -1\frac{5}{6} + \left(-8\frac{3}{8}\right)$
6. $g = 12 - 5\frac{3}{7}$ $6\frac{4}{7}$
7. $a = 2\frac{4}{5}(-10)$ -28
8. $\left(-\frac{4}{9}\right)^2 = h$ $\frac{16}{81}$

9. Explain how to compute $12 \times 3\frac{3}{4}$ using the distributive property.
    (Lesson 7-4) $12\left(3 + \frac{3}{4}\right) = 12 \cdot 3 + 12 \cdot \frac{3}{4}$

10. Marianne is conditioning for a 10-kilometer race. On the first day she ran 2 laps around the track. The second day she ran 4 laps. The third day she ran 6 laps. On what day will she reach her goal of 14 laps? *(Lesson 7-5)* **7th day**

State whether each sequence is arithmetic or geometric. Then find the next three numbers in the sequence. *(Lesson 7-6)*

11. 20, 23, 26, 29, ...

12. 768, 192, 48, ... **geometric, 12, 3, $\frac{3}{4}$**

11. **arithmetic, 32, 35, 38**

Extending the Lesson

Using Cooperative Groups Ask students to predict the next term in the sequence 1, 2, 4, 8, 16, ... Then have them work in small groups to test the formula

$$N = \frac{x^4 - 6x^3 + 23x^2 - 18x + 24}{24}$$

for values of x from 1 to 6. **1, 2, 4, 8, 16, 31; Thus, a sequence may not be accurately determined by even its first five terms.**

Cooperative Learning Activity

Sequence of Events 7-6

Number of players: 2
Materials: Spinners, index cards

• Copy onto cards the numbers shown on the back of this card, one number per card. Shuffle the cards and place them face down in a pile. Label the sections of one spinner "4," "5," "6," "7," "8," "9." These numbers tell the number of terms a sequence should have. Label equal sections of another spinner "Arithmetic" and "Geometric."

➤ One partner selects two cards and decides which number to use as the first term in his or her sequence and which to use as the common difference or ratio. Then this partner spins both spinners to find the number of terms and the type of sequence to write using the numbers on the cards. The other partner repeats the procedure. The partner with the greater last term wins the round. Play at least three rounds.

Glencoe Mathematics: Applications and Connections, Course 3

NCTM Standards: 1–5, 8

Management Tips

For Students If possible, provide isometric dot paper or a template containing hexagons for each group. This will simplify the work of drawing honeycombs and ensure more accurate results.

For the Overhead Projector
Overhead Manipulative Resources provides appropriate materials for teacher or student demonstration of the activities in this Mathematics Lab.

1 FOCUS

Introducing the Lab

Ask students to give examples of sequences that are neither arithmetic nor geometric.
Sample answer: 1, 4, 9, 16, . . .
(the sequence of perfect squares)

2 TEACH

Using Lists Due to the number of paths to cell E, students may have difficulty distinguishing the different paths in order to be sure they have drawn them all. Have students use the cell letters to write a series of letters to identify each path. For example, the three paths to cell C shown on page 276 would be represented by BC, AC, and ABC.

Objective
Discover the numbers that make up the Fibonacci Sequence.

Materials
colored pencils

Leonardo was born about A.D. 1170 in the city of Pisa, Italy. This famous mathematician was also known by the name Fibonacci. He wrote many works, but his *Liber Abaci* was the most famous. He is credited with introducing the Arabic numbers we use today to the European scholars who, at the time, were still using Roman numerals.

Leonardo loved to create interesting story problems. Many of the ones he created centered around a series of numbers that became known as the Fibonacci Sequence.

Try this!

Work in groups of three.

Study the honeycomb shown below. The bees go from cell to cell in the comb to store honey and other food stuffs. Suppose the path they take must have the letters in alphabetical order.

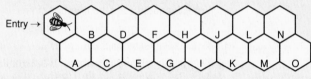

- Suppose the bee wanted to go from the entry to cell A. There is only one path possible.

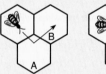

- Suppose the bee wanted to go from the entry to cell B. There are two paths possible.

- Suppose the bee wanted to go from the entry to cell C. There are three paths possible.

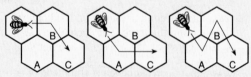

- Make a drawing of the honeycomb up to cell D. Use colored pencils to draw all the possible paths from the entry to cell D, making each path a different color. How many paths are there? 5

- Make another drawing of the honeycomb up to cell E. Use colored pencils to draw all the possible paths to cell E.
- Copy and complete the chart.

Cell	A	B	C	D	E	F
Number of paths to the cell	1	2	3	5	8	13

What do you think?

1. Each number is the sum of the previous two numbers.

1. Look for a pattern in the numbers. How is each number related to the previous numbers?

2. Without making a drawing, how many paths are there to cell G? **21** How did you arrive at this number? **add 8 and 13**

3. 21, 34, 55, 89, 144

3. The numbers in the chart are the first numbers of the Fibonacci Sequence. Find the next five numbers in the sequence.

4. Is the Fibonacci Sequence arithmetic, geometric, or neither? Explain. **Neither; there is not a common difference or common ratio.**

Applications

5. **Money** Tokens for the arcade machines cost 25¢ each. The token machine at *Laser One Arcade* will accept only half-dollars and quarters. For example, if you wanted to buy two tokens, you could use two quarters (QQ) or one half-dollar (H). There are two ways to buy two tokens. **See Solutions Manual for list.**
   a. Use Qs and Hs to list the ways to insert the coins to buy each number of tokens. Then copy and complete the chart below.

Number of Tokens	1	2	3	4	5	6	7
Ways to Buy	1	2	3	5	8	13	21

   They are the same.
   b. How do your results relate to the Fibonacci Sequence?

6. **Nature** The pine cone, pineapple, daisy, and sunflower all have characteristics of the Fibonacci Sequence. For example, look at the spirals on the bottom of a pine cone.

   a. The blue tint shows a clockwise spiral. How many clockwise spirals are there? **13 clockwise spirals**

   b. The red tint shows a counterclockwise spiral. How many counterclockwise spirals are there? **8 counterclockwise spirals**

   c. Why do we say that the pine cone is an example of Fibonacci's numbers? **8 and 13 are numbers in the Fibonacci sequence.**

Mathematics Lab 7-6B The Fibonacci Sequence **277**

Using Logical Reasoning After students find the relationship between the numbers in the sequence, help them to see the logic behind the pattern: Each cell has two cells bordering it on the left. The number of paths leading to each cell, therefore, is the sum of the number of paths leading to each of the two bordering cells.

Close

Have students write the first eight terms of a sequence beginning with the numbers 1 and 3, using the rule for the Fibonacci sequence. 1, 3, 4, 7, 11, 18, 29, 47

OPTIONS

Lab Manual You may wish to make copies of the blackline master on p. 58 of the *Lab Manual* for students to use as a recording sheet.

Lab Manual, p. 58

Name _____ Date _____

Mathematics Lab Worksheet

Use with pages 276-277

The Fibonacci Sequence

Try this!

Cell	A	B	C	D	E	F
Number of paths to the cell	1	2	3	5	8	13

What do you think?

1. The number is the sum of the two previous numbers.

2. There are 21 paths to cell G because 8 + 13 = 21.

3. 21, 34, 55, 89, 144

NCTM Standards: 1–4, 7, 9, 12, 13

Lesson Resources
- Study Guide Master 7-7
- Practice Master 7-7
- Enrichment Master 7-7
- Group Activity Card 7-7

 Transparency 7-7 contains the 5-Minute Check and a teaching aid for this lesson.

🕐 5-Minute Check
(Over Lesson 7-6)

State whether each sequence is arithmetic, geometric, or neither. Then write the next three terms of each sequence.

1. 486, 162, 54, 18, . . .
   geometric; 6, 2, $\frac{2}{3}$

2. 6, 2, −2, −6, . . .
   arithmetic; −10, −14, −18

3. 0.7, 1.1, 1.5, 1.9, . . .
   arithmetic; 2.3, 2.7, 3.1

4. 3, 6, 12, 24, . . .
   geometric; 48, 96, 192

1 FOCUS

Motivating the Lesson

Activity Have students draw an acute triangle and measure its height. Then have them draw a line on their triangle parallel to the base at a distance of one-half the height. Have them cut out their triangle and cut along the line they drew. Now have students rotate the top piece of their original triangle and align it alongside the bottom piece, as shown below.

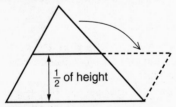

$\frac{1}{2}$ of height

Ask students what figure is formed.   parallelogram

7-7 Area of Triangles and Trapezoids

Objective
Find the areas of triangles and trapezoids.

Words to Learn
trapezoid
base
altitude
height

A hydrologist studies the movement, or stream flow, of water. The first step in determining stream flow is to find the area of a cross section of the stream. The stream bed shown at the right

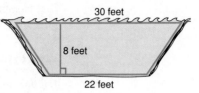

30 feet

8 feet

22 feet

approximates the shape of a trapezoid. The area of this trapezoid is a good estimate of the area of the cross section. *You will find the area of the trapezoid in Example 1.*

Remember that a **trapezoid** is a quadrilateral with exactly one pair of parallel sides called **bases.** A segment perpendicular to both bases, with endpoints on the base lines, is called the **altitude.** The length of the altitude is called the **height.**

In the trapezoid at the right, sides $\overline{GH}$ and $\overline{JK}$ are the bases. $\overline{EF}$ is an altitude.

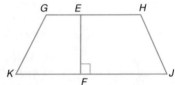

Mini-Lab

Work with a partner.

Materials: graph paper, scissors

- Copy the trapezoid at the right on a piece of graph paper. Cut it out.

- Make a cut along the dashed line. Move the parts so they form a parallelogram.

Talk About It

LOOK BACK
You can review area of parallelograms on page 75.

a. What is the length of the base and the height of the parallelogram? $b = 10$, $h = 2$

b. What is the area of the parallelogram? 20 units²

c. Explain how the height and length of the base of the parallelogram are related to the height and sum of the lengths of the bases of the original trapezoid. See margin.

OPTIONS

Bell Ringer

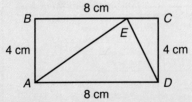

B —— 8 cm —— C

4 cm   E   4 cm

A —— 8 cm —— D

ABCD is a rectangle. Find the sum of the areas of △*AEB* and △*CDE*.
16 cm²

Additional Answer
Mini-Lab

c. The height of the parallelogram is half the height of the trapezoid and the length of the base of the parallelogram is the sum of the lengths of the bases of the trapezoid.

The Mini-Lab suggests the following rule for finding the area of a trapezoid.

Area of a Trapezoid	**In words:** The area of a trapezoid is equal to the product of half the height and the sum of the bases.
	In symbols: If a trapezoid has bases of a units and b units and a height of h units, $A = \frac{1}{2}h(a + b)$.

Example 1 *Problem Solving*

Hydrology A hydrologist needs to find the area of the cross section of the stream shown at the beginning of the lesson to complete a flood control study. What is the area of the trapezoid representing the cross section?

$A = \frac{1}{2}h(a + b)$

$A = \frac{1}{2} \cdot 8(30 + 22)$ *Replace a with 30, b with 22, and h with 8.*

$A = \frac{1}{2} \cdot 8 \cdot 52$ or 208   The area is 208 square feet.

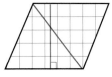

A parallelogram can also be used to find the area of a triangle. The diagonal separates a parallelogram into two congruent triangles.

The area of the parallelogram at the left is $6 \cdot 5$ or 30 square units. The area of each triangle is one half the area of the parallelogram. So, each triangle has an area of 15 square units.

Area of a Triangle	**In words:** The area of a triangle is equal to half the product of its base and height.
	In symbols: If a triangle has a base of b units and a height of h units, $A = \frac{1}{2}bh$.

Any side of a triangle can be used as a base. The height is the length of the corresponding altitude. The altitude is a line segment perpendicular to the base from the opposite vertex.

Example 2

Find the area of the triangle.

$A = \frac{1}{2}bh$

$A = 0.5(7.5)(3.75)$ *Replace b with 7.5 and h with 3.75.*

0.5 ⊠ 7.5 ⊠ 3.75 ⊟ **14.0625**

The area is 14.0625 square inches.

Lesson 7-7 Geometry Connection: Area of Triangles and Trapezoids   **279**

Reteaching Activity

Using Estimation Have students draw trapezoids and triangles on grid paper and estimate the area of each figure by counting squares. Then have them calculate the areas using the area formulas and check their answers by comparing them with their estimates.

Study Guide Masters, p. 63

Name _____   Date _____

Study Guide Worksheet 7-7

Area of Triangles and Trapezoids

The area of a trapezoid is equal to one-half its height times the sum of its bases. $A = \frac{1}{2}h(a + b)$

Example   Find the area of the trapezoid.

$A = \frac{1}{2}h(a + b)$
$A = \frac{1}{2}(6)(10\frac{1}{2} + 14\frac{1}{2})$ $h = 6, a = 10\frac{1}{2}, b = 14\frac{1}{2}$
$A = 3(25)$
$A = 75$ The area is 75 square inches.

The area of a triangle is equal to one-half its base times its height. $A = \frac{1}{2}bh$

---

2 TEACH

Using the Mini-Lab To form a parallelogram, students must invert the top part of the trapezoid and align the two parts side by side. Be sure that students align the proper sides of the two parts.

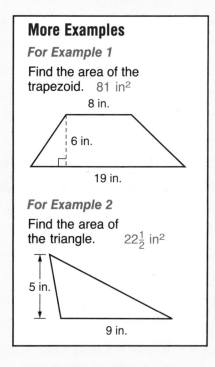

More Examples

For Example 1

Find the area of the trapezoid.   81 in²

8 in.

6 in.

19 in.

For Example 2

Find the area of the triangle. $22\frac{1}{2}$ in²

5 in.

9 in.

Teaching Tip In Example 2, point out that in an obtuse triangle, two of the altitudes fall outside the triangle. (See More Examples, Example 2.)

Checking for Understanding

Exercises 1-4 are designed to help you assess students' understanding through reading, writing, speaking, and modeling. You should work through these exercises with your students and then monitor their work on Guided Practice Exercises 5-13.

Error Analysis

Watch for students who use non-perpendicular sides of trapezoids or triangles as heights.

Prevent by pointing out that the height of a room is measured along a perpendicular, not along a slant, and that the height of a geometric figure is also a perpendicular distance.

279

Close

Have students complete these sentences: *The area of a trapezoid can be found by __?__ .* multiplying $\frac{1}{2}$ times the height times the sum of the lengths of the bases *The area of a triangle can be found by __?__ .* multiplying $\frac{1}{2}$ times the height times the length of the base

3 PRACTICE/APPLY

Assignment Guide
Maximum: 14–40
Minimum: 15–31 odd, 32–39

For **Extra Practice,** see p. 600.

Alternate Assessment

Writing   Have students work in pairs to create problems which involve finding the area of trapezoids and triangles. Have them trade problems with another pair and solve the problems they receive.

Practice Masters, p. 63

280

Checking for Understanding For answers to Exercises 1-4, see margin.

Communicating Mathematics

Read and study the lesson to answer each question.

1. **Tell** which two sides of a trapezoid are the bases.
2. **Draw** a triangle similar to the one shown at the right. Sketch an altitude.
3. **Tell** how to find the area of a triangle.
4. **Draw** a trapezoid on graph paper. Label its height and bases. Then find its area.

Guided Practice

State the measures of the base(s) and the height of each triangle or trapezoid. Then find the area.

5. $b = 2\frac{2}{3}$ ft,
$h = 3\frac{3}{4}$ ft,
$A = 5$ ft²

6. $a = 2.2$ cm,
$b = 5.8$ cm,
$h = 3.6$ cm,
$A = 14.4$ cm²

5.

6.
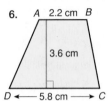

7.
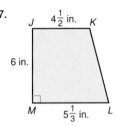

7. $a = 4\frac{1}{2}$ in.,
$b = 5\frac{1}{3}$ in.,
$h = 6$ in.,
$A = 29\frac{1}{2}$ in²

Find the area of each figure described below.

8. triangle: base, $3\frac{3}{4}$ ft; height, $4\frac{1}{2}$ ft $8\frac{7}{16}$ ft²

9. triangle: base, 9 cm; height, 2.6 cm **11.7 cm²**

10. triangle: base, 10 in.; height, 7 in. **35 in²**

11. trapezoid: bases, 12 m and 8 m; height, 9 m **90 m²**

12. trapezoid: bases, 0.3 km and 0.5 km; height, 0.2 km **0.08 km²**

13. trapezoid: bases $2\frac{1}{3}$ yd and $4\frac{1}{6}$ yd; height, 3 yd $9\frac{3}{4}$ yd²

Exercises

Independent Practice

State the measures of the base(s) and the height of each triangle or trapezoid. Then find the area.

14. $b = 12$ cm,
$h = 5$ cm,
$A = 30$ cm²

15. $a = 3\frac{1}{2}$ ft,
$b = 5\frac{1}{2}$ ft,
$h = 2\frac{2}{3}$ ft,
$A = 12$ ft²

16. $a = 12\frac{2}{3}$ in.,
$b = 7\frac{1}{2}$ in.,
$h = 5\frac{1}{4}$ in.,
$A = 52\frac{15}{16}$ in²

14.
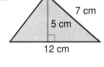

$b = 30$ cm, $h = 12$ cm,

17. $A = 180$ cm²

15.
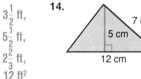

16.
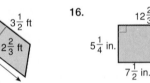

$b = 3$ ft, $h = 4$ ft,
$A = 6$ ft²

17.
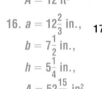

18.
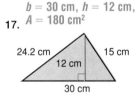

$a = 12$ yd, $b = 18$ yd,
$h = 10$ yd, $A = 150$ yd²

19.
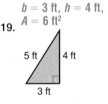

280   **Chapter 7** Rational Numbers

Additional Answers

1. The parallel sides are the bases.

2.

3. See page 281.
4. See page 281.

Find the area of each triangle described below.

	base	height	
20.	8 cm	3.8 cm	15.2 cm²
22.	$2\frac{2}{3}$ ft	$3\frac{1}{12}$ ft	$4\frac{1}{9}$ ft²
24.	20 m	17 m	170 m²

	base	height	
21.	22 yd	27 yd	297 yd²
23.	$1\frac{3}{4}$ in.	$5\frac{1}{8}$ in.	$4\frac{31}{64}$ in²
25.	16 mm	14 mm	112 mm²

26. 258 cm²
27. 255 ft²
28. 375 in²
29. 68.88 km²
30. 11.66 cm²
31. 0.204 m²

Find the area of each trapezoid described below.

	base (a)	base (b)	height
26.	19 cm	24 cm	12 cm
28.	26 in.	24 in.	15 in.
30.	4.7 cm	5.9 cm	2.2 cm

	base (a)	base (b)	height
27.	12 ft	18 ft	17 ft
29.	8.3 km	8.5 km	8.2 km
31.	0.3 m	0.72 m	0.4 m

Mixed Review

32. Write an equation to represent *three more than two times the number of cars is fifteen.* (*Lesson 2-6*) **2c + 3 = 15**

33. Solve $\frac{w}{4} = -125$. (*Lesson 3-9*) **−500**

34. **Statistics** Find the mean, median, and mode of the set {40, 27, 19, 31, 35, 23, 40, 39}. (*Lesson 4-5*) **31.75, 33, 40**

35. similar

35. **Geometry** Tell if the pair of figures at the right are congruent, similar, or neither. (*Lesson 5-6*)

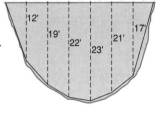

36. Write the next three terms of the sequence 80, 76, 72, 68, ... (*Lesson 7-6*) **64, 60, 56**

Problem Solving and Applications

37. **Hydrology** To get a more accurate picture of the cross section of a stream, a hydrologist takes depth readings every 5 feet and draws a sketch of the cross section. Estimate the area of the cross section.
Hint: Find the area of each small section.
570 ft²

38. The area is quadrupled.

38. **Critical Thinking** What is the effect on the area of a trapezoid if the length of each base is doubled and the height is doubled?

39. **Geography** The state of South Carolina is shaped something like a triangle.
   a. Describe how to find an estimate of the area of South Carolina. **A ≈ $\frac{1}{2}$(273)(219)**
   b. Estimate the area of South Carolina. **about 29,894 mi²**

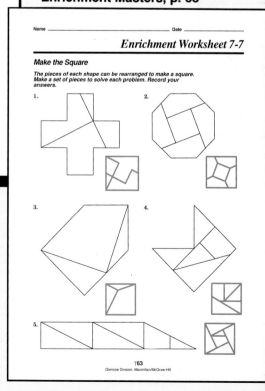

South Carolina

219 miles

273 miles

40. **Journal Entry** Write a few sentences explaining how the area of a triangle and a trapezoid are related. **See students' work.**

Lesson 7-7 Geometry Connection: Area of Triangles and Trapezoids **281**

Extending the Lesson

Using Cooperative Groups Have students work in small groups to find the amount of material needed to cover the trapezoidal sides and rectangular base of this wastebasket. **876 in²**

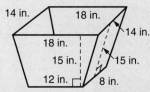

14 in. 18 in. 14 in.
18 in.
15 in. 15 in.
12 in. 8 in.

Cooperative Learning Activity

Trapezoid Trios **7-7**

Use groups of 3.
Materials: Spinners, centimeter grid paper, metric rulers, index cards

▸ Copy onto cards the following descriptions, one per card: one right angle, one obtuse angle, and two acute angles. Thoroughly mix the three cards. Label the sections of each of two spinners "3," "4," "5," "6," "7," "8." The numbers on these spinners represent the lengths in centimeters of bases of trapezoids. Label equal sections of a third spinner "3," "4," "5." These numbers represent the heights of trapezoids.

▸ Each group member spins a spinner. Then each group member selects a card and draws a trapezoid with the height and bases shown on the spinners and the angle(s) described on the card. Finally, each group member computes the area of his or her trapezoid and shares his or her work with the group.

Repeat the activity and then, as a group, write what you have observed about the areas and shapes of trapezoids.

Glencoe Mathematics: Applications and Connections, Course 3

Additional Answers

3. $A = \frac{1}{2} \cdot b \cdot h$, where the height is the length of the altitude to the base.

4. Sample answer:

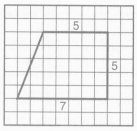

5
5
7

$A = \frac{1}{2} \cdot 5(7 + 5)$
  = 30 units²

Enrichment Masters, p. 63

Name _____ Date _____

Enrichment Worksheet 7-7

Make the Square

The pieces of each shape can be rearranged to make a square. Make a set of pieces to solve each problem. Record your answers.

1.
2.
3.
4.
5.

T63
Glencoe Division, Macmillan/McGraw-Hill

281

Management Tips

For Students   If they are using dot paper, students must use a straight edge and accurately draw segments, for their success in this lab will require them to distinguish between dots lying on a triangle and those lying inside the triangle.

For the Overhead Projector
Overhead Manipulative Resources provides appropriate materials for teacher or student demonstration of the activities in this Mathematics Lab.

1 FOCUS

Introducing the Lab

Have students describe methods for finding the areas of geometric figures.   Sample answers: use a formula; trace the figure on grid paper and count the squares inside it

Cooperative Learning

7-7B   Area and Pick's Theorem

A Follow-Up of Lesson 7-7

Objective
Connect algebra and geometry to find the area of a triangle.

Materials
dot paper or geoboards

Pick's Theorem is a formula that uses information from dot paper to find the area of a triangle. Let's investigate this formula on the following triangles.

Try this!

Work in groups of four.

* Make these triangles on your geoboard. *If you don't have a geoboard, draw them on dot paper.*

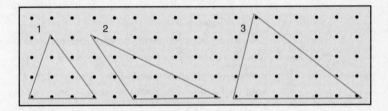

* Copy the spreadsheet below.

	A	B	C	D	E	F
1	TRIANGLE	AREA USING A = 1/2 bh	NUMBER OF DOTS ON TRIANGLE	NUMBER OF DOTS INSIDE TRIANGLE	PICK'S THEOREM	AREA USING PICK'S THEOREM
2	1	4.5	5	3	C2/2 + D2 – 1	4.5
3	2	6	8	3	C3/2 + D3 – 1	6
4	3	12	8	9	C4/2 + D4 – 1	12

Computer Hint

• • • • • • • • • •

C2/2 means divide the value in cell C2 by 2.

* Find the area of each triangle using the formula $A = \frac{1}{2}bh$. Record your findings in column B of the spreadsheet.

* Count the number of dots on the sides of the triangle. Then count the number of dots inside the triangle. Record these numbers in columns C and D of the spreadsheet.

* Use the spreadsheet formula in column E to find the result of using Pick's Theorem. Record each result in column F.

282   **Chapter 7** Rational Numbers

What do you think?

1. Describe triangles 1, 2, and 3 shown on the geoboard. See margin.

2. Compare your results in column B with your results in column F. What do you notice? They are the same.

3. If x represents the number of dots on the figure, y represents the number of dots inside the figure, and A represents the area of the figure, write a formula for Pick's Theorem. $A = \frac{x}{2} + y - 1$

4. Yes; see students' work. 4. Do you think Pick's Theorem would work for a rectangle? Show several rectangles on your geoboard to support your answer.

5. Would Pick's Theorem work for trapezoids? Show examples to support your answer. Yes; see students' work.

Extension

6. Make each of the figures below on your geoboard or dot paper.

   a. How could you find the area of each figure without using Pick's Theorem? Count the square units.

   b. Investigate Pick's Theorem with each figure. With which types of figures can you use Pick's Theorem?
   Pick's Theorem works for all of the figures below.

I.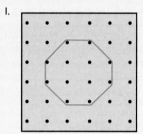

II.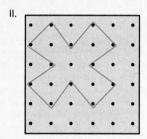

III.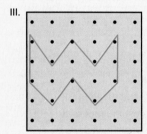

IV.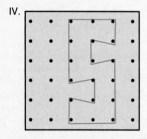

Lab 7-7B Area and Pick's Theorem   **283**

2 TEACH

Using Communication Ask students to translate the symbols in cell E4 into their own words. Divide the value in cell C4 by 2, add the value in cell D4, and subtract 1.

3 PRACTICE/APPLY

Using Problem Solving Ask students this question: *A triangle on a geoboard has an area of 20. What is the sum of the number of dots inside the triangle and half the number on the triangle?* 21

Close

Have students write a sentence or two explaining how they could find the area of a triangle drawn on dot paper. Divide the number of dots on the triangle by 2, add the number of dots inside the triangle, and subtract 1.

Additional Answer

1. triangle 1: scalene acute; triangle 2: scalene obtuse; triangle 3: scalene acute

OPTIONS

Lab Manual You may wish to make copies of the blackline master on p. 59 of the *Lab Manual* for students to use as a recording sheet.

Lab Manual, p. 59

Name _____ Date _____

Mathematics Lab Worksheet

Use with pages 282-283

Area and Pick's Theorem

Try this!

	A	B	C	D	E	F
		Area using $A = \frac{1}{2}bh$	Number of dots on triangle	Number of dots inside triangle	Pick's Theorem	Area using Pick's Theorem
1	Triangle					
2	1	$4\frac{1}{2}$	5	3	C2/2 + D2 – 1	$4\frac{1}{2}$
3	2	6	8	3	C3/2 + D3 – 1	6
4	3	12	8	9	C4/2 + D4 – 1	12

What do you think?

1. Triangle 1 has a base of 3 and a height of 4 units. Triangle 2 has a b_____ f 4 and _ _ _ _ _ _

7-8 Circles and Circumference

NCTM Standards: 1–5, 7, 9, 12, 13

Lesson Resources
- Study Guide Master 7-8
- Practice Master 7-8
- Enrichment Master 7-8
- Technology Master, p. 7
- Lab Manual, p. 60
- Group Activity Card 7-8

 Transparency 7-8 contains the 5-Minute Check and a teaching aid for this lesson.

🕐 5-Minute Check
(Over Lesson 7-7)

Find the area of each figure.

1. 120 cm²

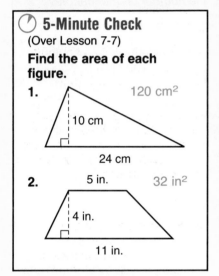

10 cm

24 cm

2. 5 in.   32 in²

4 in.

11 in.

1 FOCUS

Motivating the Lesson

Activity Have students press π on their calculators. Point out that during the 5th century, a Chinese mathematician found the rational approximation $\frac{355}{113}$ for π. Have students divide 355 by 113 and compare the quotient with π. The quotient only exceeds π by approximately 0.0000002.

2 TEACH

Using the Mini-Lab Ask students to estimate how the radius of each circular object compares to the circumference. Each is about one-sixth of the circumference.

284

Objective
Find the circumference of circles.

Words to Learn
circle
center
radius
diameter
circumference

◀LOOKBACK
You can review mean on page 145.

What is displayed on your calculator when you press $\boxed{\pi}$? Is it possible to generate the same number without using this specially-marked key?

Ancient mathematicians used a variety of numbers to approximate π in their work with circles. Before you learn about π, let's first study some terms and properties related to circles.

A **circle** is a set of points in a plane that are the same distance from a given point in the plane. The given point is called the **center.** The distance from the center to any point on the circle is called the **radius** *(r)*. The distance across the circle through the center is its **diameter** *(d)*. The **circumference** *(C)* of a circle is the distance around the circle. The diameter of a circle is twice its radius, or $d = 2r$.

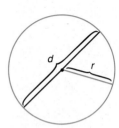

🔬 Mini-Lab

Work in groups of three or four.

Materials: tape measure, circular objects, calculator

- Collect three to five circular objects.
- Measure the diameter and circumference of each as accurately as possible. Record the measurements in a table like the one below.

Object	Diameter	Circumference	Circumference Diameter
#1			
#2			
#3			
#4			
#5			

- Divide each circumference by the corresponding diameter.

Talk About It

a. What is the mean of the quotients? *See students' work; it should be about 3.14.*

b. How does it compare to $\boxed{\pi}$? *It is about the same.*

OPTIONS

Bell Ringer

Half circles are constructed at the ends of a rectangle to create the running track shown below. How far is it around the track? Use $\pi \approx 3.14$.
about 651.2 yd

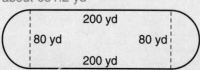

200 yd

80 yd   80 yd

200 yd

The relationship you discovered in the Mini-Lab is true for all circles. The circumference of a circle divided by its diameter is always 3.1415926.... The Greek letter π (pi) represents this number. Although π is not a rational number, the rational numbers 3.14 and $\frac{22}{7}$ are often used as approximations for π.

Circumference	**In words:** The circumference of a circle is equal to its diameter times π, or 2 times its radius times π.
	In symbols: $C = \pi d$ or $C = 2\pi r$

Example 1 *Connection*

Geometry The "spokes" of a Ferris wheel extend 21 feet from the center to the outside of the wheel.

a. How far does a car that is connected to the outside travel in one trip around?

Using $\frac{22}{7}$ for π.   *Using 3.14 for π.*

$C = 2\pi r$ $C = 2\pi r$

$C \approx 2 \cdot \frac{22}{7} \cdot 21$ $C \approx 2 \cdot 3.14 \cdot 21$

                         $C \approx 131.88$

$C \approx 2 \cdot \frac{22}{7}_{1} \cdot \frac{21}{1}^{3}$

$C \approx 132$

The car travels about 132 feet.

b. How many turns of the Ferris wheel would it take to travel 1 mile?

Divide 5,280 by 132 to find how many turns of the Ferris wheel it takes to equal 1 mile.

5280 132   40

It would take the Ferris wheel about 40 turns to travel 1 mile.

Example 2

Find the circumference of a 26-inch bicycle tire.

$C = \pi d$

$C = \pi \cdot 26$ *Replace d with 26.*

 ⊗ 26 ⊟ 81.681409

The circumference is about 81.7 inches

Lesson 7-8 Geometry Connection: Circles and Circumference   **285**

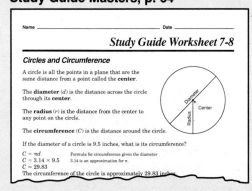
285

Alternate Assessment

Speaking Draw
the figure on
the chalkboard.
Ask students to
identify a
radius, the diameter, and the
center. $\overline{AK}$ or $\overline{KT}$; $\overline{AT}$; K

Additional Answer

23a. 5 | 8
6 | 257
7 | 1123569
8 | 23458
9 | 1347　　5 | 8 means 58

Practice Masters, p. 64

Checking for Understanding

Communicating Mathematics

Read and study the lesson to answer each question.

1. **Tell** how you can find the diameter of a circle if you know the radius. $d = 2r$

2. **Write** the formula for the circumference of a circle if you know the radius. $C = 2\pi r$

3. **Tell** how to estimate the circumference of a circle if you know the diameter. $C \approx 3d$

Answers are calculated using $\boxed{\pi}$ key on calculator and then rounding.

Guided Practice

Find the circumference of each circle described below.

4. 18 in. — 56.55 in.
5. 2.6 m — 8.17 m
6. 2.5 cm — 15.7 cm
7. 7 in. — 43.98 in.

8. The diameter is 13.6 meters. 42.73 m
9. The diameter is $5\frac{1}{4}$ inches. $16\frac{1}{2}$ in. or 16.49 in.
10. The radius is 3.5 kilometers. 21.99 km
11. The radius is $\frac{1}{2}$ foot. 3.14 ft

Exercises

Independent Practice

Find the circumference of each circle described below.

12. 21 ft — 65.97 ft
13. $4\frac{3}{8}$ in. — $27\frac{1}{2}$ in. or 27.49 in.
14. 49 cm — 153.94 cm
15. 6.78 m — 42.6 m

16. The diameter is 36 inches. 113.1 in.
17. The radius is 8 feet. 50.27 ft
18. The radius is 3.4 centimeters. 21.36 cm
19. The diameter is 8.8 meters. 27.65 m
20. The diameter is $2\frac{1}{3}$ feet. $7\frac{1}{3}$ ft or 7.33 ft.
21. The radius is $4\frac{1}{2}$ yards. $28\frac{2}{7}$ yd or 28.27 yd

Mixed Review

22. Find the value of the expression 2^6. *(Lesson 1-9)* 64

23. **Statistics** The chart below shows history test scores. *(Lesson 4-4)*

| 71 | 83 | 67 | 91 | 73 | 75 | 84 | 94 | 71 | 65 |
| 58 | 76 | 85 | 82 | 93 | 72 | 88 | 97 | 79 | 62 |

23a. See margin.

a. Make a stem-and-leaf plot of these scores.

b. In what interval do most of the scores lie? 70-79

24. State the measure of the bases and the height of the trapezoid at the right. Then find the area of the trapezoid. *(Lesson 7-7)* $a = 15$ yd, $b = 20$ yd, $h = 10$ yd, $A = 175$ yd²

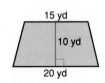
15 yd
10 yd
20 yd

286 **Chapter 7** Rational Numbers

OPTIONS

Limited English Proficiency

Tell the class that many
mathematical terms, such as radius
and diameter, were derived from
other languages. Ask LEP students
to state and define terms from their
languages. Explore relationships
between these terms and their
English counterparts. Encourage
LEP students to lead the discussion.

25. Manufacturing A label is to be placed on a can. The can has a diameter of 9.1 centimeters and a height of 7.5 centimeters. What shape and size must the label be in order to fit the can exactly? **rectangular; 28.6 cm × 7.5 cm**

26. Critical Thinking Three tennis balls are packaged one on top of the other in a can. Which measure is greater, the height or the circumference of the can? Explain. **Circumference; height = 3d, C ≈ 3.14d.**

27. Astronomy The diameter of Saturn at its equator is about 75,100 miles. Find the approximate circumference of Saturn at its equator. **about 235,933.6 miles**

28. Portfolio Suggestion Review the items in your portfolio. Make a table of contents of the items, noting why each item was chosen. Replace any items that are no longer appropriate. **See students' work.**

29. Sports The diameter of a basketball rim is 18 inches.

a. Find the circumference of the basketball rim. **56.55 inches**

b. The circumference of a standard-size basketball is 30 inches. About how much room is there between the rim and the ball if it goes exactly in the center of the rim? **about 4.2 inches**

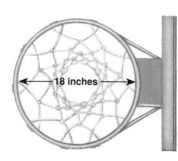

18 inches

30. Data Search Refer to pages 254 and 255. What fractional part of the total number of Cy Young Award winners are left-handed? $\frac{19}{60}$

DATA SEARCH

CULTURAL KALEIDOSCOPE

An Wang

An Wang (1920-1990) was born in Shanghai, China and later came to the United States to study technology. He graduated from Harvard University with a Ph.D. in physics. His first major invention in computer technology was the magnetic-core computer memory, which he sold to IBM. With the profits from that sale, he financed his own business and Wang Laboratories was born.

Wang soon became the front-runner in the computer industry, and his inventions are used for data and text processing, telecommunications, and network processing.

In 1986, *Forbes* magazine listed Wang as one of the wealthiest people in America. On July 4, 1986, at the 100th anniversary celebration of the Statue of Liberty, President Ronald Reagan awarded Mr. Wang the Medal of Liberty—an award to honor naturalized citizens who have made significant contributions to society.

Lesson 7-8 Geometry Connection: Circles and Circumference   **287**

Extending the Lesson

Cultural Kaleidoscope Tell students that Wang® computers were one of the first text-processing computers to be networked in an office environment. Discuss the advantages and disadvantages of such a concept.

Cooperative Learning Activity

String Thing 7-8

Number of players: 2
Materials: String, scissors, compass, index cards

♦ Cut two 1-meter-long pieces of string.

➡ In this game, the sum of the circumferences of circles you draw cannot exceed 1 meter. In each round, each partner writes on a card the measure in centimeters of the radius of a circle. Both partners flip their cards over at the same time. Then, using the same center, each partner draws on a sheet of paper a circle with the radius length shown on his or her card. Each partner takes a string, measures the circumference of his or her circle with the string, and then cuts off the length of the circumference. The partner with the larger circle wins the round, provided that this partner has enough string to measure the circumference of the circle. Try to win more rounds than your partner before you run out of string.

Glencoe Mathematics: Applications and Connections, Course 3

Enrichment Masters, p. 64

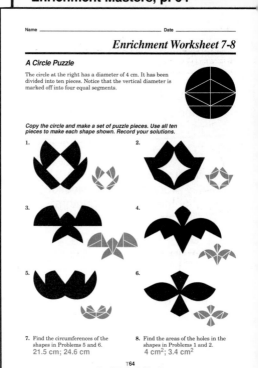

Name _____   Date _____

Enrichment Worksheet 7-8

A Circle Puzzle

The circle at the right has a diameter of 4 cm. It has been divided into ten pieces. Notice that the vertical diameter is marked off into four equal segments.

Copy the circle and make a set of puzzle pieces. Use all ten pieces to make each shape shown. Record your solutions.

1.
2.
3.
4.
5.
6.

7. Find the circumferences of the shapes in Problems 5 and 6. **21.5 cm; 24.6 cm**

8. Find the areas of the holes in the shapes in Problems 1 and 2. **4 cm²; 3.4 cm²**

T64
Glencoe Division, Macmillan/McGraw-Hill

287

NCTM Standards: 1–5, 7, 9, 12

Lesson Resources
- Study Guide Master 7-9
- Practice Master 7-9
- Enrichment Master 7-9
- Group Activity Card 7-9

 Transparency 7-9 contains the 5-Minute Check and a teaching aid for this lesson.

🕐 5-Minute Check
(Over Lesson 7-8)

Find the circumference of each circle described below.

1.
7 m

about
21.99 m

2.
12 in.

about
75.40 in.

3. The radius is 1.5 meters.
about 9.42 m

4. The diameter is $3\frac{1}{2}$ yards.
about 11 yd

---

1 FOCUS

Motivating the Lesson

Activity Have students use rulers to find the number of $\frac{1}{4}$-inch sections in $2\frac{3}{4}$ inches. 11

Write: $2\frac{3}{4} \div \frac{1}{4} = 11$

Show that the same result is obtained by multiplying $2\frac{3}{4}$ by 4.

2 TEACH

Using Properties Use the identity property of multiplication to justify the division algorithm:

$$\frac{\frac{3}{3}}{4} = \frac{3}{3} \cdot \boxed{\frac{\frac{4}{3}}{\frac{4}{3}}} = \frac{3 \cdot \frac{4}{3}}{1} = 3 \cdot \frac{4}{3}$$

$\uparrow$
1

7-9 Dividing Fractions

Objective
Divide fractions.

In 1980, only $\frac{2}{5}$ of the radio stations in the United States were FM stations. Today, nearly $\frac{1}{2}$ of the 9,356 radio stations are FM stations. Approximately how many stations are FM stations?

You could find this number in two ways.

1. Divide by 2.

9356 ÷ 2 = 4678

2. Multiply by $\frac{1}{2}$.

9356 × 0.5 = 4678 $\frac{1}{2} = 0.5$

There are about 4,678 FM stations.

In the example above, notice that dividing by 2 and multiplying by $\frac{1}{2}$ give you the same result.

❝ **When am I ever going to use this?** ❞

Suppose it takes you $\frac{3}{4}$ of a minute to answer each multiple choice question on a test. How many questions can you complete in 15 minutes?

Dividing Fractions	**In words:** To divide by a fraction, multiply by its multiplicative inverse.

Arithmetic	**Algebra**
$3 \div \frac{3}{4} = 3 \cdot \frac{4}{3}$	$\frac{a}{b} \div \frac{c}{d} = \frac{a}{b} \cdot \frac{d}{c}$, where $b, c, d \neq 0$

Example 1 *Problem Solving*

Food Mrs. Rodriguez had $\frac{1}{2}$ of a square cake left for lunch. She divided it into 6 equal parts for her family. What part of the cake will each person receive?

$$\frac{1}{2} \div 6 = \frac{1}{2} \div \frac{6}{1} \quad \text{\textit{Rename 6 as} } \frac{6}{1}.$$
$$= \frac{1}{2} \cdot \frac{1}{6} \quad \text{\textit{Dividing by} } \frac{6}{1} \text{ \textit{is the same as multiplying by} } \frac{1}{6}.$$
$$= \frac{1}{12}$$

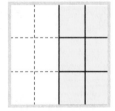

Each serving is $\frac{1}{12}$ of the cake. Compare with the model.

OPTIONS

Reteaching Activity

Using Models Have students use fraction circles to model division as groups of equal amounts.

$2\frac{1}{4} \div \frac{3}{4} = 3$

Have students use fraction circles to solve $3\frac{1}{2} \div \frac{1}{2}$. 7

Study Guide Masters, p. 65

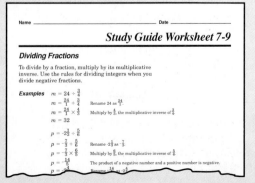

Name _____ Date _____

Study Guide Worksheet 7-9

Dividing Fractions

To divide by a fraction, multiply by its multiplicative inverse. Use the rules for dividing integers when you divide negative fractions.

Examples $m = 24 \div \frac{3}{4}$
$m = \frac{24}{1} \div \frac{3}{4}$ Rename 24 as $\frac{24}{1}$.
$m = \frac{24}{1} \times \frac{4}{3}$ Multiply by $\frac{4}{3}$, the multiplicative inverse of $\frac{3}{4}$.
$m = 32$

$p = -2\frac{1}{3} \div \frac{5}{6}$
$p = -\frac{7}{3} \div \frac{5}{6}$ Rename $-2\frac{1}{3}$ as $-\frac{7}{3}$.
$p = -\frac{7}{3} \times \frac{6}{5}$ Multiply by $\frac{6}{5}$, the multiplicative inverse of $\frac{5}{6}$.
$p = -\frac{14}{5}$ The product of a negative number and a positive number is negative.
$p = -2\frac{4}{5}$ Rename $-\frac{14}{5}$ as $-2\frac{4}{5}$.

Use the rules of signs for dividing integers when you divide rational numbers.

Solve each equation.

Fractions like $\frac{12}{-3\frac{1}{3}}$ are called complex fractions.

2 $y = \dfrac{12}{-3\frac{1}{3}}$ *Estimate: $12 \div -3 = -4$*

$y = 12 \div \left(-3\frac{1}{3}\right)$ *Remember that the fraction bar means division.*

$y = \dfrac{12}{1} \cdot \left(-\dfrac{3}{10}\right)$ *Dividing by $-3\frac{1}{3}$ or $-\frac{10}{3}$ is the same as multiplying by $-\frac{3}{10}$.*

$y = \dfrac{\overset{6}{12}}{1} \cdot \left(-\dfrac{3}{10}_{5}\right)$

$y = -\dfrac{18}{5} \text{ or } -3\frac{3}{5}$ *Rename as a mixed number in simplest form.*

3 $x = -\dfrac{9}{4} \div \left(-\dfrac{3}{8}\right)$

$x = -\dfrac{9}{4} \cdot \left(-\dfrac{8}{3}\right)$

$x = -\dfrac{\overset{3}{9}}{\underset{1}{4}} \cdot \left(-\dfrac{\overset{2}{8}}{\underset{1}{3}}\right)$

$x = 6$

4 $p = -3\frac{3}{4} \div 6\frac{2}{3}$

$p = -\dfrac{15}{4} \div \dfrac{20}{3}$

$p = -\dfrac{15}{4} \cdot \dfrac{3}{20}$

$p = -\dfrac{\overset{3}{15}}{4} \cdot \dfrac{3}{20_{4}}$

$p = -\dfrac{9}{16}$

Checking for Understanding

Communicating Mathematics

Read and study the lesson to answer each question.

1. **Tell** why b, c, or d cannot equal zero in the expression $\frac{a}{b} \div \frac{c}{d}$. **Zero cannot be a denominator.**

2. **Write** the quotient of 3 and $\frac{3}{4}$. **4**

3. **Tell** how the model at the right shows the quotient of 3 and $\frac{3}{4}$. **See margin.**

4. **Draw** a model that shows how to find the quotient of $2\frac{1}{2} \div \frac{5}{8}$. **See Solutions Manual.**

5. **Tell** whether $10 \div \frac{1}{2}$ is greater or less than 10. Explain. **Greater than; dividing by $\frac{1}{2}$ is the same as multiplying by 2.**

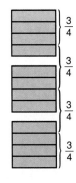

Lesson 7-9 Dividing Fractions   **289**

Gifted and Talented Needs

Have students simplify this complex fraction:

$$\cfrac{1}{5 + \cfrac{1}{5 + \cfrac{1}{5 + \frac{1}{5}}}}$$ $\dfrac{135}{701}$

Have students research Euclid's Algorithm, which is used to rename simple fractions as continued fractions.

Additional Answer

3. There are 4 sets of $\frac{3}{4}$ to equal 3.

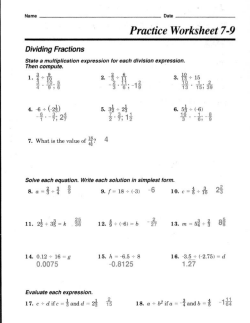

Close

Have students use the word *reciprocal* in a sentence explaining how to divide one fraction by another. **To divide one fraction by another, multiply the first fraction by the reciprocal of the second.**

3 PRACTICE/APPLY

Assignment Guide
Maximum: 16–34
Minimum: 17–27 odd, 28–34

For **Extra Practice,** see p. 601.

Alternate Assessment
Writing   Write the following equation on the chalkboard.

$$\frac{1}{x} \div \frac{1}{y} = \frac{2}{3}$$

Have students find *x* and *y*.
Sample answer: $x = 3$, $y = 2$

Additional Answer
28. $b > -8$;

```
        -10   -8   -6
```

Enrichment Masters, p. 65

Name _____ Date _____

Enrichment Worksheet 7-9

Continued Fractions

The expression at the right is an example of a *continued fraction*. The example shows how to change an improper fraction into a continued fraction.

$$1 + \cfrac{1}{1 + \cfrac{1}{1 + \frac{1}{9}}}$$

Example $\frac{72}{17} = 4 + \frac{4}{17}$

$$= 4 + \cfrac{1}{\frac{17}{4}}$$

$$= 4 + \cfrac{1}{4 + \frac{1}{4}}$$ Notice that the last fraction must be less than 1 before the process is complete.

Change each improper fraction to a continued fraction.

1. $\frac{13}{10}$ $1 + \cfrac{1}{3 + \frac{1}{3}}$

2. $\frac{17}{11}$ $1 + \cfrac{2}{3 + \frac{2}{5}}$

3. $\frac{29}{13}$ $1 + \cfrac{3}{3 + \frac{3}{4}}$

4. $\frac{17}{6}$ $2 + \cfrac{2}{2 + \frac{2}{5}}$

Write each continued fraction as an improper fraction.

5. $1 + \cfrac{1}{1 + \frac{1}{2}}$ $\frac{8}{5}$

6. $1 + \cfrac{1}{1 + \frac{1}{3}}$ $\frac{11}{7}$

7. $1 + \cfrac{1}{1 + \frac{1}{6}}$ $\frac{17}{11}$

8. $2 + \cfrac{1}{2 + \frac{1}{2}}$ $\frac{29}{12}$

9. $3 + \cfrac{1}{1 + \frac{1}{3}}$ $\frac{20}{9}$

10. $6 + \cfrac{1}{1 + \frac{1}{3}}$ $\frac{88}{13}$

T65
Glencoe Division, Macmillan/McGraw-Hill

290

Guided Practice   State a multiplication expression for each division expression. Then compute.

6. $\frac{2}{3} \div \frac{5}{6}$ $\frac{2}{3} \cdot \frac{6}{5} = \frac{4}{5}$

7. $\frac{3}{8} \div \frac{9}{10}$

8. $-\frac{5}{6} \div \frac{2}{9}$

9. $\frac{4}{9} \div 6$

7. $\frac{3}{8} \cdot \frac{10}{9} = \frac{5}{12}$

8. $-\frac{5}{6} \cdot \frac{9}{2} = -3\frac{3}{4}$

9. $\frac{4}{9} \cdot \frac{1}{6} = \frac{2}{27}$

10. $-12 \div \left(-3\frac{3}{8}\right)$
$-\frac{12}{1} \cdot \frac{8}{27} = 3\frac{5}{9}$

11. $1\frac{1}{3} \div 2\frac{2}{9}$

12. $15 \div 2\frac{8}{11}$
$\frac{15}{1} \cdot \frac{11}{30} = 5\frac{1}{2}$

13. $7\frac{5}{9} \div (-8)$
$\frac{68}{9} \cdot -\frac{1}{8} = -\frac{17}{18}$

11. $\frac{4}{3} \cdot \frac{9}{20} = \frac{3}{5}$

14. What is the value of $\frac{3\frac{3}{5}}{10}$? $\frac{9}{25}$

15. Find the quotient of -6 divided by $-1\frac{1}{2}$.   4

Exercises

Independent Practice   Solve each equation. Write each solution in simplest form.

16. $a = \frac{3}{4} \div \frac{5}{6}$ $\frac{9}{10}$

17. $10 \div (-2) = t$ -5

18. $b = \frac{8}{9} \div \frac{6}{7}$ $1\frac{1}{27}$

19. $7\frac{1}{3} \div 1\frac{2}{9} = d$ 6

20. $n = \frac{3}{8} \div (-6)$ $-\frac{1}{16}$

21. $4\frac{1}{2} \div \frac{3}{4} = h$ 6

22. $j = \frac{9}{10} \div 6$ $\frac{3}{20}$

23. $2\frac{2}{3} \div 4 = y$ $\frac{2}{3}$

24. $g = -3\frac{3}{4} \div \left(-2\frac{1}{2}\right)$ $1\frac{1}{2}$

Evaluate each expression.

25. $c \div d$ if $c = \frac{1}{2}$ and $d = 2\frac{1}{3}$ $\frac{3}{14}$

26. $a^2 \div b^2$ if $a = -\frac{2}{3}$ and $b = \frac{4}{5}$ $\frac{25}{36}$

27. $x + y \div z$ if $x = \frac{3}{4}$, $y = 0.5$, and $z = \frac{1}{4}$ $2\frac{3}{4}$ or 2.75

Mixed Review

28. Solve $\frac{b}{2} + 7 > 3$. Show the solution on the number line.   *(Lesson 2-10)*
See margin.

29. Solve $r = (-8) + 12 + 3 + 9$. Check by solving another way.   *(Lesson 3-4)*   16

30. Express 15.363636... using bar notation.   *(Lesson 6-7)* $15.\overline{36}$

31. **Geometry**   Find the circumference of a circle with a radius of 5 millimeters.   *(Lesson 7-8)*   31.4 mm

Problem Solving and Applications

32. **Advertising**   A page of sale items is to be folded into thirds before it is stapled and mailed. If the page is 11 inches long, how wide is each section? $3\frac{2}{3}$ inches

33. **Home Economics**   How many slices of pepperoni, each $\frac{1}{16}$ inch thick, can be cut from a stick 8 inches long?   128 slices

34. **Critical Thinking**   A positive number is both multiplied and divided by the same rational number *n*, where $0 < n < 1$. Which is greater, the product or the quotient? Explain your reasoning.
Quotient; dividing by a proper fraction is actually multiplying by an improper fraction.

290   **Chapter 7** Rational Numbers

OPTIONS

Extending the Lesson

Using Cooperative Groups   Ask students to solve this problem: *Use the numbers 2, 3, 4, and 5 to write a division problem with a quotient of $\frac{3}{10}$.* $\frac{3}{4} \div \frac{5}{2} = \frac{3}{10}$ Have students work in small groups to create similar problems.

Cooperative Learning Activity

It's Greek to Me   7-9

Use groups of 4.

The figure at the right is a type of *Greek square*. A Greek square can be used to create a secret code. In this Greek square, dividends are written above the columns and divisors are written to the left of the rows. Each letter, then, may be replaced by a quotient. For example, the letter A is in the first column and first row. Therefore, it could be replaced by a quotient. For example, the letter A is in the first column and first row. Therefore, it could be replaced by a quotient. For example, $\frac{2}{3} \div \frac{5}{6} = \frac{2}{3} \times \frac{6}{5} = \frac{4}{5}$. The word *code* would be written $12\frac{2}{3}/-2\frac{5}{3}/-9\frac{3}{4}/\frac{9}{10}$.

On a sheet of paper, write a secret message using the code in the Greek square. Trade papers with another group member and decipher his or her message.

	$\frac{2}{3}$	$-\frac{5}{6}$	$10\frac{1}{3}$	-8	$\frac{3}{4}$
$\frac{5}{6}$	A	B	C	D	E
$-\frac{11}{12}$	F	G	H	IJ	K
3	L	M	N	O	P
$-\frac{1}{2}$	Q	R	S	T	U
$\frac{5}{18}$	V	W	X	Y	Z

Glencoe Mathematics: Applications and Connections, Course 3

7-10 Solving Equations

Objective
Solve equations with rational number solutions.

The West Montpelier track team qualified to compete in an international track meet to be held in Montreal. One of the track members is Terry O'Malley. He read that the temperature there would be about 20 degrees Celsius (°C). His coach said they could find out the temperature in degrees Fahrenheit (°F) using the formula, $C = \frac{5}{9}(F - 32)$. What is the temperature in degrees Fahrenheit for Montreal?

You can apply the skills you have learned for rational numbers to solve equations containing rational numbers, such as $C = \frac{5}{9}(F - 32)$.

$$C = \frac{5}{9}(F - 32)$$

$$20 = \frac{5}{9}(F - 32) \qquad \textit{Replace C with 20.}$$

$$\frac{9}{5} \cdot 20 = \frac{9}{5} \cdot \frac{5}{9}(F - 32) \qquad \textit{Multiply each side by } \frac{9}{5},$$
$$\textit{the multiplicative inverse of } \frac{5}{9}.$$

$$36 = F - 32$$

$$36 + 32 = F - 32 + 32 \qquad \textit{Add 32 to each side.}$$

$$68 = F$$

The equivalent Fahrenheit temperature is 68°.

Example 1

Solve $t + 0.25 = -4.125$. Check your solution.

$$t + 0.25 = -4.125$$

$$t + 0.25 - 0.25 = -4.125 - 0.25 \qquad \textit{Subtract 0.25 from each side.}$$

4.125 [+/−] [−] 0.25 [=] ‑4.375

$$t = -4.375$$

Check: 4.375 [+/−] [+] 0.25 [=] ‑4.125 ✔

The solution is −4.375.

Lesson 7-10 Algebra Connection: Solving Equations **291**

OPTIONS

Reteaching Activity

Using Questioning Review inverse operations. Ask these questions:

• *What inverse operation should you use to solve the equation $\frac{2}{3}k = \frac{1}{2}$?* division

• *By what number should you divide each side?* $\frac{2}{3}$

• *What is the value of k?* $\frac{3}{4}$

Study Guide Masters, p. 66

Name _____ Date _____

Study Guide Worksheet 7-10

Solving Equations

Solve equations containing rational numbers the same way you solve integer equations.

Example 1 $-\frac{2}{3}m = \frac{10}{21}$
$-\frac{3}{2} \times -\frac{2}{3}m = -\frac{3}{2} \times \frac{10}{21}$ Multiply each side by $-\frac{3}{2}$, the multiplicative inverse of $-\frac{2}{3}$.
$m = -\frac{5}{7}$
Check: $-\frac{2}{3} \times (-\frac{5}{7}) \stackrel{?}{=} \frac{10}{21}$
$\frac{10}{21} = \frac{10}{21}$ ✔

Example 2 $-\frac{3}{8} = \frac{t}{5}$
$5 \times (-\frac{3}{8}) = 5 \times \frac{t}{5}$ Multiply each side by 5.
$-\frac{15}{8} = t$
$-1\frac{7}{8} = t$

NCTM Standards: 1–4, 7, 9

Lesson Resources
• Study Guide Master 7-10
• Practice Master 7-10
• Enrichment Master 7-10
• Evaluation Master, Quiz B, p. 61
• Technology Master, p. 21
• Multicultural Activity, p. 7
• Group Activity Card 7-10

 Transparency 7-10 contains the 5-Minute Check and a teaching aid for this lesson.

5-Minute Check
(Over Lesson 7-9)

Solve each equation. Write each solution in simplest form.

1. $n = 5 \div \frac{1}{3}$ 15

2. $k = \frac{3}{4} \div (-2)$ $-\frac{3}{8}$

3. $-1\frac{1}{2} \div (-1\frac{7}{8}) = y$ $\frac{4}{5}$

4. $p = -2\frac{1}{4} \div 2\frac{7}{10}$ $-\frac{5}{6}$

1 FOCUS

Motivating the Lesson

Questioning Ask students to name the freezing and boiling temperatures for water on the Fahrenheit and Celsius scales. freezing: 32°F, 0°C; boiling: 212°F, 100°C

2 TEACH

Using Questioning Have students look at the third line of the temperature conversion on page 291:

$$\frac{9}{5} \cdot 20 = \frac{9}{5} \cdot \frac{5}{9}(F - 32)$$

Ask the following questions:

• *How is the equation different from the equation above?* Each side has been multiplied by $\frac{9}{5}$.

• *Why was this done?* to eliminate fractions from the equation

291

More Examples

**Solve each equation.
Check each solution.**

For Example 1

$-11.362 = 4.37 + x$
-15.732

For Example 2

$\frac{8}{9}k = -\frac{4}{15}$ $-\frac{3}{10}$

For Example 3

$\frac{3}{4} = 11h + \left(-\frac{1}{6}\right)$ $\frac{1}{12}$

Checking for Understanding

Exercises 1-2 are designed to help you assess students' understanding through reading, writing, speaking, and modeling. You should work through these exercises with your students and then monitor their work on Guided Practice Exercises 3-11.

Additional Answer

1. Add 4 to both sides and then multiply both sides by $\frac{3}{2}$.

Practice Masters, p. 66

Name _____ Date _____

Practice Worksheet 7-10

Solving Equations

Solve each equation. Check your solution.

1. $2.3w = 6.9$ 3
2. $-\frac{1}{3}y + \frac{2}{9} = \frac{1}{2}$ $-\frac{5}{6}$
3. $4.2 = \frac{c}{0.7}$ 2.94

4. $\frac{3}{8}a - (-4) = 5$ $1\frac{2}{3}$
5. $3\frac{1}{2}m = 6\frac{2}{3}$ $1\frac{19}{21}$
6. $-\frac{t}{4} = -\frac{7}{8}$ $3\frac{1}{2}$

7. $\frac{b}{2.6} = -3.8$ -9.88
8. $-2.4y - 6.3 = -18.3$ 5
9. $7x = -23$ $-3\frac{2}{7}$

10. $\frac{x}{6.3} = 63$ 396.9
11. $b - (-0.07) = 4.5$ 4.43
12. $-\frac{2}{3}c = 8.7$ -13.05

13. $\frac{m}{4} = \frac{3}{10}$ $-\frac{1}{5}$
14. $-\frac{2}{9}k = \frac{3}{10}$ $-1\frac{1}{20}$
15. $\frac{2}{3}x - \frac{1}{5} = -2\frac{2}{15}$ $-3\frac{3}{20}$

16. $6.4s + 3.3 = 12.5$ 1.4375
17. $1\frac{1}{2}t = 3\frac{2}{3}$ $2\frac{4}{9}$
18. $-\frac{7}{8}p + 1\frac{1}{4} = 18$ $-19\frac{7}{?}$

T66
Glencoe Division, Macmillan/McGraw-Hill

292

Solve each equation. Check each solution.

2 $\frac{3}{4}y = -\frac{7}{8}$

$\frac{4}{3} \cdot \frac{3}{4}y = \left(\frac{4}{3}\right)\left(-\frac{7}{8}\right)$ *Multiply each side by $\frac{4}{3}$.*

$y = -\frac{7}{6}$ or $-1\frac{1}{6}$

Check: $\frac{3}{4}y = -\frac{7}{8}$

$\frac{1}{4}\overset{1}{\cancel{3}}\left(-\frac{7}{\cancel{6}_2}\right) \overset{?}{=} -\frac{7}{8}$

$-\frac{7}{8} = -\frac{7}{8}$ ✓

3 $7m + \left(-\frac{2}{9}\right) = \frac{5}{9}$

$7m + \left(-\frac{2}{9}\right) = \frac{5}{9}$

$7m + \left(-\frac{2}{9}\right) + \frac{2}{9} = \frac{5}{9} + \frac{2}{9}$ *Add $\frac{2}{9}$ to each side.*

$7m = \frac{7}{9}$

$7m \cdot \frac{1}{7} = \frac{7}{9} \cdot \frac{1}{7}$ *Multiply each side by $\frac{1}{7}$, the multiplicative inverse of 7.*

$m = \frac{1}{9}$

Check: $7m + \left(-\frac{2}{9}\right) = \frac{5}{9}$

$7\left(\frac{1}{9}\right) + \left(-\frac{2}{9}\right) \overset{?}{=} \frac{5}{9}$

$\frac{5}{9} = \frac{5}{9}$ ✓   The solution is $\frac{1}{9}$.

Checking for Understanding

Communicating Mathematics

Read and study the lesson to answer each question.

1. **Tell** how you would solve $\frac{2}{3}x - 4 = 8$. **See margin.**

2. **Write** an equation that you would use the multiplicative inverse of $-1\frac{5}{8}$ to solve. **Sample answer:** $-1\frac{5}{8}x - 3 = 10$

Guided Practice

Solve each equation. Check your solution.

3. $1.1 + y = -4.4$ -5.5
4. $-\frac{5}{8}x + \frac{1}{6} = \frac{3}{5}$ $-\frac{52}{75}$
5. $3.6 = \frac{c}{0.9}$ 3.24

6. $\frac{2}{3}h - (-3) = 6$ $4\frac{1}{2}$
7. $2\frac{1}{2}d = 5\frac{3}{4}$ $2\frac{3}{10}$
8. $-\frac{8t}{5} = 4$ $-2\frac{1}{2}$

9. $\frac{b}{1.5} - 13 = 2.2$ 22.8
10. $-12 = -\frac{z}{7}$ 84
11. $-11g + 15 = 12.5$ 0.227

OPTIONS

Bell Ringer

One cold winter day, the temperature in Montreal dropped to $-40°C$. What was the Fahrenheit temperature? $-40°F$ What is unusual about these two temperatures? They have the same numerical value. ($-40°$ is the only temperature for which this is true.)

Additional Answer

31d. With every 10 mph increase, the difference in stopping distance increases about 10 feet.

Exercises

Independent Practice

Solve each equation. Check your solution.

12. $2x = -12$ −6

13. $\frac{t}{3} = -6$ −18

14. $a - (-0.03) = 3.2$
3.17

15. $-\frac{1}{4}c = 3.8$ −15.2

16. $\frac{y}{3.2} = -4.5$ −14.4

17. $-1.6w + 3.5 = 0.48$
1.8875

20. −8.97

18. $\frac{n}{2} = -1.6$ −3.2

19. $\frac{6d}{2} = -0.36$ −0.12

20. $\frac{m}{2.3} - 1.3 = -5.2$

21. $k + \frac{2}{3} = -\frac{4}{9}$ $-1\frac{1}{9}$

22. $-\frac{3}{5}h = \frac{2}{3}$ $-1\frac{1}{9}$

23. $4p - \frac{1}{5} = -7\frac{2}{5}$ $-1\frac{4}{5}$

24. What is the solution of $z - \frac{2}{5} = -2$? $-1\frac{3}{5}$

Mixed Review

25. Estimate $618 + 182 + 375$ by rounding. *(Lesson 1-3)* 1,200

26. Statistics Determine whether a scatter plot of the number of base hits to the number of runs scored would show a positive, negative, or no relationship. *(Lesson 4-8)* positive

27. Solve $46 = 8k - 2$. Check your solution. *(Lesson 2-7)* 6

28. Find the LCM of 9 and 30. *(Lesson 6-9)* 90

29. Solve $g = \frac{5}{6} \div \frac{4}{3}$. *(Lesson 7-9)* $\frac{5}{8}$

Problem Solving and Applications

30. Critical Thinking Using the formula at the beginning of this lesson, explain how you could find the Fahrenheit temperature when the Celsius temperature is 0°. **See margin.**

31. Safe Driving The graph below shows the distance needed to stop an automobile traveling at various speeds. Each of the given formulas approximates the stopping distance, *d* (in feet), based on the speed, *s,* in miles per hour. Determine which speed is the closest match for each of the given formulas.

a. $d = 3s$ 35 mph

b. $d = 4s$ 55 mph

c. $d = 2\frac{1}{2}s$ 25 mph

STOPPING DISTANCE:
From eye to brain to foot to wheel to road

62 ft	25 MPH
106 ft	35 MPH
162 ft	45 MPH
228 ft	55 MPH
306 ft	65 MPH

d. Look for a pattern in the graph above. What conclusion can you make about the stopping distance and the speed of a car? **See margin.**

Lesson 7-10 Algebra Connection: Solving Equations   **293**

Extending the Lesson

Using Connections Scientists often use the Kelvin temperature scale. Kelvin and Celsius temperatures are related by the formula $K = C + 273.2$. Find the Kelvin temperature corresponding to the following temperatures.

a. 56°C
329.2°K

b. −147.7°C
125.5°K

c. 95°F
308.2°K

d. 365°F
458.2°K

Cooperative Learning Activity

It's Out of My Hand **7-10**

Number of players: 2
Materials: Index cards

↓ Copy onto cards the equations shown on the back of this card, one per card. Shuffle the cards and divide them evenly. Label the sections of a spinner "−2," "−$\frac{7}{8}$," "−$\frac{3}{5}$," "1$\frac{1}{2}$," "3.6," and "4.2." Each of these numbers is the solution to three of the equations on the cards.

↳ One partner spins the spinner. If possible, each partner then removes from his or her hand one card containing an equation for which the number on the spinner is the solution. Continue in this way, taking turns at the spinner, until one partner runs out of cards. The partner who runs out of cards first is the winner.

Glencoe Mathematics: Applications and Connections, Course 3

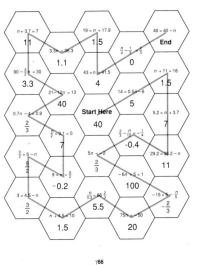

The Chapter Study Guide and Review begins with a section on Communicating Mathematics. This includes questions that review the new terms and concepts that were introduced in the chapter.

Then, the Skills and Concepts presented in the chapter are reviewed using a side-by-side format. Encourage students to refer to the Objectives and Examples on the left as they complete the Review Exercises on the right.

The Chapter Study Guide and Review ends with problems that review Applications and Problem Solving.

Additional Answer

9. Sample answer: Rewrite the mixed numbers as fractions. Multiply the numerators and multiply the denominators. Then simplify.

Chapter

7 Study Guide and Review

Communicating Mathematics

Choose the letter that best matches each phrase.

1. the sum of a whole number and a fraction g
2. the LCM of 2 and 6 c
3. a sequence whose terms increase or decrease by a constant factor h
4. a sequence having the same difference between any two consecutive terms i
5. a quadrilateral with exactly one pair of parallel sides j
6. the distance across a circle through the center e
7. the distance around a circle f
8. the number you would multiply each side of the equation $\frac{3}{4}t = -\frac{5}{8}$ by to solve it b

a. $\frac{3}{4}$
b. $\frac{4}{3}$
c. 6
d. 12
e. diameter
f. circumference
g. mixed number
h. geometric sequence
i. arithmetic sequence
j. trapezoid

9. In your own words, describe how to multiply two mixed numbers. See margin.

Self Assessment

Objectives and Examples	*Review Exercises*
Upon completing this chapter, you should be able to:	*Use these exercises to review and prepare for the chapter test.*
• add and subtract fractions with like denominators *(Lesson 7-1)* Solve $b = \frac{1}{5} - \frac{4}{5}$. $b = \frac{1-4}{5}$ or $-\frac{3}{5}$	Solve each equation. Write each solution in simplest form. 10. $\frac{2}{7} + \frac{3}{7} = n$ $\frac{5}{7}$ 11. $w = -\frac{1}{8} - \frac{5}{8}$ $-\frac{3}{4}$ 12. $x = \frac{5}{12} + \frac{7}{12}$ 1
• add and subtract fractions with unlike denominators *(Lesson 7-2)* Solve $h = \frac{1}{2} + \frac{2}{3}$. $h = \frac{3}{6} + \frac{4}{6}$ $h = \frac{7}{6}$ or $1\frac{1}{6}$	Solve each equation. Write each solution in simplest form. 13. $m = -\frac{3}{5} + \frac{1}{3}$ $-\frac{4}{15}$ 14. $z = 4 - 2\frac{3}{5}$ $1\frac{2}{5}$ 15. $t = -4\frac{2}{3} + \left(-6\frac{3}{4}\right)$ $-11\frac{5}{12}$

Objectives and Examples

Review Exercises

- multiply fractions *(Lesson 7-3)*

  Solve $f = -\dfrac{7}{8} \cdot \dfrac{1}{2}$.

  $f = \dfrac{-7 \cdot 1}{8 \cdot 2}$

  $f = -\dfrac{7}{16}$

Solve each equation. Write each solution in simplest form.

16. $p = \left(-\dfrac{1}{6}\right)\left(-\dfrac{3}{5}\right)$ $\dfrac{1}{10}$ 17. $2\dfrac{2}{5}\left(-4\dfrac{3}{8}\right) = s$ $-10\dfrac{1}{2}$

18. $-\dfrac{7}{10} \cdot \dfrac{4}{7} = k$ $-\dfrac{2}{5}$ 19. $g = \dfrac{4}{9} \cdot 5\dfrac{1}{4}$ $2\dfrac{1}{3}$

- identify and use rational number properties *(Lesson 7-4)*

  Find $3\dfrac{1}{4} \cdot 4$.

  $3\dfrac{1}{4} \cdot 4 = 4 \cdot 3\dfrac{1}{4}$

  $\qquad = 4\left(3 + \dfrac{1}{4}\right)$

  $\qquad = 4(3) + 4\left(\dfrac{1}{4}\right)$

  $\qquad = 12 + 1 \text{ or } 13$

Name the multiplicative inverse of each of the following.

20. $\dfrac{5}{7}$ $\dfrac{7}{5}$ 21. $-6\dfrac{1}{3}$ $-\dfrac{3}{19}$

Find each product.

22. $5 \cdot 7\dfrac{2}{5}$ 37 23. $\left(-\dfrac{4}{5}\right)\left(-3\dfrac{1}{2}\right)$ $2\dfrac{4}{5}$

- recognize and extend arithmetic and geometric sequences *(Lesson 7-6)*

  State whether the sequence 3, 6, 12, 24, ... is geometric. Then write the next three terms.

  Since there is a common ratio, 2, the sequence is geometric. The next three terms are 48, 96, and 192.

State whether each sequence is arithmetic, geometric, or neither. Then write the next three terms of each sequence.

24. $-10, -7, -4, -1, \ldots$ A; 2, 5, 8

25. $27, 9, 3, 1, \ldots$ G; $\dfrac{1}{3}, \dfrac{1}{9}, \dfrac{1}{27}$

26. $6, 13, 19, 24, \ldots$ N; 28, 31, 33

27. $60, 56, 52, 48, \ldots$ A; 44, 40, 36

- find the areas of triangles and trapezoids *(Lesson 7-7)*

  Find the area of the triangle.

  $A = \dfrac{1}{2}bh$

  $A = \dfrac{1}{2}(3.2)(2.4)$

  $A = 3.84$

  The area is 3.84 square feet.

  2.4 ft

  3.2 ft

Find the area of each figure described below.

28. triangle; base, $2\dfrac{1}{2}$ cm; height, $3\dfrac{1}{4}$ cm $4\dfrac{1}{16}$ cm²

29. trapezoid; bases, 10 m and 7 m; height, 6 m   51 m²

- find the circumference of circles *(Lesson 7-8)*

  Find the circumference of the circle.

  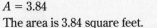

  $C = \pi d$

  $C = \pi(5)$

  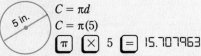

  The circumference is about 15.7 inches.

Find the circumference of each circle described below.

30. The diameter is $3\dfrac{1}{3}$ feet. $10\dfrac{10}{21}$ or 10.47 ft

31. The radius is 2.4 meters.   15.08 m

32. The radius is 19 yards.   119.38 yd

33. The diameter is 5.5 inches.   17.28 in.

Evaluation Masters, pp. 59–60

Study Guide and Review

Name _____ Date _____

Form 2A _____ **Chapter 7 Test**

Solve each equation. Write each solution in simplest form.

1. $-8\frac{5}{8} + 3\frac{7}{8} = a$
2. $\frac{9}{14} + \frac{9}{14} = b$
3. $\frac{5}{8} - \frac{5}{9} = c$
4. $d = \frac{6}{7}\left(\frac{49}{51}\right)$
5. $e = \frac{5}{8} \div 2\frac{1}{8}$
6. $-4\frac{2}{3} \div (-2\frac{6}{10}) = f$
7. $3\frac{1}{3}g = -6\frac{2}{3}$
8. $5\frac{3}{4} = h + 1\frac{3}{8}$
9. $\frac{1}{3.5} - 4.8 = -2.2$
10. $\frac{1}{3} = \frac{6}{7}j - 3\frac{3}{4}$

11. What is the multiplicative inverse of $2\frac{3}{7}$?

12. Write the first four terms in the sequence with a common difference of -3. The first term is 5.

13. The fifth term in a sequence is $\frac{5}{16}$. The common ratio is $\frac{1}{4}$. Find the previous four terms.

Find the area of each triangle described below.

	base	height
14.	11 m	16 m
15.	$2\frac{1}{2}$ ft	$4\frac{3}{4}$ ft

Find the area of each trapezoid described below.

	base a	base b	height
16.	18 mm	22 mm	14 mm
17.	4.8 cm	5.7 cm	2.6 cm

Find the circumference of each circle described below.

18. The diameter is 6.2 mi.
19. The radius is $2\frac{3}{4}$ ft.

20. One vertical line separates a circle into two parts as shown at the right. How many parts would there be if the circle had 103 vertical lines through it?

BONUS An auditorium has 20 seats in the front row and 2 seats more in each following row than in the preceding one. If there are 20 rows, what is the seating capacity of the auditorium?

1. $-4\frac{1}{2}$
2. $\frac{9}{7}$
3. $-\frac{1}{18}$
4. $\frac{14}{17}$
5. $\frac{25}{88}$
6. $1\frac{11}{17}$
7. $1\frac{19}{21}$
8. $3\frac{13}{20}$
9. 9.1
10. $-4\frac{2}{3}$
11. $\frac{3}{8}$
12. $5, 2, -1, -4$
13. $80, 20, 5, \frac{5}{4}$
14. $88\ m^2$
15. $5\frac{15}{16}\ ft^2$
16. $280\ mm^2$
17. $13.65\ cm^2$
18. $19.468\ mi$
19. $17\frac{2}{7}\ ft$
20. 104

    780 seats

59

Glencoe Division, Macmillan/McGraw-Hill

Name _____ Date _____

Form 2B _____ **Chapter 7 Test**

Solve each equation. Write each solution in simplest form.

1. $k = -7\frac{2}{5} + 4\frac{4}{5}$
2. $\frac{9}{16} + \frac{9}{16} = l$
3. $m = \frac{5}{8} - \frac{6}{7}$
4. $\left(-\frac{8}{9}\times\frac{27}{16}\right) = n$
5. $p = \frac{3}{4} \div 2\frac{1}{2}$
6. $-3\frac{1}{3} \div (-6\frac{6}{9}) = q$
7. $1\frac{1}{2} = -2\frac{3}{4}r$
8. $1\frac{3}{4} = s + 3\frac{3}{8}$
9. $1.2 = \frac{1}{2.5} + 2.6$
10. $\frac{1}{2} = -1\frac{3}{4} - \frac{9}{8}w$

11. What is the multiplicative inverse of $-3\frac{1}{2}$?

12. Name the sixth term in the sequence $20, 10, 5, 2\frac{1}{2}, \ldots$.

13. The fifth term in a sequence is 8. The common difference is -4. Find the first four terms.

Find the area of each triangle or trapezoid.

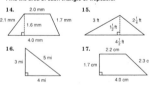

14.
15.
16.
17.

Find the circumference of each circle described below.

18. The diameter is $2\frac{1}{2}$ ft.
19. The radius is 3.6 cm.

20. Study the pattern of dots shown in the figures at the right. If the pattern continues, how many dots will be in the figure that has 9 dots in the bottom row?

BONUS The third term of an arithmetic sequence is 12. The sixth term is -6. Find the first, second, and fifth terms of the sequence.

1. $-2\frac{3}{5}$
2. $\frac{7}{8}$
3. $-\frac{13}{56}$
4. $\frac{3}{2}$
5. $-\frac{3}{10}$
6. $\frac{1}{2}$
7. $-\frac{6}{11}$
8. $-1\frac{11}{12}$
9. -3.5
10. -6
11. $-\frac{2}{7}$
12. $\frac{5}{8}$
13. $24, 20, 16, 12$
14. $4.8\ mm^2$
15. $3\frac{3}{8}\ ft^2$
16. $6\ mi^2$
17. $5.27\ cm^2$
18. $7\frac{6}{8}\ ft$
19. $22.608\ cm$
20. 45 dots

    $24, 18, 0$

60

Glencoe Division, Macmillan/McGraw-Hill

296

Objectives and Examples

- divide fractions *(Lesson 7-9)*

  Solve $r = \frac{5}{8} \div \left(-\frac{3}{4}\right)$.

  $r = \frac{5}{8} \cdot \left(-\frac{4}{3}\right)$

  $r = -\frac{5}{6}$

- solve equations with rational number solutions *(Lesson 7-10)*

  Solve $\frac{2}{3}n = \frac{5}{12}$.

  $\frac{3}{2} \cdot \frac{2}{3}n = \frac{3}{2} \cdot \frac{5}{12}$

  $n = \frac{5}{8}$

Review Exercises

Solve each equation. Write each solution in simplest form.

34. $i = -\frac{7}{9} \div \left(-\frac{2}{3}\right)$ $1\frac{1}{6}$
35. $2\frac{2}{5} \div 4 = f$ $\frac{3}{5}$
36. $3\frac{1}{7} \div \left(-2\frac{1}{5}\right) = d$ $-1\frac{3}{7}$
37. $q = \frac{3}{4} \div 3\frac{3}{5}$ $\frac{5}{24}$

Solve each equation.

38. $\frac{x}{6} = -4.3$ -25.8
39. $-6.2 = \frac{e}{1.7} + 4$ -17.34
40. $2b - \frac{4}{7} = 6\frac{1}{7}$ $3\frac{5}{14}$
41. $t - (-0.9) = 5$ 4.1

Applications and Problem Solving

42. Bob rides in the March Bike Marathon. He rides 12 miles the first day, 18 the second, 27 the third. If he continues this pattern, how many miles will Bob have ridden in all by the end of the fourth day? *(Lesson 7-5)* **97.5 miles**

43. The length of the minute hand on a clock is 9 centimeters. How far does the end of the minute hand travel as it moves from 12 to 4? *(Lesson 7-8)* **18.85 cm**

Curriculum Connection Projects

- **Business** From the Business section of today's newspaper, record the "volume" and "net change" for the "Top Percent Losers" and "Top Percent Gainers" and find total gain or loss for each stock.

- **Sports** Find the circumference of the three-point circle on a basketball court.

- **Sports** Use triangles to find the area of the infield of a baseball field.

Read More About It

Jordan, Sheryl. *A Time of Darkness.*
Keightley, Moy. *Investigating Art: A Practical Guide for Young People.*
Miller, Marvin. *You Be the Jury.*

Chapter 7 Test

1. What is the multiplicative inverse of $1\frac{1}{9}$? $\frac{9}{10}$

2. Find the product of $5\frac{1}{3}$ and $-2\frac{1}{4}$. -12

Solve each equation. Write each solution in simplest form.

3. $-6\frac{3}{7} + 4\frac{6}{7} = m$ $\ -1\frac{4}{7}$

4. $\frac{8}{15} + \frac{8}{15} = a$ $\ 1\frac{1}{15}$

5. $\frac{5}{8} - \frac{4}{5} = g$ $\ -\frac{7}{40}$

6. $\frac{33}{40} \cdot \frac{8}{9} = t$ $\ \frac{11}{15}$

7. $c = -\frac{7}{8} \div 2\frac{4}{5}$ $\ -\frac{5}{16}$

8. $5\frac{5}{6} \div \left(-1\frac{2}{3}\right) = x$ $\ -3\frac{1}{2}$

9. Write the first four terms in an arithmetic sequence with a common difference of 2. The first term is 20. **20, 22, 24, 26**

10. The fifth term of a sequence is 6. The common ratio is $\frac{1}{2}$. Find the first four terms. **96, 48, 24, 12**

Find the area of each triangle described below.

	base	height	
11.	12 m	19 m	114 m²
12.	$4\frac{1}{2}$ ft	$6\frac{3}{4}$ ft	$15\frac{3}{16}$ ft²

Find the area of each trapezoid described below.

	base (a)	base (b)	height	
13.	15 in.	26 in.	$9\frac{1}{2}$ in.	$194\frac{3}{4}$ in²
14.	3.7 mm	5.4 mm	8.2 mm	37.31 mm²

Find the circumference of each circle described below.

15. The diameter is 6.3 yards. $\approx$ **19.792 yards**

16. The radius is $2\frac{5}{8}$ meters. $\approx 16\frac{1}{2}$ **or 16.49 meters**

Solve each equation. Check your solution.

17. $2\frac{1}{2}w = 4\frac{3}{8}$ $\ 1\frac{3}{4}$

18. $\frac{a}{2.8} - 6.8 = 12$ **52.64**

19. $\frac{1}{4} = -\frac{5}{6}x + \frac{9}{16}$ $\ \frac{3}{8}$

20. **Archeology** Arrowheads from a prehistoric site in Montana have been arranged in rows in a museum showcase. The first row contains 12 arrowheads. The second row contains 10 arrowheads. The third row has 13, the fourth row has 11, and so on, until the last row contains 13 arrowheads. Find the pattern and determine how many rows of arrowheads there were in the showcase. **Subtract 2, then add 3; 8 rows.**

No; zero cannot be a denominator.

Bonus Does zero have a multiplicative inverse? Why or why not?

Chapter 7 Test **297**

Test and Review Generator software is provided in Apple, IBM, and Macintosh versions. You may use this software to create your own tests or worksheets, based on the needs of your students.

The **Performance Assessment Booklet** provides an alternate assessment for evaluating student progress. An assessment for this chapter can be found on pages 13–14.

8 Real Numbers

Previewing the Chapter

In this chapter, the filling in of the number line begun in Chapter 3 (Integers) and continued in Chapter 7 (Rational Numbers) is completed by the addition of the irrational numbers. Students work extensively with square roots before learning the definition of irrational numbers. The Pythagorean Theorem is developed and applied in a variety of ways, especially in finding distances, graphing irrational numbers, and discovering relationships in 30°–60° and 45°–45° right triangles. In the **problem-solving strategy** lesson, students learn how to solve problems by using a formula.

Lesson	Lesson Objectives	NCTM Standards	State/Local Objectives
8-1	Find square roots of perfect squares.	1–7, 12	
8-2A	Use models to estimate square roots.	1–5, 7, 8	
8-2	Estimate square roots.	1–5, 7, 8, 12	
8-3	Identify and classify numbers in the real number system.	1–4, 6, 7, 9	
8-4	Solve problems by using a formula.	1–4, 7–9	
8-5A	Explore the relationships in a right triangle.	1–5, 7, 8, 12, 13	
8-5	Use the Pythagorean Theorem.	1–5, 7–9, 12, 13	
8-6	Solve problems using the Pythagorean Theorem.	1–5, 7, 8, 12, 13	
8-6B	Use the Pythagorean Theorem to graph irrational numbers on a number line.	1–5, 7, 12, 13	
8-7	Find the distance between points in the coordinate plane.	1–5, 7, 12, 13	
8-8	Find missing measures in 30°–60° right triangles and 45°–45° right triangles.	1–5, 7–9, 12, 13	

Organizing the Chapter

LESSON PLANNING GUIDE

A complete, 1-page lesson plan is provided for each lesson in the Lesson Plans Masters Booklet.

Lesson	Materials/ Manipulatives	Extra Practice (Student Edition)	Study Guide	Practice	Enrichment	Evaluation	Technology	Lab Manual	Multicultural Activities	Application and Interdisciplinary Activities	Transparencies	Group Activity Cards
8-1	calculator	p. 601	p. 67	p. 67	p. 67				p. 8	p. 8	8-1	8-1
8-2A	tiles or base-10 blocks							p. 61				
8-2		p. 602	p. 68	p. 68	p. 68		p. 8			p. 22	8-2	8-2
8-3	calculator	p. 602	p. 69	p. 69	p. 69						8-3	8-3
8-4			p. 70	p. 70	p. 70	Quiz A, p. 70					8-4	8-4
8-5A	geoboard, rubber bands							p. 62				
8-5		p. 602	p. 71	p. 71	p. 71						8-5	8-5
8-6			p. 72	p. 72	p. 72		p. 22				8-6	8-6
8-6B	compass							p. 63				
8-7	graph paper	p. 603	p. 73	p. 73	p. 73						8-7	8-7
8-8	compass, inch ruler, protractor, scissors	p. 603	p. 74	p. 74	p. 74	Quiz B, p. 70					8-8	8-8
Study Guide and Review						Multiple Choice Test, Forms 1A and 1B, pp. 64–67 Free Response Test, Forms 2A and 2B, pp. 68–69 Cumulative Review, p. 71 (free response) Cumulative Test, p. 72 (multiple choice)						
Test												

Pacing Guide: Option I (Chapters 1–12) - 13 days; Option II (Chapters 1–13) - 12 days; Option III (Chapters 1–14) - 11 days
You may wish to refer to the complete **Course Planning Guides** on page T25.

OTHER CHAPTER RESOURCES

Student Edition
Chapter Opener, pp. 298–299
Save Planet Earth, p. 302
Mid-Chapter Review, p. 312
Portfolio Suggestions, pp. 322, 331

 Manipulatives
Overhead Manipulative Resources
Middle School Mathematics Manipulative Kit

 Software/Technology
Interactive Mathematics Tools (Macintosh)
Test and Review Generator (IBM, Apple, Macintosh)
Teacher's Guide for Software Resources

Other Supplements
Transparency 8–0
Performance Assessment, pp. 15–16
Glencoe Mathematics Professional Series
Lesson Plans, pp. 85–95

INTERDISCIPLINARY BULLETIN BOARD

Seismology Connection

Objective   Calculate tsunami speeds.

How To Use It   Have students research and display data on tsunamis and the depths of at least five points on the ocean floor. Have them use the formula given in the bulletin board to calculate the speed of a tsunami unleashed at each of the five points. You may wish to have students model tsunami action in a container of water.

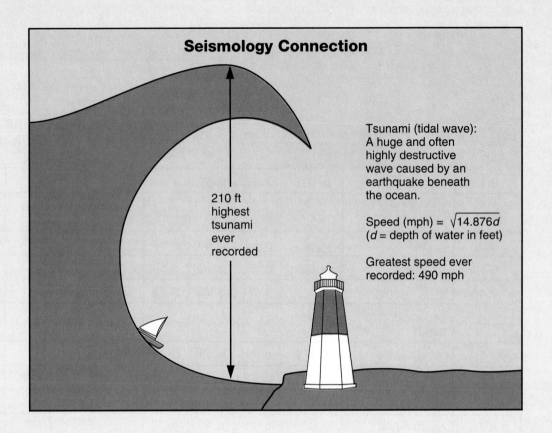

Seismology Connection

210 ft highest tsunami ever recorded

Tsunami (tidal wave): A huge and often highly destructive wave caused by an earthquake beneath the ocean.

Speed (mph) = $\sqrt{14.876d}$
(d = depth of water in feet)

Greatest speed ever recorded: 490 mph

APPLICATIONS AND CONNECTIONS

Applications	Lesson	Example	Exercise
Gardening	8-1		27
Physics	8-2	2	
Traffic Safety	8-2		22
Physics	8-2		23
Physics	8-3		38
Baseball	8-5	3	
Sports	8-5		31
Home Maintenance	8-6	2	
Skateboarding	8-6		13
Hiking	8-6		14
Landscaping	8-6		15
Construction	8-6		16
Map Making	8-7		21
Construction	8-8		17
Manufacturing	8-8		18
Connections			
Geometry	8-1	3	21
Algebra	8-3		39
Geometry	8-5		30, 33
Geometry	8-6	1	
Number Theory	8-6	3	
Computer	8-6		18
Geometry	8-7		19

TEAM ACTIVITIES

Multicultural Experiences

Outside Field Trips   Take an excursion through the business section of your town. Have students identify and list any right triangles they find in buildings and on signs.

Visit a manufacturing plant to learn how formulas are used in the design and manufacture of the company's products.

In-Class Speakers   Invite an architect or structural engineer to discuss the use of right triangles in building and bridge design.

A nursery operator can explain formulas used to create fertilizers, herbicides, and pesticides.

SUPPLEMENTARY BLACKLINE MASTER BOOKLETS

Some of the blackline masters for enhancing this chapter are shown below.

Application and Interdisciplinary Activity Masters, pp. 8, 22

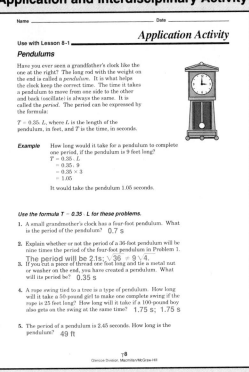

Name _____ Date _____

Application Activity

Use with Lesson 8-1

Pendulums

Have you ever seen a grandfather's clock like the one at the right? The long rod with the weight on the end is called a *pendulum*. It is what helps the clock keep the correct time. The time it takes a pendulum to move from one side to the other and back (oscillate) is always the same. It is called the *period*. The period can be expressed by the formula:

$T = 0.35 \cdot L$, where L is the length of the pendulum, in feet, and T is the time, in seconds.

Example How long would it take for a pendulum to complete one period, if the pendulum is 9 feet long?
$T = 0.35 \cdot L$
$= 0.35 \cdot 9$
$= 0.35 \times 3$
$= 1.05$

It would take the pendulum 1.05 seconds.

Use the formula $T = 0.35 \cdot L$ for these problems.

1. A small grandmother's clock has a four-foot pendulum. What is the period of the pendulum? **0.7 s**

2. Explain whether or not the period of a 36-foot pendulum will be nine times the period of the four-foot pendulum in Problem 1.
The period will be 2.1s; $\sqrt{36} \neq 9\sqrt{4}$.

3. If you cut a piece of thread one foot long and tie a metal nut or washer on the end, you have created a pendulum. What will its period be? **0.35 s**

4. A rope swing tied to a tree is a type of pendulum. How long will it take a 50-pound girl to make one complete swing if the rope is 25 feet long? How long will it take if a 100-pound boy also gets on the swing at the same time? **1.75 s; 1.75 s**

5. The period of a pendulum is 2.45 seconds. How long is the pendulum? **49 ft**

T8
Glencoe Division, Macmillan/McGraw-Hill

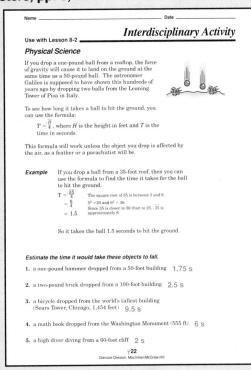

Name _____ Date _____

Interdisciplinary Activity

Use with Lesson 8-2

Physical Science

If you drop a one-pound ball from a rooftop, the force of gravity will cause it to land on the ground at the same time as a 50-pound ball. The astronomer Galileo is supposed to have shown this hundreds of years ago by dropping two balls from the Leaning Tower of Pisa in Italy.

To see how long it takes a ball to hit the ground, you can use the formula:

$T = \dfrac{\sqrt{H}}{4}$, where H is the height in feet and T is the time in seconds.

This formula will work unless the object you drop is affected by the air, as a feather or a parachutist will be.

Example If you drop a ball from a 35-foot roof, then you can use the formula to find the time it takes for the ball to hit the ground.

$T = \dfrac{\sqrt{35}}{4}$ The square root of 35 is between 5 and 6.
$= \dfrac{6}{4}$ $5^2 = 25$ and $6^2 = 36$.
$= 1.5$ Since 35 is closer to 36 than to 25, $\sqrt{35}$ is approximately 6.

So it takes the ball 1.5 seconds to hit the ground.

Estimate the time it would take these objects to fall.

1. a one-pound hammer dropped from a 50-foot building **1.75 s**

2. a two-pound brick dropped from a 100-foot building **2.5 s**

3. a bicycle dropped from the world's tallest building (Sears Tower, Chicago, 1,454 feet) **9.5 s**

4. a math book dropped from the Washington Monument (555 ft) **6 s**

5. a high diver diving from a 60-foot cliff **2 s**

T22
Glencoe Division, Macmillan/McGraw-Hill

Multicultural Activity Masters, p. 8

Name _____ Date _____

Multicultural Activity

Use with Lesson 8-1

Olga Taussky-Todd

Olga Taussky-Todd (1906–) has had a rich and varied career as a research mathematician, professor of mathematics, and author and editor of mathematical texts. Born in eastern Europe, in the region that today is Czechoslovakia, she has lived and worked in Austria, Germany, England, and the United States. For ten years, she served as the consultant in mathematics for the National Bureau of Standards in Washington, D.C. In 1957, she became the first woman appointed to the mathematics department of the California Institute of Technology.

Dr. Taussky-Todd has made contributions in many areas of mathematics and physics, but it is number theory that she calls her "dream subject." She is particularly interested in sums of square numbers. The exercises that follow will give you a chance to explore some simple sums of square numbers.

1. Every positive integer either is a square or can be expressed as a sum of square numbers.

$25 = 5^2$ $35 = 1^2 + 3^2 + 3^2 + 4^2$

Express the integers from 1 to 24 as a square or a sum of squares. *Use the least number of addends possible.*

$1 = 1^2$ $9 = 3^2$ $17 = 1^2 + 4^2$

$2 = 1^2 + 1^2$ $10 = 1^2 + 3^2$ $18 = 3^2 + 3^2$

$3 = 1^2 + 1^2 + 1^2$ $11 = 1^2 + 1^2 + 3^2$ $19 = 1^2 + 3^2 + 3^2$

$4 = 2^2$ $12 = 2^2 + 2^2 + 2^2$ $20 = 2^2 + 4^2$

$5 = 1^2 + 2^2$ $13 = 2^2 + 3^2$ $21 = 1^2 + 2^2 + 4^2$

$6 = 1^2 + 1^2 + 2^2$ $14 = 1^2 + 2^2 + 3^2$ $22 = 2^2 + 3^2 + 3^2$

$7 = 1^2 + 1^2 + 1^2 + 2^2$ $15 = 1^2 + 1^2 + 2^2 + 3^2$ $23 = 1^2 + 2^2 + 3^2 + 3^2$

$8 = 2^2 + 2^2$ $16 = 4^2$ $24 = 2^2 + 2^2 + 4^2$

2. Refer to your answers to Exercise 1. What is the greatest number of addends among all your sums? **4**

T8
Glencoe Division, Macmillan/McGraw-Hill

Technology Masters, p. 22

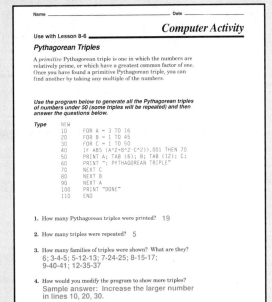

Name _____ Date _____

Computer Activity

Use with Lesson 8-6

Pythagorean Triples

A *primitive* Pythagorean triple is one in which the numbers are relatively prime, or which have a greatest common factor of one. Once you have found a primitive Pythagorean triple, you can find another by taking any multiple of the numbers.

Use the program below to generate all the Pythagorean triples of numbers under 50 (some triples will be repeated) and then answer the questions below.

```
Type   NEW
       10   FOR A = 3 TO 16
       20   FOR B = 1 TO 45
       30   FOR C = 1 TO 50
       40   IF ABS (A^2+B^2-C^2)>.001 THEN 70
       50   PRINT A; TAB (6); B; TAB (12); C;
       60   PRINT ": PYTHAGOREAN TRIPLE"
       70   NEXT C
       80   NEXT B
       90   NEXT A
       100  PRINT "DONE"
       110  END
```

1. How many Pythagorean triples were printed? **19**

2. How many triples were repeated? **5**

3. How many families of triples were shown? What are they?
6; 3-4-5; 5-12-13; 7-24-25; 8-15-17; 9-40-41; 12-35-37

4. How would you modify the program to show more triples?
Sample answer: Increase the larger number in lines 10, 20, 30.

T22
Glencoe Division, Macmillan/McGraw-Hill

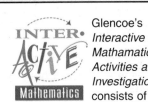

This two-page introduction to the chapter provides a visual, relevant way to engage students in the mathematics of the chapter. Questions are included that help students see the need to learn the mathematics in the chapter. Data in charts and graphs provide statistical information that students can analyze and interpret at this point as well as later in the chapter. The Chapter Project provides an activity that applies the mathematics of the chapter.

MAKING MATHEMATICS RELEVANT

Spotlight on Animals

Each of the following professions is concerned with animals. Ask students to describe how mathematics might be used in each profession. Sample answers are given.

- **veterinarian** determining medicine dosages
- **wildlife manager** estimating wildlife population sizes
- **wildlife biologist** analyzing research data
- **farmer** calculating nutritional requirements

Ask students to name other professions that deal with animals and have them describe how each might incorporate mathematics.

Using the Timeline

Ask the following questions.

- *California grizzlies became extinct 53 years after Yellowstone National Park was created. What year did the California grizzly become extinct?* 1925
- *Texas red wolves became extinct 18 years before George Bush was elected president. What year did the Texas red wolf become extinct?* 1970

Chapter

8

Real Numbers

Spotlight on Animals

Have You Ever Wondered...

- What animal can move the quickest?
- How long different animals live?

Length of Life for Animals

Mammals (Average life span in years)		Birds (Maximum life span in years)	
Chimpanzee	40-50	Blue jay	4
Elephant	60	Canada goose	32
Grizzly Bear	20	Canary	24
Horse	20-30	Cardinal	22
Lion	20-25	Ostrich (African)	50
Mouse	1-2	Penguin (king)	26
Squirrel	9	Raven	69
Tiger	11	Robin	12

Fish (Maximum life span in years)		Reptiles and amphibians (Maximum life span in years)	
Electric Eel	11	Alligator	56
Flounder	10	Bullfrog	15
Goldfish	25	Crocodile	13
Perch	11	Garter snake	6
Sea horse	4	Gila monster	20
Sturgeon	50	Rattlesnake	18
Trout (rainbow)	4	Turtle (box)	123

1872   *1916*   *1935*

1870   **1890**   **1910**   **1930**

Game of Monopoly designed

Chance

First National Park declared at Yellowstone

National Park System Formed

298

"Have You Ever Wondered?" Answers

- As a class, birds are the fastest. Of those listed, the golden eagle is the fastest.
- The average life span of various animals can be read from the chart.

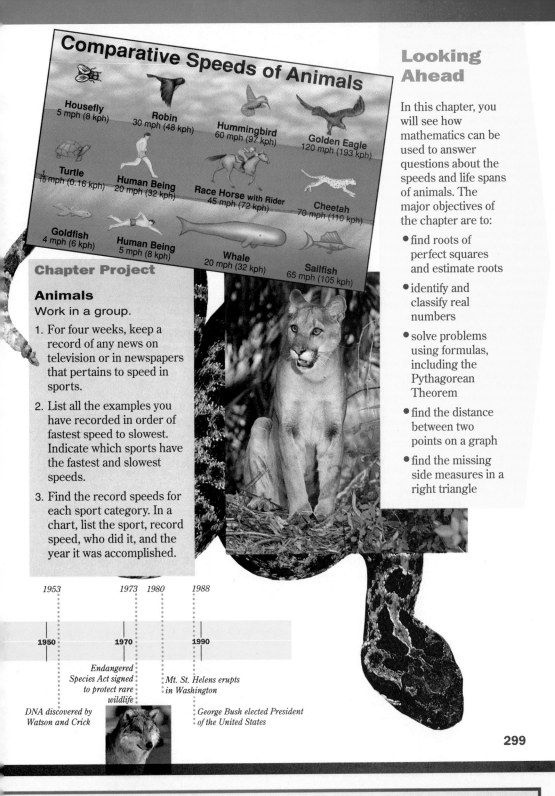

Comparative Speeds of Animals

Housefly 5 mph (8 kph)

Robin 30 mph (48 kph)

Hummingbird 60 mph (97 kph)

Golden Eagle 120 mph (193 kph)

Turtle $\frac{1}{10}$ mph (0.16 kph)

Human Being 20 mph (32 kph)

Race Horse with Rider 45 mph (72 kph)

Cheetah 70 mph (110 kph)

Goldfish 4 mph (6 kph)

Human Being 5 mph (8 kph)

Whale 20 mph (32 kph)

Sailfish 65 mph (105 kph)

Chapter Project

Animals
Work in a group.

1. For four weeks, keep a record of any news on television or in newspapers that pertains to speed in sports.

2. List all the examples you have recorded in order of fastest speed to slowest. Indicate which sports have the fastest and slowest speeds.

3. Find the record speeds for each sport category. In a chart, list the sport, record speed, who did it, and the year it was accomplished.

1953 *1973* *1980* *1988*

1950 **1970** **1990**

Endangered Species Act signed to protect rare wildlife

Mt. St. Helens erupts in Washington

DNA discovered by Watson and Crick

George Bush elected President of the United States

Looking Ahead

In this chapter, you will see how mathematics can be used to answer questions about the speeds and life spans of animals. The major objectives of the chapter are to:

- find roots of perfect squares and estimate roots

- identify and classify real numbers

- solve problems using formulas, including the Pythagorean Theorem

- find the distance between two points on a graph

- find the missing side measures in a right triangle

DATA ANALYSIS
Have students study the life-span and comparative-speed tables. Ask the following questions.

- *How do the following animals rank in speed from fastest to slowest: fastest water animal, fastest bird, fastest land animal?* fastest bird, fastest land animal, fastest water animal

- *Which animals seem to support the theory that a slow pace and low stress contribute to longevity?* turtles, alligators, and elephants

Data Search
A question related to these data is provided in Lesson 8-7, page 327, Exercise 22.

CHAPTER PROJECT
Encourage students to be attuned to sports like swimming, skating, and skiing, where speed is important. Record speeds and other speeds, like that of a baseball, can be found in almanacs and encyclopedias. Encourage students to be creative when displaying their data.

Allow five weeks to complete the project.

Chapter Opener Transparency

Transparency 8-0 is available in the Transparency Package. It provides another full-color, motivating activity that you can use to capture students' interest.

NCTM Standards: 1–7, 12

Lesson Resources
• Study Guide Master 8-1
• Practice Master 8-1
• Enrichment Master 8-1
• Multicultural Activity, p. 8
• Application Master, p. 8
• Group Activity Card 8-1

Transparency 8-1 contains the 5-Minute Check and a teaching aid for this lesson.

5-Minute Check
(Over Chapter 7)

Solve each equation. Write each solution in simplest form.

1. $e = \frac{1}{2} + \frac{5}{6}$ $1\frac{1}{3}$

2. $\left(-1\frac{1}{3}\right)\left(1\frac{1}{8}\right) = p$ $-1\frac{1}{2}$

3. State whether the sequence 18, 25, 32, 39, . . . is arithmetic, geometric, or neither. Then write the next three terms.   Arith.; 46, 53, 60

4. The base of a triangle is 12 inches long and the height is 3 inches. Find the area.   18 in²

1 FOCUS

Motivating the Lesson

Situational Problem   Ask students to find the length of a side of a square garden if the area of the garden is 400 square feet.

2 TEACH

Using Calculators   After reading the opening paragraph, have students enter this key sequence on their calculators.

776 $\boxed{x^2}$ $\boxed{\sqrt{x}}$

Point out that since the answer 776, is the same as the number entered, the operations of squaring a number and taking the square root of a number are inverse operations.

8-1 Square Roots

Objective
Find square roots of perfect squares.

Words to Learn
perfect square
square root
radical sign
principal square root

The Great Pyramid at Giza, built around 2600 B.C., is one of the "Seven Wonders of the Ancient World." It measures 776 feet on each side of the square base. The area covered by the base of the Great Pyramid can be found by using the formula $A = s^2$, where s feet is the length of the side of the base.

776 $\boxed{x^2}$ 602176

The area of the base is 602,176 square feet.

Products such as 602,176 that are squares of rational numbers are called **perfect squares.** Some other perfect squares are 25, 0.04, and $\frac{4}{9}$.

DID YOU KNOW

More than 2 million stone blocks, each weighing between 2 tons and 150 tons, were used in the construction of the Great Pyramid of Gizeh.

Notice the relationship that exists between the area of the square shown at the right and the length of its side. We say that 5 is a **square root** of 25, because $5^2 = 25$.

It is also true that $(-5)^2 = 25$. This suggests that another square root of 25 is -5.

$5^2 = 25$

Square Root	If $x^2 = y$, then x is a square root of y.

The symbol $\sqrt{}$, called a **radical sign,** is used to indicate a nonnegative, or **principal,** square root.

$\sqrt{25} = 5$ *principal square root*
$-\sqrt{25} = -5$ *negative square root*

Example 1

Find $\sqrt{144}$.
The symbol $\sqrt{144}$ indicates the principal square root.
Since $12^2 = 144$, $\sqrt{144} = 12$.

300   **Chapter 8**   Real Numbers

OPTIONS

Reteaching Activity

Using Charts   Prepare work sheets like the one below to show that squaring and finding the square root are inverse operations.

Positive Number	Square	Square Root
8	$8^2 = 64$	$\sqrt{64} = 8$
3		

Study Guide Masters, p. 67

Name _____   Date _____

Study Guide Worksheet 8-1

Square Roots

The area of a square is equal to the square of the length of its side. For the square shown, $A = 4^2 = 16$.

The length of a side of a square is equal to the square root of the area. For the square shown, 4 is the square root of 16.

If $x^2 = y$, then x is a square root of y. The symbol $\sqrt{}$ is called a radical sign. Read $\sqrt{16}$ as "the square root of 16."

Examples x $x^2 = y$ $\sqrt{y} = x$

    4        $4 \times 4 = 4^2 = 16$ $\sqrt{16} = 4$ principal square root
    -4 $-4 \times -4 = (-4)^2 = 16$ $-\sqrt{16} = -4$ negative square root
    1.5 $1.5^2 = 2.25$

Example 2

Find $-\sqrt{2.25}$.

Use your calculator.   2.25 $\boxed{\sqrt{x}}$ 1.5

The symbol $-\sqrt{}$ indicates the negative square root.

Since $1.5^2 = 2.25$, $-\sqrt{2.25} = -1.5$.

Example 3   *Connection*

Geometry   The area of a square is 256 square inches. Find its perimeter.

First find the length of each side.

256 $\boxed{\sqrt{x}}$ 16

The length of each side is 16 inches.

256 square inches

$P = 4s$
$P = 4 \cdot 16$ *Replace s with 16.*
$P = 64$ The perimeter is 64 inches.

LOOKBACK

You can review area and perimeter of squares on page 75.

Checking for Understanding

Communicating Mathematics

2. $\sqrt{100}$

Read and study the lesson to answer each question.

1. **Tell** why 36 is a perfect square. It is the square of 6.

2. **Write** the symbol for the principal square root of 100.

3. **Draw** and label a square that has an area of 16 square centimeters. See Solutions Manual.

Guided Practice

Find each square root.

4. $\sqrt{49}$ 7   5. $\sqrt{81}$ 9   6. $\sqrt{121}$ 11   7. $-\sqrt{64}$ -8

Exercises

Independent Practice

14. -17
18. -1.7

Find each square root.

8. $\sqrt{25}$ 5   9. $\sqrt{400}$ 20   10. $\sqrt{225}$ 15   11. $-\sqrt{9}$ -3

12. $\sqrt{196}$ 14   13. $\sqrt{625}$ 25   14. $-\sqrt{289}$ 15. $-\sqrt{100}$ -10

16. $\sqrt{\dfrac{4}{9}}$ $\dfrac{2}{3}$ 17. $\sqrt{0.16}$ 0.4   18. $-\sqrt{2.89}$ 19. $\sqrt{\dfrac{64}{100}}$ $\dfrac{8}{10}$

20. 15, -15; 15 is the principal square root because it is nonnegative.

20. Find two square roots of 225. Explain which is the principal square root.

21. **Geometry**   If the area of a square is 1.69 square meters, what is the length of its side? 1.3 meters

---

Have students explain the difference between the square of 9 and the square root of 9.
square of 9: 9×9 or 81; square root of 9: 3, the number which when squared equals 9

3 PRACTICE/APPLY

Assignment Guide
Maximum: 8–28
Minimum: 9–21 odd, 22–27

For **Extra Practice,** see p. 601.

Alternate Assessment

Modeling Have students use square tiles to construct squares and then to use the lengths of their sides to find the square roots of the areas.

Additional Answer
23.

Enrichment Masters, p. 67

Name _____ Date _____

Enrichment Worksheet 8-1

Properties of the Geometric Mean

The square root of the product of two numbers is called their *geometric mean.*

Numbers	Geometric Mean
a and c	$b = \sqrt{ac}$
12 and 48	$\sqrt{12 \cdot 48} = \sqrt{576} = 24$

The geometric mean has many interesting properties. For example, two numbers and their geometric mean satisfy the proportion at the right. $\dfrac{a}{b} = \dfrac{b}{c}$

Find the geometric mean, b, for each pair of numbers.

1. $a = 2$ and $c = 8$
$b = $ 4

2. $a = 4$ and $c = 9$
$b = $ 6

3. $a = 9$ and $c = 16$
$b = $ 12

4. $a = 16$ and $c = 4$
$b = $ 8

5. $a = 16$ and $c = 36$
$b = $ 24

6. $a = 12$ and $c = 3$
$b = $ 6

7. $a = 18$ and $c = 8$
$b = $ 12

8. $a = 2$ and $c = 18$
$b = $ 6

9. $a = 27$ and $c = 12$
$b = $ 18

Solve each problem.

10. For each triple of numbers in problems 1–9, draw a triangle like the one shown at the right. What property is shown?
All the triangles are right.

11. Now make this drawing for each triple of numbers. The semicircle has a diameter equal to the sum of a and c. What property do you find?
Segment with length b exactly meets the semicircle.

T67
Glencoe Division, Macmillan/McGraw-Hill

Mixed Review
22. How many yards are in 270 inches? *(Lesson 1-7)* **7.5 yards**

23. Graph the points $C(2, 5)$, $H(-3, 3)$, $E(4, 1)$, and $G(-1, -2)$ on the same coordinate plane. *(Lesson 3-10)* **See margin.**

24. Find the GCF of 12 and 63. *(Lesson 6-4)* **3**

25. Solve $3x - 5 = -6$. *(Lesson 7-11)* $-\dfrac{1}{3}$

Problem Solving and Applications

26. Critical Thinking Is the product of two perfect squares always a perfect square? Explain why or why not. **Yes; product of square roots of each perfect square is square root of new perfect square.**

27. Gardening The area of a square garden is 289 square feet. How much will it cost to fence the garden if fencing costs $0.35 per foot? **$23.80**

28. Journal Entry In your own words, write a definition of square root. **See students' work.**

Save Planet Earth

Disposable Batteries Do you have a game that requires batteries? Did you know that household batteries contain heavy metals such as mercury and cadmium? When these batteries are thrown out with the trash and taken to landfills, they break apart and release the metals into the soil. When batteries are incinerated, the toxic substances are released into the air.

Americans use 2 billion disposable batteries every year. The annual use of mercury in batteries exceeds the federal limits for trash by 400%. Prolonged exposure to mercury can make people sick and affect their behavior.

How You Can Help

- Use rechargeable batteries. Even though they contain cadmium, they last longer and do not require frequent replacement.
- If possible, recycle alkaline batteries.

302 Chapter 8 Real Numbers

OPTIONS

Extending the Lesson

Save Planet Earth Ask students to make a list of all the games and/or electronic equipment they use regularly. Have them estimate the number of batteries they use in one month. Ask them what alternatives they can use to limit the number of batteries used in one year.

Cooperative Learning Activity

Once Around 8-1

Number of players: 4
Materials: Counters, number cube

◆ Copy onto a large sheet of paper (or several smaller sheets taped together) the game board shown at the right. Make sure that a counter will fit in each box.

➤ Each group member places a counter on the "Start" square. In turn, each group member rolls a number cube and moves his or her counter the number of spaces indicated. On a separate sheet of paper write the value of the squares you land on. Do not toss the number cube after you have passed the "Start" square for a second time. Find the sum of the values you wrote. The winner is the group member with the greatest sum. Play several rounds.

Glencoe Mathematics: Applications and Connections, Course 3

8-2A Estimating Square Roots

A Preview of Lesson 8-2

Objective
Use models to estimate square roots.

Materials
tiles or
base-10 blocks

Suppose you have 50 tiles and want to arrange them into a square. Can you do it? No, a square cannot be built with 50 tiles. This suggests that 50 is not a perfect square.

In this Lab, you will estimate the square root of numbers that are not perfect squares.

Try this!

Work with a partner.

● Arrange 50 tiles into the largest square possible.

The square has 49 tiles, with one left over.

● Add tiles until you have the next larger square.

You need to add 14 tiles. This square has 64 tiles.

What do you think?

1. What is the square root of 49? 7
2. What is the square root of 64? 8
3. Between what two whole numbers is the square root of 50? 7 and 8
4. Is $\sqrt{50}$ closer to 7 or 8? Explain your reasoning.
   7; 50 is closer to 49 than 64.

Applications

For each given number, arrange tiles or base-10 blocks into the largest square possible. Then add tiles until you have the next larger square. To the nearest whole number, estimate the square root of each number.

5. 20 4   6. 76 9   7. 133 12
8. 150 12   9. 200 14   10. 2 1

Mathematics Lab 8-2A Estimating Square Roots **303**

NCTM Standards: 1–5, 7, 8

Management Tips

For Students Appoint materials managers to pass out and collect tiles or base-10 blocks.

For the Overhead Projector
Overhead Manipulative Resources provides appropriate materials for teacher or student demonstration of the activities in this Mathematics Lab.

1 FOCUS

Introducing the Lab

Ask students to solve this riddle: *What kind of trees grow best in the math lab?* trees with square roots

2 TEACH

Using Logical Reasoning Ask students to explain how they know that 50 tiles cannot be arranged into a square. There is no number which, when squared, equals 50.

3 PRACTICE/APPLY

Using Logical Thinking Ask students to find the least whole number whose square root is closer to 8 than to 7. 57

Close

Have students explain how they would use tiles to estimate $\sqrt{10}$.

OPTIONS

Lab Manual You may wish to make copies of the blackline master on p. 61 of the *Lab Manual* for students to use as a recording sheet.

Lab Manual, p. 61

Name _____ Date _____

Mathematics Lab Worksheet

Use with page 307

Estimating Square Roots

What do you think?

1. The square root of 49 is ___7___ 2. The square root of 64 is ___8___
3. The square root of 50 is between ___7 and 8___
4. ___50 is closer to 7 because 50 is closer to 49 than to 64.___

Applications

5. ___4___   6. ___9___   7. ___12___

NCTM Standards: 1–5, 7, 8, 12

Lesson Resources
- Study Guide Master 8-2
- Practice Master 8-2
- Enrichment Master 8-2
- Technology Master, p. 8
- Interdisciplinary Master, p. 22
- Group Activity Card 8-2

 Transparency 8-2 contains the 5-Minute Check and a teaching aid for this lesson.

🕐 5-Minute Check
(Over Lesson 8-1)

Find each square root.

1. $\sqrt{49}$ 7 **2.** $-\sqrt{16}$ -4

3. $\sqrt{\frac{25}{64}}$ $\frac{5}{8}$ **4.** $\sqrt{0.09}$ 0.3

5. The area of a square is 81 square inches. Find the length of a side.
9 in.

Practice Masters, p. 68

Name _____ Date _____

Practice Worksheet 8-2

Estimating Square Roots

Estimate to the nearest whole number.

1. $\sqrt{84}$ 9   2. $\sqrt{10}$ 3   3. $\sqrt{69}$ 8

4. $\sqrt{99}$ 10   5. $\sqrt{120}$ 11   6. $\sqrt{78}$ 9

7. $\sqrt{250}$ 16   8. $\sqrt{444}$ 21   9. $\sqrt{51}$ 7

10. $\sqrt{78}$ 9   11. $\sqrt{300}$ 17   12. $\sqrt{123}$ 11

13. $\sqrt{199}$ 14   14. $\sqrt{171}$ 13   15. $\sqrt{286}$ 17

16. $\sqrt{730}$ 27   17. $\sqrt{17.8}$ 4   18. $\sqrt{630}$ 25

19. $\sqrt{1,230}$ 35   20. $\sqrt{8.42}$ 3   21. $\sqrt{0.09}$ 0

22. $\sqrt{80.95}$ 9   23. $\sqrt{1.05}$ 1   24. $\sqrt{47.25}$ 7

T68
Glencoe Division, Macmillan/McGraw-Hill

304

8-2 Estimating Square Roots

Objective
Estimate square roots.

Have you ever had one of those days when everything went your way? You aced your geography test, got the last chocolate milk at lunch, and the experiment in science lab worked! More often than not, our days are not perfect and we have to make adjustments.

Similarly, most numbers are not perfect squares, and we have to approximate their square roots. For example, the number 160 is not a perfect square. However, we know that 160 is between two perfect squares, 144 and 169. So the square root of 160 is between 12 and 13.

$$144 < 160 < 169$$
$$12^2 < 160 < 13^2$$
$$12 < \sqrt{160} < 13$$

Since 160 is closer to 169 than 144, the best whole number estimate for the square root of 160 is 13.

Example 1

Estimate $\sqrt{90}$.

$81 < 90 < 100$ *81 and 100 are perfect squares.*

$9^2 < 90 < 10^2$

$9 < \sqrt{90} < 10$ Since 90 is closer to 81 than to 100, the best whole number estimate for $\sqrt{90}$ is 9.

Example 2 *Problem Solving*

Physics You can estimate the distance you can see to the horizon by using the formula $d = 1.22 \times \sqrt{h}$. In the formula d represents the distance you can see, in miles, and h represents the height your eyes are from the ground, in feet. Suppose your eyes are 5 feet from the ground. About how far can you see to the horizon?

$d = 1.22 \times \sqrt{5}$ *Replace h with 5.*

$\approx 1.22 \times 2$ *$\sqrt{5}$ is between 2 and 3.*

≈ 2.44

If your eyes are 5 feet from the ground, you can see about 2.4 miles to the horizon.

304 Chapter 8 Real Numbers

OPTIONS

Reteaching Activity

Using Communication Name a whole number. Have students write the nearest perfect squares greater than and less than the number and circle the closer number. Have them write the square root of the circled number, their estimate of the square root of the given number.

Example: (36) 39 49 6

Study Guide Masters, p. 68

Name _____ Date _____

Study Guide Worksheet 8-2

Estimating Square Roots

Many numbers are not perfect squares. You can estimate square roots for these numbers.

Example 1   Estimate $\sqrt{200}$.

$14^2 = 196$ 196 is a perfect square.
$15^2 = 225$ 225 is a perfect square.

$196 < 200 < 225$ 200 is between 196 and 225.
$14^2 < 200 < 15^2$
$14 < \sqrt{200} < 15$ The square root of 200 is between 14 and 15.

Since 200 is closer to 196 than to 225, the best whole-number estimate for $\sqrt{200}$ is 14.

$\sqrt{200} \approx 14$ The square root of 200 is about 14.

Checking for Understanding

Communicating Mathematics

Read and study the lesson to answer each question.

1. **Tell** how the drawing at the right can be used to estimate $\sqrt{12}$. $\sqrt{12}$ is between 3 and 4.

2. **Draw** a figure that can be used to explain why the square root of 75 is between 8 and 9. See Solutions Manual.

Guided Practice

Estimate to the nearest whole number.

3. $\sqrt{50}$ 7   4. $\sqrt{135}$ 12   5. $\sqrt{29}$ 5   6. $\sqrt{11}$ 3

Exercises

Independent Practice

Estimate to the nearest whole number.

7. $\sqrt{23}$ 5   8. $\sqrt{44}$ 7   9. $\sqrt{56}$ 7   10. $\sqrt{17.5}$ 4

11. $\sqrt{47}$ 7   12. $\sqrt{113}$ 11   13. $\sqrt{175}$ 13   14. $\sqrt{200}$ 14

15. $\sqrt{408}$ 20   16. $\sqrt{17.25}$ 4   17. $\sqrt{957}$ 31   18. $\sqrt{30.8}$ 6

Mixed Review

19. Solve $s = 3.6 \div 0.6$. *(Lesson 2-4)* 6

20. Solve $4\frac{2}{3} - 6\frac{1}{4} = m$. *(Lesson 7-2)* $-1\frac{7}{12}$

21. Find the principal square root of 900. *(Lesson 8-1)* 30

Problem Solving and Applications

22. **Traffic Safety**   Police officers can estimate how fast a car was going by measuring the length of its skid marks. The formula $s = \sqrt{24d}$ can be used to estimate the speed on a dry, concrete road. In the formula, s is the speed in miles per hour, and d is the distance in feet the car skidded after its brakes were applied. What was the approximate speed of a car that left skid marks for 20 feet?
approximately 22 miles per hour

23. **Physics**   Suppose you are in a hot air balloon that is flying at an altitude of 900 feet. About how far can you see to the horizon? Use the formula in Example 2 on page 304.
about 36.6 miles

24. **Critical Thinking**   A square has an area of 20 square units. Explain why the length of its side is between 4.4 and 4.5 units. $(4.4)^2 = 19.36$ and $(4.5)^2 = 20.25$; $19.36 < 20 < 20.25$; so $4.4 < \sqrt{20} < 4.5$.

Lesson 8-2   Estimating Square Roots   **305**

Extending the Lesson

Using Cooperative Groups   Show students how to find the *cube root* of a number.
cube root of 8: $\sqrt[3]{8} = 2$
    because $2 \cdot 2 \cdot 2 = 8$
cube root of -8: $\sqrt[3]{-8} = -2$
    because $(-2)(-2)(-2) = -8$
Have students work in small groups to find these cube roots.

1. $\sqrt[3]{27}$ 3   2. $\sqrt[3]{125}$ 5
3. $\sqrt[3]{-1,000}$ -10 4. $\sqrt[3]{-1}$ -1

Cooperative Learning Activity

Step by Step 8-2

Use groups of 2.
Materials: Calculator, index cards

✦   Copy onto cards the numbers shown on the back of this card, one per card. Shuffle the cards and place them face down in a pile.

➡   One partner selects a card. Then, working together, both partners obtain an estimate for the square root of this number using the following steps.

Step 1. Determine which two whole numbers the square root of the number falls between.
Step 2. Find the median of the two numbers you found in Step 1. The median gives you your first approximation for the square root of the number you selected.
Step 3. Divide the number on the card by the median you found in the previous step. Round the quotient to the nearest tenth. Find the median of this quotient and the median you found in the first step. This is your second approximation.
Step 4. Repeat Step 3 to obtain additional approximations. Stop when you get two approximations in a row that are the same rounded to the nearest tenth.
Step 5. Check the result with a calculator.
    Trade roles and repeat the activity. Continue in the same way as time allows.

Glencoe Mathematics: Applications and Connections, Course 3

305

NCTM Standards: 1–4, 6, 7, 9

Lesson Resources
- Study Guide Master 8-3
- Practice Master 8-3
- Enrichment Master 8-3
- Group Activity Card 8-3

Transparency 8-3 contains the 5-Minute Check and a teaching aid for this lesson.

🕐 5-Minute Check
(Over Lesson 8-2)

Estimate to the nearest whole number.

1. $\sqrt{52}$ 7
2. $\sqrt{13}$ 4
3. $-\sqrt{31}$ −6
4. $\sqrt{108}$ 10

5. The area of a square is 70 square meters. Estimate the length of a side to the nearest whole number.   8 m

1 FOCUS

Motivating the Lesson

Questioning   Ask students to give two examples for each of the following: (Sample answers are given.)

- whole number   7, 1
- integer   −5, 8
- rational number $\frac{7}{8}$, −5.82
- terminating decimal   0.641
- repeating decimal $0.\overline{81}$

2 TEACH

Using Calculators   To convince students that $\sqrt{2}$ is not exactly the number shown on their calculators, have them write the displayed number on paper and then multiply the displayed number by the number they wrote down. The result will be near but not equal to 2.

8-3 **The Real Number System**

Objective
Identify and classify numbers in the real number system.

Words to Learn
irrational number
real number

Swedish botanist Carolus Linnaeus (1707—1778) developed the system used today to classify every kind of living thing according to common characteristics. For example, a guinea pig is classified as a rodent, but it is also a mammal.

Kingdom						Animal
Phylum						Chordate
Class						Mammal
Order						Rodent
Family						Caviid
Genus						Cavia
Species						Porcellus
						Guinea Pig

LOOK BACK

You can review rational numbers on page 264.

(265)

In mathematics, we classify numbers that have common characteristics. So far in this text, we have classified numbers into the following sets.

Natural Numbers	{1, 2, 3, 4, …}
Whole Numbers	{0, 1, 2, 3, 4, …}
Integers	{…, -2, -1, 0, 1, 2, …}
Rational Numbers	{all numbers that can be expressed in the form $\frac{a}{b}$, where a and b are integers and $b \neq 0$}

Remember that terminating or repeating decimals are rational numbers since they can be expressed as fractions. Also, the square roots of perfect squares are rational numbers. For example, $\sqrt{0.09}$ is a rational number because $\sqrt{0.09} = 0.3$, a rational number.

We can summarize the classification of rational numbers in a Venn diagram.

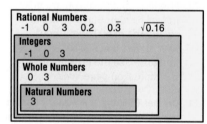

Rational Numbers
-1   0   3   0.2 $0.\overline{3}$ $\sqrt{0.16}$
   Integers
   -1   0   3
      Whole Numbers
      0   3
         Natural Numbers
         3

OPTIONS

Team Teaching

Ask the other teachers on your team to point out to students examples of classification systems in their disciplines. Suggestions for curriculum integration are:

Science: Linnaean classification

Social Studies: political units

Language: parts of speech

Numbers like $\sqrt{2}$ and $\sqrt{5}$ are the square roots of numbers that are *not* perfect squares. Notice what happens when you find these square roots with your calculator.

2 $\boxed{\sqrt{x}}$ 1.4142136 . . .   5 $\boxed{\sqrt{x}}$ 2.236068 . . .

The numbers continue forever without any pattern of repeating digits. These numbers are not rational numbers since they are not terminating or repeating decimals. Numbers like $\sqrt{2}$ and $\sqrt{5}$ are called **irrational numbers**.

Definition of Irrational Number	An irrational number is a number that cannot be expressed as $\frac{a}{b}$, where a and b are integers and b does not equal 0.

Examples

Determine whether each number is rational or irrational.

1 0.66666 . . .

This repeating number is a rational number since it can be expressed as $\frac{2}{3}$.

2 0.141141114 . . .

This decimal does not terminate and it does not repeat. It is an irrational number.

3 π

$\pi = 3.1415926 \ldots$ It is an irrational number.

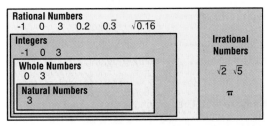

Real Numbers

Rational Numbers
-1   0   3   0.2 $0.\overline{3}$ $\sqrt{0.16}$

Integers
-1   0   3

Whole Numbers
0   3

Natural Numbers
3

Irrational Numbers
$\sqrt{2}$ $\sqrt{5}$
π

You have graphed rational numbers on a number line. But if you graphed all of the rational numbers, you would still have some "holes" in the number line. The irrational numbers "fill in" the number line. The set of rational numbers and the set of irrational numbers combine to form the set of **real numbers**.

The graph of all real numbers is the entire number line.

-4 -3 -2 -1 0 1 2 3 4 5

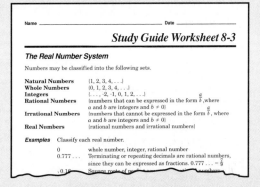

Have students give examples of rational and irrational numbers. Then have them compare and contrast the numbers.

3 PRACTICE/APPLY

Assignment Guide
Maximum: 16–41
Minimum: 17–31 odd, 33–40

For **Extra Practice,** see p. 602.

Alternate Assessment

Speaking   Name a real number. Have students state whether it is rational or irrational and explain why.

Additional Answers

1. The set of rational numbers combined with the set of irrational numbers

3.

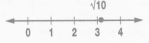

Practice Masters, p. 69

Name _____ Date _____

Practice Worksheet 8-3

The Real Number System

Name the set or sets of numbers to which each real number belongs.

1. 12
   rational, integer, whole, natural
2. $-\sqrt{25}$
   rational, integer
3. $\sqrt{13}$
   irrational

4. $\sqrt{0.36}$
   rational
5. 0.373773777 . . .
   irrational
6. 0.505050 . . .
   rational

7. 25.0
   rational, integer, whole, natural
8. $-\sqrt{40}$
   irrational
9. $\frac{3}{7}$
   rational

Find an approximation for each square root. Then graph the square root on the number line.

10. $\sqrt{8}$ 11. $\sqrt{35}$ 12. $\sqrt{71}$ 13. $\sqrt{18}$

14. $\sqrt{3}$ 15. $-\sqrt{3}$ 16. $\sqrt{5}$ 17. $-\sqrt{7}$

Solve each equation.

18. $a^2 = 196$ 19. $y^2 = 81$ 20. $c^2 = 150$
    14, -14   9, -9   ≈12.2, -12.2

21. $x^2 = 1.69$ 22. $b^2 = 0$ 23. $n^2 = 85$
    1.3, -1.3   0   ≈9.2, -9.2

T 69
Glencoe Division, Macmillan/McGraw-Hill

To graph irrational numbers, you can use a calculator or a table of squares and square roots to find approximate square roots in decimal form.

Example

4   Graph $\sqrt{2}$, $\sqrt{5}$, and π on the number line.

2 [√x] 1.4142136

5 [√x] 2.236068

[π] 3.1415927

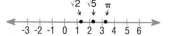

Throughout this text you have solved equations that have rational number solutions. Some equations have solutions that are irrational numbers. You can solve some equations that involve squares by taking the square root of each side.

Examples

Estimation Hint

In Example 6,
THINK
$100 < 180 < 225$
$10 < \sqrt{180} < 15$

5   Solve $x^2 = 36$.

$x^2 = 36$
$x = \sqrt{36}$ or $x = -\sqrt{36}$
$x = 6$ or $x = -6$

6   Solve $x^2 = 180$.

$x^2 = 180$
$x = \sqrt{180}$ or $-\sqrt{180}$
180 [√x] 13.416408
$x \approx 13.4$ or $x \approx -13.4$

Checking for Understanding

Communicating Mathematics

Read and study the lesson to answer each question.

1. **Write** a definition of real numbers. See margin.
2. **Tell** whether 0.010010001 . . . is a rational or irrational number. irrational
3. **Draw** a number line and graph $\sqrt{10}$. See margin.
4. **Tell** the solutions of $x^2 = 25$. 5, -5

Guided Practice

Name the set or sets of numbers to which each real number belongs.

5. $\sqrt{5}$ irrational   6. $0.\overline{27}$ rational   7. $-\sqrt{9}$ integer, rational   8. -2.5 rational

Find an approximation for each square root. Then graph the square root on the number line. See Solutions Manual for graphs.

9. $\sqrt{7} \approx 2.6$ 10. $\sqrt{8} \approx 2.8$ 11. $\sqrt{20} \approx 4.5$ 12. $-\sqrt{2} \approx -1.4$

Solve each equation.

13. $x^2 = 144$ 12, -12   14. $x^2 = 900$ 30, -30   15. $y^2 = 50$ 7.1, -7.1

308   **Chapter 8**   Real Numbers

OPTIONS

Bell Ringer

The number *k* is a perfect square. Is the square root of *k* rational or irrational? Explain.   Rational; the square root of a perfect square is a whole number, which is also a rational number.

Independent Practice

Name the set or sets of numbers to which each real number belongs.

16. 7

17. $\sqrt{11}$ irrational

18. $-\sqrt{36}$ integer, rational

19. 0.4545 . . . rational

20. $\frac{5}{8}$ rational

21. 6.06060606 rational

22. 0.121121112 . . . irrational

Find an approximation for each square root. Then graph the square root on the number line. **See Solutions Manual for graphs.**

23. $\sqrt{6} \approx 2.4$

24. $\sqrt{50} \approx 7.1$

25. $\sqrt{27} \approx 5.2$

26. $\sqrt{108} \approx 10.4$

Solve each equation. Round decimal answers to the nearest tenth.

27. $x^2 = 64$ 8, –8

28. $m^2 = 12 \approx 3.5, -3.5$

29. $y^2 = 360 \approx 19.0, -19.0$

30. $n^2 = 17 \approx 4.1, -4.1$

31. $p^2 = 1.44$ 1.2, -1.2

32. $t^2 = 1$ 1, -1

Mixed Review

33. Solve $33 = 4x - 15$. *(Lesson 2-7)* 12

34. Solve $d = 28(-12)$. *(Lesson 3-6)* –336

35. Statistics   Find the mean, median, and mode for the following set of data: 64, 52, 57, 65, 59, 61, 55, 50, 68. *(Lesson 4-5)* 59, 59, no mode

36. Find the product of $-\frac{5}{8}$ and $-3\frac{2}{5}$. *(Lesson 7-3)* $2\frac{1}{8}$

37. Estimate $\sqrt{300}$ to the nearest whole number. *(Lesson 8-2)* 17

Problem Solving and Applications

38. Physics   The formula $d = 16t^2$ represents the distance, d, in feet that an object falls in t seconds. Suppose a ball is rolled off a platform that is 25 feet above the ground. How long does it take for the ball to hit the ground? **1.25 seconds**

39. Algebra   In the geometric sequence 4, 12, __?__ , 108, 324, the missing number is called the *geometric mean* of 12 and 108. It can be found by simplifying $\sqrt{ab}$ where a and b are the numbers on either side of the geometric mean. Find the missing number. **36**

40. Critical Thinking   Name all whole numbers whose square roots are between 3 and 4. **10, 11, 12, 13, 14, 15**

41. Journal Entry   How can you remember the classifications of numbers? Can you think of a method for recalling the sets? **See students' work.**

Extending the Lesson

Using Connections   Have students research the Linnaean system to find the kingdom, phylum, class, order, family, genus, and species for humans.   Animalia; Chordata; Mammalia; Primates; Hominoidea; Homo; Homo sapiens

Cooperative Learning Activity

A Real Winner **8-3**

Number of players: 4
Materials: Index cards, spinner

▪ Copy onto cards the real numbers shown on the back of this card, one per card. Shuffle the cards and place them face down in a pile. Label the sections of a spinner "Real numbers," "Irrational numbers," "Rational numbers," "Integers," "Whole numbers," "Natural numbers."

▪ Each group member selects two cards from the pile and places them face up. One group member spins the spinner and takes all the cards showing numbers belonging to the set of numbers indicated. Keep any cards not taken by the group member who spun the spinner. Continue in the same way, taking turns at the spinner, until no cards remain in the pile. The group member who has the most cards at the end wins. Shuffle the cards and play again if time allows.

Glencoe Mathematics: Applications and Connections, Course 3

Enrichment Masters, p. 69

Name _____   Date _____

Enrichment Worksheet 8-3

What Did They Invent?

Each problem gives the name of an inventor. To find the invention, graph each set of points on the number line.

1. Whitcomb Judson P at $\sqrt{3}$, R at π, Z at 0.75, I at $\frac{3}{2}$, P at $\sqrt{6}$, E at $2\frac{7}{8}$

2. Johannes Kepler S at $\sqrt{5}$, P at $\sqrt{12}$, E at 3.75, L at $\frac{16}{13}$, C at $\frac{5}{2}$, T at $\frac{3}{8}$, O at π, E at 1.6, and E at 0.767

3. Alessandro Volta Y at $\sqrt{60}$, T at $\sqrt{30}$, A at 4.3, E at 6.2, T at $\frac{46}{9}$, R at $\sqrt{45}$, and B at $\sqrt{17}$

4. William Röntgen A at $\sqrt{32}$, Y at $6\frac{6}{8}$, X at $\frac{14}{3}$, S at $\sqrt{55}$, R at 5.3

5. Karl von Linde R at $\sqrt{140}$, G at 9.6, E at 8.5, I at $\sqrt{90}$, R at $\frac{21}{2}$, R at $\sqrt{70}$, T at $8\frac{5}{8}$, E at 100, A at 10.7, R at $9\frac{5}{11}$, T at $\sqrt{120}$, O at 11.4

T69
Glencoe Division, Macmillan/McGraw-Hill

310

NCTM Standards: 1–4, 7–9

Lesson Resources
- Study Guide Master 8-4
- Practice Master 8-4
- Enrichment Master 8-4
- Evaluation Masters, Quiz A, p. 70
- Group Activity Card 8-4

 Transparency 8-4 contains the 5-Minute Check and a teaching aid for this lesson.

🕐 5-Minute Check
(Over Lesson 8-3)

Name the set or sets of numbers to which each real number belongs.

1. $0.\overline{3}$ rational
2. $\sqrt{7}$ irrational
3. $0.212212221\ldots$ irrational
4. -5.687 rational
5. Solve the equation $x^2 = 70$. $x \approx 8.4$ or $x \approx -8.4$

---

1 FOCUS

Motivating the Lesson

Questioning   Ask students to state any formulas they already know. List these on the chalkboard, identifying the variables. Have students evaluate each formula after choosing values for the variables.

2 TEACH

Using Algebra   The problem can also be solved by using algebra to first rewrite the formula:

$$d = rt$$
$$\frac{d}{t} = \frac{rt}{t}$$
$$\frac{d}{t} = r$$

Now substitute values of d and t into the formula to find r.

8-4 Use a Formula

Objective
Solve problems by using a formula.

Motion is all around us. People walk, run, ride bicycles and skateboards, and travel from place to place in automobiles, airplanes, and trains.

The Amtrak Commuter Train #620 runs from Philadelphia to Penn Station in New York City. It leaves 30th Street Station in Philadelphia at 5:41 A.M. and arrives at Penn Station at 7:23 A.M., traveling a distance of 104 miles. Along the way, the train makes some stops to pick up more passengers. These stops take about 12 minutes in all.

You may have used the formula $d = rt$ when solving problems that involve motion. In the formula, d is the distance the object has moved, r is the rate or speed of the object, and t is the time. Use the formula $d = rt$ to find the average running speed of the train.

Explore   We know the starting time and arrival time of the train. We also know that the train was not moving for about 12 minutes. The distance between stations is 104 miles. The problem asks for the average running speed of the train.

Plan   Find the actual time that the train runs. Use the formula $d = rt$.

Solve   Subtract to find the time between the starting and arrival times.

$$\overbrace{\text{1 hour = 60 minutes}}$$

$$\overset{\frown}{7:23} - 5:41 \quad \Longrightarrow \quad \overset{\frown}{6:83} - 5:41 = 1:42$$

Subtract the time when the train was not moving.

$$1:42 - 0:12 = 1:30$$

The train runs for 1 hour and 30 minutes. Since 30 minutes is 0.5 hour, another way to express the time is 1.5 hours.

OPTIONS

Reteaching Activity

Using Communication   Students may be confused by the variables in a formula, failing to see that the formula represents an arithmetic relationship. Write formulas on the chalkboard and have students state them in sentence form. For $d = rt$, they might say, "Distance is equal to rate multiplied by time."

Study Guide Masters, p. 70

Name _____ Date _____

Study Guide Worksheet 8-4

Problem-Solving Strategy: Use a Formula

Example   Ryan wants new carpet for his room. His room is 4.5 yards wide and 5 yards long. How much will it cost to carpet Ryan's room if the carpet he wants costs $14.75 per square yard?

Explore   You know Ryan's room is 4.5 yards wide and 5 yards long. You know the carpet costs $14.75 per square yard.

Plan   Use the formula $A = lw$ to find the area of the room in square yards. Multiply the square yards by $14.75 to find the cost of the carpet.

Solve $A = lw$
$A = 5 \times 4.5$
$A = 22.5$ The area of the room is 22.5 square yards.
$22.5 \times \$14.75 = \$331.875$
Carpet for Ryan's room will cost about $331.88.

Now, substitute values into the formula $d = rt$.

$$d = rt$$
$$104 = r(1.5) \quad \textit{Replace d with 104 and t with 1.5.}$$
$$\frac{104}{1.5} = \frac{r(1.5)}{1.5} \quad \textit{Divide each side by 1.5.}$$
$$104 \boxed{÷} 1.5 \boxed{=} 69.3333333$$
$$69.3 \approx r$$

The average running speed of the train is about 69.3 miles per hour.
Examine this solution.

Checking for Understanding   1. distance = rate · time

Communicating Mathematics

Read and study the lesson to answer each question.

1. **Tell** what the variables d, r, and t represent in the formula $d = rt$.

2. **Write** the formula for the area of a rectangle. $A = \ell \cdot w$

Guided Practice   Solve. Use a formula.

3. Find the distance you travel if you drive your car at an average speed of 45 miles per hour for 3 hours.   **135 miles**

4. The formula $P = I - E$ is used to find the profit (P) when income (I) and expenses (E) are known. Find the profit if $I = \$12,995$ and $E = \$15,000$.   **-\$2,005**

5. Amtrak Commuter Train #624 leaves Philadelphia at 6:20 A.M. and arrives at Penn Station at 8:08 A.M. If this train makes the same stops as #620, find the average running speed of the train.   **65 miles per hour**

Problem Solving

Practice   Solve using any strategy.

Strategies
• • • • • • • •
Look for a pattern.
Solve a simpler problem.
Act it out.
Guess and check.
Draw a diagram.
Make a chart.
Work backward.

6. The difference between two whole numbers is 9. Their product is 360. Find the two numbers.   **15, 24**

7. A commuter-train car is 60 feet long and 12 feet wide. Find the maximum amount of carpeting needed to cover the car's floor.   **720 square feet**

8. Draw the next figure in the sequence. Write a sentence that describes the sequence.   **base length stays same, height gets bigger**

Lesson 8-4   Problem-Solving Strategy: Use a Formula   **311**

Bell Ringer

Two satellites speed toward each other, one at 16,000 miles per hour, the other at 14,000 miles per hour. They will collide in one hour. How far apart are they now?   30,000 mi

9. Mathematics and Science   Read the following paragraphs.

A flash of lightning is a huge spark of electricity that travels between a cloud and the ground or between two clouds. Lightning also causes thunder. Light from the flash travels almost instantly to your eyes. The sound of the thunder travels more slowly and arrives a few seconds later.

You can use the formula $d = 0.2t$ to find the distance between you and a thunderstorm. In the formula, d is the distance, in miles, and t is the time, in seconds. The speed of sound is about 0.2 miles per second.

a. On her way home from work, Darlene saw a flash of lightning. About 20 seconds later, she heard the thunder. How far away was the storm?   4 miles

b. Sam was watching the Weather Up-Date on television, when the weather forecaster announced that a severe thunderstorm was 4 miles west of the city. About how many seconds should Sam expect between the lightning and the sound of the thunder?   about 20 seconds

8 Assessment: Mid-Chapter Review

Find each square root. *(Lesson 8-1)*

1. $\sqrt{36}$ 6
2. $\sqrt{225}$ 15
3. $-\sqrt{25}$ −5
4. $-\sqrt{0.16}$ −0.4

Estimate to the nearest whole number. *(Lesson 8-2)*

5. $\sqrt{90}$ 9
6. $\sqrt{2}$ 1
7. $\sqrt{28}$ 5
8. $\sqrt{200}$ 14

Name the set or sets of numbers to which each real number belongs. *(Lesson 8-3)*

9. 10 natural, whole, integer, rational
10. $\sqrt{4}$ natural, whole, integer, rational
11. 0.121212… rational
12. $\sqrt{3}$ irrational

Solve each equation. Round decimal answers to the nearest tenth. *(Lesson 8-3)*

13. $x^2 = 49$ 7, −7
14. $y^2 = 50$ ≈ 7.1, −7.1

15. What is the average speed of a baseball if it takes 0.5 seconds for the ball to reach home plate, 60 feet away? Use the formula $d = rt$. *(Lesson 8-4)*   120 feet per second

312   **Chapter 8**   Real Numbers

OPTIONS

Extending the Lesson

Mathematics and Science   Ask students to explain how they would use this formula to find out how many seconds after the lightning you would hear thunder if the storm was 6 miles away. Ask students to investigate how sonar works.

Cooperative Learning Activity

Use groups of 2.
Materials: Rulers

If the Shoe Fits **8-4**

With the following formulas you can estimate the length of someone's foot in inches (L) if you know his or her shoe size (S).

for men: $S = 3L − 26$

for women: $S = 3L − 22$

Each partner secretly measures the length in inches of his or her right foot. Each partner tells the other his or her shoe size. Then each partner uses the formula to find the estimated length of the other's foot. Compare your estimate with the measurement your partner recorded for his or her foot.

Glencoe Mathematics: Applications and Connections, Course 3

312

8-5A The Pythagorean Theorem

A Preview of Lesson 8-5

Objective

Explore the relationships in a right triangle.

Materials

geoboard or dot paper

In the previous lessons, you learned about the relationship between the area of a square and the length of its side. You will use this relationship when you investigate a famous rule about right triangles. This rule is called the Pythagorean Theorem.

Try this!

Work with a partner.

- Build a triangle like the one shown on the geoboard. Remember it is called a *right triangle* because it has one right angle.

- Using the longest side of the triangle, build a square. The side of the square has the same length as the longest side of the triangle.

- The area of this square is 2 square units.

- Now build squares on the two shorter sides. Each square has an area of 1 square unit.

- The areas of the squares are 1 square unit, 1 square unit, and 2 square units.

Mathematics Lab 8-5A   The Pythagorean Theorem   **313**

NCTM Standards: 1–5, 7, 8, 12, 13

Management Tips

For Students   Students should divide the work, with one building the triangles and the other building the required squares. Partners should switch roles after they have completed the work on each triangle.

For the Overhead Projector
Overhead Manipulative Resources provides appropriate materials for teacher or student demonstration of the activities in this Mathematics Lab.

1 FOCUS

Introducing the Lab

Point out to students that this lab discusses only those triangles that are *right triangles.* Review right triangles from Lesson 5-3. Ask students why geoboards and dot paper are appropriate materials to use in this discussion.   Both geoboards and dot paper contain square grid patterns, and squares have four right angles which can be used as the right angle in a right triangle.

Using Connections After students find the area of the square on the hypotenuse, have them confirm this area using Pick's Theorem (pp. 282–283).

3 PRACTICE/APPLY

Using Models After students find a relationship between the areas of the two smaller squares and the area of the larger square, have them build a triangle that is not a right triangle and check to see if the relationship holds. It does not.

Close

Have students complete this statement: *If squares are built on the three sides of a right triangle, the ___?___ of the two smaller squares equals the ___?___ of the larger square.* sum of the areas; area

Additional Answer

1.

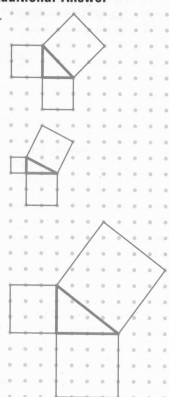

What do you think?

1. Build squares on each side of the triangles shown below. Record the areas of the squares. **See margin.**

sum of area of two smaller squares equals area of larger square

2. For each triangle, how does the area of the two smaller squares compare to the area of the larger square?

3. Build at least four different right triangles on your geoboard. Then build squares on each side. Look for a relationship between the area of the two smaller squares and the area of the larger square. Write a statement that describes the relationship. $a^2 + b^2 = c^2$ where c is length of hypotenuse

Applications

4. In a right triangle, the two shorter sides are 2 units and 3 units long. Without making a drawing, what is the area of the square built on the longest side? **13 square units**

5. In a right triangle, the longest side is 6 units long, and one of the other sides is 2 units long. What is the area of the square built on the remaining side? **32 square units**

Extension

Can you build a square with an area of 10 square meters? If you think of 10 as the sum of 1 and 9, you can build squares like the ones shown below. The square that is built on the longest side is 10 square units.

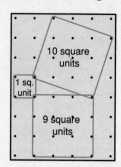

10 square units

1 sq. unit

9 square units

6. Build squares with areas of 5, 8, 13, 17, 32, 40, and 50 square units. See students' work.

OPTIONS

Lab Manual You may wish to make copies of the blackline master on p. 62 of the *Lab Manual* for students to use as a recording sheet.

Lab Manual, p. 62

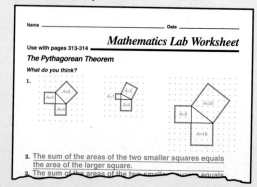

8-5 The Pythagorean Theorem

Objective
Use the Pythagorean Theorem.

Words to Learn
hypotenuse
legs
Pythagorean Theorem
converse

One of the earliest uses of mathematics was for measurement. Engineers and builders in ancient Egypt pioneered many aspects of mathematics. Every year, the Nile River flooded, covering their farmland for weeks. After the waters drained away, it was necessary to remeasure the boundaries.

About 2000 B.C., Egyptians discovered a 3-4-5 triangle. Taking a piece of rope knotted into 12 equal spaces, they stretched the rope around three stakes to form a triangle. The sides of the triangle had lengths of 3, 4, and 5 spaces. The longest side was opposite a right angle. Today, we call the longest side of a right triangle the **hypotenuse**. The sides that form the right angle are called **legs**.

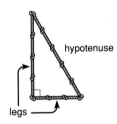

Many years later, in the fifth century B.C., a Greek mathematician, Pythagoras, and his followers learned about this 3-4-5 triangle. They noticed that if they built a square on each of the sides, the area of the two smaller squares was equal to the area of the large square.

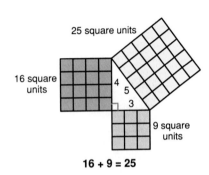

Today, we call this relationship the **Pythagorean Theorem.** It is true for *any* right triangle.

Pythagorean Theorem	**In words:** In a right triangle, the square of the length of the hypotenuse is equal to the sum of the squares of the lengths of the legs. **In symbols:** $c^2 = a^2 + b^2$

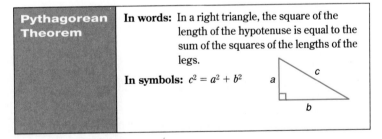

Lesson 8-5   The Pythagorean Theorem   **315**

NCTM Standards: 1–5, 7–9, 12, 13

Lesson Resources
• Study Guide Master 8-5
• Practice Master 8-5
• Enrichment Master 8-5
• Group Activity Card 8-5

Transparency 8-5 contains the 5-Minute Check and a teaching aid for this lesson.

5-Minute Check
(Over Lesson 8-4)

1. Find the distance an airplane travels in 5 hours at an average speed of 350 miles per hour. Use the formula $d = rt$.
   1,750 miles

2. Find the length of a rectangle with width 8.5 centimeters and perimeter 43 centimeters. Use the formula $P = 2\ell + 2w$ (P = perimeter, ℓ = length, w = width).
   13 cm

1 FOCUS

Motivating the Lesson

Activity   Have students cut out squares with sides of the following lengths from a sheet of graph paper: 5 units, 12 units, and 13 units. Have them arrange the squares to form a triangular figure similar to the figure in the middle of page 315.

2 TEACH

Using Models   Show that a 12-knot string forms a 3–4–5 right triangle (with a knot at each vertex). Then have students try to form a right triangle using a 30-knot string, with a knot at each vertex.   The sides measure 5 knots, 12 knots, and 13 knots.

OPTIONS

Bell Ringer

Find x. $\sqrt{3}$ or about 1.7 cm

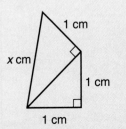

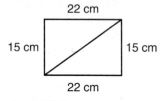
Checking for Understanding

Exercises 1–3 are designed to help you assess students' understanding through reading, writing, speaking, and modeling. You should work through these exercises with your students and then monitor their work on Guided Practice Exercises 4–8.

Error Analysis

Watch for students who always add the squares of the given sides.

Prevent by having students draw triangles, showing the known and unknown measurements, and then have them identify which measurement is the length of the hypotenuse.

1 Find the length of the hypotenuse in the triangle shown at the right.

$$c^2 = a^2 + b^2$$ *Pythagorean Theorem*

$$c^2 = 9^2 + 12^2$$ *Replace a with 9 and*
                        b with 12.

$$c^2 = 81 + 144$$

$$c^2 = 225$$

$$c = \sqrt{225}$$

$$c = 15$$ *You can ignore $-\sqrt{225}$ because it is*
              not reasonable to have a negative length.

The length of the hypotenuse is 15 feet.

12 ft

9 ft

Estimation Hint

• • • • • • • • • •

THINK:
$25 \times 25 = 625$
$30 \times 30 = 900$
$\sqrt{756}$ is between 25 and 30.

2 The hypotenuse of a right triangle is 30 meters long, and one of its legs is 12 meters long. Find the length of the other leg.

$$c^2 = a^2 + b^2$$

$$30^2 = a^2 + 12^2$$

$$900 = a^2 + 144$$

$$900 - 144 = a^2 + 144 - 144$$

$$756 = a^2$$

$$\sqrt{756} = a$$

756 $\boxed{\sqrt{x}}$ 27.495454

The length of the leg is about 27.5 meters.

30 m   12 m
a m

Example 3 *Problem Solving*

Baseball   A baseball diamond is actually a square. The distance between bases is 90 feet. When the catcher throws the ball from home plate to second base, how far does the ball travel?

$$c^2 = a^2 + b^2$$ *Pythagorean Theorem*

$$c^2 = 90^2 + 90^2$$ *Replace a and b with 90.*

$$c^2 = 8,100 + 8,100$$

$$c^2 = 16,200$$

$$c = \sqrt{16,200}$$

16,200 $\boxed{\sqrt{x}}$ 127.27922

$$c \approx 127.3$$

The distance the ball travels is about 127.3 feet.

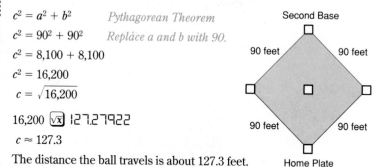

Second Base

90 feet   90 feet

90 feet   90 feet

Home Plate

316   **Chapter 8**   Real Numbers

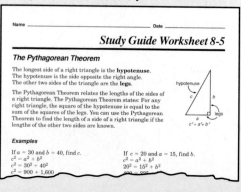

Some triangles may look like right triangles, but in reality they are not. The **converse** of the Pythagorean Theorem can be used to test whether a triangle is a right triangle.

Converse of Pythagorean Theorem	If the sides of a triangle have lengths a, b, and c units, such that $c^2 = a^2 + b^2$, then the triangle is a right triangle.

Examples

Determine whether each triangle with sides of given length is a right triangle. *Remember, the hypotenuse is the longest side.*

4 8 cm, 13 cm, 17 cm

$$c^2 = a^2 + b^2$$
$$17^2 \stackrel{?}{=} 8^2 + 13^2$$
$$289 \stackrel{?}{=} 64 + 169$$
$$289 \neq 233$$

The triangle is *not* a right triangle.

5 5 ft, 12 ft, 13 ft

$$c^2 = a^2 + b^2$$
$$13^2 \stackrel{?}{=} 5^2 + 12^2$$
$$169 \stackrel{?}{=} 25 + 144$$
$$169 = 169$$

The triangle is a right triangle.

Checking for Understanding

Communicating Mathematics

Read and study the lesson to answer each question.

1. **Tell** the area of the shaded square shown at the right. **100 square units**

2. **Draw** a right triangle and label the hypotenuse and the legs. **See margin.**

3. **Tell** whether a triangle with sides of 4, 5, and 6 inches is a right triangle. **no**

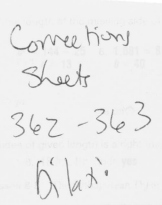

64 square units

36 square units

Guided Practice

State an equation you could us[e] [to find the missing length of the missing] triangle. Then find the missing [length.]

4. $c^2 = 144 + 81$
   $c = 15$

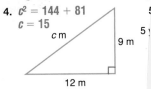

cm

9 m

12 m

Determine whether each trian[gle]

7. 10 cm, 12 cm, 15 cm **no**

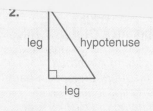

Correction Sheets
362 - 363
Dilati

Gifted and Talented Needs

Have students find the length of the diagonal ($\overline{AG}$) of this cube. (HINT: Find the length of $\overline{AC}$ in $\triangle ABC$. Then find the length of $\overline{AG}$ in $\triangle ACG$.) about 6.9 in.

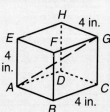

H 4 in.

E

F G

4 in.

A

D C

B 4 in.

2.

leg   hypotenuse

leg

Close

Guide students to summarize the lesson by asking the following question. *How can you find the length of a side of a right triangle if you know the lengths of the other two sides?* Substitute the known lengths into the equation $a^2 + b^2 = c^2$ and solve for the remaining variable.

3 PRACTICE/APPLY

Assignment Guide
Maximum: 9–33
Minimum: 9–25 odd, 26–33

For **Extra Practice,** see p. 602.

Alternate Assessment

Writing Have students write the Pythagorean Theorem using this figure.
$h^2 = p^2 + e^2$

p

e

h

Practice Masters, p. 71

Name _____ Date _____

Practice Worksheet 8-5

The Pythagorean Theorem

State an equation you could use to find the unknown side length in each right triangle. Then find the unknown length.

1.
c
12 in.
16 in.
$c = 20$ in.

2.
8 cm
c
15 cm
$c = 17$ cm

3.
26 yd
10 yd
b
$b = 24$ yd

Determine whether each triangle with sides of given length is a right triangle.

4. 6 cm, 8 cm, 10 cm yes

5. 9 mm, 12 mm, 16 mm no

6. 18 ft, 80 ft, 82 ft yes

7. 10 mi, 24 mi, 25 mi no

8. 15 cm, 36 cm, 39 cm yes

9. 16 yd, 30 yd, 34 yd yes

Find the unknown side lengths for each right triangle. Round decimal answers to the nearest tenth.

10. a, 24 ft; b, 32 ft
    $c = 40$ ft

11. a, 9 ft; c, 16 ft
    $b \approx 13.2$ ft

12. b, 5 in.; c, 11 in.
    $a \approx 9.8$ in.

13. a, 8 cm; b, 12 cm
    $c \approx 14.4$ cm

14. b, 15 yd; c, 21 yd
    $a \approx 14.7$ yd

15. a, 6.3 cm; c, 12.4 cm
    $b \approx 10.7$ cm

Write an equation to solve for x. Then solve. Round decimal answers to the nearest tenth.

16.
5 cm
x
6 cm
$x^2 = (5 \text{ cm})^2 + (6 \text{ cm})^2$
$x \approx 7.8$ cm

17.
x
12 in.
12 in.
$x^2 = 2(12 \text{ in.})^2$
$x \approx 17.0$ in.

18.
10 ft   10 ft
x
10 ft
$(10 \text{ ft})^2 = x^2 + (5 \text{ ft})^2$
$x \approx 8.7$ ft

T71
Glencoe Division, Macmillan/McGraw-Hill

317

Exercises

Independent Practice Find the missing measure for each right triangle. Round answers to the nearest tenth.

9. a, 9 ft; c, 12 ft $b \approx 7.9$ ft
10. a, 5 in.; b, 5 in. $c \approx 7.1$ in.
11. a, 3 m; c, 8 m $b \approx 7.4$ m
12. b, 99 mm; c, 101 mm $a = 20$ mm
13. b, 12 cm; c, 22 cm $a \approx 18.4$ cm
14. a, 48 yd; b, 55 yd $c = 73$ yd
15. a, 40 in.; c, 41 in. $b = 9$ in.
16. a, 3.5 m; b, 12.5 m $c \approx 13.0$ m

Write an equation to solve for x. Then solve. Round answers to the nearest tenth.

17.
10 in. x in.
10 in.
$x^2 = 100 + 100$; $x \approx 14.1$

18.
8 ft x ft   8 ft
←8 ft→
$64 = x^2 + 16$; $x \approx 6.9$

19.
1 cm
x cm
1 cm
1 cm
$x^2 = 1 + 2$; $x \approx 1.7$

Determine whether each triangle with sides of given length is a right triangle.

20. 5 in., 10 in., 12 in.   no
21. 1 mi, 1 mi, $\sqrt{2}$ mi   yes
22. 4 m, 7 m, 5 m   no
23. 28 cm, 197 cm, 195 cm   yes
24. 9 in., 40 in., 41 in.   yes
25. 24 mm, 143 mm, 145 mm   yes

Mixed Review
26. How many grams are in 1.25 kilograms? *(Lesson 1-6)*   1,250 grams
27. **Statistics**   Name the stems you would use to plot the following set of data: 328, 351, 336, 357, 348, 324. *(Lesson 4-4)*   32, 33, 34, 35
28. Express -3.47×10^{-5} in standard form. *(Lesson 6-11)*   -0.0000347
29. Solve $t^2 = 144$. *(Lesson 8-3)*   12, -12

Problem Solving and Applications
30. **Geometry**   Find the length of a diagonal of a rectangle with a length of 8 units and a width of 5 units.   about 9.4 units

31. **Sports**   A popular pass play in football is the "down and out." A receiver runs down the field, parallel to the sideline, then turns sharply toward the sideline to receive the ball. How far from his original position is a receiver who runs downfield 15 yards, turns and runs toward a sideline for another 8 yards?   17 yards

32. about 394 feet

32. **Data Search**   Refer to page 667. What is the length of the diagonal of a football field?

DATA SEARCH

33. **Critical Thinking**   The diagonal of a square is 8 units. Find the length of its side.   about 5.7 units

34. **Geometry**   Find the area and perimeter of the triangle shown at the right. $A = 96$ cm^2; $P = 48$ cm

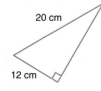
20 cm
12 cm

318   **Chapter 8**   Real Numbers

Enrichment Masters, p. 71

Name _____ Date _____

Enrichment Worksheet 8-5

Geometric Relationships

The Pythagorean Theorem can be used to express relationships between parts of geometric figures.

$d^2 = s^2 + s^2$
$d^2 = 2s^2$
$d = \sqrt{2}s$

The example shows how to write a formula for the length of the diagonal of a square in terms of the length of the side.

Develop a formula for each problem. The dotted lines have been included to help you.

1. An equilateral triangle has three sides of the same length. Express the altitude h in terms of the side s.
$h = \frac{\sqrt{3}s}{2}$

2. A regular hexagon has six sides of the same length. Express the height h in terms of the length of the side s.
$h = \sqrt{3}s$

3. A circle is circumscribed about a square. Express the radius r of the circumscribed circle in terms of the side s of the square.
$r = \frac{\sqrt{2}s}{2}$

4. A circle is inscribed in a square. Express the radius r of the inscribed circle in terms of the side s of the square.
$r = \frac{s}{2}$

5. Use the isosceles triangle below. Express the altitude h in terms of the quantity a.
$h = 3a$
5a
h
8a

6. Use the isosceles right triangle below. Express x in terms of s.
$x = \frac{\sqrt{2}s}{2}$

T71
Glencoe Division, Macmillan/McGraw-Hill

OPTIONS

Extending the Lesson

Using Cooperative Groups   Have students work in small groups to solve this problem: *A softball diamond is a square 60 feet on each side. How long will it take a ball thrown from home plate at 75 feet per second to reach second base?*   about 1.1 sec

Cooperative Learning Activity

Pythagorean Triple Take **8-5**

Number of players: 4
Materials: Index cards

• Copy onto cards the numbers shown on the back of this card, one per card. Shuffle the cards and place them face down in a pile.

➡ Each group member takes five cards. In turn, each group member removes from his or her hand any three cards showing the lengths of three sides of a right triangle and replaces them with cards from the pile. If you don't have three cards showing the lengths of three sides of a right triangle, your turn may consist of trading in one or more cards for cards from the pile. Place cards that you trade in on the bottom of the pile.

Continue in the same way until no cards remain in the pile. The group member with the most sets of three cards is the winner.

Glencoe Mathematics: Applications and Connections, Course 3

8-6 Using the Pythagorean Theorem

Objective

Solve problems using the Pythagorean Theorem.

Words to Learn

Pythagorean triple

The illustration at the right is from a Chinese work called *Chóu-peï Suan-king*, written sometime during 2000–1000 B.C. The block print shows a principle we know as the Pythagorean Theorem. Can you see several 3–4–5 right triangles in the illustration? However, the work contains no explanation relating the measures of the figures.

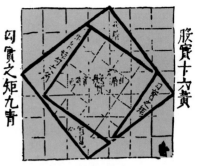

CHÓU-PEÏ SUAN-KING

You can use your knowledge of the Pythagorean Theorem to find the areas of the figures in the illustration.

Example 1 *Connection*

Geometry Find the total area of the four small triangles in the illustration above.

Explore First, let's re-draw the figure to show the inside, middle, and outside squares. You need to find the area of the shaded triangles.

Plan To find the area of the shaded triangles, you can find the area of the middle square and subtract the area of the inside square from it.

Solve The middle square is built on the hypotenuse of the 3-4-5 right triangle. Its area is the square of the hypotenuse.

$c^2 = a^2 + b^2$ *Pythagorean Theorem*
$c^2 = 3^2 + 4^2$
$c^2 = 9 + 16$ or 25

The area of the middle square is 25 square units.

Now subtract the area of the inside square. It is 4^2 or 16 square units.

$25 - 16 = 9$

The total area of the four small triangles is 9 square units.

Lesson 8-6   Using the Pythagorean Theorem   **319**

8-6 Lesson Notes

NCTM Standards: 1–5, 7, 8, 12, 13

Lesson Resources
• Study Guide Master 8-6
• Practice Master 8-6
• Enrichment Master 8-6
• Technology Master, p. 22
• Group Activity Card 8-6

Transparency 8-6 contains the 5-Minute Check and a teaching aid for this lesson.

5-Minute Check
(Over Lesson 8-5)
Find the missing measure for each right triangle.
1. *a*, 6 cm; *c*, 10 cm   8 cm
2. *a*, 8 in.; *b*, 15 in.   17 in.

Determine whether each triangle with sides of given length is a right triangle.
3. 7 mm, 12 mm, 14 mm   no
4. 9 m, 12 m, 15 m   yes

1 FOCUS

Motivating the Lesson

Questioning Point out that the Pythagorean Theorem has many everyday applications. Ask this question: *What part of a 19-inch TV set measures 19 inches?* the diagonal; In the figure, $a^2 + b^2 = 19^2$.

2 TEACH

Using Connections Students can find the primitive Pythagorean triple for a given Pythagorean triple by dividing each member of the triple by the GCF of the three numbers.

OPTIONS

Meeting Needs of Middle School Students

Middle school students profit from frequent evaluations of their progress, so assign homework nightly. Give quizzes and tests often. Mark and return all of work promptly. Give students opportunities to gauge their progress with self-assessment tests.

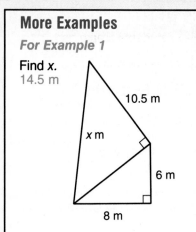
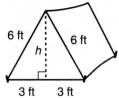
Examine   Estimate the area of each small triangle by counting squares. Then multiply by 4 to find the total area.

$2 \cdot 4 = 8$

The answer is reasonable.

The Pythagorean Theorem can be applied in many situations involving measurement.

Example 2   *Problem Solving*

Home Maintenance   For safety reasons the base of a 24-foot ladder should be at least 8 feet from the wall. How high can a 24-foot ladder safely reach?

Let *b* represent the height the ladder will reach.

24 ft

8 ft

$$c^2 = a^2 + b^2$$
$$24^2 = 8^2 + b^2$$
$$576 = 64 + b^2$$
$$576 - 64 = 64 + b^2 - 64$$
$$512 = b^2$$
$$\sqrt{512} = b$$

512 $\boxed{\sqrt{x}}$ 22.627417

The ladder can safely reach a height of about 22.6 feet.

By now you can recognize 3–4–5 as integers that satisfy the Pythagorean Theorem. Such numbers are called **Pythagorean triples.** You can use multiples to find other Pythagorean triples that are based on 3–4–5.

Mental Math Hint

• • • • • • • • • •

You can mentally find a Pythagorean triple by finding a multiple of a Pythagorean triple you already know.

Example 3   *Connection*

Number Theory   The chart below shows several Pythagorean triples. Study the pattern in the chart to find the next triple in the set.

a	b	c
3	4	5
6	8	10
9	12	15
■	■	■

a	b	c
3	4	5
6	8	10
9	12	15
12	16	20

The next triple in the set is 12–16–20.

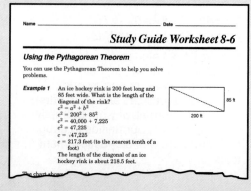

The triple 3–4–5 is called a *primitive* Pythagorean triple because the numbers are relatively prime. The triples 6–8–10, 9–12–15, and so on are in the 3–4–5 family.

Checking for Understanding

Communicating Mathematics

Read and study the lesson to answer each question.

1. **Tell** the area of the shaded square shown at the right. **5 units²**

2. **Write** two Pythagorean triples in the same family as 5–12–13.
   Sample answer: 10-24-26; 20-48-52

Guided Practice

State an equation that can be used to answer each question. Then solve. Round answers to the nearest tenth.

3. How long is each rafter?

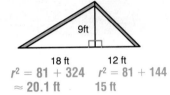

9ft

18 ft   12 ft
$r^2 = 81 + 324$ $r^2 = 81 + 144$
≈ 20.1 ft   15 ft

4. How long is the lake?

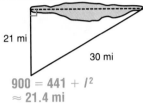

21 mi

30 mi

$900 = 441 + l^2$
≈ 21.4 mi

Exercises

Independent Practice

Solve. Round answers to the nearest tenth.

5. How high does the ladder reach? **about 14.7 ft**

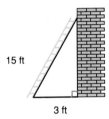

15 ft

3 ft

6. How far apart are the planes? **about 9.4 mi**

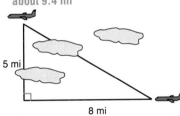

5 mi

8 mi

For Exercises 7-9, sample answers are given.

For each Pythagorean triple, find two triples in the same family.

7. 8–15–17
   16-30-34; 40-75-85

8. 7–24–25
   14-48-50; 35-120-125

9. 9–40–41
   18-80-82; 45-200-205

10. Name the family to which the triple 36–48–60 belongs. **3-4-5**

Mixed Review

11. Evaluate $4^2 - 2^3$. *(Lesson 1-9)* **8**

12. The lengths of three sides of a triangle are 12 meters, 20 meters, and 13 meters. Determine whether the triangle is a right triangle. *(Lesson 8-5)* **no**

Bell Ringer

Divide each number of the 3–4–5 primitive Pythagorean triple by 2. Do the resulting rational numbers satisfy the Pythagorean Theorem? yes

---

Close

Have students create and exchange application problems involving the Pythagorean Theorem.

3 PRACTICE/APPLY

Assignment Guide
Maximum: 5–18
Minimum: 5–17

Alternate Assessment

Writing Have students work in pairs to create problems whose solutions can be found by using the Pythagorean Theorem.

Practice Masters, p. 72

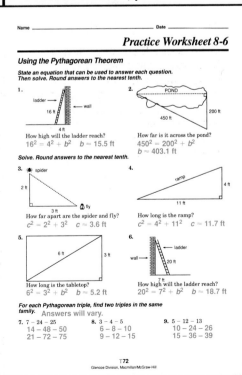

For Exercises 13-16, make a drawing of each situation. Then solve. Round answers to the nearest tenth.

13. **Skateboarding** The acceleration ramp for the skateboard competition is 20 meters long and extends 15 meters from the base of the starting point. How high is the ramp? ≈ 13.2 meters

14. **Hiking** A hiker walked 11 kilometers north, then walked 3 kilometers west. How far was she from the starting point? ≈ 11.4 kilometers

15. **Landscaping** A newly-planted tree needs to be staked with three wires. Each wire is staked 3 feet from the base of the tree and extends 5 feet high on the trunk. How much wire is needed to stake four trees? ≈ 70.0 feet

16. **Portfolio Suggestion** Select your favorite word problem from this chapter and place your solution to it in your portfolio. Attach a note explaining why it is your favorite. See students' work.

17. **Critical Thinking** Several Pythagorean triples are listed below. Study the pattern in the table.

a	b	c
3	4	5
5	12	13
7	24	25
9	40	41

a. Find the Pythagorean triple that has 11 as the measure of the shortest leg. 11-60-61

b. Find the Pythagorean triple that has 85 as the measure of the hypotenuse. 13-84-85

COMPUTER CONNECTION

18. **Computer Connection** You can also find Pythagorean triples by inputing positive integers x and y into the following program. Note that x must be greater than y.

```
10 INPUT X, Y
20 A = X^2 - Y^2: B = 2*X*Y: C = X^2 + Y^2
30 PRINT A, B, C
```

a. Write the expressions that are used to find values of a, b, and c.

b. Run the program for several values of x and y. See students' work.

18a. $a = x^2 - y^2$; $b = xy$; $c = x^2 + y^2$

Enrichment Masters, p. 72

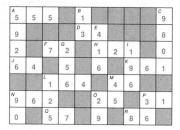

Name _____ Date _____

Enrichment Worksheet 8-6

A Cross-Number Puzzle

Use the clues at the bottom of the page to complete the puzzle.
Round computational answers to the nearest whole number.
You are to write one digit in each box.

A 5	5	5		B 1			C 9
9			D 3	E 4			8
2		F 7	G 2		H 1	2	I 1	0
J 6	4		5		6		K 9	6	1
		L 1	6	4		M 4	6	
N 9	6	2		O 2	5		P 3	1
0		Q 5	7		9		R 8	6

Across

A The square of 23.56
C The digits in the repeating block of 1/11
D Hypotenuse if legs are 16 and 30
F Perimeter of a square with area of 324
H Perfect square. Digits sum is 4.
J Hypotenuse if legs are 40 and 50
K The largest three-digit perfect square
L Twice the square root of 6,724
M Side of a square with area of 2,100
N Perfect square plus 1
O Hypotenuse if legs are 7 and 24
P 10π
Q Diagonal of square with a side of 40
R The square root of 7,400

Down

A The 4th to 8th digits of π
B Makes Pythagorean triple with 5 and 12
C The largest four-digit perfect square
E Square of hypotenuse if legs are 20 and 4
G Perfect square that is a power of 2
I The square of 14
L The square root of 15,625
M Other leg if hypotenuse is 53 and short leg is 28
N One angle of a right triangle
O Makes Pythagorean triple with 20 and 21
P Perimeter of a square with area of 81

T72
Glencoe Division, Macmillan/McGraw-Hill

322

OPTIONS

Extending the Lesson

Using Charts Have students use the chart below to find Pythagorean triples. They must choose two numbers, m and n (one odd and one even) with $m > n$.

	Side lengths		
m	n	$m^2 - n^2$	$2mn$	$m^2 + n^2$
2	1	3	4	5

Cooperative Learning Activity

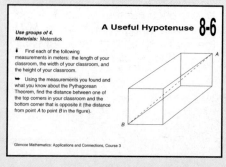

Use groups of 4.
Materials: Meterstick

A Useful Hypotenuse **8-6**

✦ Find each of the following measurements in meters: the length of your classroom, the width of your classroom, and the height of your classroom.

☛ Using the measurements you found and what you know about the Pythagorean Theorem, find the distance between one of the top corners in your classroom and the bottom corner that is opposite it (the distance from point A to point B in the figure).

Glencoe Mathematics: Applications and Connections, Course 3

Cooperative Learning

8-6B Graphing Irrational Numbers

A Follow-Up of Lesson 8-6

Objective
Use the Pythagorean Theorem to graph irrational numbers on a number line.

Materials
compass
straightedge

Most people know that Alexander Graham Bell invented the telephone. But did you know that the drawings needed to get a patent for the telephone were done by Lewis Howard Latimer (1848–1928), an African-American engineer and draftsman?

Draftsmen, inventors, and engineers often use a compass and straightedge to copy measurements accurately from one location to another. You already know how to graph integers and rational numbers on a number line. How would you graph an irrational number like $\sqrt{5}$?

Activity One

LOOKBACK

You can review perpendicular segments on page 183.

You can construct a perpendicular segment by folding the paper line at 2, making sure the two parts of the number line align when you hold the paper up to the light. The fold is a segment perpendicular to the number line.

- Draw a number line.

- At 2, construct a perpendicular line segment 1 unit in length. Draw the line segment shown in color. Label it *c*.

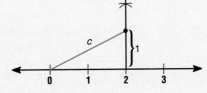

- The Pythagorean Theorem can be used to show that *c* is $\sqrt{5}$ units long.

$c^2 = a^2 + b^2$
$c^2 = 1^2 + 2^2$ *Replace a with 1 and b with 2.*
$c^2 = 5$
$c = \sqrt{5}$

- Open the compass to the length of *c*. With the tip of the compass at 0, draw an arc that intersects the number line at *B*. The distance from 0 to *B* is $\sqrt{5}$ units.

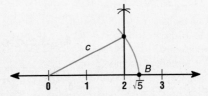

Mathematics Lab 8-6B   Graphing Irrational Numbers   **323**

Management Tips

For Students   Although students can use rulers to mark off number lines, you may prefer to have them use compasses kept at a constant radius.

For the Overhead Projector
Overhead Manipulative Resources provides appropriate materials for teacher or student demonstration of the activities in this Mathematics Lab.

1 FOCUS

Introducing the Lab

List the squares of the whole numbers 1–6 on the chalkboard. Ask students to express each of the numbers 20, 11, and 17 as the sum or difference of two squares.
$2^2 + 4^2$ or $6^2 - 4^2$; $6^2 - 5^2$;
$1^2 + 4^2$

2 TEACH

Using Logical Reasoning
Students can simply follow the instructions; however, they may develop a better understanding of graphing irrational numbers if you first discuss the logic behind the instructions: you are using the Pythagorean Theorem to construct a right triangle having a side of length equal to the length you wish to graph. This length is then copied on a number line.

Classroom Vignette

"You may wish to assign students a one-page report on the contributions of minority scientists. Challenge them to write about scientists that we know very little about and to provide pictures of these scientists. Their reports can make a very attractive bulletin board display."

Patricia S. Wilson

Patricia S. Wilson
Author

Using Logical Reasoning Of those numbers from 1–20 that are not perfect squares, ask students to find those whose square roots cannot be graphed using the method of this lab.   6, 14

Close

Ask students to summarize the lesson by completing each of the following statements using either the word *hypotenuse* or the word *leg*.

- To graph the square root of a number which is the sum of two squares, copy the length of the ___?___ of the appropriately constructed right triangle on a number line.   hypotenuse

- To graph the square root of a number which is the difference of two squares, copy the length of the ___?___ of the appropriately constructed right triangle on a number line.   leg

❝When am I ever going to use this?❞

Large toy companies, such as Mattel, employ designers and engineers to create new toys. These creative individuals draw blueprints and build models when they design new games, toys, and cars.

A background in mathematics and drafting is essential in the study of mechanical engineering and industrial design.

For more information contact:
Mattel
333 Continental Boulevard
El Segundo, California 90245

In Activity One, the irrational number that was graphed is the sum of two squares and is represented by the hypotenuse. Sometimes, the irrational number to be graphed will be the difference of two squares and can be represented by a leg of a triangle. Consider the following method for graphing $\sqrt{7}$.

Activity Two

- Draw a number line.

- At 3, construct a perpendicular line segment. Put the tip of the compass at 0. With the compass set at 4 units, construct an arc that intersects the perpendicular line segment. Label the perpendicular leg a.

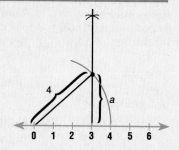

- The Pythagorean Theorem can be used to show that a is $\sqrt{7}$ units long.

$$c^2 = a^2 + b^2$$
$$4^2 = a^2 + 3^2$$
$$16 = a^2 + 9 \quad \textit{Replace c with 4 and b with 3.}$$
$$7 = a^2$$
$$\sqrt{7} = a$$

- Open the compass to the length of a. With the tip of the compass at 0, draw an arc that intersects the number line at D. The distance from 0 to D is $\sqrt{7}$ units.

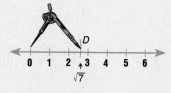

What do you think?   For answers to Exercises 1-4, see Solutions Manual.

1. Explain how to graph $\sqrt{2}$.
2. Describe two different ways to graph $\sqrt{8}$.
3. Explain how the graph of $\sqrt{2}$ can be used to locate the point that represents $\sqrt{3}$.
4. Explain how to graph $-\sqrt{5}$.

Applications   For graphs to Exercises 5-8, see Solutions Manual.

Graph each number on a number line.

5. $\sqrt{2}$ 6. $\sqrt{3}$ 7. $\sqrt{8}$ 8. $\sqrt{10}$

OPTIONS

Lab Manual You may wish to make copies of the blackline master on p. 63 of the *Lab Manual* for students to use as a recording sheet.

Lab Manual, p. 63

Name _____ Date _____

Mathematics Lab Worksheet

Use with pages 323–324

Graphing Irrational Numbers

What do you think?

1. On a number line at 1, draw a perpendicular line segment 1 unit in length. The side opposite the right angle is √2 units long. Measure this length with a compass and draw an arc that intersects the number line at D. The distance from 0 to D is √2.

2. Graph √8 as the leg of a right triangle with hypotenuse 3 and leg 1 or graph √8 as the hypotenuse of a right isosceles triangle with legs 2.

3. On a number line at √2, draw a perpendicular line

8-7 Distance on the Coordinate Plane

Objective
Find the distance between points in the coordinate plane.

One day Jim and his brother David were arguing. Their parents sent them to their room to calm down. Since they share the same room, they wanted to be as far away from each other as possible. Jim wanted to know how far he was from David. He drew a graph of their room on a grid like the one shown at the right. *The side of each square represents 1 foot.*

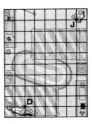

LOOK BACK

You can review the coordinate plane on page 117.

The graph looks like a coordinate plane. If we draw the *x*- and *y*- axes, David's location is represented by the ordered pair (2, 1). Jim's location is represented by the ordered pair (7, 9).

Let's see how these ordered pairs can help determine how far Jim is from David.

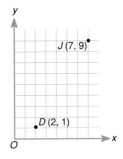

Mini-Lab

Work with a partner.
Materials: graph paper

- Graph points *D* and *J* on a coordinate plane and connect them with a line segment.

- Draw a horizontal line through *D* and a vertical line through *J*. Call the point of intersection *T*.

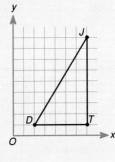

DID YOU KNOW

AT&T has a reference book listing coordinates for all locations in North America. The phone company then calculates the distance between two cities, and from this, the long distance telephone charge is determined.

Talk About It

a. What is the length of $\overline{DT}$? **5 units**

b. What is the length of $\overline{JT}$? **8 units**

c. Explain how you can find the length of $\overline{DJ}$. **Use the Pythagorean Theorem.**

Lesson 8-7 Measurement Connection: Distance on the Coordinate Plane **325**

OPTIONS

Reteaching Activity

Using Cooperative Groups Have students work in pairs, rolling two number cubes twice to form two ordered pairs and plotting the points on a coordinate plane. They then draw a right triangle with the points as the endpoints of the hypotenuse. Students then work together to find the length of the hypotenuse.

Study Guide Masters, p. 73

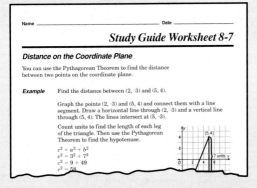

8-7 Lesson Notes

NCTM Standards: 1–5, 7, 12, 13

Lesson Resources
- Study Guide Master 8-7
- Practice Master 8-7
- Enrichment Master 8-7
- Group Activity Card 8-7

Transparency 8-7 contains the 5-Minute Check and a teaching aid for this lesson.

5-Minute Check
(Over Lesson 8-6)

1. Tony drove 12 miles south, then 16 miles west. How far is he from his starting point? 20 miles

2. Find two Pythagorean triples in the 7–24–25 family. Sample answers: 14–48–50; 21–72–75

3. Name the family to which the triple 24–45–51 belongs. 8–15–17

1 FOCUS

Motivating the Lesson

Activity Have students plot the point *P*(4, 6) on a coordinate plane drawn on graph paper. Have students use a compass set for a 5-unit radius to draw a circle with center at *P*. Then have them list as many points as possible located on the circle. Sample answers: (4, 1), (4, 11), (−1, 6), (9, 6), (0, 3), (0, 9), (1, 2), (1, 10), (7, 2), (7, 10), (8, 3), (8, 9)

2 TEACH

Using the Mini-Lab Point out that the length of $\overline{DT}$ equals the difference between the *x*-coordinates of points *J* and *D*: 7 − 2 = 5. The length of $\overline{JT}$ equals the difference between the *y*-coordinates: 9 − 1 = 8.

Checking for Understanding

Exercises 1-3 are designed to help you assess students' understanding through reading, writing, speaking, and modeling. You should work through these exercises with your students and then monitor their work on Guided Practice Exercises 4-6.

Close

State two ordered pairs. Have students explain how they would find the distance between those two points in a coordinate plane.

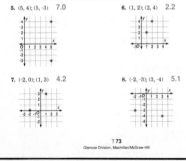 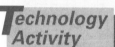

As you found in the Mini-Lab, the distance between Jim and David can be related to the hypotenuse of a right triangle.

Example

Problem Solving Hint
• • • • • • • • • •
Use a formula.

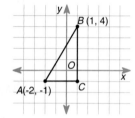

You can learn how to use a graphing calculator to find the distance between two points in Technology Activity 3 on page 660.

Find the distance between Jim and David.

Let c = the distance between Jim and David.
Let $a = 5$.
Let $b = 8$.

$$c^2 = a^2 + b^2$$
$$c^2 = 5^2 + 8^2$$
$$c^2 = 25 + 64$$
$$c^2 = 89$$
$$c = \sqrt{89}$$

89 $\boxed{\sqrt{x}}$ 9.4339811

Jim and David are about 9.4 feet apart.

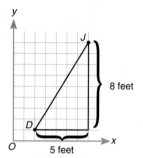

Checking for Understanding

Communicating Mathematics

Read and study the lesson to answer each question.

1. **Tell** the length of $\overline{BC}$ and $\overline{AC}$ in the figure at the right.   5 units, 3 units

2. See Solutions Manual.

2. **Write** the steps you could use to find the distance between (5, 5) and (2, 2).

3. **Draw** the triangle that you can use to find the distance between (-2, 1) and (-5, -3) on the coordinate plane.   See margin.

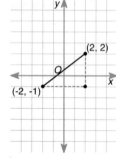

Guided Practice

Find the distance between each pair of points whose coordinates are given. Round answers to the nearest tenth.

4. 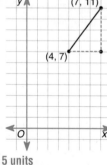 (7, 11) (4, 7)   5 units
5. 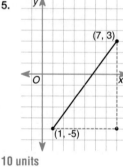 (7, 3) (1, -5)   10 units
6. (2, 2) (-2, -1)   5 units

326   **Chapter 8**   Real Numbers

OPTIONS

Bell Ringer

From a point 30 feet directly behind third base along the foul line, the leftfielder threw a baseball to first base. Recall that the distance between the bases on a baseball diamond is 90 feet. Draw a diagram. Then use mental math and a 3–4–5 family triangle to find the distance the ball traveled.   150 feet

Additional Answer

3.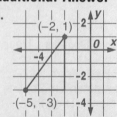

Exercises

Independent Practice

Find the distance between each pair of points whose coordinates are given. Round answers to the nearest tenth.

7.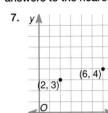

≈ 4.1 units

8.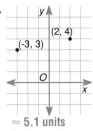

O (0, 0)

(3, -5)

≈ 5.8 units

9.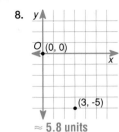

(2, 4)

(-3, 3)

≈ 5.1 units

Graph each pair of ordered pairs. Then find the distance between the points. Round answers to the nearest tenth. For graphs to Exercises 10-13, see Solutions Manual.

10. (3, 5); (3, -2) **7 units**

11. (-1, 0); (2, 7) **≈ 7.6 units**

12. (1, 5); (3, 1) **≈ 4.5 units**

13. (-2, 4); (3, -5) **≈ 10.3 units**

14. Find the distance between $A(-5, -2)$ and $C(1, -2)$. **6 units**

15. The coordinates of point R and S are (4, 3) and (1, 6). What is the distance between the points? **≈ 4.2 units**

Mixed Review

16. Solve $h - 15 = 27$. *(Lesson 2-3)* **42**

17. Solve $\frac{n}{10} = -8$. *(Lesson 7-10)* **-80**

18. **Measurement** Find the height of the tower shown at the right. *(Lesson 8-6)* **≈ 31.5 feet**

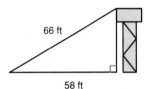

66 ft

58 ft

Problem Solving and Applications

19. **Geometry** A triangle on the coordinate plane has vertices $A(2, -1)$, $B(-2, 2)$ and $C(-6, 14)$.

   a. Draw the triangle. **See margin.**

   b. Find the perimeter of the triangle. **≈ 34.6 units**

20. **-13 or 17**

20. **Critical Thinking** The distance between points A and B is 17 units. Find the value of x if the coordinates of A and B are $(-3, x)$ and $(5, 2)$.

21. **Map Making** On a scaled street map, where the side of each square represents 1 mile, the Ball Park is located at (1, 2) and the Rollerdome is located at (6, 10). A diagonal street runs directly between the two locations. Approximately how far is it from the Ball Park to the Rollerdome? **≈ 9.4 units**

Rollerdome

Ball Park

22. **Data Search** Refer to pages 298 and 299.
   You can use the formula $d = rt$ to find the average speed (r) that an object travels, given its distance (d) and time (t). On average, how many seconds does it take for a dragonfly to travel 5 miles? **6 minutes or $\frac{1}{10}$ hour**

DATA SEARCH

Lesson 8-7 Measurement Connection: Distance on the Coordinate Plane **327**

Extending the Lesson

Science Connection Have students speak to a surveyor or cartographer to find out how triangulation is used to measure distances on Earth's surface.

Cooperative Learning Activity

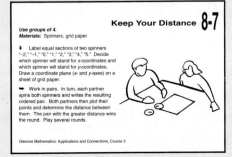

Keep Your Distance 8-7

Use groups of 4.
Materials: Spinners, grid paper

♦ Label equal sections of two spinners "-2," "-1," "0," "1," "2," "3," "4," "5." Decide which spinner will stand for x-coordinates and which spinner will stand for y-coordinates. Draw a coordinate plane (x- and y-axes) on a sheet of grid paper.

➡ Work in pairs. In turn, each partner spins both spinners and writes the resulting ordered pair. Both partners then plot their points and determine the distance between them. The pair with the greater distance wins the round. Play several rounds.

Glencoe Mathematics: Applications and Connections, Course 3

 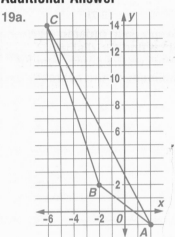
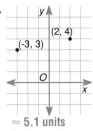
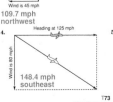

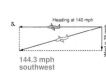

327

Lesson Resources
- Study Guide Master 8-8
- Practice Master 8-8
- Enrichment Master 8-8
- Evaluation Master, Quiz B, p. 70
- Group Activity Card 8-8

 Transparency 8-8 contains the 5-Minute Check and a teaching aid for this lesson.

🕐 **5-Minute Check**
(Over Lesson 8-7)

Graph each ordered pair. Then find the distance between the points. Round decimals to the nearest tenth.

1. (1, 2), (5, 5)   5

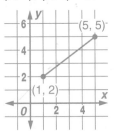

2. (−2, −2), (3, 0)   5.4

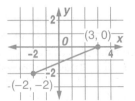

---

1 FOCUS

Motivating the Lesson

Questioning   Draw a square on the chalkboard. Draw a diagonal and ask students to describe the two triangles formed.   congruent isosceles right triangles

---

8-8 Special Right Triangles

Objective
Find missing measures in 30°-60° right triangles and 45°-45° right triangles.

In 1987, the United States regained the America's Cup trophy in yachting from Australia. *Stars and Stripes* won over *Kookaburra III* in four one-sided races. The sails on boats such as these are in the shape of right triangles.

The other two angles of the right triangle often have measurements of 30° and 60°. In a 30°–60° right triangle, the lengths of the sides are related in a special way.

🔵 Mini-Lab

Work with a partner.

Materials: compass, protractor, scissors, ruler

- Construct and cut out an equilateral triangle.
- Fold the triangle in half and cut along the fold line.
- Measure each side and each angle.
- Repeat the above steps for several other equilateral triangles.

Talk About It The hypotenuse is twice as long.

What is the relationship between the length of the hypotenuse and the length of the side opposite the 30° angle?

The relationship you discovered in the Mini-Lab is always true in a 30°–60° right triangle. The length of the side opposite the 30° angle is one-half the length of the hypotenuse.

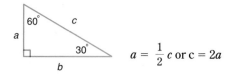

$$a = \frac{1}{2}c \text{ or } c = 2a$$

OPTIONS

Limited English Proficiency

Students will enjoy devices like puns, acronyms (see the Reteaching Activity), and silly sentences as a way of learning math and improving their English proficiency. Encourage them to create their own.

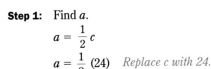

Example 1

Find the missing lengths in $\triangle PQR$.

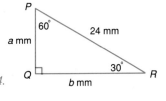

Step 1: Find a.

$$a = \frac{1}{2}c$$

$$a = \frac{1}{2}(24) \quad \textit{Replace c with 24.}$$

$$a = 12$$

Step 2: Find b.

$$c^2 = a^2 + b^2 \quad \textit{Pythagorean Theorem}$$

$$24^2 = 12^2 + b^2 \quad \textit{Replace c with 24 and a with 12.}$$

$$576 = 144 + b^2$$

$$432 = b^2 \qquad 432 \; \boxed{\sqrt{x}} \; \text{20.78461}$$

$$b \approx 20.8$$

The length of $\overline{PQ}$ is 12 millimeters, and the length of $\overline{PR}$ is about 20.8 millimeters.

Sometimes the other two angles of a right triangle have measurements of 45° and 45°. The lengths of the sides are also related in a special way.

Mini-Lab

Work with a partner.

Materials: protractor, ruler, scissors

- Construct and cut out a square.
- Fold the square in half and cut along the diagonal.
- Measure each side and each angle.
- Repeat the above steps for several other squares.

Talk About It

What is the relationship between the length of the legs in the 45°–45° right triangles? **length of legs are equal**

In a 45°–45° right triangle, the lengths of the legs are equal. $a = b$

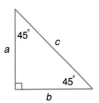

Lesson 8-8   Geometry Connection: Special Right Triangles   **329**

Using the Mini-Lab In the first Mini-Lab, students should draw a segment of arbitrary length for the base of the triangle. Setting the compass radius to the length of this segment and placing the point at each end of the segment, they should draw intersecting arcs above the segment. The point of intersection is the third vertex of the equilateral triangle.

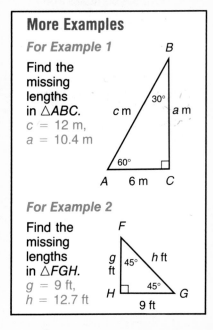

More Examples

For Example 1

Find the missing lengths in $\triangle ABC$.
$c = 12$ m,
$a = 10.4$ m

For Example 2

Find the missing lengths in $\triangle FGH$.
$g = 9$ ft,
$h = 12.7$ ft

Checking for Understanding

Exercises 1-3 are designed to help you assess students' understanding through reading, writing, speaking, and modeling. You should work through these exercises with your students and then monitor their work on Guided Practice Exercises 4-8.

Reteaching Activity

Using Language Give students the "Sshh!" rule for 30°–60° right triangles: *SSHH* means "Short Side is Half the Hypotenuse."

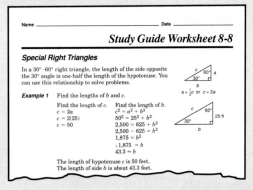

Study Guide Masters, p. 74

Name _____ Date _____

Study Guide Worksheet 8-8

Special Right Triangles

In a 30°-60° right triangle, the length of the side opposite the 30° angle is one-half the length of the hypotenuse. You can use this relationship to solve problems.

$a = \frac{1}{2}c$ or $c = 2a$

Example 1 Find the lengths of b and c.

Find the length of c.
$c = 2a$
$c = 2(25)$
$c = 50$

Find the length of b.
$c^2 = a^2 + b^2$
$50^2 = 25^2 + b^2$
$2,500 = 625 + b^2$
$2,500 - 625 = b^2$
$1,875 = b^2$
$\sqrt{1,875} = b$
$43.3 \approx b$

The length of hypotenuse c is 50 feet.
The length of side b is about 43.3 feet.

Watch for students who find relationships in 30°–60° right triangles incorrectly.

Prevent by having them draw and label a triangle using the lengths they have found; the hypotenuse should be the longest side and the side opposite the 30° angle should be the shortest.

Close

Have students compare and contrast the relationships among the length of the sides of the 30°–60° and 45°–45° right triangles.

3 PRACTICE/APPLY

Assignment Guide
Maximum: 9–20
Minimum: 9–19

For **Extra Practice**, see p. 603.

Practice Masters, p. 74

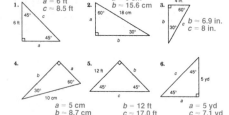

Name _____ Date _____

Practice Worksheet 8-8

Special Right Triangles

Find the unknown side lengths. Round decimals to the nearest tenth.

1. $a = 6$ ft
   $c \approx 8.5$ ft
2. $a = 9$ cm
   $b = 15.6$ cm
3. $b \approx 6.9$ in.
   $c = 8$ in.

4. $a = 5$ cm
   $b \approx 8.7$ cm
5. $b = 12$ ft
   $c \approx 17.0$ ft
6. $a = 5$ yd
   $c \approx 7.1$ yd

7. The shorter leg of a 30°-60° right triangle is 18 feet. What is the length of the other leg?
   ≈ 31.2 feet

8. One leg of a 45°-45° right triangle is 18 inches. Find the length of the hypotenuse.
   ≈ 25.5 in.

9. The length of the hypotenuse of a 30°-60° right triangle is 8.5 cm. Find the length of the side opposite the 30° angle.
   4.25 cm

10. One leg of a 45°-45° right triangle is 33.5 inches. Find the length of the hypotenuse.
    ≈ 47.4 in.

T 74
Glencoe Division, Macmillan/McGraw-Hill

330

Example 2

Find the missing lengths of △QRS.

Step 1 Find a.

$a = b$

$b = 6$

$a = 6$

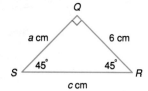

Step 2 Find c.

$c^2 = a^2 + b^2$ *The Pythagorean Theorem*

$c^2 = 6^2 + 6^2$ *Replace a and b with 6.*

$c^2 = 36 + 36$

$c^2 = 72$

$c = \sqrt{72}$

72 $\boxed{\sqrt{x}}$ 8.4852814

$c \approx 8.5$

The length of $\overline{QS}$ is 6 centimeters, and the length of $\overline{SR}$ is about 8.5 centimeters.

Checking for Understanding

Communicating Mathematics

Read and study the lesson to answer each question.

1. **Draw** a 30°–60° right triangle. Indicate which side is opposite the 30° angle. See margin.
2. **Tell** why a 45°–45° right triangle is also called an *isosceles* right triangle.
   two legs have equal length
3. **Write** a sentence describing the relationship between the hypotenuse of a 30°–60° right triangle and the leg opposite the 30° angle. $c = 2a$ where a is leg opposite 30° angle

Guided Practice

Find the lengths of the missing sides. Round answers to the nearest tenth.

4.
   $c = 10$ cm
   $b \approx 8.7$ cm

5. $a = 8$ ft
   $c \approx 11.3$ ft

6. $a = 6$ in.
   $b \approx 10.4$ in.

7. One leg of a 45°–45° right triangle is 15 centimeters long. What is the length of the other leg? 15 centimeters

8. The shorter leg in a 30°–60° right triangle is 3 inches long. What is the length of the hypotenuse? 6 inches

---

OPTIONS

Bell Ringer

Find *x*.   14.1 cm

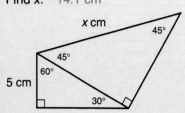

Additional Answer

1.

Exercises

Independent Practice Find the lengths of the missing sides. Round decimals to the nearest tenth.

9.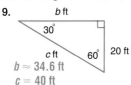
$b \approx 34.6$ ft
$c = 40$ ft

10.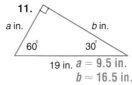
$b = 3.2$ m
$c \approx 4.5$ m

11.
19 in. $a = 9.5$ in.
$b \approx 16.5$ in.

12. One leg of a 45°–45° right triangle is 21.5 inches long. Find the length of the hypotenuse. $\approx$ 30.4 inches

13. The length of the hypotenuse of a 30°–60° right triangle is 7.5 inches. Find the length of the side opposite the 30° angle. 3.75 inches

Mixed Review 14. **Statistics** Find the median and upper and lower quartiles for the following lengths, in inches, of rope: 56, 62, 48, 71, 60, 50, 64. *(Lesson 4-6)* 60, 64, 50

15. Write $\frac{54}{81}$ in simplest form. *(Lesson 6-5)* $\frac{2}{3}$

16. Find the distance between $P(\text{-}3, 4)$ and $Q(5, \text{-}2)$. *(Lesson 8-7)* 10 units

Problem Solving and Applications 17. **Construction** Ms. Gomez wants to add an access ramp to the rear entrance of her store. The ramp makes a 30° angle with the ground. If the rear entrance is 6 feet above the ground, how long is the ramp? 12 feet

 18. **Portfolio Suggestion** Select an item from this chapter that you feel shows your best work and place it in your portfolio. Explain why you selected it.

18. See students' work.

19. **Critical Thinking** The area of a square is 400 square meters. Find the length of each of its diagonals. $\approx$ 28.3 meters

 20. **Journal Entry** Write a detailed solution of the following problem. How much material is needed to make the sail shown at the right? See margin.

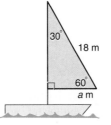

Lesson 8-8   Geometry Connection: Special Right Triangles   **331**

Extending the Lesson

Using Connections For each of several 30°–60° right triangles, have students divide the length of the longer leg by that of the shorter leg. Have them compare their results with the values in a square root table and write a sentence summarizing the results. In a 30°–60° right triangle, the length of the longer leg is $\sqrt{3}$ times the length of the shorter leg.

Cooperative Learning Activity

Two (More) Sides to the Story 8-8
Number of players: 2
Materials: Index cards, spinners

• Copy onto cards the numbers shown on the back of this card, one per card. Shuffle the cards and place them face down in a pile. Label equal sections of two spinners "30°" and "45°."

➡ Each partner selects a card. Then each partner spins one of the spinners. Try to be the first to find the lengths of the other two sides of a right triangle if the card tells the length of one side of the triangle and the spinner tells the measure of the angle opposite the side with the given length. Play several rounds.

Glencoe Mathematics: Applications and Connections, Course 3

Alternate Assessment

Speaking Draw several special right triangles on the chalkboard, indicating one length on each triangle. Have students describe how they would find the missing lengths.

Additional Answer

20. $a = \frac{1}{2} \cdot 18 = 9$;
$h = \sqrt{18^2 - 9^2} = \sqrt{243}$;
Area $= \frac{1}{2}ah = \frac{1}{2} \cdot 9 \cdot \sqrt{243}$;
The area is about 70.1 square meters of material.

Enrichment Masters, p. 74

Name _____   Date _____

Enrichment Worksheet 8-8

Tangrams

The tangram puzzle, shown at the right, is made of seven pieces. There are five 45°–45° triangles, one square, and one parallelogram.

The figure with the dotted lines shows one way to make the tangram pieces. Start by folding a square into 16 equal parts.

Create a set of tangrams. Then use all seven pieces to make each shape shown. Record your solutions.

1.
2.
3.
4.

The square and the polygons in Problems 1–4 are called *convex* because no outside angle measures less than 180°. It is possible to make 13 different convex polygons with the tangram pieces: 1 triangle, 6 quadrilaterals, 2 pentagons, and 4 hexagons.

5. Find the other 8 convex polygons. Record your solutions below.

There is more than one way to make some of the shapes.

T74
Glencoe Division, Macmillan/McGraw-Hill

331

The Chapter Study Guide and Review begins with a section on Communicating Mathematics. This includes questions that review the new terms and concepts that were introduced in the chapter.

Then, the Skills and Concepts presented in the chapter are reviewed using a side-by-side format. Encourage students to refer to the Objectives and Examples on the left as they complete the Review Exercises on the right.

The Chapter Study Guide and Review ends with problems that review Applications and Problem Solving.

Additional Answer

9. Sample answer: Rational numbers can be expressed in the form $\frac{a}{b}$, where a and b are integers and $b \neq 0$, but irrational numbers cannot be expressed in that form; rational: 0.75, irrational: $\sqrt{3}$.

Chapter

8 Study Guide and Review

Communicating Mathematics

Choose the letter of the correct word or words to complete each statement.

1. The symbol $\sqrt{}$ is used to indicate a(n) _____ square root. **b**
2. A(n) _____ is the square of a rational number. **g**
3. The set of rational numbers and the set of irrational numbers combine to form the set of _____ . **c**
4. A(n) _____ can always be expressed as a terminating or repeating decimal. **d**
5. In a right triangle, the _____ is the side opposite the right angle. **i**
6. The Pythagorean Theorem is true for any _____ . **h**
7. In a 30°–60° right triangle, the length of the side opposite the 30° angle is one-half the length of the _____ . **i**
8. Tell how you can use the Pythagorean Theorem to determine if a triangle is a right triangle. **If $c^2 = a^2 + b^2$ then the triangle is a right triangle.**
9. Explain the difference between a rational number and an irrational number. Give an example of each. **See margin.**

a. triangle
b. principal
c. real numbers
d. rational number
e. irrational number
f. square root
g. perfect square
h. right triangle
i. hypotenuse

Self Assessment

Objectives and Examples	Review Exercises
Upon completing this chapter, you should be able to:	*Use these exercises to review and prepare for the chapter test.*

- find square roots of perfect squares *(Lesson 8-1)*

  Find $\sqrt{81}$.
  Since $9^2 = 81$, $\sqrt{81} = 9$.

Find each square root.

10. $\sqrt{36}$ **6**   11. $-\sqrt{2.25}$ **-1.5**

12. $-\sqrt{\dfrac{9}{16}}$ **$-\dfrac{3}{4}$**   13. $\sqrt{\dfrac{49}{100}}$ **$\dfrac{7}{10}$**

14. $-\sqrt{169}$ **-13**   15. $\sqrt{5.29}$ **2.3**

- estimate square roots *(Lesson 8-2)*

  Estimate $\sqrt{31}$.
  $25 < 31 < 36$
  $5^2 < 31 < 6^2$
  $5 < \sqrt{31} < 6$
  Since 31 is closer to 36 than to 25, the best whole number estimate is 6.

Estimate to the nearest whole number.

16. $\sqrt{136}$ **12**   17. $\sqrt{50.2}$ **7**

18. $\sqrt{725}$ **27**   19. $\sqrt{372}$ **19**

20. $\sqrt{19.33}$ **4**   21. $\sqrt{250}$ **16**

Objectives and Examples

Review Exercises

- identify and classify numbers in the real number system *(Lesson 8-3)*

Determine whether 8.41 is a rational or irrational number.

8.41 is a terminating decimal. So it is a rational number.

Name the set or sets of numbers to which each real number belongs.

22. $\sqrt{33}$ **23.** −21

24. −0.525225 . . .   **25.** 0.686868 . . .

For answers to Exercises 22-25, see margin.

- find the length of the side of a right triangle using the Pythagorean Theorem *(Lesson 8-5)*

Find the length of the hypotenuse.

$c^2 = a^2 + b^2$
$c^2 = 6^2 + 8^2$
$c^2 = 36 + 64$
$c^2 = 100$
$c = 10$

c yd   8 yd

6 yd

The hypotenuse is 10 yards long.

Find the missing measure for each right triangle. Round decimal answers to the nearest tenth.

26. $a = 16$ ft; $c = 20$ ft $b = 12$ ft
27. $a = 5$ cm; $b = 7$ cm $c \approx 8.6$ cm
28. $b = 28$ mm; $c = 55$ mm $a \approx 47.3$ mm
29. $a = 7.5$ in.; $c = 8.5$ in. $b = 4$ in.
30. $a = 18$ m; $b = 30$ m $c \approx 35.0$ m

- solve problems using the Pythagorean Theorem *(Lesson 8-6)*

How tall is the tree? Let *b* represent the height of the tree.

$c^2 = a^2 + b^2$
$63^2 = 40^2 + b^2$
$3{,}969 = 1{,}600 + b^2$
$2{,}369 = b^2$
$48.7 \approx b$

The tree is about 48.7 feet tall.

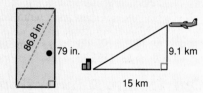

63 ft   *b* ft

40 ft

Solve. Round decimal answers to the nearest tenth.

31. How wide is the door?
36.0 in.

32. How far is the airplane from the airport?
17.5 km

86.8 in.   79 in.

9.1 km

15 km

- find the distance between two points on the coordinate plane. *(Lesson 8-7)*

Find *c*.
$c^2 = a^2 + b^2$
$c^2 = 5^2 + 3^2$
$c^2 = 34$
$c = \sqrt{34}$
$c \approx 5.8$

The distance is about 5.8 units.

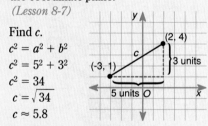

(2, 4)

c   3 units

(-3, 1)

5 units O

Graph each pair of ordered pairs. Find the distance between the points. Round decimal answers to the nearest tenth.

33. (3, 3) and (1, 6) ≈ 3.6 units
34. (-2, 1) and (3, 7) ≈ 7.8 units
35. (-2, -4) and (5, 4) ≈ 10.6 units
36. (-5, -3) and (4, -6) ≈ 9.5 units

For graphs to Exercises 33-36, see Solutions Manual.

Study Guide and Review

Chapter 8   Study Guide and Review   **333**

You may wish to use a Chapter Test from the Evaluation Masters booklet as an additional chapter review. The two free-response forms are shown below. One of the two multiple-choice forms is shown on the next page.

Evaluation Masters, pp. 68–69

Name _____ Date _____

Form 2A
Chapter 8 Test

Find each square root.
1. $\sqrt{36}$ 2. $\sqrt{\frac{16}{49}}$ 3. $-\sqrt{1.44}$

Estimate to the nearest whole number.
4. $\sqrt{30}$ 5. $\sqrt{263}$ 6. $\sqrt{141.6}$

Name the set or sets of numbers to which each number belongs.
7. $\sqrt{11}$ 8. $1.\overline{4}$ 9. $-\sqrt{64}$

Solve each equation. Round to the nearest tenth.
10. $m^2 = 29$ 11. $n^2 = 289$ 12. $p^2 = 0.81$

Determine whether each triangle with sides of given lengths is a right triangle.
13. 7 cm, 24 cm, 25 cm   14. 8 mm, 9 mm, 15 mm

Find the missing measure for each right triangle. Round answers to the nearest tenth.
15. a, 8 in.; b, 6 in.   16. b, 10 in; c, 15 m

17. Find the distance between (2, -4) and (-3, 5). Round to the nearest tenth.

Find the missing lengths. Round answers to the nearest tenth.
18.   19.
20.   21.
22.   23.

24. A ladder is leaning against a house. The top of the ladder is 15 feet from the ground, and the base of the ladder is 12 feet from the side of the house. How long is the ladder? Round to the nearest tenth.

25. Find the distance you travel if you drive your car at an average speed of 48 mph for 4.5 hours. Use the formula $d = rt$.

BONUS Solve $x^2 + x^2 = 70$. Round to the nearest tenth.

1. -6
2. $\frac{4}{7}$
3. -1.2
4. 5
5. 16
6. 12
7. irrational, real
8. rational, real
9. integer, rational, real
10. 5.4 or -5.4
11. 17 or -17
12. 0.9 or -0.9
13. right triangle
14. not a right triangle
15. 10 in.
16. 11.2 m
17. 10.3 units
18. 11.3 in.
19. 5.2 ft
20. $a = 5$ mm; $c = 7.1$ mm
21. $a = 1.8$ cm; $b = 3.0$ cm
22. $a = 3.5$ yd; $c = 4.9$ yd
23. $a = 3.2$ mi; $b = 5.5$ mi
24. 19.2 ft
25. 216 mi

5.9 or -5.9

68
Glencoe Division, Macmillan/McGraw-Hill

Name _____ Date _____

Form 2B
Chapter 8 Test

Find each square root.
1. $\sqrt{49}$ 2. $\sqrt{\frac{81}{64}}$ 3. $-\sqrt{2.25}$

Estimate to the nearest whole number.
4. $\sqrt{42}$ 5. $\sqrt{292}$ 6. $\sqrt{173.6}$

Name the set or sets of numbers to which each number belongs.
7. 0.151515111...   8. 3.14   9. -5

Solve each equation. Round to the nearest tenth.
10. $r^2 = 3$ 11. $s^2 = 121$ 12. $t^2 = 200$

Determine whether each triangle with sides of given lengths is a right triangle.
13. 60 ft, 100 ft, 80 ft   14. 5 cm, 13 cm, 12 cm

Find the missing measure for each right triangle. Round answers to the nearest tenth.
15. a, 10 in.; b, 24 in.   16. b, 15 mm; c, 17 mm

Find the missing lengths. Round answers to the nearest tenth.
17.   18.
19.   20.
21.   22.

23. Find the distance between (-3, 0) and (2, 1). Round to the nearest tenth.

24. A ten-foot ladder is leaning against a house. The base of the ladder is 5 feet from the side of the house. At what height does the ladder touch the house?

25. Find your average speed if you drive your car 420 miles for 8 hours. Use the formula $d = rt$.

BONUS A television screen has a 7-inch width and its diagonal measure is 9.5 inches. How high is the television screen?

1. -7
2. $\frac{9}{8}$
3. -1.5
4. 6
5. 17
6. 13
7. irrational, real
8. rational, real
9. integer, rational, real
10. 1.7 or -1.7
11. 11 or -11
12. 14.1 or -14.1
13. right triangle
14. right triangle
15. 26 in.
16. 8 mm
17. 13 cm
18. 6.9 in.
19. $c = 42$ in.; $b = 36.4$ in.
20. 7.4 ft
21. $a = 7.5$ mm; $b = 13.0$ mm
22. $a = b = 12.0$ mi
23. 5.1 units
24. 8.7 ft
25. 52.5 mph

6.4 in.

69
Glencoe Division, Macmillan/McGraw-Hill

334

Objectives and Examples

- find the missing measures in 30°-60° right triangles (*Lesson 8-8*)

Find the length of $\overline{AB}$ in $\triangle ABC$.

$$a = \frac{1}{2}C$$
$$a = \frac{1}{2}(16)$$
$$a = 8$$

The length of $\overline{AB}$ is 8 meters.

- find the missing measures in 45°-45° right triangles (*Lesson 8-8*)

Find the length of $\overline{YZ}$ in $\triangle XYZ$.

$$a = b$$
$$8 = b$$

The length of $\overline{YZ}$ is 8 feet.

Review Exercises

Find the missing lengths.

37.   38.
$a = 14$ in. $b \approx 8.7$ km
$b \approx 24.2$ in. $c = 10$ km

Find the missing lengths.

39.   40.
$a = 15$ mm $b = 6$ m
$c \approx 21.2$ mm $c \approx 8.5$ m

Applications and Problem Solving

41. **Skateboarding** Suppose a skateboarder travels a distance of 20 meters in 16 seconds. Find the average speed. Use the formula $d = rt$. (*Lesson 8-4*) **1.25 m/sec**

42. **Sales** How much profit does the owner of The Computer Connection make on a microcomputer that sells for $599.99 if the computer cost her $390.29, and she paid the salesperson a commission of $49.72? Use the formula $P = I - E$, where P is profit, I is income, and E is expense. (*Lesson 8-4*) **$159.98**

Curriculum Connection Projects

- **Science** Step off the length and width of a rectangular area of your school grounds. Calculate the diagonal, in steps. Then step off the diagonal to see if your answer is correct.

- **Sports** Research the dimensions of a tennis court, volleyball court, and a basketball court. Find the length of each diagonal.

Read More About It

Galen, Laura. *Out of this World: Science Fiction and Fantasy.*
Froman, Robert. *Angles Are Easy as Pie.*
Chrisman, Arthur Bowie. *Shen of the Sea.*

334 **Chapter 8** Study Guide and Review

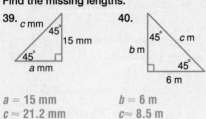

8 Test

1. Find the distance between $R(-3, -3)$ and $S(4, 5)$. Round to the nearest tenth. ≈ 10.6 units

Find each square root.

2. $-\sqrt{144}$ -12

3. $\sqrt{\dfrac{49}{64}}$ $\dfrac{7}{8}$

4. $-\sqrt{0.25}$ -0.5

Estimate to the nearest whole number.

5. $\sqrt{66}$ ≈ 8

6. $\sqrt{605}$ ≈ 25

7. $\sqrt{137.8}$ ≈ 12

8. State the Pythagorean Theorem. See Solutions Manual. For answers to Exercises 9-12, see Solutions Manual.

Name the set or sets of numbers to which each real number belongs.

9. $\sqrt{13}$

10. $-\sqrt{25}$

11. $8.1212\ldots$

12. $\sqrt{28.347}$

Solve each equation.

13. $y^2 = 80$ ≈ 8.9 or ≈ -8.9

14. $x^2 = 225.$ = 15 or -15

Find the missing measure for each right triangle. Round decimal answers to the nearest tenth.

15. $a = 1.5$ km; $b = 2$ km 2.5 km

16. $b = 20$ in.; $c = 33$ in. 26.2 in.

Determine whether each triangle with sides of given measure is a right triangle.

17. 16 cm, 34 cm, 30 cm yes

18. 12 ft, 18 ft, 23 ft no

19. A ladder is leaning against a house. The top of the ladder is 20 feet from the ground and the base of the ladder is 15 feet from the side of the house. How long is the ladder? 25 ft

20. Find the perimeter of a right triangle with legs of 9 inches and 8 inches. about 29 in.

Find the missing lengths.

21.
34 in. 60° a in.
30°
b in.
$a = 17$ in.
$b ≈ 29.4$ in.

22.
b mm
30°
a mm 60° 57 mm
$a = 28.5$ mm
$b ≈ 49.4$ mm

23.
12 yd 45° c yd
45°
b yd
$b = 12$ yd
$c ≈ 17.0$ yd

24.
20 cm
45°
a cm 45° c cm
$a = 20$ cm
$c ≈ 28.3$ cm

25. The formula for finding gas mileage is $m = \dfrac{d}{g}$, where m is miles per gallon, d is the distance traveled, and g is the number of gallons of gasoline used. Suppose your car averages 28 miles per gallon on the highway, and your car's gas tank holds 13 gallons of gasoline. Can you drive 400 miles on one tank of gas? Explain why or why not.
No; you can only go 28 · 13 or 364 miles.

Bonus In a rectangular container, all pairs of intersecting edges are perpendicular. What is the length of the diagonal of the container shown at the right? ≈ 7.1 m

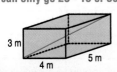
3 m
4 m
5 m

Using the Chapter Test

This page may be used as a chapter test or another chapter review.

Evaluation Masters, pp. 64–65

Name _____ Date _____

Form 1A _____ *Chapter 8 Test*

1. Find $\sqrt{81}$.
   A. 8   B. -8   C. 9   D. -9   1. ___D___
2. Find $\sqrt{\frac{25}{36}}$.
   A. $\frac{6}{6}$ B. 5   C. $\frac{5}{6}$ D. 6   2. ___C___
3. Find $\sqrt{2.56}$.
   A. 1.6   B. 16   C. 25.6   D. 0.256   3. ___A___
4. Estimate $\sqrt{44}$ to the nearest whole number.
   A. 7   B. 8   C. 6   D. 9   4. ___A___
5. Estimate $\sqrt{345}$ to the nearest whole number.
   A. 20   B. 22   C. 19   D. 21   5. ___C___
6. Estimate $\sqrt{250.9}$ to the nearest whole number.
   A. 17   B. 16   C. 14   D. 15   6. ___B___
7. Name the sets of numbers to which $\sqrt{5}$ belongs.
   A. rationals, reals   B. integers, reals   C. irrationals, reals   D. Both A and B   7. ___C___
8. Name the sets of numbers to which $\frac{7}{8}$ belongs.
   A. rationals, reals   B. integers, reals   C. irrationals, reals   D. Both A and B   8. ___A___
9. Name the sets of numbers to which $-\sqrt{9}$ belongs.
   A. rationals, reals   B. integers, reals   C. irrationals, reals   D. Both A and B   9. ___D___
10. Solve $d^2 = 55$. Round to the nearest tenth.
    A. 11   B. 5   C. 7.4   D. 7.4 or -7.4   10. ___D___
11. Solve $e^2 = 361$.
    A. 19 or -19   B. 19   C. -19   D. 36.1   11. ___A___
12. Solve $f^2 = 1.69$.
    A. 1.3   B. 1.3 or -1.3   C. -1.3   D. 0.13 or -0.13   12. ___B___
13. Which measurements belong to a right triangle?
    A. 8 in., 6 in., 10 in.   B. 14 mi, 48 mi, 50 mi   C. 3 cm, 5 cm, 7 cm   D. Both A and B   13. ___D___
14. Which measurements do not belong to a right triangle?
    A. 21 yd, 35 yd, 28 yd   B. 30 mm, 34 mm, 18 mm   C. 3 in., 4 in., 5 in.   D. Both A and B   14. ___B___

64
Glencoe Division, Macmillan/McGraw-Hill

Name _____ Date _____

Chapter 8 Test, Form 1A (continued)

In Exercises 15 and 16, find the missing measure for each right triangle. Round answers to the nearest tenth.

15. a, 5 cm; b, 18 cm
    A. 18.7 cm   B. 3.6 cm   C. 19.5 cm   D. 16.0 cm   15. ___A___
16. b, 15 ft; c, 20 ft
    A. 12 ft   B. 25 ft   C. 5 ft   D. 13.2 ft   16. ___D___
17. Find the distance between $(-2, 4)$ and $(3, -1)$. Round to the nearest tenth.
    A. 7.1 units   B. 8.0 units   C. 3.2 units   D. 4.0 units   17. ___A___

In Exercises 18-23, find the missing length. Round answers to the nearest tenth.

18. 13 in. x 13 in. 20 in.
    A. 15.2 in.   B. 14.7 in.   C. 8.3 in.   D. 10.3 in.   18. ___C___
19. x 5 cm 5 cm
    A. 7.1 cm   B. 4 cm   C. 3.2 cm   D. 8.2 cm   19. ___A___
20. 30° 10 yd 60° x
    A. 8 yd   B. 7 yd   C. 6 yd   D. 5 yd   20. ___D___
21. 45° x 45° 6 ft
    A. 3 ft   B. 8.5 ft   C. 6 ft   D. 12 ft   21. ___B___
22. 2.3 in. x 60° 30°
    A. 4.0 in.   B. 4.6 in.   C. 5.1 in.   D. 5.8 in.   22. ___A___
23. 60° 4.8 ft x 30°
    A. 2.2 ft   B. 2.1 ft   C. 2.4 ft   D. 3.0 ft   23. ___C___
24. Sandy walked 3 miles south, then walked 4 miles east. How far was Sandy from the starting point?
    A. 4 mi   B. 2 mi   C. 5 mi   D. 3 mi   24. ___C___
25. What is the average speed of a baseball if it takes 0.8 seconds for a catcher to throw the ball to the pitcher, 60 feet away? Use the formula $d = rt$.
    A. 85 ft/s   B. 75 ft/s   C. 90ft/s   D. 100 ft/s   25. ___B___

BONUS Solve $2e^2 = 10 + e^2$. Round to the nearest tenth.
    A. 1.1   B. 3.2   C. 1.1 or -1.1   D. 3.2 or -3.2   ___D___

65
Glencoe Division, Macmillan/McGraw-Hill

Test and Review Generator software is provided in Apple, IBM, and Macintosh versions. You may use this software to create your own tests or worksheets, based on the needs of your students.

The Performance Assessment Booklet provides an alternate assessment for evaluating student progress. An assessment for this chapter can be found on pages 15–16.

9 Applications with Proportion

Previewing the Chapter

This chapter introduces ratio and proportion, and develops some of the important applications of each. Students learn the distinction between ratio and rate, and explore the golden ratio. In the **problem-solving strategy** lesson, they learn to solve problems by drawing a diagram. Students then use this strategy with these applications of proportion: similar figures, scale drawings, indirect measurement, and dilations. The chapter then investigates the side relationships in right triangles and explores the sine, cosine, and tangent ratios.

Lesson	Lesson Objectives	NCTM Standards	State/Local Objectives
9-1	Express ratios as fractions in simplest form and determine unit rates.	1–5, 7, 10	
9-1B	Find the value of the golden ratio.	1–5, 7, 8, 12, 13	
9-2	Determine if a pair of ratios form a proportion and solve proportions.	1–5, 7, 9, 10	
9-3	Solve problems by using proportions.	1–5, 7, 9, 10	
9-4	Solve problems by drawing a diagram.	1–5, 7, 8	
9-5	Identify corresponding parts of similar polygons.	1–5, 7, 9, 12	
9-6	Solve problems involving similar triangles.	1–5, 7, 9, 12, 13	
9-7	Solve problems involving scale drawings.	1–5, 7, 9, 12, 13	
9-8	Graph dilations on a coordinate plane.	1–4, 7–9, 12, 13	
9-9A	Discover ratios among the sides of a right triangle.	1–5, 7, 8, 12, 13	
9-9	Find the tangent of an angle and find the measure of an angle using the tangent.	1–5, 7–9, 12, 13	
9-10	Find the sine and cosine of an angle and find the measure of an angle using sine or cosine.	1–5, 7–9, 12, 13	

Organizing the Chapter

A complete, 1-page lesson plan is provided for each lesson in the Lesson Plans Masters Booklet.

LESSON PLANNING GUIDE

| Lesson | Materials/ Manipulatives | Extra Practice (Student Edition) | Blackline Masters Booklets | | | | | | | | | |
			Study Guide	Practice	Enrichment	Evaluation	Technology	Lab Manual	Multicultural Activities	Application and Interdisciplinary Activities	Transparencies	Group Activity Cards
9-1	calculator	p. 603	p. 75	p. 75	p. 75						9-1	9-1
9-1B	drawing paper, calculator, graph paper, scissors							p. 64				
9-2	calculator	p. 604	p. 76	p. 76	p. 76		p. 9		p. 9		9-2	9-2
9-3		p. 604	p. 77	p. 77	p. 77		p. 23			p. 23	9-3	9-3
9-4			p. 78	p. 78	p. 78						9-4	9-4
9-5		p. 604	p. 79	p. 79	p. 79	Quiz A, p. 79					9-5	9-5
9-6		p. 605	p. 80	p. 80	p. 80						9-6	9-6
9-7	map of your state, scissors, tape, large drawing paper	p. 605	p. 81	p. 81	p. 81			p. 65			9-7	9-7
9-8	graph paper, inch ruler	p. 605	p. 82	p. 82	p. 82						9-8	9-8
9-9A	protractor, metric ruler, calculator							p. 66				
9-9	calculator	p. 606	p. 83	p. 83	p. 83					p. 9	9-9	9-9
9-10	calculator	p. 606	p. 84	p. 84	p. 84	Quiz B, p. 79					9-10	9-10
Study Guide and Review			Multiple Choice Test, Forms 1A and 1B, pp. 73–76 Free Response Test, Forms 2A and 2B, pp. 77–78 Cumulative Review, p. 80 (free response)									
Test			Cumulative Test, p. 81 (multiple choice)									

Pacing Guide: Option I (Chapters 1–12) - 14 days; Option II (Chapters 1–13) - 13 days; Option III (Chapters 1–14) - 12 days
You may wish to refer to the complete **Course Planning Guides** on page T25.

OTHER CHAPTER RESOURCES

Student Edition
Chapter Opener, pp. 336–337
Mid-Chapter Review, p. 352
Cultural Kaleidoscope, p. 363
Portfolio Suggestion, p. 371
Academic Skills Test, pp. 376–377

 Manipulatives
Overhead Manipulative Resources
Middle School Mathematics Manipulative Kit

 Software/Technology
Interactive Mathematics Tools (Macintosh)
Test and Review Generator (IBM, Apple, Macintosh)
Teacher's Guide for Software Resources

Other Supplements
Transparency 9–0
Performance Assessment, pp. 17–18
Glencoe Mathematics Professional Series
Lesson Plans, pp. 96–107

INTERDISCIPLINARY BULLETIN BOARD

Architecture Connection

Objective Make a scale drawing of your school.

How To Use It Obtain the outside dimensions of your school, or a building at your school. Have students work in teams to take inside measurements and create a scale drawing of the building, its rooms, and its major features.

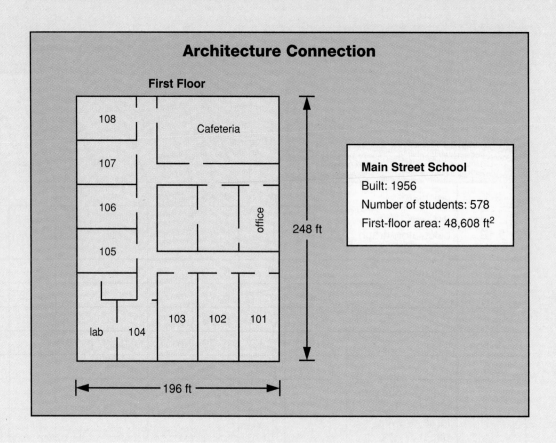

Architecture Connection

First Floor

108
107
106
105

Cafeteria

office

248 ft

lab 104 103 102 101

196 ft

Main Street School

Built: 1956

Number of students: 578

First-floor area: 48,608 ft^2

APPLICATIONS AND CONNECTIONS

Applications	Lesson	Example	Exercise
Geography	9-1	3	
Sports	9-1		42
School	9-1		43
Travel	9-1		44
Fitness	9-2	2	
Science	9-2		32
Health	9-2		33
Health	9-3	1	
Science	9-3		13
Smart Shopping	9-3		14
Photography	9-5		20
Hobbies	9-5		21
Forestry	9-6	1	
Geography	9-6	2	
Sailing	9-6		13
History	9-6		14
Architecture	9-6		15
Aviation	9-7	X	
Movies	9-7		15
Safety	9-9	1	
Surveying	9-9		25
School Clubs	9-10		25
Travel	9-10		27
Connections			
Statistics	9-3	2	15
Geometry	9-8		17

TEAM ACTIVITIES

Multicultural Experiences

Outside Field Trips Visit a survey site, where students can see how right triangles are used by surveyors to fix boundaries and find areas.

A visit to a hospital lab can show students how technicians use proportions to count blood cells, bacteria, and so on.

In-Class Speakers Invite an artist to discuss the importance of proportion and the golden ratio in art.

A draftsperson can demonstrate techniques used to make scale drawings.

SUPPLEMENTARY BLACKLINE MASTER BOOKLETS

Some of the blackline masters for enhancing this chapter are shown below.

Application and Interdisciplinary Activity Masters, pp. 9, 23

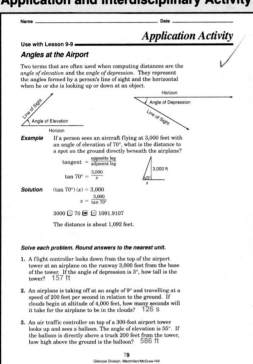

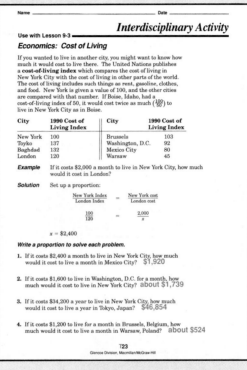

Multicultural Activity Masters, p. 9

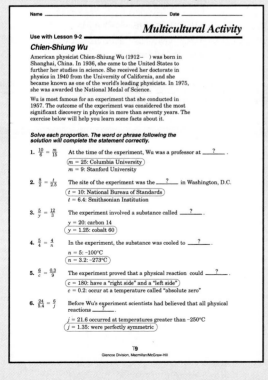

Technology Masters, p. 9

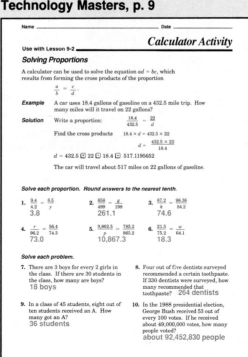

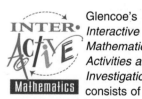
336d

MAKING MATHEMATICS RELEVANT

Spotlight on Travel and Money

Tourism is big business. Tourists spent $16.5 billion in France and $11.4 billion in Italy in 1989. California took in more than $26 billion from tourists in 1990.

Tourist dollars go farther in some places than in others. In Buenos Aires, Argentina, goods and services cost only about half of what they cost in Athens, Greece. Also affecting the value of the tourist dollar is the foreign exchange rate, which changes daily. A U.S. visitor to Italy could buy three times as many Italian lira for one U.S. dollar in 1985 as could be bought in 1970.

Chapter

9

Applications with Proportion

Spotlight on Travel and Money

Have You Ever Wondered...

- What it means when the United States dollar has an exchange rate of 1:19 with Jamaican dollars?

- What it means when the cost of living in Paris, France, is 1:1 with the cost of living in New York City?

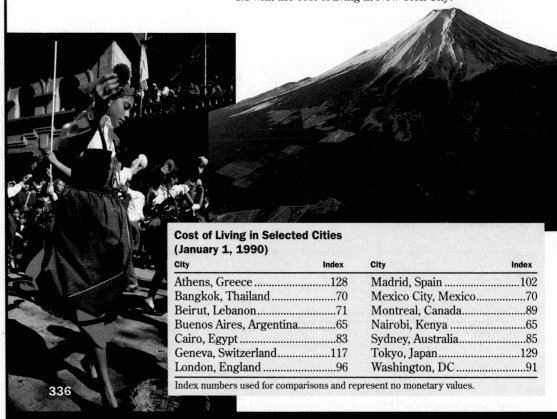

Cost of Living in Selected Cities (January 1, 1990)

City	Index	City	Index
Athens, Greece	128	Madrid, Spain	102
Bangkok, Thailand	70	Mexico City, Mexico	70
Beirut, Lebanon	71	Montreal, Canada	89
Buenos Aires, Argentina	65	Nairobi, Kenya	65
Cairo, Egypt	83	Sydney, Australia	85
Geneva, Switzerland	117	Tokyo, Japan	129
London, England	96	Washington, DC	91

Index numbers used for comparisons and represent no monetary values.

336

"Have You Ever Wondered?" Answers

- A Jamaican dollar is worth only $\frac{1}{19}$ of a U.S. dollar.
- It costs about the same amount to live in either city.

Chapter Project

Travel and Money
Working a group.

1. Design a questionnaire for your friends to find out whether they have traveled or lived in another country or state. Ask them what items, such as food, cab fare, or movies, were cheaper or more expensive than what they are at home.

2. Organize your data. Make a bar graph to compare the differentcosts of one item in different states and/or countries.

Looking Ahead

In this chapter, you will see how mathematics can be used to answer questions about travel and money. The major objectives of the chapter are to:

- express ratios as fractions and determine unit rates

- solve problems by using proportions and drawing diagrams

- solve problems involving similar triangles and scale drawings

- graph dilations on a coordinate plane

- find the tangent, sine, and cosine of an angle

Exchange Rates (January 3, 1994)

Country	Amount Equivalent to $1 U.S. Currency
Australia	1.47 dollars
Britain	0.68 pounds
Canada	1.324 dollars
France	5.91 francs
India	31.13 rupee
Japan	111.61 yen
Mexico	3.105 pesos
Poland	20,438 zloty

337

DATA ANALYSIS

Have students study the cost-of-living and exchange-rate tables. Then ask the following questions.

- *Which city is about $\frac{3}{4}$ as expensive to live in as Geneva, Switzerland?* Montreal, Canada

- *About how much is a French franc worth in U.S. currency?* about $0.17

- *About how much is a British pound worth in U.S. currency?* about $1.48

Data Search

A question related to these data is provided in Lesson 9-2, page 346, Exercise 34.

CHAPTER PROJECT

The purpose of the project is for students to work with ratios. Students should collect data that will allow them to express the results for each group they survey as a portion of the whole. Specify particular types of displays or allow students to design their own displays.

Allow several days to complete the project.

Chapter Opener Transparency

Transparency 9-0 is available in the Transparency Package. It provides another full-color, motivating activity that you can use to capture students' interest.

Lesson Resources
- Study Guide Master 9-1
- Practice Master 9-1
- Enrichment Master 9-1
- Group Activity Card 9-1

 Transparency 9-1 contains the 5-Minute Check and a teaching aid for this lesson.

5-Minute Check
(Over Chapter 8)

1. Find $-\sqrt{81}$. -9
2. Estimate $\sqrt{52}$ to the nearest whole number.
   7
3. Give an example of an irrational number.
   Sample answers: π, $\sqrt{11}$
4. A right triangle has a hypotenuse measuring 15 inches and a leg measuring 12 inches. Find the length of the other leg.   9 in.

1 FOCUS

Motivating the Lesson

Questioning   On the chalkboard, write the number of right-handed students in the class and the number of left-handed students. Ask students to suggest ways to compare the numbers.

2 TEACH

Using Connections   Point out the similarity between the terms *ratio* and *rational number*. Ask students to explain the relationship.   A rational number can be expressed in the form $\frac{a}{b}$, that is, as a ratio.

Teaching Tip   In Example 2, point out that the ratio could also be written using the foot as the common unit, without affecting the result.

$$\frac{6 \text{ inches}}{1 \text{ foot}} = \frac{\frac{1}{2} \text{ foot}}{1 \text{ foot}} = \frac{1}{2}$$

338

9-1 Ratios and Rates

Objectives
Express ratios as fractions in simplest form and determine unit rates.

Words to Learn
ratio
rate
unit rate

At the time of the 1991 All-Star Game, the Texas Rangers led the American League West division by winning 44 of their first 77 games. You can compare these two numbers using a **ratio**.

Ratio	A ratio is a comparison of two numbers by division.

The ratio that compares 44 to 77 can be written as follows.

44 to 77   44:77   44 out of 77 $\frac{44}{77}$

Since a ratio can be written as a fraction, it can also be simplified. Since 44 and 77 have a common factor of 11, the ratio $\frac{44}{77}$ is equivalent to $\frac{4}{7}$.

Examples

Express each ratio in simplest form.

1   16 brown-eyed students: 20 blue-eyed students

$$\frac{16}{20} = \frac{4}{5} \qquad \textit{Divide the numerator and denominator by their GCF, 4.}$$

LOOK BACK
You can review GCF on page 221.

The ratio in simplest form is $\frac{4}{5}$ or 4:5.

2   6 inches out of 1 foot

$$\frac{6 \text{ inches}}{1 \text{ foot}} = \frac{6 \text{ inches}}{12 \text{ inches}} \qquad \textit{1 foot = 12 inches}$$

$$\frac{6}{12} = \frac{1}{2} \qquad \textit{The GCF of 6 and 12 is 6.}$$

The ratio in simplest form is $\frac{1}{2}$ or 1 out of 2.

The ratios in Examples 1 and 2 compare quantities with the same unit or quantities that can be rewritten so that the units are the same. Often it is necessary to compare two quantities with different units. For example, $\frac{\$10.00}{8.7 \text{ gallons}}$ compares the number of dollars spent for gasoline to the number of gallons purchased. This type of ratio is called a **rate**.

OPTIONS

Team Teaching

Ratios and rates are common in all disciplines. Ask the other teachers on your team to call attention to them and to distinguish between the two. Suggestions for curriculum integration are:

Social Studies: inflation rates

Language: reading rates

Health: innoculation rates

Rate	A rate is a ratio of two measurements with different units.

When a rate has a denominator of 1, it is called a **unit rate.** This type of rate is frequently used when comparing statistics.

Example 3 *Problem Solving*

Geography In 1990, Texas had a population of 16,991,000 and covers an area of 266,807 square miles. Washington had a population of 4,761,000 with an area of 68,139 square miles. Which state was more densely populated?

First, find the rate of people per square mile for each state. Then make a comparison.

 To find the unit rate, divide both the numerator and the denominator by the denominator. Use your calculator.

Texas

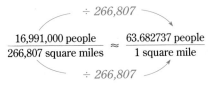

$\div 266,807$

$$\frac{16,991,000 \text{ people}}{266,807 \text{ square miles}} \approx \frac{63.682737 \text{ people}}{1 \text{ square mile}}$$

$\div 266,807$

Texas has about 63.7 people per square mile.

> **Problem Solving Hint**
> • • • • • • • • •
> You can also find the unit rate by dividing the numerator by the denominator.

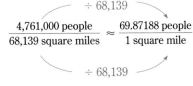

Washington

$\div 68,139$

$$\frac{4,761,000 \text{ people}}{68,139 \text{ square miles}} \approx \frac{69.87188 \text{ people}}{1 \text{ square mile}}$$

$\div 68,139$

Washington has about 69.9 people per square mile.

Washington has more people per square mile than Texas. So Washington is more densely populated.

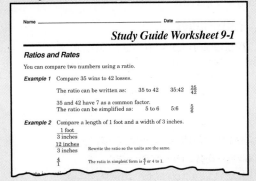

3 PRACTICE/APPLY

Alternate Assessment

Modeling   Have students count several types of classroom objects—books, writing instruments, and so on—and compare them using rates and ratios.

Additional Answers

1. A ratio is the comparison of two numbers by division with the same units of measurement, while a rate is a comparison of two numbers with different units of measurement.
2. A unit rate is frequently used when comparing statistics. Sample examples: miles per gallon; number of students per teacher
36. See below.

Practice Masters, p. 75

Name _____ Date _____

Practice Worksheet 9-1

Ratios and Rates
Express each ratio or rate as a fraction in simplest form.

1. 9 to 28 $\frac{9}{28}$
2. 30 out of 50 doctors $\frac{3}{5}$
3. 84 students to 3 teachers $\frac{28}{1}$
4. 22 players:2 teams $\frac{11}{1}$
5. 15:50 $\frac{3}{10}$
6. 19 out of 76 $\frac{1}{4}$
7. 20 wins in 32 games $\frac{5}{8}$
8. 4 boys to 6 girls $\frac{2}{3}$
9. 5 days per calendar year $\frac{1}{73}$
10. $8 for 2 tickets $\frac{4}{1}$
11. 14 wins:35 losses $\frac{2}{5}$
12. 40 minutes per hour $\frac{2}{3}$
13. 12 students:$54 $\frac{2}{9}$
14. 18 inches:1 yard $\frac{1}{2}$
15. 6 hits in 14 times at bat $\frac{3}{7}$
16. 1 inch per 1 foot $\frac{1}{12}$

Express each comparison as a rate in simplest form. Tell whether the simplest form is a unit rate.

17. 102 miles in 8 hours $\frac{51\ mi}{4h}$; no
18. 62 cubic yards to 124 carts $\frac{1\ cu.\ yd}{2\ carts}$; no
19. $84 saved in 7 weeks $\frac{$12}{1\ wk}$; yes
20. 108 students in 3 classrooms $\frac{36\ students}{1\ classroom}$; yes

Express each as a unit rate.

21. $10.81 for 23 pounds   47¢/lb
22. $269.55 for 9 tickets $29.95/ticket
23. $11.97 for 9 gallons $1.33/gal
24. $12.25 for 35 newspapers   35¢/paper

T75
Glencoe Division, Macmillan/McGraw-Hill

Checking for Understanding

Communicating Mathematics

Read and study the lesson to answer each question.

1. **Tell** the difference between a ratio and a rate. See margin.
2. **Tell** why unit rates are helpful. Give two examples. See margin.
3. **Write** a ratio about the students in your class.
   a. Write your ratio in simplest form. See students' work.
   b. Is your ratio also a rate? Why? Answers will vary.

Guided Practice

Express each ratio or rate as a fraction in simplest form.

4. 5 out of 7 people $\frac{5}{7}$
5. 2 cups to 16 cups $\frac{1}{8}$
6. 20 out of 25 free throws $\frac{4}{5}$
7. 35 wins in 55 games $\frac{7}{11}$
8. 18 brown-eyed student : 12 blue-eyed students   3 brown-eyed/2 blue-eyed
9. 1 foot per 1 yard $\frac{1}{3}$

Express each comparison as a rate in simplest form. Tell whether the simplest form is a unit rate.

10. 100 miles in 4 hours   25 miles/1 hour; unit rate
11. 24 pounds lost in 8 weeks   3 pounds/1 week; unit rate
12. 4 inches of rain in 30 days   2 inches/15 days; not a unit rate
13. 102 passengers in 9 minivans   34 passengers/3 minivans; not a unit rate

Exercises

Independent Practice

Express each ratio or rate as a fraction in simplest form.

14. 11 out of 12 $\frac{11}{12}$
15. 49 tiles:77 tiles $\frac{7}{11}$
16. 27 is to 15 $\frac{9}{5}$
17. 99 wins:99 losses $\frac{1\ win}{1\ loss}$
18. 18 boys:27 students   2 boys/3 students
19. 65 out of 105 $\frac{13}{21}$
20. 17 out of 51 $\frac{1}{3}$
21. 64 to 16 $\frac{4}{1}$
22. 165:200 $\frac{33}{40}$
23. 144 to 96 $\frac{3}{2}$
24. 188 students:$354   94 students/$177
25. 3 inches per foot $\frac{1}{4}$
26. 6 absences in 180 school days   1 absence/30 days
27. 20 minutes per hour $\frac{1}{3}$

Express each as a unit rate.

30. 15 students/ 1 teacher
32. $0.80/ 1 pound

28. $1.75 for 5 minutes $0.35/1 minute
29. $25 for 10 disks $2.50/1 disk
30. 300 students to 20 teachers
31. $420 for 15 tickets $28/1 ticket
32. $8.80 for 11 pounds
33. 96¢ per dozen $0.08/egg
34. $25,000 fifth-place prize money among 100 winners $250/winner

Mixed Review

35. Solve $2x - 8 = 12$. *(Lesson 2-7)* 10
36. **Statistics**   What is meant by the mean, median, and mode? *(Lesson 4-5)*
    See margin.

340   **Chapter 9**   Applications with Proportion

OPTIONS

Bell Ringer

A cheetah sprinted at a rate of 88 feet per second. Find its rate in miles per hour. 60 mph

Additional Answer

36. The mean is the sum of the data divided by the number of pieces of data. The median is the number in the middle when the data are arranged in order. The mode is the number in a set of data that appears most often.

37. **Probability** A cereal box stated that it may contain a prize. A consumer protection agency bought 50 boxes of the cereal. Five of them contained a prize. Estimate the probability of winning a prize when you buy a box of that brand of cereal. *(Lesson 6-8)* $\frac{1}{10}$

38. Order 7.35, $7\frac{2}{7}$, and $\frac{37}{5}$ from least to greatest. *(Lesson 6-10)* $7\frac{2}{7}$, 7.35, $\frac{37}{5}$

39. Find the next number in the sequence 3, 7, 11, __?__. *(Lesson 7-6)* 15

40. Name all the sets of numbers to which $\sqrt{100}$ belongs. *(Lesson 8-3)* natural numbers, whole numbers, integers, rational numbers, real numbers

Problem Solving and Applications

41. **Critical Thinking** Ms. Al-Khwarizmi works for a law firm from a computer in her home. The computer communicates with the law office by use of a telephone modem. The telephone bill for the modem was $7.50 for 18 minutes of use. Find the unit rate for one hour of use. **$25 per hour**

42. $\frac{3 \text{ wins}}{2 \text{ losses}}$

42. **Sports** In the first ten games of the season, the Pittsburgh Pirates won 6 games. What is their win:loss ratio in simplest terms?

43. Eisenhower Middle School

43. **School** Eisenhower Middle School has 24 computers and 432 students. Thales Central Middle School has 567 students and 27 computers. In which school would you have a better chance of getting computer time?

DATA SEARCH

44a. 59 miles per hour

44. **Data Search** Refer to page 666. Enrique Perez can drive from Charlotte, North Carolina to Birmingham, Alabama in about 7 hours.

   a. Find the unit rate of miles per hour or average speed of the car.

   b. If the speed limit is 55 miles per hour, should the State Trooper give him a ticket for speeding? **yes**

45. **Mathematics and Sports** Read the following paragraphs.

The modern game of baseball was invented by Abner Doubleday at Cooperstown, New York in 1839. In 1845, Alexander J. Cartwright established standard rules for the game and organized the Knickerbocker Baseball Club of New York.

Since the beginning of baseball, statisticians have kept track of players' performances. For example, a player's batting average is really a ratio.

$$\frac{\text{number of hits}}{\text{number of times at bat}} = \text{batting average}$$

In the 1991 baseball season, Jeff Treadway led the Atlanta Braves in individual batting with 98 hits in 306 times at bat. To the nearest thousandth, what was his batting average? **0.320**

Lesson 9-1 Ratios and Rates **341**

Extending the Lesson

Mathematics and Sports Ask students to write a ratio describing the relationship between a team's win-loss record and the total number of games played. Have students read the sports section of a local newspaper and calculate the team winning percentage for various teams during the current season.

Cooperative Learning Activity

Go the Distance 9-1

Use groups of 4.

Materials: Yard stick, watch or clock with second hand, masking tape, objects that can be rolled

▸ Use masking tape to mark off a distance of 15 feet in the classroom or in the hallway. Each group member walks 15 feet at his or her normal pace, while the other group members record the time in seconds it takes to walk this distance. Then each group member rolls an object such as a ball or a roll of tape 15 feet, while group members record the time it takes for the object to roll 15 feet.

▸ For each person and object divide the distance traveled (15 feet) by the number of seconds. This gives you the unit rate. Now multiply the denominator by 3,600 to change the unit from seconds to hours and divide the numerator by 5,280 to change feet to miles. Compare the speeds in miles per hour.

Glencoe Mathematics: Applications and Connections, Course 3

NCTM Standards: 1–5, 7, 8, 12, 13

Management Tips

For Students Careful square counting is critical for success in this lab. Urge all members of each group to agree on the location of each new cut before it is made.

For the Overhead Projector
Overhead Manipulative Resources provides appropriate materials for teacher or student demonstration of the activities in this Mathematics Lab.

1 FOCUS

Introducing the Lab

Ask students to find a decimal approximation for the expression $\frac{1 + \sqrt{5}}{2}$. 1.618034 Write the approximation on the chalkboard and promise to return to it later in the lab.

9-1B The Golden Ratio

A Follow-Up of Lesson 9-1

Objective
Find the value of the golden radio.

Materials
graph paper
scissors
calculator
drawing paper

The ancient Greeks were concerned with aesthetics. That means they wanted to know what made some things more pleasing to look at than other things. For example, many Greek philosophers and mathematicians searched for the perfect, beautiful rectangle. In these rectangles, the ratio of the length to the width always resulted in the same ratio. This ratio became known as the **golden ratio,** and the rectangles were called **golden rectangles.**

Try this!

Work in groups of three.

- Cut a rectangle out of graph paper that is 34 squares by 21 squares. Find the ratio of length to width and record your result. Express the ratio as a decimal. $\frac{34}{21} \approx 1.62$

- **Step 1** Draw a square so that the edge along the width of the square is one side of the square. Cut this square from the rectangle.

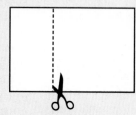

Step 2 Measure the new rectangle that remains. Record its length and width. Express the ratio of length to width as a decimal. Record your result. $\frac{21}{13} \approx 1.62$

- Repeat Steps 1 and 2 with your new rectangle. Record the measurements and ratio. $\frac{13}{8} \approx 1.63$

- Continue repeating the steps and recording your information until the remaining rectangle is 1 square by 2 squares. $\frac{8}{5} \approx 1.6$; $\frac{5}{3} \approx 1.67$; $\frac{3}{2} \approx 1.5$; $\frac{2}{1} \approx 2.0$

What do you think? 1. Except for 2.0, all are near 1.6.

1. Make a conjecture about the ratios you recorded.

2. Does your conjecture hold true for any rectangle? Draw several rectangles to support your answer. No; see students' work.

3. If the rectangle above were described as a golden rectangle, what do you think is the value of the golden ratio? about 1.6

Applications For Exercises 4-6, see students' work.

Investigate the ratio of the two measurements in each situation. Which ones are close to the golden ratio?

4. Find a painting of a landscape. Measure the height of the painting and the distance from the horizon line to the bottom of the painting.

5. Measure the height of each person in your group. Then measure the distance from the floor to each person's navel.
   a. Find the ratio for each person.
   b. Find the average ratio for the group.

6. Measure the height of your face and the width of your face at your cheekbone. Compare your ratio with those in your group.

The ancient Greeks considered the value of the golden ratio to be 1.618. In Exercises 7–9, a rectangle has been drawn. Measure each rectangle and determine how closely it resembles a golden rectangle.

7. The Parthenon   8. Bill Clinton   9. Augustus
   (Greece, 450 B.C.)   (1994)   (Rome, 20 B.C.)

For Exercises 7-9, see students' work.

Extension

10. The spiral of the chambered nautilus follows the pattern of the golden rectangle.
    a. Trace the figure at the right. It is a smaller version of the golden rectangle you cut apart at the beginning of this lesson. See students' work.

    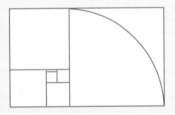

    b. An arc connects the opposite corners of the large square. Sketch an arc that connects the opposite corners of the next largest square. Continue the process. See students' work.

Mathematics Lab 9-1B   The Golden Ratio   **343**

343

OPTIONS

Lab Manual You may wish to make copies of the blackline master on p. 64 of the *Lab Manual* for students to use as a recording sheet.

Lab Manual, p. 64

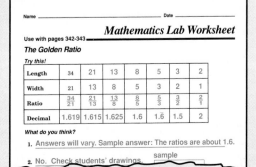

Name _____   Date _____

Mathematics Lab Worksheet

Use with pages 342-343

The Golden Ratio

Try this!

Length	34	21	13	8	5	3	2
Width	21	13	8	5	3	2	1
Ratio	$\frac{34}{21}$	$\frac{21}{13}$	$\frac{13}{8}$	$\frac{8}{5}$	$\frac{5}{3}$	$\frac{3}{2}$	$\frac{2}{1}$
Decimal	1.619	1.615	1.625	1.6	1.6	1.5	2

What do you think?

1. Answers will vary. Sample answer: The ratios are about 1.6.

2. No. Check students' drawings.   sample

2 TEACH

Using Connections After students have finished cutting squares, ask them to write the sequence of side lengths of the squares they cut off. Then ask them to identify the sequence. 21, 13, 8, 5, 3, 2; part of the Fibonacci sequence

3 PRACTICE/APPLY

Using Logical Reasoning Ask students to find the dimensions of the next larger golden rectangle, after the 34 units by 21 units rectangle they began with. 55 units by 34 units

Close

Have students give general definitions of the golden ratio and the golden rectangle, and name places the latter appears in art, architecture, and nature. Then draw attention to the decimal approximation of $\frac{1 + \sqrt{5}}{2}$ recorded on the chalkboard earlier (during Introducing the Lab). State that this is the exact ratio of length to width in a golden rectangle.

NCTM Standards: 1–5, 7, 9, 10

Lesson Resources
- Study Guide Master 9-2
- Practice Master 9-2
- Enrichment Master 9-2
- Technology Master, p. 9
- Multicultural Activity, p. 9
- Group Activity Card 9-2

 Transparency 9-2 contains the 5-Minute Check and a teaching aid for this lesson.

🕐 5-Minute Check
(Over Lesson 9-1)

Express each ratio or rate as a fraction in simplest form.

1. 8 out of 12 $\frac{2}{3}$
2. 12 girls : 20 students $\frac{3}{5}$
3. 9 inches per foot $\frac{3}{4}$

Express each as a unit rate.

4. $17.40 in 3 hours
   $5.80 per hour
5. $0.56 for 16 radishes
   $0.035 per radish

---

1 FOCUS

Motivating the Lesson

Questioning Have students read the first sentence of the lesson. Poll the class to find the number of students who watch six or more hours of television per day. Ask students to suggest ways to compare their viewing habits with those of Montana and North Dakota students.

2 TEACH

Using Connections Point out that in a proportion, the unit rates are equal.

$$\frac{3}{50} = \frac{1,200}{20,000}$$

↑   ↑

unit   unit
rate: rate:
$\frac{0.06}{1}$ $\frac{0.06}{1}$

9-2 Proportions

Objectives
Detemine if a pair of ratios form a proportion and solve proportions.

Words to Learn
proportion
cross product

TEEN SCENE
If you are an "average" teenager, you might watch television about 22 hours per week. Of those 22 hours, advertisements take 3 to 4 hours. That's about 15% of the time you spend watching television.

A recent survey reported that 3 out of 50 eighth-graders in Montana and North Dakota watch television six or more hours a day.

The ratio *3 out of 50* can be expressed as the fraction $\frac{3}{50}$. The report means that $\frac{3}{50}$ of the eighth-graders surveyed watch television six or more hours a day. There are about 20,000 eighth-graders in Montana and North Dakota. You can estimate how many of them watch television six or more hours a day by finding equivalent fractions.

This means that 3 out of 50 is equivalent to 1,200 out of 20,000. Therefore, about 1,200 eighth-graders in Montana and North Dakota watch television six or more hours a day. The equation $\frac{3}{50} = \frac{1,200}{20,000}$ states that the two ratios are equivalent. This is an example of a **proportion.**

Proportion	**In words:** A proportion is an equation that shows that two ratios are equivalent.
	Arithmetic **Algebra**
	$\frac{3}{50} = \frac{1,200}{20,000}$ $\frac{a}{b} = \frac{c}{d}, b \neq 0, d \neq 0$

There are two ways to determine if a pair of ratios form a proportion. The following example shows one way.

Example 1

Jane made 9 out of 12 free throws, and Alesha made 18 out of 24. Do these ratios form a proportion?

You can write each ratio in simplest form and compare them.

$$\frac{9}{12} = \frac{3}{4} \qquad \frac{18}{24} = \frac{3}{4}$$

Since both ratios simplify to $\frac{3}{4}$, they are equivalent.
The ratios do form a proportion.

OPTIONS

Reteaching Activity

Using Patterns Have students find the prices of 1 through 4 tapes at $4 per tape and the four resulting ratios, $\frac{\text{tapes}}{\text{price}} \left(\frac{1}{4}, \frac{2}{8}, \frac{3}{12}, \frac{4}{16} \right)$. Point out the pattern of numerators and denominators. Show that any pair of these ratios form a proportion.

Study Guide Masters, p. 76

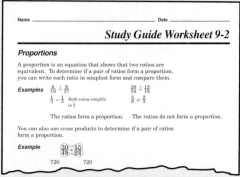

Name _____ Date _____

Study Guide Worksheet 9-2

Proportions

A proportion is an equation that shows that two ratios are equivalent. To determine if a pair of ratios form a proportion, you can write each ratio in simplest form and compare them.

Examples $\frac{6}{15} \stackrel{?}{=} \frac{9}{27}$ $\frac{20}{24} \stackrel{?}{=} \frac{12}{18}$
$\frac{1}{3} = \frac{1}{3}$ Both ratios simplify to $\frac{1}{3}$ $\frac{5}{6} \neq \frac{2}{3}$

The ratios form a proportion.   The ratios do not form a proportion.

You can also use cross products to determine if a pair of ratios form a proportion.

Example $\frac{30}{48} \stackrel{?}{=} \frac{15}{24}$
     720   720

The proportion in Example 1 can also be verified by using **cross products.** In the proportion shown at the right, $9 \cdot 24$ and $12 \cdot 18$ are cross products.

$$\frac{9}{12} = \frac{18}{24}$$
216   216

Since the products are equal, the ratios form a proportion.

Property of Proportions	**In words:** The cross products of a proportion are equal.
	In symbols: If $\frac{a}{b} = \frac{c}{d}$, then $ad = bc$. If $ad = bc$, then $\frac{a}{b} = \frac{c}{d}$.

If one value in a proportion is not known, you can use cross products to solve the proportion.

Example 2   *Problem Solving*

Fitness   To burn off a 12-ounce can of regular cola, you have to cycle for 24 minutes at 13 mph. How long would you have to cycle at 13 mph to burn off a 16-ounce bottle of cola?

Write a proportion. Let m represent the number of minutes.

$$\begin{array}{ll} ounces \rightarrow & \dfrac{12}{24} = \dfrac{16}{m} \leftarrow ounces \\ minutes \rightarrow & \qquad\qquad \leftarrow minutes \end{array}$$

Calculator Hint
· · · · · · · · · ·
To solve a proportion using a calculator, find one cross product. Then divide by the remaining number.

Do not press $=$ until after you divide.

Find the cross products. Then solve for m.

$$\frac{12}{24} = \frac{16}{m}$$
$$12 \cdot m = 24 \cdot 16$$
$$12m = 384$$
$$\frac{12m}{12} = \frac{384}{12}$$

24 ☒ 16 ÷ 12 🟰 ᴣᴢ

$$m = 32$$

You would have to cycle for 32 minutes at 13 mph to burn off a 16-ounce bottle of cola.

Checking for Understanding

Communicating Mathematics

Read and study the lesson to answer each question.

1. **Tell** two methods for determining if two ratios form a proportion.   See margin.
2. **Write** two ratios that do not form a proportion. Explain why they do not.
   Answers will vary. The cross products are not equal.

Lesson 9-2   Proportions   **345**

Bell Ringer

Find two solutions to the proportion $\frac{4}{x} = \frac{x}{9}$.   6 and -6

Additional Answer

1. Write each ratio in simplest form. The two ratios form a proportion if their simplest forms are equal. Another method is to find the cross products of the two ratios. The ratios form a proportion if the cross products are equal.

More Examples

For Example 1

Holly was absent from school 8 out of 36 days and Juan was absent 9 out of 45 days. Do these ratios form a proportion?   no

For Example 2

Denise needed 4 hours to paint 1,280 square feet of wall space. How much time would she need to paint 1,600 square feet of space?   5 h

Checking for Understanding

Exercises 1-2 are designed to help you assess students' understanding through reading, writing, speaking, and modeling. You should work through these exercises with your students and then monitor their work on Guided Practice Exercises 3-10.

Practice Masters, p. 76

Name _____ Date _____

Practice Worksheet 9-2

Proportions

Tell whether each pair of ratios forms a proportion.

1. $\frac{8}{12}, \frac{12}{18}$ yes   2. $\frac{4}{8}, \frac{5}{9}$ no

3. $\frac{5}{10}, \frac{6}{12}$ yes   4. $\frac{8}{10}, \frac{12}{15}$ yes

5. $\frac{9}{12}, \frac{12}{18}$ no   6. $\frac{15}{10}, \frac{6}{8}$ yes

7. $\frac{28}{35}, \frac{8}{10}$ yes   8. $\frac{16}{18}, \frac{24}{27}$ yes

9. $\frac{8}{12}, \frac{7}{14}$ no   10. $\frac{15}{45}, \frac{24}{63}$ no

Solve each proportion.

11. $\frac{6}{x} = \frac{10}{15}$ 2   12. $\frac{m}{4} = \frac{7}{14}$ 2

13. $\frac{8}{14} = \frac{12}{y}$ 21   14. $\frac{25}{15} = \frac{8}{6}$ 10

15. $\frac{5}{10} = \frac{4}{n}$ 8   16. $\frac{6}{21} = \frac{4}{6}$ 14

17. $\frac{x}{13} = \frac{12}{26}$ 6   18. $\frac{9}{d} = \frac{15}{40}$ 24

19. $\frac{16}{20} = \frac{c}{15}$ 12   20. $\frac{3}{d} = \frac{c}{4}$ $1\frac{5}{12}$

21. $\frac{n}{85} = \frac{7}{119}$ 5   22. $\frac{44}{72} = \frac{x}{108}$ 66

T76
Glencoe Division, Macmillan/McGraw-Hill

346

Error Analysis

Watch for students who multiply numerators and multiply denominators to find cross products.

Prevent by stressing the term *cross product* and depicting it as a pair of crossing lines, indicating how the products are to be found.

Close

Have students name ratios that form a proportion with $\frac{2}{3}$.

Sample answers: $\frac{4}{6}, \frac{6}{9}$

3 PRACTICE/APPLY

Assignment Guide
Maximum: 11–34
Minimum: 11–25 odd, 27–33

For **Extra Practice,** see p. 604.

Alternate Assessment

Speaking Write simple proportions on the chalkboard with one term missing, for example, $\frac{1}{2} = \frac{x}{6}$. Have students find the missing term using mental math.

$x = 3$

Enrichment Masters, p. 76

346

346

Guided Practice Tell whether each pair of ratios form a proportion.

3. $\frac{16}{12}, \frac{12}{9}$ yes
4. $\frac{7}{6}, \frac{6}{7}$ no
5. $\frac{75}{100}, \frac{3}{4}$ yes
6. $\frac{3}{11}, \frac{55}{200}$ no

Solve each proportion.

7. $\frac{3}{5} = \frac{c}{10}$ 6
8. $\frac{a}{0.9} = \frac{0.6}{2.7}$ 0.2
9. $\frac{120}{b} = \frac{24}{60}$ 300
10. $\frac{3}{7} = \frac{2.1}{d}$ 4.9

Exercises

Independent Practice Tell whether each pair of ratios form a proportion.

11. $\frac{8}{12}, \frac{10}{15}$ yes
12. $\frac{3}{2}, \frac{4}{6}$ no
13. $\frac{10}{12}, \frac{5}{6}$ yes
14. $\frac{2}{7}, \frac{6}{21}$ yes

15. $\frac{6}{9}, \frac{8}{12}$ yes
16. $\frac{10}{16}, \frac{25}{45}$ no
17. $\frac{75}{100}, \frac{4}{3}$ no
18. $\frac{18}{14}, \frac{54}{42}$ yes

Solve each proportion.

19. $\frac{5}{4} = \frac{y}{12}$ 15
20. $\frac{4}{100} = \frac{12}{n}$ 300
21. $\frac{2}{34} = \frac{5}{x}$ 85
22. $\frac{9}{1} = \frac{n}{14}$ 126

23. $\frac{2}{3} = \frac{7}{y}$ 10.5
24. $\frac{0.35}{3} = \frac{c}{18}$ 2.1
25. $\frac{n}{2} = \frac{7}{4}$ 3.5
26. $\frac{10}{6} = \frac{y}{26}$ $43\frac{1}{3}$

Mixed Review

27. Solve $480 \div (-40) = t$. *(Lesson 3-7)* -12

28. **Geometry** Find the value of x in the figure at the right. *(Lesson 5-1)* 40°

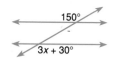

29. Solve $\left(-2\frac{6}{7}\right)\left(-5\frac{3}{5}\right) = y$. *(Lesson 7-3)* 16

30. Express *240 shrimp in 6 pounds* as a unit rate. *(Lesson 9-1)* 40 shrimp/1 pound

Problem Solving and Applications

31. **Critical Thinking** Solve $\frac{9}{x} = \frac{x}{16}$. 12, -12

32. **Science** Light travels approximately 1,860,000 miles in 10 seconds. How long will it take light to travel the 93,000,000 miles from the sun to Earth?

32. 500 seconds, or $8\frac{1}{3}$ minutes

33. **Health** Take your pulse to count the number of times your heart beats in 15 seconds. Let c = this count. Substitute your value for c into the proportion $\frac{c}{15} = \frac{p}{60}$. Then solve for p and you will know your pulse rate per minute. Answers will vary.

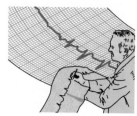

DATA SEARCH

34. **Data Search** Refer to pages 336 and 337. How many U.S. dollars are equivalent to 2,500 Japanese yen? about $22

346 **Chapter 9** Applications with Proportion

OPTIONS

Extending the Lesson

Using Cooperative Groups If the numerator of one fraction and the denominator of the other fraction in a proportion are equal, the equal terms are called *mean proportionals*:
$\frac{1}{6} = \frac{6}{36}$. Thus, 6 is the mean proportional between 1 and 36. Have students find the mean proportional for 2 and 8, and 8 and 18. 4; 12

Cooperative Learning Activity

Destination Unknown 9-2

Number of players: 3 or 4
Materials: Spinners

• Label equal sections of one spinner "10," "25," "35," "40," "50," "55." These numbers indicate speed in miles per hour. Label equal sections of a second spinner "0.5," "0.4," "0.3," "0.2," "1," and "2." These numbers indicate number of hours traveled.

➡ The object of this game is to be the first to "travel" 200 miles. One group member spins both spinners. He or she can then determine the distance "traveled" on this turn by writing and solving a proportion. (For example, a spin of 10 and 0.2 means that you traveled 10 miles per hour for 0.2 hours, so you would write $\frac{10}{1} = \frac{x}{0.2}$. Solving for x, this is a distance of 10 • 0.2, or 5, miles.) Continue in the same way, taking turns at the spinner, until the sum of the distances found by one group member is 200 miles.

Glencoe Mathematics: Applications and Connections, Course 3

9-3 Using Proportions

Objective
Solve problems by using proportions.

In Home Economics class, Wai Lui used $1\frac{1}{4}$ cups of sugar in a recipe that made 25 cookies. If he wanted to make 60 cookies, how much sugar should he use?

This problem can be solved using a proportion. In the proportion below, c represents the number of cups of sugar needed for the 60 cookies.

Technology Activity

You can learn how to use a spreadsheet to solve proportions in Technology Activity 4 on page 661.

$$\begin{array}{c} cups \rightarrow \\ cookies \rightarrow \end{array} \quad \frac{1\frac{1}{4}}{25} = \frac{c}{60} \quad \begin{array}{c} \leftarrow \ cups \\ \leftarrow \ cookies \end{array}$$

You will solve this problem in Exercise 5.

This proportion involves two rates. Remember you must always write the proportions so that the units correspond.

Example 1 · *Problem Solving*

Health Out of 60 blood cells on a microscope slide, there are 35 red blood cells. How many red blood cells would be expected in a blood sample of 75,000 blood cells?

Explore $\frac{35}{60}$ is the ratio of red cells to all blood cells. The sample has 75,000 blood cells.

66 When am I ever going to use this?

Suppose you want to triple a recipe for banana bread. The ingredients must stay in the same proportion for the bread to taste the same. When you multiply the amount of each ingredient by three, you are using proportions.

Plan Let r represent the number of red cells. Write a proportion.

$$\begin{array}{c} red\ blood\ cells \rightarrow \\ all\ blood\ cells \rightarrow \end{array} \quad \frac{35}{60} = \frac{r}{75,000} \quad \begin{array}{c} \leftarrow\ red\ blood\ cells \\ \leftarrow\ all\ blood\ cells \end{array}$$

Solve Solve the proportion.

$$\frac{35}{60} = \frac{r}{75,000}$$

35 $\boxed{\times}$ 75000 $\boxed{\div}$ 60 $\boxed{=}$ `43750`

$$r = 43,750$$

43,750 red blood cells would be expected in a sample of 75,000 blood cells.

Lesson 9-3 Using Proportions **347**

Lesson Resources
• Study Guide Master 9-3
• Practice Master 9-3
• Enrichment Master 9-3
• Technology Master, p. 23
• Interdisciplinary Master, p. 23
• Group Activity Card 9-3

 Transparency 9-3 contains the 5-Minute Check and a teaching aid for this lesson.

5-Minute Check
(Over Lesson 9-2)
Tell whether each pair of ratios form a proportion.
1. $\frac{4}{3}, \frac{6}{8}$ no
2. $\frac{4}{10}, \frac{10}{25}$ yes

Solve each proportion.
3. $\frac{10}{n} = \frac{6}{9}$ 15
4. $\frac{15}{35} = \frac{k}{14}$ 6

1 FOCUS

Motivating the Lesson

Questioning Ask students the following question: *In a survey of 20 voters, 10 said they preferred candidate Green. Of 1 million voters, how many would be expected to vote for candidate Green?* 500,000

2 TEACH

Using Problem Solving Using the proportion $\frac{2}{3} = \frac{6}{9}$ as a model, ask students whether the following proportions are true.

a. $\frac{2}{6} = \frac{3}{9}$ true
b. $\frac{2}{9} = \frac{3}{6}$ false
c. $\frac{3}{2} = \frac{9}{6}$ true

OPTIONS

Reteaching Activity

Using Calculators Show that students can solve a proportion by multiplying along the diagonal containing two of the known terms, then dividing by the remaining known term.

$$\frac{35}{84} = \frac{x}{156}$$

35 $\boxed{\times}$ 156 $\boxed{\div}$ 84 $\boxed{=}$ 65

Study Guide Masters, p. 77

Name _____ Date _____

Study Guide Worksheet 9-3

Using Proportions

You can use proportions to solve problems.

Example Of the 360 members of the kennel club who were surveyed, 190 said they would try a new dog food. If the kennel club has 2,100 members, how many could be expected to try the new dog food?

Let t represent the number of members who might try the new dog food. Write a proportion.

$$\frac{190}{360} = \frac{t}{2,100} \quad \begin{array}{l} \leftarrow \text{ Will try new dog food} \\ \leftarrow \text{ Kennel club members} \end{array}$$

$360t = 190 \times 2,100$ Cross multiply.
$360t = 399,000$
$t \approx 1,108$

About 1,108 members of the kennel club

347

348

Examine   Check your solution by substituting 43,750 for r in your original ratios. Simplify each ratio.

$$\frac{35}{60} = \frac{7}{12} \qquad \frac{43,750}{75,000} = \frac{7}{12}$$

Since both ratios are equivalent to the same fraction, they form a proportion. So, 43,750 is correct.

Example 2   *Connection*

Statistics   The Student Council at Walnut Springs Middle School decided to sell school sweatshirts as a fundraiser. They surveyed 75 students. Of those students, 53 said they would buy a sweatshirt. If there are 1,023 students in the school, about how many will buy a sweatshirt?

Let s represent the number of sweatshirts. Write a proportion.

$$\frac{53}{75} = \frac{s}{1,023}$$

53 ⊗ 1023 ÷ 75 ⊜ 722.92

$$s = 722.92$$

About 723 students will buy a sweatshirt.

Checking for Understanding

Communicating Mathematics   Read and study the lesson to answer each question.

1. **Show** how to use a calculator to solve $\frac{25}{x} = \frac{15}{9}$. See margin.

2. **Tell** which proportions from the list below could be used to solve the problem. Be prepared to defend your answer.

   If 12 eggs cost 96¢, how much will 6 eggs cost? a, b, c, f

   a. $\frac{12}{0.96} = \frac{6}{x}$ b. $\frac{0.96}{12} = \frac{x}{6}$ c. $\frac{12}{6} = \frac{0.96}{x}$

   d. $\frac{12}{x} = \frac{0.96}{6}$ e. $\frac{x}{12} = \frac{6}{0.96}$ f. $\frac{6}{12} = \frac{x}{0.96}$

Guided Practice   Write a proportion to solve each problem. Then solve.

3. 40 ounces costs $43. 25 ounces costs x. $\frac{40}{43} = \frac{25}{x}$; $26.88

4. 10 pounds cooks in 4 hours. y pounds cooks in 5.6 hours. $\frac{10}{4} = \frac{y}{5.6}$; 14 pounds

5. Refer to the cookie problem at the beginning of this lesson. How much sugar will Wai need to make 60 cookies? 3 cups

348   **Chapter 9**   Applications with Proportion

OPTIONS

Limited English Proficiency

Use foreign currency exchange rates to demonstrate proportions. Have students find the amount of their native currency that is equivalent to $1 US. Write this as a fraction and show that it forms a proportion with any other fraction representing equivalent amounts of their native currency and US currency.

Interactive Mathematics Tools

This multimedia software provides an interactive lesson that is tied directly to Lesson 9-1. Students will use ratios to convert between currencies.

Exercises

*Independent
Practice*

Use a proportion to solve each problem.

90 lines

7. $262\frac{1}{2}$ minutes

6. 60 lines can be printed in 10 seconds. k lines can be printed in 15 seconds.

7. Sue can type 2 pages in 15 minutes. How many minutes will it take her to type 35 pages?

8. The average heart beats 72 times in 60 seconds. How many times does it beat in 15 seconds? **18 times**

9. 24 cans of soft drink cost $6.24. x cans cost $4.68. **18 cans**

Mixed Review

10. Express $9\frac{3}{5}$ as a decimal. *(Lesson 6-6)* **9.6**

11. What is the negative square root of 64? *(Lesson 8-1)* **-8**

12. Solve $\frac{3}{7} = \frac{n}{28}$. *(Lesson 9-2)* **12**

*Problem Solving
and
Applications*

13. **Science** The ratio of a person's weight on the moon to his or her weight on Earth is 1:6. If you weigh 126 pounds on Earth, how much would you weigh on the moon? **21 pounds**

14. **Smart Shopping** The Winn-Dixie store sells 8 cans of Cool Cola for $2.59. Super-Duper sells 6 cans of Cool Cola for $1.79. Which is the better buy?
6 cans for $1.79

15. **Statistics** A political advisor surveyed 150 voters before election day to find their preference for mayor. The results are shown in the table below.

Candidate	Number
Alvarez	45
Cruz	54
Hoffman	33
Newton	18

Suppose 250,000 voters are expected to vote in the election. Predict the number of votes each candidate will receive.
Alvarez 75,000 votes
Cruz 90,000 votes
Hoffman 55,000 votes
Newton 30,000 votes

16. **Critical Thinking** Three friends, Arturo, Beth, and Carmen, invested $200, $300, and $500 respectively in a business. Profits will be divided in the same ratio as the investment. If the business made a profit of $1,500, what is each investor's share in the profit? **Arturo $300; Beth $450; Carmen $750**

Lesson 9-3 Using Proportions **349**

Extending the Lesson

Using Connections Have students contact statisticians, pollsters, demographers, or public opinion surveyors to find out how statistical samples are taken and how proportions are used to form projections based on survey results.

Cooperative Learning Activity

Ample Proportions 9-3

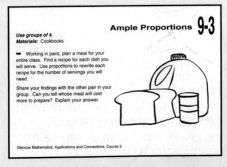

Use groups of 4.
Materials: Cookbooks

➤ Working in pairs, plan a meal for your entire class. Find a recipe for each dish you will serve. Use proportions to rewrite each recipe for the number of servings you will need.

Share your findings with the other pair in your group. Can you tell whose meal will cost more to prepare? Explain your answer.

T77

Glencoe Mathematics: Applications and Connections, Course 3

Close

Have students create and exchange word problems involving proportions.

3 PRACTICE/APPLY

Assignment Guide
Maximum: 6–16
Minimum: 6–16

For **Extra Practice**, see p. 604.

Alternate Assessment

Writing A motorist drove 110 miles in 2 hours. Have students write and solve a problem involving the same unit rate but a different time.

Enrichment Masters, p. 77

Name _____ Date _____

Enrichment Worksheet 9-3

People of the United States

A national census is taken every ten years. Our last census, in 1990, revealed that there are about 250,000,000 people in the United States, and that about 8 out of 100 of these people were 5-13 years old. To find the number of people in the United States 5-13 years old, use the ratio of people 5-13 years old and create a proportion.

$$\frac{8}{100} = \frac{n}{250,000,000}$$

To solve the proportion, find cross-products.
$8 \times 250,000,000 = 2,000,000,000$ and $n \times 100 = 100\,n$.
Then divide. $2,000,000,000 \div 100 = 20,000,000$.

In 1990, about 20,000,000 people in the United States were 5-13 years old.

Use the approximate ratios in each exercise to create a proportion, given that there are 250,000,000 people in the United States. Then solve and choose the correct answer from the choices at the right.

1. The United States is a diverse collection of different races and ethnic origins. Asians or Pacific Islanders account for about $\frac{1}{100}$ of the population of the United States. About how many people of Asian or Pacific-Island origin live in the United States? **C**   A. 200,000,000

2. African-Americans account for about $\frac{9}{100}$ of the population of the United States. About how many African-American people live in the United States? **E**   B. 22,500,000

3. People of Hispanic origin account for about $\frac{9}{100}$ of the population of the United States. About how many people of Hispanic origin live in the United States? **B**   C. 7,500,000

4. Caucasian people account for about $\frac{4}{5}$ of the population of the United States. About how many people of white or Caucasian origin live in the United States? **A**   D. 2,000,000

5. People of American-Indian, Eskimo, or Aleut origin account for about $\frac{1}{100}$ of the population of the United States. About how many people of American-Indian, Eskimo, or Aleut origin live in the United States? **D**   E. 30,000,000

T77

Glencoe Division, Macmillan/McGraw-Hill

NCTM Standards: 1–5, 7, 8

Lesson Resources
- Study Guide Master 9-4
- Practice Master 9-4
- Enrichment Master 9-4
- Group Activity Card 9-4

 Transparency 9-4 contains the 5-Minute Check and a teaching aid for this lesson.

🕐 5-Minute Check
(Over Lesson 9-3)

Use a proportion to solve each problem.

1. Jack earned $50 in 8 hours. How much will he earn in 10 hours? $62.50

2. Andrea used 4 cups of flour to make 30 pancakes. How many pancakes could she make using 2.4 cups of flour? 18 pancakes

---

1 FOCUS

Motivating the Lesson

Questioning Ask students to find the next term in the sequence 1, 2, 3, . . . and explain their reasoning. Point out that several answers are possible. Sample answers: 4 (whole numbers); 5 (add the two previous terms)

2 TEACH

Using Logical Reasoning Ask students the following question: *There are 466 pairs of rabbits in an enclosure in March and 754 pairs in April. If the number of pairs follows the Fibonacci sequence, how many pairs were there in February?* 288 pairs

350

9-4 Draw a Diagram

Objective
Solve problems by drawing a diagram.

The famous mathematician, Fibonacci, liked to invent problems to solve. One concerns a pair of rabbits.

Suppose you place a pair of adult rabbits in an enclosure on January 1. Every month, each adult pair of rabbits produces a pair of baby rabbits. These baby rabbits begin to give birth two months after their own birth. How many pairs of rabbits will there be on the following January 1?

One way to solve this problem is to draw a diagram. Diagrams are useful because they can help you decide how to solve the problem. They can also help you organize your information.

Explore Every adult pair of rabbits produces a pair of baby rabbits each month. In two months, the babies begin to reproduce.

Plan Organize the information in a drawing. Then look for a pattern.

Solve In the drawings, *R* stands for a pair of adult rabbits, *b* stands for a pair of baby rabbits, and *r* stands for a pair of rabbits that are not old enough to reproduce.

Date	Number of Pairs of Rabbits
January 1 R	1
February 1 R → b	2
March 1 b ← R r	3
April 1 r b ← R R → b	5
May 1 b ← R r b ← R R → b r	8
June 1 r b ← R b ← R r R → b b ← R r R → b	13

350   **Chapter 9**   Applications with Proportion

OPTIONS

Reteaching Activity

Using Cooperative Groups Have students work in small groups to draw diagrams to find the maximum number of pieces that can be cut from circular pizzas using the given number of straight cuts (they need *not* go through the center):

a. 1   2   **b.** 2   4

c. 3   7   **d.** 4   11

Study Guide Masters, p. 78

Name _____ Date _____

Study Guide Worksheet 9-4

Problem-Solving Strategy: Draw a Diagram

Example The streets in Sachi's city are arranged in square blocks. Sachi left her house and walked 5 blocks east and 2 blocks north to Jim's house. She and Jim walked 1 block north, 3 blocks west and 1 block north to school. After school Sachi walked 2 blocks west and 2 blocks south to Bella's house. How far from Bella's house is Sachi's house?

Explore You know the number of blocks and the directions Sachi walked to arrive at each location.
You want to find how far Bella's house is from Sachi's house.

Plan Draw a diagram to show Bella's route.

Solve

It is clear that the drawing is becoming unmanageable. So, let's look for a pattern in the number of pairs of rabbits.

LOOK BACK

You can review the
Fibonacci Sequence
on page 276.

$$1 \quad 2 \quad 3 \quad 5 \quad 8 \quad 13$$

You may recognize this sequence of numbers as the Fibonacci Sequence. Each number is the sum of the previous two numbers. *The Fibonacci Sequence actually begins with two 1s.*

Extend the sequence to find the number of pairs of rabbits on January 1.

1	2	3	5	8	13	21	34	55	89	144	233	377
J	F	M	A	M	J	J	A	S	O	N	D	J

On January 1, you will have 377 pairs of rabbits!

Examine Make a model using different color counters to picture each generation.

Checking for Understanding

1. Diagrams help organize information and help you decide how to solve the problem.

Communicating Mathematics

Read and study the lesson to answer each question.

1. **Tell** two reasons why a diagram is useful in solving problems.

2. **Tell** how many pairs of rabbits you would have on the following February 1.
   610 pairs

Guided Practice

Solve. Make a drawing.

3. A section of a theater is arranged so that each row has the same number of seats. Andrew is seated in the fifth row from the front and the third row from the back. His seat is sixth from the left and second from the right. How many seats are in this section? **49 seats**

4. Sixteen players are competing in a bowling tournament. Each player in the competition bowls against another opponent and is eliminated after one loss. How many games does the winner play? **4 games**

Lesson 9-4 Problem-Solving Strategy: Draw a Diagram **351**

Bell Ringer

You have four sticks of one length and four more exactly half the length of the first four. Show how to enclose exactly three squares of equal area with the eight sticks.

Checking for Understanding

Exercises 1-2 are designed to help you assess students' understanding through reading, writing, speaking, and modeling. You should work through these exercises with your students and then monitor their work on Guided Practice Exercises 3-4.

Close

Tell students to begin with three adult pairs of rabbits. Ask them to write the sequence representing the number of pairs of rabbits each month for the first six months. 3, 6, 9, 15, 24, 39

3 PRACTICE/APPLY

Assignment Guide
Maximum: 5–10
Minimum: 5–9
All: Mid-Chapter Review

Practice Masters, p. 78

Name _____ Date _____

Practice Worksheet 9-4

Problem-Solving Strategy: Draw a Diagram
Solve. Make a drawing.

1. The riser platform for the school chorus has four levels. Each level holds 4 chorus members more than the level below it. If the bottom level holds 12 chorus members, how many chorus members does the top level hold?
   24 members

2. A section of the school auditorium is set up so that each row has the same number of seats. Charlene is seated in the seventh row from the back and the eighth row from the front of this section. Her seat is the fourth from the right and the seventh from the left. How many seats are in this section?
   14 rows 140 seats
   10 seats

3. Eight tennis players are competing in the tournament finals. Each plays against an opponent, and the loser of that contest is eliminated. How many games must the winner of the tournament play?
   4 games

Solve using any strategy.

4. How many diagonals does an octogon have?
   20

5. The product of a number and twice the number is 50. What is the number?
   5 or −5

6. A stack of cubes is piled 8 cubes high, 5 cubes wide, and 10 cubes deep. Each cube contains 27 spheres, and each sphere contains 5 tiny jellybeans. How many jellybeans are in the stack?
   54,000 jellybeans

T78
Glencoe Division, Macmillan/McGraw-Hill

Modeling   Have students use two sizes or colors of counters representing adult and baby rabbits to model rabbit reproduction through several generations.

Problem Solving

Solve using any strategy.

5. When a number is decreased by four, the result is -23. What is the number? **-19**

Strategies
. . . .
Look for a pattern.
Solve a simpler problem.
Act it out.
Guess and check.
Draw a diagram.
Make a chart.
Work backward.

6. How many different three-member teams can be formed from six players? **20 teams**

7. There are eight people at a business meeting. Each person shakes hands with everyone else exactly once. How many handshakes occur? **28 handshakes**

8. Ms. Straub's dance class is standing evenly spaced in a circle. If the sixth person is directly opposite the sixteenth person, how many people are in the circle? **20 people**

9. Two sides of a triangle have the same length. The third side is 2 meters long. If the perimeter of the triangle is 20 meters, find the lengths of the sides. **9 meters**

COMPUTER CONNECTION

10. **Computer Connection**   A Fibonacci ratio is found by dividing each term of the Fibonacci sequence by the next term. The BASIC program at the right can be used to print Fibonacci ratios.

    a. Run the program to determine the value of the Fibonacci ratio. **0.618033989**

    b. Compare the Fibonacci ratio to the golden ratio found on page 342. How are they the same? **Both ratios lie between 0.6 and 0.625.**

```
10 LET X = 1
20 LET Y = 1
30 LET Z = X/Y
40 PRINT Z
50 LET W = X + Y
60 LET X = Y
70 LET Y = W
80 LET N = N + 1
85 IF N = 15 THEN 95
90 GOTO 30
95 END
```

---

9 Assessment: Mid-Chapter Review

Express each ratio or rate as a fraction in simplest form. *(Lesson 9-1)*

1. 15 out of 20 $\frac{3}{4}$

2. $500 from 320 students $\frac{\$25}{16 \text{ students}}$

3. 80¢ per dozen $\frac{\$0.80}{1 \text{ dozen}}$ or $\frac{\$0.20}{3}$

Solve each proportion. *(Lesson 9-2)*

4. $\frac{2}{5} = \frac{x}{250}$ **100**

5. $\frac{7.5}{a} = \frac{3}{4}$ **10**

6. $\frac{6.5}{19.5} = \frac{13}{y}$ **39**

Solve.

7. A 10-acre field produced 750 bushels of corn. At that rate, how much corn can be produced from a 14-acre field? *(Lesson 9-3)* **1,050 bushels**

8. Patrice lives nine blocks west of Julio. Julio lives four blocks east of Margie. Where does Margie live in relationship to Patrice? *(Lesson 9-4)* **5 blocks east of Patrice**

Enrichment Masters, p. 78

Enrichment Worksheet 9-4

Diagrams

Stories can sometimes travel quickly. Let's say someone told a story to two friends, and each of these two friends in turn told the story to three other friends. How many people in all have been told the story?

Diagrams are useful problem-solving tools. Indicate the original storyteller with a dot.

The original storyteller told two friends; extend the diagram with two new dots.

Each of these two friends told three other friends; extend the diagram to show six more dots.

The diagram helps us see that eight people have been told the story.

Draw a diagram and answer the following questions.

1. A football coach wanted to change the time of football practice, so the coach told two players of the time change. Each of these two players were to tell three other players of the time change. Each of those three players were to tell four other players of the time change. How many players were to be told of the time change?
Diagrams will vary; 32 players.

2. In December, some people enjoy singing a song called "The Twelve Days of Christmas." In the song, a person receives a gift of a partridge in a pear tree on the first day. On the second day, the person receives two turtle doves and a partridge in a pear tree. On the third day, three French hens, two turtle doves, and a partridge in a pear tree are received. This pattern continues for a total of 12 days. After 12 days, how many gifts are received?
Diagrams will vary; 364 gifts.

3. A creature in no particular hurry and with nothing better to do is at the bottom of a 15-foot well. Each day the creature climbs up three feet toward the top of the well, then slides back down one foot toward the bottom of the well each night. At that rate, how many days will it take the creature to climb out of the well? (Think before you answer!)
Diagrams will vary; 7 days.

OPTIONS

Extending the Lesson

Using Cooperative Groups   Have students work in small groups to solve this problem: *Draw a diagram showing how a cake can be cut into eight equal pieces using three straight cuts.*

Cooperative Learning Activity

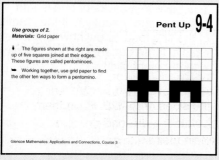

Use groups of 2.
Materials: Grid paper

◆   The figures shown at the right are made up of five squares joined at their edges. These figures are called pentominoes.

➡   Working together, use grid paper to find the other ten ways to form a pentomino.

Pent Up **9-4**

Glencoe Mathematics: Applications and Connections, Course 3

Geometry Connection

9-5 Similar Polygons

Objective

Identify corresponding parts of similar polygons.

Words to Learn

polygon
pentagon
similar polygons

LOOKBACK

You can review similar figures on page 198.

The largest office building in the world is the Pentagon in Washington, D.C. It has a floor area of 6,500,000 square feet. Notice how the figure outlining the courtyard has the same shape as the outer walls of the Pentagon.

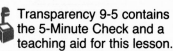

In mathematics, a **polygon** is a simple, closed figure in a plane formed by three or more sides. A **pentagon** is a polygon with five sides. The pentagons shown below have the same shape, but differ in size. These pentagons are **similar polygons**.

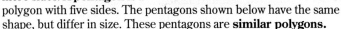

pentagon *ABCDE* ~ pentagon *VWXYZ*
The symbol ~ *means similar to.*

Notice that the corresponding angles are congruent.

$$\angle A \cong \angle V \quad \angle B \cong \angle W \quad \angle C \cong \angle X \quad \angle D \cong \angle Y \quad \angle E \cong \angle Z$$

A special relationship also exists among the corresponding sides of the polygons. Let's compare the ratios of the lengths of the corresponding sides.

$$\frac{AB}{VW} = \frac{7.5}{5} \text{ or } \frac{3}{2} \qquad \frac{BC}{WX} = \frac{7.5}{5} \text{ or } \frac{3}{2} \qquad \frac{CD}{XY} = \frac{9}{6} \text{ or } \frac{3}{2}$$

$$\frac{DE}{YZ} = \frac{6}{4} \text{ or } \frac{3}{2} \qquad \frac{AE}{VZ} = \frac{6}{4} \text{ or } \frac{3}{2}$$

As you can see, the ratios of the lengths of the corresponding sides all equal $\frac{3}{2}$. Since they are all equivalent, you can form proportions using corresponding sides.

Similar Polygons	Two polygons are similar if their corresponding angles are congruent and their corresponding sides are in proportion.

OPTIONS

Reteaching Activity

Using Models Have students draw a triangle labeled *ABC* and measure the lengths of its sides. Have them draw $\overline{DE} \parallel \overline{BC}$ (*D* on $\overline{AB}$ and *E* on $\overline{AC}$) and measure the lengths of the sides of △*ADE*. Have them calculate $\frac{AD}{AB}$, $\frac{AE}{AC}$, and $\frac{DE}{BC}$, and explain their findings. The ratios are equal; △*ADE* and △*ABC* are similar.

Study Guide Masters, p. 79

Name _____ Date _____

Study Guide Worksheet 9-5

Similar Polygons

A polygon is a closed figure in a plane and is formed by three or more line segments that meet only at their endpoints.

Two polygons are similar if their corresponding angles are congruent and their corresponding sides are in proportion.

Example $\angle A \cong \angle X$ $\frac{XY}{AB} = \frac{9}{12} = \frac{3}{4}$

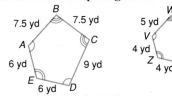

$\angle B \cong \angle Y$ $\frac{YZ}{BC} = \frac{12}{16} = \frac{3}{4}$

$\angle C \cong \angle Z$ $\frac{XZ}{AC} = \frac{15}{20} = \frac{3}{4}$

The corresponding angles are equal.
The corresponding sides are in proportion.
△*ABC* ~ △*XYZ* The symbol ~ means "is similar to."

You can use proportions to solve problems involving similar figures.

NCTM Standards: 1–5, 7, 9, 12

Lesson Resources
• Study Guide Master 9-5
• Practice Master 9-5
• Enrichment Master 9-5
• Evaluation Master, Quiz A, p. 79
• Group Activity Card 9-5

Transparency 9-5 contains the 5-Minute Check and a teaching aid for this lesson.

5-Minute Check
(Over Lesson 9-4)

Solve by drawing a diagram.

1. Don is shorter than Carla. Beth is taller than Andy but shorter than Don. List the four from shortest to tallest. Andy, Beth, Don, Carla

2. Myra drove 12 miles east, 10 miles south, 17 miles west, and 10 miles north. How far was she from her starting point? 5 mi due west

1 FOCUS

Motivating the Lesson

Questioning Ask students to give examples of pairs of objects that have the same shape but different sizes. Sample answers: a photo and its enlargement; different sizes of the same T-shirt

2 TEACH

Using Connections Have students name several Pythagorean triples in the 3–4–5 family. Point out that all are similar since corresponding angles are congruent and corresponding sides are in proportion.

353

More Examples

For the Example

The triangles below are similar. Find the length of $\overline{MN}$. 20 m

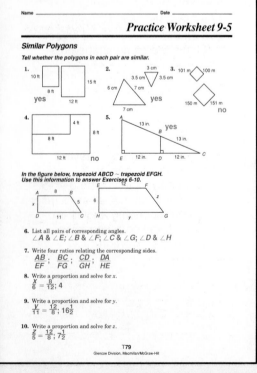

N
78°
x m
M 65° 37° P
25 m

H
12 m 78°
G 65° 37° K
15 m

Checking for Understanding

Exercises 1-3 are designed to help you assess students' understanding through reading, writing, speaking, and modeling. You should work through these exercises with your students and then monitor their work on Guided Practice Exercises 4–8.

Practice Masters, p. 79

Estimation Hint
• • • • • • • • • •
Often you can tell which angles are corresponding by estimating their angle measure instead of measuring each angle.

Proportions are useful in finding the missing length of a side in any pair of similar polygons.

Example

The two quadrilaterals below are similar. Find the length of side $\overline{AB}$.

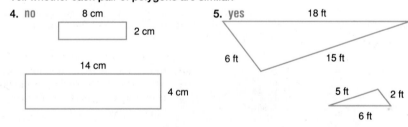

D
8 ft
12 ft C
4 ft
A x ft B

H
G
6 ft
E 21 ft F

$\overline{BC}$ corresponds to $\overline{FG}$ and $\overline{AB}$ corresponds to $\overline{EF}$, so you can write a proportion. Then use the values from the quadrilaterals to find the missing measure.

$$\frac{BC}{FG} = \frac{AB}{EF}$$
$$\frac{4}{6} = \frac{x}{21} \quad \textit{Substitute values from the quadrilaterals.}$$
$$4 \cdot 21 = 6 \cdot x \quad \textit{Find the cross products.}$$
$$84 = 6x$$
$$14 = x$$

The length of $\overline{AB}$ is 14 feet.

Checking for Understanding

Communicating Mathematics Read and study the lesson to answer each question.

1. **Write** a definition of similar polygons. See margin.

2. **Draw** two similar polygons and explain how you know which parts are corresponding. See students' work.

3. **Tell** the difference between similar polygons and congruent polygons.
See Solutions Manual.

Guided Practice Tell whether each pair of polygons are similar.

4. no
8 cm
2 cm
14 cm
4 cm

5. yes
18 ft
6 ft 15 ft
5 ft 2 ft
6 ft

OPTIONS

Multicultural Education

Mathematical talent may appear at an early age. African-American J. Ernest Wilkins, Jr., entered the University of Chicago at age thirteen, graduated at sixteen, and earned his doctorate degree three years later. One of America's top mathematicians, Wilkins has been president of the American Nuclear Society.

Additional Answer

1. Similar polygons have congruent corresponding angles and their corresponding sides are in proportion.

Refer to the Example on page 354.

6. Find the length of $\overline{GH}$. **12**   7. Find the length of $\overline{EH}$. **18**

8. If the length of $\overline{BC}$ is 8 units, how would your answers to Exercises 6 and 7 change? **They would be half of the original lengths.**

Exercises

Independent Practice

Tell whether each pair of polygons are similar.

9. yes

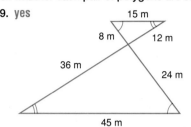

10. yes

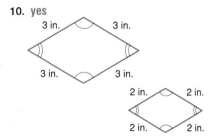

11. $\angle EAD$, $\angle CAB$; $\angle AED$, $\angle ACB$; $\angle ADE$, $\angle ABC$

12. $\dfrac{AD}{AB} = \dfrac{AE}{AC}$, $\dfrac{AD}{AB} = \dfrac{ED}{CB}$, $\dfrac{AE}{AC} = \dfrac{EB}{CB}$

In the figure at the right, $\triangle ABC \sim \triangle ADE$. Use this information to answer Exercises 11-14.

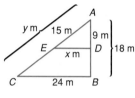

11. List all pairs of corresponding angles.

12. Write three ratios relating the corresponding sides.

13. Write a proportion and solve for *x*. $\dfrac{x}{24} = \dfrac{9}{18}$, **12**

14. Write a proportion and solve for *y*. $\dfrac{15}{y} = \dfrac{9}{18}$, **30**

Mixed Review

15. Write $4 \cdot 4 \cdot 8 \cdot 8 \cdot 4$ as an expression using exponents. *(Lesson 1-9)* $4^3 \cdot 8^2$

16. Order 23, -8, 0, -16, 51, -51, and -30 from greatest to least. *(Lesson 3-2)* **51, 23, 0, -8, -16, -30, -51**

17. Solve $a = \dfrac{7}{12} \div \dfrac{3}{4}$. *(Lesson 7-9)* $\dfrac{7}{9}$

18. **Cooking** Nancy used 6 tablespoons of ground coffee to make 3 cups of coffee. If she wanted to make 5 cups of coffee, how many tablespoons of ground coffee should she use? *(Lesson 9-3)* **10 tablespoons**

Problem Solving and Applications

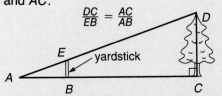

19. **Critical Thinking** The symbol for similar is ~ and the symbol for congruent is ≅. The symbols are related in the same way that the two words are related. What is this relationship? **See Solutions Manual.**

20. **Photography** The 4 in. by 5 in. portrait proofs for the school yearbook must be reduced to fit three across on a page. The ratio of the original to the reduced print needed to do this is 8:5. Find the dimensions of the pictures as they will appear in the yearbook. $2\frac{1}{2} \times 3\frac{1}{8}$

21. **Hobbies** Craig likes to build models of antique cars. At a recent car show, he took photographs of a 1934 Buick coupe, which was 174 inches long and 66 inches high. He wants his model to be 6 inches long. To the nearest tenth of an inch, what will be the height of his model? **2.3 inches**

Lesson 9-5 Geometry Connection: Similar Polygons **355**

Extending the Lesson

Using Cooperative Groups Have pairs of students find the height of a tall object (*CD*) using a yardstick (*EB*) and measuring distances *AB* and *AC*.

$\dfrac{DC}{EB} = \dfrac{AC}{AB}$

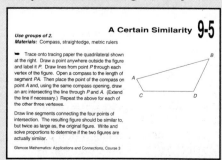

Cooperative Learning Activity

A Certain Similarity 9-5

Use groups of 2.
Materials: Compass, straightedge, metric rulers

➡ Trace onto tracing paper the quadrilateral shown at the right. Draw a point anywhere outside the figure and label it *P*. Draw lines from point *P* through each vertex of the figure. Open a compass to the length of segment *PA*. Then place the point of the compass on point *A* and, using the same compass opening, draw an arc intersecting the line through *P* and *A*. (Extend the line if necessary.) Repeat the above for each of the other three vertexes.

Draw line segments connecting the four points of intersection. The resulting figure should be similar to, but twice as large as, the original figure. Write and solve a proportion to determine if the two figures are actually similar.

Glencoe Mathematics: Applications and Connections, Course 3

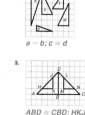

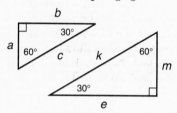
Name _____ Date _____

Enrichment Worksheet 9-5

Similar and Congruent Figures

If a 4-inch by 5-inch photograph is enlarged to an 8-inch by 10-inch photograph, the photographs are said to be *similar*. They have the same shape, but they do not have the same size. If a 4-inch by 5-inch photograph is duplicated and a new 4-inch by 5-inch photograph is made, the photographs are said to be *congruent*. They have the same size and shape.

In each exercise, identify which of the triangles are congruent to each other and identify which of the shapes are similar to each other. Use the symbol ≅ for congruence and the symbol ~ for similarity.

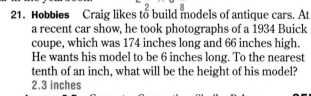

1.   2.

$a \sim b; c \cong d$

$a \cong b; b \sim c; a \sim c$

3.   4.

$ABD \cong CBD; HKJ \cong NML;$
$HKJ \sim ABD; HKJ \sim CBD;$
$LMN \sim DBC; LMN \sim DBA$

$ABH \cong CKL; CDP \sim MNP;$
$QRT \sim MNP; QRT \sim CDP$

5.

$BCG \cong JKM;$
$AQH \cong LHQ;$
$BTD \sim BCG;$
$JKM \sim JNP;$
$BTD \sim JNP;$
$BCG \sim JNP;$
$BTD \sim JKM$

T79

Glencoe Division, Macmillan/McGraw-Hill

355

Lesson Resources
- Study Guide Master 9-6
- Practice Master 9-6
- Enrichment Master 9-6
- Group Activity Card 9-6

 Transparency 9-6 contains the 5-Minute Check and a teaching aid for this lesson.

⏱5-Minute Check
(Over Lesson 9-5)

1. Tell whether the rectangles are similar.
   no

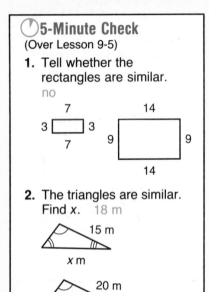

2. The triangles are similar. Find x.   18 m

1 FOCUS

Motivating the Lesson

Situational Problem On a sunny day, you are looking up at your kite which has gotten caught at the very top of a tall tree. How could you determine the height of the tree?

2 TEACH

Using Communication Explain that methods of indirect measurement assume all measurements have been increased or decreased proportionally. The ratio of two known measurements can be applied to two other similarly related measures, one of which is unknown.

Objective
Solve problems involving similar triangles.

Words to Learn
indirect measurement

You will be asked to solve the map problem in Exercise 8.

9-6 Indirect Measurement

For geography class, Marcia had to draw a map of the United States on a poster. In the atlas she has, the distance on the map from Buffalo to Tampa Bay is 5.4 cm. The distance from Buffalo to Houston is 6.7 cm. The distance from Tampa Bay to Houston is 4.2 cm. On her poster, the distance from Buffalo to Tampa Bay is 21.6 cm. Without measuring, what should the other two distances be?

If Marcia measures the distances between the other two cities on her poster, she makes a direct measurement. When we use proportions to find a measurement, we use **indirect measurement.**

Example 1   *Problem Solving*

Forestry   The park ranger wanted to estimate the height of a tree that had been planted five years ago. At 2:00 P.M., her shadow was 3 feet long. The shadow of the tree was 19 feet long. If the ranger is $5\frac{1}{2}$ feet tall, how tall is the tree?

Explore   Make a drawing and fill in the information you know. Draw similar triangles.

   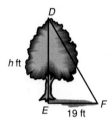

Mental Math Hint
• • • • • • • • • •
Sometimes you can solve a proportion mentally by using equivalent fractions.
$$\frac{3}{18} = \frac{6}{h}$$
THINK: $3 \cdot 2 = 6$
$18 \cdot 2 = 36$
So, $h = 36$

Plan   Write a proportion from the information in the drawing. Let h = the tree's height.

ranger's shadow → $\dfrac{3}{19}$ = $\dfrac{5\frac{1}{2}}{h}$ ← ranger's height
tree's shadow →   ← tree's height

Solve
$$\frac{3}{19} = \frac{5\frac{1}{2}}{h}$$

$3 \cdot h = 19 \cdot 5\frac{1}{2}$ *Find the cross product.*

$3h = 104\frac{1}{2}$ *Divide each side by 3.*

$h = 34\frac{5}{6}$ The tree is about 35 feet high.

OPTIONS

Reteaching Activity

Using Applications Have students stretch a string from a point on a wall (P) to a point on the floor (A) and then position a 12-inch ruler as shown in the figure. Students should measure AC and AF, find PF using $\frac{PF}{BC} = \frac{AF}{AC}$, and check by measuring PF.

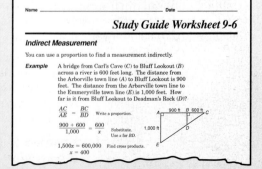

Study Guide Masters, p. 80

Name _____   Date _____

Study Guide Worksheet 9-6

Indirect Measurement

You can use a proportion to find a measurement indirectly.

Example   A bridge from Carl's Cave (C) to Bluff Lookout (B) across a river is 600 feet long. The distance from the Arborville town line (A) to Bluff Lookout is 900 feet. The distance from the Arborville town line to the Emmeryville town line (E) is 1,000 feet. How far is it from Bluff Lookout to Deadman's Rock (D)?

$\frac{AC}{AE} = \frac{BC}{BD}$ Write a proportion.

$\frac{900 + 600}{1,000} = \frac{600}{x}$ Substitute. Use x for BD.

$1,500x = 600,000$ Find cross products.

$x = 400$

Example 2 *Problem Solving*

Geography   Use the diagram below to find how far is it from Tybert to Crawford by boat. The triangles are similar triangles.

Explore   The distance from Tybert (T) to Crawford (C) is equal to the distance from Tybert to Lorain (L), 60 miles, plus the distance from Lorain to Crawford (C). Similar triangles can help us find the distance from Lorain to Crawford.

Plan   Let the first letters of the cities represent the vertices of the triangles. So, $\triangle LTD \sim \triangle LCM$. Now write a proportion.

$$\frac{MC}{CL} = \frac{DT}{TL} \quad \rightarrow \quad \frac{30}{x} = \frac{45}{60}$$

Solve $\dfrac{30}{x} = \dfrac{45}{60}$

$30 \boxed{\times}\ 60 \boxed{\div}\ 45 \boxed{=}\ 4\square$ So, $40 = x$.

The distance from Tybert to Crawford by boat is $60 + 40$ or 100 miles.

Examine   Estimate the distance by comparing it to those on the map. Does it seem reasonable?

Checking for Understanding   3. See Solutions Manual.

Communicating Mathematics

Read and study the lesson to answer each question.

1. **Tell** what is meant by indirect measurement.   See Solutions Manual.

2. **Write** a proportion that you can solve mentally.   Answers will vary.

3. **Draw** a diagram like the one in Example 1, in which the ranger's shadow is 9 feet, the tree's shadow is 15 feet, and the ranger is 6 feet tall.

4. **Tell** a situation where you could use indirect measurement.   Sample answer given: finding the height of a building.

Guided Practice   Draw a diagram of the situation. Then write a proportion and solve it.

5. A flagpole casts a shadow 8.75 feet long at the same time that a 5-story office building, 60 feet tall, casts a 15-foot shadow. How tall is the flagpole?   35 feet

6. A guy wire is attached to the top of a telephone pole and goes to the ground 9 feet from its base. When Jarem stands under the guy wire so that his head touches it, he is 2 feet 3 inches from where the wire goes into the ground. If Jarem is 5 feet tall, how tall is the telephone pole?   20 feet

Lesson 9-6   Indirect Measurement   **357**

"Lay a mirror on the ground between the school and a student so he or she can see the top of the school in the mirror. Have others measure the distances from the mirror to the school and to the student, and from the student's eyes to his or her feet. Have them set up a proportion to find the school's height."

Classroom Vignette

Lorraine J. Gowens

Lorraine Gowens, Teacher
Ridgeview Middle School, Columbus, OH

More Examples

For Example 1

The boat sail reaches 8 feet above the water. How tall is the cliff?   192 ft

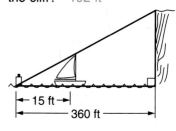

For Example 2

The triangles are similar. Find *AB*, the distance across the canyon.   175 ft

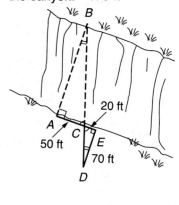

Practice Masters, p. 80

Name _____   Date _____

Practice Worksheet 9-6

Indirect Measurement

For Exercises 1-3, draw a diagram of the situation. Then write a proportion and solve it.

1. A photograph measuring 8 inches wide and 10 inches long is enlarged to make a wall mural. The mural is 60 inches wide. How long is the mural? $\frac{8}{10} = \frac{60}{X}$; 75 in.

2. Lena is $5\frac{1}{2}$ feet tall and casts an 8-foot shadow. At the same time, a flagpole casts a 48-foot shadow. How tall is the flagpole? $\frac{5\frac{1}{2}}{8} = \frac{X}{48}$; 33 ft

3. Bobbi is 30 inches tall and casts a 12-inch shadow. At the same time, her teddy bear casts a 9-inch shadow. How tall is Bobbi's bear? $\frac{30}{12} = \frac{X}{9}$; $22\frac{1}{2}$ in.

Write a proportion to solve each problem. Assume the triangles are similar.

4. Bob and Ted carefully place wooden stakes to measure the length of Muddy Pond. How long is Muddy Pond? $\frac{30}{50} = \frac{100}{X}$; $166\frac{2}{3}$ ft

5. Janice is trimming a large piece of parachute fabric to make a store-window display 6-feet high. When she discards the scrap, how long will the remaining piece of fabric be? $\frac{9}{12} = \frac{6}{X}$; 8 ft

T80
Glencoe Division, Macmillan/McGraw-Hill

357

Exercises

Independent Practice

Write a proportion to solve each problem. Assume the triangles are similar.

7. Find the distance across Clarence Lake if Town Road and Park Lane are perpendicular. **12.5 km**

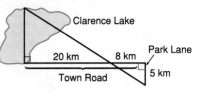

Clarence Lake
Town Road   20 km   8 km   Park Lane   5 km

8. Refer to the poster problem at the beginning of the lesson. What is the length from Tampa Bay to Houston and the length of Buffalo to Houston on Marcia's poster?
Tampa Bay to Houston 16.8 cm; Buffalo to Houston 26.8 cm

9. The state highway department is investigating the possibility of building a tunnel through the mountain from Picketon to Skylight. The surveyors provided the map shown at the right. How long would the tunnel be? **45 miles**

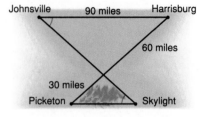

Johnsville   90 miles   Harrisburg
60 miles
30 miles
Picketon   Skylight

Mixed Review

10. Solve $n = -28 + 73$ *(Lesson 3-3)* **45**

11. Find the LCM of 48 and 60. *(Lesson 6-9)* **240**

12. **Geometry**   In the figures at the right, $\triangle ABC \sim \triangle DEF$. Write three ratios relating the corresponding sides. *(Lesson 9-5)* $\frac{AC}{DF}, \frac{AB}{DE}, \frac{BC}{EF}$

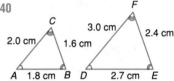

C   3.0 cm   F   2.4 cm
2.0 cm   1.6 cm
A   1.8 cm   B   D   2.7 cm   E

Problem Solving and Applications

13. **Sailing**   A tugboat known to be 33.85 feet tall is tied up next to the *Velsheda*, the world's tallest single-masted yacht. The tugboat casts a 5-foot shadow while the *Velsheda* casts a 25-foot shadow. How tall is the *Velsheda*? **169.25 feet**

14. **History**   The Pyramid of the Sun at Teotihuacán in northeastern Mexico casts a shadow 13.3 meters long. At the same time, a 1.83-meter tall man casts a shadow 0.4 meters long. How tall is the Pyramid of the Sun? **60.8475 meters**

15. **Architecture**   At 1:00 P.M. in Paris, the shadow of the Eiffel Tower is 123.24 feet long. When the sun is at the same angle in Chicago, the Sears Tower, the world's tallest building, casts a 181.75-foot shadow. If the Sears Tower is 1,454 feet tall, how tall is the Eiffel Tower? **985.92 feet**

16. **Critical Thinking**   What factors might cause you to get an incorrect measurement when using the indirect measurement method? **See Solutions Manual.**

17. **Journal Entry**   Write a plan for measuring the height of your school building by the indirect measurement method. Include a drawing with your plan.

See students' work.

358   **Chapter 9**   Applications with Proportion

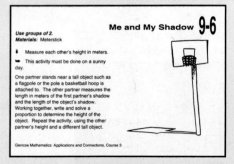

9-7 Scale Drawings

Objective
Solve problems involving scale drawings.

A **scale drawing** is used to represent something that is too large or too small to be conveniently drawn actual size. The scale is determined by the ratio of a given length on the drawing to its corresponding length in reality. Blueprints and maps are commonly-used scale drawings.

Example *Problem Solving*

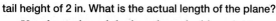

Aviation   Denise Cortez works for American Airlines in Dallas, Texas. She makes blueprints for the design layouts of new planes. On a blueprint of a Boeing 747, the scale is $\frac{1}{8}$ in. = 1 ft, or $\frac{1}{8}$ in.:1 ft. The drawing of the plane has a length of $18\frac{1}{8}$ in., a wingspan of 15 in., and a tail height of 2 in. What is the actual length of the plane?

Use the scale and the length on the blueprint to form a proportion. Then solve the proportion.

$$\frac{\frac{1}{8} \text{ in.}}{1 \text{ ft}} = \frac{18\frac{1}{8} \text{ in.}}{x \text{ ft}}$$

$$\frac{1}{8}x = 18\frac{1}{8} \qquad \textit{Find the cross products.}$$

$$8\left(\frac{x}{8}\right) = 8\left(18\frac{1}{8}\right) \qquad \textit{Multiply each side by 8.}$$

$$x = 145 \qquad \text{The Boeing 747 is 145 feet long.}$$

Mini-Lab

Work in groups of eight.

Materials: a map of your state, scissors, large pieces of drawing paper, tape

- Cut the map into 8 congruent rectangles. Each member of the group receives a rectangle of the map.
- Using a scale of 1:3, draw an enlargement of your piece of the map. Include large cities and important geographical features.
- Have your group tape together their enlargements to form the new map. Then, tape together the original map.

Talk About It

a. **They are in proportion. The new map is 3 times larger than the original map.**

a. Compare the dimensions of the new map to the original one. What do you find?

b. Measure the distance between the same two cities on each map. Compare these measurements to the scale. **The distance on the new map is 3 times the distance on the original map.**

Lesson 9-7   Scale Drawings   **359**

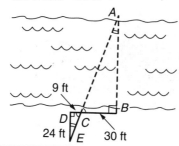

359

1 FOCUS

Motivating the Lesson

Questioning Ask students this riddle: *How are sketches of a fish and a balance alike?* They are both *scale* drawings.

2 TEACH

More Examples

For the Example

In a drawing of a giraffe drawn to the scale $\frac{1}{2}$ in. = 1 ft, the giraffe is $8\frac{1}{2}$ inches tall. What is the giraffe's actual height? 17 ft

Close

Have students explain the meaning of the scale shown on their state map.

3 PRACTICE/APPLY

Assignment Guide
Maximum: 9–17
Minimum: 9–16

For **Extra Practice**, see p. 605.

Enrichment Masters, p. 81

Name _____ Date _____

Enrichment Worksheet 9-7

Scale Drawings

The figure at the right has an area of 6 square units. If the figure represented a map, and were drawn to a scale of 1 unit = 3 feet, the lengths of the sides would be 6 ft and 9 ft. So, the figure would represent an area of 54 square feet.

The ratio of the actual area of the figure to the scale area of the figure can be expressed as a ratio:

$\frac{\text{actual area}}{\text{scale area}} = \frac{6}{54} = \frac{1}{9}$ or 1 to 9

Find the actual area and the scale area of these figures, then determine the ratio of actual area to scale area.

1. Scale: 1 unit = 4 ft
   actual area ___15___
   scale area ___240___
   ratio _1 to 16_

2. Scale: 1 unit = 50 cm
   actual area ___16___
   scale area ___40,000___
   ratio _1 to 2,500_

3. Scale: 1 unit = 8 mi
   actual area ___12___
   scale area ___768___
   ratio _1 to 64_

4. Scale: 1 unit = 12 m
   actual area ___30___
   scale area ___4,320___
   ratio _1 to 144_

5. Scale: 1 unit = 18 in.
   actual area ___10___
   scale area ___3,240___
   ratio _1 to 324_

6. Scale: 1 unit = 6 km
   actual area ___24___
   scale area ___864___
   ratio _1 to 36_

T81
Glencoe Division, Macmillan/McGraw-Hill

360

Checking for Understanding

Communicating Mathematics

Read and study the lesson to answer each question.
1. **Tell** what is meant by a scale drawing. **See Solutions Manual.**
2. **Tell** how scale drawings relate to proportions. **See Solutions Manual.**
3. **Write** two situations in real life where scale drawings are used.

Guided Practice
3. Sample answers: road maps, house plans

4. Refer to the Example on page 359. Find the actual length of the wingspan and the tail. **wingspan 120 ft; tail 16 ft**

The distance on a map is given. Find the actual distance, if the scale on the map is 1 in.:60 mi.

5. 3 in. **180 mi**
6. $2\frac{1}{4}$ in. **135 mi**
7. $4\frac{1}{8}$ in. **$247\frac{1}{2}$ mi**
8. $\frac{5}{8}$ in. **$37\frac{1}{2}$ mi**

Exercises

Independent Practice

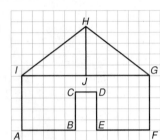

The figure at the right is a scale drawing of a playhouse. In the drawing, the side of each square represents 2 feet. Find the actual size of each segment.

9. the width of the house, *IG* **24 ft**
10. the width of the door, *CD* **4 ft**
11. the height of the wall, *AI* **10 ft**
12. the height of the roof, *JH* **9 ft**

Mixed Review

13. **Statistics** Find the interquartile range for 79, 84, 81, 84, 73, 75, 80, and 78. *(Lesson 4-6)* **6**

14. In the afternoon, the Empire State Building in New York City casts a shadow 156.25 feet long. At the same time, a nearby four-story office building, 84 feet high, casts a shadow 10.5 feet long. How tall is the Empire State Building? *(Lesson 9-6)* **1,250 ft**

Problem Solving and Applications

15. **Movies** The model of the bee used in the movie *Honey, I Shrunk the Kids* was built from a scale drawing. If the length of the drawing of the bee is 32 cm, what is the length of the model? *scale: 1 cm = 12 cm* **384 cm**

16. **12 units²; 192 ft²; the area of the model is $\frac{1}{16}$ the area of the real figure; to compare the areas, square the scale factor.**

16. **Critical Thinking** In the figure at the right, the scale is 1 unit = 4 feet. Find the area of the scale drawing. Then find the area of the real figure. Compare the two numbers. Make a conjecture about your findings.

17. **Journal Entry** Make a scale drawing of your bedroom. Be sure to include the scale. **See students' work.**

OPTIONS

Extending the Lesson

Business Connection Have students solve this problem:
Wyoming is shaped approximately like a rectangle measuring 360 miles by 280 miles. A mapmaker used the scale 1 in. = x mi to draw the largest possible map of Wyoming on an $8\frac{1}{2}$ inch by 11 inch sheet. Find x to the nearest mile. **33 mi**

Cooperative Learning Activity

Floor Plan **9-7**

Use groups of 2.
Materials: $\frac{1}{4}$-inch grid paper, yardstick, masking tape

➤ Each partner uses grid paper to make a scale drawing of a design that will be made on the floor with masking tape. Write the scale on the sheet of grid paper next to your drawing. (Make sure that a figure with the actual measurements indicated on your plan can be created in the classroom.) Partners trade completed drawings and use the scale and the drawing to create the actual design on the floor with masking tape.

Check your partner's work.

Glencoe Mathematics: Applications and Connections, Course 3

9-8 Dilations

Objective
Graph dilations on a coordinate plane.

Words to Learn
dilation
scale factor

A dilated image is usually named using the same letters as the original figure, but with primes, as in △ABC ~ △A'B'C'.

Have you ever wondered how movies appear on the screen in a movie theater? Light from a movie projector passes through each 35-mm frame of the film and projects a larger image onto the screen, which might be more than 100 feet wide. The process of enlarging or reducing an image in mathematics is called a **dilation.**

Because a dilated image is the same shape as the original, the two images are similar. The ratio of the new image to the original is called the **scale factor.**

Example

Graph △ABC with vertices A(4, 6), B(10, 2), and C(14, 10). Graph its dilation with a scale factor of 1.5.

Graph the three vertices and connect them to form the triangle. Label the vertices.

To find the vertices of the dilation, multiply each coordinate in the ordered pairs by 1.5.

$$A(4, 6) \rightarrow (4 \cdot 1.5, 6 \cdot 1.5) \rightarrow A'(6, 9)$$
$$B(10, 2) \rightarrow (10 \cdot 1.5, 2 \cdot 1.5) \rightarrow B'(15, 3)$$
$$C(14, 10) \rightarrow (14 \cdot 1.5, 10 \cdot 1.5) \rightarrow C'(21, 15)$$

Now graph A', B', and C'. Connect them to form △A'B'C'. △A'B'C' is the dilation of △ABC with a scale factor of 1.5.

To check your graph, draw lines through the origin and each of the vertices of the original figure. If the vertices of the dilated figure don't lie on those same lines, you've made a mistake.

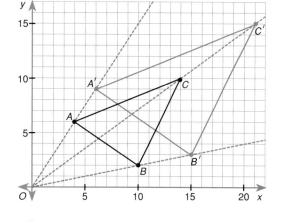

What happens if the scale factor of the dilation is less than 1, or perhaps equal to 1? Try this Mini-Lab to find the answer.

Lesson 9-8 Geometry Connection: Dilations **361**

9-8 Lesson Notes

NCTM Standards: 1–4, 7–9, 12, 13

Lesson Resources
• Study Guide Master 9-8
• Practice Master 9-8
• Enrichment Master 9-8
• Group Activity Card 9-8

 Transparency 9-8 contains the 5-Minute Check and a teaching aid for this lesson.

5-Minute Check
(Over Lesson 9-7)

A drawing of a train uses the scale 1 in. = 12 ft.

1. How long will a 60-foot locomotive appear in the drawing?   5 in.

2. In the drawing, the caboose is $2\frac{1}{4}$ inches long. Find its actual length.   27 ft

1 FOCUS

Motivating the Lesson

Activity   Display a photo of yourself or a student. Ask students to compare and contrast the photo image and the real person.

2 TEACH

More Examples

For the Example

Graph △ABC with vertices A(2, 0), B(0, 1), and C(3, 2). Graph its dilation with a scale factor of 3.

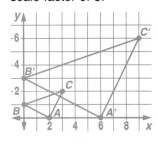

OPTIONS

Reteaching Activity

Using Models   Use a number line to show dilations in one dimension.

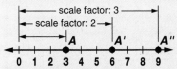

After several one-dimensional dilations, extend the idea to a two-dimensional graph.

Study Guide Masters, p. 82

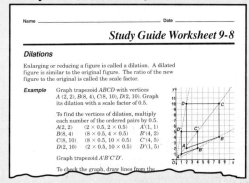

361

Using the Mini-Lab
Point out that the vertices of the dilated triangle lie on the lines drawn from the origin through the vertices of the original triangle, just as in the Example.

Checking for Understanding

Exercises 1-3 are designed to help you assess students' understanding through reading, writing, speaking, and modeling. You should work through these exercises with your students and then monitor their work on Guided Practice Exercises 4-7.

Close

Ask students to compare and contrast a geometrical figure with a dilation of the figure.

3 PRACTICE/APPLY

Assignment Guide
Maximum: 8–17
Minimum: 8–17

For **Extra Practice,** see p. 605.

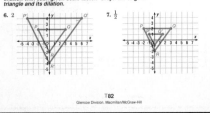

Mini-Lab

Work with a partner.
Materials: graph paper, ruler

- Graph △ABC from the Example on page 361 on a coordinate grid.
- Find the coordinates for a dilation with a scale factor of $\frac{1}{2}$.
  A'(2, 3); B'(5, 1); C'(7, 5)
- Graph △A'B'C'.

Talk About It a. Is half the size of the original.

a. How does the dilated image relate in size to the original?

b. Graph a dilation of △ABC with a scale factor of 1. How do the two triangles compare? They are the same triangle.

Checking for Understanding

Communicating Mathematics

Read and study the lesson to answer each question.

1. **Tell** what a dilation is. the enlarging or reducing of an image in mathematics

2. Multiply each member of the ordered pair (x, y) by the scale factor.

2. **Write** a general rule for finding the new coordinates of any ordered pair (x, y) for a dilation with a scale factor of k. (x, y) → (_?_ , _?_)

3. **Draw** a figure on a coordinate plane. Then draw the dilations of the figure if the scale factor is greater than 1, less than 1, and equal to 1. See students' work.

Guided Practice

In the figure, △A'OB' is a dilation of △AOB.

4. Find the image of A(3, 4) for a dilation with a scale factor of 2. (6, 8)

5. Find the image of A(3, 4) for a dilation with a scale factor of 5. (15, 20)

6. Find the scale factor if OA = 16, OB = 20 and OA' = 48. 3

7. Find the length of $\overline{A'B'}$ if AB = 20 and the scale factor is $\frac{5}{4}$. 25

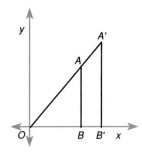

Exercises

Independent Practice

8. Graph the segment GH with G(-2, -2) and H(3, -3). Then graph its image for a dilation with a scale factor of 6. See Solutions Manual.

9. Graph segment QR with Q(-6, -6) and R(12, -12). Then graph its image for a dilation with a scale factor of $\frac{3}{4}$. See Solutions Manual.

OPTIONS

Meeting Needs of Middle School Students

Students of all ability levels need to feel challenged. Offer enrichment activities and exercises to all students, stimulating their curiosity, challenging their ability, and giving them that gratifying sense that they are moving into new territory.

For answers to Exercises 10-12, see Solutions Manual.

Triangle *PQR* has vertices *P*(-4, 12), *R*(-2, -4), and *Q*(8, 6). Find the coordinates of its image for a dilation with each given scale factor. Graph △*PQR* and its dilation.

10. 2　　　　　　　11. $\frac{1}{4}$　　　　　　　12. 1

Mixed Review　**13.** Solve $1.29b = 5.16$ *(Lesson 2-4)*　4

14. Use divisibility rules to determine whether 284 is divisible by 6. Explain why or why not. *(Lesson 6-1)*　See margin.

15. The distance between two cities on a map is $2\frac{3}{8}$ inches. Find the actual distance between the cities if the scale on the map is 1 inch:300 miles. *(Lesson 9-7)*　$712\frac{1}{2}$ miles

Problem Solving and Applications

16. Negative scale factors invert the original graph.

17c. See Solutions Manual.
d. perimeter 126 units; area 972 units²

16. Critical Thinking　Graph △*PQR* with vertices *P*(1, 1), *Q*(1, 4), and *R*(5, 1). Then graph its image for a dilation with a scale factor of -1. Make a conjecture about dilations with negative scale factors.

17. Geometry　Graph polygon *ABCD* with vertices *A*(3, 3), *B*(15, 3), *C*(15, 12), and *D*(3, 12).

　a. What type of polygon is *ABCD*?　rectangle

　b. Find its perimeter and area.　perimeter 42 units; area 108 units²

　c. Graph the image of polygon *ABCD* for a dilation with a scale factor of 3.

　d. Find the perimeter and area of polygon *A'B'C'D'*.

　e. Write a ratio in simplest form comparing the perimeter of *A'B'C'D'* to the perimeter of *ABCD*.　$\frac{3}{1}$

　f. Write a ratio in simplest form comparing the area of *A'B'C'D'* to the area of *ABCD*.　$\frac{9}{1}$

　g. Make a conjecture about your findings.　See margin.

CULTURAL KALEIDOSCOPE

Faith Ringgold

As a child, Faith Ringgold was a chronic asthmatic who spent much of her childhood at home learning from her parents. She learned an appreciation for art and creating designs from cloth.

In 1948, she tried to enroll in college as a liberal arts student, but was rejected because she was a woman. Instead, she enrolled in the school of education and taught for the next twenty years in New York City Public Schools. However,

she continued to study art. Through her students, she learned new ways to see and appreciate fabric and patterns and to express her African-American heritage in her work.

Ms. Ringgold is known for the quilting in her artwork. She uses bright colors and bold patterns to tell stories. Each piece fits into the story and expresses ideas and feelings through color, shape, and form.

Lesson 9-8　Geometry Connection: Dilations　**363**

Extending the Lesson

Cultural Kaleidoscope　Ask students to discuss ways in which proportion may be important in designing a quilt. Discuss why the ratios of color, shape, and form need to be balanced in any type of art.

Cooperative Learning Activity

Reflecting on Dilations 9-8

Use groups of 2.
Materials: Grid paper, colored pencils

◆ Each partner draws the coordinate plane shown on the back of this card on grid paper.

◆ One partner graphs *ABC* with vertices *A*(0,0), *B*(4,5), and *C*(4,0). The other partner graphs *DEF* with vertices *D*(0,0), *E*(5,4), and *F*(5,0). Each partner then graphs the dilation of his or her figure with a scale factor of 2.

Draw the reflections of triangles *ABC* and *A'B'C'* or *DEF* and *D'E'F'* over the *x*-axis. Then draw the reflection of the entire figure in quadrants I and IV over the *y*-axis. Use colored pencils to shade the resulting triangles. Compare your work with the work done by your partner.

Glencoe Mathematics: Applications and Connections, Course 3

Alternate Assessment

Speaking　On the chalkboard, write an ordered pair and the image of the ordered pair after applying a scale factor. Have students name the scale factor.

Additional Answers

14. No; 284 is divisible by 2 but not divisible by 3.

17g. The perimeter of the dilation of a polygon is equal to the perimeter of the original polygon times the scale factor. The area of the dilation of the polygon is equal to the area of the original polygon times the square of the scale factor.

Enrichment Masters, p. 82

Name _____　Date _____

Enrichment Worksheet 9-8

Dilation and Area

A dilation of a shape creates a new shape that is similar to the original. The ratio of the new image to the original is called the *scale factor*.

Plot and draw each shape. Then perform the dilation of each shape using a scale factor of two. After the new image has been drawn, determine the area of both the original shape and its dilation.

1. △ (2, 1) (7, 1) (4, 4)
　Area of original _____
　7.5 sq. units
　Area of dilation _____
　30 sq. units

2. ○ with radius (1, 2) to (4, 2)
　Area of original _____
　28.26 sq. units
　Area of dilation _____
　113.04 sq. units

3. ▱ (-3, 2), (-3, -2), (4, -2), (4, 2)
　Area of original _____
　28 sq. units
　Area of dilation _____
　112 sq. units

4. ▱ (-3, 3), (-3, -3), (3, -3), (3, 3)
　Area of original　36 sq. units
　Area of dilation　144 sq. units

5. What general statement can be made about the area of a figure when compared to its area after being dilated by scale factor 2?　Accept logical responses; the area of a figure is 4 times greater when dilated by scale factor 2.

T82
Glencoe Division, Macmillan/McGraw-Hill

363

Management Tips

For Students The results of the lab will be most convincing if group members draw 30°–60° right triangles of different sizes.

For the Overhead Projector
Overhead Manipulative Resources provides appropriate materials for teacher or student demonstration of the activities in this Mathematics Lab.

1 FOCUS

Introducing the Lab

Ask students to name relationships among the lengths of the legs, *a* and *b,* of a right triangle, and the hypotenuse, *c.*
Sample answers: $c^2 = a^2 + b^2$; $c > a$; $c > b$

2 TEACH

Using Diagrams Use the figure below to clarify "opposite" and "adjacent."

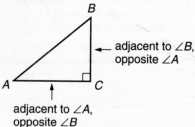

adjacent to ∠B, opposite ∠A

adjacent to ∠A, opposite ∠B

3 PRACTICE/APPLY

Using Connections Have students review the relationships among the sides of special triangles derived in Lesson 8-8.

Close

Have students name the ratios for ∠A:
$\frac{opposite}{adjacent}$, $\frac{opposite}{hypotenuse}$, $\frac{adjacent}{hypotenuse}$
$\frac{a}{b}$, $\frac{a}{c}$, $\frac{b}{c}$

Cooperative Learning

9-9A Right Triangles

A Preview of Lesson 9-9 and Lesson 9-10

Objective
Discover ratios among the sides of a right triangle.

Materials
protractor
metric ruler
calculator

Any triangle that contains a right angle is called a right triangle. Mathematicians have been studying the relationships among the sides of right triangles since before 2000 B.C.

Try this!

Work in groups of three.

● Each person should draw a right triangle *ABC* in which $m\angle A = 30°$, $m\angle B = 60°$, and $m\angle C = 90°$.

● Use your ruler to measure the side opposite the 30° angle. Record the measurement to the nearest millimeter.

● The leg adjacent to an angle is the side of the angle that is not the hypotenuse. Measure the leg adjacent to the 30° angle and record the measurement.

● Measure the hypotenuse and record the measurement.

● Use your measurements and your calculator to find each ratio for the 30° angle.

$$\text{ratio 1: } \frac{\text{opposite leg}}{\text{adjacent leg}}$$

$$\text{ratio 2: } \frac{\text{opposite leg}}{\text{hypotenuse}}$$

$$\text{ratio 3: } \frac{\text{adjacent leg}}{\text{hypotenuse}}$$

● Repeat the above procedure for the 60° angle.

What do you think?

1. Compare your ratios with the others in your group. How do they compare? Ratios are the same.

2. Make a conjecture about the ratio of the sides of any 30°–60° right triangle. Ratio equals 1:2.

3. Repeat the activity for 45°–45° right triangles. What do you find? Ratio equals 1:1.

Extension

4. For each triangle in your group find the value of (ratio 2)² + (ratio 3)². What do you discover? It equals 1.

OPTIONS

Lab Manual You may wish to make copies of the blackline master on p. 66 of the *Lab Manual* for students to use as a recording sheet.

Lab Manual, p. 66

Name _____ Date _____

Mathematics Lab Worksheet

Use with page 364

Right Triangles

Try this!
Answers will vary.

	30°-angle	60°-angle
Length of side opposite		
Length of side adjacent		

Length of hypotenuse

Sample answers are rounded to the nearest thousandth.	30°-angle	60°-angle
Ratio 1: $\frac{\text{opposite leg}}{\text{adjacent leg}}$	0.577	1.732

9-9 The Tangent Ratio

Objectives
Find the tangent of an angle and find the measure of an angle using the tangent.

Words to Learn
tangent

The industrial technology class plans to add a wheelchair ramp to the emergency exit of the auditorium as a class project. They know that the landing is 3 feet high and that the angle the ramp makes with the ground cannot be greater than 6°. What is the minimum distance from the landing that the ramp should start? *This problem will be solved in Example 1.*

Problems like the one above involve a right triangle. Right triangles and the relationships among their sides have been studied for thousands of years. One ratio, called the **tangent,** compares the measure of leg opposite an angle with the measure of the leg adjacent to that angle. The symbol for the tangent of angle *A* is tan *A*.

Tangent	If *A* is an acute angle of a right triangle, $$\tan A = \frac{\text{measure of the leg opposite } \angle A}{\text{measure of the leg adjacent to } \angle A}.$$

You can also use the symbol for tangent to write the tangent of an angle measure. The tangent of a 60° angle is written as tan 60°. If you know the measures of one leg and an acute angle of a right triangle, you can use the tangent to solve for the measure of the other leg.

Example 1   *Problem Solving*

Safety   Solve the problem about the wheelchair ramp.
First draw a diagram.

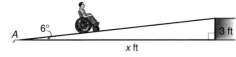

$m\angle A = 6°$
leg adjacent to $\angle A = x$ feet
leg opposite $\angle A = 3$ feet

Now substitute these values into the definition of tangent.

$\tan 6° = \dfrac{3}{x}$ ← *opposite leg*
            ← *adjacent leg*

$(\tan 6°)(x) = 3$ *Multiply each side by x.*

$x = \dfrac{3}{\tan 6°}$ *Divide each side by tan 6°.*

You can now use your calculator to find the value of *x*.

3 ÷ 6 [TAN] = 28.543093

The ramp must begin about 28.5 feet from the landing.

If your calculator does not have a TAN key, you can use the table on page 583.

Lesson 9-9   Measurement Connection: The Tangent Ratio   **365**

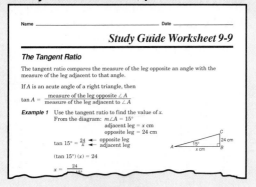

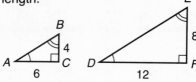
365

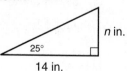
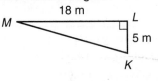
Checking for Understanding

Exercises 1-3 are designed to help you assess students' understanding through reading, writing, speaking, and modeling. You should work through these exercises with your students and then monitor their work on Guided Practice Exercises 4-13.

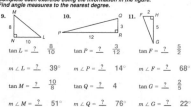
366

You can also use your calculator to find the measure of an acute angle of a right triangle when you know the measures of the two legs.

Example 2

Find the measure of ∠A.

From the figure, you know the values of the two legs. Use the definition of tangent.

$$\tan A = \frac{\text{opposite leg}}{\text{adjacent leg}}$$

$$\tan A = \frac{6}{10}$$

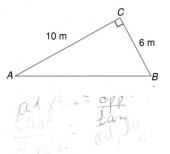

Now use your calculator.

6 ÷ 10 = INV TAN 30.963757

The measure of ∠A is about 31°.

Checking for Understanding   For answers to Exercises 1-2, see margin.

Communicating Mathematics

Read and study the lesson to answer each question.

1. **Write** a definition of the tangent ratio.

2. **Tell** how to use the tangent ratio to find the measure of a leg of a right triangle.

3. **Tell** how to find the measure of an angle in a right triangle when you know the measures of the two legs. **Find the ratio of the leg opposite the angle to the one adjacent to the angle. Then use the inverse of the tangent function on a calculator.**

Guided Practice

Use the figures at the right for Exercises 4–11. Write the ratios in simplest form. Find angle measures to the nearest degree.

4. Find tan *J*. $\frac{3}{5}$ 5. Find tan *S* $\frac{5}{3}$
6. Find tan *K*. $\frac{9}{5}$ 7. Find tan *T*. $\frac{5}{9}$
8. Find *m*∠*J*. 31°   9. Find *m*∠*S*. 59°
10. Find *m*∠*K*. 61°   11. Find *m*∠*T*. 29°

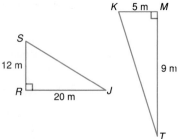

12. If the leg opposite the 53° angle in a right triangle is 4 inches long, how long is the other leg to the nearest tenth of an inch? **3.0 inches**

13. If the leg adjacent to a 29° angle in a right triangle is 9 feet long, what is the measure of the other leg to the nearest foot? **5 ft**

366   **Chapter 9**   Applications with Proportion

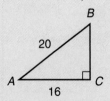

Exercises

Independent Practice

Complete each exercise using the information in the figure. Find angle measures to the nearest degree.

14.
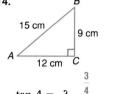

$$\tan A = \underline{\ ?\ } \quad \frac{3}{4}$$
$$\tan B = \underline{\ ?\ } \quad \frac{4}{3}$$
$$m\angle A = \underline{\ ?\ } \quad 37°$$
$$m\angle B = \underline{\ ?\ } \quad 53°$$

15.
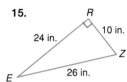

$$\tan Z = \underline{\ ?\ } \quad \frac{12}{5}$$
$$\tan E = \underline{\ ?\ } \quad \frac{5}{12}$$
$$m\angle Z = \underline{\ ?\ } \quad 67°$$
$$m\angle E = \underline{\ ?\ } \quad 23°$$

16.
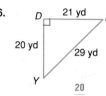

$$\tan F = \underline{\ ?\ } \quad \frac{20}{21}$$
$$\tan Y = \underline{\ ?\ } \quad \frac{21}{20}$$
$$m\angle F = \underline{\ ?\ } \quad 44°$$
$$m\angle Y = \underline{\ ?\ } \quad 46°$$

Find the value of x to the nearest tenth or nearest degree.

17. 6.9 in.
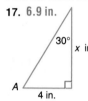

18.

19. 3.6 km
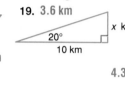

20.
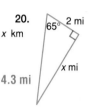
4.3 mi

Mixed Review

21. Geometry Draw an isosceles, right triangle. *(Lesson 5-3)* See students' work.

22. Solve $7\frac{3}{8} = 2\frac{9}{16} + j$. *(Lesson 7-2)* $4\frac{13}{16}$

23. Graph line segment EF with endpoints $E(2, 6)$ and $F(4, -4)$. Then graph its image for a dilation with a scale factor of $\frac{1}{2}$. *(Lesson 9-8)* See Solutions Manual.

Problem Solving and Applications

24. Critical Thinking In this lesson, you have learned about the tangent of acute angles. Use your calculator to investigate the tangent of the following angle measures. What do you discover? See Solutions Manual.

90°	120°	150°	180°	210°
240°	270°	300°	330°	360°

25. Surveying A surveyor is measuring the width of a river for a proposed bridge. A theodolite is used by the surveyor to measure angles. The distance from where the surveyor is standing to the proposed bridge site is 40 feet. The angle from where the surveyor is to the bridge site across the river is 50°. Find the length of the bridge. about 48 feet

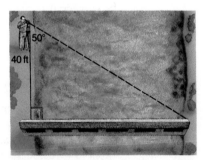

Lesson 9-9   Measurement Connection: The Tangent Ratio   **367**

Extending the Lesson

Using Cooperative Groups Have students work in small groups using a calculator to find the values of tan x for $x = 0°, 5°, 10°, 15°, \ldots,$ 90°. (HINT: When students receive an error message after trying to find tan 90°, have them find tan 89° and then point out that tan 90° is infinite.) Then have students use the values to draw a graph of $y = \tan x$. See students' work.

Cooperative Learning Activity

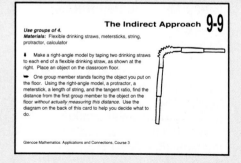

The Indirect Approach 9-9

Use groups of 4.
Materials: Flexible drinking straws, metersticks, string, protractor, calculator

* Make a right-angle model by taping two drinking straws to each end of a flexible drinking straw, as shown at the right. Place an object on the classroom floor.
➡ One group member stands facing the object you put on the floor. Using the right-angle model, a protractor, a meterstick, a length of string, and the tangent ratio, find the distance from the first group member to the object on the floor *without actually measuring this distance*. Use the diagram on the back of this card to help you decide what to do.

Glencoe Mathematics: Applications and Connections, Course 3

Error Analysis

Watch for students who use the hypotenuse as an opposite or adjacent side.

Prevent by stressing that the terms opposite and adjacent refer only to the legs of right triangles.

Close

Have students write a sentence or two explaining how to find the tangent of an angle.

3 PRACTICE/APPLY

Assignment Guide
Maximum: 14–25
Minimum: 14–25

For **Extra Practice,** see p. 606.

Alternate Assessment

Writing Have students use the figure to find tan 37° and tan 53°.
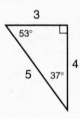
$\frac{3}{4}$ or 0.75;
$\frac{4}{3}$ or $1.\overline{3}$

Enrichment Masters, p. 83

Name _____ Date _____

Enrichment Worksheet 9-9

On a Clear Day You Can See Forever?
If you've ever watched a submarine movie, you've probably seen the captain of the submarine look through a periscope. Have you ever wondered how far the captain could see?

The equation that approximates the distance that someone can see is $d = 1.5\sqrt{h}$ where d is the distance in miles and h is the height in feet of the observer above the surface.
When using this formula, remember that it gives answers only for ideal conditions. Viewing conditions on Earth are typically less than ideal.

Use the equation $d = 1.5\sqrt{h}$ and your calculator to answer the following questions. When necessary, round your answers to the nearest hundredth.

1. A submarine captain is looking through a periscope that is 1 foot above the water. How far is the captain able to see? 1.5 mi

2. An airplane is flying at an altitude of 6.5 miles. When looking out the window, how far would an observer be able to see? (5,280 feet =1 mile) 277.88 mi

3. The Sears Tower in Chicago is 1,464 feet tall. If the observation deck is located at a height of 1,350 feet above ground, how far would a person on the observation deck be able to see? 55.11 mi

4. A sailor is standing in the crow's-nest of a sailing ship. The crow's-nest is an observation area located high above the ship on a mast. The sailor in the crow's-nest is 120 feet above the surface of the water. How far is the sailor able to see? 16.43 mi

5. Using a periscope, a submarine captain sights a rowboat that is floating at a distance of 1.84 miles from the ship. How far is the periscope above water? 1.5 ft

6. When looking out the window of an airplane, an observer is able to see a distance of 150 miles. At what height is the airplane flying? 10,000 ft

T83
Glencoe Division, Macmillan/McGraw-Hill

9-10 The Sine and Cosine Ratios

NCTM Standards: 1–5, 7–9, 12, 13

Lesson Resources
- Study Guide Master 9-10
- Practice Master 9-10
- Enrichment Master 9-10
- Evaluation Master, Quiz B, p. 79
- Group Activity Card 9-10

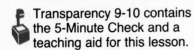 Transparency 9-10 contains the 5-Minute Check and a teaching aid for this lesson.

5-Minute Check
(Over Lesson 9-9)

1. Find *x* to the nearest tenth. 14.6 ft

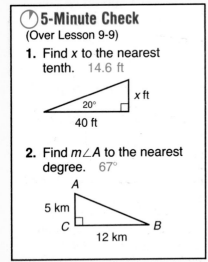

2. Find *m∠A* to the nearest degree. 67°

1 FOCUS

Motivating the Lesson

Questioning Have students read the first paragraph of the lesson. Ask them to explain why the angle cannot be found using the tangent ratio. The tangent ratio can be used when the lengths of the two legs of a right triangle are known; in this situation, the length of only one leg is known (along with the length of the hypotenuse).

2 TEACH

Using Logical Reasoning To decide which trigonometric ratio to use, note the acute angle and two sides whose measures you know or want to know. Relate the sides to the angle using the terms *opposite, adjacent,* and/or *hypotenuse*. Choose the ratio involving those terms.

368

Objective
Find the sine and cosine of an angle and find the measure of an angle using sine or cosine.

Words to Learn
trigonometry
sine
cosine

Toni decided to make a scale drawing of the Leaning Tower of Pisa for her project in art class. She knows the tower is 177 feet tall and tilts $16\frac{1}{2}$ feet off the perpendicular. First, she wants to draw the angle representing the tilt of the tower. What should be the measure of the angle? *This problem will be solved in Example 3.*

16½ ft

177 ft

When you look at the diagram, you see that you know the measures of one leg and the hypotenuse. These are not the measures you need to use the tangent ratio you learned about in Lesson 9-9. The tangent ratio is only one of several ratios used in the study of **trigonometry.**

Two other ratios in trigonometry are the **sine** ratio and the **cosine** ratio. They can be written as sin *A* and cos *A*. They are defined below.

	If *A* is an acute angle of a right triangle,
Sine	$\sin A = \dfrac{\text{measure of the leg opposite } \angle A}{\text{measure of the hypotenuse}}$
Cosine	$\cos A = \dfrac{\text{measure of the leg adjacent to } \angle A}{\text{measure of the hypotenuse}}$

Example 1

Use △*ABC* to find sin *A*, cos *A*, sin *B*, and cos *B*.

$$\sin A = \frac{BC}{AB} \qquad\qquad \sin B = \frac{AC}{AB}$$

$$= \frac{4}{5} \text{ or } 0.8 \qquad\qquad = \frac{3}{5} \text{ or } 0.6$$

$$\cos A = \frac{AC}{AB} \qquad\qquad \cos B = \frac{BC}{AB}$$

$$= \frac{3}{5} \text{ or } 0.6 \qquad\qquad = \frac{4}{5} \text{ or } 0.8$$

5 yd 4 yd 3 yd

368   **Chapter 9**   Applications with Proportion

OPTIONS

Gifted and Talented Needs

A wealth of fascinating material awaits the motivated student who wishes to delve further into trigonometry. Suggest that students explore the following topics in an algebra text: solving right triangles; applying trigonometric ratios; graphing trigonometric ratios; trigonometric identities.

You can also find the sine and cosine of an angle if you know its measure by using your calculator.

sin 63° → 63 [SIN] 0.8910065   cos 63° → 63 [COS] 0.4539905

sin 63° ≈ 0.891   cos 63° ≈ 0.454

In Lesson 9-9, you learned you could use the tangent ratio to find missing lengths of sides or angle measures in a right triangle. The same is true of the sine and cosine ratios.

Example 2

Find the length of $\overline{XY}$ in $\triangle XYZ$.

You know the measure of $\angle X$ and the length of the hypotenuse. You can use the cosine ratio.

$$\cos X = \frac{XY}{XZ} \qquad \frac{adjacent\ leg}{hypotenuse}$$

$$\cos 35° = \frac{n}{25} \qquad \text{Substitute 35° for X, n for XY, and 25 for XZ.}$$

$$\cos 35° \, (25) = \frac{n}{25} \, (25) \qquad \text{Multiply each side by 25.}$$

$$25 \cdot \cos 35° = n$$

Now use your calculator.

25 [×] 35 [COS] [=] 20.478801

The length of $\overline{XY}$ is about 20.48 kilometers.

Example 3 *Problem Solving*

Find the angle that Toni needs to draw for her scale drawing of the Leaning Tower of Pisa.

Explore We know the leg opposite the angle and the hypotenuse. We can use the sin A.

Plan Substitute the known values in the definition.

$$\sin A = \frac{16.5}{177}$$

Solve $$\sin A = \frac{16.5}{177}$$

Use your calculator.

16.5 [÷] 177 [=] [INV] [SIN] 5.3488982

Toni must draw an angle of about 5°.

Examine Toni knows the angle in her drawing will be very narrow. 5° is a very small angle, so it is a reasonable answer.

16.5 ft

177 ft

A

Lesson 9-10   Measurement Connection: The Sine and Cosine Ratios   **369**

DID YOU KNOW

The Leaning Tower of Pisa took 199 years to build. It was completed in 1372. The ground beneath the tower started to sink after the first three stories were built. Since 1911, the tower has increased its lean by an average of 0.05 inch per year.

More Examples

For Example 1

Find sin *M*, cos *M*, sin *N*, and cos *N*.
$\frac{12}{13}, \frac{5}{13}, \frac{5}{13}, \frac{12}{13}$

13 yd   12 yd   5 yd

For Example 2

Find *KH* to the nearest tenth.
8.2 m

11 m   42°   x m

For Example 3

Find $m\angle R$ to the nearest degree.   45°

24 in.   17 in.

Checking for Understanding

Exercises 1-3 are designed to help you assess students' understanding through reading, writing, speaking, and modeling. You should work through these exercises with your students and then monitor their work on Guided Practice Exercises 4-13.

Error Analysis

Watch for students who use the wrong trigonometric ratio.

Prevent by teaching the mnemonic SOHCAHTOA (Sine Opposite Hypotenuse; Cosine Adjacent Hypotenuse; Tangent Opposite Adjacent).

Close

Have students explain the differences among the sine, cosine, and tangent ratios.

Reteaching Activity

Using Charts Have students complete the chart for $\triangle ABC$.

B   10   6   A   8   C

	$\angle A$	$\angle B$
opposite	6	8
adjacent	8	6
hypotenuse	10	10
sine	0.6	0.8
cosine	0.8	0.6
tangent	0.75	1.3

Study Guide Masters, p. 84

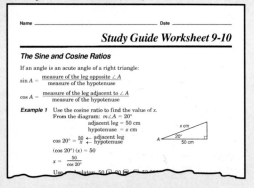

Name _____ Date _____

Study Guide Worksheet 9-10

The Sine and Cosine Ratios

If an angle is an acute angle of a right triangle:

$\sin A = \frac{\text{measure of the leg opposite } \angle A}{\text{measure of the hypotenuse}}$

$\cos A = \frac{\text{measure of the leg adjacent to } \angle A}{\text{measure of the hypotenuse}}$

Example 1 Use the cosine ratio to find the value of x.
From the diagram: $m\angle A = 20°$
adjacent leg = 50 cm
hypotenuse = x cm
$\cos 20° = \frac{50}{x} ←$ adjacent leg
$(\cos 20°)(x) = 50$
$x = \frac{50}{\cos 20°}$

x cm   20°   50 cm

Assignment Guide
Maximum: 14–28
Minimum: 14–27

For **Extra Practice,** see p. 606.

Alternate Assessment

Speaking Draw a right triangle on the chalkboard, indicating the lengths of its sides. Give the fractional value of one of the three trigonometric ratios and have students name the ratio you are using.

Additional Answers

1. The sine ratio of an acute angle equals the measure of the leg opposite that angle divided by the measure of the hypotenuse. The cosine ratio of an acute angle equals the measure of the leg adjacent to that angle divided by the measure of the hypotenuse.
3. See below.

Practice Masters, p. 84

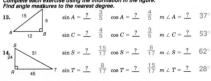

Checking for Understanding

Communicating Mathematics

Read and study the lesson to answer each question.
1. **Write** what the sine and cosine ratios are. **See margin.**
2. trigonometry
2. **Tell** which branch of mathematics uses the sine, cosine, and tangent ratios.
3. **Show** how you could use the sine or cosine to find the missing measure of one of the legs if you know the hypotenuse and an acute angle. **See margin.**

Guided Practice

Use the figures at the right for Exercises 4–13. Write the ratios in simplest form. Find angle measures to the nearest degree.

4. $\frac{3}{5}$ 5. $\frac{4}{5}$
7. $\frac{3}{5}$ 8. $\frac{4}{5}$
10. $\frac{5}{13}$
11. $\frac{5}{13}$

4. Find cos A.   5. Find sin A.
6. Find $m\angle A$. 53° 7. Find sin B.
8. Find cos B.   9. Find $m\angle B$. 37°
10. Find cos Y.   11. Find sin X.
12. Find $m\angle X$. 23° 13. Find $m\angle Y$. 67°

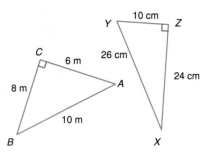

Exercises

Independent Practice

Complete each exercise using the information in the figure. Round angles to the nearest degree.

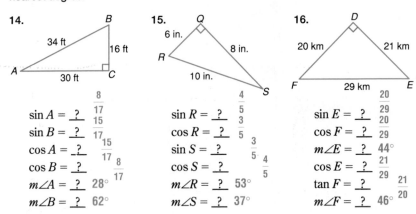

14.
$$\sin A = \underline{?}\ \frac{8}{17}$$
$$\sin B = \underline{?}\ \frac{15}{17}$$
$$\cos A = \underline{?}\ \frac{15}{17}$$
$$\cos B = \underline{?}\ \frac{8}{17}$$
$$m\angle A = \underline{?}\ 28°$$
$$m\angle B = \underline{?}\ 62°$$

15.
$$\sin R = \underline{?}\ \frac{4}{5}$$
$$\cos R = \underline{?}\ \frac{3}{5}$$
$$\sin S = \underline{?}\ \frac{3}{5}$$
$$\cos S = \underline{?}\ \frac{4}{5}$$
$$m\angle R = \underline{?}\ 53°$$
$$m\angle S = \underline{?}\ 37°$$

16.
$$\sin E = \underline{?}\ \frac{20}{29}$$
$$\cos F = \underline{?}\ \frac{20}{29}$$
$$m\angle E = \underline{?}\ 44°$$
$$\cos E = \underline{?}\ \frac{21}{29}$$
$$\tan F = \underline{?}\ \frac{21}{20}$$
$$m\angle F = \underline{?}\ 46°$$

Find the value of x to the nearest tenth or to the nearest degree.

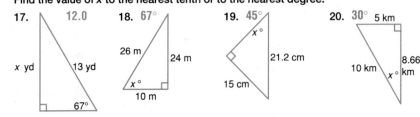

17.   18. 67°   19. 45°   20. 30° 5 km

OPTIONS

Bell Ringer
The sine of an angle is $\frac{8}{17}$. What is the cosine of the angle? $\frac{15}{17}$

Additional Answer

3. If the missing leg measure is opposite the known acute angle, use the sine ratio. If the missing leg measure is adjacent to the known acute angle, use the cosine ratio.

Mixed Review

22. 0.00092

21. Solve $g = -5(12)(3)$. *(Lesson 3-6)* **-180**

22. Express 9.2×10^{-4} in standard form. *(Lesson 6-11)*

23. Use the triangle at the right to find tan A. *(Lesson 9-9)* $\frac{3}{4}$

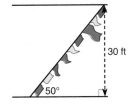

C, 10 in., 6 in., A, 8 in., B

Problem Solving and Applications

24. **Critical Thinking** Look at your results in Exercises 14–16. Make a conjecture about the sine and cosine of complementary angles. **They are the same.**

25. **School Clubs** The Student Government wants to hang banners from all of the school clubs on a wire for the Club Appreciation Assembly. They propose stringing a wire from the ceiling at the front of the auditorium to a spot on the floor so that it makes a 50° angle with the floor. If the ceiling is 30 feet high, at least how long must the wire be? **about 39.2 feet**

30 ft, 50°

26. **Guess and Check** Suppose A represents the tangent ratio, B represents the cosine ratio, and C represents the sine ratio. Which of the following proportions is true? Be prepared to defend your answers. **e, f**

a. $\dfrac{A}{B} = C$ b. $\dfrac{A}{C} = B$ c. $\dfrac{B}{C} = A$

d. $\dfrac{B}{A} = C$ e. $\dfrac{C}{A} = B$ f. $\dfrac{C}{B} = A$

28. See students' work.

29. See students' work.

27. **Travel** Many tourists travel to New York City during the holidays to see the decorated tree placed at Rockefeller Center near the skating rink. One year the tree was 63.2 feet tall. A guy wire was attached to the top of the tree and made a 72° angle with the ground. To the nearest foot, how long was that wire? **66 ft**

28. **Journal Entry** Write and solve a problem in which a trigonometric ratio can be used. Include a drawing as part of the solution.

29. **Portfolio Suggestion** Select one of the graphs from this chapter that you found especially challenging. Place it in your portfolio.

Lesson 9-10 Measurement Connection: The Sine and Cosine Ratios **371**

Enrichment Masters, p. 84

Name _____ Date _____

Enrichment Worksheet 9-10

Sine and Cosine Ratios

In this figure, sine A is equal to the measure of the leg opposite angle A divided by the measure of the hypotenuse.

Cosine A is equal to the measure of the leg adjacent to angle A divided by the measure of the hypotenuse.

Altitude

Use the sine and cosine ratios and your calculator to determine the answers to the following exercises. When necessary, round your answers to the nearest hundredth.

1. A Doppler radar station tracking a storm has located a cloud formation it suspects to be a developing tornado. The elevation angle to the cloud formation is 30 degrees and the slant range is 50 miles. Determine the horizontal distance to the suspect cloud formation and its altitude.

50 mi, 30°

horizontal distance **43.30** mi   altitude **25** mi

2. A radar installation is tracking an object of unknown origin. Data indicates that the object is hovering at a slant range of 80 miles and an elevation angle of 20 degrees. Compute the horizontal distance to the object and its altitude.

80 mi, 20°

horizontal distance **75.18** mi   altitude **27.36** mi

3. A plane climbing at a constant elevation angle has flown a distance of 11 miles since takeoff, as measured along its line of flight. The plane has an altitude of 3 miles. Find the elevation angle of the plane.

11 mi, 3 mi

elevation angle **15.83** degrees

4. A parabolic dish antenna is aimed at a satellite with a slant range of 26,590 miles. The elevation angle is 57 degrees. Determine the altitude of the satellite.

altitude **22,300.25** mi

84

Glencoe Division, Macmillan/McGraw-Hill

Extending the Lesson

Using Charts Have students complete this chart for at least five angles.

$m\angle A$	$\dfrac{\sin A}{\cos A}$	$\tan A$

Have students suggest how the tangent of an angle and the quotient of the sine and cosine are related. **They are equal.**

Cooperative Learning Activity

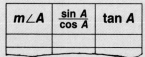

Will You Cosine? 9-10

Number of players: 2
Materials: Index cards, spinner, calculator

♦ Copy onto cards the angle measures shown on the back of this card, one per card. Shuffle the cards and place them face down in a pile. Label equal sections of a spinner "5 cm," "6 cm," "8 cm," "10 cm," "13 cm," "15.5 cm."

➥ One partner selects a card, and the other partner spins the spinner. Try to be the first to find the length of the hypotenuse of a triangle that has an acute angle equal in measure to the measure shown on the card and a side that is equal in length to the length shown on the spinner. (Hint: It may help to draw a diagram.)

Continue in this way until no cards remain. Determine which partner won more rounds.

Glencoe Mathematics: Applications and Connections, Course 3

371

Using the Chapter Study Guide and Review

The Chapter Study Guide and Review begins with a section on Communicating Mathematics. This includes questions that review the new terms and concepts that were introduced in the chapter.

Then, the Skills and Concepts presented in the chapter are reviewed using a side-by-side format. Encourage students to refer to the Objectives and Examples on the left as they complete the Review Exercises on the right.

The Chapter Study Guide and Review ends with problems that review Applications and Problem Solving.

Additional Answer

8. Sample answer: The scale is determined by finding the ratio of the distance on a drawing to the same distance in real life.

---

9 Study Guide and Review

Communicating Mathematics

Choose the letter that best matches each phrase.

1. an example of a ratio h
2. an example of a proportion i
3. an example of a rate f
4. figures that have the same shape but may differ in size c
5. finding a measurement using proportions b
6. the process of enlarging or reducing an image in mathematics e
7. a branch of mathematics that uses the sine, cosine, and tangent ratios g

a. direct measurement
b. indirect measurement
c. similar figures
d. congruent figures
e. dilation
f. 3 miles in 7 hours
g. trigonometry
h. $\dfrac{3}{7}$
i. $\dfrac{3}{7} = \dfrac{9}{21}$

8. In your own words, explain how the scale of a scale drawing is determined. **See margin.**

Self Assessment

Objectives and Examples	Review Exercises
Upon completing this chapter, you should be able to:	*Use these exercises to review and prepare for the chapter test.*
• express ratios as fractions in simplest form *(Lesson 9-1)* Express the ratio 8 out of 12 in simplest form. $\dfrac{8}{12} = \dfrac{2}{3}$	Express each ratio or rate as a fraction in simplest form. 9. 10 green apples:20 red apples $\dfrac{1}{2}$ 10. 20 centimeters per meter $\dfrac{1}{5}$ 11. 36 to 5 $\dfrac{36}{5}$ 12. 4 men:20 people $\dfrac{1}{5}$
• solve proportions *(Lesson 9-2)* Solve $\dfrac{x}{3} = \dfrac{10}{15}$. $15x = 3(10)$ *Cross products.* $15x = 30$ $x = 2$	Solve each proportion. 13. $\dfrac{3}{8} = \dfrac{n}{40}$ $n = 15$ 14. $\dfrac{6}{r} = \dfrac{15}{20}$ $r = 8$ 15. $\dfrac{d}{18} = \dfrac{9}{4}$ $d = 40.5$ 16. $\dfrac{0.5}{30} = \dfrac{0.25}{b}$ $b = 15$

Objectives and Examples

- solve problems by using proportions *(Lesson 9-3)*

  If 3 cassettes cost $26.97, how much will 1 cassette cost?

  $$\frac{3}{26.97} = \frac{1}{x}$$
  $$3x = 26.97$$
  $$x = 8.99$$

  One cassette costs $8.99.

- identify corresponding parts of similar polygons *(Lesson 9-5)*

  Two polygons are similar if their corresponding angles are congruent and their corresponding sides are in proportion.

- solve problems involving similar triangles *(Lesson 9-6)*

  How far is Malden from Bristow?

  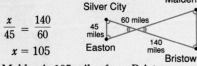

  Silver City   Malden

  $$\frac{x}{45} = \frac{140}{60}$$

  45 miles   60 miles

  $$x = 105$$ Easton   140 miles   Bristow

  Malden is 105 miles from Bristow.

- solve problems involving scale drawings *(Lesson 9-7)*

  The scale of a model car is $\frac{1}{2}$ in.:1 ft. If the model is 7 inches long, how long is the actual car?

  $$\frac{\frac{1}{2}\text{in.}}{7\text{ in.}} = \frac{1\text{ ft}}{x\text{ ft}}$$
  $$\frac{1}{2}x = 7$$
  $$x = 14 \qquad \text{The car is 14 feet long.}$$

- graph dilations on a coordinate plane *(Lesson 9-8)*

  In a dilation with a scale factor of k, the ordered pair (x, y) becomes the ordered pair (kx, ky).

Review Exercises

Use a proportion to solve each problem.

17. Vicki earns $70 in 8 hours. How much will she earn in 20 hours? $175

18. A snail moves 6 inches in 3 minutes. How far does the snail move in 5 minutes? 10 in.

19. It costs $1.20 to copy 10 pages. How many pages can be copied for $3.00? 25 pages

Tell whether each pair of polygons are similar.

20.   4 m   7 m
      3 m   3 m
      not similar

21.   3 in.   4 in.
      8 in.   6 in.
      similar

Write a proportion to solve the following problem.

22. Sonia is standing next to a flagpole. She casts a shadow 6 feet 8 inches long, while the flagpole casts a shadow 26 feet 8 inches long. If Sonia is 5 feet tall, how tall is the flagpole? 20 ft

The distance on a map is given. Find the actual distance, if the scale on the map is 2 cm:35 km.

23. 6 cm 105 km
24. 9 cm 157.5 km
25. 3.2 cm 56 km
26. 4.6 cm 80.5 km
27. 8.4 cm 147 km

Graph △*HIJ* with vertices *H*(2, 4), *I*(-6, -4), and *J*(6, -8). Find the coordinates for a dilation with each scale factor. Graph the dilation. See Solutions Manual.

28. $\frac{1}{2}$
29. 2
30. $\frac{1}{4}$

You may wish to use a Chapter Test from the Evaluation Masters booklet as an additional chapter review. The two free-response forms are shown below. One of the two multiple-choice forms is shown on the next page.

Evaluation Masters, pp. 77–78

374

Objectives and Examples

Review Exercises

● find the tangent of an angle
 (*Lesson 9-9*)
 Find the tangent of ∠Y.
 $\tan Y = \frac{3}{4} = 0.75$

Find each ratio using the information in △ABC.
31. tan A 0.4167
32. tan B 2.4

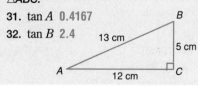

● find the sine and cosine of an angle
 (*Lesson 9-10*)
 Find the sine and cosine of ∠D.
 $\sin D = \frac{6}{10} = 0.6$
 $\cos D = \frac{8}{10} = 0.8$

Find each ratio using the information in △RQS.
33. sin Q 0.8824
34. sin R 0.4706
35. cos Q 0.4706
36. cos R 0.8824

Applications and Problem Solving

37. **Hobbies** Eddie has 128 baseball cards in his collection. Fifty-six of the cards are of Los Angeles Dodgers players. Find the ratio of the Dodgers cards to all of the cards. (*Lesson 9-1*) $\frac{7}{16}$

38. The Fort Couch Middle School Chess Club has eight members. Recently, each member agreed to play every other member exactly once. How many games will be played in all? (*Lesson 9-4*)
 28 games

Curriculum Connection Projects

● **Astronomy** Find the ratio of Earth's distance from the sun to each of the other eight planets' distances from the sun.

● **History** Find the ratio of the length to the height of the Greek Parthenon. Compare this ratio to the golden ratio.

● **Music** Find the ratio of the frequency of middle C on the musical scale to the frequency of the other notes of the scale.

Read More About It

Crichton, Michael. *Jurassic Park*.
McCauley, David. *Castle*.
Wood, Paul W. *Starting with Stained Glass*.

374   **Chapter 9**   Study Guide and Review

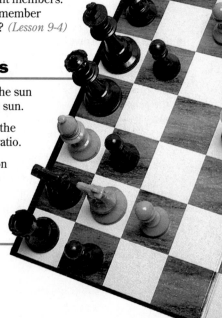

Chapter 9 Test

Express each ratio or rate as a fraction in simplest form.

1. 8 misses in 20 tries $\frac{2}{5}$

2. 9 out of 14 $\frac{9}{14}$

3. 12 wins:4 losses $\frac{3}{1}$

4. 38 to 24 $\frac{19}{12}$

5. Express *290 miles in 5 hours* as a unit rate. **58 miles per hour**

Solve each proportion.

6. $\frac{5}{6} = \frac{11}{x}$ $x = 13.2$
7. $\frac{n}{30} = \frac{5}{10}$ $n = 15$
8. $\frac{9}{33} = \frac{b}{11}$ $b = 3$
9. $\frac{2}{y} = \frac{8}{5}$ $y = 1.25$

10. Do $\frac{32}{88}$ and $\frac{12}{36}$ form a proportion? **no**

11. A car uses 4 gallons to travel 96 miles. How many gallons are used to travel 60 miles?
    2.5 gallons

Determine if each pair of polygons below are similar.

12.  **yes**

13.  **no**

The distance on a map is given. Find the actual distance, if the scale on the map is 1 in.:100 mi.

14. 4 in. **400 miles**
15. $\frac{1}{4}$ in. **25 miles**
16. $3\frac{1}{8}$ in. **312.5 miles**

17. Polygon $ABCD$ has vertices $A(4, 3)$, $B(-3, 2)$, $C(-1, -4)$, and $D(5, -5)$. Find the vertices for a dilation with a scale factor of 3. **(12, 9), (-9, 6), (-3, -12), (15, -15)**

Complete each exercise using the information in $\triangle ABC$. Round angle measures to the nearest degree.

18. $\tan A = $ _?_ **0.75**
19. $m\angle A = $ _?_ **37°**
20. $\cos B = $ _?_ **0.6**
21. $m\angle B = $ _?_ **53°**
22. $\sin B = $ _?_ **0.8**
23. $m\angle C = $ _?_ **90°**

24. At 2:00 P.M., the shadow of Mr. Harris' house is 20 feet long. At the same time, the shadow of a tree in his backyard is 30 feet long. If Mr. Harris' house is 24 feet tall, how tall is the tree? **36 feet tall**

25. A photographer hangs her prints to dry on a cord using clothespins. If she has 10 clothespins, what is the greatest number of photos she can hang? Assume that each photo needs two clothespins. **9**

Bonus If A is an acute angle of a right triangle, explain why $\tan A = \frac{\sin A}{\cos A}$. **See Solutions Manual.**

Chapter 9 Test 375

Using the Chapter Test

This page may be used as a chapter test or another chapter review.

Evaluation Masters, pp. 73–74

Form 1A — Chapter 9 Test

1. Express the ratio *9 inches out of 1 foot* in simplest form. **D**
   A. $\frac{9}{1}$ B. $\frac{1}{4}$ C. $\frac{9}{12}$ D. $\frac{3}{4}$
2. Express the ratio *18 blue-eyed students*: 20 brown-eyed students in simplest form. **B**
   A. $\frac{3}{4}$ B. $\frac{9}{10}$ C. $\frac{4}{5}$ D. $\frac{90}{100}$
3. Express *$1.44 per dozen* as a unit rate. **D**
   A. $12.00 B. $17.28 C. $1.20 D. $0.12
4. Solve $\frac{36}{a} = \frac{8}{3}$. **C**
   A. 15 B. 14 C. $13\frac{1}{2}$ D. 13
5. Solve $\frac{2}{6} = \frac{b}{36}$. **A**
   A. 8 B. 6 C. $\frac{1}{2}$ D. 7
6. Solve $\frac{c}{15} = \frac{16}{20}$. **D**
   A. 11 B. 15 C. 13 D. 12
7. Solve $\frac{2}{5} = \frac{38}{d}$. **B**
   A. 90 B. 95 C. 105 D. 100
8. Solve $\frac{27}{e} = \frac{3}{2}$. **C**
   A. 9 B. 12 C. 18 D. 16
9. A car uses 8 gallons of gasoline to travel 192 miles. How many gallons are needed to go 144 miles? **D**
   A. 10 B. 4 C. 8 D. 6
10. A soup recipe calls for 3 pounds of potatos for 18 servings. How many pounds of potatos are needed for 48 servings? **B**
    A. 6 B. 8 C. 10 D. 12
11. Rectangle $ABCD \sim$ rectangle $EFGH$. Which angle corresponds to $\angle D$? **D**
    A. $\angle E$ B. $\angle F$ C. $\angle G$ D. $\angle H$
12. For the rectangles above, which side corresponds to $\overline{FG}$? **B**
    A. $\overline{AB}$ B. $\overline{BC}$ C. $\overline{CD}$ D. $\overline{AD}$
13. The two triangles at the right below are similar. What is the length of $\overline{EF}$? **D**
    A. 9 m B. 8 m C. 10 m D. 12 m

73
Glencoe Division, Macmillan/McGraw-Hill

Chapter 9 Test, Form 1A (continued)

14. There are five members in the Ciarcia family. If every member hugs every other member, how many hugs take place? **C**
    A. 8 B. 6 C. 10 D. 12
15. A tree casts a shadow 9 meters long at the same time that a building, 54 meters tall, casts an 18-meter shadow. How tall is the tree? **A**
    A. 27 m B. 25 m C. 30 m D. 28 m
16. The distance on a map is 2 inches. Find the actual distance, if the scale on the map is 1 in. : 30 mi. **D**
    A. 15 mi B. 32 mi C. 45 mi D. 60 mi
17. The distance on a map is $2\frac{3}{4}$ inches. Find the actual distance if the scale on the map is 1 in. : 60 mi. **A**
    A. 165 mi B. 21 mi C. 180 mi D. 150 mi
18. Triangle ABC has vertices $A(-2, -4)$, $B(-3, 1)$, and $C(2, 2)$. Find the vertices for a dilation with a scale factor of 0.5. **C**
    A. $A(1, -2), B(1.5, -0.5), C(1, -1)$ B. $A(-1, -3), B(-2, 2), C(1, 1)$
    C. $A(-1, -2), B(-1.5, 0.5), C(1, 1)$ D. $A(-3, -5), B(-4, 0), C(1, 1)$

Complete Exercises 19-24 using the information in $\triangle ABC$. Round angle measures to the nearest degree.

19. Find $\tan A$. **B**
    A. $\frac{3}{5}$ B. $\frac{4}{5}$ C. $\frac{3}{4}$ D. $\frac{4}{3}$
20. Find $m\angle A$. **D**
    A. 37° B. 90° C. 47° D. 53°
21. Find $\sin B$. **C**
    A. $\frac{4}{5}$ B. $\frac{4}{3}$ C. $\frac{3}{5}$ D. $\frac{3}{4}$
22. Find $\cos B$. **A**
    A. $\frac{4}{5}$ B. $\frac{4}{3}$ C. $\frac{3}{5}$ D. $\frac{3}{5}$
23. Find $m\angle B$. **A**
    A. 37° B. 90° C. 47° D. 53°
24. Find $m\angle C$. **D**
    A. 37° B. 47° C. 53° D. 90°
25. Find the value of x to the nearest tenth in $\triangle DEF$. **A**
    A. 13.9 ft B. 12.2 ft C. 8 ft D. 27.7 ft

BONUS How many terms are in the sequence 18, 24, 30, 36, . . . , 624? **A**
    A. 102 B. 98 C. 105 D. 100

74
Glencoe Division, Macmillan/McGraw-Hill

Test and Review Generator software is provided in Apple, IBM, and Macintosh versions. You may use this software to create your own tests or worksheets, based on the needs of your students.

The **Performance Assessment Booklet** provides an alternate assessment for evaluating student progress. An assessment for this chapter can be found on pages 17–18.

375

Academic Skills Test

Academic Skills Test

Directions: Choose the best answer. Write A, B, C, or D.

1. Sue bought grocery items for the
C following prices: $1.39, $2.89, 58¢, and $1.19. The best estimate of the total cost is

   A $4   B $5

   C $6   D $9

2. Which equation is equivalent to
C $\frac{c}{5} = 2.5$?

   A $\frac{c}{5} = \frac{2.5}{5}$

   B $\frac{c}{5} = 2.5 \cdot 5$

   C $\frac{c}{5} \cdot 5 = 2.5 \cdot 5$

   D $\frac{c}{5} = 2.5 \div 5$

3. If $\frac{x}{5} + 4 = 32$, what is the value of x?
D

   A 5.6   B 7.2

   C 28   D 140

4. $(-8)^3 =$
A

   A –512   B –24

   C 24   D 512

5.
B

Quiz Score	Number of Students
9-11	3
12-14	4
15-17	9
18-20	6

How many students had scores less than 15?

   A 4   B 7

   C 16   D none of these

6. 8th Graders Monthly Allowances ($)
A

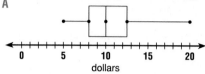

If the box-and-whisker plot represents 30 students, about how many students receive $10 or less?

   A 15   B 10

   C 5   D 3

7. Use the box-and-whisker plot in
D problem 6. Which average could be misleading?

   A mean   B median

   C mode   D none of these

8. In the figure below, $x \parallel y$. If $d = 72°$,
B what is the value of e?

   A 180

   B 108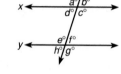

   C 90

   D 72

9. A four-sided figure with only one pair
D of parallel sides is a

   A rectangle   B rhombus

   C parallelogram   D trapezoid

10. What is the greatest common factor of
B 14 and 50?

   A 1   B 2

   C 50   D 700

11. To use a calculator to divide 6 by $2\frac{1}{8}$,
C what decimal number should you enter for $2\frac{1}{8}$?

A 12.75 **B** 2.18

C 2.125 **D** 0.125

12. If $x + 2\frac{2}{3} = -4\frac{1}{3}$, what is the value
D of x?

A $1\frac{2}{3}$ **B** $-1\frac{2}{3}$

C -6 **D** -7

13. What are the next two terms in the
D sequence 2, 5, 10, 17, . . . ?

A 22, 27 **B** 24, 31

C 26, 35 **D** 26, 37

14. What is the area of this figure?
C

A 40 sq ft

B 64 sq ft

C 88 sq ft

D 110 sq ft

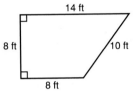

15. $-\sqrt{0.81} =$
B

A -0.09 **B** -0.9

C 0.09 **D** 0.9

16. To the nearest inch, how long is the
C diagonal of a 20 in. by 50 in. window?

A 100 in. **B** 70 in.

C 54 in. **D** 29 in.

17. To the nearest foot, what is the
C value of c?

A 25

B 50

C 100

D 150

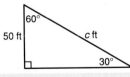

18. On a trip, the Browns drive 102 miles
B in 2 hours. If they continue at the same rate, which proportion will give h, the total number of hours, for a 450-mile trip?

A $\frac{102}{2} = \frac{h}{450}$ **B** $\frac{102}{2} = \frac{450}{h}$

C $\frac{2}{h} = \frac{450}{102}$ **D** $\frac{h}{2} = \frac{102}{450}$

19. $\triangle MNO$ is similar to $\triangle PQR$. What side
C corresponds to $\overline{NO}$?

A $\overline{NM}$

B $\overline{PQ}$

C $\overline{QR}$

D $\overline{RP}$

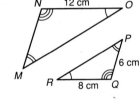

20. Use the similar triangles shown in
B problem 19. What is the length of $\overline{MN}$?

A 8 cm **B** 9 cm

C 10 cm **D** 11 cm

10 Applications with Percent

Previewing the Chapter

This chapter introduces percent by connecting it with proportions, a topic from the previous chapter. This enables students to see percent as a continuation of past work rather than as a new and discrete topic. All facets of percent are explored, including relationships with fractions and decimals, large and small percents, estimation, and the percent equation. Applications of percent which are highlighted are circle graphs, percent of change, discount, and simple interest. In the **problem-solving strategy** lesson, students learn to solve problems by solving a simpler problem.

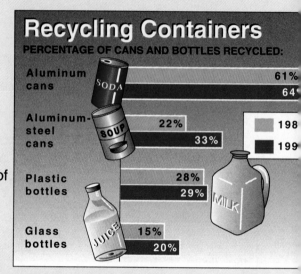

Recycling Containers
PERCENTAGE OF CANS AND BOTTLES RECYCLED:

Aluminum cans — 61%, 64%

Aluminum-steel cans — 22%, 33%

Plastic bottles — 28%, 29%

Glass bottles — 15%, 20%

198... 199...

Lesson	Lesson Objectives	NCTM Standards	State/Local Objectives
10-1	Express fractions as percents.	1–5, 7, 9	
10-1	Solve problems using the percent proportion.	1–5, 7, 9	
10-2	Express decimals and fractions as percents.	1–5, 7, 9	
10-2	Express percents as fractions and decimals.	1–5, 7, 9	
10-3	Express percents greater than 100 or less than 1 as decimals and fractions.	1–5, 7, 9	
10-4	Solve problems by first solving a simpler problem.	1–5, 7, 8, 12	
10-5	Estimate by using fractions, decimals, and percents interchangeably.	1–5, 7, 10, 12, 13	
10-5B	Estimate area using nonstandard units of measure.	1–5, 7, 13	
Decision Making	Analyze data and make a decision.	1–4, 7	
10-6	Solve problems using the percent equation.	1–5, 7, 9	
10-7	Construct circle graphs.	1–5, 10, 12, 13	
10-8	Find the percent of increase or decrease.	1–5, 7, 9	
10-9	Solve problems involving discounts.	1–5, 7, 9	
10-10	Solve problems involving simple interest.	1–5, 7, 9	

Organizing the Chapter

A complete, 1-page lesson plan is provided for each lesson in the Lesson Plans Masters Booklet.

LESSON PLANNING GUIDE

Lesson	Materials/ Manipulatives	Extra Practice (Student Edition)	Study Guide	Practice	Enrichment	Evaluation	Technology	Lab Manual	Multicultural Activities	Application and Interdisciplinary Activities	Transparencies	Group Activity Cards
10-1	calculator	p. 606	p. 85	p. 85	p. 85						10-1	10-1
10-2	graph paper, colored pencils, calculator	p. 607	p. 86	p. 86	p. 86			p. 67			10-2	10-2
10-3	graph paper, colored pencils, calculator	p. 607	p. 87	p. 87	p. 87						10-3	10-3
10-4			p. 88	p. 88	p. 88						10-4	10-4
10-5		p. 607	p. 89	p. 89	p. 89	Quiz A, p. 88					10-5	10-5
10-5B	measuring tape							p. 68				
10-6	graph or newspaper article, calculator	p. 608	p. 90	p. 90	p. 90		p. 10			p. 10	10-6	10-6
10-7	compass, protractor, calculator	p. 608	p. 91	p. 91	p. 91			p. 69	p. 10	p. 24	10-7	10-7
10-8	scissors, graph paper, calculator	p. 608	p. 92	p. 92	p. 92						10-8	10-8
10-9	calculator	p. 609	p. 93	p. 93	p. 93						10-9	10-9
10-10	calculator	p. 609	p. 94	p. 94	p. 94	Quiz B, p. 88	p. 24				10-10	10-10
Study Guide and Review			Multiple Choice Test, Forms 1A and 1B, pp. 82–85 Free Response Test, Forms 2A and 2B, pp. 86–87									
Test			Cumulative Review, p. 89 (free response) Cumulative Test, p. 90 (multiple choice)									

Blackline Masters Booklets

Pacing Guide: Option I (Chapters 1–12) - 14 days; Option II (Chapters 1–13) - 13 days; Option III (Chapters 1–14) - 12 days
You may wish to refer to the complete **Course Planning Guides** on page T25.

OTHER CHAPTER RESOURCES

Student Edition
Chapter Opener, pp. 378–379
Mid-Chapter Review, p. 396
Decision Making, pp. 398–399
Portfolio Suggestion, p. 402

Manipulatives
Overhead Manipulative Resources
Middle School Mathematics Manipulative Kit

Software/Technology
Interactive Mathematics Tools (Macintosh)
Test and Review Generator (IBM, Apple, Macintosh)
Teacher's Guide for Software Resources

Other Supplements
Transparency 10–0
Performance Assessment, pp. 19–20
Glencoe Mathematics Professional Series Lesson Plans, pp. 108–118

INTERDISCIPLINARY BULLETIN BOARD

Health Connection

Objective Express real-world facts as percents.

How To Use It Have students research and display data on an organ or system of the human body. Ask them to take measurements on themselves (for example, pulse rate, aerobic capacity) and use percents to compare these measurements with the average measurement they discover through their research.

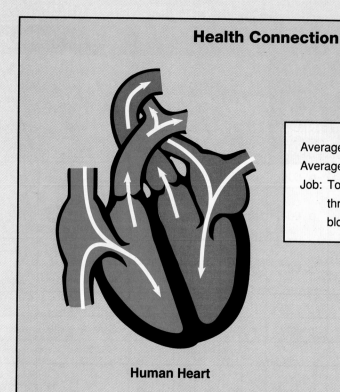

Health Connection

Average weight: $\frac{1}{2}$ pound

Average rate: 72 beats per minute

Job: To pump 5 quarts of blood through 60,000 miles of blood vessels

Human Heart

APPLICATIONS AND CONNECTIONS

Applications	Lesson	Example	Exercise
Consumer Awareness	10-1	1	
Smart Shopping	10-1	2	
Sports	10-1		40
Recycling	10-1		42
Economics	10-3		37
Consumer Awareness	10-3		39
Consumer Math	10-5	5	
Ecology	10-5		38
Entertainment	10-6	3	
Taxes	10-6		34
Sales	10-6		37, 39
Education	10-6		38
Research	10-7		16
Nutrition	10-7		17
Business	10-8	1	
Earning Money	10-8	2	
Traffic Safety	10-8		24
Telecommunication	10-9		31
Earning Money	10-10	1	
Consumer Math	10-10	2	
Finance	10-10	3	33, 36
Connections			
Geometry	10-2		44
Geometry	10-5	6	
Statistics	10-5		39
Statistics	10-7		9, 15
Probability	10-7		10

TEAM ACTIVITIES

Multicultural Experiences

Outside Field Trips Try to arrange field trips that will illustrate the use of percents in everyday life. At a mall, students can look for sales and calculate the discount rates.

At a bank, students can learn the differences among the various interest rates charged and paid by the bank.

In-Class Speakers Invite an accountant to discuss the calculation of sales, income, and other taxes.

A merchant can explain how he or she decides on the discount rates for a sale.

SUPPLEMENTARY BLACKLINE MASTER BOOKLETS

Some of the blackline masters for enhancing this chapter are shown below.

Application and Interdisciplinary Activity Masters, pp. 10, 24

Name _____ Date _____

Applications Activity

Use with Lesson 10-6

Business Management: Calculating Depreciation

When something loses value, it is said to **depreciate**. If you buy a new car for $12,000, it may be worth only $8,000 two years later. The car has depreciated in value by $4,000. People often have to figure out how much an item depreciates so that they will know how much tax they must pay on it. The government allows you to use certain formulas to calculate depreciation. The simplest to calculate is **straight-line** depreciation. Each year, you depreciate an item by the same percentage.

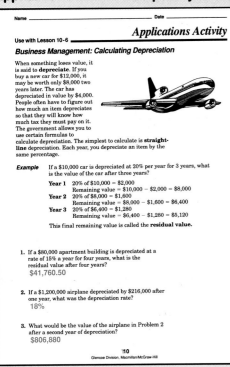

Example If a $10,000 car is depreciated at 20% per year for 3 years, what is the value of the car after three years?

Year 1 20% of $10,000 = $2,000
Remaining value = $10,000 − $2,000 = $8,000
Year 2 20% of $8,000 = $1,600
Remaining value = $8,000 − $1,600 = $6,400
Year 3 20% of $6,400 = $1,280
Remaining value = $6,400 − $1,280 = $5,120

This final remaining value is called the **residual value**.

1. If a $80,000 apartment building is depreciated at a rate of 15% a year for four years, what is the residual value after four years?
$41,760.50

2. If a $1,200,000 airplane depreciated by $216,000 after one year, what was the depreciation rate?
18%

3. What would be the value of the airplane in Problem 2 after a second year of depreciation?
$806,880

T10
Glencoe Division, Macmillan/McGraw-Hill

Name _____ Date _____

Interdisciplinary Activity

Use with Lesson 10-7

Geography

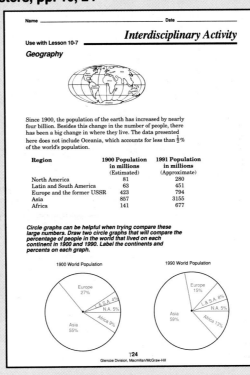

Since 1900, the population of the earth has increased by nearly four billion. Besides this change in the number of people, there has been a big change in where they live. The data presented here does not include Oceania, which accounts for less than $\frac{1}{2}$% of the world's population.

Region	1900 Population in millions (Estimated)	1991 Population in millions (Approximate)
North America	81	280
Latin and South America	63	451
Europe and the former USSR	423	794
Asia	857	3155
Africa	141	677

Circle graphs can be helpful when trying compare these large numbers. Draw two circle graphs that will compare the percentage of people in the world that lived on each continent in 1900 and 1990. Label the continents and percents on each graph.

T24
Glencoe Division, Macmillan/McGraw-Hill

Multicultural Activity Masters, p. 10

Name _____ Date _____

Multicultural Activity

Use with Lesson 10-7

Who Are the People of the United States?

Every ten years, the United States government must take a census, or count, of the population. The purpose of the census is not only to find out how many people live in the country, but also to gather data that helps us see ourselves a little more clearly—who we are, where we come from, how we live. The graph at the right was created using data collected in the 1990 census.

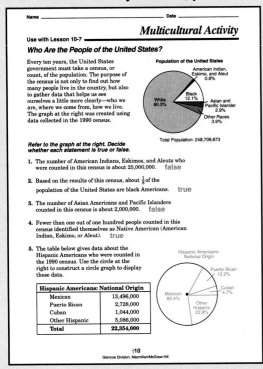

Refer to the graph at the right. Decide whether each statement is true or false.

1. The number of American Indians, Eskimos, and Aleuts who were counted in this census is about 25,000,000. false

2. Based on the results of this census, about $\frac{1}{8}$ of the population of the United States are black Americans. true

3. The number of Asian Americans and Pacific Islanders counted in this census is about 2,000,000. false

4. Fewer than one out of one hundred people counted in this census identified themselves as Native American (American Indian, Eskimo, or Aleut). true

5. The table below gives data about the Hispanic Americans who were counted in the 1990 census. Use the circle at the right to construct a circle graph to display these data.

Hispanic Americans: National Origin	
Mexican	13,496,000
Puerto Rican	2,728,000
Cuban	1,044,000
Other Hispanic	5,086,000
Total	**22,354,000**

T10
Glencoe Division, Macmillan/McGraw-Hill

Technology Masters, p. 24

Name _____ Date _____

Computer Activity

Use with Lesson 10-10

Simple Interest

Example Mario needs to borrow $8,100 to buy a new car. His payments will last 36 months at a rate of 9% per year (simple interest). What is his monthly payment?

Solution The interest would be calculated by using the formula $I = PRT$, or $I = 8,100 \times 0.09 \times \frac{36}{12} = \$2,187$. Therefore, the total amount of the loan is $8,100 + $2,187 = $10,287. Each payment would be $\frac{10,287}{36}$, or $285.75.

The BASIC program below can be used to find the simple interest and the monthly payment on a loan of P dollars at a rate of R percent for N months.

```
TYPE    NEW
  10    PRINT "SIMPLE INTEREST"
  20    INPUT "PRINCIPAL AMOUNT" ; P
  30    INPUT "RATE (AS A DECIMAL)" ; R
  40    INPUT "NUMBER OF MONTHS" ; N
  50    LET T = N/12
  60    LET I = P * R * T
  70    PRINT "THE AMOUNT OF INTEREST IS":I
  80    LET A = INT(((P + I)/N) * 100 + .5)/100
  90    PRINT "MONTHLY PAYMENT : " ; A
 100    END
```

Use the program to find the monthly payment for each of the following loans.

1. Aretha borrowed $5,200 at 8% for 30 months. What is the amount of simple interest she will have to pay on the loan? What is her monthly payment? $1,040; $208.00

2. Mindy borrowed $1,850 at 9.75% for 15 months. What is the amount of simple interest she will have to pay on the loan? What is her monthly payment to the nearest cent?
$225.47; $138.36

3. Kim needed a loan of $11,500 at 10.5% to buy a car. If his budget only allowed for a payment of $300 a month, how many months would he have to make payments? 58

T24
Glencoe Division, Macmillan/McGraw-Hill

RECOMMENDED OUTSIDE RESOURCES

Books/Periodicals

Mett, C.L., *Writing in Mathematics: Evidence of Learning Through Writing,* Clearing House, 62:293–6, March, 1989.

Schulte, Albert P., ed., *Teaching Statistics and Probability, 1981 Yearbook,* NCTM, 1981.

Films/Videotapes/Videodiscs

Equations in Algebra, Chicago, IL: International Film Bureau, Inc., 1963.

Multiplying Options and Subtracting Bias, Reston, VA: NCTM, 1981.

Software

Survival Math, (Apple II), Wings for Learning/Sunburst

For addresses of companies handling software, please refer to page T24.

Glencoe's *Interactive Mathamatics: Activities and Investigations* consists of 18 units that may be used as alternatives or supplemental material for *Mathematics: Applications and Connections.* The suggested units for this chapter are Unit 13, *Start your Engines* and Unit 16, *Growing Pains.* See page T18 for more information.

378d

MAKING MATHEMATICS RELEVANT

Spotlight on Recycling

Americans are making great strides in recycling. In 1988, we recycled 13 percent of the total amount of waste we generated, twice the 1960 rate. Unfortunately, the amount of waste generated in 1988 was 50 percent higher than the amount generated in 1960. Moreover, there are vast amounts of additional materials used to sustain our way of life, the raw materials used to produce consumable goods. On a per capita basis in 1991, the average American used 40 pounds of petroleum and coal, 30 pounds of other minerals, 26 pounds of agricultural products, and 19 pounds of forest products every day. Figures like these, which are vital to the future health of the country, are compiled and analyzed by environmental scientists.

Chapter

10 Applications with Percent

Spotlight on Recycling

Have You Ever Wondered...

- If more containers are being recycled each year?

- If the amount of waste disposed of has increased or decreased over the past 10 years?

WHERE DOES YOUR WASTE GO?
(in pounds per person per day)

Year	Waste Generated	Waste Recycled	Combustion for Energy	Combustion (no Energy)	Landfill Deposits
1960	2.67	0.18	—	0.82	1.67
1965	3.00	0.19	0.01	0.75	2.05
1970	3.27	0.23	0.02	0.66	2.37
1975	3.26	0.25	0.02	0.45	2.54
1980	3.61	0.35	0.06	0.27	2.93
1985	3.71	0.38	0.17	0.10	3.06
1986	3.80	0.42	0.22	0.07	3.09
1987	3.92	0.45	0.36	0.05	3.06
1988	4.00	0.52	0.59	0.02	2.87

"Have You Ever Wondered?" Answers

- More containers were recycled in 1990 than in 1989.

- The amount of waste has increased.

Recycling

Working a group.

1. For two weeks, keep track of what you throw away each day.

2. Make a chart showing the type and amount of trash you throw away each day.

3. Indicate what can be recycled or reused. Include information about what kinds of recycling programs are available in your area.

4. Suggest ways that you can reduce the amount of waste you contribute to landfills

Looking Ahead

In this chapter, you will see how mathematics can be used to answer questions about recycling. The major objectives of the chapter are to:

- express fractions and decimals as percents and vice versa

- solve problems using percents

- construct circle graphs

- find the percent of increase or decrease

- solve problems involving discounts or simple interest

379

DATA ANALYSIS

Have students study the waste table and the recycling graph. Ask the following questions.

- *In what year did daily landfill deposits decrease for the first time?* 1987

- *What is the meaning of the 33% figure in the bar graph?* In 1990, Americans recycled 33% of the aluminum-steel cans produced.

Data Search

A question related to these data is provided in Lesson 10-7, page 405, Exercise 18.

CHAPTER PROJECT

Help students prepare a chart for keeping track of what they throw away. You may want to extend the project to include the trash disposed of in their homes. Make a few students responsible for researching recycling services in your area.

At the conclusion of the project, discuss how students can apply what they have learned. For example, have them make a list of supplies they would take on a 5-day hiking trip if they could not leave any trash along the way.

Allow three weeks to complete the project.

Chapter Opener Transparency

Transparency 10-0 is available in the Transparency Package. It provides another full-color, motivating activity that you can use to capture students' interest.

NCTM Standards: 1–5, 7, 9

Lesson Resources
- Study Guide Master 10-1
- Practice Master 10-1
- Enrichment Master 10-1
- Group Activity Card 10-1

 Transparency 10-1 contains the 5-Minute Check and a teaching aid for this lesson.

⏱ 5-Minute Check
(Over Chapter 9)

1. If 5 apples cost $1.35, how much will 7 apples cost? $1.89

2. The triangles are similar. Find *x*. 21 m

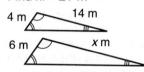
4 m 14 m
6 m *x* m

3. A map uses the scale 3 cm = 36 km. What actual distance is represented by a map distance of 10 cm?
120 km

4. Find sin *A*, cos *A*, and tan *A*.
$\frac{3}{5}, \frac{4}{5}, \frac{3}{4}$

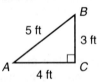
B
5 ft
3 ft
A
4 ft
C

---

1 FOCUS

Motivating the Lesson

Questioning Ask students to name everyday situations in which the word *percent* is used.

2 TEACH

Using Questioning Ask the following series of questions: *How many squares of a 10-by-10 grid would you shade to represent 20%? 9%? 63%? n%?*
20; 9; 63; *n*

10-1 The Percent Proportion

Objectives
Express fractions as percents. Solve problems using the percent proportion.

Words to Learn
percent
percentage
base
rate
percent proportion

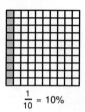

The word *percent* and the symbol % are so common in magazines and newspapers, radio and TV, that you may take percents for granted. From an 87% on your health test and shooting 74% from the foul line, to buying in-line skates at 15% off and paying 6% sales tax, you are constantly bombarded with percents.

A **percent** is a ratio that compares a number to 100. Percent also means *hundredths,* or *per hundred.* The models below represent 50%, 25%, and 10%.

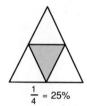
$\frac{1}{2}$ = 50%

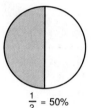
$\frac{1}{4}$ = 25%

$\frac{1}{10}$ = 10%

Whenever you split the cost of a CD with your sister, or share a pizza, you usually work with fractions. But how often do you cut a pizza into a hundred parts? How can you express eating three pieces of pizza out of a total of eight pieces as a percent?

By looking at the model at the right or the number line below, you can see that $\frac{3}{8}$ is less than $\frac{1}{2}$ and greater than $\frac{1}{4}$. You can estimate that $\frac{3}{8}$ is between 50% and 25%.

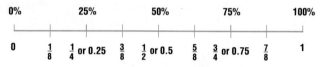

0%   25%   50%   75%   100%

0   $\frac{1}{8}$ $\frac{1}{4}$ or 0.25 $\frac{3}{8}$ $\frac{1}{2}$ or 0.5 $\frac{5}{8}$ $\frac{3}{4}$ or 0.75 $\frac{7}{8}$ 1

LOOKBACK

You can review ratios on page 338 and proportions on page 344.

To find the percent (*x*), you can solve this proportion.

$$\frac{3}{8} = \frac{x}{100}$$ *3 pieces out of 8 eaten*

$3 \cdot 100 = 8x$ *Write the cross products.*

$300 = 8x$ *Divide each side by 8.*

300 ÷ 8 = 37.5

$x = 37.5$

The solution is 37.5. So, $\frac{3}{8}$ or 37.5% of the pizza was eaten.

OPTIONS

Team Teaching

Urge the other teachers on your team to employ percents whenever possible. Encourage them to frame questions in each of the three possible forms. Point out the importance of visual representations of percents, such as circle graphs, bar graphs, and so on.

 Interactive Mathematics Tools

This multimedia software provides an interactive lesson that is tied directly to Lesson 10–1. Students will use fraction grids to explore fractions and percents.

In the pizza proportion, 3 is called the **percentage** (P). The number 8 is called the **base** (B). The ratio $\frac{37.5}{100}$ is called the **rate.**

$$\frac{3}{8} = \frac{37.5}{100} \quad \rightarrow \quad \frac{\text{Percentage}}{\text{Base}} = \text{Rate}$$

If r represents the percent, the proportion can be written as $\frac{P}{B} = \frac{r}{100}$. This proportion is called the **percent proportion.** You can think of the percent proportion as a comparison. In the pizza proportion, the part eaten is compared to the whole pizza.

$$\begin{array}{ll} \textit{slices of pizza eaten} \rightarrow & \dfrac{3}{8} = \dfrac{37.5}{100} \leftarrow \textit{percent eaten} \\ \textit{slices in whole pizza} \rightarrow & \leftarrow \textit{percent in whole} \end{array}$$

You can use the percent proportion to solve percent problems.

Example 1 *Problem Solving*

Consumer Awareness The purchase price of a CD player is $127. The state tax rate is 6% of the purchase price. Find the total price.

$$\frac{P}{B} = \frac{r}{100}$$

$$\frac{P}{127} = \frac{6}{100} \qquad \textit{Replace B with 127 and r with 6.}$$

$$P \cdot 100 = 127 \cdot 6 \quad \textit{Find the cross products.}$$

$127 \; \boxed{\times} \; 6 \; \boxed{\div} \; 100 \; \boxed{=} \; \text{7.62} \quad \textit{Find } 127 \cdot 6. \textit{ Then divide by 100.}$

$$P = 7.62 \qquad \textit{The tax is \$7.62.}$$

The total cost is $127 + $7.62 or $134.62.

Example 2 *Problem Solving*

Smart Shopping A bicycle is on sale for $115. This is 80% of the regular price. What is the regular price?

$$\frac{P}{B} = \frac{r}{100}$$

$$\frac{115}{B} = \frac{80}{100} \qquad \textit{Replace P with 115 and r with 80.}$$

$$115 \cdot 100 = B \cdot 80 \quad \textit{Find the cross products.}$$

$$11{,}500 = 80B \qquad \textit{Divide each side by 80.}$$

$11500 \; \boxed{\div} \; 80 \; \boxed{=} \; \text{143.75}$

$$143.75 = B$$

The regular price is $143.75.

Lesson 10-1   The Percent Proportion   **381**

3 PRACTICE/APPLY

Assignment Guide
Maximum: 15–42
Minimum: 15–33 odd, 34–42

For **Extra Practice,** see p. 606.

Alternate Assessment

Modeling Have students use visual representations of percents similar to those on page 380 to illustrate examples of percents.

Additional Answers

1. A percent is a ratio that compares a number to 100.

2. $\frac{53}{100} = \frac{x}{215}$

3. $\frac{3}{8} = \frac{37.5}{100} = 37.5\%$

Practice Masters, p. 85

Example 3

Express $\frac{3}{5}$ as a percent.

$$\frac{P}{B} = \frac{r}{100}$$

$$\frac{3}{5} = \frac{r}{100} \qquad \textit{Replace P with 3 and B with 5.}$$

$$3 \cdot 100 = 5 \cdot r \qquad \textit{Find the cross products.}$$

$$300 = 5r \qquad \textit{Divide each side by 5.}$$

$$300 \;\boxed{\div}\; 5 \;\boxed{=}\; 60$$

$$60 = r \qquad \frac{3}{5} \text{ is equivalent to 60\%.}$$

Checking for Understanding   For answers to Exercises 1-3, see margin.

Communicating Mathematics

Read and study the lesson to answer each question.

1. **Tell** what is meant by percent.
2. **Write** a proportion you would use to find 53% of 215.
3. **Tell** why 37.5% of the figure at the right is shaded.

Guided Practice

Express each fraction as a percent.

4. $\frac{17}{25}$ 68%   5. $\frac{35}{100}$ 35%   6. $\frac{7}{8}$ 87.5%   7. $\frac{9}{10}$ 90%   8. $\frac{1}{20}$ 5%

Match each question with its corresponding proportion.

9. 24 is 25% of what number? b   a. $\frac{24}{25} = \frac{r}{100}$

10. 24 is what percent of 25? a   b. $\frac{24}{B} = \frac{25}{100}$

11. What number is 25% of 24? c   c. $\frac{P}{24} = \frac{25}{100}$

Write a percent proportion to solve each problem. Round answers to the nearest tenth.

12. Find 19% of 532. $\frac{19}{100} = \frac{P}{532}$ $P \approx 101.1$

13. Find 12.5% of 88. $\frac{12.5}{100} = \frac{P}{88}$ $P = 11$

14. If a man weighs 185 pounds, his body contains about 111 pounds of water. The water weight is what percent of his body weight?
    $\frac{111}{185} = \frac{r}{100}$ $r = 60$ $\frac{111}{185} = 60\%$

Exercises

Independent Practice

Express each fraction as a percent.

15. $\frac{9}{100}$ 9%   16. $\frac{1}{8}$ 12.5%   17. $\frac{7}{10}$ 70%   18. $\frac{3}{4}$ 75%   19. $\frac{23}{50}$ 46%

20. $\frac{5}{8}$ 62.5%   21. $\frac{2}{3}$ $66\frac{2}{3}\%$ 22. $\frac{27}{30}$ 90%   23. $\frac{4}{5}$ 80%   24. $\frac{15}{40}$ $37\frac{1}{2}\%$

OPTIONS

Bell Ringer

One year Mrs. Grady's store made a good profit. The next year the profit increased 100%. The next year it decreased 100%. How much profit was there the third year? $0

Write a percent proportion to solve each problem. Round answers to the nearest tenth. **For proportions to Exercises 25-33, see margin.**

25. What is 35% of 230? **80.5**
26. Find 37.5% of 104. **39**
27. 50 is what percent of 400? **12.5%**
28. 17.8 is what percent of 178? **10%**
29. 57 is 30% of what number? **190**
30. 80 is 45% of what number? **177.8**
31. Twenty-eight is 25% of what number? **112**
32. Fifteen is 40% of what number? **37.5**
33. Jim has autographs from 16 of the 25 members of the Pittsburgh Pirates. The number of autographs is what percent of the team? **64%**

Mixed Review

34. Mr. and Mrs. Dixon are having their living room ceiling painted. The living room is 14 feet wide and 20 feet long. A painter charges 24¢ for each square foot to be painted. How much will it cost the Dixons to have their ceiling painted? *(Lesson 1-1)* **$67.20**

35. **Statistics** Refer to the line plot in the Example on page 137. Find the median and upper and lower quartiles of the data in the line plot. *(Lesson 4-6)* **21; 23; 17**

36. **Geometry** Refer to the figure in Example 2 on page 178. Find $m\angle 8$. *(Lesson 5-1)* **80°**

37. Write $\frac{40}{72}$ in simplest form. *(Lesson 6-5)* **$\frac{5}{9}$**

38. Find $\sqrt{220}$ to the nearest tenth. *(Lesson 8-3)* **14.8**

39. In the figure at the right, find the value of x to the nearest degree. *(Lesson 9-10)* **23°**

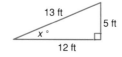

Problem Solving and Applications

40. **Sports** Eleven out of 48 members of the football team are on the field. What percent of the team members are playing? **22.9%**

41. **Critical Thinking** Katrina made 56% of her free throws in the first half of the basketball season. If she makes 7 shots out of the next 13 attempts, will it help or hurt her average? Explain. **See margin.**

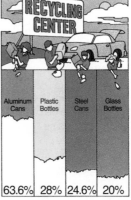

42. **Recycling** The graph at the right shows what products in the United States were recycled most often in 1990.

42a. about 86.5 billion

a. Americans recycled a record 63.6% of the aluminum cans produced. If 55 billion cans were recycled, how many were produced?

b. Lake Charleston estimates it recycled 2,500 of the 6,250 glass bottles purchased in 1991. How does this compare with the national average in 1990? **It is twice the national average.**

Lesson 10-1 The Percent Proportion **383**

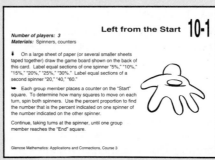
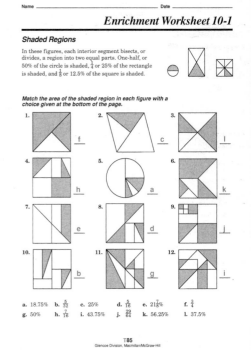
383

Lesson Resources
- Study Guide Master 10-2
- Practice Master 10-2
- Enrichment Master 10-2
- Lab Manual, p. 67
- Group Activity Card 10-2

 Transparency 10-2 contains the 5-Minute Check and a teaching aid for this lesson.

⏱ 5-Minute Check
(Over Lesson 10-1)

Express each fraction as a percent.

1. $\frac{19}{100}$ 19%   **2.** $\frac{2}{5}$ 40%

Write a percent proportion to solve each problem.

3. What is 20% of 25?   5

4. 18 is 45% of what number?   40

5. 9 is what percent of 12?
75%

---

1 FOCUS

Motivating the Lesson

Questioning   Ask students to find different ways to name these numbers: 3^3; $\sqrt{81}$; $0.\overline{4}$; 2.6×10^{-4}.   27; 9; $\frac{4}{9}$; 0.00026

2 TEACH

More Examples

Express each decimal as a percent.

For Example 1

0.1   10%

For Example 2

0.91   91%

For Example 3

0.222   22.2%

10-2 Fractions, Decimals, and Percents

Objectives
Express decimals and fractions as percents. Express percents as fractions and decimals.

Jackie wants to buy a new skateboard. She finds two stores that have the same model on sale. If the original price is the same at both stores, which store offers the better sale price?

To find the better price, you need to compare $\frac{2}{3}$ and 70%.

One way to compare them is to express $\frac{2}{3}$ and 70% as decimals and compare the decimals.

$$\frac{2}{3} = 2 \div 3$$

$$2 \boxed{\div} 3 \boxed{=} 0.6666667$$

$$\frac{2}{3} \approx 0.67$$

$$70\% = \frac{70}{100} \quad \textit{Definition of percent}$$
$$= 0.70 \text{ or } 0.7$$

Since 0.70 is greater than 0.67, Henry's offers the better sale price.

LOOK BACK

You can review expressing fractions as decimals on page 227.

You learned how to express fractions as decimals in Chapter 6, and in Lesson 10-1 you learned how to express fractions as percents. Fractions, decimals, and percents are different ways to name the same number.

To express a decimal as a percent, first write the decimal as a fraction with a denominator of 100. Then, express the fraction as a percent.

Examples

Mental Math Hint

• • • • • • • • • • •

In Examples 1–3, notice the percent has the same number as the result of multiplying the decimal by 100.

Express each decimal as a percent.

1 0.6
$$0.6 = 0.60$$
$$= \frac{60}{100} \text{ or } 60\%$$

2 0.78
$$0.78 = \frac{78}{100} \text{ or } 78\%$$

3 0.354
$$0.354 = \frac{354}{1,000}$$
$$= \frac{35.4}{100} \text{ or } 35.4\%$$

Divide the numerator and the denominator by 10, so that the denominator is 100.

OPTIONS

Multicultural Education
Women hoping to become mathematicians have always faced obstacles; mathematics was considered "man's work." The belief that men are better than women at math is fading and opportunities for women are increasing. More than 1,000 women belong to the organization American Women in Mathematics.

To express a fraction as a percent, you can solve a percent proportion or you can use a calculator to express the fraction as a decimal. Then express the decimal as a percent like you did in Examples 1–3.

Examples

Express each fraction as a percent.

4 $\dfrac{2}{25}$

$2 \; \boxed{\div} \; 25 \; \boxed{=} \; \boxed{0.08}$

$\dfrac{2}{25} = 0.08 \;\rightarrow\; \dfrac{8}{100} = 8\%$

5 $\dfrac{1}{6}$

$1 \; \boxed{\div} \; 6 \; \boxed{=} \; \boxed{0.1666667}$

$\dfrac{1}{6} \approx 0.17 \;\rightarrow\; \dfrac{17}{100} = 17\%$

The following chart provides commonly-used fractions and their percent equivalents.

Mental Math Hint
• • • • • • • • • •
It is helpful to know fraction-percent equivalencies by memory.

Fraction-Percent Equivalencies

Fraction	Percent	Fraction	Percent	Fraction	Percent
$\frac{1}{2}$	50%	$\frac{1}{5}$	20%	$\frac{5}{6}$	$83\frac{1}{3}\%$
$\frac{1}{3}$	$33\frac{1}{3}\%$	$\frac{2}{5}$	40%	$\frac{1}{8}$	$12\frac{1}{2}\%$
$\frac{2}{3}$	$66\frac{2}{3}\%$	$\frac{3}{5}$	60%	$\frac{3}{8}$	$37\frac{1}{2}\%$
$\frac{1}{4}$	25%	$\frac{4}{5}$	80%	$\frac{5}{8}$	$62\frac{1}{2}\%$
$\frac{3}{4}$	75%	$\frac{1}{6}$	$16\frac{2}{3}\%$	$\frac{7}{8}$	$87\frac{1}{2}\%$

Mini-Lab

Work with a partner.

Materials: 10 × 10 grid, colored pencils

• Shade a 5 × 5 section in one corner of the grid.

• Use a different colored pencil to shade each of the other three 5 × 5 corner sections.

Talk About It

a. How many small squares are in the grid? 100

b. How many small squares are in each colored section? 25

c. What percent is represented by each colored section? 25%

d. How many 5 × 5 sections are there? 4

e. What fraction of the grid is represented by each colored section? $\frac{1}{4}$

Lesson 10-2 Fractions, Decimals, and Percent **385**

Using the Mini-Lab Have students complete this statement, which is illustrated by the lab:
__?__ is __?__ percent of __?__.
25; 25; 100

Teaching Tip In Example 4, point out that the problem could also have been solved by first renaming $\frac{2}{25}$ as the equivalent fraction $\frac{8}{100}$.

More Examples

Express each fraction as a percent.

For Example 4

$\frac{47}{50}$ 94%

For Example 5

$\frac{7}{9}$ about 78%

Express each percent as a fraction in the simplest form.

For Example 6

28% $\frac{7}{25}$

For Example 7

95% $\frac{19}{20}$

For Example 8

$18\frac{3}{4}\%$ $\frac{3}{16}$

Express each percent as a decimal.

For Example 9

33%   0.33

For Example 10

70%   0.7

For Example 11

19.45%   0.1945

Checking for Understanding

Exercises 1-3 are designed to help you assess students' understanding through reading, writing, speaking, and modeling. You should work through these exercises with your students and then monitor their work on Guided Practice Exercises 4-15.

Reteaching Activity

Using Charts To help students see relationships among fractions, decimals, and percents, make charts like this one for them to complete.

	Fraction	Decimal	Percent
$\frac{1}{4}$		0.25	25%
0.7	$\frac{7}{10}$		70%
5%	$\frac{1}{20}$	0.05	

Study Guide Masters, p. 86

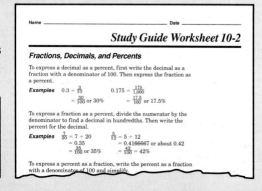

Name _____ Date _____

Study Guide Worksheet 10-2

Fractions, Decimals, and Percents

To express a decimal as a percent, first write the decimal as a fraction with a denominator of 100. Then express the fraction as a percent.

Examples $0.3 = \frac{3}{10}$ $0.175 = \frac{175}{1,000}$
$= \frac{30}{100}$ or 30% $= \frac{17.5}{100}$ or 17.5%

To express a fraction as a percent, divide the numerator by the denominator to find a decimal in hundredths. Then write the percent for the decimal.

Examples $\frac{7}{20} = 7 \div 20$ $\frac{5}{12} = 5 \div 12$
$= 0.35$ $= 0.4166667$ or about 0.42
$= \frac{35}{100}$ or 35% $= \frac{42}{100} = 42\%$

To express a percent as a fraction, write the percent as a fraction with a denominator of 100 and simplify.

385

Watch for students who express fractions as percents incorrectly, and vice-versa.

Prevent by having students memorize the fraction-percent equivalencies on page 385 and use them as a guide in estimating answers.

Close

Have students write a fraction, a decimal, and a percent, and explain how to express each in the other two forms.

3 PRACTICE/APPLY

Assignment Guide
Maximum: 16–44
Minimum: 17–37 odd, 38–44

For **Extra Practice,** see p. 607.

Alternate Assessment

Modeling Have students shade part of a 10 × 10 grid, then tell what fraction, decimal, and percent of the entire grid they shaded.

Practice Masters, p. 86

Name _____ Date _____

Practice Worksheet 10-2

Fractions, Decimals, and Percents

Express each decimal as a percent.

1. 0.04 4%   2. 0.4 40%   3. 0.625 62.5%

4. 0.3 30%   5. 0.13 13%   6. 0.123 12.3%

7. 0.21 21%   8. 0.25 25%   9. 0.603 60.3%

Express each percent as a fraction in simplest form.

10. 15% $\frac{3}{20}$ 11. 32% $\frac{8}{25}$ 12. 67% $\frac{67}{100}$

13. 62.5% $\frac{5}{8}$ 14. 18% $\frac{9}{50}$ 15. 23% $\frac{23}{100}$

16. 10% $\frac{1}{10}$ 17. 1.5% $\frac{3}{200}$ 18. 3.2% $\frac{4}{125}$

Express each percent as a decimal.

19. 8% 0.08   20. 32% 0.32   21. 15% 0.15

22. 16.23% 0.1623   23. 15.7% 0.157   24. 2.01% 0.0201

25. 3.2% 0.032   26. 80% 0.8   27. 1.32% 0.0132

Determine which is greater.

28. $\frac{1}{8}$ or 16% $\frac{1}{6}$ 29. 42% or $\frac{2}{8}$ 42%   30. $\frac{23}{10}$ or 23% $\frac{23}{10}$

T86
Glencoe Division, Macmillan/McGraw-Hill

386

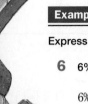

To express a percent as a fraction, express the percent in the form $\frac{r}{100}$ and simplify.

Examples

Express each percent as a fraction in simplest form.

6 6%

$$6\% = \frac{6}{100}$$
$$= \frac{3}{50}$$

7 45%

$$45\% = \frac{45}{100}$$
$$= \frac{9}{20}$$

8 $87\frac{1}{2}\%$

$$87\frac{1}{2}\% = \frac{87\frac{1}{2}}{100}$$
$$= 87\frac{1}{2} \div 100$$
$$= \frac{\overset{7}{\cancel{175}}}{2} \times \frac{1}{\underset{4}{\cancel{100}}}$$
$$= \frac{7}{8}$$

To express a percent as a decimal, express the percent in the form $\frac{r}{100}$ and then express the fraction as a decimal.

Examples

Express each percent as a decimal.

9 75%

$$75\% = \frac{75}{100} \text{ or } 0.75$$

10 20%

$$20\% = \frac{20}{100} \text{ or } 0.20 \text{ or } 0.2$$

11 5.5%

$$5.5\% = \frac{5.5}{100}$$
$$= \frac{55}{1,000} \quad \textit{Multiply the numerator and the denominator by 10, so that the numerator is a whole number.}$$
$$= \frac{55}{1,000} \text{ or } 0.055$$

Checking for Understanding   For answers to Exercises 1-3, see margin.

Communicating Mathematics

Read and study the lesson to answer each question.

1. **Tell** how to express a decimal as a percent.
2. **Tell** how you would express a percent as a fraction.
3. **Write** a shortcut that you might use to express a decimal as a percent.

OPTIONS

Bell Ringer

Ivory® soap is advertised as "$99\frac{44}{100}$ percent pure!" Express its purity as a fraction in lowest terms. $\frac{1,243}{1,250}$

Additional Answers

1. Write the decimal as a fraction with a denominator of 100, then express the fraction as a percent.

2. Express the percent in the form $\frac{r}{100}$ and simplify.

3. Multiply the decimal by 100, then add a percent sign.

Express each decimal as a percent.

4. 0.7 **70%**   5. 0.605 **60.5%**   6. 0.26 **26%**   7. 0.02 **2%**

Express each percent as a fraction in simplest form.

8. 65% $\frac{13}{20}$ 9. 6.5% $\frac{13}{200}$ 10. 12.5% $\frac{1}{8}$ 11. 96% $\frac{24}{25}$

Express each percent as a decimal.

12. 78% **0.78**   13. 9% **0.09**   14. 12.3% **0.123**   15. 8.4% **0.084**

Exercises

Determine which is greater.

16. 15% or $\frac{1}{8}$ **15%**   17. 0.3 or 3.2% **0.3**   18. $\frac{1}{4}$ or 28% **28%**

Express each decimal as a percent.

19. 0.18 **18%**   20. 0.08 **8%**   21. 0.704 **70.4%**

22. 0.039 **3.9%**   23. 0.553 **55.3%**   24. 0.6306 **63.06%**

Express each percent as a fraction in simplest form.

25. 58% $\frac{29}{50}$ 26. 37% $\frac{37}{100}$ 27. 44.5% $\frac{89}{200}$

28. $83\frac{1}{3}$% $\frac{5}{6}$ 29. 18.25% $\frac{73}{400}$ 30. $12\frac{3}{4}$% $\frac{51}{400}$

Express each percent as a decimal.

31. 28% **0.28**   32. 74% **0.74**   33. 84.25% **0.8425**

34. 81.5% **0.815**   35. 38.4% **0.384**   36. 9.01% **0.0901**

37. Express the ratio 11:55 as a decimal, as a percent, and as a fraction in simplest form. **0.2; 20%; $\frac{1}{5}$**

38. Solve $r = 9 + (-14) + 5 + (-21)$. Check by solving another way. *(Lesson 3-4)* **−21**

39. Factor −162 completely. *(Lesson 6-2)* **$-2 \cdot 3^4$**

40. Solve $\frac{z}{3} = -2.4$. *(Lesson 7-10)* **−7.2**

41. **Geometry** How can you tell if two polygons are similar? *(Lesson 9-5)* **See margin.**

42. Find 28% of 250. *(Lesson 10-1)* **70**

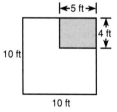

43. **Critical Thinking** A pizza with a diameter of 8 inches costs $6. A pizza with a diameter of 16 inches costs $12.

   a. The area of the 8-inch pizza is what percent of the area of the 16-inch pizza? **25%**

   b. Which is the better buy? Explain. **See margin.**

44. **Geometry** What percent of the area of the square at the right is shaded? Express the percent as a decimal. **20%; 0.20**

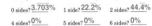

Lesson 10-2 Fractions, Decimals, and Percent   **387**

Additional Answers

41. The polygons have the same shape, but differ in size.

43b. The 16-inch pizza for $12 is the better buy because it costs about $0.06 per in² while the 8-inch pizza for $6 costs about $0.12 per in².

Enrichment Masters, p. 86

Name _____   Date _____

Enrichment Worksheet 10-2

Block Party

1. This model is made up of 27 cubes and has a length of 3 cubes, a width of 3 cubes, and a height of 3 cubes.

   The entire model will be painted yellow, then broken apart into individual cubes.

   What percent of the cubes will be painted yellow on:

   0 sides? **3.703%**   1 side? **22.2%**   2 sides? **44.4%**   3 sides? **29.629%**

   4 sides? **0%**   5 sides? **0%**   6 sides? **0%**

2. This model is made up of 64 cubes and has a length of 4 cubes, a width of 4 cubes, and a height of 4 cubes.

   The entire model will be painted orange, then broken apart into individual cubes.

   What percent of the cubes will be painted orange on:

   0 sides? **12.5%**   1 side? **37.5%**   2 sides? **37.5%**   3 sides? **12.5%**

   4 sides? **0%**   5 sides? **0%**   6 sides? **0%**

3. This model is made up of 125 cubes and has a length of 5 cubes, a width of 5 cubes, and a height of 5 cubes.

   The entire model will be painted purple, then broken apart into individual cubes.

   What percent of the cubes will be painted purple on:

   0 sides? **21.6%**   1 side? **43.2%**   2 sides? **28.8%**   3 sides? **6.4%**

   4 sides? **0%**   5 sides? **0%**   6 sides? **0%**

Extending the Lesson

Using Cooperative Groups Have students brainstorm to create a list of book or movie titles, slogans, or well-known phrases that contain fractions, decimals, or percents. Have them rewrite each phrase using the two other forms of the value.

Cooperative Learning Activity

Get Sets 10-2

Number of players: 4
Materials: index cards

▪ Copy onto cards the fractions, decimals, and percents shown on the back of this card, one per card. Shuffle the cards and place them face down in a pile. Each player takes six cards.

➡ The object of the game is to get rid of all of the cards in your hand by forming sets of three cards that name the same number. For example, cards with $\frac{1}{2}$, 0.5, and 50% would form one set.

Each player removes from his or her hand any set of three matching cards. Decide which group member will go first. The first player takes the top card from the pile and decides whether to keep it or to discard it by placing it face up next to the pile. Since no player may have more than six cards in his or her hand, it may be necessary to place one of the cards in your hand face up in the discard pile if you keep a card from the pile. Continue, with each group member drawing a card and removing sets of three cards, until one group member has played all of his or her cards.

Glencoe Mathematics: Applications and Connections, Course 3

NCTM Standards: 1–5, 7, 9

Lesson Resources
- Study Guide Master 10-3
- Practice Master 10-3
- Enrichment Master 10-3
- Group Activity Card 10-3

 Transparency 10-3 contains the 5-Minute Check and a teaching aid for this lesson.

⏱ 5-Minute Check
(Over Lesson 10-2)

1. Which is greater, 5 or 5%? 5

2. Express 0.2 as a percent. 20%

3. Express 45% as a fraction in simplest form. $\frac{9}{20}$

4. Express 8% as a decimal. 0.08

1 FOCUS

Motivating the Lesson

Questioning A coach said that in order for the team to win, each player would have to give a 110% effort. Explain. Each player would have to perform even better than their previous best performance.

2 TEACH

Using the Mini-Lab Ask students the following series of questions: *How many squares out of 400 would you shade to represent 1%? $\frac{1}{2}$%? $\frac{1}{4}$%?* 4; 2; 1

10-3 Large and Small Percents

Objective
Express percents greater than 100 or less than 1 as decimals and fractions.

Jason organized a neighborhood carnival to raise money for the Muscular Dystrophy Association. In order to make his goal, he needed to collect $30 an hour. The first hour he collected $35. What percent of his hourly goal did he collect the first hour?

100% of his hourly goal is $30, so Jason collected more than 100% of his hourly goal.

You can use the percent proportion to find the exact percent.

$$\frac{P}{B} = \frac{r}{100}$$

$$\frac{35}{30} = \frac{r}{100}$$

$$35 \cdot 100 = 30 \cdot r$$

$$3{,}500 = 30r$$

3500 ÷ 30 = 116.66667

$$116.67 \approx r$$

Estimation Hint
• • • • • • • • • •
THINK:
30 is 100% of 30.
3 is 10% of 30.
6 is 20% of 30.
35 is almost 120% of 30.

During the first hour, Jason collected about 117% of his hourly goal.

🔲 Mini-Lab

Work with a partner.
Materials: graph paper, colored pencils

- Draw a 10 × 10 square on a piece of graph paper. Separate the square into 10 equal parts as shown at the right.
- If the 10 × 10 square represents 100%, shade a region that represents 50%.
- Shade a region that represents 1%.

Talk About It Shade $\frac{1}{2}$ of the 1% region.

a. How can you shade a region to represent $\frac{1}{2}$%?

b. Would a $\frac{1}{2}$% region be larger or smaller than the 1% region? smaller

c. How would a $\frac{1}{2}$ % region compare to the 50% region?

c. 50% region is 100 times bigger than the $\frac{1}{2}$% region.

OPTIONS

Reteaching Activity

Using Cooperative Groups
Prepare several pairs of cards with fractional percents and their decimal equivalents. Each player is dealt 6 cards. In turn, players draw from the remaining cards or pick the card discarded by the previous player, and then discard. The winner is the first player to match 3 pairs.

Study Guide Masters, p. 87

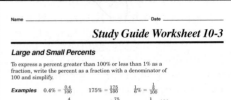

Name _____ Date _____

Study Guide Worksheet 10-3

Large and Small Percents

To express a percent greater than 100% or less than 1% as a fraction, write the percent as a fraction with a denominator of 100 and simplify.

Examples $0.4\% = \frac{0.4}{100}$ $175\% = \frac{175}{100}$ $\frac{1}{6}\% = \frac{\frac{1}{6}}{100}$

$= \frac{4}{1{,}000}$ $= 1\frac{75}{100}$ $= \frac{1}{6} \div 100$

$= \frac{1}{250}$ $= 1\frac{3}{4}$ $= \frac{1}{6} \times \frac{1}{100}$

$= \frac{1}{600}$

To express a percent greater than 100% or less than 1% as a decimal, write the percent as a fraction with a denominator of 100 and then express the fraction as a decimal.

Examples $254\% = \frac{254}{100}$ $0.05\% = \frac{.05}{100}$ $\frac{5}{8}\% = \frac{\frac{5}{8}}{100}$

To express a percent greater than 100 or less than 1 as a fraction or a decimal, you can use the same procedure you used for percents from 1 to 100.

Examples

Express each percent as a fraction or mixed number in simplest form.

1 0.2%

$$0.2\% = \frac{0.2}{100}$$
$$= \frac{2}{1,000}$$
$$= \frac{1}{500}$$

2 135%

$$135\% = \frac{135}{100}$$
$$= 1\frac{35}{100}$$
$$= 1\frac{7}{20}$$

3 $\frac{1}{8}$%

$$\frac{1}{8}\% = \frac{\frac{1}{8}}{100}$$ *The fraction bar indicates division.*
$$= \frac{1}{8} \div 100$$
$$= \frac{1}{8} \times \frac{1}{100}$$ *To divide by 100, multiply by its multiplicative inverse, $\frac{1}{100}$.*
$$= \frac{1}{800}$$

Express each percent as a decimal.

LOOKBACK

You can review division of fractions on page 288.

4 123%

$$123\% = \frac{123}{100} \text{ or } 1.23$$

5 0.9%

$$0.9\% = \frac{0.9}{100}$$
$$= \frac{9}{1,000} \text{ or } 0.009$$

Checking for Understanding For answers to Exercises 1-4, see margin.

Communicating Mathematics

Read and study the lesson to answer each question.

1. **Write** a shortcut you might use to express a percent greater than 100 as a decimal.

2. **Draw** a model of 150%.

3. **Tell** how you would draw a model of $\frac{1}{4}$%.

4. **Tell** how you know that 50% is not equal to $\frac{1}{2}$%.

Lesson 10-3 Large and Small Percents **389**

Interactive Mathematics Tools

This multimedia software provides an interactive lesson that is tied directly to Lesson 11–1. Students will use changeable quadrilaterals to explore the area of parallelograms.

Additional Answers

1. Move the decimal point two places to the left and drop the percent sign.

2. ☐ ☐

3. Draw a 10-by-10 square on a piece of graph paper. Shade $\frac{1}{4}$ of a region that represents 1%.

4. 50% = 0.5 and $\frac{1}{2}$% = 0.005

More Examples

Express each percent as a fraction or mixed number in simplest form.

For Example 1

0.7% $\frac{7}{1,000}$

For Example 2

225% $2\frac{1}{4}$

For Example 3

$\frac{3}{4}$% $\frac{3}{400}$

Express each percent as a decimal.

For Example 4

314.6%   3.146

For Example 5

0.4%   0.004

Checking for Understanding

Exercises 1-4 are designed to help you assess students' understanding through reading, writing, speaking, and modeling. You should work through these exercises with your students and then monitor their work on Guided Practice Exercises 5-14.

Practice Masters, p. 87

Name _____ Date _____

Practice Worksheet 10-3

Large and Small Percents

Express each percent as a fraction or mixed number in simplest form.

1. 0.15% $\frac{3}{2000}$ 2. 250% $\frac{5}{2}$ 3. 0.06% $\frac{3}{5,000}$

4. 0.5% $\frac{1}{200}$ 5. 165% $1\frac{13}{20}$ 6. 350% $3\frac{1}{2}$

7. 0.25% $\frac{1}{400}$ 8. 0.1% $\frac{1}{1,000}$ 9. 110% $1\frac{1}{10}$

10. $62\frac{1}{2}$% $\frac{5}{8}$ 11. $\frac{3}{4}$% $\frac{3}{400}$ 12. 150% $1\frac{1}{2}$

Express each percent as a decimal.

13. 316% 3.16   14. 0.02% 0.0002   15. 0.15% 0.0015

16. 2,345% 23.45   17. $\frac{1}{4}$% 0.0025   18. $\frac{1}{2}$% 0.005

Complete with < or > to make a true statement.

19. A percent less than 100 is a number _____ 1. <

20. A percent greater than 1% is a number _____ $\frac{1}{100}$. >

21. A number less than 1 is a percent _____ 100. <

22. A mixed number is a percent _____ 100%. >

87

Glencoe Division, Macmillan/McGraw-Hill

389

390

Guided Practice

Express each percent as a fraction in simplest form.

5. 0.02% $\frac{1}{5,000}$ 6. 0.1% $\frac{1}{1,000}$ 7. 175% $1\frac{3}{4}$ 8. $\frac{1}{5}$% $\frac{1}{500}$

Express each percent as a decimal.

9. 178% **1.78**   10. 201.2% **2.012**   11. 0.6% **0.006**   12. 0.05% **0.0005**

Replace each ■ with $<$ or $>$ to make a true statement.

13. A percent greater than 100 is a number ■ 1. $>$

14. A percent less than 1 is a number ■ $\frac{1}{100}$. $<$

Exercises

Independent Practice

Express each percent as a fraction or mixed number in simplest form. 18. $123\frac{23}{250}$

15. 0.3% $\frac{3}{1,000}$ 16. 0.04% $\frac{1}{2,500}$ 17. 760% $7\frac{3}{5}$ 18. 12,309.2%

19. 243% $2\frac{43}{100}$ 20. $\frac{3}{4}$% $\frac{3}{400}$ 21. $\frac{4}{25}$% $\frac{1}{625}$ 22. $33\frac{1}{3}$% $\frac{1}{3}$

Express each percent as a decimal.   **0.10088**

23. 212% **2.12**   24. 1,819% **18.19**   25. 0.03% **0.0003**   26. 10.088%

27. $\frac{7}{10}$% **0.007**   28. $\frac{13}{20}$% **0.0065**   29. 0.008% **0.00008**   30. $16\frac{2}{5}$% **0.164**

31. Order 0.8, 67%, 7 and $\frac{3}{8}$% from least to greatest. $\frac{3}{8}$%, 67%, 0.8, 7

Mixed Review

32. Solve $2.4m = 14.4$ *(Lesson 2-4)* **6**

33. Express 0.000084 in scientific notation. *(Lesson 6-11)* $\mathbf{8.4 \times 10^{-5}}$

34. **Geometry** Refer to the illustration in Exercise 5 on page 321. How high will the ladder reach if the bottom of the ladder is 4 feet from the wall? *(Lesson 8-6)* $\approx$ **14.5 feet**

35. Name the eighth term in the sequence 81, 27, 9, ... *(Lesson 7-6)* $\frac{1}{27}$

36. Express 38.5% as a decimal and as a fraction in simplest form. *(Lesson 10-2)* $0.385 = \frac{77}{200}$

Problem Solving and Applications

37. **Economics** Between 1980 and 1989, the number of people in the United States reporting annual incomes of more than $500,000 increased by 9.85%. Express the percent of increase as a decimal. **0.0985**

38. **Critical Thinking** The price of gasoline has doubled in the last decade. Explain whether or not this means that the price has increased by 200%. **See Solutions Manual.**

39. **Consumer Awareness** The purchase price of a camera is $84. The state tax rate is 5.5% of the purchase price. Explain whether or not this means that the total cost is 105.5% of the purchase price. **See Solutions Manual.**

40. **Journal Entry** Write a sentence explaining how you can tell when a decimal represents more than 100% or less than 1%. **See students' work.**

10-4 Solve a Simpler Problem

Objective

Solve problems by first solving a simpler problem.

An understudy is an actor who learns the part of another actor in case a substitute is needed. There are 32 students trying out for the spring drama production. Twenty-five% of them will serve as understudies. How many students will be understudies?

Explore *What do you know?*
There are 32 students trying out and 25% of them will be understudies.
What are you trying to find out?
How many students will be understudies.

Plan Instead of multiplying 25% and 32, look for a simpler way to solve the problem. Use mental math and the fraction equivalent to 25%.

Solve The product of 25% and 32 is the same as the product of $\frac{1}{4}$ and 32, because $25\% = \frac{1}{4}$.

$32 \times \frac{1}{4} = 32 \div 4$ or 8

Multiplying by $\frac{1}{4}$ is the same as dividing by 4.

Examine Since the number of students trying out (32) is a multiple of 4, it is simpler to find $\frac{1}{4}$ of 32 mentally than to use 25%.

Solving a simpler problem is a strategy that also involves setting aside the original problem and solving one or more simpler, similar problems.

Example

What is the total number of squares of any size in the 6×6 square at the right?

Find the number of squares in a 1×1 square, a 2×2 square, and a 3×3 square. Look for a pattern that you can extend to a 6×6 square.

1×1 square
□ 1×1's: 1 $1 = 1^2$

2×2 square
1×1's: 4 $4 = 2^2$
$\underline{+\ 2 \times 2's: 1}$ $1 = 1^2$
5

3×3 square
1×1's: 9 $9 = 3^2$
2×2's: 4 $4 = 2^2$
$\underline{+\ 3 \times 3's: 1}$ $1 = 1^2$
14

Notice that the total number of squares is the sum of the numbers of squares up to that point. For a 6×6 square, there would be:
$1^2 + 2^2 + 3^2 + 4^2 + 5^2 + 6^2 = 1 + 4 + 9 + 16 + 25 + 36$
$= 91$ squares

Lesson 10-4 Problem-Solving Strategy: Solve a Simpler Problem **391**

OPTIONS

Reteaching Activity

Using Charts Review the fraction-percent equivalencies chart on page 385. Show how to find a product involving a percent by writing a simpler problem involving a fraction.

Example: $37\frac{1}{2}\%$ of $16 = \frac{3}{8} \times \frac{16}{1}$
$= 3 \times 2$
$= 6$

Motivating the Lesson

Situational Problem Show the class a photo of a large crowd of people. Ask students how they would determine the number of people in the photo.

2 TEACH

More Examples

For the Example

How many toothpaste boxes would appear in a 12-row display? **144 boxes**

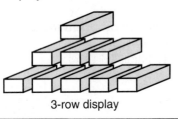

3-row display

3 PRACTICE/APPLY

Assignment Guide

Maximum: 7–14

Minimum: 7–14

Enrichment Masters, p. 88

Name _____ Date _____

Enrichment Worksheet 10-4

Solve a Simpler Problem

The game pictured at the right contains two discs of decreasing size on a peg. The goal of the game is to move both discs to another peg, moving one disc at a time, and never putting the larger disc on top of the smaller disc.

If discs and pegs are not available, the game can be simulated with coins or other objects of different sizes. Using the squares below, place two objects of different sizes on the square marked B, with the smaller object on top of the larger. Move the larger object to square A (one move). Move the smaller object to square C (one move). Then move the smaller object to square C (one move). The objects have now been moved to a different location, and it can be said that moving two objects requires a minimum of 3 moves.

A	B	C

Repeat this activity using three, four, and five objects. Complete the table, then look for a pattern and predict the number of moves that would be required to move 10 objects.

Number of Objects	Minimum Number of Moves
1	1
2	3
3	7
4	15
5	31
10	1,023

For n objects, the minimum number of moves is $2^n - 1$.

T88
Glencoe Division, Macmillan/McGraw-Hill

Checking for Understanding
For answers to Exercises 1-2, see Solutions Manual.

Communicating Mathematics

Read and study the lesson to answer each question.

1. **Tell** how you can use fraction-decimal-percent equivalencies to solve a problem.

2. **Tell** how solving a simpler problem can save time.

Guided Practice   Solve by solving a simpler problem.

3. Find 20% of 525. **105**

4. Find the sum of the whole numbers from 1 to 200. **20,100**

5. There are 210 people visiting the Exhibit Hall. Thirty percent of them are students. How many visitors are students? **63 visitors**

6. How many cuts are needed to separate a long board into 19 smaller parts? **18 cuts**

Problem Solving

Practice   Solve using any strategy.

Strategies

• • • • • • •

Look for a pattern.

Solve a simpler problem.

Act it out.

Guess and check.

Draw a diagram.

Make a chart.

Work backward.

7. Tracie bought a leather jacket for $220. She paid $14.30 in sales tax. What was the sales tax rate? **6.5%**

8. A number is tripled and then -16 is added to it. The result is 2. What is the number? **6**

9. A frozen lean dinner entree contains 200 calories. About 25% of its calories are from fat. How many calories are from fat? **about 50 calories**

10. Benjamin bought some cans of peaches for $1.29 each and some cartons of cream for $2.16 each. He spent a total of $12.51. How many of each item did he buy? **3 cans of peaches; 4 cartons of cream**

11. Four-fifths of the state tax returns filed were residents of the state for the entire year. If 160,000 returns were filed, how many people were residents for the entire year? **128,000 people**

9 clothespins

12. Which is the least number of clothespins you need to hang 8 towels on a clothesline to dry? Assume it takes 2 clothespins to hang one towel.

DATA SEARCH

13. **Data Search**   Refer to page 666. What fraction of home buyers had incomes of $40,000 or less? $\frac{1}{4}$

14. Maryann just got a job at the Too Good Yogurt Stand. The manager gave her 3 shirts and 3 pairs of pants to wear as a uniform. She has a red shirt, a gray shirt, and a white shirt and a black pair of pants, a navy blue pair of pants, and a white pair of pants. How many different combinations of uniforms can she choose from? **9 combinations**

OPTIONS

Extending the Lesson

Using Cooperative Groups Have students work in small groups to solve this problem by first solving a simpler problem: *Find the sum*

$\frac{1}{2} + \frac{1}{2^2} + \frac{1}{2^3} + \ldots + \frac{1}{2^{10}}$. $\frac{1,023}{1,024}$

Cooperative Learning Activity

The Squares Go Where? 10-4

Use groups of 2.
Materials: Grid paper, scissors, colored pencils

♦ Cut out two grids like the one shown on the back of this card.

☛ Each partner uses the clues given below to find the pattern by shading squares.

• The bottom row has no shaded squares.

• $33\frac{1}{3}\%$ of the squares are shaded.

• 50% of a row with any shaded squares has shaded squares.

• $66\frac{2}{3}\%$ of the squares in each column are not shaded.

• 33 of the rows have no shaded squares.

• 50% of the columns have a shaded square at the top.

• 80% of the shaded squares touch more than one corner of another square.

• 0% of the shaded squares share a common side.

Glencoe Mathematics: Applications and Connections, Course 3

10-5 Percent and Estimation

Objective
Estimate by using fractions, decimals, and percents interchangeably.

In 1990, *Putt-Putt Golf of America*® surveyed 3,400 customers. One of the items on the survey asked for the players' age. About 11% of those surveyed said they were between the ages of 13 and 15. About how many of those surveyed were in this age group?

You can estimate the number of 13–15 year olds that were surveyed by using the fraction method.

11% is slightly more than 10% or $\frac{1}{10}$.

$\frac{1}{10}$ of 3,400 is 340.

About 340 players surveyed were 13–15 years old.

Examples

1 Estimate 13% of 48.

13% is about 12.5% or $\frac{1}{8}$.
$\frac{1}{8}$ of 48 is 6.

13% of 48 is about 6.

2 Estimate 0.6% of 205.

0.6% is about half of 1%, 205 is slightly more than 200.
1% of 200 is 2 and $\frac{1}{2}$ of 2 is 1.

0.6% of 205 is about 1.

You can review compatible numbers on page 12.

3 Estimate 25% of 78.

25% = $\frac{1}{4}$ and 78 is about 80, which is compatible with $\frac{1}{4}$.
$\frac{1}{4}$ of 80 is 20.
25% of 78 is about 20.

4 Estimate 30% of $118.

30% is about $33\frac{1}{3}$% or $\frac{1}{3}$ and $118 is about $120, which is compatible with $\frac{1}{3}$. $\frac{1}{3}$ of $120 is $40.
30% of $118 is about $40.

Lesson 10-5 Percent and Estimation **393**

10-5 Lesson Notes

NCTM Standards: 1–5, 7, 10, 12, 13

Lesson Resources
- Study Guide Master 10-5
- Practice Master 10-5
- Enrichment Master 10-5
- Evaluation Master, Quiz A, p. 88
- Group Activity Card 10-5

Transparency 10-5 contains the 5-Minute Check and a teaching aid for this lesson.

5-Minute Check
(Over Lesson 10-4)

Solve by first solving a simpler problem.

1. Find 25% of 48.   12

2.

1-square   2-square   3-square

How many squares must be added to a 20-by-20 square to create a 21-by-21 square?   41

1 FOCUS

Motivating the Lesson

Questioning   Ask students to think of two percents with simple fraction equivalents that are near each of these percents: $11\frac{6}{7}$%, 22%, 82.6%.   Sample answers: 10% $\left(\frac{1}{10}\right)$ and $12\frac{1}{2}$% $\left(\frac{1}{8}\right)$; 20% $\left(\frac{1}{5}\right)$ and 25% $\left(\frac{1}{4}\right)$; 80% $\left(\frac{4}{5}\right)$ and $83\frac{1}{3}$% $\left(\frac{5}{6}\right)$

2 TEACH

Using Logical Reasoning   After going over the lesson introduction, ask students to think of a way to estimate 89% of 3,400 without using percents.   Subtract 340 from 3,400 (about 3,100).

OPTIONS

Limited English Proficiency

Make these suggestions to help students read their math books.
1. Keep paper and pencil handy. Jot down main ideas, good examples, and questions.
2. Read slowly. Reread as often as necessary until you understand the content.
3. If previous material is referenced, review it at once.

Problem Solving Hint

• • • • • • • • • •

Use the *solve a simpler problem* strategy.

Estimation Hint

• • • • • • • • • •

To find the area of an irregular region, determine how many squares contain any part of the region and the number of full squares within the region. Then find the mean of the two measures.

$$\frac{15 + 35}{2} = 25$$

Example 5   *Problem Solving*

Consumer Math   Rick took his mother out to dinner for her birthday. When the bill came, Rick's mother reminded him that it is customary to tip the server about 15% of the bill. If the bill was for $19.60, what should Rick leave for the tip?

A 10% tip is easy to figure. A 15% tip is equal to a 10% tip plus half of a 10% tip.

$19.60 is almost $20.
10% of 20 is 2.
So, 15% of $20 is $2 + $\frac{1}{2} \cdot$ $2 or $3.
Rick should leave a $3 tip.

Example 6   *Connection*

Geometry   Estimate what percent of the area of the large square is shaded.

About 25 squares are shaded out of 49.
$\frac{25}{49}$ is about $\frac{25}{50}$ or $\frac{1}{2}$.
$\frac{1}{2}$ = 50%.
About 50% is shaded.

Checking for Understanding

Communicating Mathematics

Read and study the lesson to answer each question.

1. **Tell** how you can estimate 23% of $98.95 using fractions and compatible numbers.   **See margin.**

2. **Draw** a triangle on graph paper. Shade about $\frac{1}{3}$ of the area.   **See students' work.**

3. **Tell** how you can estimate a 15% tip on a $24.90 dinner.   **See margin.**

Guided Practice

Determine which is the better estimate.

4. 46% of 80   a   a. less than 40   b. greater than 40
5. 22% of 300   b   a. less than 60   b. greater than 60
6. 107% of $42   b   a. less than $42   b. greater than $42
7. $\frac{1}{4}$% of 4,000   a   a. less than 40   b. greater than 40

Estimate.   **Sample answers given.**

8. 32% of 89   **30**   9. 14% of 78   **10**   10. 88% of 61   **54**

Estimate the percent.

11. 7 out of 16   **50%**   12. 8 out of 13 $66\frac{2}{3}$%   13. $\frac{15}{11}$ **150%**

OPTIONS

Reteaching Activity

Using Cooperative Groups   Have group members choose a store item to place on sale, such as a shirt. Each member draws a sign stating the percent of discount ("Now at 75% of the regular price."). Members then work together to estimate the sale price indicated by each sign. Repeat with several items.

Study Guide Masters, p. 89

Name _____   Date _____

Study Guide Worksheet 10-5

Percent and Estimation

You can use compatible numbers to estimate with percents.

Examples   Estimate 35% of 360.
35% is about $\frac{1}{3}$. $\frac{1}{3}$ is compatible with 360.
$\frac{1}{3}$ of 360 is 120. 35% of 360 is about 120.

Estimate 24% of 158.
24% is about $\frac{1}{4}$, and 158 is about 160. $\frac{1}{4}$ and 160 are compatible numbers. $\frac{1}{4}$ of 160 is 40. 24% of 158 is about 40.

Estimate 19 out of 48.
19 is about 20. 48 is about 50.
20 out of 50 is $\frac{2}{5}$ or 40%. 19 out of 48 is about 40%.

Estimate the percent of the area shaded. Sample answers given.

14.
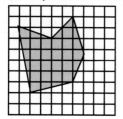
28%

15.
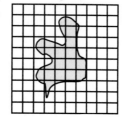
20%

Exercises

Independent Practice

Estimate. Sample answers given.

16. 73% of 65 48
17. 16% of 55 9
18. 19% of 72 14
19. 68% of 33 22
20. 29% of 50 15
21. 12.4% of 39 5

22. How would you determine if 8% of 400 is greater than 4% of 180? See margin.
23. What compatible numbers could you use to estimate 32% of 154? 30% and 150

Estimate the percent of the area shaded. Sample answers given.

24.
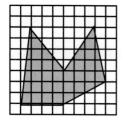
36%

25.
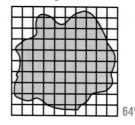
64%

Estimate the percent. Sample answers given.

26. 4 out of 25 20%
27. 24 out of 62 40%
28. 61 out of 88 $66\frac{2}{3}$%
29. 12 out of 60 20%
30. 7 out of 56 12.5%
31. 38 out of 159 25%

32. How would you estimate Janice's foul shooting percent if she made 13 foul shots in 22 attempts? Round 13 to 15 and 22 to 20; 75%.

Mixed Review

33. **58.5 ft²**
34. $\frac{1}{6}$

33. **Geometry** Find the area of a parallelogram whose height is 6.5 feet and whose base is 9 feet. *(Lesson 2-9)*
34. **Probability** Two dice are rolled. Find the probability that the sum of the numbers showing is seven. *(Lesson 6-8)*
35. Express the ratio $\frac{\$2.88}{9 \text{ ounces}}$ as a unit rate. *(Lesson 9-1)* $\frac{\$0.32}{1 \text{ ounce}}$
36. Express $\frac{2}{5}$% as a fraction in simplest form. *(Lesson 10-3)* $\frac{1}{250}$

Problem Solving and Applications

37. **Critical Thinking** If x is 285% of y, then y is about what percent of x? 35%
38. **Ecology** In a survey of 1,413 shoppers, 6% said they would be willing to pay more for environmentally safe products. About how many shoppers said they would pay more? about 70 shoppers

Lesson 10-5 Percent and Estimation **395**

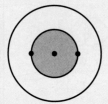
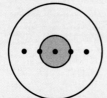
Close

Have students explain how to use compatible numbers to estimate solutions to percent problems.

3 PRACTICE/APPLY

Assignment Guide
Maximum: 16–40
Minimum: 17–31 odd, 33–39
All: Mid-Chapter Review

For **Extra Practice,** see p. 607.

Alternate Assessment

Modeling Have students shade irregular regions on sections of graph paper and tell how to estimate the percent of each section that is shaded.

Additional Answer

22. Using compatible numbers, 10% of 400 is 40 and 5% of 200 is 10, so 8% of 400 is greater than 4% of 180.

Practice Masters, p. 89

395

39. Statistics The graph at the right represents the six beverages with the highest consumption rates outside the home. If each household surveyed consumed four drinks, estimate the number of each type consumed.

What's to Drink?

Soft Drinks	37%
Coffee	22%
Tea	16%
Milk	2%
Bottled Water	1%
All Other Beverages	22%

10,930 households surveyed

Beverage	Estimate
Soft drinks	17,600
Coffee	8,800
Tea	7,200
Other	8,800
Milk	880
Bottled water	440

40. Journal Entry Write a few sentences explaining a method of estimating with percents. **See students' work.**

10 Assessment: **Mid-Chapter Review**

Write a proportion to solve each problem. *(Lesson 10-1)*

1. What number is 40% of 60? **24**   2. Seventy-five is 30% of what number? **250**

Express each fraction as a percent. *(Lesson 10-1)*

3. $\frac{44}{100}$ **44%**   4. $\frac{2}{3}$ **$66\frac{2}{3}$%**   5. $\frac{5}{8}$ **62.5%**   6. $\frac{2}{5}$ **40%**   9. **0.375**, $\frac{3}{8}$

Express each percent as a decimal and as a fraction in simplest form. *(Lessons 10-2, 10-3)*

7. 80% **0.80**, $\frac{4}{5}$ 8. 9% **0.09**, $\frac{9}{100}$ 9. $37\frac{1}{2}$%   10. 7.09% **0.0709**, $\frac{709}{10,000}$

11. 0.4% **0.004**, $\frac{1}{250}$ 12. 118% **1.18**, $1\frac{9}{50}$ 13. $\frac{7}{8}$% **0.00875**, $\frac{7}{800}$ 14. $1\frac{3}{50}$% **0.0106**, $\frac{53}{5,000}$

15. There are 24 girls on the cheerleading squad. If 25% of them are freshmen, how many cheerleaders are freshmen? *(Lesson 10-4)* **6 cheerleaders**

Determine which is the best estimate. *(Lesson 10-5)*

16. 47.5% of 600 **c**   a. 3   b. 30   c. 300
17. 17% of 42 **b**   a. 0.8   b. 8   c. 80
18. 7 out of 41 **b**   a. 1.7%   b. 17%   c. 170%
19. $\frac{9}{16}$% of 415 **c**   a. 200   b. 20   c. 2
20. 108% of 1,988 **c**   a. 22   b. 220   c. 2,200

OPTIONS

Extending the Lesson

Using Connections Have students read about mapmaking or speak to a cartographer to learn the methods used to estimate the areas of irregular regions on the surface of Earth.

Cooperative Learning Activity

Use groups of 2.
Materials: Centimeter grid paper

Lend a Hand **10-5**

• Each partner places the fingers and thumb of one hand together and traces the outline of the hand onto centimeter grid paper. Extend the lines to form a closed figure. Then shade the figure. Trade papers with your partner.

➡ Estimate what percent of the grid paper is shaded. (Hint: To estimate the area of an irregular figure, find the median of the number of completely shaded squares and the number of partially shaded squares.)

Glencoe Mathematics: Applications and Connections, Course 3

10-5B Percent Scavenger Hunt

A Follow-Up of Lesson 10-5

Objective
Estimate area using nonstandard units of measure.

Materials
measuring tape

Look at the door of your classroom. Can you imagine using the door as a tool for measuring area? In this lab you will do that as you go on a scavenger hunt for the area of other objects.

Try this!

Work with a partner.

- Copy the table below. Look at the door. Now look for an object with a surface whose area appears to be about 50% of the area of the door. Write this object in the first row of the second column of your table. Continue this procedure until you complete the second column of the table.

- Using a measuring tape, find the dimensions of the door and the other objects you identified in the second column. Complete the two middle columns of your table.

- Express the ratio of the area of each object in the second column to the area of the door. Express each result as a percent in the last column.

Estimated Area of the Door	Object	Area of Object	Area of Door	Ratio of Areas (%)
50%				
25%				
$133\frac{1}{3}$ %				
$\frac{5}{8}$				
0.9				
0.5%				

For answers to Exercises 1-2, see students' work.

What do you think?

1. Select one of the objects you chose. Explain how you used fractions or percents for your estimation.

2. Discuss with another pair of classmates how you can estimate area by comparing areas. Present an estimation problem to the class that could be solved using the same procedure.

Mathematics Lab 10-5B Percent Scavenger Hunt **397**

NCTM Standards: 1–5, 7, 13

Management Tips

For Students Be sure students choose all six objects for the second column before they begin using their measuring tapes.

For the Overhead Projector *Overhead Manipulative Resources* provides appropriate materials for teacher or student demonstration of the activities in this Mathematics Lab.

1 FOCUS

Introducing the Lab

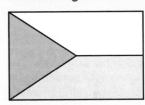

Sketch this drawing of the Czechoslovakian flag. Ask students to estimate the area of each section as a percent of the whole. actual percents: triangle, 25%; trapezoids, $37\frac{1}{2}$% each

2 TEACH

Using Patterns Ask students to give reasons why they might have over- or underestimated the areas.

3 PRACTICE/APPLY

Using Connections A biologist counted 312 cells in region A, which is 2.1% of the area of the culture. Estimate the number of cells in the culture. about 15,000

Close

Name an object in the room. Have students estimate its area, explaining their method.

OPTIONS

Lab Manual You may wish to make copies of the blackline master on p. 68 of the *Lab Manual* for students to use as a recording sheet.

Lab Manual, p. 68

Name _____ Date _____

Mathematics Lab Worksheet

Use with page 397

Percent Scavenger Hunt

Try this! Answers will vary.

Estimated Area of the Door	Object	Area of Object	Area of Door	Ratio of Areas (%)
50%				
25%				
$133\frac{1}{3}$%				
$\frac{5}{8}$				

397

DECISION MAKING

Decision Making

NCTM Standards: 1–4, 7

Objective Analyze data and make a decision.

1 FOCUS

Introducing the Situation

Only two restaurants in town sell hot dogs. At one the price is $1.75, at the other the price is $2.75. Ask students to give reasons why they might choose to buy the $2.75 hot dog. Sample answers: tastes better, more toppings, better quality

2 TEACH

Using Cooperative Groups

Students should calculate the cost of each hot dog on the menu. Encourage groups to search for a fifth, more profitable, kind of hot dog.

Checking for Understanding

Ask students to find the profit on 1 hot dog, 1 bun, and $\frac{1}{3}$ cup of hot dog chili if the finished hot dog is sold for $1.50. $49\frac{1}{2}$¢

Planning a Fund-Raising Event

Situation

The Pep Club is planning a fund-raising activity scheduled to take place at the All-State Baseball Championship being held at your school. The club has decided to sell hot dogs. You have been assigned the task of organizing the toppings you will use to offer four kinds of hot dogs. How much should you charge for each kind of hot dog to make a profit?

Hidden Data

Getting the supplies: Who will do the shopping before the game?
Preparation of the food: Where will the food be stored and cooked?
Attendance: How many people are expected to attend each game?
Complimentary condiments: Will you offer some ingredients without charge? What would they be?

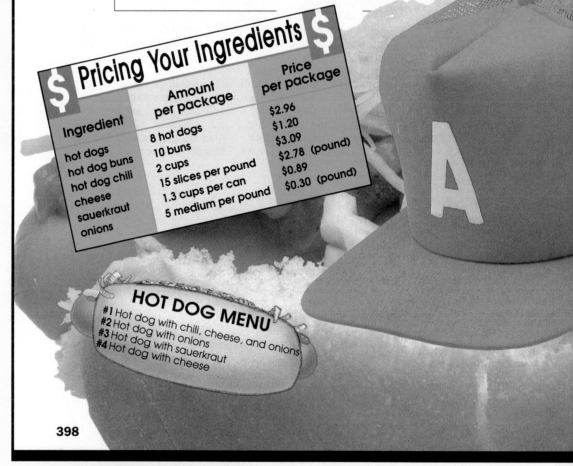

$ Pricing Your Ingredients $

Ingredient	Amount per package	Price per package
hot dogs	8 hot dogs	$2.96
hot dog buns	10 buns	$1.20
hot dog chili	2 cups	$3.09
cheese	15 slices per pound	$2.78 (pound)
sauerkraut	1.3 cups per can	$0.89
onions	5 medium per pound	$0.30 (pound)

HOT DOG MENU

#1 Hot dog with chili, cheese, and onions
#2 Hot dog with onions
#3 Hot dog with sauerkraut
#4 Hot dog with cheese

398

Classroom Vignette

"As my students were working on this activity, I challenged each group to take a poll about food. They could choose the questions to ask and the way to display their data. I was really surprised by the variety of responses they generated!"

Kay McClain

Kay McClain
Author

Analyzing the Data

1. About how much does one plain hot dog with bun cost?
2. About how much does one slice of cheese cost?
3. How much does hot dog #1 cost to prepare?

Making a Decision

4. **About how much** profit do you wish to make on each sale?
5. **Will you** encourage people to buy the hot dog with the most toppings to make a larger profit? Explain.
6. **How will you** know if the prices you select are reasonable?
7. **What special arrangements** will you have to make to prepare the food and keep it warm?

Instructions
To concession stand workers

#1 **CHILI-CHEESE-ONIONS**
Use: 1 hot dog/ 1 bun
$\frac{1}{4}$ cup chili
1 slice cheese
2 tablespoons onion

#2 **ONIONS ONLY**
Use: 1 hot dog/ 1 bun
3 tablespoons onion

#3 **SAUERKRAUT ONLY**
Use: 1 hot dog/ 1 bun
$\frac{1}{3}$ cup sauerkraut

#4 **CHEESE ONLY**
Use: 1 hot dog/ 1 bun
2 slices cheese

Making Decisions in the Real World

8. **Gather information** about the cost of a hot dog with similar toppings at fast food restaurants, stadiums, and the school cafeteria. Where were the hot dogs more expensive? How did this price compare with your prices?

399

Analyzing the Data

Emphasize that in order for students to find the total cost of the ingredients needed to prepare one hot dog of each kind, they must first find the unit rate for each package of ingredients.

Answers

1. $0.49
2. about $0.19
3. about $1.09

3 PRACTICE/APPLY

Making a Decision

Each group should prepare a written report answering the questions in the lesson, stating the selling prices the group has agreed upon, and outlining the reasons behind the decision. You may want groups to consider these questions:

- *Why might you want to change hot dog prices after the event has begun?*
- *Would doing so be a good idea? Why or why not?*

Making Decisions in the Real World

Interested students can talk to business people to learn about the role of supply and demand in the setting of prices in a free-market economy.

NCTM Standards: 1–5, 7, 9

Lesson Resources
- Study Guide Master 10-6
- Practice Master 10-6
- Enrichment Master 10-6
- Technology Master, p. 10
- Application Master, p. 10
- Group Activity Card 10-6

 Transparency 10-6 contains the 5-Minute Check and a teaching aid for this lesson.

🕐 5-Minute Check
(Over Lesson 10-5)

Estimate. Estimates may vary.

1. 26% of 40   10
2. 0.4% of 398   2
3. 32.8% of $180 $60
4. 39% of 36   14
5. Sketch an equilateral triangle with about 76% of its area shaded.   Sample answer:

---

1 FOCUS

Motivating the Lesson

Situational Problem   Sketch a circle graph with five unequal sections. Have students estimate the percent represented by each section.

2 TEACH

Using Connections   Reassure students that the equation $P = R \cdot B$ is merely a different form of the percent proportion, not a whole new approach to percents. When they use the equation, students should write the percent as a decimal.

10-6 The Percent Equation

Objective
Solve problems using the percent equation.

In 1991, nearly 400,000 foreign students were studying at United States colleges. How many of the students were from Asia?

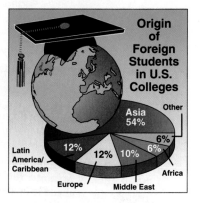

Origin of Foreign Students in U.S. Colleges

Asia 54%
Other
6%
6%
Latin America/Caribbean 12%
12% 10%
Africa
Europe
Middle East

Estimation Hint
• • • • • • • • • •
THINK:
54% is slightly more than 50%.
$50\% = \dfrac{1}{2}$
$\dfrac{1}{2}$ of 400,000 is 200,000.

You can use an equation to solve this problem.

Let s = the number of students from Asia. Write an equation. Write the percent as a decimal.

$s = 0.54 \cdot 400{,}000$

0.54 ⊠ 400000 🟰 216000

$s = 216{,}000$

There were 216,000 students from Asia studying in the United States. *Compared to the estimate, the answer is reasonable.*

TEEN SCENE

About 5.5% of incoming college freshmen chose business administration as their major in 1990, up one percent from 1989.

You can express the percent proportion you studied in Lesson 10-1 in a form that is easier to use when the rate and base are known.

$$\dfrac{P}{B} = \dfrac{r}{100} \qquad \textit{Write the percent proportion.}$$

$$\dfrac{P}{B} \cdot B = \dfrac{r}{100} \cdot B \qquad \textit{Multiply each side by B.}$$

$$P = \dfrac{r}{100} \cdot B \qquad \textit{Remember, the ratio } \dfrac{r}{100} \textit{ is called the rate.}$$

$$P = R \cdot B \qquad \textit{Let R represent } \dfrac{r}{100}. \textit{ Replace } \dfrac{r}{100} \textit{ with R.}$$

The equation is now in the form $P = R \cdot B$. You can use this equation to solve percent problems like the one at the beginning of the lesson.

Example 1

Find 6% of $725.   *Estimate: 1% of 700 is 7; 6 · 7 = 42*

What number   is   6%   of   725?

$\quad P \qquad = \quad 0.06 \quad \cdot \quad 725 \qquad$ *Write in $P = R \cdot B$ form.*
P represents the percentage.

0.06 ⊠ 725 🟰 43.5

$\qquad P = 43.5$

6% of $725 is $43.50.   *Compare with the estimate.*

OPTIONS

Reteaching Activity

Using Cooperative Groups
Separate students into groups of three. One student writes a percent problem in sentence form. A second student writes the percent proportion for the problem and the third writes the percent equation. Students compare the two, making changes if needed. Repeat several times.

Study Guide Masters, p. 90

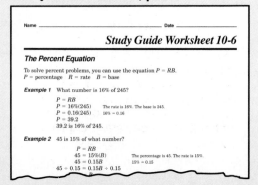

Name _____ Date _____

Study Guide Worksheet 10-6

The Percent Equation

To solve percent problems, you can use the equation $P = RB$.
P = percentage R = rate B = base

Example 1   What number is 16% of 245?

$P = RB$
$P = 16\%(245)$ The rate is 16%. The base is 245.
$P = 0.16(245)$ 16% = 0.16
$P = 39.2$
39.2 is 16% of 245.

Example 2   45 is 15% of what number?

$P = RB$
$45 = 15\%(B)$ The percentage is 45. The rate is 15%.
$45 = 0.15B$ 15% = 0.15
$45 \div 0.15 = 0.15B \div 0.15$

Example 2

12 is 40% of what number?   *Estimate: 40% is about $\frac{1}{2}$. $\frac{1}{2} \cdot 12$ is $\frac{1}{2}$ of 24.*

$$P = R \cdot B$$
$12 = 0.4 \cdot B$ *Replace P with 12 and R with 40% or 0.4*
$12 = 0.4B$ *Solve for B.*

$12 \boxed{\div} 0.4 \boxed{=} 30$ *Divide each side by 0.4.*

$30 = B$

12 is 40% of 30.   *Check your answer by finding 40% of 30.*

Example 3   *Problem Solving*

Entertainment   The price of a home video game system is $198. If the sales tax on the video game is $8.91, what is the sales tax rate?

$$P = R \cdot B$$
$8.91 = R \cdot 198$ *Replace P with 8.91 and B with 198.*

$8.91 \boxed{\div} 198 \boxed{=} 0.045$ *Divide each side by 198.*

$R = 0.045$ or 4.5%

The sales tax rate is 4.5%.

Checking for Understanding

Communicating Mathematics

1. $28 = R \cdot 34$

Read and study the lesson to answer each question.

1. **Write** an equation in the form $P = R \cdot B$ that you would use to determine the percent score of correctly answering 28 out of 34 questions on a history test.

2. **Tell** what number you would use for R in the equation $P = R \cdot B$ if the rate is 35%. $R = 0.35$

3. **Tell** whether the percentage is greater than or less than the base, when the rate is less than 100%. less than

For equations for Exercises 4–12, see Solutions Manual.

Guided Practice

Write an equation in the form $P = R \cdot B$ for each problem. Then solve.

4. What number is 47% of 52? 24.44
5. What number is 56% of 80? 44.8
6. What percent of 52 is 25? ≈ 48.1%
7. What percent of 3,600 is 2? ≈ 0.06%
8. $48 is 30% of what amount? $160
9. $64 is what percent of $78? ≈ 82.1%
10. What percent of 4.8 is 1.12? $23\frac{1}{3}$%
11. Find 16.5% of 60. 9.9
12. Thirty percent of what amount is $5,000? $16,666.67

Lesson 10-6   Algebra Connection: The Percent Equation   **401**

Error Analysis

Watch for students who fail to write percents as decimals in the percent equation.

Prevent by having students estimate answers before using the equation.

Close

Ask students to compare and contrast the percent equation and the percent proportion as means of solving percent problems.

3 PRACTICE/APPLY

Assignment Guide
Maximum: 13–40
Minimum: 13–27 odd, 29–36

For **Extra Practice,** see p. 608.

Alternate Assessment

Speaking Have students explain the meaning of the equation $P = R \cdot B$ in their own words.

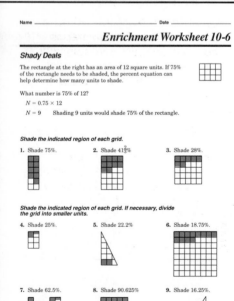
402

Exercises

Independent Practice

Solve.

13. What is 81% of 11.2? **9.072**
14. What percent of 90 is 36? **40%**
15. Fifty is 10% of what number? **500**
16. Find 0.5% of 3,200. **16**
17. What is 7.4% of 40? **2.96**
18. What percent of 21 is 96? $\approx$ **457.1%**
19. 20% of what number is 65? **325**
20. Find 28% of $231.90. $\approx$ **$64.93**

21. 120%
22. $33\frac{1}{3}$%

21. Sixty-six is what percent of 55?
22. $17 is what percent of $51?
23. $54 is 108% of what amount? **$50**
24. What is 124% of 72? **89.28**
25. Sixteen is $66\frac{2}{3}$% of what number? **24**
26. $6 is what percent of $50? **12%**
27. $6,899.70 is 105.5% of how many dollars? **$6,540**
28. There are 35 students. Eight of them are wearing orange. What percent are wearing orange? $\approx$ **22.9%**

Mixed Review

29. **Algebra** In trapezoid $STUV$, $m\angle S = 90°$, $m\angle T = 3x°$, $m\angle U = 60°$, and $m\angle V = 90°$. Find the value of x. *(Lesson 5-4)* **40**

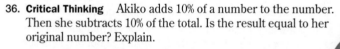

30. Find the multiplicative inverse of $-\frac{1}{a}$. *(Lesson 7-4)* **$-a$**
31. If $x^2 = 121$, what is the value of x? *(Lesson 8-3)* **11, -11**
32. Estimate 20.5% of 89. *(Lesson 10-5)* **18**

Problem Solving and Applications

35. See students' work.

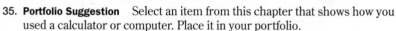

36. No; sample answer: $100 + 0.1($100) = $110, $110 − 0.1($110) = $99, not $100.

37. $242.64

33. **Royalties** Marcela writes songs and receives a royalty of 8% of the CD sales. Last month she received a check for $3,896. How much money was spent on the CDs with her songs? **$48,700**
34. **Taxes** Mrs. Harper stayed overnight at a hotel during a mathematics teachers' convention. The cost of the room was $84 and the room tax was $10.92. What was the tax rate? **13%**
35. **Portfolio Suggestion** Select an item from this chapter that shows how you used a calculator or computer. Place it in your portfolio.
36. **Critical Thinking** Akiko adds 10% of a number to the number. Then she subtracts 10% of the total. Is the result equal to her original number? Explain.
37. **Sales** Jeremiah Morrison bought a new electric guitar and amplifier for $229.99. In addition, he paid a $5\frac{1}{2}$% state sales tax. What is the total amount he paid?
38. **Education** Bryan scored 84% on his language arts test. If he answered 21 questions correctly, how many questions were on the test? **25 questions**
39. **Sales** The sales tax on a $21 purchase was $1.47. What was the rate of sales tax? **7%**
40. **Make Up a Problem** Find a graph or newspaper article that involves the use of percents. Write a problem that can be solved using the equation $P = R \cdot B$. **See students' work.**

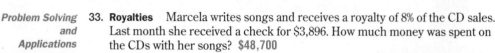

402 **Chapter 10** Applications with Percent

OPTIONS

Extending the Lesson

Using Cooperative Groups Have students survey the class to find the ancestral birthplace of each student. (Include North America if there are Native Americans in the class.) Have them determine the percent in each category and display the results.

Cooperative Learning Activity

Use groups of 2.
Materials: Index cards, spinners

y not x? **10-6**

● Copy onto cards the questions shown on the back of this card, one question per card. Shuffle the cards and place them face down in a pile. Label equal sections of one spinner "4," "15," "25," "30," "50," "75," "80," "125." Label equal sections of a second spinner "2," "12," "20," "25," "40," "60," "90," "120." Decide which spinner you will use to replace the variable x and which spinner you will use to replace the variable y in the percent questions. (Partners must choose different spinners.)

➡ One partner selects the top card from the pile. Each partner then spins a spinner. Partners replace x and y in the question on the card with the numbers on the spinners and then write an equation in P = R • B form. The partner with the greater solution wins the round. Play several rounds, taking turns selecting a card.

Glencoe Mathematics: Applications and Connections, Course 3

10-7 Circle Graphs

Objective
Construct circle graphs.

Words to Learn
circle graph

The table below shows the average attendance at four major attractions.

Average Visitors Per Day in 1991	
Dollywood—Pigeon Forge, Tennessee	4,408
Opryland, USA—Nashville, Tennessee	5,303
Disneyland—Anaheim, California	31,983
Disney World/Epcot Center—Orlando, Florida	77,135

In Chapter 4, you learned how to make stem-and-leaf plots to display sets of data, and you learned how to summarize data in a box-and-whisker plot. How do you display a comparison of parts of a set of data to the whole set? For example, how would you compare Dollywood visitors to the total visitors at all four attractions?

A good way to display this information is to use a *circle graph*. A **circle graph** is used to compare parts of a whole. Study the example to find out how to make a circle graph.

Example

Construct a circle graph using the data in the table above.

- Find the total number of visitors.

  4408 $\boxed{+}$ 5303 $\boxed{+}$ 31983 $\boxed{+}$ 77135 $\boxed{=}$ **118829**

Since you are comparing the number of visitors at each park to the total, each ratio represents a percent of the whole circle.

- Find the ratio that compares the visitors at each park to the total number of visitors. Round each ratio the the nearest thousandth.

  Dollywood: $\frac{4,408}{118,829}$

  4408 $\boxed{\div}$ 118829 $\boxed{=}$ **0.0370953**   *0.0370953 ≈ 0.037 or 3.7%*

  Opryland, USA: $\frac{5,303}{118,829}$

  5303 $\boxed{\div}$ 118829 $\boxed{=}$ **0.0446272**   *0.0446272 ≈ 0.045 or 4.5%*

  Disneyland: $\frac{31,983}{118,829}$

  31983 $\boxed{\div}$ 118829 $\boxed{=}$ **0.2691515**   *0.2691515 ≈ 0.269 or 26.9%*

  Disney World: $\frac{77,135}{118,829}$

  77135 $\boxed{\div}$ 118829 $\boxed{=}$ **0.6491261**   *0.6491261 ≈ 0.649 or 64.9%*

Lesson 10-7   Statistics Connection: Circle Graphs   **403**

10-7 Lesson Notes

NCTM Standards: 1–5, 10, 12, 13

Lesson Resources
- Study Guide Master 10-7
- Practice Master 10-7
- Enrichment Master 10-7
- Lab Manual, p. 69
- Multicultural Activity, p. 10
- Interdisciplinary Master, p. 24
- Group Activity Card 10-7

 Transparency 10-7 contains the 5-Minute Check and a teaching aid for this lesson.

5-Minute Check
(Over Lesson 10-6)
1. What is 29% of 63?
   18.27
2. What percent of 80 is 15?
   18.75%
3. 15% of what number is 5.4?   36
4. At a hardware store, Jack paid $1.42 sales tax on a total purchase of $28.40. What was the sales tax rate?   5%

1 FOCUS

Motivating the Lesson

Situational Problem   Show a few examples of circle graphs from newspapers and magazines. Choose one of special interest and ask students how it was constructed.

2 TEACH

Using Connections   Ask students the following question: *Of the types of data displays you have already studied, which might be good for displaying comparisons between the number of visitors at each of the four attractions?*   probably the best would be a bar graph, which is useful for comparing large numbers

---

OPTIONS

Reteaching Activity

Using Models   Have students choose an example of a circle graph in a magazine or newspaper. Have them convert its percents to degrees and then check the angles in the drawing with a protractor. Ask them to describe how they could have drawn the graph knowing only the percents.

Study Guide Masters, p. 91

Name _____ Date _____

Study Guide Worksheet 10-7

Circle Graphs

A circle graph shows how a whole is divided into parts.

The chassis of a race car cost $220,000. The engine cost $90,000. The tires and wheels cost $3,000. You can represent this data in a circle graph.

To make a circle graph for this data, first find the total cost of the race car: $220,000 + $90,000 + $3,000 = $313,000

Then find the ratio that compares the cost of each of the parts to the total cost. Round to the nearest thousandth.

Chassis   220,000 ÷ 313,000 ≈ 0.701
Engine   90,000 ÷ 313,000 ≈ 0.288
Tires & Wheels 3,000 ÷ 313,000 ≈ 0.01

Race Car Costs

Chassis
70%

403

404

- Since there are 360° in a circle, multiply each ratio by 360 to find the number of degrees for each section of the graph. Round to the nearest degree.

  Dollywood: 0.037 ☒ 360 🟰 13.32   *13.32 ≈ 13°*

  Opryland, USA: 0.045 ☒ 360 🟰 16.2   *16.2 ≈ 16°*

  Disneyland: 0.269 ☒ 360 🟰 96.84   *96.84 ≈ 97°*

  Disney World: 0.649 ☒ 360 🟰 233.64   *233.64 ≈ 234°*

- Use a compass to draw a circle and a radius as shown at the right.

- Use a protractor to draw an angle of 13°. *Actually, you can start with any of the four angles.*

- From the new radius, draw the next angle. Repeat for the remaining angles. Label each section and give the graph a title.

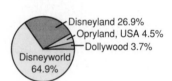
Disneyland 26.9%
Opryland, USA 4.5%
Dollywood 3.7%
Disneyworld 64.9%

Visitors at Selected Parks

Checking for Understanding

Communicating Mathematics

Read and study the lesson to answer each question.

1. **Tell** why circle graphs are used to show data. They compare parts of a whole.
2. **Tell** how to find the number of degrees for a section of a circle graph that represents the number of girls in your math class. See Solutions Manual.
3. **Write** what the sum of the percents in a circle graph should be. 100%
4. **Draw** a circle graph to represent the percent of girls and the percent of boys in your class today. See students' work.

Guided Practice

Use the table at the right to answer Exercises 5–8.

5. What is the expected total of the percent column? 100%
6. What is the expected total of the degree column? 360°
7. Copy and complete the table.
8. Make a circle graph of the data. See Solutions Manual.

Monthly Budget			
Category	Amount	% of total	Degrees in graph
Housing	$775	31%	112°
Food	$375	15%	54°
Insurance	$225	9%	32°
Transportation	$475	19%	68°
Other	$650	26%	94°
Total	$2,500	100%	360°

404   **Chapter 10**   Applications with Percent

OPTIONS

Meeting Needs of Middle School Students

Students receive large amounts of information each day in school. Set reasonable goals for what you will cover in class but be prepared to change plans. A little time for thinking and questioning will serve students better than a last-minute burst of new material.

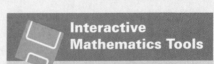

Interactive Mathematics Tools

This multimedia software provides an interactive lesson that is tied directly to Lesson 10-7. Students will explore the relationship between the angles in a circle graph.

Exercises

Independent Practice
9. See Solutions Manual.

9. **Statistics** The chart shows the number of patents issued to foreign inventors on an average day in the United States. Make a circle graph to display the data.

Country	Number
Canada	5
Great Britain	8
France	8
West Germany	22
Japan	47

10. **Probability** What is the probability of selecting a free prize in a classroom raffle if there are 2 winning tickets out of a total of 9 tickets? Make a circle graph to show the probability of winning and of losing. **22%; See Solutions Manual.**

Mixed Review

11. Find the absolute value of -28. *(Lesson 3-1)* **28**

12. Find the LCM of 18, 34, and 6. *(Lesson 6-9)* **306**

13. What percent of 32 is 12? *(Lesson 10-6)* **37.5%**

Problem Solving and Applications

14. **Critical Thinking** Pam was preparing a circle graph to display the data in the chart at the right. When she multiplied each ratio by 360 to find the degrees of each section, she noticed the total was 361°. Why is the total more than 360° and how can Pam get the correct total? **See margin.**

Areas (in square miles) of the Oceans of the World	
Pacific Ocean	64,186,300
Atlantic Ocean	33,420,000
Indian Ocean	28,350,500
Arctic Ocean	5,105,700

15. **Statistics** On an average day in the United States 2,749 people enroll in a foreign language course. Of these, the average enrollments are: Chinese, 46; Japanese, 64; Russian, 93; French, 754; and Spanish, 1,127. Make a circle graph to display the data. **See Solutions Manual.**

16. **Research** Take a survey of the people in your class on the amount of time they spent watching television during the past 24 hours. Make a circle graph to show what percent of the class watched less than one hour, 1–2 hours, 2–3 hours, or more than 3 hours. **See students' work.**

17. **Nutrition** A restaurant's survey asked each customer how often they eat salad. The results are listed in the chart at the right. Make a circle graph of the data. **See Solutions Manual.**

Frequency of eating salad	number
once or twice a day	100
several times a week	270
once a week	60
1–3 times a month	50
less than once a month	20

18. For graphs to Exercises 18a-c., see Solutions Manual.

DATA SEARCH

18. **Data Search** Refer to pages 378 and 379.

   a. Construct a circle graph to display what happened to the waste generated per person per day in 1960.

   b. Construct a circle graph to display what happened to the waste generated per person per day in 1988.

   c. What conclusion can you make by comparing the two graphs?

Lesson 10-7 Statistics Connection: Circle Graphs **405**

Extending the Lesson

Using Connections Have students keep a record of how they spent their time over a 24-hour period. Have them organize the data into several broad categories and then draw a circle graph displaying the data.

Cooperative Learning Activity

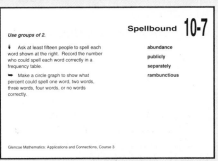

Spellbound **10-7**

Use groups of 2.

❧ Ask at least fifteen people to spell each word shown at the right. Record the number who could spell each word correctly in a frequency table.

➡ Make a circle graph to show what percent could spell one word, two words, three words, four words, or no words correctly.

abundance
publicly
separately
rambunctious

Glencoe Mathematics: Applications and Connections, Course 3

Error Analysis

Watch for students who find angle measures incorrectly.

Prevent by having students add the measures of all sections before drawing their graphs. The sum should be 360°.

Close

Have students describe the kind of data that can usefully be displayed in a circle graph.

3 PRACTICE/APPLY

> **Assignment Guide**
> **Maximum:** 9–18
> **Minimum:** 9–15, 17

For **Extra Practice,** see p. 608.

Alternate Assessment

Writing Have students work in pairs to write an explanation of the steps for creating a circle graph to display a given set of data.

Additional Answer

14. The total is more than 360° because Pam rounded incorrectly. She should round all her ratios to the same place value.

Enrichment Masters, p. 91

Name _____ Date _____

Enrichment Worksheet 10-7

The Department of the Treasury

From October, 1989 through September, 1990, $1,031,462,000,000 was received by the United States Department of the Treasury. The circle graph shows how the government spent that money.

Federal Government Expenditures

Determine the amount of this income that was spent on:

1. National defense and international relations $278,494,740,000
2. General debt interest $144,404,680,000
3. State and local governments $103,146,200,000
4. Insurance trusts $30,943,860,000
5. Social security $257,865,500,000
6. General expenditures $216,607,020,000

Given that there are 360° in a circle, find the number of degrees of each section of the circle graph. Round to the nearest whole degree.

7. National defense and international relations 97°
8. General debt interest 50°
9. State and local governments 36°
10. Insurance trusts 11°
11. Social security 90°
12. General expenditures 76°

T91
Glencoe Division, Macmillan/^-Graw-Hill

NCTM Standards: 1–5, 7, 9

Lesson Resources
- Study Guide Master 10-8
- Practice Master 10-8
- Enrichment Master 10-8
- Group Activity Card 10-8

 Transparency 10-8 contains the 5-Minute Check and a teaching aid for this lesson.

🕐 5-Minute Check
(Over Lesson 10-7)

Do You Watch Monday Night Football?	
Always	24
Sometimes	5
Never	11

Use the results of a survey of 40 eighth graders shown in the table above for Exercises 1–2.

1. Find the percent of the total for each category in the table. 60%; 12.5%; 27.5%

2. In a circle graph displaying the survey results, how many degrees should be used for each section? 216°; 45°; 99°

1 FOCUS

Motivating the Lesson

Questioning A sportscaster said that a player's performance was "100% improved over last year." Ask students to explain the statement. The player was doing twice as well as last year.

2 TEACH

Using the Mini-Lab Have students think of the short rectangle as the long one after it has lost some squares. The *amount* of change in area is 4 squares. The *percent* of change in area is a comparison of the amount of change, 4, to the original area, 11.

406

10-8 Percent of Change

Objective
Find the percent of increase or decrease.

Ronald Reagan was the fortieth president of the United States. During his first term, the number of people who were unemployed was 10,678,000. By the end of his second term, 6,701,000 people were unemployed. You can express the decrease from about 11 million to about 7 million by using percents.

Mini-Lab

Work with a partner.
Materials: graph paper, pencil, scissors

- Draw a rectangle 11 units long and 1 unit wide on graph paper. Draw another rectangle 7 units long and 1 unit wide.

- Cut out the shorter rectangle and place it over the longer rectangle. Shade the squares that are not covered.

Talk About It

a. Describe the relationship between the area of the longer rectangle and the area of the shorter rectangle.

b. What do the shaded squares represent?

c. What is the ratio of the area of the shaded squares to the total area of the longer rectangle? Express the ratio as a percent.

a. The area of the longer rectangle is 4 square units more than the shorter one.
b. $\frac{4}{11}$ of the total area of the large rectangles.
c. 4:11; ≈ 36.4%

The Mini-Lab shows how you can find the estimated percent decrease in the number of unemployed people. You can compute the actual percent of decrease by using the percent equation and a calculator.

- Subtract to find the amount of decrease.
  10678000 ⊟ 6701000 ⊟ ∃Ч77000

Estimation Hint
• • • • • • • • • • •
THINK:
$\frac{4,000,000}{10,000,000} = \frac{4}{10}$
$\frac{4}{10} = 40\%$

- Use the form $P = R \cdot B$. Compare the amount of decrease to the original amount.

  3,977,000   *is*   *what percent*   *of*   *10,678,000?*

  3,977,000   =   R   ·   10,678,000

  3977000 ⊡ 10678000 ⊟ 0.∃72ЧЧ8

  $R \approx 0.37$ or 37%

  The unemployment rate decreased about 37%.

406   **Chapter 10**   Applications with Percent

OPTIONS

Reteaching Activity

Using Cooperative Groups Have groups of three students spin a spinner twice, recording both numbers spun. The first student states the change from the first number to the second number. The second student states the fraction comparing the change and the first number. The third student finds the percent of change.

Study Guide Masters, p. 92

Name _____ Date _____

Study Guide Worksheet 10-8

Percent of Change

To find the percent of increase or decrease, first find the amount of the increase or decrease. Then find the ratio of that amount to the original amount and express it as a percent.

Example 1 Two years ago a bicycle shop sold 675 bicycles. This year, 865 bicycles were sold. To the nearest percent, what is the percent of increase?

   865 − 675 = 190   Find the amount of increase.
   $\frac{190}{675} = 28\%$ Compare the amount of increase to the original amount.

   Bicycle sales increased about 28%.

Example 2 The population of West Valley was 26,892 ten years ago. Today the population of West Valley is 22,160. To the nearest percent, what is the percent of decrease in the population?

You can also use the percent proportion to find the percent of change. The base represents the original amount and the amount of change is the percentage.

Example 1 *Problem Solving*

Business John Clark sells the merchandise in his sporting goods store for more than what he pays for it. This increase in price is called the *markup*. It is used to cover expenses and make a profit. Mr. Clark's cost for a pair of roller blades is $30. If he sells them for $48, what is his markup rate?

$$48 - 30 = 18 \qquad \textit{Find the amount of increase.}$$
$$\frac{18}{30} = \frac{r}{100} \qquad \textit{Write the percent proportion.}$$
$$\qquad\qquad\qquad \textit{The original amount is \$30.}$$
$$18 \cdot 100 = 30 \cdot r \qquad \textit{Find the cross products.}$$
$$1{,}800 = 30r \qquad \textit{Divide each side by 30.}$$
$$1800 \; \boxed{\div} \; 30 \; \boxed{=} \; \boxed{60}$$
$$60 = r$$

The markup rate is 60%.

Estimation Hint
• • • • • • • • • •
THINK: $\frac{20}{30} = \frac{2}{3}$
Since $\frac{18}{30} < \frac{20}{30}$,
the percent of increase is less than $66\frac{2}{3}\%$.

Example 2 *Problem Solving*

Earning Money At the beginning of the year, Shawna received an allowance of $8 per week. Now that she has a job after school she receives $3 per week. Find the percent of decrease in her allowance.

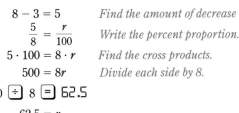

$$8 - 3 = 5 \qquad \textit{Find the amount of decrease}$$
$$\frac{5}{8} = \frac{r}{100} \qquad \textit{Write the percent proportion.}$$
$$5 \cdot 100 = 8 \cdot r \qquad \textit{Find the cross products.}$$
$$500 = 8r \qquad \textit{Divide each side by 8.}$$
$$500 \; \boxed{\div} \; 8 \; \boxed{=} \; \boxed{62.5}$$
$$62.5 = r$$

The percent of decrease is 62.5%.

Checking for Understanding For answers to Exercises 1-3, see margin.

Communicating Mathematics

Read and study the lesson to answer each question.

1. **Tell** what the first step is when finding the percent of change.
2. **Tell** how you know which number to use as the base when finding a percent of change.
3. **Draw** a picture to show a decrease of 20%.

Lesson 10-8   Percent of Change   **407**

Multicultural Education

The table at the right shows the number of U.S. citizens receiving doctoral degrees from colleges and universities in 1988 and a comparison to the number received 10 years earlier, in 1978. Use the table to illustrate percent of change and to stimulate discussion about higher education in the United States.

Doctoral Recipients: U.S. Citizens by Ethnic Group

	1988	10-Year Change
African-American	805	−22%
Asian	612	+57%
Hispanic	594	+26%
Native American	93	+55%
White	20,685	−5%
Race unknown	383	—
All U.S. Citizens	23,172	−8%

More Examples

For Example 1

Find the markup rate on a lamp purchased by a store owner for $35 and priced at $49.   40%

For Example 2

In one year, the number of whooping cranes at a wildlife refuge dropped from 32 to 28. Find the percent of decrease.   12.5%

Checking for Understanding

Exercises 1-3 are designed to help you assess students' understanding through reading, writing, speaking, and modeling. You should work through these exercises with your students and then monitor their work on Guided Practice Exercises 4-9.

Additional Answers

1. Subtract to find the amount of change.
2. Use the original amount.
3.
   decrease of 20%

Practice Masters, p. 92

407

Close

Have students explain the difference between the amount of change from one number to another, and the percent of change between the numbers.

3 PRACTICE/APPLY

Assignment Guide
Maximum: 10–25
Minimum: 11–19 odd, 20–24

For **Extra Practice,** see p. 608.

Alternate Assessment

Modeling   Place 10 tiles in a row. State a percent of change that is a multiple of 10%. Have students add or subtract tiles, as necessary, to show the percent of change in the number of tiles.

Additional Answer

23. The store lost money because 50% of the list price is greater than 50% of the original number.

Enrichment Masters, p. 92

Name _____ Date _____

Enrichment Worksheet 10-8

Percent of Change

Changes in elevation experienced by mountain climbers can be described using percents. To describe a change in elevation, determine the amount of increase or decrease, then use the percent equation.

Example 1   An expedition began a day's climb at 4,000 feet and made camp at the end of the day at 6,200 feet. By what percent did the elevation of the climbers increase?

Find the amount of increase.	6,200 − 4,000 = 2,200
Use the percent equation.	2,200 is what percent of 4,000?
Divide both sides by 4,000.	$\frac{2,200}{4,000} = \frac{4,000R}{4,000}$
The elevation increased by 55%.	$0.55 = R$

Example 2   An expedition ended a day's descent at 9,600 feet after beginning the day's descent at 12,000 feet. By what percent did the elevation of the climbers decrease?

Find the amount of decrease.	12,000 − 9,600 = 2,400
Use the percent equation.	2,400 is what percent of 12,000?
Divide both sides by 12,000.	$\frac{2,400}{12,000} = \frac{12,000R}{12,000}$
The elevation decreased by 20%.	$0.20 = R$

This chart contains information about a climbing expedition. Use the information from the mountain pictured here, the percent equation, and your calculator to complete the chart. When necessary, round your answer to the nearest whole percent.

	Starting Location	Ending Location	Change in Elevation
1.	Base Camp I	Camp Charity	60% increase
2.	Base Camp III	Camp Patience	11% decrease
3.	Camp Hope	Base Camp II	25% increase
4.	Camp Energy	Base Camp I	60% decrease
5.	Camp Faith	Base Camp III	9% decrease
6.	Camp Faith	Summit	8% increase
7.	Camp Patience	Base Camp II	21% decrease
8.	Camp Hope	Camp Energy	35% decrease

Summit (20,320 ft)

Camp Faith (18,800 ft) •
Base Camp III (17,100 ft) •
Camp Patience (15,200 ft) •
Base Camp II (12,000 ft) •
Camp Hope (9,600 ft) •
Camp Energy (6,200 ft) •
Camp Charity (4,000 ft) •
Base Camp I (2,500 ft) •

T92
Glencoe Division, Macmillan/McGraw-Hill

Guided Practice

Estimate the percent of change. Sample answers given.

4. old: $4
   new: $6   **50%**

5. old: $56.12
   new: $62   **10%**

6. new: $88
   old: $76 $16\frac{2}{3}$**%**

Find the percent of change. Round to the nearest whole percent.

7. old: $3
   new: $2   **33%**

8. old: $72
   new: $80   **11%**

9. old: $533
   new: $600   **13%**

Exercises

Independent Practice

Estimate the percent of change. Sample answers given.

10. old: $5
    new: $7   **40%**

11. old: $48.88
    new: $36.99   **25%**

12. old: $44
    new: $39   **10%**

Find the percent of change. Round to the nearest whole percent.

13. old: $6
    new: $5   **17%**

14. old: $48
    new: $64   **33%**

15. old: $221
    new: $300   **36%**

16. old: $21
    new: $30   **43%**

17. old: $90
    new: $80   **11%**

18. old: $315
    new: $400   **27%**

19. Find the percent of change in taxes if the old taxes were $54.00 and the new taxes are $57.78. **7%**

Mixed Review

20. How many pints are in 9 cups? *(Lesson 1-7)* **4.5 pints**

21. **Geometry**   The length of a leg of a 45°–45° right triangle is 6.5 feet. Find the length of the hypotenuse to the nearest tenth. *(Lesson 8-8)* **9.2 feet**

22. **Statistics**   On an average Saturday, Kelly spends 9 hours sleeping, 4 hours watching TV, 1.5 hours eating, 5 hours with her friends, and 4.5 hours with her family. Make a circle graph to display the data. *(Lesson 10-7)*
    See Solutions Manual.

Problem Solving and Applications

23. **Critical Thinking**   A store has a 50% markup on sweaters. But, the sweaters do not sell well at the listed price. So, the sweaters are put on sale at 50% of the listed price. All the sweaters are sold. Did the store break even, make a profit, or lose money? Explain. **See margin.**

24. **Traffic Safety**   The graph at the right shows the percentage of drivers who wore seat belts each year from 1982 to 1991.
    a. What is the percent of increase from 1982 to 1991 in the percentages of drivers using seat belts? **355%**
    b. For which year was the rate of increase greatest? **1985**

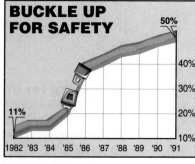

25. **Journal Entry**   Write one or two sentences explaining how to find a percent of change. **See students' work.**

OPTIONS

Extending the Lesson

Using Connections   Have students research and report on the *Consumer Price Index,* an index of prices used for measuring changes in the cost of basic goods and services in comparison with a fixed base period.

Cooperative Learning Activity

Number of players: **4**
Materials: Index cards, spinners

Time for a Change 10-8

♦ Copy onto cards the numbers 15, 33, 47, 50, 78, and 95, one number per card. Shuffle the cards and place them face down in a pile. Label equal sections of two spinners with the digits 0 through 9. Decide which spinner will stand for digits in tens place and which spinner will stand for digits in ones place.

➡ One group member selects the top card from the pile. Then, in turn, each group member spins both spinners, records the resulting two-digit number, and computes the percent of change from the number on the card. The group member with the largest percent of increase or smallest percent of decrease wins the round. Continue in this way, taking turns selecting a card, until no cards remain in the pile.

Glencoe Mathematics: Applications and Connections, Course 3

10-9 Discount

Objective
Solve problems involving discounts.

Words to Learn
discount
sale price

The 18-speed mountain bike Diana wants to buy usually sells for $198. If she buys it on sale at 25% off, how much will she pay?

The amount by which the regular price is reduced is called the **discount.** The **sale price** is the price after the discount has been subtracted.

You can find the sale price in one of two ways.

Estimation Hint
• • • • • • • • • •
THINK
$25\% = \frac{1}{4}$
$\frac{1}{4}$ of 200 is 50.
The discount is about $50. The sale price is about $200 − $50 or $150.

Method 1
Find the amount of the discount.
25% of $198 is the discount.

$0.25 \boxed{\times} 198 \boxed{=} 49.5$

Diana will save $49.50.

Subtract the discount from the regular price.

$198 \boxed{-} 49.5 \boxed{=} 148.5$

The sale price is $148.50.

Method 2
Find the percent paid.
$100\% − 25\% = 75\%$

Diana will pay 75% of the regular price.

Find the amount paid.
75% of $198 is the sale price.

$0.75 \boxed{\times} 198 \boxed{=} 148.5$

Example *Problem Solving*

Smart Shopping   Mitchell Li bought a pair of pants that had been reduced from $39 to $32. What was the percent of discount?

$39 − 32 = 7$ *Find the discount amount.*

$7 \quad is \ what \ percent \ of \quad 39?$

$7 \quad = \quad R \quad \cdot \quad 39$ *Write in $P = R \cdot B$ form.*

$7 \boxed{\div} 39 \boxed{=} 0.1794872$ *Divide each side by 39.*

$R \approx 0.1794872$ or about 0.18

The percent of discount is about 18%.

Lesson 10-9   Discount   **409**

Technology Activity

You can learn how to use a spreadsheet to find the sale price of an item in Technology Activity 5 on page 662.

NCTM Standards: 1–5, 7, 9

Lesson Resources
• Study Guide Master 10-9
• Practice Master 10-9
• Enrichment Master 10-9
• Group Activity Card 10-9

 Transparency 10-9 contains the 5-Minute Check and a teaching aid for this lesson.

⏱ 5-Minute Check
(Over Lesson 10-8)
1. The average number of students per class in a school fell from 25 to 19. Find the percent of decrease.   24%
2. Kwai's test score average rose from 80 to 84. Find the percent of increase.   5%

1 FOCUS

Motivating the Lesson

Questioning   Ask students to give reasons why a store might have a sale.   Sample answers: to attract customers, to reduce inventory, to raise quick cash

2 TEACH

Using Logical Reasoning   Ask students which of the two methods described they think is the more efficient way of finding a sale price.   Answers will vary. Students will probably agree that since finding the "percent paid" can be done mentally, Method 2 is faster.

Teaching Tip   In the Example, point out that the "percent of discount" is the "percent of change" discussed in the previous lesson.

OPTIONS

Reteaching Activity

Using Models   Provide copies of sale ads from newspapers or magazines. Have students write problems based on the information in the ads. Students should then exchange problems and solve.

Study Guide Masters, p. 93

Name _____ Date _____

Study Guide Worksheet 10-9

Discount

The amount by which the regular price is reduced is called the discount. The sale price is the price after the discount has been subtracted.

Example 1   A VCR that usually sells for $365 is on sale for 20% off. What is the sale price?

Method 1
Find the amount of the discount.
$0.20 \times \$365 = \$73$ discount

Subtract the discount from the regular price.
$\$365 − \$73 = \$292$

Method 2
Find the percent paid.
$100\% − 20\% = 80\%$ paid

Find the amount paid.
$0.80 \times \$365 = \$292$

The sale price is $292.

409

410

Checking for Understanding

Communicating Mathematics

Read and study the lesson to answer each question.

1. **Tell** how to find the price of a $35 sweater on sale at 20% off. See margin.

2. **Write** the equation you would use to find the rate of discount on a video tape that is on sale for $3.74 less than the regular price of $19.98. $R = \dfrac{3.74}{19.98}$

Guided Practice

Find the discount to the nearest cent.

3. $49 athletic shoes, 20% off $9.80

4. $300 stereo, $33\frac{1}{3}$% off $100

5. $8.60 tie, 40% off $3.44

6. $38.50 dress, 15% off $5.78

Find the sale price of each item.

7. $899 sofa, 10% off $809.10

8. $210 suit, 5% off $199.50

9. $37.95 sweatsuit, 25% off $28.46

10. $40 jacket, 30% off $28

Find the percent of discount.

11. regular price: $65 ≈ 38.5%
discount: $25

12. regular price: $40 12.5%
sale price: $35

Exercises

Independent Practice

Find the amount of discount and the sale price of each item to the nearest cent.

13. $29.95 jeans, 25% off $7.49; $22.46

14. $3 socks, 30% off $0.90; $2.10

15. $14.50 CD, 15% off $2.18; $12.32

16. $13 book, 20% off $2.60; $10.40

17. $119.50 lamp, $\frac{1}{3}$ off $39.83; $79.67

18. $3.59 tennis balls, $\frac{1}{4}$ off $0.90; $2.69

Find the percent of discount.

19. regular price: $89
discount: $22.25 25%

20. regular price: $75
discount: $30 40%

21. regular price: $72
sale price: $36 50%

22. regular price: $108
sale price: $72 $33\frac{1}{3}$%

23. What is the discount on a $22.75 shirt on sale for 15% off? $3.41

24. What is the sale price of a $169.95 camera on sale at 10% off? $152.95

25. Find the discount rate on a $20 watch that regularly sells for $25. 20%

26. What is the regular price of a pair of jeans that sold for $25.95 at a 30% off sale? $37.07

Mixed Review

27. Solve $n - 12 = 8$. *(Lesson 2-2)* 20

28. Solve $-3\frac{5}{8}(-5\frac{1}{4}) = s$. Write the solution in simplest form. *(Lesson 7-3)* $19\frac{1}{32}$

29. **Geometry** Find the value of x in the figure at the right. Round your answer to the nearest tenth. *(Lesson 9-9)* 7.2

30. **Consumer Math** Find the percent of change in gasoline prices if the old price per gallon was $1.15 and the new price is $1.19. *(Lesson 10-8)* 3.5%

OPTIONS

Bell Ringer

Because of inflation, a store owner raised the price of a $500 refrigerator by 10%. When it did not sell at the new price, the owner dropped the price 10%. What was the new selling price? $495

31. Telecommunication When you call long distance within your calling zone at night or on weekends, you get discounts off the regular cost. The times and discount rates are shown in the chart at the right.

a. The regular cost of a call is $7.60. What is the discount if the call is made at 11:15 P.M.? **$4.56**

b. The regular cost of a call is $4.20. If the call is made Wednesday at 6:00 P.M., what is the cost? **$2.94**

c. Bill made a call and is charged $10.70. What percent of discount did he receive if the regular cost is $26.75? **60%**

LONG DISTANCE CALLING	M	T	W	T	F	S	S
8 A.M. to 5 P.M.							
5 P.M. to 11 P.M.							
11 P.M. to 8 A.M.							

☐ Weekday (full rate)
☐ Evening (30% discount)
☐ Night and Weekend (60% discount)

32. Critical Thinking A jewelry store is having a 25% off sale. On Saturday only, all sale items are marked an additional 10% off. The Saturday sale price offers what rate of discount from the original price? **32.5%**

33. Critical Thinking During a one-day sale, a bedspread is discounted 25% to $51.

a. What was the original price? **$68**

b. After the sale is over, what must the percent of increase be to return the price of the bedspread to the original price? $33\frac{1}{3}\%$

34. Mathematics and Marketing Read the following paragraphs.

Marketing involves many activities that direct the flow of goods and services from producers to consumers. Consumer goods are sold through a variety of channels including retail stores, which often offer lower prices and a large selection of product.

Careful studies of consumers and their buying habits enable marketers to determine the best times to have promotions or sales. Marketers often use spreadsheet software to calculate the percent of decrease for different items.

This spreadsheet shows data for one store's sale merchandise. The percent of decrease is found by entering a formula into a cell. The formula in cell E2 is C2/B2*100. Find the values in cells E3 and E4.

	A	B	C	D	E
1	ITEM	REGULAR PRICE	DISCOUNT	DISCOUNT PRICE	PERCENT DECREASE
2	REFRIGERATOR	$900.00	$102.60	$797.40	11.4
3	MICROWAVE	$450.00	$90.00	$360.00	20
4	DRYER	$389.50	$54.53	$334.97	14

Lesson 10-9 Discount **411**

Extending the Lesson

Mathematics and Marketing Ask students to name the formula that is stored in cell D. Discuss why this software can also be useful to store managers.

Cooperative Learning Activity

Markdown Showdown **10-9**

Number of players: 2
Materials: Index cards, spinners

◆ Copy onto cards the dollar amounts shown on the back of this card, one per card. Label equal sections of two spinners "10%," "20%," "25%," "33⅓%," "40%," "50%."

➡ One partner selects a card. Then each partner spins a spinner. The percent on the spinner stands for the discount on an item with the price shown on the card. Each partner then writes his or her discounted price. Each partner spins a spinner a second time and writes the price after another discount has been taken. The partner who must pay the least after two discounts wins the round. Play several rounds, taking turns selecting a card.

Glencoe Mathematics: Applications and Connections, Course 3

Close

Have students write a few sentences explaining these terms: *regular price, sale price, discount, percent of discount.*

3 PRACTICE/APPLY

Assignment Guide

Maximum: 13–34
Minimum: 13–25 odd, 27–33

For **Extra Practice,** see p. 609.

Alternate Assessment

Speaking Have students choose a newspaper sale ad and give an explanation of the discounts and sale prices shown.

Enrichment Masters, p. 93

Name _____ Date _____

Enrichment Worksheet 10-9

The Cost of Using

The percent equation can be used to describe the percent by which something depreciates, or loses its value during the course of time.

Example In 1991, the average purchase price of a new automobile was $17,000. One year later, an automobile that was purchased new in 1991 typically was worth $11,500. By what percent did the automobile depreciate during the first year of ownership?

Solution First find the amount of decrease.
$17,000 − $11,500 = $5,500
Then write and solve the percent equation.

$5,500 is what percent of $17,000?
$5,500 = R × $17,000
0.3235294 = R

The automobile depreciated about 32.4% during the first year of ownership. It could also be said that the automobile lost about ⅓ of its value.

Advertisements such as these regularly appear in the classified pages of newspapers. Find the percent of depreciation in each advertisement.

1. For sale: Ford 2 dr, 5 speed, air, sport wheels, mint. Bought new 8 months ago for $9,600, yours for $7,200. Must sell—baby on way. **25%**

2. For sale: Washer/dryer combo. Antique white, electric, like new—18 mos. old. Paid $950, asking $500. **47.4%**

3. For sale: Honda 4 dr, auto, air, ABS, the works. 1 year old—12,400 mi. Purchase price—$16,000. Your price—$12,800 firm. **20%**

4. For sale: Dishwasher, 2 racks, full factory warranty. Never used—won in contest. List: $840. I will deliver for $588 cash. **30%**

5. For sale: Mountain bike. 20-inch frame. 26 × 1.60 new tires. Used but not abused. Bought last summer for $320. $150 or best offer. **53.1%**

6. For sale: Personal Computer. XT Model. 20 Mhz/386. 80 meg hard drive. 3.5 and 5.25 floppy drives. Color VGA monitor. 24-pin dot matrix printer with lots of software. $1,600 new—yours for $450. **71.9%**

T93
Glencoe Division, Macmillan/McGraw-Hill

NCTM Standards: 1–5, 7, 9

Lesson Resources

- Study Guide Master 10-10
- Practice Master 10-10
- Enrichment Master 10-10
- Evaluation Master, Quiz B, p. 88
- Technology Master, p. 24
- Group Activity Card 10-10

 Transparency 10-10 contains the 5-Minute Check and a teaching aid for this lesson.

🕐 5-Minute Check
(Over Lesson 10-9)

1. Find the amount of a 25% discount on a $12 tie. $3

2. Find the sale price of a $34.50 blouse selling for 30% off. $24.15

3. A $60 clock sold for $48. Find the percent of discount.   20%

1 FOCUS

Motivating the Lesson

Situational Problem   Ask students how much money Christopher Columbus would have in his account today if he had invested $100 at 6% simple interest on his first trip to America.

2 TEACH

Using Discussion   Ask students to explain why a bank is willing to pay you interest to keep your money.   The bank loans your money to other people at a higher interest rate.

10-10   Simple Interest

Objective
Solve problems involving simple interest.

Words to Learn

interest
principal
rate
time

Stephen Sopher found a United States savings bond his uncle bought when he was born. The savings bond had matured and was worth $50 eight years ago. Stephen is curious about how much the savings bond is worth now. If the savings bond earned $6\frac{1}{4}$% simple interest annually for the last 8 years, what is its value now?

Simple **interest** (*I*) is calculated on the **principal** (*p*), which is the amount of money in an account. The **rate** (*r*), is a percent, and the **time** (*t*), is given in years. You can use the formula below to find out how much interest Stephen's savings bond earned over the past eight years.

$$interest = principal \cdot rate \cdot time$$
$$I = prt$$
$$I = 50 \cdot 0.0625 \cdot 8$$

50 ⊠ 0.0625 ⊠ 8 ⊟ **25**   So, *I* = 25.

The savings bond earned $25 interest in the last eight years. Stephen's savings bond is now worth $75.

Example 1   *Problem Solving*

Earning Money   Yolanda sold calendars to her paper route customers and opened a savings account with the $300 she earned. Her account earns $5\frac{3}{4}$% interest annually. If she does not withdraw or deposit any money for 15 months, how much will be in her account?

First, find the amount of interest earned by using the simple interest formula.

$I = prt$ *Replace p with 300, r with 0.0575, and t*
$I = 300 \cdot 0.0575 \cdot \dfrac{15}{12}$ *with $\dfrac{15}{12}$ since 15 months is $\dfrac{15}{12}$ year.*

300 ⊠ 0.0575 ⊠ 15 ⊟ 12 ⊟ **21.5625**

$I = 21.5625$

The interest earned after 15 months is $21.56.

Then, add the interest to the savings: 300 ⊞ 21.56 ⊟ **321.56**.

After 15 months, the account will contain $321.56.

DID YOU KNOW

Outstanding consumer credit increased from $131.6 billion in 1970 to $728.9 billion in 1988.

OPTIONS

Gifted and Talented Needs

Most interest charged is *compound* interest, which adds the accrued interest to the principal each compounding period. Have students research compound interest, then study local bank interest rates and compounding periods to see which bank offers its customers the best deals.

 Interactive Mathematics Tools

This multimedia software provides an interactive lesson that is tied directly to Lesson 10–10. Students will explore compound interest.

Interest is charged to you when you borrow money. When this happens, the principal is the amount borrowed. If merchandise is bought using a credit card, a bank or the store is actually lending the money.

Example 2 *Problem Solving*

Consumer Math Jessica's mother used her credit card to purchase a $380 stereo. The bank that issued the credit card charges an annual interest rate of 19.8%. Each month they charge interest on the unpaid balance of the account. If Jessica's mother does not make any more purchases and makes a $50 payment, how much interest will she be charged next month?

By making a $50 payment, the balance, p, for the next month is $330.

$I = prt$

$I = 330 \cdot 0.198 \cdot \dfrac{1}{12}$ *Replace p with 330, r with 0.198, and t with $\dfrac{1}{12}$.*

330 $\boxed{\times}$ 0.198 $\boxed{\div}$ 12 $\boxed{=}$ 5.445

Jessica's mother will be charged $5.45 in interest next month.

Example 3 *Problem Solving*

Finance Dan's father borrowed $7,800 to buy a new car. He paid the money back in equal payments of $243.75 for the next 48 months. Find the simple interest rate on his loan.

First, find the amount he repaid.   →   48 $\boxed{\times}$ 243.75 $\boxed{=}$ 11700

Then find the amount of interest.   →   11700 $\boxed{-}$ 7800 $\boxed{=}$ 3900

$I = prt$

$3{,}900 = 7{,}800 \cdot r \cdot 4$ *Replace I with $3{,}900$, p with $7{,}800$ and t*
$3{,}900 = 31{,}200r$ *with 4 since 48 months is 4 years.*

3900 $\boxed{\div}$ 31200 $\boxed{=}$ 0.125   *Divide each side by $31{,}200$.*

The simple interest rate on the loan was 12.5%.

Checking for Understanding

Communicating Mathematics

Read and study the lesson to answer each question.

1. **Write** how you would express nine months in the simple interest formula. $\dfrac{3}{4}$ year

2. **Tell** the difference between the principal used to find interest on a loan and on a savings account.   See margin.

3. **Tell** why it is a good idea to pay off the entire balance on credit card accounts each month.   To avoid paying interest and to have a good credit rating.

More Examples

For Example 1

Willis invested $2,800 in a savings account at $6\frac{1}{2}$% simple interest. Find the amount in the account after 42 months. $3,437

For Example 2

A credit card company charges 18.9% annual interest on the unpaid balance each month. Find the monthly interest on an $863 unpaid balance. $13.59

For Example 3

Renatta repaid a $4,000 college loan at the rate of $85 per month for five years. Find the simple interest rate on the loan.   5.5%

Checking for Understanding

Exercises 1-3 are designed to help you assess students' understanding through reading, writing, speaking, and modeling. You should work through these exercises with your students and then monitor their work on Guided Practice Exercises 4-13.

Error Analysis

Watch for students who write time incorrectly in the formula $I = prt$.

Prevent by having students identify each variable, including the proper units. Have them identify the time period in the interest rate and the time units to verify that they correspond.

$i = 5\%$ per $\boxed{\text{year}}$
$t = 3\frac{1}{2}\ \boxed{\text{years}}$

Additional Answer

2. The principal on a loan is the amount of money borrowed. The principal on a savings account is the amount of money in the account.

Reteaching Activity

Using Cooperative Groups   Have pairs of students simulate a savings account using play money. The "banker" announces the rate and the "saver" states the length of time and deposits money in the account. The banker calculates the annual interest and pays that amount. Players then switch roles.

Study Guide Masters, p. 94

Name _____   Date _____

Study Guide Worksheet 10-10

Simple Interest

To find simple interest, use the formula $I = prt$. Interest (I) is the charge for the use of money. Principal (p) is the amount of money. Rate (r) is a percent per period. Time (t) is the time the money is used.

Example 1   Find the interest earned on $490 deposited in a savings account at $8\frac{1}{2}$% per year for 6 months.

$I = prt$ $p = \$490,\ r = 8\frac{1}{2}\%$ or 0.085,
$I = 490(0.085)(\frac{6}{12})$ $t = 6$ out of 12 months or $\frac{6}{12}$
$I = 20.825$ or 20.83

Find the total amount of money in the savings account.
$490.00 + \$20.83 = \$510.83$ Add the interest to the original amount.

Example 2   Find the annual rate of simple interest ...

413

Close

Have students explain the meaning of the formula $I = prt$ in their own words.

3 PRACTICE/APPLY

Assignment Guide

Maximum: 14–37

Minimum: 15–27 odd, 28–36

For **Extra Practice,** see p. 609.

Alternate Assessment

Speaking Have students tell the number they would write in the formula $I = prt$ for each of the following:

- $p = \$5,000$ 5,000
- $r = 9\frac{1}{2}\%$ 0.095
- $t = 3$ months 0.25

Have students use $I = prt$ and the values above to compute the interest. $118.75

Practice Masters, p. 94

Name _____ Date _____

Practice Worksheet 10-10

Simple Interest

Find the simple interest to the nearest cent.

1. $250 at 20% for 1 year
$50

2. $300 at 15% for 14 months
$52.50

3. $75 at 6.5% for 9 months
$3.66

4. $625 at 18.5% for 1 year
$115.63

5. $3,284 at 15.5% for 2 years
$1,018.04

6. $6,850 at 16% for 30 months
$2,740

7. $170.32 at 3% for 4 years
$20.44

8. $2,341 at 16.2% for 6 months
$189.62

Find the total amount in each account.

9. $300 at 6% for 3 years
$354

10. $275 at 5.5% for 20 months
$300.21

11. $1,000 at 5.5% for 9 months
$1,041.25

12. $16.28 at 3% for 6 years
$19.21

13. $298.97 at 4.5% for 3 months
$302.33

14. $7,184 at 5.25% for 10 months
$7,498.30

Find the annual rate of simple interest.

15. principal: $5,000   interest: $650   time: 3 years 4.3%

16. principal: $4,840   interest: $199.95   time: 9 months 5.5%

17. principal: $21.50   interest: $1.72   time: 2 years 4%

18. principal: $725   interest: $130.50   time: 18 months 12%

T 94
Glencoe Division, Macmillan/McGraw-Hill

414

Find the simple interest to the nearest cent.

4. $345 at $6\frac{1}{4}\%$ for 6 months $10.78
5. $400 at 15% for 18 months $90
6. $1,088 at 18% for 1 year $195.84
7. $62.25 at 5.5% for 9 months $2.57

Find the total amount in each account.

8. $615 at 7% for 8 months $643.70
9. $120 at $12\frac{3}{4}\%$ for $1\frac{1}{2}$ years. $142.95
10. $118 at 5.5% for 19 months $128.28
11. $217.75 at 6% for 36 months $256.95

Find the annual rate of simple interest.

12. interest: $31.50; principal: $700; time: 9 months 6%
13. interest: $142.80; principal: $560; time: 2 years 12.75%

Exercises

Find the simple interest to the nearest cent.

14. $205 at $6\frac{1}{4}\%$ for 9 months $9.61
15. $500 for 15 months at 12% $75
16. $78.75 at 6.5% for 8 months $3.41
17. $2,108 for 2 years at 16% $674.56
18. $100 at 5% for 18 months $7.50
19. $4,000 at 13.5% for 21 months $945

Find the total amount in each account.

20. $708 at 8% after 6 months $736.32
21. $200 at 6.75% after 9 months $210.13
22. $235 at 5.25% after 14 months $249.39
23. $176.77 at 6% after 6 years $240.41
24. $1,860 at $7\frac{1}{2}\%$ after 5 years $2,557.50
25. $10,000 at 13% after 6 months $10,650

Find the annual rate of simple interest.

26. principal: $4,000; total amount: $5,920; time: 3 years 16%
27. principal: $3,200; total amount: $3,632; time: 18 months 9%

28. Midori borrowed $9,800 and paid back $257.25 a month for five years. What was the annual rate of simple interest? 11.5%

29. Number of people who watch 0–5 hours is three times the number of people who watch 15–17 hours.

29. **Statistics**   Refer to the graph in Example 1 on page 133. How does the number of people who watch 0–5 hours compare to the number of people who watch 15–17 hours? *(Lesson 4-2)*

30. Solve $6p = \frac{5}{9}$. *(Lesson 7-10)* $\frac{5}{54}$

31. On a map, the distance between two cities is $2\frac{3}{4}$ inches. Find the actual distance between the cities if the scale is 1 in.:20 mi. *(Lesson 9-7)* 55 miles

32. **Smart Shopping**   Find the amount of discount and the sale price of a pair of $89 shoes on sale for 30% off. *(Lesson 10-9)* $26.70; $62.30

OPTIONS

Bell Ringer

In 1990, the U.S. Government paid $264.8 billion in interest on money it had borrowed. Find the amount spent on interest per U.S. resident (1990 population: 248 million).
about $1,068

33. Finance   Doug's savings account earned $27.93 interest in 6 months. The interest rate is $5\frac{1}{4}$%. How much was in his account to earn that amount of simple interest? **$1,064**

34. Critical Thinking   Maura can use her credit card to get a cash advance from an automatic teller machine or she can get a loan from her credit union. The interest rate on cash advances is 1.5% per month and the credit union rate is 16% per year. Which is better for Maura? Explain. **See margin.**

35. Critical Thinking   Heather paid $50 for a United States savings bond that will double in value in 8 years. What is the simple interest rate on this savings bond? **12.5%**

36. Finance   Tim opened a savings account several years ago and deposited $100. He never made any more deposits or withdrawals. His last statement from the bank listed the balance at $191. If the account earned a simple interest rate of 7%, how long ago did Tim open his savings account? **13 years**

COMPUTER
CONNECTION

37. Computer Connection   A spreadsheet like the one shown below can be used to generate a simple interest table for various account balances.

	A	B	C	D	E
1	Principal	Rate	Time	Interest	New Balance
2					
3	500	=B2/100	=C2	=A3*B3*C3	=A3+D3
4	1000	=B2/100	=C2	=A4*B4*C4	=A4+D4
5	1500	=B2/100	=C2	=A5*B5*C5	=A5+D5
6	2000	=B2/100	=C2	=A6*B6*C6	=A6+D6
7	2500	=B2/100	=C2	=A7*B7*C7	=A7+D7
8	3000	=B2/100	=C2	=A8*B8*C8	=A8+D8
9	3500	=B2/100	=C2	=A9*B9*C9	=A9+D9

For answers to
Exercises
37a-d, see margin.

a. Why is the rate in column B divided by 100?

b. Suppose you want to make a table to find the balance if the interest rate is $5\frac{1}{2}$% and the time period is 3 years. What value will be in cell E6?

c. Your teacher asks you to add a new row to the spreadsheet to represent a principal of $4,000. List each of the cell entries (A10, B10, C10, D10, E10) you would enter.

d. How would you modify the spreadsheet if you wanted to calculate the simple interest on a principal of $900 at a rate of 6% for a 15-month period?

Lesson 10-10   Simple Interest   **415**

Additional Answers

34. The loan from the credit union; the interest rate charged by the credit union is $1\frac{1}{3}$% per month.

37. a. to change the percent to a decimal

b. 2330

c. A10: 4000;
B10: B2/100;
C10: =C2;
D10: =A10*B10*C10;
E10: =A10+D10

d. Sample answer: Enter 6 in B2; enter 15 in C2; change A3 to 900; change C3 to =C2/12.

Enrichment Masters, p. 94

Extending the Lesson

Using Cooperative Groups   Have students work in small groups to solve this problem: *How many years will it take the accumulated interest to exceed the principal at these simple interest rates: 6%, 8%, 10%?*

16.7 years; $12\frac{1}{2}$ years; 10 years

Cooperative Learning Activity

The Chapter Study Guide and Review begins with a section on Communicating Mathematics. This includes questions that review the new terms and concepts that were introduced in the chapter.

Then, the Skills and Concepts presented in the chapter are reviewed using a side-by-side format. Encourage students to refer to the Objectives and Examples on the left as they complete the Review Exercises on the right.

The Chapter Study Guide and Review ends with problems that review Applications and Problem Solving.

Additional Answers

8. Sample answer: Express the fraction as a decimal. Then multiply the decimal by 100 and add a percent sign.
9. Sample answer: Express the percent as a fraction with a denominator of 100. Then simplify.
10. Interest = 400(0.055)(1)

Chapter

10 Study Guide and Review

Study Guide and Review

Communicating Mathematics

State whether each sentence is *true* or *false.* If false, replace the underlined word or number to make a true sentence.

1. A percent is a ratio that compares a number to <u>10</u>. **false; 100**
2. The decimal <u>0.25</u> is equivalent to 2.5%. **false; 0.025**
3. 12 is 10% of <u>120</u>. **true**
4. The amount by which a regular price is reduced to find the sale price is called the <u>discount</u>. **true**
5. The <u>interest</u> is the amount of money in an account. **false; balance**
6. To express a <u>percent</u> as a fraction, express the percent in the form $\frac{r}{100}$ and simplify. **true**
7. A <u>circle</u> graph is used to compare parts of a set of data to the whole set. **true**
8. Explain how to express a fraction as a percent. **For answers to Exercises 8-10, see margin.**
9. Tell how to express 160% as a mixed number.
10. Write how you would find the simple interest on $400 invested at $5\frac{1}{2}$% for 1 year.

Self Assessment

Objectives and Examples

Upon completing this chapter, you should be able to:

Review Exercises

Use these exercises to review and prepare for the chapter test.

- solve problems using the percent proportion *(Lesson 10-1)*

  96 is what percent of 240?
  $$\frac{96}{240} = \frac{r}{100}$$
  $$96(100) = 240(r)$$
  $$r = 40$$
  So, 96 is 40% of 240.

  Use a proportion to solve each problem.
  11. What is 28% of 400? **112**
  12. 54 is what percent of 180? **30%**
  13. 61.5 is 75% of what number? **82**
  14. 220 is what percent of 800? **27.5%**
  15. Find 62.5% of 128. **80**

- express percents as fractions and decimals *(Lesson 10-2)*

  Express 40% as a fraction.
  $$40\% = \frac{40}{100} = \frac{2}{5}$$

  Express each percent as a fraction in simplest form.
  16. 65% $\frac{13}{20}$ 17. 8% $\frac{2}{25}$
  18. 30% $\frac{3}{10}$ 19. 17.5% $\frac{7}{40}$

Objectives and Examples

- express percents greater than 100 or less than 1 as decimals and fractions *(Lesson 10-3)*

  Express 120% as a mixed number.

  $120\% = \dfrac{120}{100} = 1\dfrac{20}{100} = 1\dfrac{1}{5}$

- estimate by using fractions, decimals, and percents interchangeably *(Lesson 10-5)*

  Estimate 20% of 32.

  $20\% = \dfrac{1}{5}$ *Round 32 to 30.*

  $\dfrac{1}{5}$ of 30 is 6.   So, 20% of 32 ≈ 6.

- solve problems using the percent equation *(Lesson 10-6)*

  Find 15% of 600.

  $P = R \cdot B$
  $P = 0.15 \cdot 600$ *R = 15% or 0.15,*
  $P = 90$ *B = 600*

- construct circle graphs *(Lesson 10-7)*

  A circle graph is used to compare parts of a set of data to the whole set.

- find the percent of increase or decrease *(Lesson 10-8)*

  Find the percent of increase of a sweater that had cost $20 and now costs $25.

  $25 - 20 = 5$

  $\dfrac{P}{B} = \dfrac{r}{100}$
  $\dfrac{5}{20} = \dfrac{r}{100}$ *P = 5, B = 20*
  $r = 25$

  The percent of increase is 25%.

- solve problems involving discounts *(Lesson 10-9)*

  What is the sale price of a $15 CD on sale at 10% off?

  $0.10 \cdot 15 = 1.50$
  $15 - 1.50 = 13.50$
  The sale price is $13.50.

Review Exercises

Express each percent as a fraction or mixed number in simplest form.

20. 145% $1\dfrac{9}{20}$ 21. $\dfrac{4}{5}\%$ $\dfrac{1}{125}$

22. 428% $4\dfrac{7}{25}$ 23. $\dfrac{3}{7}\%$ $\dfrac{3}{700}$

Estimate. Sample answers given.

24. 8% of 64 5   25. 66% of 31 20

26. 59% of 80 48   27. 26% of 37 9

28. 98% of 20 20   29. 49% of 56 28

Solve.

30. What is 36% of 75? 27

31. What percent of 80 is 15? 18.75%

32. Find 30% of $128.50. $38.55

33. Forty-two is 28% of what number? 150

34. Make a circle graph of the number of hours each week that you study, talk on the telephone, watch television, and sleep. See students' work.

Find the percent of change. Round to the nearest whole percent.

35. old: $30 20% increase
    new: $36

36. old: $250 16% decrease
    new: $210

37. old: $48 25% increase
    new: $60

Find the amount of discount and the sale price of each item. $10.99, $43.96

38. $54.95 video game, 20% off

39. $60 watch, 15% off $9, $51

40. $120 bicycle, 30% off $36, $84

41. $84 clock, $\dfrac{1}{4}$ off $21, $63

Chapter 10   Study Guide and Review   **417**

You may wish to use a Chapter Test from the Evaluation Masters booklet as an additional chapter review. The two free-response forms are shown below. One of the two multiple-choice forms is shown on the next page.

Evaluation Masters, pp. 86–87

Name _____ Date _____

Form 2A _____ **Chapter 10 Test**

1. Eighteen is $37\frac{1}{2}$% of what number?
2. What is $\frac{1}{2}$% of 1,200?
3. Sixty-four is 20% of what number?
4. What percent of 51 is 17?   5. What percent of 51 is 85?
6. Express $\frac{9}{5}$ as a percent.

Express each percent as a decimal and as a fraction.

7. 11.75%   8. 230%   9. 65%   10. $\frac{3}{4}$%

Refer to the table at the right to answer the following questions.

Number of marbles in a bag	
red	8
blue	10
yellow	2

11. What percent of all the marbles are blue?
12. If the data in the table were used to make a circle graph, what would be the number of degrees for each section of the graph?
13. Dee received a score 80 out of 100 on a science test. On the next test he received a score of 72 out of 100. Find the percent of decrease.

Find the amount of discount and the sale price of each item.

14. $15 cap, 10% off   15. $399 television, 30% off
16. $18 video, $\frac{1}{6}$ off   17. $49.50 sweater, 15% off
18. Find the discount rate if the regular price is $80 and the sale price is $52.

Determine which is the best estimate.

19. $\frac{8}{15}$% of 509   a. 2.5   b. 25   c. 250
20. 33% of 92   a. 3   b. 30   c. 300
21. 37.9% of 79   a. 30   b. 300   c. 3,000
22. 198% of 3,989   a. 80   b. 800   c. 8,000
23. Find the annual rate of simple interest for a loan if the principal borrowed is $5000, the interest paid is $650, and the length of the loan is 18 months.
24. Find the total amount in a savings account if the principal is $800, the interest rate is $5\frac{3}{4}$%, and the time is 6 months.
25. The lockers in the hall outside the library are numbered consecutively. They start with number 273 and end with 349. How many lockers is this?

BONUS A shirt is discounted 30%. Then another 20% discount is given on the discounted price. What percent of the original price is the final price?

1.	48
2.	6
3.	320
4.	$33\frac{1}{3}$%
5.	$166\frac{2}{3}$%
6.	180%
7.	$0.1175; \frac{47}{400}$
8.	$2.30; \frac{23}{10}$
9.	$0.65; \frac{13}{20}$
10.	$0.0075; \frac{3}{400}$
11.	50%
12.	red, 144°; blue, 180°; yellow, 36°
13.	10%
14.	$1.50; $13.50
15.	$119.70; $279.30
16.	$2.25; $15.75
17.	$7.43; $42.07
18.	35%
19.	a
20.	b
21.	a
22.	c
23.	$8\frac{2}{3}$%
24.	$823
25.	77 lockers
	56%

86
Glencoe Division, Macmillan/McGraw-Hill

Name _____ Date _____

Form 2B _____ **Chapter 10 Test**

1. Sixteen is $62\frac{1}{2}$% of what number?
2. What is $\frac{1}{4}$% of 2,800?
3. Seventy-two is 30% of what number?
4. What percent of 66 is 22?
5. What percent of 24 is 54?
6. Express $\frac{11}{8}$ as a percent.

Express each percent as a decimal and as a fraction.

7. 18.25%   8. 195%   9. 85%   10. $\frac{7}{8}$%

Refer to the table at the right to answer the following questions.

Number of marbles in a bag	
red	14
blue	3
yellow	8

11. What percent of all the marbles are red?
12. If the data in the table were used to make a circle graph, what would be the number of degrees for each section of the graph? Round to the nearest degree.
13. Chari scored 75 out of 100 on a mathematics test. On the next test she scored 90 out of 100. Find the percent of increase.

Find the amount of discount and the sale price of each item.

14. $18 visor, 15% off   15. $275 VCR, 20% off
16. $14.95 CD, $\frac{1}{4}$ off   17. $39.49 shirt, 25% off
18. Find the discount rate if the regular price is $90 and the sale price is $60.

Determine which is the best estimate.

19. $1\frac{8}{9}$% of 198   a. 4   b. 40   c. 400
20. 51% of 79   a. 4   b. 40   c. 400
21. 19.5% of 203   a. 4   b. 40   c. 400
22. 302% of 5,938   a. 180   b. 1,800   c. 18,000
23. Find the annual rate of simple interest for a loan if the principal borrowed is $4000, the interest paid is $620, and the length of the loan is 2 years.
24. Find the total amount in a savings account if the principal is $800, the interest rate is $5\frac{1}{4}$%, and the time is 15 months.
25. Find the sum of the first 100 odd numbers.

BONUS How many squares are on a 10-by-10 checkerboard?

1.	25.6
2.	7
3.	240
4.	$33\frac{1}{3}$%
5.	225%
6.	$137\frac{1}{2}$%
7.	$0.1825; \frac{73}{400}$
8.	$1.95; \frac{39}{20}$
9.	$0.85; \frac{17}{20}$
10.	$0.00875; \frac{7}{800}$
11.	56%
12.	red, 202°; blue, 43°; yellow, 115°
13.	20%
14.	$2.70; $15.30
15.	$55; $220
16.	$3.74; $11.21
17.	$9.87; $29.62
18.	$33\frac{1}{3}$%
19.	a
20.	b
21.	b
22.	c
23.	7.75%
24.	$852.50
25.	10,000
	385

87
Glencoe Division, Macmillan/McGraw-Hill

Objectives and Examples

- solve problems involving simple interest *(Lesson 10-10)*

  Find the simple interest of $250 at 6% for 8 months.
  $$I = 250 \cdot 0.06 \cdot \frac{8}{12}$$
  $$= 10$$
  The interest is $10.

Review Exercises

Find the simple interest to the nearest cent.

42. $820 at $7\frac{1}{2}$% for 1 year **$61.50**
43. $1,728 at 5.75% for 9 months **$74.52**
44. $96 at 6% for 15 months **$7.20**
45. $240 at $6\frac{1}{4}$% for 18 months **$22.50**

Applications and Problem Solving

46. Randy hired a rock band to play at the Snowflake Dance. They charge $2,000 per performance. The manager required a 15% deposit. How much did Randy pay on deposit? *(Lesson 10-4)* **$300**

47. **Smart Shopping**   Emilio wants to buy a CD player that costs $149.95. If he waits until the CD player is on sale at 20% off to buy it, how much will he save? *(Lesson 10-9)* **$29.99**

48. **Statistics**   55% of Mrs. Kackley's math class are boys. What fraction of her class are boys? *(Lesson 10-2)* $\frac{11}{20}$

49. **Taxes**   Find the percent of change if the sales tax increased from 5% to $5\frac{1}{2}$%. *(Lesson 10-8)* **10% increase**

Curriculum Connection Projects

- **Home Economics**   Survey your class to find how many like each flavor of potato chips. Find the percent of the class that likes each flavor. Draw a circle graph of your results.

- **Health**   Have a friend measure your pulse while you are resting and again after you have run in place for 2 minutes. Find the percent of increase in your heart rate.

- **Consumer Awareness**   Find how much interest you would pay in a year if you used a credit card to pay for a CD player.

Read More About It

Corcoran, Barbara. *The Strike.*
Cribb, Joe. *Money.*
Dickens, Charles. *The Christmas Carol.*
Scott, Elain. *The Banking Book.*

Solve.

1. Seventeen is $33\frac{1}{3}$% of what number? **51**   2. What is $\frac{3}{4}$% of 2,400? **18**

3. Fifty-eight is 80% of what number? **72.5**   4. What percent of 45 is 18? **40%**

5. What percent of 28 is 42? **150%**   6. Express $\frac{8}{5}$ as a percent. **160%**

Express each percent as a decimal and as a fraction.

7. 12.8% **0.128; $\frac{16}{125}$**   8. 285% **2.85; $2\frac{17}{20}$**   9. 35% **0.35; $\frac{7}{20}$**   10. $\frac{1}{4}$% **0.0025; $\frac{1}{400}$**

Refer to the table at the right to answer the following questions.

Number of marbles in a bag	
red	6
blue	4
green	10

11. What is the percent of blue marbles to the total number of marbles? **20%**

12. If the data in the table were used to make a circle graph, what would be the number of degrees for each section of the graph? **red-108°; blue-72°; green-180°**

13. Rachel received a score of 70 out of 100 on an English test. On the next test she received a score of 84 out of 100. Find the percent of increase. **20%**

Find the amount of discount and the sale price of each item.

14. $28 shirt, 15% off **$4.20; $23.80**   15. $299 recliner, 20% off **$59.80; $239.20**

16. $16 sweatshirt, $\frac{1}{4}$ off **$4; $12**   17. $59.90 lamp, 10% off **$5.99; $53.91**

18. Find the discount rate if the regular price is $60 and the sale price is $42. **30% off**

Determine which is the best estimate.

19. $\frac{7}{16}$% of 595 **a**   a. 3   b. 30   c. 300

20. 24% of 60 **b**   a. 1.5   b. 15   c. 150

21. 12.3% of 74 **b**   a. 90   b. 9   c. 0.9

22. 204% of 1,309 **c**   a. 26   b. 260   c. 2,600

23. Find the annual rate of simple interest for a loan if the principal borrowed is $3,000, the interest paid is $540, and the length of the loan is 18 months. **12%**

24. Find the total amount in a savings account if the principal is $600, the interest rate is $5\frac{1}{2}$%, and the time is 9 months. **$624.75**

25. The lockers in the hall outside Sam's homeroom are numbered consecutively and start with number 265 and end with number 357. How many lockers are in the hall? **93**

Bonus Express 100% as a fraction in simplest form. $\frac{1}{1}$ or 1

Using the Chapter Test

This page may be used as a chapter test or another chapter review.

Evaluation Masters, pp. 82–83

Name _____ Date _____

Form 1A _____ *Chapter 10 Test*

1. Express $\frac{3}{8}$ as a percent.
   A. 12%   B. $12\frac{1}{2}$%   C. 40%   D. $37\frac{1}{2}$%   1. ___D___

2. What is 45% of 260?
   A. 117   B. 1.17   C. 11.7   D. 11,700   2. ___A___

3. 100 is what percent of 500?
   A. 500%   B. 2%   C. 5%   D. 20%   3. ___D___

4. 56 is 20% of what number?
   A. 70   B. 280   C. 40   D. 90   4. ___B___

5. Express 0.03 as a percent.
   A. $3\frac{1}{3}$%   B. 30%   C. 3%   D. $33\frac{1}{3}$%   5. ___C___

6. Express $10\frac{1}{4}$% as a fraction.
   A. $\frac{41}{4}$ B. $\frac{41}{4}$ C. $\frac{41}{400}$ D. $\frac{41}{200}$ 6. ___C___

7. Express $87\frac{1}{2}$% as a decimal.
   A. 0.875   B. 8.75   C. 0.0875   D. 87.5   7. ___A___

8. Express $183\frac{1}{3}$% as a fraction or mixed number in simplest form.
   A. $1\frac{5}{6}$ B. $183\frac{1}{3}$ C. $\frac{5}{3}$ D. $\frac{13}{6}$ 8. ___A___

9. Express $\frac{13}{25}$% as a decimal.
   A. 52   B. 0.52   C. 0.052   D. 0.0052   9. ___D___

10. Estimate 32% of 121.
    A. 4   B. 40   C. 400   D. 0.4   10. ___B___

11. Estimate the percent: 24 out of 77
    A. $\frac{3}{4}$%   B. $66\frac{2}{3}$%   C. $33\frac{1}{3}$%   D. $\frac{1}{3}$%   11. ___C___

12. Find 15% of $250.20.
    A. $38.00   B. $37.50   C. $375.30   D. $37.53   12. ___D___

13. 120% of what number is 72?
    A. 60   B. 8.64   C. 86.4   D. 0.016   13. ___A___

14. $26 is what percent of $39?
    A. 150%   B. $66\frac{2}{3}$%   C. 15%   D. $33\frac{1}{3}$%   14. ___B___

15. Find the percent of change in taxes if the old taxes were $48.00 and the new taxes are $53.76.
    A. 13%   B. $12\frac{1}{2}$%   C. 12%   D. 10.7%   15. ___C___

16. Find the percent of change in taxes if the old taxes were $36 and the new taxes are $30.
    A. 20%   B. $18\frac{1}{2}$%   C. $83\frac{1}{3}$%   D. $16\frac{2}{3}$%   16. ___D___

Name _____ Date _____

Chapter 10 Test, Form 1A (continued)

17. If the data in the table were used to make a circle graph, what would be the number of degrees for the section of the graph for the blue marbles?
    A. 96°   B. 144°   C. 150°   D. 50°   17. ___B___

Number of marbles in a bag	
red	8
blue	12
green	10

18. Find the amount of discount and the sale price of $4.25 socks, 10% off.
    A. $0.40; $3.85   B. $0.10; $4.15   C. $0.42; $3.83   D. $0.43; $3.82   18. ___D___

19. Find the amount of discount and the sale price of an $18 book, $\frac{1}{3}$ off.
    A. $6; $12   B. $5.40; $12.60   C. $5; $13   D. $6.20; $11.80   19. ___A___

20. Find the percent of discount when the regular price is $288 and the discount is $36.
    A. 13%   B. 12.5%   C. $13\frac{1}{3}$%   D. 14%   20. ___B___

21. Find the simple interest to the nearest cent: $250 at $7\frac{1}{2}$% for 6 months.
    A. $9.00   B. $112.50   C. $938   D. $9.38   21. ___D___

22. Find the total amount: $375 at 5.75% after 18 months.
    A. $32.34   B. $323.44   C. $3.23   D. $407.34   22. ___D___

23. Find the annual rate of simple interest: principal: $5,000; interest: $2,025; time: 3 years.
    A. 15%   B. $13\frac{1}{2}$%   C. $14\frac{1}{2}$%   D. 14%   23. ___B___

24. Alvin borrowed $6,500 and paid back $211.25 a month for four years. What was the annual rate of simple interest?
    A. 15%   B. $13\frac{1}{2}$%   C. 14%   D. $14\frac{1}{2}$%   24. ___C___

25. Find the sum of the first 100 even numbers. The first even number is 2.
    A. 9,900   B. 10,100   C. 1,000   D. 10,000   25. ___B___

BONUS A compact disc player sold originally for $160. The price was increased by 12.5%. The player was sold later with the price reduced $\frac{1}{3}$. What was the final sales price?
    A. $105   B. $110   C. $120   D. $100   ___C___

Test and Review Generator software is provided in Apple, IBM, and Macintosh versions. You may use this software to create your own tests or worksheets, based on the needs of your students.

The **Performance Assessment Booklet** provides an alternate assessment for evaluating student progress. An assessment for this chapter can be found on pages 19–20.

11 Algebra: Functions and Graphs

Previewing the Chapter

This chapter introduces the relationship that has been described as the most important in all of mathematics, the function. Students learn to complete function tables, graph ordered pairs, and draw the lines or curves suggested by the plotted points. Linear and quadratic functions are singled out for attention, and students learn to solve systems of equations graphically. The **problem-solving strategy** lesson explains how to use a graph to solve problems. Students then apply this strategy and their knowledge of functions to slope and to translations, reflections, and rotations.

Lesson	Lesson Objectives	NCTM Standards	State/Local Objectives
11-1	Complete function tables.	1–4, 7–9	
11-2	Graph functions by using function tables.	1–5, 7–9, 12	
11-3	Find solutions for equations with two variables.	1–5, 7–9	
11-4A	Graph a relationship that can be described by a linear function.	1–5, 8, 10	
11-4	Graph linear functions by plotting points.	1–5, 7–9, 12	
11-5	Solve systems of linear equations by graphing.	1–4, 7–9, 12	
11-6	Solve problems by using a graph.	1–4, 7, 8, 10	
11-7	Graph quadratic functions.	1–4, 7–9, 12	
11-8	Graph translations on a coordinate plane.	1–5, 7–9, 12	
11-8B	Use translations and slope to find other solutions of a linear function.	1–5, 7, 8, 12	
11-9	Graph reflections on a coordinate plane.	1–5, 7–9, 12	
11-10	Graph rotations on a coordinate plane.	1–5, 7–9, 12	

Organizing the Chapter

A complete, 1-page lesson plan is provided for each lesson in the Lesson Plans Masters Booklet.

LESSON PLANNING GUIDE

Lesson	Materials/ Manipulatives	Extra Practice (Student Edition)	Blackline Masters Booklets									
			Study Guide	Practice	Enrichment	Evaluation	Technology	Lab Manual	Multicultural Activities	Application and Interdisciplinary Activities	Transparencies	Group Activity Cards
11-1		p. 609	p. 95	p. 95	p. 95		p. 11				11-1	11-1
11-2		p. 610	p. 96	p. 96	p. 96						11-2	11-2
113		p. 610	p. 97	p. 97	p. 97						11-3	11-3
11-4A	large rubber band, 2 paper clips, inch ruler, marbles, paper cup							p. 70				
11-4	graph paper	p. 610	p. 98	p. 98	p. 98						11-4	11-4
11-5	calculator, graph paper	p. 611	p. 99	p. 99	p. 99	Quiz A, p. 97	p. 25			p. 11	11-5	11-5
11-6			p. 100	p. 100	p. 100						11-6	11-6
11-7	calculator, graph paper	p. 611	p. 101	p. 101	p. 101					p. 25	11-7	11-7
11-8	graph paper, colored pencils	p. 611	p. 102	p. 102	p. 102						11-8	11-8
11-8B	graph paper							p. 71				
11-9	graph paper, scissors	p. 612	p. 103	p. 103	p. 103			p. 72			11-9	11-9
11-10	protractor, graph paper	p. 612	p. 104	p. 104	p. 104	Quiz B, p. 97				p. 11	11-10	11-10
Study Guide and Review			Multiple Choice Test, Forms 1A and 1B, pp. 91–94 Free Response Test, Forms 2A and 2B, pp. 95–96 Cumulative Review, p. 98 (free response)									
Test			Cumulative Test, p. 99 (multiple choice)									

Pacing Guide: Option I (Chapters 1–12) - 14 days; Option II (Chapters 1–13) - 13 days; Option III (Chapters 1–14) - 13 days
You may wish to refer to the complete **Course Planning Guides** on page T25.

OTHER CHAPTER RESOURCES

Student Edition
Chapter Opener, pp. 420–421
Mid-Chapter Review, p. 438
Save Planet Earth, p. 441
Portfolio Suggestion, p. 449

Manipulatives
Overhead Manipulative Resources
Middle School Mathematics Manipulative Kit

Software/Technology
Interactive Mathematics Tools (Macintosh)
Test and Review Generator (IBM, Apple, Macintosh)
Teacher's Guide for Software Resources

Other Supplements
Transparency 11–0
Performance Assessment, pp. 21–22
Glencoe Mathematics Professional Series
Lesson Plans, pp. 119–130

INTERDISCIPLINARY BULLETIN BOARD

Science Connection

Objective Find examples of translations, reflections, rotations, and symmetry in nature.

How To Use It Have students research transformations and symmetries in nature and display them in photos or drawings. For each item, they should identify the transformation and indicate the symmetries in the figure.

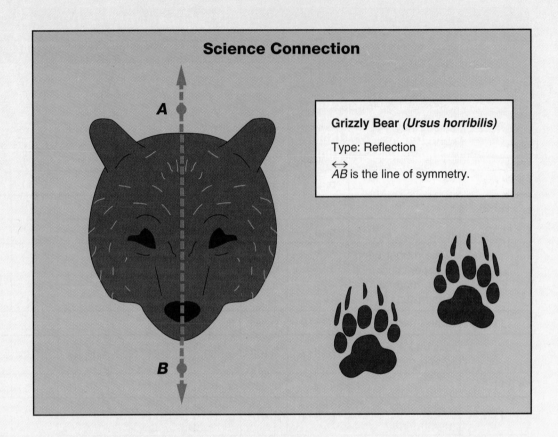

Science Connection

A

B

Grizzly Bear (Ursus horribilis)

Type: Reflection

$\overleftrightarrow{AB}$ is the line of symmetry.

APPLICATIONS AND CONNECTIONS

Applications	Lesson	Example	Exercise
Meteorology	11-2	1	
Domestic Engineering	11-2		15
Biology	11-3		23
Fund Raising	11-3		24
Weather	11-4		21
Physics	11-4		22
Smart Shopping	11-5	1	
Home Maintenance	11-5		26
Physics	11-7	1	24
Business	11-7		25
Video Games	11-8		16
Entertainment	11-10		17
Connections			
Computer	11-1		22
Number Sense	11-3	2	17, 21
Geometry	11-5		27
Geometry	11-7	2	26
Algebra	11-8	2	
Algebra	11-9		14
Geometry	11-10		16

TEAM ACTIVITIES

Multicultural Experiences

Outside Field Trips Look for experiences that illustrate linear relationships in everyday life. At a supermarket, students can record weights and prices of several packages of meat or cheese as ordered pairs, and then graph the linear functions.

At the city taxation department, students can learn how taxes are related linearly to the incomes or values being taxed.

In-Class Speakers Invite a newspaper illustrator to discuss how current-event statistics are incorporated into graphical displays.

A travel agent can explain the linear relationship between U.S. and foreign currencies.

SUPPLEMENTARY BLACKLINE MASTER BOOKLETS

Some of the blackline masters for enhancing this chapter are shown below.

Application and Interdisciplinary Activity Masters, pp. 11, 25

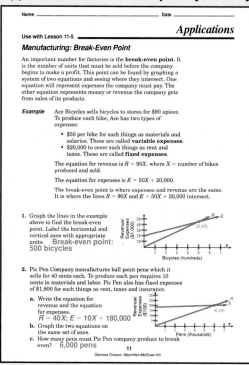

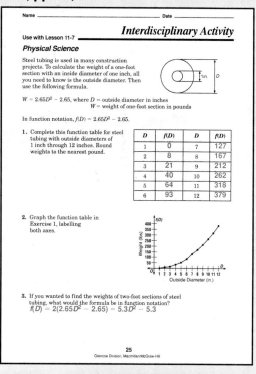

Multicultural Activity Masters, p. 11

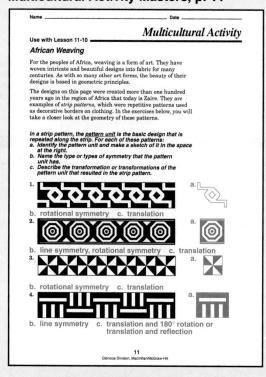

Technology Masters, p. 11

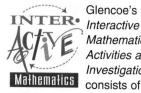

RECOMMENDED OUTSIDE RESOURCES

Books/Periodicals

National Coalition of Advocates for Students, *New Voices: Immigrant Students in U.S. Public Schools,* Boston, MA, 1988.

Edwards, Edgar L., ed., *Algebra for Everyone,* Reston, VA: NCTM, 1990.

Films/Videotapes/Videodiscs

Equations in Algebra, Chicago, IL: International Film Bureau, Inc., 1963.

Software

Geometric Connectors: Transformations, (Apple II, IBM/Tandy), Wings for Learning/Sunburst

For addresses of companies handling software, please refer to page T24.

INTER·ACTIVE Mathematics

Glencoe's *Interactive Mathematics: Activities and Investigations* consists of 18 units that may be used as alternatives or supplemental material for *Mathematics: Applications and Connections.* The suggested units for this chapter are Unit 15, *On the Move,* and Unit 16, *Growing Pains.* See page T18 for more information.

This two-page introduction to the chapter provides a visual, relevant way to engage students in the mathematics of the chapter. Questions are included that help students see the need to learn the mathematics in the chapter. Data in charts and graphs provide statistical information that students can analyze and interpret at this point as well as later in the chapter. The Chapter Project provides an activity that applies the mathematics of the chapter.

MAKING MATHEMATICS RELEVANT

Spotlight on Oceans

As ocean depth increases, so does the difficulty of sustaining life. Refer students to the graph relating depth and temperature. Sunlight penetrates only about 1,000 feet, so below that depth the ocean is dark. In addition, water pressure increases dramatically with depth. Each cubic foot of ocean water weighs 64 pounds. Ask students to find the weight of water pressing down on each square foot of the surface of a submersible at the deepest point of the Pacific Ocean, the Mariana Trench, which is 35,840 feet deep.   2,293,760 pounds

Using the Timeline

Ask the following questions.

- *How much time elapsed between the sinking of the Titanic and the discovery of its wreckage?*   73 years

- *In what year were East and West Germany created?*   1945

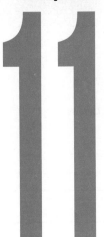

Chapter

11

Algebra: Functions and Graphs

Spotlight on Oceans

Have You Ever Wondered...

- What happens to the temperature of the ocean water as depth increases?

- What kinds of life live at different depths in the ocean?

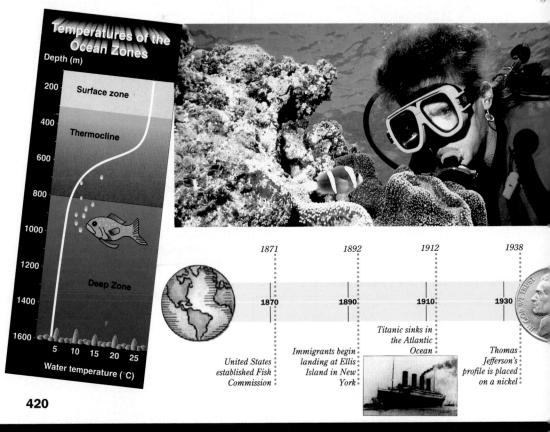

Temperatures of the Ocean Zones

Depth (m)

200 — Surface zone
400 — Thermocline
600
800
1000
1200
1400 — Deep Zone
1600

Water temperature (°C)   5 10 15 20 25

1871   United States established Fish Commission
1892   Immigrants begin landing at Ellis Island in New York
1912   Titanic sinks in the Atlantic Ocean
1938   Thomas Jefferson's profile is placed on a nickel

1870   1890   1910   1930

420

"Have You Ever Wondered?" Answers

- Generally, the temperature decreases as depth increases.
- Students can see from the chart the various forms of life that exist at different depths in the ocean.

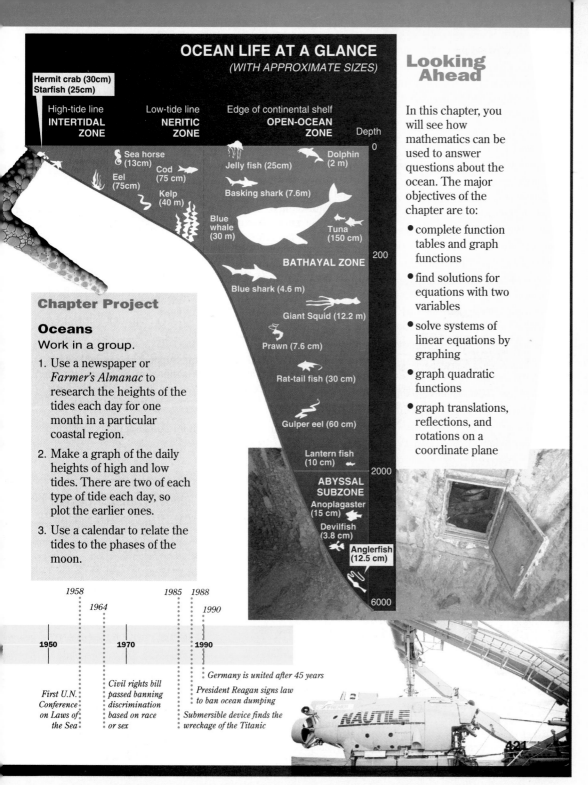

OCEAN LIFE AT A GLANCE
(WITH APPROXIMATE SIZES)

Hermit crab (30cm)
Starfish (25cm)

| High-tide line | Low-tide line | Edge of continental shelf |
| INTERTIDAL ZONE | NERITIC ZONE | OPEN-OCEAN ZONE |

Depth 0

Sea horse (13cm)
Eel (75cm)
Cod (75 cm)
Kelp (40 m)
Jelly fish (25cm)
Dolphin (2 m)
Basking shark (7.6m)
Blue whale (30 m)
Tuna (150 cm)

200

BATHAYAL ZONE

Blue shark (4.6 m)
Giant Squid (12.2 m)
Prawn (7.6 cm)
Rat-tail fish (30 cm)
Gulper eel (60 cm)
Lantern fish (10 cm)

2000

ABYSSAL SUBZONE
Anoplagaster (15 cm)
Devilfish (3.8 cm)
Anglerfish (12.5 cm)

6000

Chapter Project

Oceans

Work in a group.

1. Use a newspaper or *Farmer's Almanac* to research the heights of the tides each day for one month in a particular coastal region.

2. Make a graph of the daily heights of high and low tides. There are two of each type of tide each day, so plot the earlier ones.

3. Use a calendar to relate the tides to the phases of the moon.

1958   1985 1988
   1964   1990

1950   **1970**   **1990**

First U.N. Conference on Laws of the Sea
Civil rights bill passed banning discrimination based on race or sex
Germany is united after 45 years
President Reagan signs law to ban ocean dumping
Submersible device finds the wreckage of the Titanic

NAUTILE

421

Looking Ahead

In this chapter, you will see how mathematics can be used to answer questions about the ocean. The major objectives of the chapter are to:

- complete function tables and graph functions

- find solutions for equations with two variables

- solve systems of linear equations by graphing

- graph quadratic functions

- graph translations, reflections, and rotations on a coordinate plane

---

DATA ANALYSIS

Have students study the ocean-life graph. Ask the following questions.

- *At what depths is the greatest variety of sea life found?* 0–200 meters

- *At what depth does the edge of the continental shelf begin?* 200 meters

Data Search

A question related to these data is provided in Lesson 11-6, page 441, Exercise 12.

CHAPTER PROJECT

Tide forecasts for each month are usually given on the first day of the month in newspapers and almanacs. Students should find that tides near the shore rise as high as 1.8–2.5 meters.

This project gives students an opportunity to graph tide height as a function of the time of the month. They can then make a connection between tides, the moon, and gravity. Incoming tides are highest and outgoing tides lowest when the moon is full or new.

Allow five weeks to complete the project.

Chapter Opener Transparency

Transparency 11-0 is available in the Transparency Package. It provides another full-color, motivating activity that you can use to capture students' interest.

NCTM Standards: 1–4, 7–9

NCTM Standards: 1–4, 7–9

Lesson Resources
- Study Guide Master 11-1
- Practice Master 11-1
- Enrichment Master 11-1
- Technology Master, p. 11
- Group Activity Card 11-1

 Transparency 11-1 contains the 5-Minute Check and a teaching aid for this lesson.

🕐 5-Minute Check
(Over Chapter 10)

1. Express 60% as a fraction in simplest form.
   $\frac{3}{5}$

2. Find 75% of 32. 24

3. The price of a shirt was reduced from $30 to $24. Find the percent of decrease. 20%

4. A $40 radio was offered at 15% off. Find the sale price. $34

1 FOCUS

Motivating the Lesson

Questioning A baseball player said that good hitting is a *function* of natural ability and hard work. Ask students to explain. Natural ability and hard work are the raw materials that produce good hitting.

2 TEACH

Using Diagrams Depict functions as machines that operate on domain values and turn them into range values.

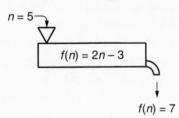

$n = 5$

$f(n) = 2n - 3$

$f(n) = 7$

11-1 Functions

Objective
Complete function tables.

Words to Learn
function
domain
range

DID YOU KNOW

The heaviest domestic dog is the St. Bernard, which weighs up to 100 kilograms and stands 70 centimeters high at the shoulders.

Do you have a pet? Nearly one-third of all American households have some sort of pet. The most popular pet among households with children is a dog. To help humans relate to how old their dog is, veterinarians have used the rule that one year of a dog's life is equivalent to seven years of human life. So a dog 10 years old is 70 years old in human years.

For every dog age, there is a corresponding human age. This relationship is an example of a **function.** In a function, one or more operations are performed on one number to get another. Thus, the second number is a function of the first.

A function is often written as an equation. Suppose the variable n is used for the first number, or input. The symbol for the second number, or output, is $f(n)$. This is read *the function of n* or, more simply, *f of n*. The function for relating dog years to human years is $f(n) = 7n$.

Let's use a table to evaluate the function for equating dog years and human years.

Example 1

Copy and complete the table at the right to find out the human ages of dogs ages 3 through 6.

Tables like these are called function tables.

INPUT dog years	RULE	OUTPUT human years
n	$7n$	$f(n)$
3		
4		
5		
6		

To find each output, substitute each dog's age for n and multiply by 7.

$f(n) = 7n$
$f(3) = 7 \cdot 3$ or 21
$f(4) = 7 \cdot 4$ or 28
$f(5) = 7 \cdot 5$ or 35
$f(6) = 7 \cdot 6$ or 42

The dog ages in human years are 21, 28, 35, and 42.

INPUT	RULE	OUTPUT
n	$7n$	$f(n)$
3	7(3)	21
4	7(4)	28
5	7(5)	35
6	7(6)	42

Interactive Mathematics Tools

This multimedia software provides an interactive lesson that is tied directly to Lesson 11–1. Students will explore linear functions and graphs.

Study Guide Masters, p. 95

Name _____ Date _____

Study Guide Worksheet 11-1

Functions

A function connects a number, n, to another number, $f(n)$, by a rule. Read $f(n)$ *the function of n*. The set of input values, values of n, is called the domain. The set of output values, values of $f(n)$, is called the range.

Example A temperature given in degrees Fahrenheit has a corresponding Celsius temperature. Let n equal degrees Fahrenheit. The domain is {0, 32, 65, 98.6}. Use the rule $(n - 32) \div 1.8$. Substitute as shown in the function table. The

Fahrenheit n	$(n - 32) \div 1.8$	Celsius $f(n)$
0	$(0 - 32) \div 1.8$	-17.8
32	$(32 - 32) \div 1.8$	0
65	$(65 - 32) \div 1.8$	18.3
98.6	$(98.6 - 32) \div 1.8$	37

The set of input values in a function is called the **domain.** The set of output values is called the **range.** So the domain contains all values of n, and the range contains all values of $f(n)$.

Example 2

Make a function table to find the range of $f(n) = 3n + 5$ if the domain is $\{-2, -1, 0, 3, 5\}$.

First make the function table. List the values in the domain, the input values.

n	3n + 5	f(n)
-2		
-1		
0		
3		
5		

Substitute each member of the domain into the function to find the values of $f(n)$, the output values.

n	3n + 5	f(n)
-2	3(-2) + 5	-1
-1	3(-1) + 5	2
0	3(0) + 5	5
3	3(3) + 5	14
5	3(5) + 5	20

The range is $\{-1, 2, 5, 14, 20\}$.

Checking for Understanding

Communicating Mathematics

Read and study the lesson to answer each question.

1. **Tell** another name for the set of input numbers. domain
2. **Tell** another name for the set of output numbers. range
3. **Write** in your own words a definition for function. See students' work.
4. **Tell** how to find $f(6)$ if $f(n) = 2n^2 - 18$. $f(6) = 2(6)^2 - 18 = 54$

Guided Practice

Complete each function table.

5. $f(n) = -5n$

n	-5n	f(n)
-4	-5(-4)	20
-2	-5(-2)	10
0	-5(0)	0
2.5	-5(2.5)	-12.5

6. $f(n) = 2n + (-6)$

n	2n + (-6)	f(n)	
-2		-10	2(-2) + (-6)
-1		-8	2(-1) + (-6)
0		-6	2(0) + (-6)
1		-5	$2\left(\frac{1}{2}\right) + (-6)$
2			

7. Find $f(-3)$ if $f(n) = -2n - 4$. 2
8. Find $f\left(\frac{1}{3}\right)$ if $f(n) = 15 - 3n$. 14
9. Find $f(0.25)$ if $f(n) = 100n$. 25

Lesson 11-1 Functions **423**

"To help my students make the connection between mathematical and English terms, I ask them, "If I told you that I feel like I just can't *function*, how is my use of the word *function* similar to the mathematical term?" A student said that I wouldn't be *operating normally*."

Classroom Vignette

Linda Dritsas

Linda Dritsas
Author

More Examples

For Example 1

Complete the table to find out the number of yards in measurements of 12 feet through 15 feet.

INPUT	RULE	OUTPUT
n	$\frac{1}{3}n$	f(n)
12	$\frac{1}{3}(12)$	4
13	$\frac{1}{3}(13)$	$4\frac{1}{3}$
14	$\frac{1}{3}(14)$	$4\frac{2}{3}$
15	$\frac{1}{3}(15)$	5

For Example 2

Make a function table to find the range of $f(n) = -2x - 4$ if the domain is $\{-2, 0, 2, 4\}$.
The range is $\{0, -4, -8, -12\}$.

Checking for Understanding

Exercises 1-4 are designed to help you assess students' understanding through reading, writing, speaking, and modeling. You should work through these exercises with your students and then monitor their work on Guided Practice Exercises 5-9.

Practice Masters, p. 95

Close

Have students define a function using the words *rule, domain,* and *range.* Sample answer: A function is a *rule* that states how to convert values from the *domain* into values in the *range.*

3 PRACTICE/APPLY

Assignment Guide
Maximum: 10–22
Minimum: 10–21

For **Extra Practice,** see p. 609.

Alternate Assessment

Speaking Write a function on the chalkboard. Name values from the domain and have students name the corresponding values in the range.

Additional Answer

18. Sample answer:

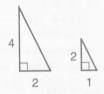

Enrichment Masters, p. 95

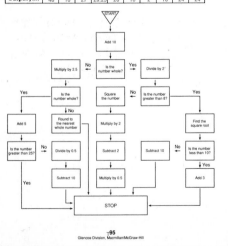
Exercises

Complete each function table.

Independent Practice

10. $f(n) = n + 5$

n	n + 5	f(n)
-2	-2 + 5	3
-1	-1 + 5	4
0	0 + 5	5
1	1 + 5	6
2	2 + 5	7

11. $f(n) = 3n$

n	3n	f(n)
-1	-3	3(-1)
0	0	3(0)
$\frac{2}{3}$	2	$3\left(\frac{2}{3}\right)$
1	3	3(1)

12. $f(n) = 2n + 3$

n	2n + 3	f(n)
-2.5		-2	2(-2.5) + 3
-1.5		0	2(-1.5) + 3
0.5		4	2(0.5) + 3
1		5	2(1) + 3
2		7	2(2) + 3

13. $f(n) = -0.5n + 1$

n	-0.5n + 1	f(n)
-4		3	-0.5(-4) + 1
-2		2	-0.5(-2) + 1
0		1	-0.5(0) + 1
2.5		-0.25	-0.5(2.5) + 1
8		-3	-0.5(8) + 1

14. Find $f(-8)$ if $f(n) = 3n + 24$. **0**

15. Find $f\left(\frac{4}{5}\right)$ if $f(n) = -5n - 4$. **-8**

16. Find $f(1.5)$ if $f(n) = n^2 + 1$. **3.25**

17. Find $f(-3.4)$ if $f(n) = 2n^2 - 5$. **18.12**

Mixed Review

18. Geometry Draw two similar right triangles. *(Lesson 5-6)* **See margin.**

19. Geometry If the length of the hypotenuse of a 30°–60° right triangle is 12 centimeters, find the length of the side opposite the 30° angle. *(Lesson 8-8)* **6 cm**

20. Finance Mrs. Sanchez borrowed $3,200 to build a garage. She made 12 monthly payments of $292 to pay back the simple interest loan. Find the interest on her loan. *(Lesson 10-10)* **$304**

Problem Solving and Applications

21. Critical Thinking Use $f(n)$ to write the equation that describes the function represented by the table at the right.
$f(n) = n + 5$

n	f(n)
-3	2
-1	4
1	6
3	8

COMPUTER CONNECTION

22. Computer Connection The number of hours each employee works is entered in column A, the hourly wage is entered in column B, and the fee for cleaning uniforms is in column C. Column D records the pay before taxes. The formula in cell D1 is A1 * B1 − C1. The formula acts like the rule of a function. Find the pay for each employee.

	A	B	C	D
1	40	$4.30	$5	$167
2	32	$5.75	$4	$180
3	30	$6.00	$6	$174
4	27	$4.80	$3	$126.60

424 **Chapter 11** Algebra: Functions and Graphs

OPTIONS

Extending the Lesson
Using Cooperative Groups Have students work in groups to define the function for each table.

n	f(n)
8	2
6	0
3	-3

n	f(n)
-1	-7
0	-2
1	3

n	f(n)
1	2
2	5
3	10

$f(n) = n - 6$; $f(n) = 5n - 2$;
$f(n) = n^2 + 1$

Cooperative Learning Activity

Lap It Up **11-1**

Number of players: 2
Materials: Index cards, number cube, counters

♦ Copy onto cards the equations shown on the back of this card, one per card. Shuffle the cards and divide them evenly. Copy the game board shown below onto a large sheet of paper (or several smaller sheets taped together).

➤ One partner rolls a number cube. The other partner then places face up a card from his or her hand, and the first partner uses the equation on the card to find the output for the input indicated on the number cube. The output tells the number of spaces forward or backward the first player is to move his or her counter. Trade roles and repeat the procedure. Continue in this way until one partner has made two laps around the board, shuffling and reusing cards as necessary.

Glencoe Mathematics: Applications and Connections, Course 3

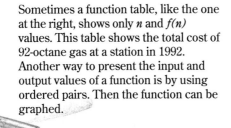

11-2 Graphing Functions

Objective
Graph functions by using function tables.

Sometimes a function table, like the one at the right, shows only n and $f(n)$ values. This table shows the total cost of 92-octane gas at a station in 1992. Another way to present the input and output values of a function is by using ordered pairs. Then the function can be graphed.

Gallons	Total Cost ($)
n	$f(n)$
1	1.16
2	2.32
3	3.48
4	4.64

To form ordered pairs, let the x-coordinate be the value of n. The y-coordinate is the value of $f(n)$. For the table, the ordered pairs are as follows.

(1, 1.16), (2, 2.32), (3, 3.48), (4, 4.64)

The graph of these ordered pairs is shown at the right. Notice that the x-axis is labeled n and the y-axis is labeled $f(n)$. *What pattern do the points suggest?*

Example 1 *Problem Solving*

Meteorology In December 1991, a rain system hit central Texas dumping several inches of rain in a few days. The Colorado River crested at over 46 feet, which was 7 feet, or 84 inches, above flood stage. After cresting, the river fell at a rate of 4 inches per hour. If n represents the number of hours, $f(n) = 84 - 4n$ represents the height of the river above flood stage after each hour. Draw a graph of this function.

First, make a function table and find the values of $f(n)$ for each value of n in the table. Then write the ordered pairs.

Graph the ordered pairs. Draw the line the points suggest.

LOOKBACK
You can review graphing points on page 117.

n	$84 - 4n$	$f(n)$	$(n, f(n))$
1	$84 - 4(1)$	80	(1, 80)
3	$84 - 4(3)$	72	(3, 72)
5	$84 - 4(5)$	64	(5, 64)
7	$84 - 4(7)$	56	(7, 56)

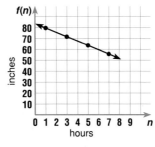

Lesson 11-2   Graphing Functions   **425**

OPTIONS

Reteaching Activity

Using Communication Students may be overly concerned about guessing the pattern suggested by an array of points. Have them concentrate instead on completing function tables and graphing points. To check their understanding of graphing, point to ordered pairs and have them identify the coordinates.

Study Guide Masters, p. 96

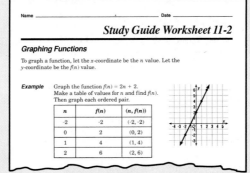

425

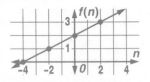

Not all graphs of functions form a line, and the graphs of many functions lie in more than the first quadrant.

Example 2

Problem Solving Hint

• • • • • • • • • • •

Look for a pattern in the positions of the points. Use the pattern to draw the complete graph.

Graph the function $f(n) = n^2$.

Make a table of values for n and find $f(n)$.

n	$f(n)$	$(n, f(n))$
-4	16	(-4, 16)
-3	9	(-3, 9)
-1	1	(-1, 1)
0	0	(0, 0)
1	1	(1, 1)
2	4	(2, 4)
4	16	(4, 16)
5	25	(5, 25)

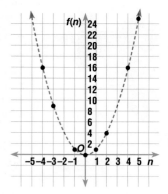

Then graph each ordered pair.

There are infinitely many values possible for n. If you graphed all these values, the points would suggest a smooth curve. Draw the curve suggested by our points.

Checking for Understanding 2. $f(0)$ is the height when the river crested.

Communicating Mathematics

Read and study the lesson to answer each question.   See Solutions Manual.

1. **Write** how you can use a function table to graph a function.

2. **Tell** what $f(0)$ means in terms of the flood described in Example 1.

3. **Tell** how long it would take the Colorado River to recede at the rate of 4 inches per hour. What type of weather might affect this? 21 hours, more rain

4. **Show** which axes are used for the input numbers and output numbers when graphing a function. Input numbers are on the x-axis and output numbers are on the y-axis.

Guided Practice

Copy and complete each function table. Then graph the function.   See Solutions Manual for graphs.

5. $f(n) = n + 4$

n	$f(n)$	$(n, f(n))$
-1	3	(-1, 3)
1	5	(1, 5)
2	6	(2, 6)
4	8	(4, 8)
5	9	(5, 9)

6. $f(n) = \dfrac{8}{n}$

n	$f(n)$	$(n, f(n))$
$\frac{1}{2}$	16	$\left(\frac{1}{2}, 16\right)$
2	4	(2, 4)
4	2	(4, 2)
8	1	(8, 1)
16		

$\frac{1}{2}, \left(16, \frac{1}{2}\right)$

Interactive Mathematics Tools

This multimedia software provides an interactive lesson that is tied directly to Lesson 11–2. Students will explore linear and quadratic functions and graphs.

Answer to More Examples, Example 1

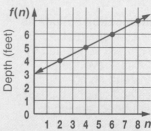

Exercises For graphs to Exercises 7-9, see Solutions Manual.

Independent Practice

Complete each function table. Then graph the function.

7. $f(n) = 3n + 1$

n	f(n)	(n, f(n))
0	1	(0, 1)
1	4	(1, 4)
2	7	(2, 7)
3	10	(3, 10)

8. $f(n) = 6n$

n	f(n)	(n, f(n))
-1	-6	(-1, -6)
1	6	(1, 6)
2.5	15	(2.5, 15)
3.5	21	(3.5, 21)
4	24	(4, 24)

9. $f(n) = \dfrac{16}{n}$

n	f(n)	(n, f(n))
8	2	(8, 2)
2	8	(2, 8)
4	4	(4, 4)
$\frac{8}{3}$	6	$\left(\frac{8}{3}, 6\right)$

10. Choose values for *n* and graph $f(n) = 0.25n + 3$. **See Solutions Manual.**

11. Choose values for *n* and graph $f(n) = n^2 + (-2)$. **See Solutions Manual.**

Mixed Review

12. Geometry Find the circumference of a circle with a radius of 2.7 millimeters. *(Lesson 7-8)* **16.96 mm**

13. Find $f\left(-\dfrac{3}{4}\right)$ if $f(n) = 8n - 1$. *(Lesson 11-1)* **-7**

Problem Solving and Applications

For graph, see Solutions Manual.

14. Critical Thinking Graph the absolute value function $f(n) = |n + 2|$. Describe the shape and range of this graph. **V-shape with vertex at (-2, 0)**

15. Domestic Engineering Suppose a coffee pot heats up at a rate of 8°C per minute. The water put into the pot is at 20°C.

a. Graph the function $f(n) = 8n + 20$ to see how the temperature of the water in the pot rises. **See Solutions Manual.**

b. In a coffee pot, does the temperature continue to rise forever? Explain your answer. Does this affect the domain? **See Solutions Manual.**

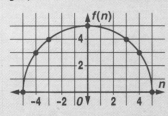

16. Critical Thinking The Post Office rounds the weight of a letter up to the next ounce when figuring the cost of mailing a letter. The first table below shows the postal rates for first-class mail as of March, 1992.

a. Use the information in the table to complete the function tables.

Oz	Cost
1	29¢
2	52¢
3	75¢
4	98¢

n oz	f(n) cents
0.1	29
0.3	29
0.6	29
1.0	29

n oz	f(n) cents
1.1	52
1.5	52
1.9	52
2.0	52

n oz	f(n) cents
2.1	75
2.4	75
2.8	75
3.0	75

n oz	f(n) cents
3.1	98
3.2	98
3.7	98
4.0	98

b. Graph the ordered pairs that can be formed from these function tables. What pattern do you notice? **For graph, see Solutions Manual; stair steps**

c. This type of function is called a *step function*. Why do you think this name was chosen? **looks like steps**

17. Journal Entry Does graphing a function help you better understand the real-life situation that the equation describes? Explain. **See students' work.**

Lesson 11-2 Graphing Functions **427**

Extending the Lesson

Using Cooperative Groups Have students work in small groups to graph the function $f(n) = \sqrt{25 - n^2}$.

Cooperative Learning Activity

No Pain, No Gain **11-2**

Use groups of 4.
Materials: Grid paper

➡ The table on the back of this card shows the number of calories used per minute for certain activities and body weights. Each group member uses the table to write a function that equates the number of minutes spent doing one of the activities shown in the table to the number of calories used for the body weight nearest his or her own. Each group member then copies onto a sheet of paper and completes the function table shown at the right. Finally, each group member graphs the ordered pairs that can be formed from the function table.

Share your work with the other group members.

n minutes	t(n) calories used
1	
15	
30	
45	
60	

Glencoe Mathematics: Applications and Connections, Course 3

Close

Guide students to summarize the lesson by asking the following question. *How can you graph a function?* Make a table of values for *n*. Find *f(n)* for each *n*. Graph each ordered pair *(n, f(n))* and then draw the line or curve suggested by the points.

3 PRACTICE/APPLY

Assignment Guide
Maximum: 7–17
Minimum: 7–11 odd, 12–16

For **Extra Practice,** see p. 610.

Alternate Assessment

Speaking Have students graph the ordered pairs, *(n, f(n))*, below.
(−4, 2), (−2, 4), (−1, 8),
(4, −2), (2, −4), (1, −8)
Ask students to suggest the shape of the graph. Have them verify their guess by graphing more ordered pairs which satisfy $f(n) = \dfrac{-8}{n}$.

Enrichment Masters, p. 96

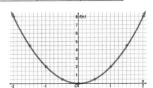

Name _____ Date _____

Enrichment Worksheet 11-2

Graphing Functions

Depending on the scale of a graph, the graphed shape of a function can be made to appear very different from one graph to another.

Given the function $f(n) = 2n^2$, find the values of f(n) for each value in the table. Write the ordered pairs, then draw the graph of the function on each grid.

n	$2n^2$	f(n)	(n, f(n))
-2	$2(-2)^2$	8	(-2, 8)
$-\frac{3}{2}$	$2(-\frac{3}{2})^2$	$4\frac{1}{2}$	$(-\frac{3}{2}, 4\frac{1}{2})$
-1	$2(-1)^2$	2	(-1, 2)
$-\frac{1}{2}$	$2(-\frac{1}{2})^2$	$\frac{1}{2}$	$(-\frac{1}{2}, \frac{1}{2})$
0	$2(0)^2$	0	(0, 0)
$\frac{1}{2}$	$2(\frac{1}{2})^2$	$\frac{1}{2}$	$(\frac{1}{2}, \frac{1}{2})$
1	$2(1)^2$	2	(1, 2)
$\frac{3}{2}$	$2(\frac{3}{2})^2$	$4\frac{1}{2}$	$(\frac{3}{2}, 4\frac{1}{2})$
2	$2(2)^2$	8	(2, 8)

1. Examine each graph of the function $f(n) = 2n^2$. What do you notice about the graphs?
   The graphs are not duplicates of each other.

2. Explain why the graphs are different.
   The graphs are drawn with different scales.

T96
Glencoe Division, Macmillan/McGraw-Hill

427

Lesson Resources
- Study Guide
- Practice Ma
- Enrichment
- Group Activity Card

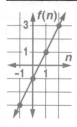
Transpa
the 5-M
teachin

⏱ **5-Minute Check**
(Over L
Comple
for *f(n)*
graph the func

n	f(n)	(n, f(n))
−1	−3	(−1, −3)
0	−1	(0, −1)
1	1	(1, 1)
2	3	(2, 3)

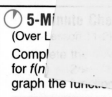

1 FOCUS

Motivating the Lesson

Questioning Write the formula $C = \pi d$ on the chalkboard. Ask students to explain how they can find the circumference of a circle if they know the diameter. Multiply the diameter by π.

2 TEACH

Using Connections Continue the relationship between functions and formulas suggested in the first paragraph of the lesson by completing a table of values for one of the formulas listed below the paragraph.

11-3 Equations with Two Variables

All of the functions we have used in Lessons 11-1 and 11-2 have been written using $f(n)$. Many functions do not use this notation. Instead they use two variables—one represents the input and the other represents the output. You are already familiar with many of these functions.

Changing Celsius to Fahrenheit	$F = \dfrac{9}{5}C + 32$
Rectangle with area of 64 square units	$64 = \ell w$
Parallelogram with perimeter of 36 units	$36 = 2a + 2b$
The distance you can run at 5 miles per hour	$d = 5t$

When you find values for the two variables that make the equation true, these values form an ordered pair that is a solution of the equation. Most equations with two variables have an infinite number of solutions.

In equations with two variables, one variable represents the input and the other represents the output of the function. When x and y are used, x usually represents the input.

Example 1

LOOKBACK

You can review solving equations on page 67.

Find four solutions for $3x - 6 = y$. Write the solutions as a set of ordered pairs.

First make a function table to find the ordered pairs. Use x for n and y for $f(n)$.

Choose any four values for x. Then complete the table.

The set of ordered pairs that are solutions for an equation is called a solution set for the equation.

x	3x − 6	y	(x, y)
-2	3(-2) − 6	-12	(-2, -12)
0	3(0) − 6	-6	(0, -6)
1	3(1) − 6	-3	(1, -3)
5	3(5) − 6	9	(5, 9)

Four solutions for the equation $3x - 6 = y$ are $\{(-2, -12), (0, -6), (1, -3), (5, 9)\}$.

In Example 1, we found four ordered pairs that were solutions for $3x - 6 = y$. There are many more. *Can you name another?*

OPTIONS

Reteaching Activity

Using Cooperative Groups Give each group of students an equation and a range of values from which to choose a value of x. Then have them find four solutions.

Example 2 *Problem Solving*

Number Sense One number is one less than three times another number. Determine which ordered pairs in the set {(-1, -4), (0, 2), $\left(\frac{1}{3}, 1\right)$, (1.5, 3), (2, 5)} are solutions for the two numbers.

First, translate the verbal sentence to an equation. Let x = one number and y = the other number. The equation that describes the problem is $y = 3x - 1$.

Let's test each ordered pair in the equation.

Test (-1, -4)　　$y = 3x - 1$
$-4 \stackrel{?}{=} 3(-1) - 1$　　*Replace y with -4 and x with -1.*
$-4 \stackrel{?}{=} -3 - 1$
$-4 = -4$ ✔　　　(-1, -4) is a solution.

Test (0, 2)

$2 \stackrel{?}{=} 3(0) - 1$

$2 \neq -1$

(0, 2) is not a solution.

Test $\left(\frac{1}{3}, 1\right)$

$1 \stackrel{?}{=} 3\left(\frac{1}{3}\right) - 1$

$1 \neq 0$

$\left(\frac{1}{3}, 1\right)$ is not a solution.

Test (1.5, 3)
$3 \stackrel{?}{=} 3(1.5) - 1$
$3 \neq 3.5$
(1.5, 3) is not a solution.

Test (2, 5)
$5 \stackrel{?}{=} 3(2) - 1$
$5 = 5$ ✔
(2, 5) is a solution.

The ordered pairs (-1, -4) and (2, 5) are solutions.

Checking for Understanding

Communicating Mathematics

Read and study the lesson to answer each question.

1. **Write** a sentence to tell how finding solutions to an equation with two variables is like finding ordered pairs of a function. See margin.

2. **Show** how you could use the method in Example 2 to check the solutions in Example 1. See Solutions Manual.

Guided Practice

3. $\left(\frac{1}{2}, 2\right)$ and (3, -3) are solutions.

3. Determine which ordered pairs in the set {(-2, -1), $\left(\frac{1}{2}, 2\right)$, (0, 1), (3, -3)} are solutions for the equation $y = -2x + 3$.

Copy and complete the table for each equation.

4. $y = x + 1$

x	y
-3	-2
-1	0
1	2
2	3

5. $y = -0.5x$

x	y
-4	2
2	-1
0	0
6	-3

6. $y = 5x - 2$

x	y
$\frac{4}{5}$	-6
2	8
7	1
15	3

7. Find four solutions to $y = x + 3$. Sample answers: (0, 3), (-1, 2), (5, 8), (-4, -1)

Lesson 11-3 Equations with Two Variables　　**429**

More Examples

For Example 1

Find four solutions for $-2x + 5 = y$. Write the solutions as a set of ordered pairs. Sample answer: $\{(-1, 7), (0, 5), (1, 3), (2, 1)\}$

For Example 2

One number is three more than half another number. Determine which ordered pairs in the set $\{(0, 3), (-2, 2), (4, -1), \left(1, 3\frac{1}{2}\right)\}$ are solutions for the two numbers. $(0, 3), (-2, 2), \left(1, 3\frac{1}{2}\right)$

Checking for Understanding

Exercises 1-2 are designed to help you assess students' understanding through reading, writing, speaking, and modeling. You should work through these exercises with your students and then monitor their work on Guided Practice Exercises 3-7.

Team Teaching

An equation with two variables shows the relationship between two quantities. Urge the other teachers on your team to use equations whenever possible to show the relationship between two quantities.

Additional Answer

1. (x, y) is the solution to an equation with two variables; this is also an ordered pair of a function.

429

Watch for students who evaluate expressions incorrectly.

Prevent by having students review evaluating algebraic expressions in Lesson 2-1.

Close

Have students choose an equation with two variables and write three solutions of the equation as a set of ordered pairs.

3 PRACTICE/APPLY

Assignment Guide

Maximum: 8–24

Minimum: 8–23

For **Extra Practice**, see p. 610.

Alternate Assessment

Speaking Write the equation $y = 2x - 1$ on the chalkboard. Name a value for x. Have students name the corresponding value for y and the ordered pair.

Additional Answer

24. $75,000; $75,000–$100,000; $102,500–$125,000; $127,500–$150,000

Enrichment Masters, p. 97

Name _____ Date _____

Enrichment Worksheet 11-3

Equations with two Variables

The distance an object has fallen can be predicted using the equation $S = \sqrt{64d}$, where S = the speed of the object in feet per second and d = the distance in feet.

Example An object has fallen from a tall building. Find the distance the object has fallen when the object reaches a speed of 72 feet per second.

Solution

$S = \sqrt{64d}$

$72 = \sqrt{64d}$ Input the speed of 72 feet per second.

$(72)^2 = (\sqrt{64d})^2$ Square both sides to remove the radical.

$5,184 = 64d$ Solve for d by dividing both sides by 64.

$81 = d$

The object has fallen 81 feet.

Given the equation $S = \sqrt{64d}$, use your calculator to complete the following table. Then graph your answers.

Speed S	64	16	48	96	32	80	96
Distance d	64	4	36	144	16	100	144

T97
Glencoe Division, Macmillan/McGraw-Hill

430

Exercises

Independent Practice

Copy and complete the table for each equation.

8. $y = 0.2x + 7$

x	y
-5	6
0	7
5	8
10	9

9. $y = \dfrac{x}{3} + 4$

x	y
-3	3
3	5
6	6
8	$6\frac{2}{3}$

10. $y = -5x - 1$

x	y
-2	9
-1	4
0	-1
2	-11
4	-21

For sample answers to Exercises 11-16, see Solutions Manual.

Find four solutions of each equation.

11. $y = 2x + 1$ **12.** $y = -x + 1$ **13.** $y = \dfrac{x}{2} + 3$

14. $y = 2.5x + 1$ **15.** $y = -2x + 3$ **16.** $y = 15x - 57$

17. Number Sense *Twice the sum of two numbers is 16.* Determine which ordered pairs from the set $\{(12, 4), (6, 2), (3, 5), (-45, 53)\}$ are solutions for the verbal sentence. **{(6, 2) (3, 5), (-45, 53)}**

Mixed Review

18. Use mental math to find $8(35)$. *(Lesson 1-2)* **280**

19. Express $2.\overline{44}$ as a mixed number in simplest form. *(Lesson 6-7)* **$2\frac{4}{9}$**

20. Choose values for n and graph $f(n) = \dfrac{n}{2} - 1$. *(Lesson 11-2)* **See Solutions Manual.**

Problem Solving and Applications

21. Number Sense Write an equation for each verbal sentence. Find three solutions for each equation. **For answers to Exercises a-c, see Solutions Manual.**
  a. The second number is nine more than the first.
  b. The second number is three more than twice the first.
  c. The sum of two numbers is 0.

22. Critical Thinking The equations $y = 3x - 1$ and $6x - 2y = 2$ have the same solution set. **For answers to Exercises a-b, see Solutions Manual.**
  a. Find four ordered pairs to show this statement is true.
  b. Why does $y = 3x - 1$ seem easier to solve than $6x - 2y = 2$?

23. Biology You can tell the approximate temperature in degrees Fahrenheit by counting the chirps a cricket makes in 15 seconds. The rule is $t = c + 40$. Complete the table to find the temperature for each number of chirps.

chirps in 15 seconds (c)	12	23	31	47	50
temperature in °F (t)	52	63	71	87	90

24. Data Search Refer to page 666. Buyers can usually borrow about $2\frac{1}{2}$ times their annual income for a home mortgage. What amounts could be borrowed at each income level on the graph? **See margin.**

OPTIONS

Extending the Lesson

Using Problem Solving The *Cartesian product* of set A and set B is the set of all possible ordered pairs having the first coordinate from set A and the second from set B. Have students find the Cartesian product of $A = \{0, 1\}$ and $B = \{0, 2\}$. **{(0, 0), (0, 2), (1, 0), (1, 2)}**

Cooperative Learning Activity

Use groups of 2.

Drive Safely 11-3

↓ Suppose that you and your partner are writing a booklet on safe driving practices. For the section on the importance of observing the speed limit, you want to include a table showing the distance in feet it takes a car to stop when traveling at a certain speed on a dry, concrete surface.

→ On a sheet of paper copy the table shown below. Complete the table using the formula $d = 0.042s^2 + 1.1s$, where d is the distance and s is the speed in miles per hour. (Round the distances to the nearest foot.) Write a paragraph that explains the table and tells what it means in terms of driving safely.

Speed (mph)	15	20	25	30	35	40	45	50	55	60	65	70	75
Distance (feet)													

Glencoe Mathematics: Applications and Connections, Course 3

Cooperative Learning

11-4A Graphing Linear Functions

A Preview of Lesson 11-4

Objective
Graph a relationship that can be described by a linear function.

Materials
large rubber band
2 paper clips
ruler
paper cup
marbles

When scientists perform experiments, they often graph the relationships they find and look for a pattern in the points they graph.

Try this

Work in groups of four.

- Punch a small hole in the bottom of the cup. Place one paper clip onto the rubber band. Push the other end of the rubber band through the hole in the bottom of the cup. Attach the other paper clip to act as a hook.

- Have one person hold the suspended cup. Drop one marble into the cup. Record the distance from the base of the paper clip to the bottom of the cup.

- Drop another marble in. Record the distance again.

- Keep dropping marbles in and recording distances until you have 10 sets of distances.

What do you think?

1. Make a table of ordered pairs. Let *x* represent the number of marbles and *y* represent the distance from the paper clip to the bottom of the cup. **For answers to Exercises 1-2, see students' work.**
2. Suppose you were to graph these ordered pairs. Make a guess about the pattern they might show. Then graph the ordered pairs.
3. Was your guess correct? What pattern do the points seem to suggest? **linear pattern (straight line)**

LOOKBACK

You can review scatter plots on page 157.

Extension

4. **Statistics** Make a scatter plot by graphing the data from all groups in your class. See if you can find a linear pattern. In statistics, this line is called the *best-fit line*. The line does not go through all the points. It is used to write an equation to generalize a set of data. **See students' work.**

Mathematics Lab 11-4A Graphing Linear Functions **431**

NCTM Standards: 1–5, 8, 10

Management Tips

For Students Urge students to create the system carefully and then measure the distance as accurately as possible.

For the Overhead Projector
Overhead Manipulative Resources provides appropriate materials for teacher or student demonstration of the activities in this Mathematics Lab.

1 FOCUS

Introducing the Lab

Ask students to describe what happens to a grocery store scale when another orange of the same size is added to an orange already on the scale. The weight readout doubles.

2 TEACH

Using Logical Reasoning Ask students if the pattern they see in their measurements would continue indefinitely. Only to a point; the rubber band will eventually reach its elastic limit.

3 PRACTICE/APPLY

Using Connections Have students read about Robert Hooke (1635–1703), who studied the behavior of elastic materials.

Close

Have students state a relationship between the weight held by a spring and the distance the spring stretches.

OPTIONS

Lab Manual You may wish to make copies of the blackline master on p. 70 of the *Lab Manual* for students to use as a recording sheet.

Lab Manual, p. 70

Name _____ Date _____

Mathematics Lab Worksheet

Use with page 431 _____

Graphing Linear Functions

Try this! Answers will vary.

What do you think?
Answers will vary.

Number of marbles	Distance from base of clip to bottom of cup
1	
2	
3	
4	
5	
6	

1.

x	*y*
1	
2	
3	
4	
5	

Lesson Resources
• Study Guide Master 11-4
• Practice Master 11-4
• Enrichment Master 11-4
• Group Activity Card 11-4

 Transparency 11-4 contains the 5-Minute Check and a teaching aid for this lesson.

⏱ 5-Minute Check
(Over Lesson 11-3)

1. Complete the table for the equation $y = 3x - 4$.

x	y
−4	−16
0	−4
3	5
6	14

2. Find four solutions for the equation $y = -x + 2$. Write the solutions as a set of ordered pairs.
Sample answer: $\{(-1, 3), (0, 2), (1, 1), (2, 0)\}$

---

1 FOCUS

Motivating the Lesson

Situational Problem Sketch the graph at the right, which shows a company's profits increasing at a constant rate over time. Ask students to name other situations that could be represented by such a graph.

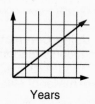

2 TEACH

Using the Mini-Lab Ask students to explain why the graph appears only in the first quadrant. In this situation, neither time nor distance can be negative.

11-4 Graphing Linear Functions

Objective
Graph linear functions by plotting points.

Words to Learn
linear function

How long will the batteries last in this toy? Battery companies spend millions of dollars each year to convince you that their batteries last the longest.

The formula, $d = rt$, where d is the distance, r is the rate, and t is the time, can be used to find how far this toy will go. Suppose this toy travels in a straight line at a rate of 0.5 feet per second. By substituting 0.5 for r, the formula becomes $d = 0.5t$.

Mini-Lab

Draw a graph of all ordered pairs that are solutions of the equation $d = 0.5t$.
Materials: graph paper

• Make a function table to find ten solutions for the equation.

• The solutions include the ordered pairs, (3, 1.5), (5, 2.5), (6, 3), (10, 5), and so on. *(6, 3) means the toy travels 3 feet in 6 seconds.*

t	d	(t, d)
3	1.5	(3, 1.5)
5	2.5	(5, 2.5)
6	3	(6, 3)
10	5	(10, 5)

Technology Activity
You can use a graphing calculator to explore graphs of linear equations in Technology Activity 6 on page 663.

• Graph all the ordered pairs and look for a pattern in the points. *Since all the coordinates are positive, you need only show the first quadrant of the coordinate plane.*

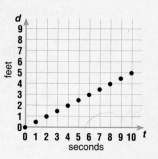

Talk About It

a. What figure is suggested by these ten points? **line**

b. Sketch this figure. **See students' work.**

c. Find four more solutions. Do they lie on the figure you sketched? **yes**

d. What conclusion could you make about other solutions of $d = 0.5t$? **They lie on the line, too.**

OPTIONS

Reteaching Activity

Using Cooperative Groups Have students work in pairs to make a function table showing the number of inches in whole numbers of feet from 1 to 10. Have them list the ordered pairs (ft, in.) and graph the function.

Study Guide Masters, p. 98

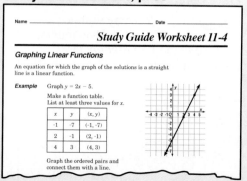

Name _____ Date _____

Study Guide Worksheet 11-4

Graphing Linear Functions

An equation for which the graph of the solutions is a straight line is a linear function.

Example   Graph $y = 2x - 5$.

Make a function table. List at least three values for x.

x	y	(x, y)
−1	−7	(−1, −7)
2	−1	(2, −1)
4	3	(4, 3)

Graph the ordered pairs and connect them with a line.

In the Mini-Lab, you saw that all solutions of the equation suggested a straight line. An equation in which the graphs of the solutions form a line is called a **linear function.**

The graphs of linear functions that interpret real-life activities often lie in the first quadrant. However, most linear functions lie in at least two quadrants of the coordinate plane.

Example

Graph $y = -3x + 10$.

First make a function table.
List at least three values for x.

x	y	(x, y)
-3	19	(-3, 19)
0	10	(0, 10)
3	1	(3, 1)

Graph the ordered pairs.
Connect them with a line.
Put arrows on the ends of the line to show that the line continues indefinitely.

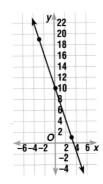

Checking for Understanding

Communicating Mathematics

Read and study the lesson to answer each question.   See margin.

1. **Write** a sentence explaining why the graph of a linear function is a line.

2. **Tell** why you should graph at least three ordered pairs when only two points are needed to draw the line. The third point is for a check.

3. **Show** how you would label the axes to graph the ordered pairs (10, 50), (20, 100), (30, 150), (40, 200). Label the x-axis 0, 10, 20, 30, 40 and label the y-axis 0, 50, 100, 150, 200.

Guided Practice

Copy and complete each function table. Then graph the function. For graphs to Exercises 4-7, see Solutions Manual.

4. $y = 5x$

x	y	(x, y)
-4	-20	(-4, -20)
-1	-5	(-1, -5)
0	0	(0, 0)
2	10	(2, 10)

5. $y = 25 - x$

x	y	(x, y)
-5	30	(-5, 30)
0	25	(0, 25)
5	20	(5, 20)
10	15	(10, 15)

6. Graph $y = 3x + 1$.

7. Graph $y = 15 - 3x$.

Lesson 11-4   Graphing Linear Functions   **433**

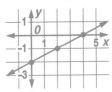
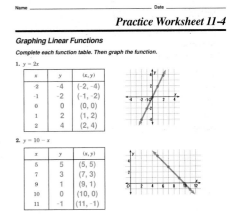

Have students write a sentence or two defining a linear function and how to graph it.

3 PRACTICE/APPLY

Assignment Guide
Maximum: 8–24
Minimum: 9–15 odd, 17–23

For **Extra Practice**, see p. 610.

Alternate Assessment

Speaking Use an overhead projector to show the graph of a line. Name the *x*- or *y*-coordinate of points on the line and have students name the other coordinate.

Enrichment Masters, p. 98

Name _____ Date _____

Enrichment Worksheet 11-4

In Too Deep

The pressure of water is determined by the linear function $P = 62.4d$, where P = water pressure in pounds per square foot and d = depth in feet. The water pressure for the swimming pool can be determined by substituting 3 feet and 8 feet into the linear function $P = 62.4d$.

At 3 feet:
$P = 62.4(3)$
$P = 187.2$ lb/sq ft

At 8 feet:
$P = 62.4(8)$
$P = 499.2$ lb/sq ft

The depth of famous ocean trenches and basins is given in the table. Determine the water pressure by using the linear function $P = 62.4d$.

Name	Location	Depth in ft	Water Pressure in lb/sq ft
Mariana Trench	Pacific Ocean	35,840	2,236,416
Puerto Rico Trench	Atlantic Ocean	28,232	1,761,676.8
Java Trench	Indian Ocean	23,376	1,458,662.4
Eurasia Basin	Arctic Ocean	17,881	1,115,774.4
Ionian Basin	Mediterranean Sea	16,896	1,054,310.4

Using the linear function $P = 62.4d$, find the depths of these underwater locations. Choose the letter of the correct answer from the list. The letters of the correct answers will spell the name of a famous Pacific Ocean trench.

Name	Location	Water Pressure in lb/sq ft	Depth in ft
Tonga Trench	Pacific Ocean	2,211,019.2	Y
Romanche Gap	Atlantic Ocean	1,582,089.6	A
Ob Trench	Indian Ocean	1,407,307.2	P

A. 25,354	C. 27,313	E. 24,721	H. 32,995	K. 35,513
L. 31,998	N. 22,675	P. 22,553	R. 20,325	T. 23,560
U. 24,836	V. 34,995	W. 25,386	Y. 35,433	Z. 26,457

T98
Glencoe Division, Macmillan/McGraw-Hill

434

Exercises

Independent Practice

Graph each function. **For graphs to Exercises 8-16, see Solutions Manual.**

8. $y = 8x$
9. $y = -4x$
10. $y = 5x + 3$
11. $y = 6x + 5$
12. $y = 5x - 10$
13. $y = 1.5x + 2.5$
14. $y = \dfrac{x}{3} + 5$
15. $y = 6 - \dfrac{x}{2}$
16. $y = 75 - 3x$

Mixed Review

17. **Algebra** Write *six more dollars than Atepa has* as an algebraic expression. *(Lesson 2-6)* **A + 6**

18. **Geometry** Make an Escher-like drawing for the pattern shown at the right. Use two rows of three squares as your base. *(Lesson 5-7)* **See Solutions Manual.**

19. **Geometry** Find the area of a triangle whose base **4.375 in²** is 2.5 inches and whose height is 3.5 inches. *(Lesson 7-7)*

20. Find four solutions for $y = \dfrac{x}{3} + 8$. Write the solution set. *(Lesson 11-3)* **Sample answer: {(0, 8), (3, 9), (-3, 7), (-6, 6)}**

Problem Solving and Applications

21. **Weather** Suppose you didn't know the formula for changing temperatures in degrees Celsius to degrees Fahrenheit, but you could remember that the freezing points for water are 0°C and 32°F and the boiling points are 100°C and 212°F.
    a. Write two ordered pairs that relate Celsius and Fahrenheit. **(0, 32) (100, 212)**
    b. Graph the linear function that contains these two points. **See Solutions Manual.**
    c. How could you use this graph to find other equivalents of other Celsius and Fahrenheit temperatures? **Find the coordinates of other points on the graph.**

22. **Physics** When there is a storm, you see the lightning before you hear the thunder. If you see a flash of lightning and hear the thunder 5 seconds later, the lightning is about 1 mile away. If *t* is the time in seconds and *d* is the distance in miles, the function that describes this relationship is $t = 5d$. Graph this function. **See Solutions Manual.**

23. **Critical Thinking** Graph the functions $y = 5x$ and $y = 5x + 5$ on the same coordinate plane. Describe what type of lines these are. **See Solutions Manual; parallel lines.**

24. **Journal Entry** Write a few sentences that tell an advantage to looking at the graph of a function rather than just looking at its table of values. **See students' work.**

434 **Chapter 11** Algebra: Functions and Graphs

OPTIONS

Extending the Lesson

Using Cooperative Groups In the figure at the right, line 1 is steeper than line 2. Have students work in small groups to create a method for measuring the steepness (or slope) of a line.

Cooperative Learning Activity

Number of players: 2
Materials: Grid paper

It's a Hit **11-4**

Copy onto cards the equations shown on the back of this card, one per card. Shuffle the cards and place them face down in a pile. Write the equations on a sheet of paper.

Each partner selects a card and graphs the equation shown. (Remember, to graph a linear function, make a function table to find ordered pairs.) Then partners take turns trying to guess which equation the other partner graphed by calling out ordered pairs. If the ordered pair names a point on the line you graphed, say "Hit." If the ordered pair does not name a point on the line you graphed, say "Miss." Try to be the first to guess which of the equations you wrote on the sheet of paper and the cards your partner graphed. (Hint: You should be able to guess the equation after you have guessed any two points on the line.)

Glencoe Mathematics: Applications and Connections, Course 3

11-5 Graphing Systems of Equations

Objective
Solve systems of linear equations by graphing.

Words to Learn

system of equations

Miss Taggers is the eighth grade girls' basketball coach at Union Middle School. She asked the video club to video tape all the home games. The club needs to rent a camcorder while theirs is being repaired.

Video Town charges a $30 rental fee plus $35 per day. All-Pro Rental Services charges a $45 rental fee and $30 per day for the same camcorder. Which company should they rent from?

You can make a graph of the information to help you answer this question. Let x represent the number of days for each rental. Let y represent the total cost for the rental. An equation can be written for each store.

Video Town: $y = 30 + 35x$ **All-Pro Rental:** $y = 45 + 30x$

Example 1 *Problem Solving*

Smart Shopping Use a graph to determine which store offers the better deal in renting a video camcorder.

Graph both equations on the same coordinate plane. You can use a calculator to quickly find the y-values for each x.

For $x = 4$, in $y = 30 + 35x$: 30 [+] 35 [×] 4 [=] $\mathsf{170}$

Calculator Hint

It is sometimes helpful to use the memory key [STO], or [M+], when evaluating equations with great numbers or decimals. In the equation $4{,}235x + 26 = y$, you can store 4,235 in the memory and use the [RCL] key to enter it instead of keying in all four digits each time.

Video Town $y = 30 + 35x$	
x	y
1	65
2	100
3	135
4	170

All-Pro $y = 45 + 30x$	
x	y
1	75
2	105
3	135
4	165

Now graph each function. Since the y values are great, let each unit on the y-axis equal $10.

The graphs intersect at (3, 135).

Up to a 3-day rental, Video Town is cheaper.

For a 3-day rental, they cost the same.

For more than a 3-day rental, All-Pro is cheaper.

Lesson 11-5 Graphing Systems of Equations **435**

NCTM Standards: 1–4, 7–9, 12

Lesson Resources
- Study Guide Master 11-5
- Practice Master 11-5
- Enrichment Master 11-5
- Evaluation Master, Quiz A, p. 97
- Technology Master, p. 25
- Application Master, p. 11
- Group Activity Card 11-5

Transparency 11-5 contains the 5-Minute Check and a teaching aid for this lesson.

5-Minute Check
(Over Lesson 11-4)
Graph the function
$y = 2x + 3$.

1 FOCUS

Motivating the Lesson

Questioning A car rental agency charges $24 per day to rent a car, plus $0.09 per mile. Ask students to write an algebraic expression for the one-day charge if a renter drives m miles.
$24 + 0.09m$

2 TEACH

Using the Mini-Lab Have students study the two equations, propose a third equation that might graph as a line parallel to the first two graphs and test their proposal. Any equation of the form $y = x + C$ (where C represents a constant) will work.

435

More Examples

For Example 1

Baby Bert weighed 6 pounds at birth and gained 2 pounds per month. Baby Beth weighed 12 pounds at birth and gained 1 pound per month. Letting x represent their age in months and y represent their weight, an equation can be written for each child.

Bert: $y = 6 + 2x$
Beth: $y = 12 + x$

Use a graph to determine when the babies' weights were the same. at 6 mo.

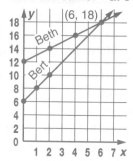

For Example 2

Graph the system of equations $y = -2x + 1$ and $y = 3x - 4$. Then find the solution of the system. $(1, -1)$

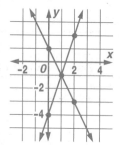

Checking for Understanding

Exercises 1-5 are designed to help you assess students' understanding through reading, writing, speaking, and modeling. You should work through these exercises with your students and then monitor their work on Guided Practice Exercises 6-13.

In Example 1, the graph of the ordered pair (3, 135) is a point on both lines. This means (3, 135) is a solution to both equations. When you find a common solution for two or more equations, you have solved a **system of equations.** The ordered pair for the point where the graphs of the equations meet is the solution for the system of equations. To check a solution for a system, you must check that solution in *each* of the equations of the system.

Example 2

Graph the system of equations $y = 2x + 1$ and $y = -x + 7$. Then find the solution to the system.

Make a table for each equation.

$y = 2x + 1$	
x	y
-1	-1
0	1
3	7

$y = -x + 7$	
x	y
-2	9
0	7
2	5

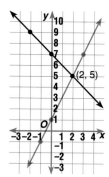

Graph each equation. Locate the point where they intersect.

The lines intersect at the point whose coordinates are (2, 5). So, the solution for the system of equations is (2, 5).

Check your solution in *both* equations.

$y = 2x + 1$
$5 \stackrel{?}{=} 2(2) + 1$ $x = 2, y = 5$
$5 \stackrel{?}{=} 4 + 1$
$5 = 5$ ✔

$y = -x + 7$
$5 \stackrel{?}{=} -(2) + 7$ $x = 2, y = 5$
$5 \stackrel{?}{=} -2 + 7$
$5 = 5$ ✔

The solution checks in both equations.

Mini-Lab

Work with a partner. Graph the system of equations $y = x + 3$ and $y = x - 2$ on the same coordinate plane.
Materials: graph paper

- Make a table for each equation.
- Graph the ordered pairs and draw the lines.

Talk About It
a. What type of lines are these? parallel lines
b. Where do these lines meet? nowhere
c. What can you conclude about the solution to this system of equations? no solution

OPTIONS

Reteaching Activity

Using Cooperative Groups Have students work in pairs, each using a sheet of transparent paper. Students draw and number coordinate axes identically, then secretly choose and graph an equation. Students then hold their sheets together and read the solution of their system of equations.

Study Guide Masters, p. 99

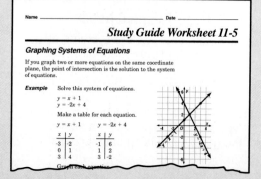

Checking for Understanding

For answers to Exercises 1-4, see margin.

Communicating Mathematics

Read and study the lesson to answer each question.

1. **Tell** what is meant by a system of equations.
2. **Write** a sentence to describe the solutions for a system of equations.
3. **Show** why (1, 3) is the solution for the system $x + y = 4$ and $2x - y = -1$.
4. **Draw** the graphs of a system of equations that has no solution.
5. **Tell** the solution for the system of equations at the right. (-3, -1)

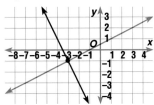

Guided Practice

Lines *a, b, c,* and *d* are graphs of four equations. Use the graphs to find the solution for each system of equations.

6. equations *a* and *b* (6, 2)
7. equations *a* and *c* (-4, -4)
8. equations *a* and *d* (1, -1)
9. equations *b* and *c* (0, 4)
10. equations *b* and *d* (-3, 5)
11. equations *c* and *d* (-1, 2)

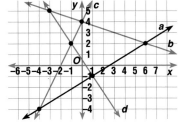

For graphs to Exercises 12-13, see Solutions Manual.

12. Solve the system $y = 3 + x$ and $y = 2x + 5$ by graphing. (-2, 1)
13. Solve the system $y = 3x + 1$ and $y = 3x - 1$ by graphing. no solution

Exercises

Independent Practice

Solve each system of equations by graphing.

For graphs to Exercises 14-19, see Solutions Manual.

14. $y = x - 4$
    $y = -4x + 16$
    (4, 0)

15. $y = x$
    $y = -x + 4$
    (2, 2)

16. $y = 2x$
    $y = -2x + 4$
    (1, 2)

17. $y = 4x - 15$
    $y = x + 3$
    (6, 9)

18. $y = -2x - 6$
    $y = -2x - 3$
    no solution

19. $y = -x - 1$
    $y = -2x + 4$
    (5, -6)

20. Find the solution for the system $y = 4x - 13$ and $y = -\frac{1}{2}x + 5$. (4, 3)
21. Find the solution for the system $2x + y = 5$ and $x - y = 1$. (2, 1)

Lesson 11-5 Graphing Systems of Equations **437**

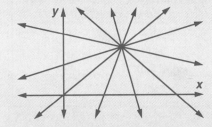
Additional Answers

1. two or more equations
2. The solution is coordinates of the point where the graphs of the equations meet, or there is no solution if the graphs do not meet.
3. $1 + 3 = 4$ and $2(1) - 3 = 2 - 3 = -1$
4. any graphs which are parallel lines

Error Analysis

Watch for students who solve systems of equations incorrectly because they draw graphs carelessly.

Prevent by insisting they use sharpened pencils and straight-edges, and that they check the solution in <u>both</u> equations.

Close

State that the graphs of two equations intersect at the point whose coordinates are (4, 6). Ask students to tell what they can conclude. The values $x = 4$ and $y = 6$ satisfy both equations. The point (4, 6) is the solution for the system of equations.

3 PRACTICE/APPLY

Assignment Guide
Maximum: 14–28
Minimum: 15–21 odd, 22–28
All: Mid-Chapter Review

For **Extra Practice,** see p. 611.

Practice Masters, p. 99

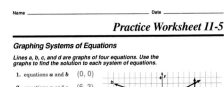

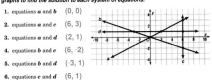
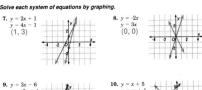
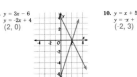
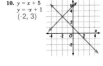

Name _____ Date _____

Practice Worksheet 11-5

Graphing Systems of Equations

Lines a, b, c, and d are graphs of four equations. Use the graphs to find the solution to each system of equations.

1. equations *a* and *b* (0, 0)
2. equations *a* and *c* (6, 3)
3. equations *a* and *d* (2, 1)
4. equations *b* and *c* (6, -2)
5. equations *b* and *d* (-3, 1)
6. equations *c* and *d* (6, 1)

Solve each system of equations by graphing.

7. $y = 2x + 1$
   $y = 4x - 1$
   (1, 3)

8. $y = -2x$
   $y = 3x$
   (0, 0)

9. $y = 3x - 6$
   $y = -2x + 4$
   (2, 0)

10. $y = x + 5$
    $y = -x + 1$
    (-2, 3)

11. Find the solution for the system $y = \frac{2}{3}x + 7$ and $y = 3x + 2$. (2, 8)

12. Find the solution for the system $y - 2x = 1$ and $2x + y = -7$. (-2, -3)

T99
Glencoe Division, Macmillan/McGraw-Hill

437

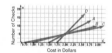
438

---

22. **Statistics** Determine whether a scatter plot of the speed of a car and the stopping distance would show a positive, negative, or no relationship. *(Lesson 4-8)* **positive**

23. Replace ● with >, <, or = in $\frac{5}{6}$ ● $\frac{7}{9}$. *(Lesson 6-10)* **>**

24. Find the best integer estimate for $\sqrt{60}$. Then check your estimate by using a calculator. *(Lesson 8-2)* **about 8**

25. Graph $y = 3x + 1$. *(Lesson 11-4)* **See margin.**

26. **Home Maintenance** Mr. Gill needs some rewiring done in his garage. One electrician he called charges a $35 house call fee plus $25 per hour for labor. A second electrician charges a $20 house call fee plus $30 per hour for labor.

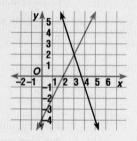

   a. Graph the equations $C = 25t + 35$ and $C = 30t + 20$ to represent the fees charged by each electrician. **See Solutions Manual.**

   b. At what time are their charges equal? **three hours**

   c. Mr. Gill estimates the job will take 16 hours to complete. Which electrician should he use? **first electrician**

27. **Geometry** 27a. See Solutions Manual.   b. (2, 9)

   a. Graph the equations $y = 2x + 5$ and $y = -\frac{1}{2}x + 10$.

   b. What is the solution of this system of equations?

   c. Measure the angles formed by these two lines. What type of lines are they? **perpendicular lines**

28. **Critical Thinking**

   a. Graph $2x + y = 6$ and $4x + 2y = 12$. **See Solutions Manual.**

   b. What do you notice about these two lines? **same line**

   c. What do you think is the solution of this system? **all points on the line (an infinite number of solutions)**

For graphs to Exercises 2 and 4, see Solutions Manual.

11

Assessment: **Mid-Chapter Review**

3. Sample answers: {(0, 4), (3, 5), (−3, 3), (−6, 2)}

1. Make a function table for $f(n) = -2n + 5$. *(Lesson 11-1)* **See margin.**

2. Use the table in Exercise 1 to graph $f(n) = -2n + 5$. *(Lesson 11-2)*

3. Find four solutions of $y = \frac{x}{3} + 4$. *(Lesson 11-3)*

4. Graph $y = 10 - 2x$. *(Lesson 11-4)*

5. What is the solution of the system of equations graphed at the right? *(Lesson 11-5)* **(3, 2)**

OPTIONS

Extending the Lesson

Using Problem Solving Felicia is six years older than Ahmad but eight years less than twice his age. Let x represent Ahmad's age and y represent Felicia's age.

$$y = x + 6$$
$$y = 2x - 8$$

Graph the equations and find Ahmad's and Felicia's ages.
Ahmad is 14, Felicia is 20.

Cooperative Learning Activity

Get It Out of Your System **11-5**

Use groups of 2.
Materials: Spinner, grid paper

▸ Label equal sections of a spinner "I," "II," "III," "IV." These numbers stand for quadrants I through IV.

▸ One partner spins the spinner. Try to be the first to use graphing to find a system of two of the equations shown below whose solution is in the quadrant indicated on the spinner. Taking turns at the spinner, repeat the procedure two more times. (You may not use any equation more than once.) Try to win two out of the three rounds.

$y = -x + 4$	$y = 3 - x$
$y = x - 1$	$y = 2x - 1$
$y = -7x + 8$	$y = -x + 15$
$y = 2x + 8$	$y = 5x - 12$

Glencoe Mathematics: Applications and Connections, Course 3

11-6 Use a Graph

Objective

Solve problems by using a graph.

Mrs. Degas works as a consultant for mass media corporations. She makes recommendations to companies about new products and trends in television technology. During a recent presentation, she used the graph below to show the amount of change in TV gadgets over a 45-year period. How long did it take for color televisions to become a part of almost all the homes in America?

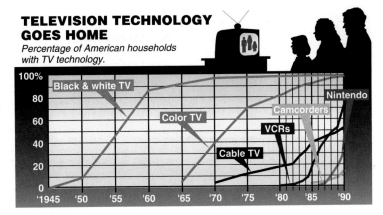

TELEVISION TECHNOLOGY GOES HOME
Percentage of American households with TV technology.

❝ When am I ever going to use this? ❞

Graphs are often used to do comparison shopping. You may use a graph to decide which bank offers the best deal on a credit card or short term loan.

Explore   *What do you know?*
The graph shows the percentage of American households with TV technology.
The graph also shows the beginning years for each type of TV technology.

What do you need to find out?
How long did it take for color television to become a part of almost all American households?

Plan   Find when color television first appeared.
Follow the line from that point to the year where the line nears 100%. The number of years will be the difference of the dates for the two points.

Solve   The line for color television begins at 1965. It continues upward until it levels off near 100% at 1989.
Subtract these two years: 1989 − 1965 = 24
It took 24 years for color TV to become a part of almost all American households.

Lesson 11-6   Problem-Solving Strategy: Use a Graph   **439**

Study Guide Masters, p. 100

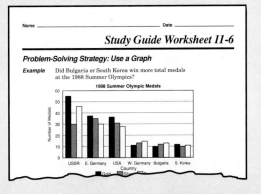

Name _____ Date _____

Study Guide Worksheet 11-6

Problem-Solving Strategy: Use a Graph

Example   Did Bulgaria or South Korea win more total medals at the 1988 Summer Olympics?

1988 Summer Olympic Medals

11-6 Lesson Notes

NCTM Standards: 1–4, 7, 8, 10

Lesson Resources
• Study Guide Master 11-6
• Practice Master 11-6
• Enrichment Master 11-6
• Group Activity Card 11-6

 Transparency 11-6 contains the 5-Minute Check and a teaching aid for this lesson.

🕐 5-Minute Check
(Over Lesson 11-5)
Solve each system of equations by graphing.

1. $y = 3x - 1$
$y = x + 5$ (3, 8)

2. $y = -x + 4$
$y = 2x + 7$ (−1, 5)

3. $y = -4x + 1$
$y = 2x - 5$ (1, −3)

4. $y = 6x - 15$
$y = 5x - 11$ (4, 9)

1 FOCUS

Motivating the Lesson

Questioning   Ask students to estimate the date of each of the following inventions: gasoline-engine automobile; bicycle; FM radio; ballpoint pen; artificial heart.   1889; 1885; 1933; 1838; 1982

2 TEACH

Using Questioning   Vary your questions which involve reading a graph by occasionally requiring students to begin by finding a value on the vertical axis. For example, ask: *In what year did about 50% of American homes have black-and-white television sets?*   about 1956

Checking for Understanding

Exercises 1-2 are designed to help you assess students' understanding through reading, writing, speaking, and modeling. You should work through these exercises with your students and then monitor their work on Guided Practice Exercises 3-5.

Additional Answers

1. Sample answer: Increases do not occur at a regular rate.
2. See below.
5. See below.

Practice Masters, p. 100

Name _____ Date _____

Practice Worksheet 11-6

Problem-Solving Strategy: Use a Graph

Use the graph at the right for Exercises 1-3.

1. Estimate the amount of revenue for AT&T in 1988. Actual is $35.22 billion.
2. During which year did AT&T's revenue decrease? 1987
3. In which year was AT&T's revenue increase greatest? 1991

Use the graph at the right for Exercises 4-6.

4. Estimate the amount of income for AT&T in 1991. Actual is $0.52 billion.
5. What does the 1988 graph point indicate? A loss of $1.67 billion.
6. Compare the graphs for AT&T Revenue and AT&T Income. Does a growth in revenue assure a growth in income? Explain. No. Revenues increase from 1988-1991, but income fluctuates.

Use the graph below for Exercises 7-9.

SHARE OF WORLD MOTOR VEHICLE PRODUCTION, 1950-89

7. Examine the graph for the years 1960-1965. How do the three motor vehicle production lines compare? Explain. Both U.S. and European shares drop, while Japanese share increases.
8. Which motor vehicle producer's rate had the greatest change between 1950 and 1989? Which had the least change? U.S. changed 53.5%; Europe changed 18.7%.
9. In 1989, what share of world motor vehicle production was held by producers that are not represented by lines on the graph? 12.4%

T100
Glencoe Division, Macmillan/McGraw-Hill

A client asks Ashley how many years it took for VCRs to become as popular as cable television. How do you think she should respond?

The point where VCRs became as popular as cable television is the point where their graphs intersect, which is about 1988. Even though cable television existed 10 years before VCRs, use the first year they both existed, 1980. To find how long this took, subtract 1980 from 1988.

$$1988 - 1980 = 8$$

It took about 8 years for VCRs to become as popular as cable television.

Checking for Understanding

Communicating Mathematics

Read and study the lesson to answer each question. For answers to Exercises 1-2, see margin.

1. **Tell** why the graphs of the different technologies are not straight lines.
2. **Write** a sentence to explain how to determine when half of the households had color TV.

Guided Practice

Use the graph at the right for Exercises 3-5.

3. Estimate the amount of money banks lent businesses in April 1991. about $660 billion
4. In which month did business loans see its biggest increase? from March to April
5. Describe the overall trend in bank lending. See margin.

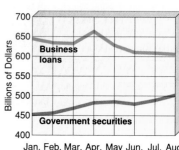

BANKING, 1991

Problem Solving

Practice

Solve using any strategy.

6. Which graph below shows a consistent growth in profits made from carnation sales over the last 14 Valentine's Days? Explain your answer. b., a. declines and c. varies.

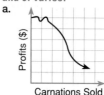
a.

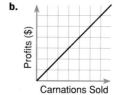
b.

c.

7. A number is doubled and then -19 is added to it. The result is 11. What is the number? 15

OPTIONS

Bell Ringer

Name a non-TV technology which if graphed on the "Wave of Television Gadgetry" graph it would show a general downward trend. Sample answers: rotary telephones, manual typewriters

Additional Answers

2. The scale is in years and most TV gadgets were not even invented until the mid-1900's.
5. There was a decrease in business loans and an increase in government securities.

Strategies

Look for a pattern.
Solve a simpler problem.
Act it out.
Guess and check.
Draw a diagram.
Make a chart.
Work backward.

8. Risa, James, and Corrine each have different stones in their class rings. Their stones are onyx, sapphire, and amethyst. James's stone is not amethyst. Risa wishes hers was onyx. Corrine's stone is blue. What kind of stones does each student have? **See margin.**

Use the graph below for Exercises 9-11.

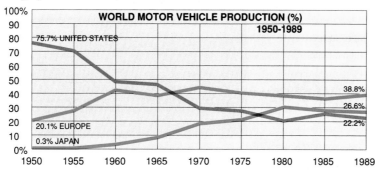

9. During which 5-year period did the United States' percent of motor vehicle production drop most significantly? **1955-1960**

10. Estimate in what year Japanese production of motor vehicles first equaled production in the United States. **1977**

    See margin.

11. Describe the trend in motor vehicle production suggested by this graph.

DATA SEARCH

12. **Data Search** Refer to pages 420 and 421.
    Make a scatter plot of the average size of marine organisms versus the depth of the water in which they are found. **See Solutions Manual.**

Save Planet Earth

Appliances in the Home   Energy specialists agree that we can have a significant impact on the environment if we maintain major appliances like refrigerators, air conditioners, and washing machines to make sure they are kept in peak working condition.

How you can help

- Use the microwave or toaster oven instead of heating up the oven in the stove. Both are more energy-efficient than a conventional oven.
- Don't switch your air conditioner to a colder setting when you turn it on. It won't cool the room any faster, but it will waste energy.
- Since washers use 32 to 59 gallons of water per cycle, you'll save water if you wait until you have a full load of wash to do. If you must do a smaller load, choose the appropriate water level.

Lesson 11-6   Problem-Solving Strategy: Use a Graph   **441**

Extending the Lesson

Save Planet Earth   Ask students to make a list of other ways they could save energy around the home. Emphasize that every contribution, no matter how small, will have an impact on the environment.

Cooperative Learning Activity

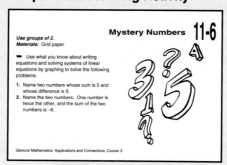

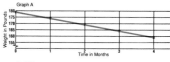

NCTM Standards: 1–4, 7–9, 12

Lesson Resources
• Study Guide Master 11-7
• Practice Master 11-7
• Enrichment Master 11-7
• Interdisciplinary Master, p. 25
• Group Activity Card 11-7

 Transparency 11-7 contains the 5-Minute Check and a teaching aid for this lesson.

⏱ 5-Minute Check
(Over Lesson 11-6)

The graph below represents a person jogging at a constant rate. Copy and then continue the graph, showing the person stopping, then jogging again at a rate slower than before.

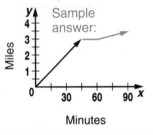

Sample answer:

---

1 FOCUS

Motivating the Lesson

Questioning Ask students to explain why the higher your eye level is above the ground, the farther out to sea you can see.

The diagram shows how the Earth's curvature affects visibility.

---

2 TEACH

Using Connections Many comets travel on paths to and from the sun that are shaped similar to parabolas. The graph shown in Example 3 would be representative of a typical path for such a comet, with the sun located at $\left(0, 9\frac{7}{8}\right)$.

442

11-7 Graphing Quadratic Functions

Objective
Graph quadratic functions.

Words to Learn
quadratic function

 **DID YOU KNOW**

Eyeglasses are worn by 431 of every 1,000 boys and men and 509 of every 1,000 girls and women. By the time they are 45 years old, 883 of every 1,000 Americans wear glasses or contact lenses.

If an oil tanker is 4 miles from shore, will you be able to see it? The answer depends on where you are standing.

In order to see an object d miles from shore, the eyes of a person with 20/20 vision must be at a certain height, $f(d)$. This can be described by the function $f(d) = \frac{2}{3}d^2$. Since the greatest power in this function is 2, it is called a **quadratic function.**

If you wanted to know how high your eye level needs to be for every mile you wanted to see from shore, you could evaluate $f(d)$ for several values of d. A better way is to graph the function. To graph a quadratic function, follow the same steps you used to graph a linear function.

Example 1 *Problem Solving*

Physics Graph $f(d) = \frac{2}{3}d^2$ to find the height your eyes need to be to see an oil tanker 4 miles from shore.

Make a function table.

d	$f(d)$	$(d, f(d))$
1	$\frac{2}{3}(1) \approx 0.7$	$(1, 0.7)$
2	$\frac{2}{3}(2)^2 \approx 2.7$	$(2, 2.7)$
3	$\frac{2}{3}(3)^2 = 6$	$(3, 6)$
4	$\frac{2}{3}(4)^2 \approx 10.7$	$(4, 10.7)$

Graph the ordered pairs.

Notice that the points suggest a curve. Sketch a smooth curve to connect the points. The height needed to see an oil tanker 4 miles from shore is about 11 feet.

OPTIONS

Meeting Needs of Middle School Students

Middle school students want to know you care about them personally. Make a point of finding out about what goes on in their lives outside of class. Mention their achievements in class. Encourage them to share their interests and concerns in class discussions.

 Interactive Mathematics Tools

This multimedia software provides an interactive lesson that is tied directly to Lesson 11-7. Students will use changeable graphs to explore parabolas.

Example 2 *Connection*

Geometry   The area of a square is found by using the formula $A = s^2$. Graph this quadratic function to estimate the area of a square whose side is 3.5 units long.

Make a table. Then graph the ordered pairs.

s	A	(s, A)
1	1	(1, 1)
1.5	2.25	(1.5, 2.25)
2	4	(2, 4)
2.5	6.25	(2.5, 6.25)
3	9	(3, 9)
4	16	(4, 16)

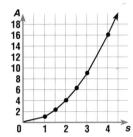

Graph the ordered pairs. Draw a smooth curve to connect the points.

The area of a square with sides 3.5 units long is about 12 square units.

The graphs of many quadratic functions used in real-life applications are only in the first quadrant. Actually, the graph of a quadratic function or equation can be in any quadrant.

Example 3

Graph $y = -2x^2 + 10$.

Make a table. Graph the ordered pairs.

x	$-2x^2 + 10$	y	(x, y)
-2	$-2(-2)^2 + 10$	2	(-2, 2)
-1.5	$-2(-1.5)^2 + 10$	5.5	(-1.5, 5.5)
-1	$-2(-1)^2 + 10$	8	(-1, 8)
0	$-2(0)^2 + 10$	10	(0, 10)
1	$-2(1)^2 + 10$	8	(1, 8)
2	$-2(2)^2 + 10$	2	(2, 2)
2.5	$-2(2.5)^2 + 10$	-2.5	(2.5, -2.5)

The graphs of the ordered pairs suggest a downward curve. Connect the points with a smooth curve.

A graph that has this shape is called a parabola. A parabola can also curve upward, to the left, or to the right.

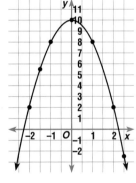

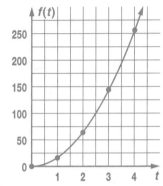
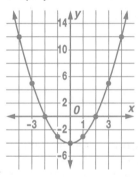

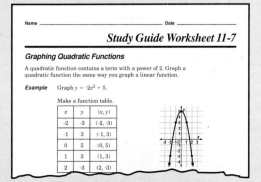

Error Analysis

Watch for students who draw parabolas by connecting ordered pairs with line segments.

Prevent by pointing out that parabolas are continuous curves. Ordered pairs should be connected with smooth curves.

Close

Have students explain the differences between the equations and graphs of linear functions and quadratic functions.

3 PRACTICE/APPLY

Assignment Guide

Maximum: 8–28

Minimum: 9–17 odd, 19–24, 26, 27

For **Extra Practice,** see p. 611.

Alternate Assessment

Writing Have students write an example of a quadratic function and then explain how its graph is related to that of $y = x^2$.

Practice Masters, p. 101

444

Checking for Understanding

Communicating Mathematics

Read and study the lesson to answer each question.

1. **Tell** what the greatest power is in a quadratic function. 2   See Solutions Manual.
2. **Draw** the general shape of the graph of a quadratic function. See Solutions Manual.
3. **Write** a sentence to explain why the graphs in Examples 1 and 2 only used the first quadrant of the coordinate plane. There are no negative numbers in the domain or range.

Guided Practice

Complete each function table. Then graph the function. For graphs to Exercises 4-7, see Solutions Manual.

4. $f(x) = x^2$

x	f(x)	(x, f(x))
-2	4	(-2, 4)
-1	1	(-1, 1)
0	0	(0, 0)
1	1	(1, 1)
2	4	(2, 4)

5. $y = x^2 - 1$

x	y	(x, y)
-2	3	(-2, 3)
-1	0	(-1, 0)
0	-1	(0, -1)
1	0	(1, 0)
2	3	(2, 3)

6. $y = 2x^2 + 1$

x	y	(x, y)
-2	9	(-2, 9)
-1.5	5.5	(-1.5, 5.5)
0	1	(0, 1)
3	19	(3, 19)
4	33	(4, 33)

7. $f(x) = -x^2$

x	f(x)	(x, f(x))
-3	-9	(-3, -9)
-1	-1	(-1, -1)
0	0	(0, 0)
1.5	-2.25	(1.5, -2.25)
2	-4	(2, -4)

Exercises

Independent Practice

Graph each quadratic function. For graphs to Exercises 8-16, see Solutions Manual.

8. $f(n) = 3n^2$
9. $f(n) = 5n^2 + 1$
10. $f(n) = -n^2$
11. $y = -2x^2$
12. $y = \frac{1}{2}x^2 + 2$
13. $y = 1.5x^2 - 1$
14. $y = -1.5x^2 - 1$
15. $f(n) = 10 - n^2$
16. $y = x^2 + x$

17. Determine which ordered pairs from the set $\{(-2, 8), (-1, -7), (0, -4), (1, -1), (2, -8)\}$ are solutions for $y = 3x^2 - 4$. {(-2, 8), (0, -4), (1, -1)}

18. Determine which ordered pairs from the set $\{(-2, 2), (-1.5, -3.75), (2, 0), (3.5, -8.75), (0, 0)\}$ are solutions for $f(x) = -x^2 + x$. {(-1.5, -3.75), (3.5, -8.75), (0, 0)}

Mixed Review

19. Evaluate $6a^2 + b$ if $a = 4$ and $b = 1$. *(Lesson 2-1)* 97
20. Solve $j = -496 \div 16$. *(Lesson 3-7)* -31
21. Evaluate $a + b - c$ if $a = \frac{1}{2}$, $b = 4\frac{3}{5}$, and $c = 1\frac{3}{4}$. *(Lesson 7-2)* $3\frac{7}{20}$
22. Solve the system $y = -x + 5$ and $y = 2x - 4$ by graphing. *(Lesson 11-5)* For graph, see margin; (3,2).

444   **Chapter 11**   Algebra: Functions and Graphs

OPTIONS

Gifted and Talented Needs

Have students investigate graphs of quadratics of the form $y = Ax^2 + C$. Ask them to consider these questions:

1. How does the value of A affect the width of the parabola?
2. How does the value of C affect the position of the parabola on the axes?

Additional Answer

22.

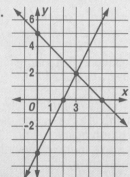

23. Critical Thinking Study your graphs in Exercises 8–16. See margin.
  a. Which graphs turn upward and which turn downward?
  b. Study the quadratic equations. Describe how you can look at the equation and tell if the graph turns upward or downward without graphing it.

24. Physics If a ball is thrown into the air, its height (in feet) at time t (in seconds) is given by the function $h(t) = 96t - 16t^2$. Make a graph of this function for the first six seconds a ball is in the air. See Solutions Manual.

25. Business The Solar Heating Company makes circular thermal blankets for swimming pools. The area of the material in each blanket can be described by the function $f(r) = \pi(r + 0.5)^2$, where r is the radius in feet. Graph this function. See Solutions Manual.

26. Geometry The area of a square can be described by the function $f(s) = s^2$. The perimeter of a square can be described by the function $f(s) = 4s$.
  a. Graph these two functions on the same coordinate plane. See Solutions Manual.
  b. When do the area and the perimeter have the same measure? when $s = 4$

27. Critical Thinking

27a. See Solutions Manual.
b. See margin.
c. It is moved up 2 units.

  a. Graph $y = x^2$, $y = \frac{1}{2}x^2$, and $y = 2x^2$ on the same coordinate plane.
  b. How do the graphs of $y = \frac{1}{2}x^2$ and $y = 2x^2$ differ from the graph of $y = x^2$?
  c. Graph $y = x^2 + 2$. How does it differ from the graph of $y = x^2$?
  d. Make a statement about how numbers multiplied by x^2 or added to x^2 affect the position of the graph. See margin.

GROWING CREDIT CARD USE
(Visa and MasterCard)

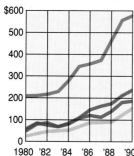

— Total credit card spending
— Bank card spending
— Total credit card debt
— Bank card debt

28. Mathematics and Consumer Credit Read the following paragraphs.

> One type of consumer loan is the installment loan. These loans are repaid in two or more payments and usually include car loans, home equity loans, personal loans, and credit card purchases.
>
> Although credit card spending makes shopping easier, it is also a very expensive way to shop if you pay installments. Finance charges on credit cards generally run higher than those of personal and business loans, and their annual percentage rate can go as high as 23%.

Credit card spending has increased dramatically since 1980.
  a. Use the graph at the left to determine the increase of total credit card spending from 1980 to 1990. almost $400 billion
  b. During what years did bank card spending begin to increase? 1983-1984

Lesson 11-7 Graphing Quadratic Functions **445**

Extending the Lesson

Mathematics and Consumer Credit Ask students to study the graph carefully and make a list of the reasons they think consumer debt has increased so dramatically over this 10-year period. Discuss why consumers use credit cards if the interest rates are so high.

Cooperative Learning Activity

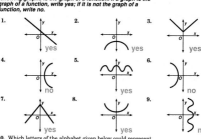

Shed Some Light on Parabolas **11-7**

Number of players: 2
Materials: Spinners, index cards

Copy onto cards the equations shown on the back of this card, one per card. Shuffle the cards and place them face down in a pile. Label equal sections of two spinners "−6," "−4," "−3," "−1," "0," "2," "5," "6." Decide which spinner names x-coordinates and which spinner represents y-coordinates.

If you lay a flashlight down on a sheet of paper, the beam it casts on the paper suggests a parabola. (Try some time.)

One partner spins both spinners and plots the point named on a coordinate grid. The other partner selects the top card from the pile and graphs the quadratic function. If the first partner's point lies within the resulting "beam" (parabola), the partner who graphed the quadratic function gets 1 point. If the point is outside the "beam" (parabola), the partner who plotted the point gets 1 point. Trade roles and repeat the activity. Continue until all the cards have been selected. The partner with the most points wins.

Glencoe Mathematics: Applications and Connections, Course 3

Additional Answers

23. a. upward: 8, 9, 12, 13, 16; downward: 10, 11, 14, 15
  b. If the squared term is positive, then it turns upward. If the squared term is negative, then it turns downward.

27. b. The graph of $y = \frac{1}{2}x^2$ is wider than the graph of $y = x^2$ and the graph of $y = 2x^2$ is narrower than the graph of $y = x^2$.
  d. Graphs of positive numbers less than 1 multiplied by x^2 have a wider graph than $y = x^2$. Graphs of numbers greater than 1 multiplied by x^2 have a narrower graph than $y = x^2$. If the number is negative, the graph opens downward. Graphs of numbers added to x^2 are the graph of $y = x^2$ shifted up for positive numbers or shifted down for negative numbers.

Enrichment Masters, p. 101

Name _____ Date _____

Enrichment Worksheet 11-7

Vertical-Line Test

Not every graph that appears in mathematics and elsewhere is necessarily the graph of a function. A vertical-line test is used to determine if a graph is the graph of a function.

A graph is the graph of a function if any vertical line intersects the graph at no more than one point. For example, the circle at the right is not the graph of a function because a vertical line can intersect the graph at more than one point. However, since any vertical line would intersect the straight line at only one point, the straight line is the graph of a function.

Using the vertical-line test, determine whether each of the following graphs is the graph of a function. If a graph is the graph of a function, write yes; if it is not the graph of a function, write no.

1. yes   2. yes   3. yes
4. no   5. yes   6. no
7. yes   8. yes   9. no

10. Which letters of the alphabet given below could represent the graph of a function? V and W

A B C D E F G H I J K L M
N O P Q R S T U V W X Y Z

T101
Glencoe Division, Macmillan/McGraw-Hill

445

NCTM Standards: 1–5, 7–9, 12

Lesson Resources
- Study Guide Master 11-8
- Practice Master 11-8
- Enrichment Master 11-8
- Group Activity Card 11-8

Transparency 11-8 contains the 5-Minute Check and a teaching aid for this lesson.

🕐 5-Minute Check
(Over Lesson 11-7)

Graph the quadratic function $y = 2 - x^2$.

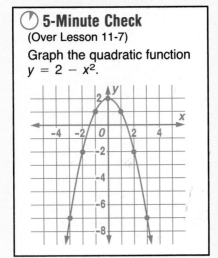

1 FOCUS

Motivating the Lesson

Questioning Sketch a pair of congruent triangles (with different labels for the vertices). Have students name ways in which the triangles are identical and ways they are different. Sample answer: same shape, size, and area; different labels and positions

2 TEACH

Using the Mini-Lab Tell students that although every point on the triangle must be translated as directed, they should concentrate on the vertices. Have them mark the horizontal and vertical path of each translated vertex.

446

Objective
Graph translations on a coordinate plane.

Words to Learn
translation

Most adventure movies today involve the use of special effects. These special effects are an application of *motion geometry*. Filmmakers use computers to move objects to create different illusions. In Chapter 5, you learned that a sliding motion in a certain direction is called a **translation.**

Mini-Lab

◀ **LOOK BACK**

You can review translations on page 202.

Work with a partner.
Materials: graph paper, straightedge, colored pencils

- Graph $\triangle ABC$ with vertices $A(-7, 3)$, $B(-2, 2)$, and $C(-4, 5)$ on a coordinate plane.

- Trace $\triangle ABC$ and cut it out.

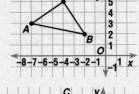

- Place the cutout over $\triangle ABC$. Then translate the cutout 4 units left. Then translate it 3 units down. Trace the cutout with a colored pencil.

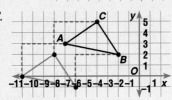

Talk About It

a. Name the three ordered pairs that describe the location of the three vertices after the translation. *A'*(-11, 0), *B'*(-6, -1), *C'*(-8, 2)

b. Compare the coordinates of the vertices of the translation to the coordinates of the original vertices. What do you notice? See margin.

If you think of movements in terms of positive and negative, to the left or down is negative, and to the right or up is positive. If we look at the results from the Mini-Lab, the translation can be written as (-4, -3). If we add -4 to the *x*-coordinate and -3 to the *y*-coordinate of each vertex of the original triangle, the results are the coordinates of the vertices of the translated triangle.

446   **Chapter 11**   Algebra: Functions and Graphs

OPTIONS

Limited English Proficiency

Spend additional time explaining unfamiliar terms in the lesson such as *translation.* Research terms that are different in other cultures. Have the students with limited English proficiency compare how the meanings of the terms are similar and how they are different.

Additional Answer
Mini-Lab

b. The new *x* values are 4 less than the old *x* values, and the new *y* values are 3 less than the old *y* values.

Translation	In words: To translate a point as described by an ordered pair, add the coordinates of the ordered pair to the coordinates of the point.
	Arithmetic **Algebra**
	(2, 3) moved (1, 1) (x, y) moved (a, b)
	becomes (3, 4) becomes $(x + a, y + b)$

Example 1

The vertices of △RST are R(-2, 1), S(1, 3), and T(3, 0). Graph △RST. Then graph the triangle after a translation 5 units right and 2 units up.

The location of a point after being moved is often written using a prime. So the new coordinates of R are written as R', S as S', and T as T'. *R' is read R prime.*

vertex   5 right, 2 up   translation

$R(-2, 1) + (5, 2) \rightarrow R'(3, 3)$
$S(1, 3) + (5, 2) \rightarrow S'(6, 5)$
$T(3, 0) + (5, 2) \rightarrow T'(8, 2)$

The coordinates of the vertices are R'(3, 3), S'(6, 5), and T'(8, 2).

Graph R', S', and T' and draw the triangle.

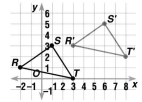

Sometimes you may need to know how a figure was moved. You can use your knowledge of translations and algebra to find the ordered pair that describes the translation.

Example 2 *Connection*

Algebra   Rectangle *RICK* has vertices R(1, 3), I(4, 0), C(3, -1), and K(0, 2). Use an equation to find the ordered pair that describes the translation if R' has coordinates (4, -1). Then graph rectangle R'I'C'K'.

Let *(a, b)* represent the ordered pair for the translation.

We know that $R(1, 3) + (a, b) \rightarrow R'(4, -1)$. Let's write an equation for each coordinate.

x-coordinate   *y-coordinate*
$1 + a = 4$ $3 + b = -1$
$a = 3$ $b = -4$

Lesson 11-8   Geometry: Translations   **447**

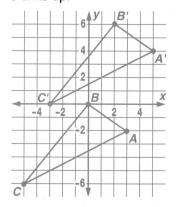
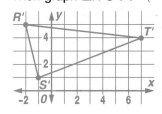

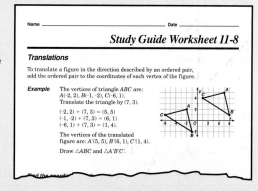
447

Close

Close

Have students write a problem which states the coordinates of the vertices of a figure and a translation. Then have them exchange problems and graph the translated figure.

3 PRACTICE/APPLY

Assignment Guide
Maximum: 8–17
Minimum: 8–17

For **Extra Practice,** see p. 611.

Alternate Assessment

Modeling   Have students place congruent triangles at different positions on a coordinate axes and name ordered pairs that describe the translation from one position to the other.

Additional Answer

2. Each point of a figure is translated 2 units to the left and 3 units up.

Practice Masters, p. 102

Name _____ Date _____

Practice Worksheet 11-8

Translations

Name the coordinates of the ordered pair needed to translate each point A to point B.

1.

2.

(4, -6)   (180, 110)

3. Translate △ABC with vertices A(-1, 4), B(0, 0), and C(2, 3) five units right and two units down. Then graph △A'B'C'.

4. Rectangle QRST has vertices Q(-1, -2), R(-2, 1), S(4, 3), and T(5, 0). Find the coordinates of the vertices of Q'R'S'T' after a translation described by (1, -2). Q'(0, -4), R'(-1, -1), S'(5, 1), T'(6, -2)

5. The coordinates of the vertices of △ABC are A(3, -1), B(0, 2) and C(3, 2). Find the coordinates of the vertices of △A'B'C', which is △ABC translated by (-3, -2). Then graph △ABC and its translation. A'(0, -3), B'(-3, 0), C'(0, -4)

6. Square ABCD has vertex A(-5, -12). When translated, A' has coordinates (6, 10). Describe the translation using an ordered pair. (11, 22)

T102
Glencoe Division, Macmillan/McGraw-Hill

A positive value for *a* means move 3 units right. A negative value for *b* means move 4 units down. The ordered pair for the translation is (3, -4).

Now use (3, -4) to find the coordinates of *I', C'*, and *K'*.

$$I(4, 0) + (3, -4) \rightarrow I'(7, -4)$$
$$C(3, -1) + (3, -4) \rightarrow C'(6, -5)$$
$$K(0, 2) + (3, -4) \rightarrow K'(3, -2)$$

To check your work, graph rectangle *RICK* and rectangle *R'I'C'K'*. Is the translation correct?

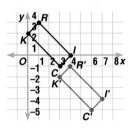

Checking for Understanding

Communicating Mathematics

Read and study the lesson to answer each question.

1. **Tell** what type of movement results from a translation. **slide**
2. **Write** a sentence to describe the translation named by (-2, 3). **See margin.**
3. **Draw** a triangle on a coordinate plane. Show the position of the triangle after a translation named by (-2, 3). **See students' work.**

Guided Practice

Name the coordinates of the ordered pair needed to translate each point *A* to point *B* to complete each scene.

4.

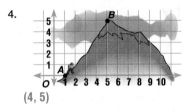

5.

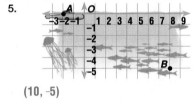

(4, 5)   (10, -5)

6. Translate △*PQR* with vertices *P*(0, 0), *Q*(-3, -4), and *R*(1, 3) 6 units left and 3 units up. Then graph △*P'Q'R'*. **P'(-6, 3), Q'(-9, -1), R'(-5, 6)   See Solutions**
7. Square *WXYZ* has vertices *W*(2, 1), *X*(4, 3), *Y*(2, 5), and *Z*(0, 3). Find the **Manual** coordinates of the vertices of *W'X'Y'Z'* after a translation described by (-1, 3). **W'(1, 4), X'(3, 6), Y'(1, 8), Z'(-1, 6)**

Exercises   For graphs to Exercises 8-9, see Solutions Manual.

Independent Practice

Find the coordinates of the vertices of each figure after the translation described. Then graph the figure and its translation.   **A'(1, 1), B'(4, 6), C'(8, 0)**

8. △*ABC* with vertices *A*(-5, -2), *B*(-2, 3), and *C*(2, -3), translated by (6, 3)
9. rectangle *PQRS* with vertices *P*(-4, 1), *Q*(2, 4), *R*(3, 2), and *S*(-3, -1), translated by (-1, 4) **P'(-5, 5), Q'(1, 8), R'(2, 6), S'(-4, 3)**

OPTIONS

Bell Ringer

The translation of a geometrical figure is described by the ordered pair (3, −5). What ordered pair describes the translation back to the original figure?   (−3, 5)

10. Three vertices of rectangle *RSTU* are *R*(-5, 5), *S*(-1, 5), and *T*(-1, 1).   **See margin.**
    a. Graph the three vertices and find the fourth vertex of the rectangle.
    b. Find the coordinates of the vertices of *R'S'T'U'* after a translation described by (8, -5). Graph *R'S'T'U'*.

11. Triangle *RST* has vertex *R*(-2, 3). When translated, *R'* has coordinates (3, 5). Describe the translation using an ordered pair.   **(5, 2)**

12. Pentagon *ABCDE* has vertices *A*(-2, -1), *B*(0, -1), *C*(1, 1), *D*(-1, 3), and *E*(-3, 1). After a translation, the coordinates of *C'* are (-1, 2).
    a. Describe the translation using an ordered pair.   **(-2, 1)**
    b. Graph pentagon *ABCDE* and pentagon *A'B'C'D'E'*.   **See Solutions Manual.**

Mixed Review

13. **Geometry**   The lengths of the sides of a triangle are 24 feet, 10 feet, and 26 feet. Determine whether the triangle is a right triangle.   *(Lesson 8-5)*   **yes**

14. Graph the quadratic function $y = 2x^2 - 8$.   *(Lesson 11-7)*   **See Solutions Manual.**

Problem Solving and Applications

16a. See margin.
17. back to its original position, since (-3, 5) + (3, -5) → (0, 0)

15. **Make a Model**   Marc misread the row and seat assignment on his theater ticket. Instead of seat (C, 3), he had seat (G, 13).
    a. Use a graph to model this situation.   **See Solutions Manual.**
    b. Tell the number of seats over and back he must move.   **over 4, back 10**

16. **Video Games**   Nintendo® estimates that in 1991, 35% of the homes in the United States will have a Nintendo® game system. Study the graph below.
    a. Name each translation that moves Mario from each year to the next year.
    b. Approximately how many households had Nintendo® in 1991?   **33 million households**
    c. Study the pattern of the increases. Describe how you think Nintendo® could analyze their success.   **See margin.**

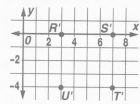

Nintendo in US Households

Households (millions)

'86: 5
'87: 11
'88: 20
'89: 28
'90: 33

17. **Critical Thinking**   A triangle is translated by (3, -5). Then the result is translated by (-3, 5). Without graphing, what is the final position of the triangle? Write an argument to defend your answer.

18. **Portfolio Suggestion**   Review the items in your portfolio. Make a table of contents of the items, noting why each item was chosen. Replace any items that are no longer appropriate.   **See students' work.**

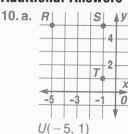

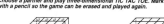
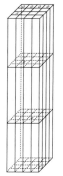

Extending the Lesson

Using Cooperative Groups   Have students brainstorm in small groups to make a list of applications for the translation of figures.   Sample answer: A single shape is repeated through translation to create a wallpaper pattern.

Cooperative Learning Activity

Triangle Demolition Derby   **11-8**

Use groups of 2.
Materials: Index cards, spinners, grid paper, colored pencils

▪ Copy onto cards the vertices of triangles shown on the back of this card. Shuffle the cards and place them face down in a pile. Label equal sections of two spinners "-4," "-3," "-2," "-1," "1," "2," "3," "4." Decide which spinner names *x*-coordinates and which spinner names *y*-coordinates.

▪ Each group member selects a card from the pile and graphs the triangle described on the same coordinate plane. Then, in turn, each group member spins both spinners and uses the resulting ordered pair to translate his or her original figure. If your translation touches or overlaps with another group member's translation, award yourself 1 point.

Repeat the procedure several times, reshuffling the cards when necessary. The group member with the most points wins.

Glencoe Mathematics: Applications and Connections, Course 3

NCTM Standards: 1–5, 7, 8, 12

Management Tips

For Students For students' ease in counting squares, stress the importance of a sharp, straight line connecting $A(1, -3)$ and $B(3, 1)$ when they copy the graph.

For the Overhead Projector *Overhead Manipulative Resources* provides appropriate materials for teacher or student demonstration of the activities in this Mathematics Lab.

Lab Manual You may wish to make copies of the blackline master on p. 71 of the *Lab Manual* for students to use as a recording sheet.

1 FOCUS

Introducing the Lab

Ask students to explain what it means to say that one hillside is steeper than another.

2 TEACH

Using Discussion Point out that for a given line, the ratio $\frac{y \text{ move from } A \text{ to } B}{x \text{ move from } A \text{ to } B}$ remains constant for any two points A and B on the line.

3 PRACTICE/APPLY

Using Logical Reasoning Ask students to find the y move from one point on the line to another if the x move were 12.   24

Close

A line has a slope of $\frac{5}{3}$. Ask students to explain what this means.

Cooperative Learning

11-8B Slope

A Follow-Up of Lesson 11-8

Objective
Use translations and slope to find other solutions of a linear function.

Materials
graph paper
straightedge

Remember that the graphs of linear functions are lines. The steepness of a line is called its **slope.** The slope is also related to the translation that relates any two points on the line.

Try this

- Copy the graph shown at the right.
- Name the ordered pair that describes the translation from A to B. (2, 4)
- The slope of the line is defined as $\frac{y \text{ move from } A \text{ to } B}{x \text{ move from } A \text{ to } B}$. Use the translation to define the slope of this line.

$\frac{4}{2} = 2$

- Use the slope to translate point B to a new location. Label this point C.
- Use the slope to translate point C to a new location. Label this point D.

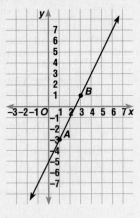

What do you think?

1. What do you notice about points A, B, C, and D? on same line
2. Find the ordered pair that describes the translation from B to A. (-2, -4)
   a. Write this as the slope.
   b. How does this compare to the slope from A to B? same

2a. $\frac{-4}{-2} = 2$

3. The line is the graph of the function $y = 2x - 5$.
   a. Use a table to find two other solutions for the function. Write them as ordered pairs. Sample answer: (4, 3), (0, -5)
   b. Find a translation that relates one ordered pair to the other. (4, 8)
   c. Write the translation as the slope. How does this slope compare with the slope from A to B? $\frac{8}{4} = 2$; same

Extension

One solution and the slope of the graph of a function are given.
a. Use the ordered pair and the slope to graph the function. See Solutions Manual.
b. Name two other solutions. Sample answers given.

4. $(3, 2)$, $\frac{1}{2}$ (5, 3), (7, 4)   5. $(-2, -4)$, $\frac{-4}{3}$ 6. $(0, 0)$, $\frac{2}{1}$
                                          (-5, 0), (1, -8)   (1, 2), (-1, -2)

450   Chapter 11   Algebra: Functions and Graphs

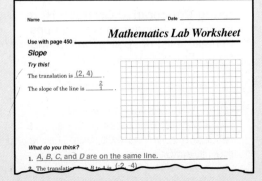

Interactive Mathematics Tools

This multimedia software provides an interactive lesson that is tied directly to Lesson 11-8B. Students will use changeable graphs to explore slopes of lines.

Lab Manual, p. 71

Name _____   Date _____

Mathematics Lab Worksheet

Use with page 450

Slope

Try this!

The translation is (2, 4) .

The slope of the line is $\frac{2}{1}$.

What do you think?

1. *A, B, C,* and *D* are on the same line.

2. The translation from *B* to *A* is (-2, -4).

11-9 Reflections

Objective
Graph reflections on a coordinate plane.

Words to Learn
symmetric
line of symmetry
reflection

Advertisers are always trying to catch your eye with flashy new designs and logos. Most of these new creations are generated using a computer. Graphic designers develop many designs using figures that can be folded into two identical parts. Each part of these designs is **symmetric** to the other part. In Chapter 5, you learned that this fold line is called the **line of symmetry.** One part of the figure is a **reflection** of the other part.

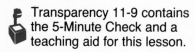

LOOKBACK

You can review reflections and symmetry on pages 192 and 193.

When a figure is reflected on a coordinate plane, every point of the original figure has a corresponding point on the other side of the line of symmetry.

Mini-Lab

Work with a partner.
Materials: graph paper, straightedge, scissors

* Graph △*ABC* with vertices *A*(2, 3), *B*(7, 1), and *C*(5, 5).

* Count how many units point *A* is from the *x*-axis. Then count that many units on the opposite side of the axis. Label this point, *A'*.

* Count how many units *B* and *C* are from the *x*-axis. Use the same method to graph points *B'* and *C'*.

* Draw △*A'B'C'*. Cut out the coordinate plane and fold it along the *x*-axis.

Talk About It

a. What do you notice about the two triangles when you fold the paper? *same triangle*

b. Compare the coordinates of *A* with *A'*, *B* with *B'*, and *C* with *C'*. What pattern do you notice? *same x value, opposite y value*

Lesson 11-9   Geometry Connection: Reflections   **451**

NCTM Standards: 1–5, 7–9, 12

Lesson Resources
* Study Guide Master 11-9
* Practice Master 11-9
* Enrichment Master 11-9
* Lab Manual, p. 72
* Group Activity Card 11-9

Transparency 11-9 contains the 5-Minute Check and a teaching aid for this lesson.

1 FOCUS

Motivating the Lesson

Questioning   Display an ink blot image and its reflection. Ask students to compare and contrast the two figures.

2 TEACH

Using the Mini-Lab   Point out that the *x*-coordinates of vertices *A, B,* and *C* do not change when they are reflected over the *x*-axis. However, their *y*-coordinates do change.

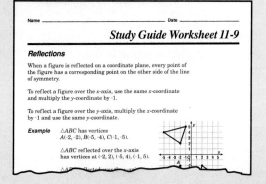

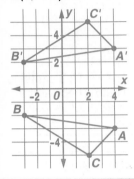
The reflection in the Mini-Lab is a reflection over the x-axis. The x-axis is the line of symmetry. Each point of △A′B′C′ corresponds to a point of △ABC. The coordinates of the points also correspond in a special way.

Reflection over the x-axis	**In words:** To reflect a point over the x-axis, use the same x-coordinate and multiply the y-coordinate by -1.
	Arithmetic (2, 3) becomes (2, -3) **Algebra** (x, y) becomes (x, -y)

What do you suppose happens if you reflect the figure over the y-axis?

Example

Reflect trapezoid PQRS over the y-axis if the vertices are P(4, -2), Q(8, -2), R(8, 4), and S(2, 4).

Count how many units each vertex is from the y-axis and graph the corresponding point on the opposite side of the axis.

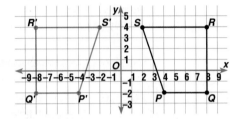

Compare the original coordinates to those of the reflected points. What do you notice?

Reflection over the y-axis	**In words:** To reflect a point over the y-axis, multiply the x-coordinate by -1 and use the same y-coordinate.
	Arithmetic (2, 3) becomes (-2, 3) **Algebra** (x, y) becomes (-x, y)

Checking for Understanding

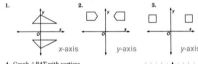

Communicating Mathematics

Read and study the lesson to answer each question. For answers to Exercises 2-3, see margin.

1. **Tell** how the meaning of a mirror reflection relates to a geometric reflection. See Solutions Manual.

2. **Write** a quick way to remember each rule for reflecting a figure over one of the axes.

3. **Draw** the figure at the right. Then draw all of the lines of symmetry.

Name the line of symmetry for each pair of figures.

4.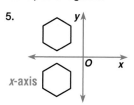
y-axis

5.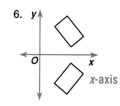
x-axis

6. y

x-axis

7. Graph △*COW* with vertices *C*(3, 3), *O*(0, 0), and *W*(6, -1).
   a. Reflect △*COW* over the *x*-axis. **C'(3, -3), O'(0, 0), W'(6, 1)**
   b. Reflect △*COW* over the *y*-axis. **C'(-3, 3), O'(0, 0), W'(-6, -1)**

Exercises 8a. *R'*(8, 4), *A'*(3, 8), *P'*(2, 2)

Independent Practice

8. Graph △*RAP* with vertices *R*(-8, 4), *A*(-3, 8), and *P*(-2, 2). **See Solutions Manual.**
   a. Find the coordinates of the vertices after a reflection over the *y*-axis.
   b. Graph △*R'A'P'*. **See Solutions Manual.**

9a. *M'*(1, -2), *O'*(0, 0), *N'*(-5, 0), *Y'*(-4, -2)

9. Graph parallelogram *MONY* with vertices *M*(1, 2), *O*(0, 0), *N*(-5, 0), and *Y*(-4, 2). **See Solutions Manual.**
   a. Find the coordinates of the vertices after a reflection over the *x*-axis.
   b. Graph parallelogram *M'O'N'Y'*. **See Solutions Manual.**

10a-b. See Solutions Manual.

10. Graph rectangle *EASY* with vertices *E*(-3, 3), *A*(3, 3), *S*(3, -3), and *Y*(-3, -3).
    a. Reflect rectangle *EASY* over the *x*-axis.
    b. On the same coordinate plane, reflect rectangle *EASY* over the *y*-axis.
    c. Write a statement comparing your three graphs. **All three graphs coincide.**

Mixed Review

11. Solve $\frac{2}{n} = \frac{7}{98}$. *(Lesson 9-2)* **28**

12. Translate △*ABC* 2 units right and 3 units up if its vertices are *A*(-3, -2), *B*(-1, 1), and *C*(2, -1). Graph △*ABC* and △*A'B'C'*. *(Lesson 11-8)* **For graph, see Solutions Manual; A'(-1, 1), B'(1, 4), C'(4, 2)**

Problem Solving and Applications

13. **Critical Thinking** An isosceles triangle has one vertex at (0, 6) and another at (-3, 0). Use reflections to graph two different triangles that meet these requirements. **See Solutions Manual.**

14. **Algebra** Quadratic functions have vertical lines of symmetry.
    a. Complete the table at the right for the function $f(n) = n^2$.
    b. Graph these ordered pairs. Then use symmetry to complete the other half of the graph. **See Solutions Manual.**

n	f(n)
0	0
1	1
2	4
3	9
4	16

Lesson 11-9 Geometry Connection: Reflections **453**

Extending the Lesson

Using Connections Ask students to find examples of company logos with one or more lines of symmetry. Have students copy the logos, draw the lines of symmetry, and display the drawings on the bulletin board.

Cooperative Learning Activity

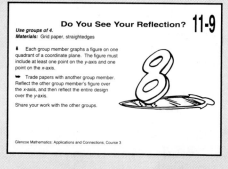

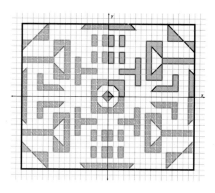

NCTM Standards: 1–5, 7–9, 12

Lesson Resources
- Study Guide Master 11-10
- Practice Master 11-10
- Enrichment Master 11-10
- Evaluation Master, Quiz B, p. 97
- Multicultural Activity, p. 11
- Group Activity Card 11-10

 Transparency 11-10 contains the 5-Minute Check and a teaching aid for this lesson.

🕐 5-Minute Check
(Over Lesson 11-9)

△**ABC** has vertices **A(−3, 1), B(0, −2),** and **C(5, −1). Find the coordinates of the vertices after a reflection over the given axis.**

1. *x*-axis   A′(−3, −1), B′(0, 2), C′(5, 1)
2. *y*-axis   A′(3, 1), B′(0, −2), C′(−5, −1)

1 FOCUS

Motivating the Lesson

Questioning An L-shaped piece of cardboard is attached to the minute hand of a clock as shown in the diagram at the right. Ask students to sketch the positon of the L at 15, 30, and 45 minutes after the hour.

2 TEACH

Using the Mini-Lab This lab generates a great deal of information. Stress the importance of a carefully planned and organized approach to data recording.

11-10 **Rotations**

Objective
Graph rotations on a coordinate plane.

Words to Learn
rotation

LOOKBACK
You can review rotations on page 203.

The first windmills were found in A.D. 644 in Persia (now known as Iran) and used to grind grain. In A.D. 1220, Ghenghis Kahn captured Persian mill builders to take them to China to build windmills for irrigating fields. The most familiar windmills are those in the Netherlands. These mills were used to pump water from the soggy lands uncovered after the dikes were built.

The air flowing through the vanes of the windmills creates a movement called **rotation.** In Chapter 5, you learned that rotations move a figure about a central point.

Mini-Lab

Work in groups of three.
Materials: protractor

- The graph models the vanes of a Dutch windmill. Record the coordinates of each lettered point.

- Measure ∠*COG*, ∠*GOK*, ∠*KOP*, and ∠*POC*. Record your measurements.

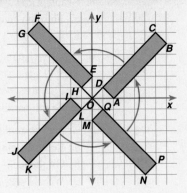

- As the windmill turns, each point of one vane will occupy the previous location of the corresponding point on another vane. Make a list of the corresponding vertices of the four vanes.

Talk About It
a. What shape is each vane of the windmill? **rectangle**
b. Which direction is this windmill turning? **counterclockwise**
c. How do the coordinates of the vertices of vane *ABCD* compare with those of vane *EFGH*? **See margin.**
d. How many degrees did the vane rotate to move from point *C* to point *G*? **90°**
e. Compare the coordinates of the vertices of vane *ABCD* with those of vane *IJKL*. **See margin.**
f. How many degrees did the vane rotate to move from point *C* to point *K*? **180°**

OPTIONS

Multicultural Education
Cultural groups use a wide variety of different designs in their art. They base most of their designs, however, on a very small number of symmetries. The Anasazi, Native Americans who inhabited the American Southwest until about 1300 A.D., based 50 percent of their designs on 180° rotational symmetry.

Additional Answers
Mini-Lab

c. They are switched and then the *x*-coordinate of each point is multiplied by −1.
e. Both coordinates of each point are multiplied by −1.

As you discovered in the Mini-Lab, the coordinates of rotated points are related for every 90° they turn.

Rotation of 90° counter-clockwise	**In words:** To rotate a figure 90° counterclockwise, switch the coordinates of each point and then multiply the first coordinate by -1. **Arithmetic** **Algebra** $A(2, 3) \rightarrow A'(-3, 2)$ $A(x, y) \rightarrow A'(-y, x)$
Rotation of 180°	**In words:** To rotate a figure 180°, multiply both coordinates of each point by -1. **Arithmetic** **Algebra** $A(2, 3) \rightarrow A'(-2, -3)$ $A(x, y) \rightarrow A'(-x, -y)$

Examples

1 Triangle *ABC* has vertices *A*(1, 3), *B*(6, 7), and *C*(9, 1). Graph △*ABC* and rotate it 180°. Then graph △*A'B'C'*.

To rotate △*ABC* 180°, multiply each coordinate by -1.

$A(1, 3) \rightarrow A'(-1, -3)$
$B(6, 7) \rightarrow B'(-6, -7)$
$C(9, 1) \rightarrow C'(-9, -1)$

Now graph the ordered pairs for points *A'*, *B'*, and *C'* and draw △*A'B'C'*.

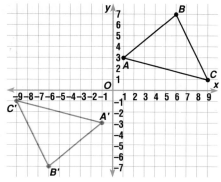

Estimation Hint
• • • • • • • • • • •
You can mentally check your figure by laying the corner of another piece of paper at the origin. Move it until *A* and *A'* lie on the edges of the paper. If you can't do this, you've probably made a mistake.

2 Use △*ABC* from Example 1. Rotate it 90° counterclockwise. Then graph △*A'B'C'*.

To rotate △*ABC* 90° counterclockwise, switch the coordinates and multiply the first by -1.

$A(1, 3) \rightarrow (3, 1) \rightarrow A'(-3, 1)$
$B(6, 7) \rightarrow (7, 6) \rightarrow B'(-7, 6)$
$C(9, 1) \rightarrow (1, 9) \rightarrow C'(-1, 9)$

Now graph the ordered pairs for points *A'*, *B'*, and *C'* and draw △*A'B'C'*.

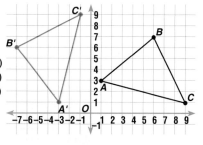

Lesson 11-10   Geometry Connection: Rotations   **455**

More Examples

For Example 1

Triangle *MNP* has vertices *M*(−2, −3), *N*(−3, 1), and *P*(−1, −1). Graph △*MNP* and rotate it 180°. Then graph △*M'N'P'*.

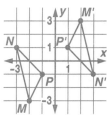

For Example 2

Use △*MNP* above. Rotate it 90° counterclockwise. Then graph △*M'N'P'*.

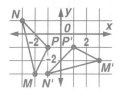

Checking for Understanding

Exercises 1-3 are designed to help you assess students' understanding through reading, writing, speaking, and modeling. You should work through these exercises with your students and then monitor their work on Guided Practice Exercises 4-8.

Close

Have students write a paragraph explaining the differences between translating a point, reflecting it over an axis, and rotating it through an angle.

Reteaching Activity

Using Manipulatives   Attach the right angle of a 45°–45° right triangle to the origin of a coordinate system. Label one of the other vertices *P* and the third vertex *P'*. Have students place *P* at any point and read the coordinates of *P'*, the 90° counterclockwise rotation image of *P*.

Study Guide Masters, p. 104

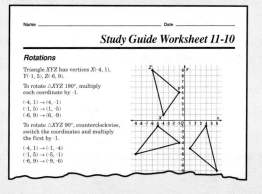

3 PRACTICE/APPLY

Practice Masters, p. 104

Name _____ Date _____

Practice Worksheet 11-10

Rotations

Determine whether each pair of figures represents a rotation. Write yes or no.

1. yes 2. no 3. yes

4. Graph rectangle *WORK* with vertices $W(1, 3)$, $O(4, 6)$, $R(6, 4)$, and $K(3, 1)$.
   a. Rotate the rectangle 90° counterclockwise.
   b. Rotate the rectangle 180°.

5. Examine the figure at the right.
   a. Does the figure have rotational symmetry? yes
   b. If so, find the degree turns that show this symmetry.
      60°, 120°, 180°, 240°, 300°, 360°

6. Quadrilateral *NEAL* has vertices $N(3, 5)$, $E(4, 4)$, $A(3, 2)$ and $L(1, 3)$.
   a. Graph quadrilateral *NEAL* and its 90° counterclockwise rotation *N'E'A'L'*.
   b. Rotate *N'E'A'L'* 90° counterclockwise.
   c. Rotate quadrilateral *NEAL* 180°.
      Explain the result.
      Rotation in c is the same as rotation in a followed by rotation in b.
      $2 \times 90° = 180°$

7. A triangle is rotated 90° counterclockwise. The coordinates of the vertices of the rotated triangle are $(3, 2)$, $(-1, 3)$, and $(2, -3)$. What are the coordinates of the original triangle?
   $(2, -3)$, $(3, 1)$, $(-3, -2)$

T104
Glencoe Division, Macmillan/McGraw-Hill

456

LOOKBACK

You can review rotational symmetry on page 193.

In Chapter 5, you learned that some figures have line symmetry. Other figures have rotational symmetry. That is, if you turn them around their center point, there is at least one other position in which the figure looks the same as it did originally.

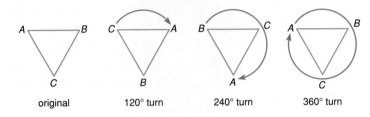

| original | 120° turn | 240° turn | 360° turn |

While the vertices are in different locations, the figure itself looks the same after each turn. An equilateral triangle has rotational symmetry at clockwise turns of 120°, 240°, and 360°.

Checking for Understanding

Communicating Mathematics

Read and study the lesson to answer each question.

1. **Tell** three examples of rotating objects you see every day. See margin.

2. **Tell** what quadrant a triangle will be in if it is rotated 180° from its location in the second quadrant. fourth quadrant

3. **Show** how you could use the 90° rotation to find a 180° rotation if you forgot the rule for 180°. Do the 90° rotation twice.

Guided Practice

Determine whether each pair of figures represents a rotation. Write *yes* or *no*.

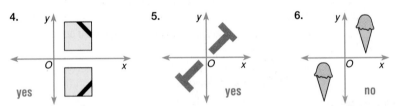

4. yes 5. yes 6. no

For answers to 7a-b, see Solutions Manual.

7. Graph rectangle *HAIR* with vertices $H(-3, 4)$, $A(-5, 4)$, $I(-5, -2)$, and $R(-3, -2)$.
   a. Rotate the rectangle 90° counterclockwise, and graph *H'A'I'R'*.
   b. Rotate the rectangle 180°, and graph *H'A'I'R'*.

8. An equilateral triangle has rotational symmetry. What other figures can you draw that have sides with equal length and rotational symmetry? Sample answers: square, hexagon

---

OPTIONS

Bell Ringer

Find the coordinates of the point $A(1, 2)$, after a 270° clockwise rotation. $(-2, 1)$

Exercises

Independent Practice

9. Triangle *RST* has vertices *R*(-1, -3), *S*(-6, -9), and *T*(-8, -5).

   a. Graph △*RST*. **See Solutions Manual.**

   b. Find the coordinates of the vertices of △*R'S'T'* after a 90° counterclockwise rotation. ***R'*(3, -1), *S'*(9, -6), *T'*(5, -8)**

   c. Graph △*R'S'T'*. **See Solutions Manual.**

10. Trapezoid *ABCD* has vertices *A*(3, -2), *B*(7, -2), *C*(9, -7), and *D*(1, -7).

    a. Graph trapezoid *ABCD* and its 180° rotation. **See Solutions Manual.**

    b. Rotate trapezoid *A'B'C'D'* 180°. What is the result? **trapezoid *ABCD***

11. A triangle is rotated 180°. The coordinates of the vertices of the rotated triangle are (4, -1), (1, -4), and (5, 8). What are the coordinates of the original triangle? **(-4, 1), (-1, 4), (-5, -8)**

12. Copy the figure at the right.

    a. Does this figure have rotational symmetry? **yes**

    b. If so, find the degree turns that show this symmetry. **72°, 144°, 216°, 288°, 360°**

Mixed Review

13. Solve *s* − 34 = 71. Check your solution. *(Lesson 2-3)* **105**

14. Find the GCF of 84 and 36. *(Lesson 6-4)* **12**

15. Graph square *BART* with vertices *T*(1, -1), *R*(3, -1), *A*(3, -3), and *B*(1, -3). *(Lesson 11-9)*

    a. Reflect square *BART* over the *x*-axis. **For answers to a-b,**

    b. Reflect square *BART* over the *y*-axis. **see Solutions Manual.**

Problem Solving and Applications

16. **Geometry** Graph pentagon *EIGHT* with vertices *E*(-6, 5), *I*(-2, 5), *G*(-2, 2), *H*(-4, 1), and *T*(-6, 2). **See Solutions Manual for a-c.**

    a. Reflect *EIGHT* over the *x*-axis. Then reflect *E'I'G'H'T'* over the *y*-axis.

    b. Graph *EIGHT* on another coordinate plane. Rotate it 180°.

    c. Write a sentence comparing your two graphs.

17. **Entertainment** In a standard deck of playing cards, the 10 of hearts has rotational symmetry. What other cards have rotational symmetry? **See margin.**

18. **Critical Thinking** Find a rule for rotating a figure 90° in a clockwise direction. **See margin.**

 19. **Journal Entry** Write a few sentences telling how you think rotations and reflections might be used in computer design. Include specific examples. **See students' work.**

Lesson 11-10 Geometry Connection: Rotations **457**

Enrichment Masters, p. 104

Name _____ Date _____

Enrichment Worksheet 11-10

Rotations

Rotations occur when a figure or object (like the blade of a fan) moves about a pivot, or central point. Rotations can occur in clockwise or counterclockwise directions.

Using the origin (0, 0) as the pivot point, rotate the pattern in Quadrant I 90° counterclockwise. After this rotation has been completed, rotate the pattern 90° counterclockwise into Quadrant III, then rotate the pattern 90° counterclockwise into Quadrant IV.

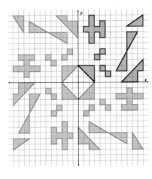

T104
Glencoe Division, Macmillan/McGraw-Hill

Extending the Lesson

Using Connections Ask students to find out why a time-exposure of the night sky taken through a telescope pointed directly at the North Star produces a photo showing rotation arcs of stars, centered at the North Star. The arcs are caused by the rotation of Earth about an axis pointed at the North Star.

Cooperative Learning Activity

Rotation Sensation 11-10

Number of players: 4
Materials: Index cards, spinner, grid paper

◆ Label equal sections of a spinner "I," "II," "III," "IV."

➥ Each group member graphs a triangle in a different quadrant of a different coordinate plane. Then one group member spins the spinner. The spinner indicates the quadrant into which a player can "move" a triangle by rotating it 90° counterclockwise. (For example, if the spinner lands on "I" in the first round, the group member who graphed a triangle in quadrant IV rotates his or her figure 90° counterclockwise. The other players cannot move.)

Continue, taking turns at the spinner, until one group member has graphed a triangle in every quadrant using 90° counterclockwise rotations.

Glencoe Mathematics: Applications and Connections, Course 3

The Chapter Study Guide and Review begins with a section on Communicating Mathematics. This includes questions that review the new terms and concepts that were introduced in the chapter.

Then, the Skills and Concepts presented in the chapter are reviewed using a side-by-side format. Encourage students to refer to the Objectives and Examples on the left as they complete the Review Exercises on the right.

The Chapter Study Guide and Review ends with problems that review Applications and Problem Solving.

Additional Answer

8. Substitute the values into the original equation and check to see that a true sentence results.

Chapter

11 Study Guide and Review

Communicating Mathematics

Choose a word from the list at the right to correctly complete each sentence.

1. The __?__ is the set of input values of a function. domain
2. The __?__ is the set of output values of a function. range
3. The set of ordered pairs that are solutions for an equation is called a __?__ for the equation. solution set
4. A function in which the graphs of the solutions form a line is called a __?__ function. linear
5. A function in which the greatest power is two is called a __?__ function. quadratic
6. The movement of a figure 2 units right and 4 units down is a __?__. translation
7. $A(2, 1) \rightarrow A'(-2, 1)$ describes a __?__ over the y-axis. reflection

| linear |
| quadratic |
| solution set |
| reflection |
| translation |
| domain |
| range |

8. Tell how to determine if an ordered pair is a solution of a function. See margin.
9. Describe how to rotate a triangle 90° counterclockwise. Switch the coordinates of each point and multiply the first one by -1.

Self Assessment

Objectives and Examples	*Review Exercises*
Upon completing this chapter, you should be able to:	*Use these exercises to review and prepare for the chapter test.*

- complete function tables *(Lesson 11-1)*

  Find $f(4)$ if $f(n) = 3n - 1$.

  $f(4) = 3(4) - 1$
  $f(4) = 12 - 1$
  $f(4) = 11$

Copy and complete the function table.

10. $f(n) = 2 - 4n$

n	$2 - 4n$	$f(n)$
-1	$2 - 4(-1)$	6
0	$2 - 4(0)$	2
2	$2 - 4(2)$	-6

- graph functions using function tables *(Lesson 11-2)*

  Graph $f(n) = n + 1$.

n	$f(n)$	$(n, f(n))$
-2	-1	(-2, -1)
0	1	(0, 1)
2	3	(2, 3)

Make a function table for each function. Then graph the function.

11. $f(n) = 4n + 1$
12. $f(n) = \frac{1}{2}n - 2$
13. $f(n) = -3n$

For graphs to Exercises 11-13, see Solutions Manual.

Objectives and Examples

- find solutions of equations with two variables *(Lesson 11-3)*

  Find a solution of $y = 6x + 8$.

  Let $x = 2$. Then $y = 6(2) + 8 = 20$.
  A solution of $y = 6x + 8$ is $(2, 20)$.

- graph linear functions by plotting points *(Lesson 11-4)*

  Make a function table and choose at least three values for x. Then graph the ordered pairs and connect them with a line.

- solve systems of linear equations by graphing *(Lesson 11-5)*

  The coordinates of the point where the graphs of the equations intersect is the solution to the system of equations.

- graph quadratic functions by plotting points *(Lesson 11-7)*

  Make a function table. Then graph the ordered pairs and draw a smooth curve connecting the points.

- graph translations on a coordinate plane *(Lesson 11-8)*

  To translate a point as described by the ordered pair *(a, b)*, add *a* to the *x*-coordinate and add *b* to the *y*-coordinate.

  For graphs to Exercises 27-28, see Solutions Manual.

- graph reflections on a coordinate plane *(Lesson 11-9)*

  To reflect a point over the *x*-axis, use the same *x*-coordinate and multiply the *y*-coordinate by -1.

  $$A(1, 2) \quad \rightarrow \quad A'(1, -2)$$

  To reflect a point over the *y*-axis, multiply the *x*-coordinate by -1 and use the same *y*-coordinate.

  $$B(-2, 3) \quad \rightarrow \quad B'(2, 3)$$

Review Exercises

Find four solutions of each equation.

14. $y = -1.5x - 1$ For answers to Exercises 14-16, see margin.
15. $y = x + 4$
16. $y = -5x + 7$

Graph each linear function.

17. $y = -6x$
18. $y = 2x + 7$ For graphs to Exercises 17-20, see Solutions Manual.
19. $y = -3.5x + 1.5$
20. $y = \dfrac{x}{2} - 1$

Solve each system of equations by graphing.

21. $y = 6x$
    $y = x + 5$ (1, 6)

22. $y = 4x - 6$
    $y = x + 3$ (3, 6)

Graph each quadratic function.

23. $y = \dfrac{1}{2}x^2 + 3$
24. $y = x^2 - 1$ For graphs to Exercises 23-26, see Solutions Manual.
25. $f(n) = 4 - n^2$
26. $y = -1.25x^2 - 1.5$

Graph each figure and its translation.

27. rectangle *RSTU* with vertices $R(-4, 1)$, $S(-2, 1)$, $T(-2, -1)$, and $U(-4, -1)$, translated by $(3, 4)$
28. $\triangle DEF$ with vertices $D(1, 1)$, $E(2, 4)$, and $F(4, 2)$, translated by $(-5, -3)$

29. Graph rectangle *ABCD* with vertices $A(2, 5)$, $B(6, 5)$, $C(6, 3)$, and $D(2, 3)$ and its reflection over the *x*-axis.

30. Graph $\triangle CAR$ with vertices $C(-4, -5)$, $A(-3, -2)$, and $R(-5, -3)$ and its reflection over the *y*-axis.
    $C'(4, -5)$, $A'(3, -2)$, $R'(5, -3)$
    For graphs in Exercises 29-30, see Solutions Manual.

29. $A'(2, -5)$, $B'(6, -5)$, $C'(6, -3)$, $D'(2, -3)$

Additional Answers

14. Sample answer: $\{(0, -1), (2, -4), (-2, 2), (-4, 5)\}$
15. Sample answer: $\{(0, 4), (1, 5), (-1, 3), (2, 6)\}$
16. Sample answer: $\{(0, 7), (1, 2), (2, -3), (-1, 12)\}$

You may wish to use a Chapter Test from the Evaluation Masters booklet as an additional chapter review. The two free-response forms are shown below. One of the two multiple-choice forms is shown on the next page.

Evaluation Masters, pp. 95–96

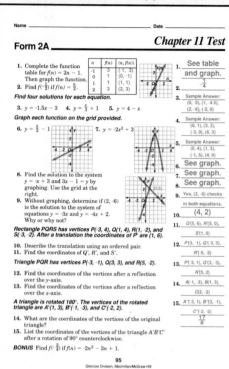

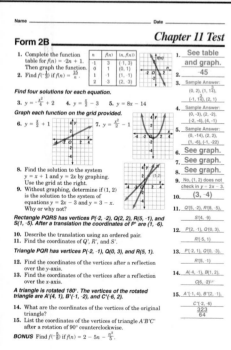

Objectives and Examples

- graph rotations on a coordinate plane
  (Lesson 11-10)

  To rotate a point 90° counterclockwise, switch the coordinates and multiply the first coordinate by -1.
  $$C(3, 4) \rightarrow C'(-4, 3)$$

  To rotate a point 180°, multiply both coordinates by -1.
  $$D(-2, 4) \rightarrow D'(2, -4)$$

Review Exercises

31. Graph square *LATE* with vertices $L(1, 4)$, $A(4, 7)$, $T(7, 4)$, and $E(4, 1)$ and its rotation of 90° counterclockwise.

32. Graph $\triangle XYZ$ with vertices $X(3, 1)$, $Y(5, -2)$, and $Z(2, -4)$ and its 180° rotation. $X'(-3, -1)$, $Y'(-5, 2)$, $Z'(-2, 4)$

31. $L'(-4, 1)$, $A'(-7, 4)$, $T'(-4, 7)$, $E'(-1, 4)$

For graphs to Exercises 31-32, see Solutions Manual.

33. It will never occur since the graphs of their profit equations never meet.

Applications and Problem Solving

33. **Business** One company's profits can be described by the equation $y = 300x - 400$. Another company's profits can be described by the equation $y = 300x + 100$. They plan to merge when their profits are the same amount. At what point will that occur? Explain your answer. *(Lessons 11-5 and 11-6)*

34. **Geometry** Find the base and height of three different triangles whose area is 12 square inches. Write the solutions as ordered pairs. *(Lesson 11-3)*
    Sample answer: (2, 12), (3, 8), (4, 6)

Curriculum Connection Projects

- **Drafting** Graph large block versions of your initials, labeling the *x*- and *y*-coordinates of key points on each letter. Then graph a translation, a reflection, and a rotation of your initials.

- **Physical Education** As muscles are used continuously, they tire. Have a friend hold a math book in his/her hand with the arm outstretched. Measure the distance from the floor to your friend's hand every 30 seconds for 5 minutes. Graph your results.

Read More About It

Harman, Carter. *A Skyscraper Goes Up.*
Dobbler, Lavina. *I Didn't Know That.*
Dickenson, Peter. *Eva.*
Jonas, Ann. *Round Trip.*

11 Test

For answers to Exercises 1-2, see Solutions Manual.

Make a function table for each function. Then graph the function.

1. $f(n) = -4n$
2. $f(n) = 2n - 2$

3. Find $f\left(-\dfrac{1}{4}\right)$ if $f(n) = \dfrac{16}{n}$. **-64**

Find four solutions for each equation. For answers to Exercises 4-7, see Solutions Manual.

4. $y = \dfrac{x}{4} + 1$
5. $y = -2.5x - 5$
6. $y = 3 - x$
7. $y = 9x - 15$

Graph each function. For graphs to Exercises 8-11, see Solutions Manual.

8. $y = \dfrac{x}{3} - 2$
9. $y = -\dfrac{1}{2}x^2 + 6$
10. $f(n) = 3n^2 - 1$
11. $y = 35 - 4x$

12. Find the solution for the system $5x + 2 = y$ and $2x - 1 = y$ by graphing. **(-1, -3)**

13. Without graphing, determine if (3, 10) is the solution to the system of equations $y = \dfrac{1}{3}x + 7$ and $y = 4x - 5$. Why or why not? **See Solutions Manual.**

Rectangle *PQRS* has vertices *P*(-5, -2), *Q*(-3, -2), *R*(-3, -5), and *S*(-5, -5). After a translation, the coordinates of *P'* are (2, 7).

14. Describe the translation using an ordered pair. **(7, 9)**

15. Find the coordinates of *Q'*, *R'*, and *S'*. **Q'(4, 7), R'(4, 4), S'(2, 4)**

Triangle *CAT* has vertices *C*(-5, 2), *A*(-2, 3), and *T*(-3, 6). **C'(5, 2), A'(2, 3), T'(3, 6)**

16. Find the coordinates of the vertices after a reflection over the *y*-axis.

17. Find the coordinates of the vertices after a reflection over the *x*-axis. **C'(-5, -2), A'(-2, -3), T'(-3, -6)**

Triangle *ABC* is rotated 180°. The vertices of the rotated triangle are *A'*(4, 4), *B'*(1, 2), and *C'*(3, 1).

18. What are the coordinates of △*ABC*? **A(-4, -4), B(-1, -2), C(-3, -1)**

19. List the coordinates of triangle *A'B'C'* after a rotation of 90° counterclockwise. **A''(-4, 4), B''(-2, 1), C''(-1, 3)**

20. **Business** About how much higher was the daily circulation of the *Denver Post* in 1991 than in 1989? **about 14,000**

Bonus Find a rule involving ordered pairs for reflecting a point over the line $y = x$. **Switch the coordinates of the points.**

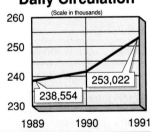

The Denver Post Daily Circulation

(Scale in thousands)

260
250
240 — 253,022
238,554
230

1989   1990   1991

Chapter 11 Test   **461**

Using the Chapter Test

This page may be used as a chapter test or another chapter review.

Evaluation Masters, pp. 91–92

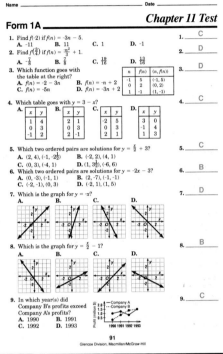

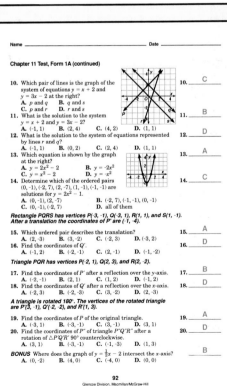

461

12 Area and Volume

Previewing the Chapter

This chapter brings algebra and geometry together to explore area and volume. Students' understanding of three-dimensional figures is deepened through lessons on drawing solid figures and drawing nets, and in the **problem-solving strategy** lesson on making models. Formulas are developed for the area of circles and the surface areas of prisms, cylinders, and spheres. Students find volumes of prisms, cylinders, pyramids, cones, and spheres. Students study precision of measurement and significant digits to further their understanding of measurements used in the applications in this chapter.

Lesson	Lesson Objectives	NCTM Standards	State/Local Objectives
12-1	Find the area of circles.	1–5, 7, 9, 11, 12	
12-2	Solve problems by making a model.	1–4, 7, 12	
12-3	Sketch three-dimensional figures from different perspectives.	1–4, 12, 13	
12-3B	Recognize a solid from its net and sketch it.	1–4, 12	
12-4	Find the surface area of rectangular and triangular prisms.	1–4, 7, 12	
12-5	Find the surface area of circular cylinders.	1–4, 7, 12, 13	
12-6	Find the volume of prisms and circular cylinders.	1–4, 7, 12	
12-6B	Investigate how surface area and volume are related.	1–4, 7, 12, 13	
12-7	Find the volume of pyramids and circular cones.	1–4, 7, 9, 12	
12-7B	Explore the surface area and volume of a sphere.	1–4, 7, 9, 12	
12-8	Describe a measurement using precision and significant digits.	1–5, 7, 13	

Organizing the Chapter

A complete, 1-page lesson plan is provided for each lesson in the Lesson Plans Masters Booklet.

LESSON PLANNING GUIDE

Lesson	Materials/ Manipulatives	Extra Practice (Student Edition)	Study Guide	Practice	Enrichment	Evaluation	Technology	Lab Manual	Multicultural Activities	Application and Interdisciplinary Activities	Transparencies	Group Activity Cards
12-1	calculator	p. 612	p. 105	p. 105	p. 105				p. 12	p. 12	12-1	12-1
12-2	cubes		p. 106	p. 106	p. 106						12-2	12-2
12-3	dot paper, cubes		p. 107	p. 107	p. 107						12-3	12-3
12-3B	scissors, graph paper, tape							p. 73				
12-4	graph paper, scissors, tape	p. 613	p. 108	p. 108	p. 108	Quiz A, p. 106					12-4	12-4
12-5	small can, graph paper, scissors, calculator	p. 613	p. 109	p. 109	p. 109					p. 26	12-5	12-5
12-6	calculator	p. 613	p. 110	p. 110	p. 110						12-6	12-6
12-6B	soft drink can, calculator							p. 74				
12-7	calculator	p. 614	p. 111	p. 111	p. 111		p. 26				12-7	12-7
12-7B	3 styrofoam balls, scissors, tape, straight pins							p. 75				
12-8			p. 112	p. 112	p. 112	Quiz B, p. 106	p. 12				12-8	12-8
Study Guide and Review			Multiple Choice Test, Forms 1A and 1B, pp. 100–103 Free Response Test, Forms 2A and 2B, pp. 104–105 Cumulative Review, p. 107 (free response)									
Test			Cumulative Test, p. 108 (multiple choice)									

Blackline Masters Booklets

Pacing Guide: Option I (Chapters 1–12) - 13 days; Option II (Chapters 1–13) - 12 days; Option III (Chapters 1–14) - 11 days
You may wish to refer to the complete **Course Planning Guides** on page T25.

OTHER CHAPTER RESOURCES

Student Edition
Chapter Opener, pp. 462–463
Cultural Kaleidoscope, p. 473
Mid-Chapter Review, p. 481
Portfolio Suggestion, p. 489
Academic Skills Test, pp. 498–499

 Manipulatives
Overhead Manipulative Resources
Middle School Mathematics Manipulative Kit

 Software/Technology
Interactive Mathematics Tools (Macintosh)
Test and Review Generator (IBM, Apple, Macintosh)
Teacher's Guide for Software Resources

Other Supplements
Transparency 12–0
Performance Assessment, pp. 23–24
Glencoe Mathematics Professional Series
Lesson Plans, pp. 131–141

This two-page introduction to the chapter provides a visual, relevant way to engage students in the mathematics of the chapter. Questions are included that help students see the need to learn the mathematics in the chapter. Data in charts and graphs provide statistical information that students can analyze and interpret at this point as well as later in the chapter. The Chapter Project provides an activity that applies the mathematics of the chapter.

MAKING MATHEMATICS RELEVANT

Spotlight on Sports

The largest stadium in the world is Strahov Stadium in Prague, Czechoslovakia, with a capacity of 240,000 spectators. Ask students to use the seating-capacity chart to solve the following problems.

- *Find the gross ticket receipts if the Rose Bowl is sold out at $25 per ticket.* $2,600,000

- *How much more would be taken in at Strahov Stadium at the same price per ticket?* $3,400,000

- *If each spectator at Strahov Stadium is alloted 9 square feet of space and an acre is composed of 43,560 square feet, how many acres are allotted for spectator seating at the stadium?* about 49.6 acres

Chapter

12

Area and Volume

Spotlight on Sports

Have You Ever Wondered...

- Which stadium in the United States can seat the most people?

- Which holds more air, a basketball or a volleyball?

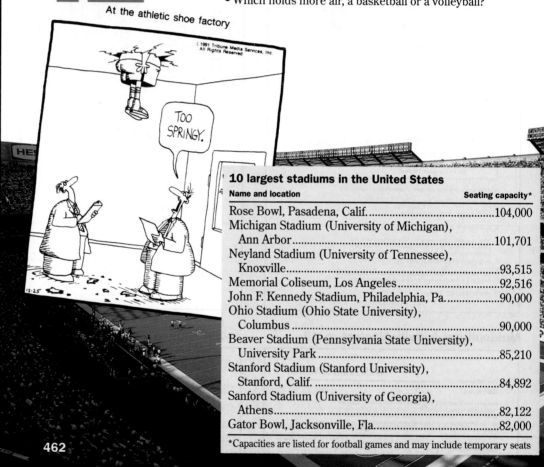

At the athletic shoe factory

10 largest stadiums in the United States

Name and location	Seating capacity*
Rose Bowl, Pasadena, Calif.	104,000
Michigan Stadium (University of Michigan), Ann Arbor	101,701
Neyland Stadium (University of Tennessee), Knoxville	93,515
Memorial Coliseum, Los Angeles	92,516
John F. Kennedy Stadium, Philadelphia, Pa.	90,000
Ohio Stadium (Ohio State University), Columbus	90,000
Beaver Stadium (Pennsylvania State University), University Park	85,210
Stanford Stadium (Stanford University), Stanford, Calif.	84,892
Sanford Stadium (University of Georgia), Athens	82,122
Gator Bowl, Jacksonville, Fla.	82,000

*Capacities are listed for football games and may include temporary seats

462

"Have You Ever Wondered?" Answers

- The Rose Bowl seats the most people.

- Students can see from the chart that the circumference of a basketball is greater than that of a volleyball. They should understand that a basketball must therefore hold more air.

Organizing the Chapter

A complete, 1-page lesson plan is provided for each lesson in the Lesson Plans Masters Booklet.

LESSON PLANNING GUIDE

Lesson	Materials/ Manipulatives	Extra Practice (Student Edition)	Blackline Masters Booklets									
			Study Guide	Practice	Enrichment	Evaluation	Technology	Lab Manual	Multicultural Activities	Application and Interdisciplinary Activities	Transparencies	Group Activity Cards
12-1	calculator	p. 612	p. 105	p. 105	p. 105				p. 12	p. 12	12-1	12-1
12-2	cubes		p. 106	p. 106	p. 106						12-2	12-2
12-3	dot paper, cubes		p. 107	p. 107	p. 107						12-3	12-3
12-3B	scissors, graph paper, tape							p. 73				
12-4	graph paper, scissors, tape	p. 613	p. 108	p. 108	p. 108	Quiz A, p. 106					12-4	12-4
12-5	small can, graph paper, scissors, calculator	p. 613	p. 109	p. 109	p. 109					p. 26	12-5	12-5
12-6	calculator	p. 613	p. 110	p. 110	p. 110						12-6	12-6
12-6B	soft drink can, calculator							p. 74				
12-7	calculator	p. 614	p. 111	p. 111	p. 111		p. 26				12-7	12-7
12-7B	3 styrofoam balls, scissors, tape, straight pins							p. 75				
12-8			p. 112	p. 112	p. 112	Quiz B, p. 106	p. 12				12-8	12-8
Study Guide and Review			Multiple Choice Test, Forms 1A and 1B, pp. 100–103 Free Response Test, Forms 2A and 2B, pp. 104–105 Cumulative Review, p. 107 (free response)									
Test			Cumulative Test, p. 108 (multiple choice)									

Pacing Guide: Option I (Chapters 1–12) - 13 days; Option II (Chapters 1–13) - 12 days; Option III (Chapters 1–14) - 11 days
You may wish to refer to the complete **Course Planning Guides** on page T25.

OTHER CHAPTER RESOURCES

Student Edition
Chapter Opener, pp. 462–463
Cultural Kaleidoscope, p. 473
Mid-Chapter Review, p. 481
Portfolio Suggestion, p. 489
Academic Skills Test, pp. 498–499

 Manipulatives
Overhead Manipulative Resources
Middle School Mathematics Manipulative Kit

 Software/Technology
Interactive Mathematics Tools (Macintosh)
Test and Review Generator (IBM, Apple, Macintosh)
Teacher's Guide for Software Resources

Other Supplements
Transparency 12-0
Performance Assessment, pp. 23–24
Glencoe Mathematics Professional Series
Lesson Plans, pp. 131–141

INTERDISCIPLINARY BULLETIN BOARD

Environmental Connection

Objective Find volumes of cylinders.

How To Use It Have students calculate the volumes of the primary and secondary containers shown in the bulletin board. Using estimation and guess-and-check, they should then find the approximate dimensions of the secondary container. You can give them additional problems by changing the percentage difference between the volumes of the containers. You may wish to have students construct a model of a double-walled container.

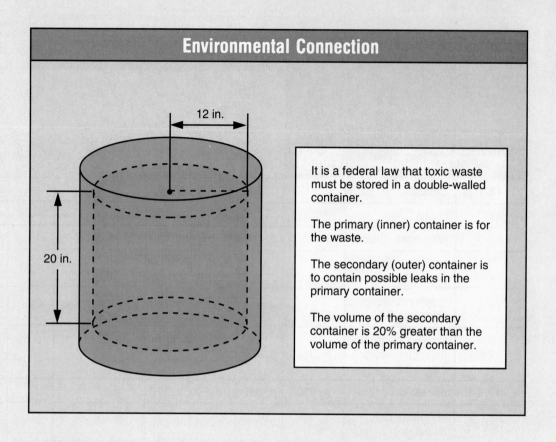

Environmental Connection

12 in.

20 in.

It is a federal law that toxic waste must be stored in a double-walled container.

The primary (inner) container is for the waste.

The secondary (outer) container is to contain possible leaks in the primary container.

The volume of the secondary container is 20% greater than the volume of the primary container.

APPLICATIONS AND CONNECTIONS

Applications	Lesson	Example	Exercise
Road Construction	12-1	2	
Smart Shopping	12-1		23
Home Decorating	12-3		15
Physics	12-4	X	
Science	12-4		19
Design	12-4		21
Food	12-5		18
Design	12-5		20
Manufacturing	12-5		21
Home Economics	12-6	3	
Marketing	12-6		24
Food	12-7	2	
Manufacturing	12-7		19
Health	12-8	1	
Research	12-8		21
Clothing	12-8		22
Connections			
Probability	12-1	3	21
Geometry	12-8	3	
Computer	12-8		23

TEAM ACTIVITIES

Multicultural Experiences

Outside Field Trips Look for experiences that will allow students to see three-dimensional geometric figures in everyday life. Tour the business section of your city and have students look for and list examples of prisms, cylinders, pyramids, cones, and spheres that they see.

Visit an architect's office to see how models of proposed buildings are created.

In-Class Speakers Invite a mechanical engineer to explain how decisions about size and design of products and product containers are made.

A draftsperson can show how three-dimensional drawings and nets are created.

SUPPLEMENTARY BLACKLINE MASTER BOOKLETS

Some of the blackline masters for enhancing this chapter are shown below.

Application and Interdisciplinary Activity Masters, pp. 12, 26

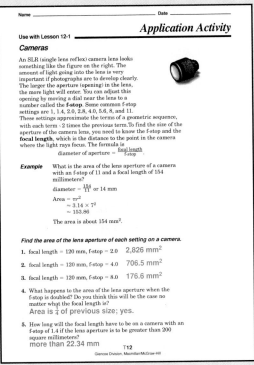

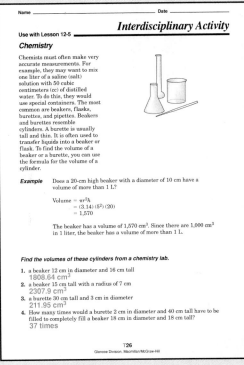

Multicultural Activity Masters, p. 12

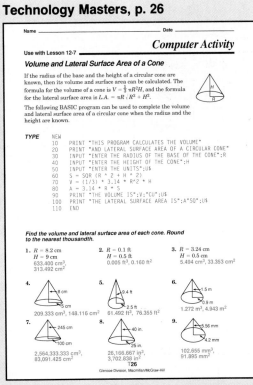

Technology Masters, p. 26

RECOMMENDED OUTSIDE RESOURCES

Books/Periodicals

Goldberg, H. and P. Wagreich, *Focus on Integrating Science and Math,* Science and Children, 26:22–4, February, 1989.

Resource Center on Educational Equity, *Critical Thinking in the Middle Grades: State Initiatives for Improved Teaching and Learning,* Washington, DC, 1990.

Films/Videotapes/Videodiscs

Classic Antics in Mathematics, Glendale, CA: AIMS Instructional Media, 1976.

Volume and Capacity, Oxford Films, 1974.

Software

Perimeter, Area, & Volume, (Apple II, IBM/Tandy), Gamco Industries

For addresses of companies handling software, please refer to page T24.

Glencoe's *Interactive Mathematics: Activities and Investigations* consists of 18 units that may be used as alternatives or supplemental material for *Mathematics: Applications and Connections.* The suggested unit for this chapter is Unit 14, *Run for Cover.* See page T18 for more information.

462

12

Area and Volume

Spotlight on Sports

Have You Ever Wondered...

- Which stadium in the United States can seat the most people?

- Which holds more air, a basketball or a volleyball?

At the athletic shoe factory

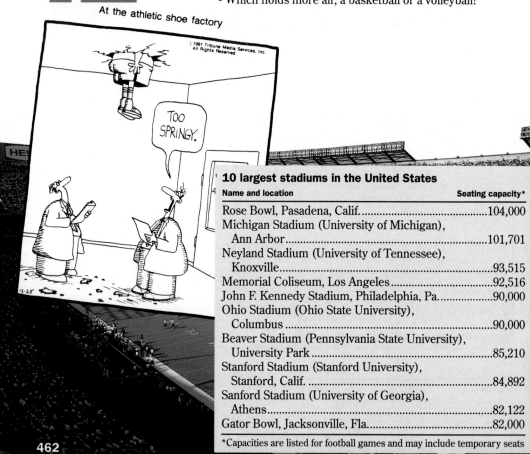

10 largest stadiums in the United States

Name and location	Seating capacity*
Rose Bowl, Pasadena, Calif.	104,000
Michigan Stadium (University of Michigan), Ann Arbor	101,701
Neyland Stadium (University of Tennessee), Knoxville	93,515
Memorial Coliseum, Los Angeles	92,516
John F. Kennedy Stadium, Philadelphia, Pa.	90,000
Ohio Stadium (Ohio State University), Columbus	90,000
Beaver Stadium (Pennsylvania State University), University Park	85,210
Stanford Stadium (Stanford University), Stanford, Calif.	84,892
Sanford Stadium (University of Georgia), Athens	82,122
Gator Bowl, Jacksonville, Fla.	82,000

*Capacities are listed for football games and may include temporary seats

462

Chapter Project

Sports

Work in a group.

1. Keep a record of any objects you see or use in a week that are in the shape of a circle, a sphere, or a cylinder. Include as many sports objects as you can.

2. Measure the circumference of the curved edge or surface of each of these objects.

3. Prepare a chart or graph to compare the circumferences of these objects.

Offical Sizes of the Balls Used in Various Sports

Basketball
Circumference 30 inches....weight 20-22 ounces

Baseball
Circumference 9-9.25 inches....weight 5-5.25 ounces

Soccer
Circumference 27-28 inches....weight 14-16 ounces

Volleyball
Circumference 26 inches....weight 9.25 ounces

Tennis
Circumference 7.75-8.25 inches....weight 2-2.062 ounces

Polo
Circumference 9.5-11 inches....weight 3.5-4.5 ounces

Ping-Pong
Circumference 4.4-4.7 inches....weight 0.083-0.091 ounces

Football
11 inches long, 7 inch diameter in center....weight 14-15 ounces

Looking Ahead

In this chapter, you will see how mathematics can be used to answer questions about sports. The major objectives of the chapter are to:

- find the area of circles
- solve problems by making a model
- find the surface area of prisms and cylinders
- sketch three-dimensional figures and find the volume of the figures
- describe a measurement by using precision and significant digits

463

DATA ANALYSIS

Have students study the ball-size chart. Ask the following questions.

- *Which two balls are closest to each other in circumference? in weight?* baseball and polo ball; soccer ball and football
- *Which ball has the smallest density (ratio of weight to volume)?* ping-pong ball

Data Search

A question related to these data is provided in Lesson 12-5, page 481, Exercise 22.

CHAPTER PROJECT

Encourage students to be alert in their observations. Common circular objects such as buttons, watch faces, and eyeglass lenses could easily be overlooked. Presentations can be in the form of drawings or models. Students should indicate the diameter or circumference of each object. You can extend the project by having students research the diameters of the planets, of circular buildings, or of other large objects, in order to gain some perspective.

Allow ten days to complete the project.

Chapter Opener Transparency

Transparency 12-0 is available in the Transparency Package. It provides another full-color, motivating activity that you can use to capture students' interest.

Lesson Resources
- Study Guide Master 12-1
- Practice Master 12-1
- Enrichment Master 12-1
- Multicultural Activity, p. 12
- Application Master, p. 12
- Group Activity Card 12-1

 Transparency 12-1 contains the 5-Minute Check and a teaching aid for this lesson.

⏱ 5-Minute Check
(Over Chapter 11)

1. Graph the linear function $y = 2x - 1$.

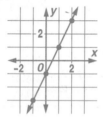

Find the coordinates of $P(-1, 2)$ after each transformation.

2. reflection over the y-axis
   $P'(1, 2)$

3. translation by $(3, -1)$
   $P'(2, 1)$

1 FOCUS

Motivating the Lesson

Questioning Have students read the first paragraph of the lesson. Then ask this question: *If the pizza pans were 16-inch and 12-inch squares, which offer would be the better buy?* two mediums for $9.99

2 TEACH

Using Logical Reasoning
Students may object to the "parallelogram" on page 464 since it has curved edges. Explain that as the number of wedges that the circle is cut into increases, the side of the figure more and more closely approximates a line segment.

464

12-1 Area of Circles

Objective
Find the area of circles.

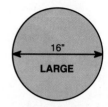

The first pizza made with tomatoes and cheese was created for Queen Marghenta of Italy in 1889. The pizza maker, Raffaele Esposito, used ingredients that matched the colors of the Italian flag: red (tomatoes), white (mozzarella cheese), and green (basil).

Georgio shows the actual pans he uses in his pizzeria so customers can see the size of the pizza they are ordering. If you can get one large pizza for $8.99, or two medium pizzas for $9.99, which offer is the better buy?

16" LARGE   12" MEDIUM

In order to solve this problem, we need to find the area of each size of pizza. The formula for the area of a circle is related to the formula for the area of a parallelogram.

Suppose you draw several radii of a circle equally-spaced. Then cut the circle along the radii to form wedge-like pieces. Rearrange the pieces to form a parallelogram-shaped figure.

  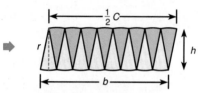

The length of each wedge from the point to its edge is the same as the radius of the circle. So the height of the parallelogram is r. The curved sides of the wedges form the circumference of the circle. The base of the parallelogram is made of half of these curves, or half the circumference of the circle.

LOOK BACK
You can review circles on page 284.

$$A = bh \qquad \textit{area of parallelogram}$$
$$A = \frac{1}{2}C \cdot r \qquad b = \frac{1}{2}C, h = r$$
$$A = \frac{1}{2} \cdot 2\pi r \cdot r \qquad C = 2\pi r$$
$$A = \pi r^2$$

So, the formula for the area of a circle is $A = \pi r^2$.

| **Area of a Circle** | **In words:** The area (A) of a circle equals π times the radius (r) squared. |
| | **In symbols:** $A = \pi r^2$ |

464   **Chapter 12**   Area and Volume

OPTIONS

Limited English Proficiency

Help students distinguish between circumference and area. Compare circumference with the perimeter of a figure. Remind students that π is a symbol used throughout the world to represent the ratio between the circumference of a circle and its diameter.

 Interactive Mathematics Tools

This multimedia software provides an interactive lesson that is tied directly to Lesson 12–1. Students will use changeable graphs to explore the area and circumference of circles.

Example 1

Find the area of a circle with a radius of 8 inches to the nearest square inch.

Using paper and pencil

$A = \pi r^2$

$A \approx 3.14(8^2)$ *Use 3.14 for π.*

$A \approx 3.14(64)$

$A \approx 200.96$

The area of the circle is about 201 square inches.

Using a calculator

Use the π key.

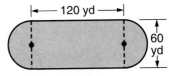

You can use the area formula for circles to find areas of circular-shaped objects. Since most calculators have a π key, we will use a calculator to compute the measurements in this chapter.

Example 2 *Problem Solving*

Estimation Hint
• • • • • • • • • •
Since $\pi \approx 3$, you can estimate the area of any circle by squaring the radius and multiplying by 3.

Road Construction A Kentucky visitors' center along I-75 is surrounded by a circular driveway. Find the cost of repaving this driveway if repaving costs $0.89 per square foot.

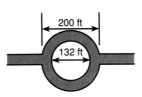

Notice that the edges of the driveway are formed by two circles. The area of the driveway would be the area of the larger circle minus the area of the smaller circle.

Remember that the radius of a circle is half its diameter.

area of large circle

$d = 200$, so $r = \frac{200}{2}$ or 100

$A = \pi r^2$

$A = \pi \cdot 100^2$

$A \approx 31{,}415.927$

area of small circle

$d = 132$, so $r = \frac{132}{2}$ or 66

$A = \pi r^2$

$A = \pi \cdot 66^2$

$A \approx 13{,}684.778$

area of driveway = area of large circle − area of small circle

$A \approx 31{,}415.927 - 13{,}684.778$ or $17{,}731.149$

The area of the driveway is about 17,731 square feet. The cost of paving would be $0.89 \cdot 17{,}731$ or $15,780.59.

Remember that the probability of an event is defined as the ratio of the number of ways something can happen to the total possible outcomes. Probability can also be related to the area of a figure.

Lesson 12-1 Area of Circles **465**

More Examples

For Example 1

Find the area of a circle with a diameter of 28 centimeters to the nearest square centimeter. 616 cm²

For Example 2

Find the area inside the track. about 10,027.43 yd²

For Example 3

What percent of the figure is shaded? about 21.5%

Teaching Tip In Example 1, ask why the results of the two methods are different. Different approximations of π are used in the calculations.

Checking for Understanding

Exercises 1-4 are designed to help you assess students' understanding through reading, writing, speaking, and modeling. You should work through these exercises with your students and then monitor their work on Guided Practice Exercises 5-8.

Notice to Teachers

Throughout the remainder of this Teacher's Wraparound Edition, all the answers involving π are calculated using the π key on the calculator. If students use $\frac{22}{7}$ or 3.14 for π in finding solutions, their answers will differ from those given here.

Reteaching Activity

Using Models Have students draw circles on graph paper using a compass. Have them count squares to find the radius and use the estimation hint on page 465 to estimate each area. Then have them calculate each area using the formula and compare their results with their estimates.

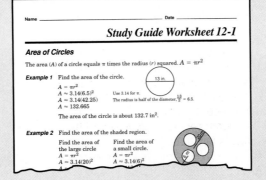

Study Guide Masters, p. 105

Study Guide Worksheet 12-1

Area of Circles

The area (A) of a circle equals π times the radius (r) squared. $A = \pi r^2$

Example 1 Find the area of the circle. 13 in.

$A = \pi r^2$
$A \approx 3.14(6.5)^2$ Use 3.14 for π.
$A \approx 3.14(42.25)$ The radius is half of the diameter, $\frac{13}{2} = 6.5$.
$A \approx 132.665$

The area of the circle is about 132.7 in².

Example 2 Find the area of the shaded region.

Find the area of the large circle.
$A = \pi r^2$
$A \approx 3.14(20)^2$

Find the area of a small circle.
$A = \pi r^2$
$A \approx 3.14(6)^2$

465

Close

Have students compare and contrast the area and circumference of a circle, and explain how to find each measure.

3 PRACTICE/APPLY

Assignment Guide
Maximum: 9–23
Minimum: 9–17 odd, 18–23

For **Extra Practice,** see p. 612.

Alternate Assessment

Modeling Have students choose circular objects in the room, measure their radii, and calculate their areas.

Additional Answers

1. Since r is given in units, r^2 would result in square units.
2. Let $\pi \approx 3$. So $A = \pi r^2$ becomes $A \approx 3(5^2)$ or $75\ m^2$.
3. Divide the diameter by 2 to get the radius. Then use the formula.

Practice Masters, p. 105

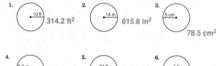

Name _____ Date _____

Practice Worksheet 12-1

Area of Circles

Find the area of each circle to the nearest tenth.

1. 314.2 ft² (10 ft)
2. 615.8 in² (14 in)
3. 78.5 cm² (5 cm)
4. 124.7 m² (6.3 m)
5. 452.4 ft² (24 ft)
6. 19.6 ft² (5 ft)

7. Find the area of a circle that has a diameter of 60 feet.
2,827.4 ft²

8. Find the area of a circle that has a radius of 22 feet.
1,520.5 ft²

9. Find the diameter of a circle that has an area of 36π square inches.
12 in.

Find the area of each shaded region.

10. 24.8 ft² (5 ft, 3 ft)
11. 13.7 ft² (8 ft, 8 ft)
12. 7.9 ft² (5 ft, 3 ft)

13. A circular flower garden has a diameter of 16 feet. At the center of the garden is a circular pool 5 feet in diameter. If a coin is tossed at random into the garden, what is the probability that the coin will land in the pool? about 1/10

T105
Glencoe Division, Macmillan/McGraw-Hill

466

Example 3 *Connection*

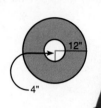

Probability Suppose you throw a dart at random at the dart board at the right and you hit the board. What is the probability that the dart lands in the red section?

To find the probability of landing in the red section, you need to know the area of the red section and the area of the entire dart board.

area of red section = area of dart board − area of inner circle

$$= \pi \cdot (12)^2 \quad - \quad \pi \cdot (4)^2$$
$$= 144\pi - 16\pi \text{ or } 128\pi$$

$$P(\text{landing in red section}) = \frac{\text{area of red section}}{\text{total area}}$$
$$= \frac{128\pi}{144\pi} \quad \textit{The GCF of the numerator}$$
$$\textit{and denominator is } 16\pi.$$
$$= \frac{8}{9}$$

The probability of landing in the red section of the dart board is $\frac{8}{9}$.

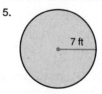

Mental Math Hint

Use the distributive property to combine numbers containing π.

$144\pi - 16\pi =$

$(144 - 16)\pi =$

$128\pi.$

Checking for Understanding For answers to Exercises 1–3, see margin.

Communicating Mathematics

Read and study the lesson to answer each question.

1. **Tell** why the area of a circle is always given in square units.

2. **Tell** how you can estimate the area of a circle whose radius is 5 meters.

3. **Tell** how you would find the area of a circle if you only know the diameter of the circle.

4. **Show** how you would find the area of the semicircle shown at the right.
$$A = \frac{1}{2}(\pi r^2) = \frac{1}{2}\pi(10)^2 \approx 157\ m^2$$

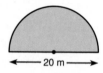

← 20 m →

Guided Practice

Find the area of each circle to the nearest tenth.

Answers are calculated using the π key on a calculator and then rounded.

5. (7 ft)
153.9 ft²

6. (3.2 km)
32.2 km²

7. 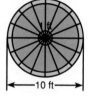 (11 yd)
95.0 yd²

8. Jolie dropped a dime down a wishing well without looking. There's a bucket at the bottom of the well. What is the probability the dime will land in the bucket? $\frac{1}{100}$

← 10 ft →

466 **Chapter 12** Area and Volume

OPTIONS

Bell Ringer

The circumference of a circle is 56.52 inches. What is the area of the circle to the nearest square inch? Use 3.14 for π.   254 in²

Exercises

Independent Practice

Find the area of each circle to the nearest tenth.

9. 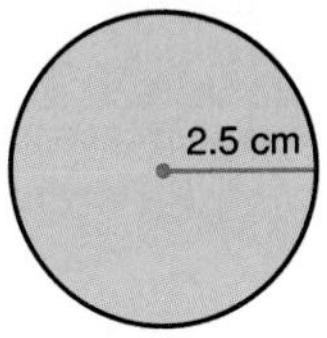

19.6 cm²

10. 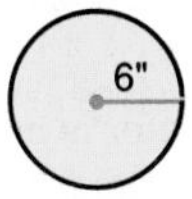

113.1 in²

11. 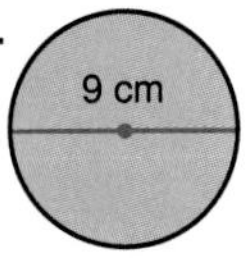

63.6 cm²

12. Find the area of a circle whose radius is 13 feet. 530.9 ft²

13. Find the area of a circle whose diameter is 10 meters. 78.5 m²

14. Find the radius of a circle whose area is 49π square inches. 7 in.

Find the area of each shaded region. Answers rounded to nearest tenth.

15. 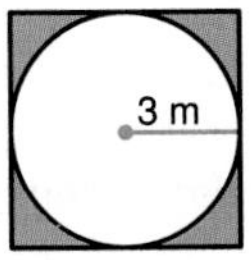

7.7 m²

16. 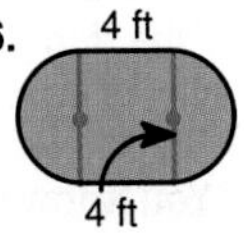

28.6 ft²

17. 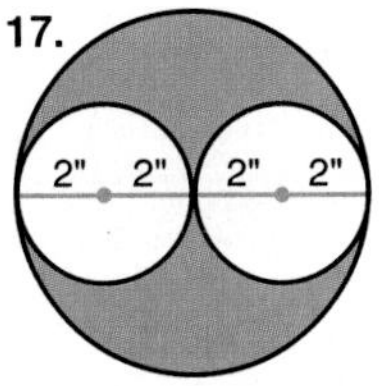

25.1 in²

Mixed Review

18. **Algebra** Find the value of x in $\triangle RST$ if $m\angle R = 54°$, $m\angle S = 90°$, and $m\angle T = 3x°$. *(Lesson 5-3)* 12

19. Find the distance between points $A(-5, -4)$ and $B(3, -2)$. Express your answer to the nearest tenth. *(Lesson 8-7)* 8.2 units

20. **Geometry** Graph $\triangle HIJ$ with vertices $H(2, 2)$, $I(4, -1)$, and $J(1, -2)$. Then graph $\triangle H'I'J'$ after a rotation of 90° counterclockwise. *(Lesson 11-10)* See margin.

Problem Solving and Applications

21. **Probability** Louie is blindfolded and throws darts at the dart board shown at the right.
   a. What is the area of each ring of the board?
   b. Suppose Louie hits the board each time he throws a dart. What is the probability of landing in the white ring? $\frac{1}{3}$

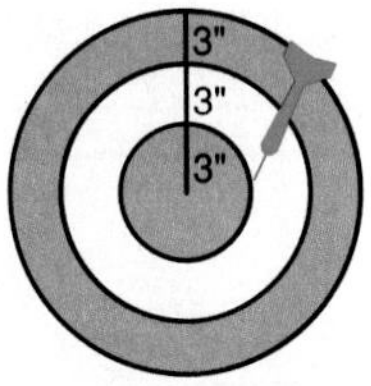

21a. 28.3 in², 84.8 in², 141.4 in²

22. **Critical Thinking** What happens to the circumference and area of a circle when the length of the radius is doubled? Make a drawing. Circumference doubles. Area quadruples.

23. **Smart Shopping** Refer to the pizza problem at the beginning of the lesson.
   a. Find the area of the large pizza and two medium pizzas.
   b. Use a calculator to find the cost per square inch of each pizza deal. Use your calculator displays to find which costs less per square inch.
   c. Now use your results rounded to the nearest cent. Which is the better deal? $L = \$0.04$, $M = \$0.04$, they have same price per square inch.

23a. $L = 201.06$ in², $M = 226.19$ in²
23b. $L = \$0.0447126$, $M = \$0.0441655$

Additional Answer

20. 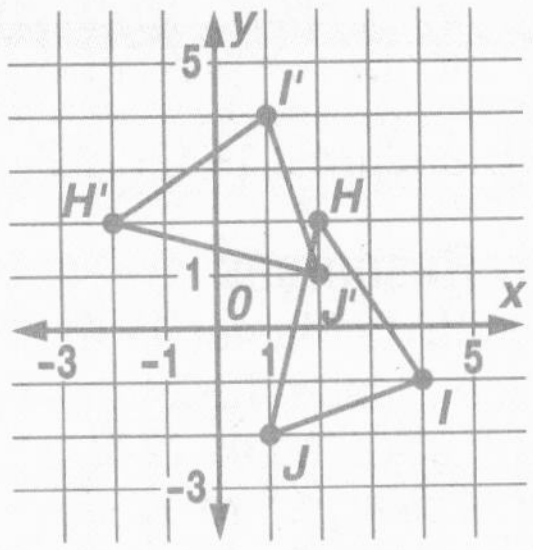

Enrichment Masters, p. 105

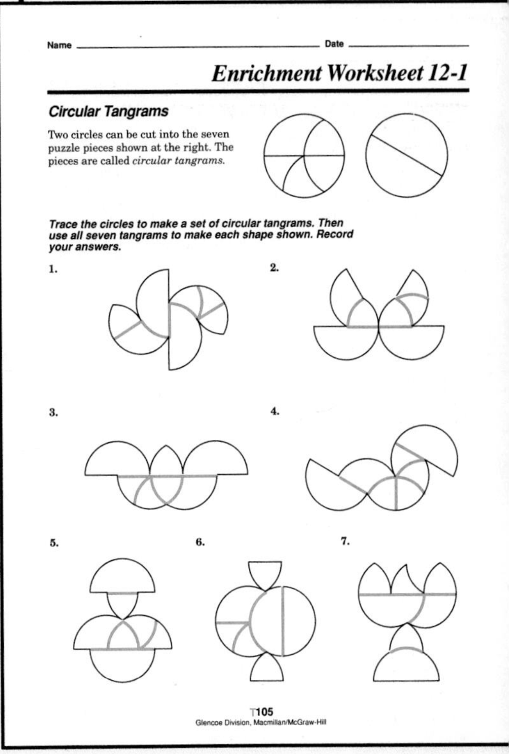
Name ______ Date ______

Enrichment Worksheet 12-1

Circular Tangrams

Two circles can be cut into the seven puzzle pieces shown at the right. The pieces are called *circular tangrams.*

Trace the circles to make a set of circular tangrams. Then use all seven tangrams to make each shape shown. Record your answers.

1. 2. 3. 4. 5. 6. 7.

T105
Glencoe Division, Macmillan/McGraw-Hill

Extending the Lesson

Using Drawings Have students use compasses to draw the figure below. Then have them use the formula given to find the total area of the shaded regions. Answers depend on the radius.

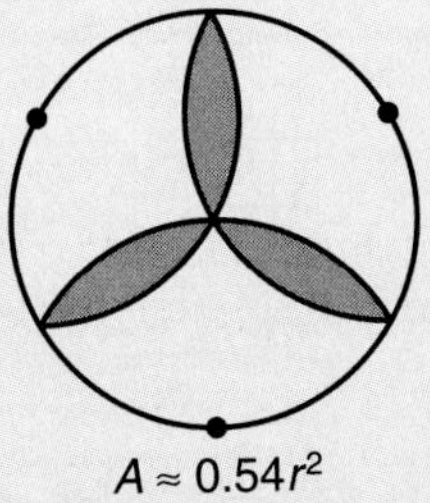

$A \approx 0.54r^2$

Cooperative Learning Activity

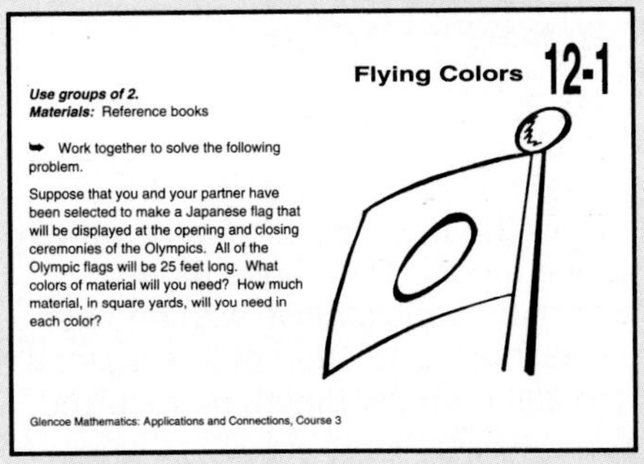
Flying Colors **12-1**

Use groups of 2.
Materials: Reference books

➡ Work together to solve the following problem.

Suppose that you and your partner have been selected to make a Japanese flag that will be displayed at the opening and closing ceremonies of the Olympics. All of the Olympic flags will be 25 feet long. What colors of material will you need? How much material, in square yards, will you need in each color?

Glencoe Mathematics: Applications and Connections, Course 3

NCTM Standards: 1–4, 7, 12

Lesson Resources
- Study Guide Master 12-2
- Practice Master 12-2
- Enrichment Master 12-2
- Group Activity Card 12-2

 Transparency 12-2 contains the 5-Minute Check and a teaching aid for this lesson.

🕐 5-Minute Check
(Over Lesson 12-1)

1. Find the area to the nearest tenth of a circle whose radius is 4 m. 50.3 m²

2. Find the area to the nearest tenth of the shaded region in the figure below. 75.40 cm²

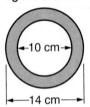
←10 cm→

←14 cm→

Practice Masters, p. 106

Name _____ Date _____

Practice Worksheet 12-2

Problem-Solving Strategy: Make a Model
Solve. Use the make-a-model strategy.

1. A memorial waterfall is built of granite cubes using the plans shown below.

TOP   SIDE   FRONT

a. How many cubes of granite are needed? 64
b. If each cube measures 2 feet on an edge, how high is the waterfall? 10 ft
c. If each cube weighs 1,176 pounds, what is the total weight of the waterfall when dry? 75,264 pounds

2. A retaining wall is made of cubes of stone using the plans below. How many cubes are needed for the wall? 75 cubes

TOP   SIDE   FRONT

Solve using any strategy.

3. The student government club sells flowers as a fund-raiser. The club buys flowers for 50¢ each, or $5 a dozen, and sells them for $1 each.
a. How much will 75 flowers cost the club? $31.50
b. How much profit will the club earn selling 75 flowers? $43.50

4. Jimmy has three cubes each measuring a different whole number of inches on an edge. When he stacks them, the stack is six inches high. What is the length of the edge of each cube? 1 in., 2 in., and 3 in.

T106
Glencoe Division, Macmillan/McGraw-Hill

468

12-2 Make a Model

Objective
Solve problems by making a model.

Materials
cubes

A set designer is creating a mirrored staircase for a dance number. The plan shows the top, front, and side views. How many cubes are needed to build the staircase?

top   side   front

Example

Make a model to determine how many cubes are needed to build the staircase for the dance number.

Explore   *What do you know?*
You know the shape and dimensions of the staircase from the squares shown on the plan.

What do you need to find out?
You need to find the number of cubes the designer needs to build the staircase.

Plan   Use each of the views of the staircase to determine the dimensions. Then use cubes to build a model.

Solve   The view from the top shows 15 cubes arranged in a rectangle, 5 cubes by 3 cubes.
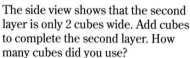

The side view shows that the second layer is only 2 cubes wide. Add cubes to complete the second layer. How many cubes did you use?

The side view also shows that the top layer is only 1 cube wide. Add cubes to complete the top layer.
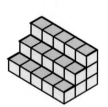

The front view shows 3 layers of 5 cubes each. Look at the front of your model to make sure you have this number of layers and cubes.

Total the number of cubes you used in each layer.

15 + 10 + 5 = 30 cubes

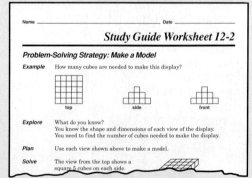

OPTIONS

Reteaching Activity

Using Models   Have students construct a model like the staircase shown in the lesson. Have them draw the top, side, and front views of their model. Then have them exchange their views with another classmate and attempt to construct a model from the diagrams received.

Study Guide Masters, p. 106

Name _____ Date _____

Study Guide Worksheet 12-2

Problem-Solving Strategy: Make a Model

Example   How many cubes are needed to make this display?

top   side   front

Explore   What do you know?
You know the shape and dimensions of each view of the display.
You need to find the number of cubes needed to make the display.

Plan   Use each view shown above to make a model.

Solve   The view from the top shows a square 5 cubes on each side.

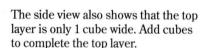

Examine Turn your model to make sure that each view is correct. If your model matches each view, the model is correct.

Checking for Understanding

For answers to Exercises 1-2, see Solutions Manual.

Communicating Mathematics

Read and study the lesson to answer each question.

1. **Tell** how you determined how many cubes were in each layer.

2. **Show** another way to build the model by starting with the side view first.

Guided Practice

Solve. Use the make-a-model strategy.

3. Cindy is placing glass decorations near the ceiling at a door entrance she is designing. Find how many glass cubes she needs for two decorations with the plans shown below. **12 cubes**

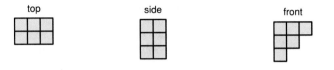

top   side   front

Problem Solving

Practice

Solve using any strategy.

4. Use the model in the Example to determine how many mirrored tiles would be needed to cover the staircase if each tile is the same size as a face of one of the cubes. **6 + 6 + 6(5) = 42 tiles**

5. Natasha paid $45 for a perm that was on sale at 40% off. What was the original price of the perm? **$75**

6. Toni, Matsue, and Juana all like pizza. One likes her pizza plain. One likes her pizza with mushrooms. One likes her pizza with anchovies. Use the following clues to find out which kind of pizza each girl likes.

- Toni doesn't know the girl who likes her pizza plain.
- Matsue's favorite kind of pizza is cheaper than pizza with mushrooms.
- The girl who likes mushrooms is Toni's cousin.

Strategies

• • • • • • •

Look for a pattern.
Solve a simpler problem.
Act it out.
Guess and check.
Draw a diagram.
Make a chart.
Work backward.

6. Toni: anchovy, Matsue: plain, Juana: mushroom

7. Edu-Toys is designing a new package to hold a set of 30 alphabet blocks. Each block is a cube with each edge of the cube being 2 inches long. A box of which dimensions will hold the set of blocks without the need for some type of filler? **c**

a. 8 inches by 4 inches by 12 inches

b. 3 inches by 6 inches by 13 inches

c. 6 inches by 4 inches by 10 inches

---

1 FOCUS

Motivating the Lesson

Questioning Ask students to describe situations when a model might help clarify a situation or solve a problem.

2 TEACH

More Examples

For the Example

Arrange 12 cubes so that the least possible number of cube faces are showing.

3 PRACTICE/APPLY

Assignment Guide
Maximum: 4–7
Minimum: 4–7

Enrichment Masters, p. 106

Name _____ Date _____

Enrichment Worksheet 12-2

From a Different Point of View

The numbers 1 through 6 are arranged on a cube so that the sum of the numbers on opposite faces is always 7. There are two ways to do this. One way is shown at the right.

Solve each problem. Use or build models if you wish.

1. One view of the number cube described above is given. Draw all 24 possible views in the space below.

Draw each figure as if you were standing behind it.

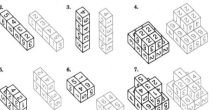

8. There is a second way to arrange the numbers 1 through 6 so that the sum on opposite faces is 7. In the space at the right, draw the view of this other number cube, showing the faces with 5, 3, and 6.

T106
Glencoe Division, Macmillan/McGraw-Hill

NCTM Standards: 1–4, 12, 13

Lesson Resources
- Study Guide Master 12-3
- Practice Master 12-3
- Enrichment Master 12-3
- Group Activity Card 12-3

Transparency 12-3 contains the 5-Minute Check and a teaching aid for this lesson.

⏱ 5-Minute Check
(Over Lesson 12-2)

How many cubes are needed to construct a model with these views: 18

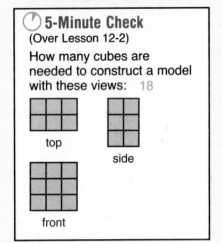

top

side

front

1 FOCUS

Motivating the Lesson

Questioning   Display a cardboard box in various positions. Ask students the following questions.

- *How many sides, including the top and bottom, are there?*   6
- *What is the greatest number of sides you can see at once?*   3

2 TEACH

Using Models   Have a model of a rectangular prism available for student study (for example, a shoe box). Have students identify the faces, bases, vertices, and edges.

12-3   Three-Dimensional Figures

Objective
Sketch three-dimensional figures from different perspectives.

Words to Learn
solid
face
edge
vertex
base

DID YOU KNOW

Edmonia Lewis was born in upstate New York. Her mother was a Chippewa Indian and her father was a freedperson. One of her works is a bust of Henry Wadsworth Longfellow, done for the Harvard College Library.

Edmonia Lewis (1845–1890) was America's first African-American woman to be recognized as a talented sculptor. She strove to capture the emotions of the people in her sculptures, unlike many of her contemporaries.

Sculpture is a three-dimensional art. The sculptor must look at the sculpture from many perspectives to make sure each detail has been captured. In geometry, we study three-dimensional figures called **solids** that have certain details that make them unique. Some common solids are shown below.

rectangular prism   triangular prism   pyramid   cone   cylinder

Before sculpting, many artists sketch different perspectives of their figures. In geometry, it is often helpful to sketch figures before solving a problem related to those figures.

Example 1

Use dot paper to sketch a rectangular prism that is 4 units long, 3 units high, and 5 units deep.

Step 1   Lightly draw the edges of the bottom of the prism that are 4 units by 5 units. Complete the other two bottom edges.

Step 2   Lightly draw vertical segments at the vertices of the base. Each segment is 3 units high.

Step 3   Complete the top of the prism.

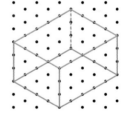

Step 4   Go over your lines. Use dashed lines for the edges of the prism you can't see from your perspective and solid lines for the edges you can see.

470   **Chapter 12**   Area and Volume

OPTIONS

Gifted and Talented Needs

Have students investigate the relationship among the numbers of faces (*F*), edges (*E*), and vertices (*V*) of a prism. Have them compile a table of values of *F*, *E*, and *V* for a variety of prisms. Then have them try to discover **Euler's formula,** which relates the three values.

$$V - E + F = 2$$

You could draw several other perspectives of the same prism. Suppose you sat it up on end or rolled it over on its side.

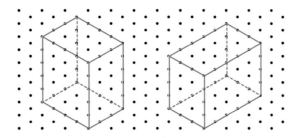

Prisms, like the ones above, have flat surfaces. The surfaces of a prism are called **faces.** The faces meet to form the **edges** of the prism. The edges meet at corners called **vertices.**

All prisms have at least one pair of faces that are parallel and congruent. These are called **bases** and are used to name the prism. The prisms shown above are *rectangular prisms.* As you can see, the bases of a rectangular prism change depending on how the prism is positioned.

Examples

Tell the dimensions of the base and height of each rectangular prism.

2

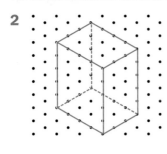

The base is 3 units by 4 units. The height is 5 units.

3

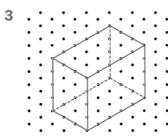

The base is 5 units by 3 units. The height is 4 units.

Other geometric shapes can be used for the bases of a prism.

Lesson 12-3 Three-Dimensional Figures **471**

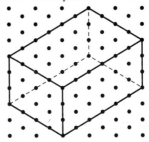
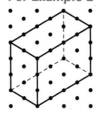
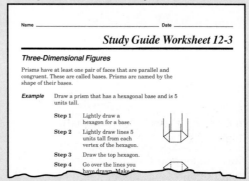

Error Analysis

Watch for students who cannot distinguish hidden from visible edges.

Prevent by using a model of a rectangular prism to show which parts of the prism are visible and which are not.

Close

Have students write a few sentences defining these terms: *face, edge, base, vertex.*

3 PRACTICE/APPLY

Assignment Guide
Maximum: 6–17
Minimum: 6–16

Alternate Assessment

Writing Have students draw a rectangular prism and on their drawing indicate a face, a vertex, an edge, and a base.

Practice Masters, p. 107

Name _____ Date _____

Practice Worksheet 12-3

Three-Dimensional Figures

1. Tell the dimensions of the prism shown at the right.
   1 unit long, 3 units high, and 4 units deep

2. What is the height of the prism? 3 units

3. What type of prism is this? rectangular prism

4. Draw another view of this prism showing a height of 1 unit.
   Answers may vary.

5. Draw another view of this prism showing a height of 3 units.
   Answers may vary.

6. Draw a view of a prism that has a triangle as a base, and is 4 units high.
   Answers may vary.

7. Draw a view of a prism that has a pentagon for a base.
   Answers may vary.

8. Draw a view of a cone.
   Answers may vary.

9. Draw a bird's-eye view of the cone in Exercise 8 as it would appear from directly overhead. Describe the bird's-eye view.
   a circle

10. What is the greatest number of cubes with a one-inch edge that can be cut from a cube that has a three-inch edge? 27

T107
Glencoe Division, Macmillan/McGraw-Hill

Example 4

Draw a pentagonal prism that has a height of 4 units.

Step 1 Lightly draw a pentagon for the base.

Step 2 Lightly draw lines 4 units high from each vertex of the pentagon. Then draw the top pentagon.

Step 3 Go over the lines you have drawn. Make the edges you can see solid and use dashed lines for the edges you can't see.

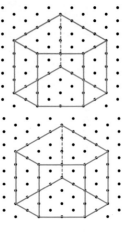

Checking for Understanding

Communicating Mathematics

Read and study the lesson to answer each question.

1. **Tell** which solids pictured in this lesson have one or more surfaces that can be rectangles. **any prism, a pyramid**

2. **Write** the steps you would use to draw a prism that has a triangle for a base. **2. See margin.**

3. **Show** how to determine which lines are solid and which lines are dashed in a geometric drawing. **See margin.**

Guided Practice

4. 2 × 3 × 5 units
4. Tell the dimensions of the prism shown at the right.

5. Draw another view of the pentagonal prism in Example 4. **See margin.**

Exercises 6. 4 × 4 × 4 units

Independent Practice

6. Tell the dimensions of the prism shown at the right.
   a. What is the height of the prism? **4 units**
   b. What type of prism is this? **cube**

7. Draw three views of a rectangular prism that is 3 units by 2 units by 1 unit. **See margin.**

8. Draw a prism that has a hexagon as a base and is 3 units tall. **See margin.**

9. See margin.
9. Explain how you would draw a pyramid that has a parallelogram as a base.

10. Write a few sentences to tell how you would draw a cylinder. Then draw one.
    Draw an oval for the base, draw two edges, draw oval for top.
    For drawing, see students' work.

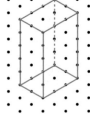

472   Chapter 12   Area and Volume

OPTIONS

Meeting Needs of Middle School Students

Middle school students, like learners of all ages, need to be challenged within a structured and supportive environment. To help them succeed, provide a setting that is high on expectations, interaction, and activity. Encourage your students to reach high, and coach them to use their talents to get there.

Additional Answers

2. Draw a triangle for the base. Draw a segment from each vertex so that all the segments are congruent and parallel. Connect the ends of the segments to form the other triangular base.

3. The edges you can see from your perspective are solid. The dashed lines are for edges you cannot see from your perspective.

11. Make a Model of the figure described at the right. Then make a drawing of your model. See Solutions Manual.

side   top   front

Mixed Review **12. Statistics** Find the interquartile range of the set {73, 70, 71, 64, 74, 71, 78, 68, 79}. *(Lesson 4-6)* **7**

13. Solve $\frac{3}{17} = \frac{n}{68}$. *(Lesson 9-2)* **12**

14. Geometry Find the area of a circle whose diameter is 12.4 meters. *(Lesson 12-1)* **120.8 m²**

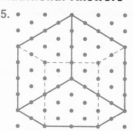

Problem Solving and Applications **15. Home Decorating** Miki has eight plastic milk crates that he can arrange in his room to store his books, Nintendo® games, and music. His mom has said he can arrange them in his room any way he wishes. Draw at least three ways he can arrange the crates so that he can store items in each of them. See Solutions Manual.

16. Critical Thinking Copy the figure at the right, which is the outline of two prisms laying side by side. One prism is 3 units by 1 unit by 1 unit. The other prism is 3 units by 3 units by 1 unit. Complete the drawing to show each prism.

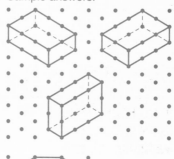

17. Journal Entry Write a list of several careers that would involve drawing three-dimensional figures. Tell how they would use them. See students' work.

CULTURAL KALEIDOSCOPE

Federico Peña

In 1983, Federico Peña became the first Hispanic to be elected mayor of Denver, Colorado. He graduated from college with a degree in law and practiced law for 10 years before becoming mayor. During Mayor Peña's two terms in office, Colorado was devastated by one of the worst recessions in the state's history. Despite the economic conditions, Mayor Peña's focus was to change the economy and create new jobs and industry for the people of Denver.

Perhaps his most significant contribution

was winning voter approval for the construction of Denver International Airport, the only major airport project to be approved in the United States since 1970. More than 60 design and engineering firms submitted ideas for this 54 square mile airport site.

Other accomplishments of Mayor Peña include bringing the Colorado Rockies, a National League expansion baseball team, to Denver and winning voter approval for a 937,000-square foot convention center.

Extending the Lesson

Cultural Kaleidoscope Discuss with students the ways in which architects utilize the strategy of making a model when designing a project the size of the Denver International Airport.

Cooperative Learning Activity

Use groups of 2.
Materials: Unit cube

A New View 12-3

➡ You know that the way the bases of a rectangular prism are drawn changes depending on how the prism is positioned. What if the prism stays in the same place and your position changes? Suppose that the figures below show a cube whose sides are 8 feet long. Describe your position in relation to the cube for each view shown. (Hint: Use a unit cube to visualize the larger cube.)

Share your results with other pairs. Did you get the same answers?

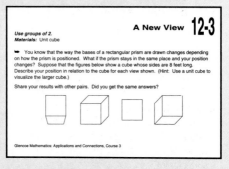

Glencoe Mathematics: Applications and Connections, Course 3

Additional Answers

5.

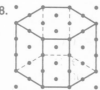

7. Sample answers:

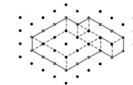

8.

9. Draw a parallelogram for the bases. Choose a point above the parallelogram. Connect this point to each vertex of the base.

Enrichment Masters, p. 107

Name _____ Date _____

Enrichment Worksheet 12-3

Tessellated Patterns for Solid Shapes

Tessellations made from equilateral triangles can be used to build many three-dimensional solid figures.

Follow the directions to fold and glue (or tape) each shape. Make the triangles at least 2 inches on each side. When you have finished each model, describe it in words.

1. Fold 5 over 1 and glue down. Repeat, in this order: fold 6 over 7, fold 2 over 6.

2. Cut on the dotted line. Then fold 5 over 3 and glue down. Repeat, in this order: fold 6 over 5, fold 7 over 12, fold 2 over 9.

Pyramid with 4 faces (tetrahedron)

Double pyramid with 6 faces

3. Cut on the dotted lines. Then fold 7 over 2 and glue down. Repeat, in this order: fold 14 over 7, fold 1 over 16, fold 12 over 4, fold 10 over 1.

4. Cut on the dotted lines. Then fold 1 over 2 and glue down. Repeat, in this order: fold 9 over 10, fold 4 over 20, fold 14 over 6, fold 5 over 1, fold 11 over 21, fold 26 over 17, fold 28 over 11, fold 31 over 30.

 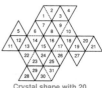

Double pyramid with 8 faces (octahedron)

Crystal shape with 20 faces (icosahedron)

T107
Glencoe Division, Macmillan/McGraw-Hill

473

NCTM Standards: 1–4, 12

Management Tips

For Students The triangles in the pattern are equilateral, with edges of 5 units and heights of about $4\frac{1}{3}$ units.

For the Overhead Projector
Overhead Manipulative Resources provides appropriate materials for teacher or student demonstration of the activities in this Mathematics Lab.

1 FOCUS

Introducing the Lab

Ask students to give examples of objects that can be formed from patterns.

2 TEACH

Using Problem Solving Ask students to draw the solid formed in the *Try this!* from a perspective showing all four triangular faces.

top
view

3 PRACTICE/APPLY

Using Logical Reasoning Ask students what changes they would make in the pattern to create a net for a pyramid with 5 triangular faces. Change the square to a pentagon and add another equilateral triangle to the pattern.

Close

Have students explain how they could make a net from a paper model of a solid. Unfold the model into a flat pattern.

12-3B Nets

A Follow-Up of Lesson 12-3

Objective
Recognize a solid from its net and sketch it.

Materials
scissors
graph paper
tape

Every solid with at least one flat surface can be formed from a pattern called a **net.**

Try this!

Work in groups of four.

- Draw the figure shown at the right on graph paper. *What geometric figures form the parts of this net?*
  4 triangles and 1 square

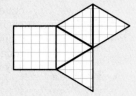

- Cut the figure out and fold along the heavy lines. Tape the edges together to form a solid.

- Have each person in the group sketch their perspective of the solid formed when the edges were taped together.

What do you think? 1. pyramid

1. What solid did you form when the edges were taped together?

2. Compare your sketch of the solid with others in your group. What differences and similarities do you see? See students' work.

3. Study your model. Is there another net that would produce this same solid? If so, draw it. Yes. For drawings, see Solutions Manual.

4. Describe the solid formed by each net. Then sketch the solid.

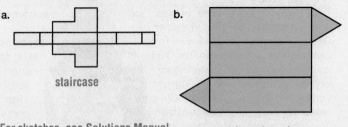

a.

staircase

b.

For sketches, see Solutions Manual.

triangular prism

Application

5. **Manufacturing** The Blocko Company uses nets of plastic to form cubes used for support in cloth-covered alphabet blocks. Use graph paper to draw all possible nets they might consider to manufacture a cube. See Solutions Manual.

OPTIONS

Lab Manual You may wish to make copies of the blackline master on p. 73 of the *Lab Manual* for students to use as a recording sheet.

Lab Manual, p. 73

Name _____ Date _____

Mathematics Lab Worksheet

Use with page 474

Nets

Try this!

What geometric figures form the parts of this net?
The net contains four triangles and one square.

Sketch your perspective. Check students' drawings; samples are shown.

What do you think?
1. pyramid
2. Answers will vary.

12-4 Surface Area of Prisms

Objective
Find the surface area of rectangular and triangular prisms.

Words to Learn
surface area
triangular prism

After measuring cooling rates in a science lab, Monica was trying to determine why her solution cooled at a different rate than Larry's solution. They each had the same amount of solution, and each block of ice placed in the solution had the same weight. The only noticeable difference was the shape of the two blocks of ice.

Monica's cube

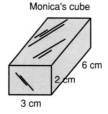

Before the experiment, Monica's block measured 3 centimeters wide, 6 centimeters long, and 2 centimeters thick. Larry's block measured 3 centimeters wide, 4 centimeters long, and 3 centimeters thick. Their teacher suggested that finding the surface area of each block of ice would explain the difference in cooling rates.

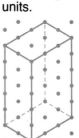

Larry's cube

An ice cube is an example of a rectangular prism. To find the **surface area** of a prism, you need to find the area of each face and then add.

Mini-Lab

Work with a partner.

Materials: graph paper, scissors, tape

- Draw the pattern shown at the right on graph paper and cut it out. *This pattern is an example of a net.*
- Fold the pattern along the lines and tape the edges to form a rectangular prism.

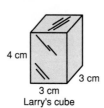

Talk About It

a. What is the length, width, and height of the prism? $4 \times 4 \times 12$ units

b. What is the area of each base? 16 units²

c. What is the area of each of the other four faces? 48 units²

d. What is the total surface area? 224 units²

Lesson 12-4 Surface Area of Prisms **475**

Interactive Mathematics Tools

This multimedia software provides an interactive lesson that is tied directly to Lesson 12-4. Students will explore the volume and surface area of a cube or prism.

Study Guide Masters, p. 108

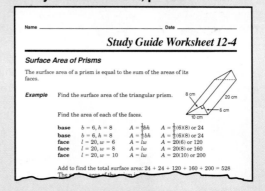

5-Minute Check
(Over Lesson 12-3)

1. Draw a rectangular prism measuring $5 \times 3 \times 2$ units.

2. Draw a triangular prism with a height of 3 units.
   Sample answer:

1 FOCUS

Motivating the Lesson

Questioning Ask the following question. *Which will evaporate faster, a wide shallow pool or a deep narrow pool of the same length and containing the same amount of water? Explain.* The shallow pool; more surface area is exposed for evaporation.

2 TEACH

Using the Mini-Lab Ask students to calculate the increase in total surface area if the prism measured $4 \times 5 \times 12$ units. 32 units²

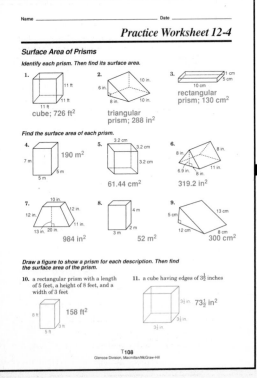

476

A **triangular prism** is a prism whose bases are triangles. In Lesson 12-3, we learned that geometric figures can be drawn from several perspectives. The prism at the right is drawn so that the bases are *not* on the top and bottom.

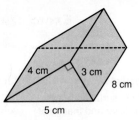
4 cm, 3 cm, 8 cm, 5 cm

Example *Problem Solving*

Physics When light travels through a prism, it is refracted to form the colors of the rainbow. A special coating can be placed on a prism like the one shown above to enhance the brilliance of the rainbow. The amount of coating needed is based on the surface area of the prism. Find the surface area of the prism.

To find the surface area of this prism, we need to find the area of each of the faces. Since the bases are triangles, use the formula $A = \frac{1}{2}bh$ to find the area of each triangle. The other three faces are rectangles.

face	dimensions	area	
one base	$b = 4, h = 3$	$A = \frac{1}{2}(4)(3)$ or	6
second base	$b = 4, h = 3$	$A = \frac{1}{2}(4)(3)$ or	6
face	$b = 8, h = 3$	$A = 8(3)$ or	24
face	$b = 8, h = 4$	$A = 8(4)$ or	32
face	$b = 8, h = 5$	$A = 8(5)$ or	40
		TOTAL	108

The surface area of the prism is 108 square inches.

Checking for Understanding

Communicating Mathematics

Read and study the lesson to answer each question.

1. **Tell** what figures you see when you view a triangular prism from different perspectives. triangle, rectangle, parallelogram

2. **Draw** a rectangular prism that has all six sides congruent. What do we call this shape? See students' work; cube.

3. **Write** a quick way to find the surface area of the prism in the Mini-Lab without finding the area of each face. Sample answer: 2($\ell h + \ell w + wh$)

Guided Practice

Identify each prism. Then find its surface area.

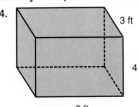

4. 3 ft, 4 ft, 6 ft — rectangular prism; 108 ft²
5. 4 m, 3.46 m, 7 m, 4 m, 4 m — triangular prism; 97.84 m²
6. 2 in., 12 in., 15 in. — rectangular prism; 468 in²

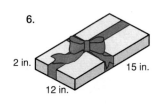

Classroom Vignette

"You may want to extend this lesson by giving each student a sheet of graph paper and a number that represents the surface area of a prism. Using the graph paper, students construct a prism having the required surface area."

Robert Daniels

Robert Daniels, Teacher
Buckeye Valley Middle School, Radnor, OH

Exercises

Independent Practice

Find the surface area of each prism.

7.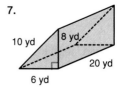

10 yd, 8 yd, 20 yd, 6 yd

8.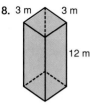

3 m, 3 m, 12 m

9.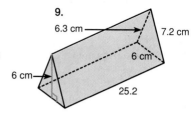

6.3 cm, 7.2 cm, 6 cm, 6 cm, 25.2

7. 528 yd²
8. 162 m²
9. 527.4 cm²
10. 37 $\frac{1}{2}$ ft² or 37.5 ft²
11. 64.5 m²
12. 372 in²

10.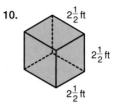

$2\frac{1}{2}$ ft, $2\frac{1}{2}$ ft, $2\frac{1}{2}$ ft

11.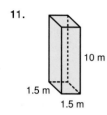

10 m, 1.5 m, 1.5 m

12.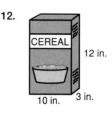

CEREAL, 12 in., 10 in., 3 in.

Draw a figure to show a prism for each description. Then find the surface area of the prism. **For figures, see Solutions Manual.**

13. a rectangular prism with a length of 4 centimeters, a width of 7 centimeters, and a height of 3 centimeters 122 cm²

14. a triangular prism whose bases are right triangles with sides 5 meters, 12 meters, and 13 meters and whose height is 10 meters 360 m²

15. a rectangular prism with all edges 8 feet long 384 ft²
    17. No, the last 2 digits are not divisible by 4.

Mixed Review
16. Evaluate the expression $2^4 \cdot 4^3$. *(Lesson 1-9)* 1,024

17. Use divisibility rules to determine if 726 is divisible by 4. *(Lesson 6-1)*

18. Draw a hexagonal prism that is 5 units tall. *(Lesson 12-3)* See margin.
    19. Monica's cube—it has the greatest surface area.

Problem Solving and Applications
19. **Science** Refer to the science experiment on page 475. Which block of ice would cool the solution the quickest? Explain your answer.

20. **Critical Thinking** Suppose you had eight identical wooden blocks you are gluing together to form a prism. What is the shape of the prism that would require the least amount of paint to cover it? cube

21. **Design** Mr. Mayoree has been commissioned to build a glass display case in the shape of a trapezoidal prism. The case will be made of panes of glass held together by brass edging. Find how many square inches of glass he needs to build this display case. 8,100 in²

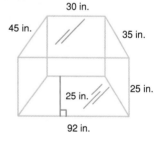

30 in., 45 in., 35 in., 25 in., 25 in., 92 in.

22. **Journal Entry** Find an example of a prism in your house and measure it. Write a sentence about how surface area can be used with this object. See students' work.

Lesson 12-4 Surface Area of Prisms **477**

Extending the Lesson

Using Cooperative Groups Have students work in small groups to solve this problem: *After the surface of a cube is painted, the cube is cut into 64 smaller cubes.*
How many have no faces painted? 8
1 face painted? 24
2 faces painted? 24
3 faces painted? 8

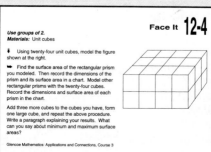

Cooperative Learning Activity

Use groups of 2.
Materials: Unit cubes

Using twenty-four unit cubes, model the figure shown at the right.

Find the surface area of the rectangular prism you modeled. Then record the dimensions of the prism and its surface area in a chart. Model other rectangular prisms with the twenty-four cubes. Record the dimensions and surface area of each prism in the chart.

Add three more cubes to the cubes you have, form one large cube, and repeat the above procedure. Write a paragraph explaining your results. What can you say about minimum and maximum surface areas?

Glencoe Mathematics: Applications and Connections, Course 3

Face It 12-4

Close

Ask students to explain how they can find the surface area of a prism. Find the area of each face and add.

3 PRACTICE/APPLY

Assignment Guide
Maximum: 7–22
Minimum: 7–15 odd, 16–21

For **Extra Practice,** see p. 613.

Alternate Assessment

Writing Have students work in pairs to create problems involving the surface area of prisms.

Additional Answer

18. Sample answer:

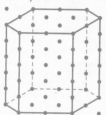

Enrichment Masters, p. 108

Name _____ Date _____

Enrichment Worksheet 12-4

The Five Platonic Solids

There are only five regular convex solids. They are called the *Platonic Solids* and are shown here.

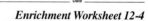

tetrahedron   hexahedron   octahedron   icosahedron   dodecahedron

1. Write the name of each Platonic Solid under its net.

dodecahedron   tetrahedron   hexahedron

octahedron   icosahedron

2. Complete this chart for the Platonic Solids.

	Tetrahedron	Hexahedron	Octahedron	Icosahedron	Dodecahedron
Number of Faces	4	6	8	20	12
Number of Edges	6	12	12	30	30
Number of Vertices	4	8	6	12	20

3. Write an equation relating the number of faces, edges, and vertices of the Platonic Solids. This equation is called Euler's Formula and is true for all simple polyhedra. $V - E + F = 2$

T108
Glencoe Division, Macmillan/McGraw-Hill

477

NCTM Standards: 1–4, 7, 12, 13

Lesson Resources
- Study Guide Master 12-5
- Practice Master 12-5
- Enrichment Master 12-5
- Interdisciplinary Master, p. 26
- Group Activity Card 12-5

 Transparency 12-5 contains the 5-Minute Check and a teaching aid for this lesson.

⏱ 5-Minute Check
(Over Lesson 12-4)

Find the surface area of each prism.

1.

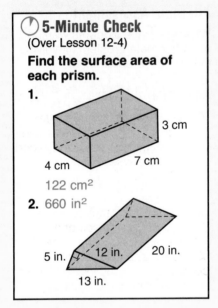

3 cm

4 cm   7 cm

122 cm²

2. 660 in²

5 in.   12 in.   20 in.

13 in.

1 FOCUS

Motivating the Lesson

Activity Display a rectangular prism and a cylinder. Ask students to describe similarities and differences between the two objects.

2 TEACH

Using the Mini-Lab Show students a can label to convince them that the side of a circular can is actually a rectangle.

Objective
Find the surface area of circular cylinders.

Words to Learn
circular cylinder

12-5 Surface Area of Cylinders

In Lesson 4-3, you read about a potato chip taste test. One of the brands that rated in the "good" category was packaged in a tube-shaped container. These containers are examples of cylinders. A cylindrical container is relatively easy to manufacture and, once filled, can be sealed to keep the contents fresh.

Most of the cylinders we see are called **circular cylinders.** The bases of a circular cylinder are two parallel, congruent circular regions.

As with prisms, you find the surface area of the cylinder by finding the area of the two bases and adding the area of the side. However, the "side" of a cylinder is one curved surface.

←7.4 cm→

24 cm

Mini-Lab

Work in groups of three.

Materials: small can, graph paper, scissors

- Trace the bases of the can on graph paper. Cut out the circles.
- Measure the height of the can. Cut a long strip of graph paper so that its width is the height of the can. Wrap the strip around the can. Cut the excess paper off so that the strip just fits around the can.
- Record the dimensions of your three pieces of graph paper to the nearest centimeter. Estimate the total area of the three pieces of graph paper.
- Tape the pieces together to form a cylinder.

LOOK BACK

You can review circumference on page 284.

b. They are approximately the same.

rectangle

Talk About It
a. What is the shape of the paper that goes around the can?
b. Find the circumference of the circles to the nearest centimeter. How does this compare with the length of the strip?
c. When you tape your cylinder together, the length of the strip becomes what measurement of the circle? **circumference**
d. Draw a net for a cylinder. **See margin.**

OPTIONS

Multicultural Education

There are only five solids whose faces are regular congruent polygons (one such solid is the cube). They are called the *Platonic solids* after the Greek philosopher Plato. Have students do research to find the names of the five solids and to build a model of each.

Additional Answer

Mini-Lab

d. Sample answer:

In the Mini-Lab, you see that the curved side of the cylinder can be flattened into a rectangle. The rectangle has the same height as the cylinder. Its length is the same measurement as the circumference of the base.

Example 1

Find the surface area of the cylinder to the nearest hundredth.

The circular base of the cylinder has a diameter of 10 meters. This means the radius is 5 meters. The height of the cylinder is 2 meters.

area of one base (πr^2) $\pi \cdot 5^2$ → $\boxed{\pi}$ $\boxed{\times}$ 5 $\boxed{x^2}$ $\boxed{+}$

area of other base (πr^2) $\pi \cdot 5^2$ → $\boxed{\pi}$ $\boxed{\times}$ 5 $\boxed{x^2}$ $\boxed{+}$

area of rectangle $(C \cdot h)$ $\pi(10) \cdot 2$ → $\boxed{\pi}$ $\boxed{\times}$ 10 $\boxed{\times}$ 2

total area   → $\boxed{=}$ 219.91149

The area of the cylinder is about 219.91 square meters.

1. Find 2 × the area of the base + h × circumference of the base.

Checking for Understanding

Communicating Mathematics

Read and study the lesson to answer each question.

1. **Write** in your own words how to find the surface area of a cylinder.
2. **Write** a list of at least three products that are usually packaged in cylinder-shaped containers. **See students' work.**

   The value of π is approximate.
3. **Tell** why the surface area of the cylinder in Example 1 is an approximation.
4. **Draw** the shapes you see when you look at the top, bottom, and side of a cylinder. **circles, rectangle**

Guided Practice

Find the surface area of each cylinder. **Answers rounded to nearest tenth.**

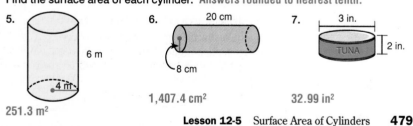

5. 6 m, 4 m
251.3 m²

6. 20 cm, 8 cm
1,407.4 cm²

7. 3 in., 2 in. TUNA
32.99 in²

Lesson 12-5   Surface Area of Cylinders   **479**

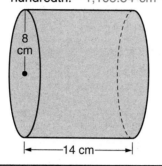
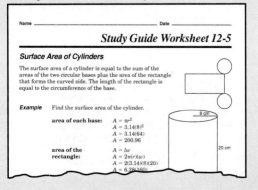
479

480

Exercises

Find the surface area of each cylinder.

8.  11 yd
5 yd
502.7 yd²

9. 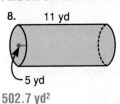 TOMATO SOUP
10.5 cm
6.5 cm
280.8 cm²

10.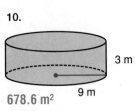
3 m
9 m
678.6 m²

Draw each cylinder. Then find its surface area. For drawings, see Solutions Manual.

11. The radius of the base is 3 inches and its height is 5 inches. **150.8 in²**

12. The diameter of the base is 30 centimeters and its height is 12 centimeters.

13. The area of its base is 24.2 square meters and its height is 20 meters. **397.2 m²**

See margin.

14. Solve $6b - 5 < 7$. Show the solution on a number line. *(Lesson 2-10)*

12. 2,544.7 cm²

15. Solve $h = 8\frac{3}{4} \div \frac{1}{2}$. *(Lesson 7-9)* **$17\frac{1}{2}$**

16. Express 35.2% as a decimal. *(Lesson 10-3)* **0.352**

17. **Geometry** Draw a rectangular prism that is 5 inches long, 3 inches wide, and 2 inches tall. Then find the surface area of the prism. *(Lesson 12-4)* **62 in²**

18. **Food** Wisconsin produces more cheese than any other state in the United States. When cheese is made, the curd is pressed into large hoops lined with cheesecloth. The cheese is then removed from the hoops and sliced into wheels. Some cheeses are sealed in wax or a thin plastic film to protect their moisture. Find the surface area of the plastic film on the small cheese wheel shown at the right. **201.1 in²**

4 in.
8 in.

19. **Critical Thinking** Will the surface area of a cylinder increase more if you double the height or double the radius of the base? Give examples to support your answer. **Double the radius; see students' work.**

20. **Design** The model at the right is a preliminary sketch of a type of trash can for the school cafeteria. The school plans to paint them using the school's colors.

a. Find the surface area of the container. **30.5 ft²**

b. The enamel paint they are going to use covers 200 square feet per gallon. Approximately how many trash cans can be covered with 1 gallon of paint? **7 trash cans**

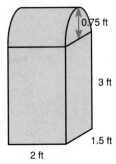
0.75 ft
3 ft
1.5 ft
2 ft

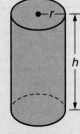

21. **Manufacturing** Morton® salt packages its table salt in cylinder-shaped containers whose base has a diameter of $3\frac{1}{2}$ inches and whose height is $5\frac{1}{2}$ inches. Morton places a label around the curved surface of the cylinder. If the label is placed $\frac{1}{4}$ inch from the top and bottom, what is the surface area of the label? **about 55 in²**

22. **Data Search** Refer to pages 462 and 463. Find the approximate areas of the circles formed by the edges of a basketball, a baseball, and a soccer ball when they are cut exactly through their centers.
basketball: 71.62 in², baseball: 6.81 in², soccer: 62.39 in²

12 Assessment: Mid-Chapter Review

1. Find the area of a circle whose radius is 6 cm. *(Lesson 12-1)*
about 113.1 cm²

2. **Probability** Shu Ping likes to play a game at the arcade where he rolls a ball up a ramp and it lands in one of four hoops. What is the probability that Shu Ping will score 50 points on the first ball?
(Lesson 12-1) $\frac{1}{16}$

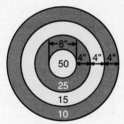

3. Use cubes to build a model of the solid from the perspectives shown. *(Lesson 12-2)*
See students' work.

side   top   front

4. Sketch two different views of a rectangular prism that is 4 feet wide by 3 feet tall by 1 foot long. *(Lesson 12-3)* **See Solutions Manual.**

Find the surface area of each solid. *(Lessons 12-4, 12-5)*

5.

20 m
10 m
1,885 m²

6.
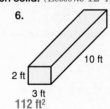
10 ft
2 ft
3 ft
112 ft²

7.

15 in.
9 in.
30 in.
12 in.
1,188 in²

Lesson 12-5 Surface Area of Cylinders **481**

Extending the Lesson

Using Formulas Have students calculate the surface areas of several cylinders using the method shown in the lesson. Then have them compare each answer with the value they obtain by substituting r and h in the expression $2\pi r(r + h)$. Have them make a conjecture about the surface area of a cylinder.
surface area = $2\pi r(r + h)$

Cooperative Learning Activity

Net a Cylinder 12-5

Use groups of 4.
Materials: Construction paper, compass, metric ruler, scissors, tape

➤ Each group member uses the figure shown at the right to draw a net for a cylinder on construction paper. Cut along the solid lines, fold along the dashed lines, and tape the tabs.

Each group member should share his or her model with the group. Tell the circumference of the circle you used, the height of the rectangle, and the total surface area.

circumference of circle

Glencoe Mathematics: Applications and Connections, Course 3

Enrichment Masters, p. 109

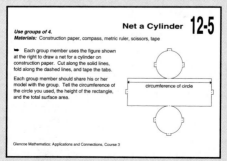

Name _____ Date _____

Enrichment Worksheet 12-5

Sliced Solids

In the diagrams on this page, a plane slices through a solid figure. The intersection of the plane with the solid is called a *cross section*. The drawings for each problem show a sliced solid and the dimensions of the resulting cross section.

Find the surface areas of the two solids that result from the slice.

1. One-fourth of the cube is sliced off the top.
8 in.
8 in.
192 in², 320 in²

2. One-third of the prism is sliced off the back.
7 in.
5 in.
9 in.
142 in², 214 in²

3. The cube is sliced in half.
10 cm
14.1 cm
441 cm², 441 cm²

4. The cylinder is sliced in half.
16 m
20 m
1,023.72 m², 1,023.72 m²

5. The cylinder is sliced in half.
100 m
80 m
17,584 m², 17,584 m²

6. The prism is sliced in half.
56.6 ft
40 ft   40 ft
8,430 ft², 8,430 ft²

T109
Glencoe Division, Macmillan/McGraw-Hill

481

NCTM Standards: 1–4, 7, 12

Lesson Resources
- Study Guide Master 12-6
- Practice Master 12-6
- Enrichment Master 12-6
- Group Activity Card 12-6

 Transparency 12-6 contains the 5-Minute Check and a teaching aid for this lesson.

🕐 5-Minute Check
(Over Lesson 12-5)

Find the surface area of the cylinder.   1,130.97 in²

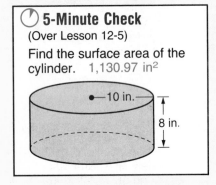

1 FOCUS

Motivating the Lesson

Activity   Blow up a balloon. Ask students to describe the difference between the surface area and the volume of the balloon.   The surface area is the area of the balloon material. The volume is the amount of air inside.

2 TEACH

Using Logical Reasoning   Ask students to find the dimensions of another rectangular prism (different than the one shown on page 482) with a volume of 24 cm³. Sample answers: 1 × 2 × 12 cm; 2 × 2 × 6 cm

---

12-6   Volume of Prisms and Cylinders

Objective

Find the volume of prisms and circular cylinders.

Words to Learn

volume

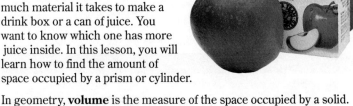

In Lessons 12-4 and 12-5, you found the amount of material it takes to make prisms and cylinders. However, if you are very thirsty, you don't care how much material it takes to make a drink box or a can of juice. You want to know which one has more juice inside. In this lesson, you will learn how to find the amount of space occupied by a prism or cylinder.

In geometry, **volume** is the measure of the space occupied by a solid. It is measured in cubic units. Two common units of measure for volume are the cubic centimeter (cm³) and the cubic inch (in³).

In Lesson 12-2, you used cubes to make models of solid shapes. The prism model at the right was built with 24 cubes. If each cube is a centimeter cube, the volume of the prism is 24 cubic centimeters.

The dimensions of the prism are 2 centimeters by 3 centimeters by 4 centimeters. The model is made of 4 layers. Each layer contains 6 cubes. Notice that 6 is the area of the base, found by multiplying $3 \cdot 2$.

Volume of a Rectangular Prism	**In words:** The volume (V) of a rectangular prism is the area of the base (B) times the height (h).
	In symbols: $V = Bh$ or, since $B = \ell w$, $V = \ell wh$

Example 1

Find the volume of a rectangular prism with length 15 inches, width 13 inches, and height 17 inches.

First draw the prism and label the dimensions.

$V = \ell wh$

$V = 15(13)(17)$ $\ell = 15, w = 13, h = 17$

15 ☒ 13 ☒ 17 ☰ ∃∃।5

The prism has a volume of 3,315 cubic inches.

OPTIONS

Limited English Proficiency

Use models to clarify the vocabulary and to help students distinguish between volume and surface area. Have students indicate the bases of cylinders and prisms, and explain how they would find the area of each solid.

To find the volume of any other type of prism, you can still use the $V = Bh$ formula.

Example 2

Find the volume of the triangular prism.

First find the area of the base, which is a triangle.

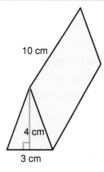

10 cm

4 cm

3 cm

$A = \dfrac{1}{2}bh$ *Formula for area of a triangle.*

$A = \dfrac{1}{2} \cdot 3 \cdot 4$ *Replace b with 3 and h with 4.*

$A = 6$ *The area of the base is 6 cm².*

Now find the volume of the prism.

$V = Bh$ *Formula for the area of a prism*

$V = 6 \cdot 10$ *Replace B with 6 and h with 10.*

$V = 60$ The volume of the triangular prism is 60 cm³.

To find the volume of a cylinder, you again use the formula, $V = Bh$. However, since the area of the base of a cylinder is the area of a circle (πr^2), the formula becomes $V = \pi r^2 h$.

Volume of a Cylinder	**In words:** The volume (V) of a cylinder is the area of the base (B) times the height (h).
	In symbols: $V = Bh$ or $V = \pi r^2 h$

Example 3   *Problem Solving*

Home Economics   You bought a 10-pound sack of sugar. The sack is a rectangular prism 9 inches by 8 inches by 5 inches. You have two cylinder-shaped canisters into which the sugar can be poured. Which canister is better suited to hold the sugar?

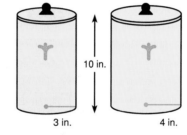

10 in.

3 in.   4 in.

First find the volume of the sugar.

$V = \ell w h$

$V = 9 \cdot 8 \cdot 5$ or 360 in³

Now find the volume of each cylinder.

$V = \pi r^2 h$ $V = \pi r^2 h$

$V = \pi (3)^2 \cdot 10 \approx 282.74$ in³ $V = \pi (4)^2 \cdot 10 \approx 502.65$ in³

The first canister is not large enough to contain the sugar. The second canister is the better choice.

Lesson 12-6   Volume of Prisms and Cylinders   **483**

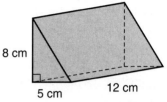
Reteaching Activity

Using Models   State the dimensions of a rectangular prism. Have students use centimeter cubes to build a prism having those dimensions. Have students count the cubes in their model. Show that the same number results from multiplying the three dimensions.

Study Guide Masters, p. 110

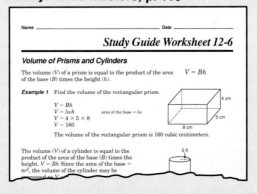

Name _____   Date _____

Study Guide Worksheet 12-6

Volume of Prisms and Cylinders

The volume (V) of a prism is equal to the product of the area $V = Bh$
of the base (B) times the height (h).

Example 1   Find the volume of the rectangular prism.

4 cm

5 cm

8 cm

$V = Bh$
$V = lwh$ area of the base = lw
$V = 4 \times 5 \times 8$
$V = 160$

The volume of the rectangular prism is 160 cubic centimeters.

The volume (V) of a cylinder is equal to the product of the area of the base (B) times the height. $V = Bh$ Since the area of the base = πr^2, the volume of the cylinder may be expressed as V...

5 ft

483

Assignment Guide
Maximum: 12–26
Minimum: 13–19 odd, 21–25

For **Extra Practice,** see p. 613.

Alternate Assessment

Speaking Name the area of the base and the height of a prism or cylinder. Have students state the volume.

Additional Answers

1. All volumes can be found using the formula $V = Bh$.
2. In a prism, $B = \ell w$. In a cylinder, $B = \pi r^2$.
3. A square has only two dimensions. Volume requires three dimensions.

Practice Masters, p. 110

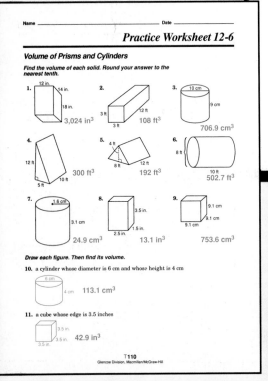

Checking for Understanding   For answers to Exercises 1-3, see margin.

Communicating Mathematics

Read and study the lesson to answer each question.

1. **Write** a sentence to state how the volume formulas for the rectangular prism, triangular prism, and cylinder are alike.

2. **Write** a sentence to state how the volume formula for a rectangular prism is different from the formula for a cylinder.

3. **Tell** why it is impossible to find the volume of a square.

4. **Draw** a cube and find its volume. What is a short way to write the formula for the volume of a cube? **See students' work.** $V = s^3$

5. **Tell** why the volumes of the cylinders in Example 3 are approximations.
The value of π is approximate.

Guided Practice

6. 120 m³
7. 314.2 ft³
8. 60 yd³
9. 141.4 cm³
10. 18 in³
11. 1,125.7 cm³

Find the volume of each solid. Round answers to the nearest tenth.

6.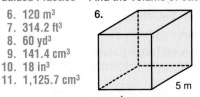
4 m   5 m   6 m

7.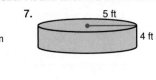
5 ft   4 ft

8.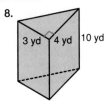
3 yd   4 yd   10 yd

9.
6 cm   5 cm

10.
JUICE   4 in.   1.5 in.   3 in.

11.
5.25 cm   Green Beans   13 cm

Exercises

Independent Practice

12. 392 yd³
13. 1,032.2 cm³
14. 100 ft³
15. 1.728 cm³
16. 70 ft³
17. 5,513.5 mm³

Find the volume of each solid. Round answers to the nearest tenth.

12.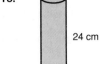
8 yd   7 yd   7 yd

13.
24 cm   7.4 cm

14.
2 ft   10 ft   10 ft

15.
1.2 cm   1.2 cm   1.2 cm

16.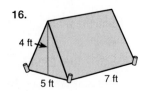
4 ft   5 ft   7 ft

17.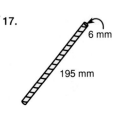
6 mm   195 mm

OPTIONS

Bell Ringer

A cube has a volume of 64 cm³.
What is its surface area?   96 cm²

Draw each figure. Then find its volume. For drawings, see students' work.

18. Find the volume of a cylinder whose diameter is 12 meters and is 14 meters tall. **1,583.4 m³**

19. Find the volume of a triangular prism that is 10 feet tall and has a base that is a right triangle with legs 5 feet and 12 feet. **300 ft³**

20. Find the volume of a pentagonal prism that is 5 centimeters tall and has a base that has an area of 25.4 square centimeters. **127 cm³**

Mixed Review

21. **Geometry** Draw two congruent trapezoids. *(Lesson 5-6)* See students' work.

22. Find the best integer estimate for $-\sqrt{76}$. Then check your estimate by using a calculator. *(Lesson 8-2)* **−9**

23. Find the surface area of a cylinder 9 centimeters tall with a radius of 4 centimeters. *(Lesson 12-5)* **326.73 cm²**

Problem Solving and Applications

24. **Marketing** The graph uses cylinders to show the change in sales of music media from 1986 to 1992.

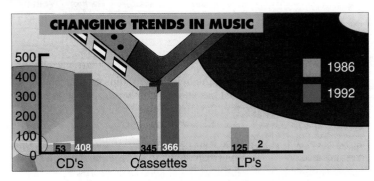

24a. LP's

a. Which type of music medium had a decrease in sales from 1986 to 1992?

b. Which type of music medium had the greatest percentage increase in sales? **CD's**

c. Write a sentence to explain why you think the amounts in each category increased or decreased. **See margin.**

d. Suppose you built a three-dimensional model of this graph and the diameter of each cylinder was 50 millimeters. What would be the volume of each cylinder, if each million sold was 1 millimeter high? **See margin.**

25. **Critical Thinking** A rectangular ditch is dug to hold a pipe being installed for a drainage system. What is the volume of dirt to be filled in around the pipe? *Assume the pipe is the same length as the ditch.* **about 259 ft³**

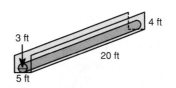

26. **Journal Entry** Write about some real objects that will help you remember what a cube and a cylinder look like. Do you think that any of these objects were designed to have a specific volume? **See students' work.**

Lesson 12-6 Volume of Prisms and Cylinders   **485**

Extending the Lesson

Using Lists A rectangular prism has a volume of 36 cm³. Have students make a list showing all the possible whole-number dimensions of the prism. $1 \times 1 \times 36$; $1 \times 2 \times 18$; $1 \times 3 \times 12$; $1 \times 4 \times 9$; $1 \times 6 \times 6$; $2 \times 2 \times 9$; $2 \times 3 \times 6$; $3 \times 3 \times 4$

Cooperative Learning Activity

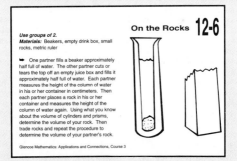

On the Rocks 12-6

Use groups of 2.
Materials: Beakers, empty drink box, small rocks, metric ruler

➡ One partner fills a beaker approximately half full of water. The other partner cuts or tears the top off an empty juice box and fills it approximately half full of water. Each partner measures the height of the column of water in his or her container in centimeters. Then each partner places a rock in his or her container and measures the height of the column of water again. Using what you know about the volume of cylinders and prisms, determine the volume of your rock. Then trade rocks and repeat the procedure to determine the volume of your partner's rock.

Glencoe Mathematics: Applications and Connections, Course 3

Additional Answers

24. c. Sample answer: CDs became more affordable, have better sound quality, and can hold more songs. The quality and convenience of LPs was less than that of CDs and cassettes.
    d. CD 1986: 104,065.3 mm³
      CD 1992: 801,106.1 mm³
      LP 1986: 245,436.9 mm³
      LP 1992: 3,927.0 mm³
      Cassette 1986: 677,405.9 mm³
      Cassette 1992: 718,639.3 mm³

Enrichment Masters, p. 110

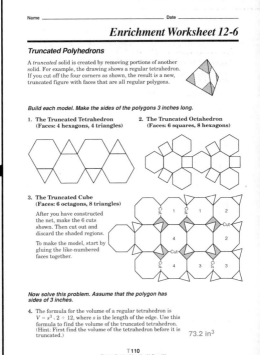

Name _____   Date _____

Enrichment Worksheet 12-6

Truncated Polyhedrons

A *truncated* solid is created by removing portions of another solid. For example, the drawing shows a regular tetrahedron. If you cut off the four corners as shown, the result is a new, truncated figure with faces that are all regular polygons.

Build each model. Make the sides of the polygons 3 inches long.

1. The Truncated Tetrahedron (Faces: 4 hexagons, 4 triangles)

2. The Truncated Octahedron (Faces: 6 squares, 8 hexagons)

3. The Truncated Cube (Faces: 6 octagons, 8 triangles)

After you have constructed the net, make the 6 cuts shown. Then cut out and discard the shaded regions.

To make the model, start by gluing the like-numbered faces together.

Now solve this problem. Assume that the polygon has sides of 3 inches.

4. The formula for the volume of a regular tetrahedron is $V = s^3 \cdot \sqrt{2} \div 12$, where s is the length of the edge. Use this formula to find the volume of the truncated tetrahedron. (Hint: First find the volume of the tetrahedron before it is truncated.) **73.2 in³**

T-110
Glencoe Division, Macmillan/McGraw-Hill

485

NCTM Standards: 1–4, 7, 12, 13

Management Tips

For Students Students should make several measurements of height and radius and record the mean of each set in the chart.

For the Overhead Projector *Overhead Manipulative Resources* provides appropriate materials for teacher or student demonstration of the activities in this Mathematics Lab.

1 FOCUS

Introducing the Lab

Ask students to list several factors that a manufacturer might take into consideration when choosing a product container.

2 TEACH

Using Logical Reasoning Point out that since the radius is *squared* in the formula for the volume of a cylinder, students must alter the height more than the radius in their search for equal volumes.

3 PRACTICE/APPLY

Using Problem Solving Ask students to find the dimensions of the rectangular prism with volume 64 cm³ and the smallest possible surface area. 4 cm × 4 cm × 4 cm

Close

Have students explain why a manufacturer would minimize surface area rather than volume.

Additional Answer

4a. Sample answer: The circumference of a can is about the same as the circumference of the glass bottle used previously.

486

Objective
Investigate how surface area and volume are related.

Materials
soft drink can
calculator

Containers are often manufactured so that the least amount of materials is used for a given volume. This is an application of surface area and volume.

Try this!

Work in groups of three.

- Find the height and radius of the base of a soft drink can to the nearest millimeter. Find the volume and surface area. Record your findings in the first row of a chart like the one below.

Cylinder	Height	Radius	Volume	Surface Area
soft drink can	120	33	410,543	31,723
#1				
#2				

DID YOU KNOW

The first aluminum soft drink can appeared on grocery shelves in 1963.

- Alter the height and radius measurements to create a new cylinder that has approximately the same volume as the soft drink can. Then find the surface area of this cylinder. Record your findings in the second row of the chart.

- Use your calculator to create four more cylinders that have approximately the same volume as the soft drink can. Record your findings in the appropriate rows.

What do you think? For Exercises 1-2, see students' work.

1. What dimensions resulted in the greatest surface area?

2. What dimensions resulted in the least surface area?

3. When the radius is greater than the radius of the original can, what happens to the height of the cylinder? It is less than the original.

Application

4. **Manufacturing** If you were manufacturing a soft drink can, which dimensions would you probably want to use for your can? Explain your answer. Answers will vary.

   a. Why do you think soft drink manufacturers have chosen the size that is used? See margin.

   b. If it costs 0.016¢ per square inch to manufacture a can, how much would a company save in producing 100,000 cans by changing to a smaller surface area for the same volume? Answers will vary.

486 **Chapter 12** Area and Volume

OPTIONS

Lab Manual You may wish to make copies of the blackline master on p. 74 of the *Lab Manual* for students to use as a recording sheet.

Lab Manual, p. 74

Name _____ Date _____

Mathematics Lab Worksheet

Use with page 486

Surface Area and Volume

Try this! Sample answers are given.

Cylinder	Height (mm)	Radius (mm)	Volume (mm³)	Surface Area (mm²)
Soft drink can	120	33	410,543	31,723
#1	60	47	416,386	31,598
#2	240	23	398,856	38,007
#3	30	66	410,543	39,810
#4	13	99	400,279	69,666
#5	1,080	11	410,543	75,404

12-7 Volume of Pyramids and Cones

Objective
Find the volume of pyramids and circular cones.

Words to Learn
altitude
circular cone

You can review ratios on page 338.

The model shows how many pyramid-fulls of sand it takes to fill the prism.

The volume of the pyramid of Quetzacoatl in Cholula, Mexico is reported to be about 116 million cubic feet. If a rectangular prism having the same dimensions as the pyramid were built, it would have a volume of 348 million cubic feet.

What is the ratio of the volume of the pyramid to the volume of the prism?

$$\frac{\text{volume of pyramid}}{\text{volume of prism}} = \frac{116 \text{ million ft}^3}{348 \text{ million ft}^3} \text{ or } \frac{1}{3}$$

This ratio suggests that the volume of a pyramid is one-third the volume of the prism into which it will fit. So, $V = \frac{1}{3}Bh$.

Volume of a Pyramid	**In words:** The volume of a pyramid equals one-third the area of the base (B) times the height (h). **In symbols:** $V = \frac{1}{3}Bh$

The segment that goes from the vertex of a pyramid to its base and is perpendicular to the base is called the **altitude.** The height of a pyramid is measured along the altitude. Like prisms, a pyramid can be named by the shape of its base.

Example 1

Find the volume of the square pyramid.

$V = \frac{1}{3}Bh$

$V = \frac{1}{3}s^2h$ *Since the base is a square, $B = s^2$.*

$V = \frac{1}{3} \cdot (4)^2 \cdot 6$ *Replace s with 4 and h with 6.*

$V = \frac{96}{3}$ or 32

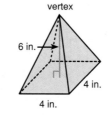

The volume of the square pyramid is 32 cubic inches.

Lesson 12-7   Volume of Pyramids and Cones   **487**

OPTIONS

Reteaching Activity

Using Connections Have students use reference materials to find the dimensions of the Great Pyramid at Giza, Egypt, then calculate its volume. The pyramid has a square base 756 feet on a side and it was originally 481 feet tall, giving it a volume of about 91.6 million cubic feet.

Study Guide Masters, p. 111

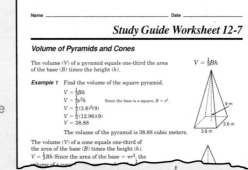

12-7 Lesson Notes

NCTM Standards: 1–4, 7, 9, 12

Lesson Resources
• Study Guide Master 12-7
• Practice Master 12-7
• Enrichment Master 12-7
• Technology Master, p. 26
• Group Activity Card 12-7

 Transparency 12-7 contains the 5-Minute Check and a teaching aid for this lesson.

5-Minute Check
(Over Lesson 12-6)

1. Find the volume of a rectangular prism that is 5 centimeters long, 4 centimeters wide, and 8 centimeters tall. 160 cm³

2. Find the volume of the cylinder. 301.59 in³

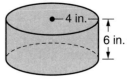

1 FOCUS

Motivating the Lesson

Questioning Have students read the first paragraph of the lesson. Then ask the following questions.

• *How many cubic feet are there in a cubic yard?* 27

• *Find the volume of the pyramid in cubic yards.* about 4.3 million cubic yards

2 TEACH

Using Mental Math Ask students to solve the following problems mentally.

• *What is the volume of a pyramid with base area 6 square inches and height 4 inches?* 8 in³

• *What is the volume of a cone with base area 15 cm² and height 7 cm?* 35 cm³

487

More Examples

For Example 1

Find the volume of the triangular pyramid.
80 m³

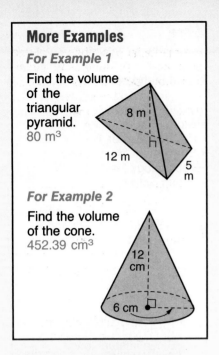

8 m

12 m

5 m

For Example 2

Find the volume of the cone.
452.39 cm³

12 cm

6 cm

Checking for Understanding

Exercises 1-3 are designed to help you assess students' understanding through reading, writing, speaking, and modeling. You should work through these exercises with your students and then monitor their work on Guided Practice Exercises 4-6.

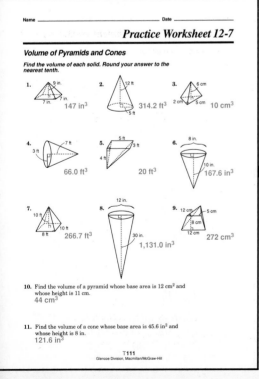

Remember that the formula for volume of a cylinder was derived from the $V = Bh$ formula. A **circular cone** can fit inside a cylinder in the same way a pyramid fits inside a prism. The relationship of the volumes is also the same.

Volume of a Cone	**In words:** The volume (V) of a cone equals one-third the area of the base (B) times the height (h).
	In symbols: $V = \frac{1}{3}Bh$ or $V = \frac{1}{3}\pi r^2 h$

Example 2 *Problem Solving*

Food Drumstick® ice cream treats are ice cream cones filled to the top by combinations of ice cream, fudge, nuts, and other ingredients. The level cone is covered by paper to protect it. Find the volume of the Drumstick® treat shown at the right.

2.5 cm

15 cm

$V = \frac{1}{3}Bh$

$V = \frac{1}{3}(\pi r^2)h$ *Replace B with πr^2.*

$V = \frac{1}{3}(\pi \cdot 2.5^2) \cdot 15$ *Replace r with 2.5 and h with 15.*

$V = 1 \boxed{\div} 3 \boxed{\times} \boxed{\pi} \boxed{\times} 2.5 \boxed{x^2} \boxed{\times} 15 \boxed{=} 98.174771$

The volume of the Drumstick® is about 98.17 cubic centimeters.

Checking for Understanding

Communicating Mathematics

Read and study the lesson to answer each question.

1. **Tell** what shape forms the faces of any pyramid regardless of the shape of the base. triangles

2. Each can be defined as $V = \frac{1}{3}Bh$.

2. **Write** a sentence to tell how the formulas for the volume of a pyramid and the volume of a cone are alike.

3. **Show** which figure at the right has a greater volume. pyramid (333.3̄ cm³) is greater than cone (261.8 cm³)

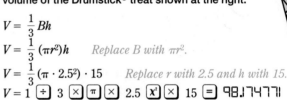

10 m
10 m
10 m

10 m
10 m

OPTIONS

Bell Ringer

Find the volume of the cone.
about 8,796.46 ft³

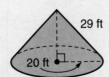

29 ft

20 ft

Guided Practice   Find the volume of each solid. Round answers to nearest tenth.

4.

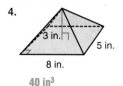

3 in. 5 in.
8 in.
40 in³

5.

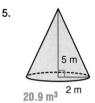

5 m
2 m
20.9 m³

6.

7 yd
6 yd 8 yd
56 yd³

Exercises

Independent
Practice
Find the volume of each solid. Round answers to the nearest tenth.

7.

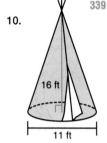

6 m 9 m
339.3 m³

8.

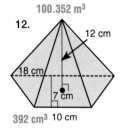

7 in.
6 in.
8 in.
112 in³

9. 2.4 m

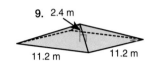

11.2 m   11.2 m
100.352 m³

10.

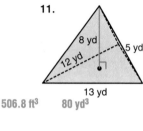

16 ft
11 ft

11.

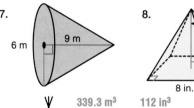

8 yd
12 yd 5 yd
13 yd
506.8 ft³   80 yd³

12.

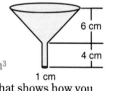

12 cm
18 cm
7 cm
392 cm³ 10 cm

13. Find the volume of a pyramid 9 cm tall, with a base area of 15 cm². **45 cm³**

14. Find the volume of a cone 12 feet tall, with a base area of 235.2 square feet.

Mixed Review   15. Write the next four terms of an arithmetic sequence that begins with 21 and
14. 940.8 ft³   has a common difference of 6. *(Lesson 7-5)* **27, 33, 39, 45**

16. Graph △*DEF* with vertices *D*(3, 6), *E*(10, 8), and *F*(9, 3). Then graph with a
scale factor of 2. *(Lesson 9-8)* **D'(6, 12), E'(20, 16), F'(18, 6)**

17. Find the volume of a cylinder whose diameter is 8 feet and height is 10 feet
tall. *(Lesson 12-6)* **502.65 ft³**

Problem Solving   18. **Critical Thinking**   Suppose the dimensions of a prism are doubled. What
and   changes would have to be made in the dimensions of a pyramid that fits
Applications   inside the original prism so that the ratio of the volumes of
18. The dimen-   the new pyramid and new prism would still be 1:3?
sions of the
pyramid   19. **Manufacturing**   The funnel at the right holds
would also   the honey that goes into Nature's Best cookies.
need to be   What is the maximum volume of the funnel?
doubled.   *Hint: What two solids make up this funnel?* **about 229 cm³**

20. **Portfolio Suggestion**   Select an item from this chapter that shows how you
used a calculator or computer. Place it in your portfolio. **See students' work.**

12 cm
6 cm
4 cm
1 cm

Lesson 12-7   Volume of Pyramids and Cones   **489**

Extending the Lesson

Using Cooperative Groups   Have
students work in small groups to find
the volume of
the *frustum*
(lower section)
of the cone.
980.18 in³

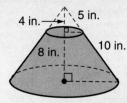

4 in. 5 in.
8 in. 10 in.

Cooperative Learning Activity

Not Your Cup of Tea **12-7**

Use groups of 2.
Materials: Construction paper, compass, protractor, metric ruler, tape

➡ Suppose that you and your partner are designing a drinking cup. The cup must have a
flat bottom so that it will not tip over.

Make a model of your drinking cup out of construction paper. Base your design on a cone.
Draw a circle, including its diameter. Then draw an angle that has the center of the circle as
its vertex and two radii as sides, cut the angle out, and tape the edges together to form a
cone. (You may want to try several different cones.) Determine what portion of the cone you
want your drinking cup to be. Use what you know about the volume of a cone to find the cup's
volume. Cut out the portion of the cone that is your cup to show its size and shape. (The
model will not have a bottom, of course.) Share your work with other pairs.

Glencoe Mathematics: Applications and Connections, Course 3

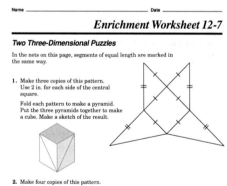

490

NCTM Standards: 1–4, 7, 9, 12

Management Tips

For Students   To avoid pin loss, students should keep their pins stuck in one of the styrofoam balls until needed.

For the Overhead Projector
Overhead Manipulative Resources provides appropriate materials for teacher or student demonstration of the activities in this Mathematics Lab.

1 FOCUS

Introducing the Lab

Display a world map. Ask students to explain the distortions.   The planet Earth is a sphere. The surface of a sphere cannot be flattened without distortion.

2 TEACH

Using Drawings   To obtain a tight fit around the ball, students must cut the ball exactly in half and trace the circle as close to the size of the cross-section of the ball as possible.

3 PRACTICE/APPLY

Using Problem Solving   A cross-section of a tennis ball has an area of 5 in². Ask students to find the surface area of the ball.
20 in²

Close

A sphere has a radius of 3 cm. Ask students to find the surface area and volume of the sphere.
113.10 cm²; 113.10 cm³

Cooperative Learning
12-7B   Exploring Spheres
A Follow-Up of Lesson 12-7

Objective
Explore the surface area and volume of a sphere.

Materials
3 styrofoam balls
scissors
tape
straight pins

Balls are examples of spheres. Spheres, like circles, have a radius and circumference. Spheres also have surface area and volume.

Try this!

- Cut one ball in half. Trace around the edge to draw a circle. Cut out the circle.

- Fold the circle in half three times. Unfold and cut the 8 sections apart. Tape them in the pattern shown.

- Use pins to attach the pattern to another ball the same size as the first.

What do you think?

1. What part of the ball did the circle cover? $\frac{1}{4}$

2. How many patterns would it take to cover the entire ball? **4 patterns**

3. What is the area of each 8-section pattern? πr^2

4. Write an expression for the surface area of the ball. $4\pi r^2$

Extension

5. Suppose you cut a ball into small wedges so that each wedge has its vertex at the center.
   a. What shape does each wedge resemble? **pyramid**
   b. Describe the height and the base of that shape in relationship to the sphere? $h = r$ **of sphere, base = part of surface area**
   c. Write a sentence to describe each step for the following development of the formula for volume of a sphere.   **See Solutions Manual.**
   $V = \frac{1}{3}B_1h + \frac{1}{3}B_2h + \frac{1}{3}B_3h + \ldots$
   $V = \frac{1}{3}B_1r + \frac{1}{3}B_2r + \frac{1}{3}B_3r + \ldots$
   $V = \frac{1}{3}r(B_1 + B_2 + B_3 + \ldots)$
   $V = \frac{1}{3}r$ (surface area of the sphere)
   $V = \frac{1}{3}r(4\pi r^2)$ or $\frac{4}{3}\pi r^3$ *The formula for the volume of a sphere.*

OPTIONS

Lab Manual   You may wish to make copies of the blackline master on p. 75 of the *Lab Manual* for students to use as a recording sheet.

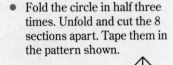

Name _____   Date _____

Mathematics Lab Worksheet
Use with page 490
Exploring Spheres
What do you think?

1. The circle covered ___$\frac{1}{4}$___ of the ball.

2. It would take ___4___ patterns to cover the entire ball.

3. The area of each 8-section pattern is ___πr^2___.

4. Surface area of the ball = ___$4\pi r^2$___

Extension

5. a. Each wedge resembles ___a pyramid___.

   b. The height of the pyramid would be ___the radius of the sphere.___

12-8 Precision and Significant Digits

Objective

Describe a measurement using precision and significant digits.

Words to Learn

precision
significant digits

The winners in some high school track and field events are determined by the distances they achieve. Events involving shorter distances, such as high jump and shot put are measured to the nearest quarter inch. Events involving longer distances, such as the discus and javelin throws, are measured to the nearest half inch.

The **precision** of a measurement depends on the unit being used. The smaller the unit the more precise the measurement is.

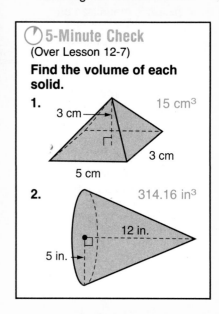

Example 1 *Problem Solving*

Health The school nurse measures the heights of kindergarten students at the beginning of the year. How precise must the measurements be?

● If she measures them to the nearest foot, some students would show no growth.

● If she measured them to the nearest inch, many would show growth.

● If she measured them to the nearest half-inch, most would show growth.

● Measuring them to the nearest tenth-inch would be more precise, but very difficult to do accurately.

So, the nearest half-inch would probably be precise enough.

The digits used in your measurements are **significant digits.** Significant digits are all the digits of a measurement that are known to be accurate plus one estimated digit.

Suppose you wanted to measure the side of a triangle. The ruler you are using is marked in centimeters.

You can see that the side is longer than 4 centimeters, but shorter than 5. You estimate that the measurement is about 0.8 of the way from 4 to 5 centimeters. Your measurement is 4.8 centimeters. The measurement has two significant digits, the 4 that you know is accurate and the 8 that you estimate.

Lesson 12-8 Precision and Significant Digits **491**

12-8 Lesson Notes

NCTM Standards: 1–5, 7, 13

Lesson Resources

• Study Guide Master 12-8
• Practice Master 12-8
• Enrichment Master 12-8
• Evaluation Master, Quiz B, p. 106
• Technology Master, p. 12
• Group Activity Card 12-8

Transparency 12-8 contains the 5-Minute Check and a teaching aid for this lesson.

5-Minute Check
(Over Lesson 12-7)

Find the volume of each solid.

1.

3 cm

15 cm³

3 cm

5 cm

2.

314.16 in³

12 in.

5 in.

1 FOCUS

Motivating the Lesson

Activity Display a postage scale and a bathroom scale. Ask students the following question. *Which scale would be best for weighing a pencil? Justify your answer.* Postage scale; it gives more precise readings for small items.

2 TEACH

Using Problem Solving Ask students the following question. *The width of a photo is measured as 8.3 cm. Between what two measurements is the actual width?* 8.25 cm and 8.35 cm

491

492

When determining significant digits, zeros sometimes pose a problem. If a zero does not fall between two significant digits and is only a placeholder for the placement of the decimal point, it is not a significant digit.

Number	20.3	4,200	0.00251	0.0580
Number of Significant Digits	3	2	3	3

Example 2

A pipe is measured as 12.73 meters long. Analyze this measurement.

To analyze a measurement, you use significant digits to determine how precise this measurement is.

● There are four significant digits. This means you know 12.7 to be accurate and the 3 in the hundredths place is an estimate. So, the measurement is exact to 0.1 meter.

● The estimated hundredths digits tells you the length is closer to 12.73 meters than to 12.7 or 12.8 meters.

When measurements are added, the sum can be no more precise than the least precise measurement. The least precise measurement has the fewest significant digits.

Example 3 *Connection*

Geometry   The lengths of the sides of a triangle are measured as 18.64 cm, 7.092 cm, and 10.4 cm. Find the perimeter.

$P = 18.64 + 7.092 + 10.4$ or 36.132 cm

The least precise measurement is 10.4. Its last significant digit is in the tenths place. Round the answer to tenths.

$36.132 \rightarrow 36.1$ The perimeter is about 36.1 cm.

Checking for Understanding 1. No, because of the density of numbers.

Communicating Mathematics

Read and study the lesson to answer each question.

1. **Tell** if it is truly possible to measure something exactly. Explain your answer.

2. **Tell** what unit of measure you would use to say how far you live from school. Tell why you chose this unit. Answers will vary.

3. **Show** how precise your measurements can be using the ruler below. sixteenth of an inch

4. A flag is 5.50 feet long.
   a. How many significant digits does this measurement have? **3**
   b. How precise is this measurement? **Closer to 5.5 ft than 5.51 ft.**

5. See margin.
6. **34.3 oz; tenths of an ounce is a more precise unit than an ounce or a pound.**

5. Suppose each number in the table at the top of page 492 represents the measured lengths of boards in meters. How precise is each measurement?

6. Which would be the most precise measurement for a can of tomatoes: 2 pounds, 34 ounces, or 34.3 ounces? Explain your answer.

7. In 1990, the United States school systems spent $212,900,000,000 on education. Analyze this measurement. **Accurate to $212 billion; 9 hundred million is estimate; it is closer to $212.9 billion than to $212.8 or $213.0 billion.**

Exercises

Independent Practice

Use significant digits to analyze each measurement. **See Solutions Manual.**

8. 5.2 feet
9. 3.08 inches
10. 0.034 mm
11. 4.003 miles
12. 0.20020 cm
13. 4,300 km

14. Which is the more precise measurement for the length of a pencil, 18 cm or 18.0 cm? Explain your answer. **18.0, accurate to nearest cm**

15. Which is the more precise measurement for the height of the Statue of Liberty, 100 yards or 305 feet? **305 feet**

16. A wire's length is measured as 0.02 meters.
    a. How many significant digits are there in 0.02? **1**
    b. Suppose the measurement was actually 2.2 centimeters. How many significant digits are there in 2.2? **2**
    c. Compare the preciseness of these two measurements. **0.02 meters is an estimate of 2 centimeters. 2.2 cm is accurate to 2 cm with estimate of 0.2 cm.**

Mixed Review

17. **Statistics**   Refer to the data in Exercise 35 on page 158. Make a back-to-back stem-and-leaf plot of the data. *(Lesson 4-4)* **See Solutions Manual.**

18. Express 9.4×10^{-5} in standard form. *(Lesson 6-11)* **0.000094**

19. **Geometry**   Find the volume of a cone whose radius is 3.5 meters and whose height is 12 meters. *(Lesson 12-7)* **153.94 m³**

Problem Solving and Applications

20. **Critical Thinking**   To be precise when multiplying measurements, your rounded answer should have the same number of significant digits as the least precise measurement. With that in mind, find the area of a circle whose radius is 4.2 centimeters. **55.4 cm²**

21. **Data Search**   Refer to page 668. How precise are the time measurements for the 1,500-meter race? **nearest tenth of a second**

22. **Clothing**   Men's dress shirts are sized according to neck size. The sizes may range from $14\frac{1}{2}$ to $17\frac{1}{2}$ in half-inch intervals. A size $16\frac{1}{2}$ means the shirt fits a man whose neck is $16\frac{1}{2}$ inches around. How do these shirt sizes relate to precision? **See Solutions Manual.**

23. **Computer Connection**   The following program finds the volume of a sphere. How precise is the output of the program? **Accurate to next to last digit of input.**

```
10    INPUT R
20    PRINT 4/3 * 3.141592654 * R^3
```

Checking for Understanding

Exercises 1-3 are designed to help you assess students' understanding through reading, writing, speaking, and modeling. You should work through these exercises with your students and then monitor their work on Guided Practice Exercises 4-7.

Close

Have students define precision and explain why it is important in measurement.

3 PRACTICE/APPLY

Assignment Guide
Maximum: 8–23
Minimum: 8–20, 22

Alternate Assessment

Speaking   Write a measurement on the chalkboard. Have students state the number of significant digits and the degree of precision of the number.

Enrichment Masters, p. 112

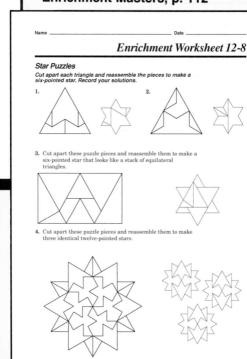

Extending the Lesson

Using Manipulatives   Borrow several measuring devices from the science department in your school. Have students make a list of the devices, together with the precision of each item. Possible devices include pH meters, graduated cylinders, thermometers, micrometers, and various scales and balances.

Cooperative Learning Activity

Number of players: 4
Materials: Index cards

Precision Decision 12-8

♦ Copy onto cards the measurements shown on the back of this card, one per card. Shuffle the cards and divide them evenly.

➡ One group member places one card face up. Then each of the other group members does the same. The four measurements represent the lengths of the sides of a quadrilateral. The group member who placed the first card face up writes the perimeter of a figure with these dimensions on a sheet of paper. (Remember, the sum of measurements can be no more precise than the least precise measurement.) Continue in this way, taking turns being the first to place a card face up, until all of the cards have been played. Try to have the greatest number of most precise measurements of the perimeters of quadrilaterals.

Glencoe Mathematics: Applications and Connections, Course 3

Chapter

12 Study Guide and Review

Study Guide and Review

Communicating Mathematics

Choose the letter of the correct word or words to complete each statement.

1. In geometry, three-dimensional figures are called ___?___ . f
2. ___?___ is the measure of the space occupied by a solid. i
3. The flat surfaces of a prism are called ___?___ . g
4. The area of a ___?___ is π times the radius squared. d
5. The ___?___ of a measurement depends on the unit being used. e
6. The bases of a ___?___ are two parallel, congruent circular regions. b
7. The volume of a ___?___ is one-third the area of the base times the height. a

   8. Sample answer: Find the sum of the surface areas of the 6 faces.

8. Write in your own words how to find the surface area of a rectangular prism.
9. What geometric shape describes the curved surface of a cylinder? rectangle
10. Explain how to find the volume of a cylinder if you know the diameter and the height.

$V = \pi \left(\dfrac{d}{2}\right)^2 h$

a. pyramid
b. cylinder
c. rectangular prism
d. circle
e. precision
f. solids
g. faces
h. surface area
i. volume

Self Assessment

Objectives and Examples	Review Exercises
Upon completing this chapter, you should be able to:	Use these exercises to review and prepare for the chapter test.

● find the area of circles *(Lesson 12-1)*

Find the area of a circle with a radius of 6 feet to the nearest foot.

$A = \pi r^2$

$A \approx 3.14(6^2)$

$A \approx 113.04$

The area of the circle is *about* 113 square feet.

Find the area of each circle to the nearest tenth.

11.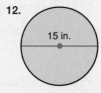

4 m

50.3 m²

12.

15 in.

176.7 in²

Objectives and Examples

- sketch three-dimensional figures from different perspectives *(Lesson 12-3)*

  Make the edges you can see solid and the edges you can't see dashed.

- find the surface area of rectangular and triangular prisms *(Lesson 12-4)*

  To find the surface area of a prism, find the area of each face. Then add all the areas.

- find the surface area of circular cylinders *(Lesson 12-5)*

  Surface area = areas of base + base + curved surface

  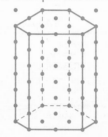

  $\pi r^2 + \pi r^2 + 2\pi rh$

- find the volume of prisms and circular cylinders *(Lesson 12-6)*

  Find the volume of the rectangular prism.

  $V = \ell wh$

  $V = 2(3)(5)$ or 30

  The prism has a volume of 30 cubic meters.

- find the volume of pyramids and circular cones *(Lesson 12-7)*

  Find the volume of the square pyramid.

  $V = \frac{1}{3}Bh$

  $V = \frac{1}{3}(3 \cdot 3)7$ or 21

  The volume of the square pyramid is 21 cubic feet.

  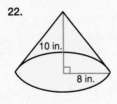

Review Exercises

Sketch each solid. See margin.

13. a rectangular prism that is 3 units by 4 units by 6 units

14. a prism that has a hexagon as a base and is 6 units tall

15. a rectangular prism with all edges 4 units

Draw each prism. Then find its surface area.

16. a rectangular prism with a length of 2 feet, a width of 3 feet, and a height of 5 feet 62 ft²

17. a rectangular prism with all edges 3 centimeters long 54 cm²

Draw a cylinder. Then find its surface area.

18. The radius of the base is 5 meters and its height is 8 meters. 408.41 m²

19. The diameter of the base is 40 yards and its height is 16 yards. 4,523.89 yd²

Draw each figure. Then find its volume.

20. a cylinder with a radius of 8 inches and is 12 inches tall 2,412.74 in³

21. a rectangular prism with a length of 6 meters, a width of 9 meters, and a height of 7 meters 378 m³

Find the volume of each solid.

22.

670.2 in³

23.

6 mm³

Additional Answers

13.

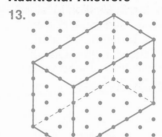

14. Sample answer:

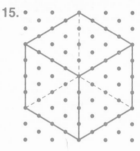

15.

Chapter 12   Study Guide and Review   **495**

You may wish to use a Chapter Test from the Evaluation Masters booklet as an additional chapter review. The two free-response forms are shown below. One of the two multiple-choice forms is shown on the next page.

Evaluation Masters, pp. 104–105

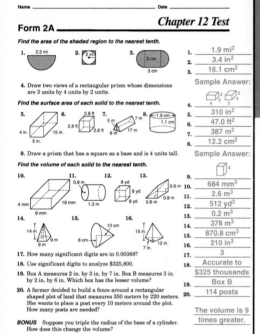

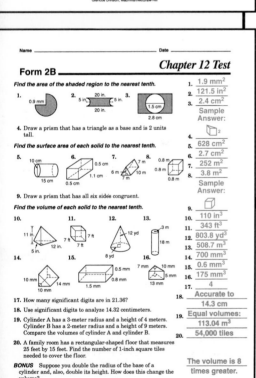

Objectives and Examples	Review Exercises
• describe a measurement using precision and significant digits *(Lesson 12-8)*	Tell how many significant digits are in each measurement.

Analyze 4.07 meters.

There are three significant digits. 4.0 is accurate and the 7 in the hundredths place is an estimate. The measurement is closer to 4.07 meters than it is to 4 meters or 4.1 meters.

24. 0.04 millimeters **1** **25.** 12.8 feet **3**

26. 2,400 yards **2** **27.** 28.20 meters **4**

28. 0.3009 centimeters **4**

29. Use significant digits to analyze 5.02 miles. **29. Accurate to 5.0 miles, 2 hundredths is an estimate.**

Applications and Problem Solving

30. Music Find the area of the top of a compact disc if its diameter is 12 centimeters and the diameter of the hole in its center is 1.5 centimeters. *(Lesson 12-1)* **111.33 cm²**

31. Art An artist is creating a pyramid piece of art using differently-colored marble cubes. There is one cube on the top, two cubes in the next layer, three cubes in the next layer, and so on until 10 layers are completed. How many cubes did the artist use to create this piece of art? *(Lesson 12-2)* **55 cubes**

32. Food A cardboard salt container is in the shape of a circular cylinder. The top has a diameter of 8.4 centimeters, and the container is 13.8 centimeters tall. Find the volume of this container. *(Lesson 12-6)* **764.76 cm³**

Curriculum Connection Projects

- **Consumer Awareness** Find the surface area and the volume of two sizes of your favorite canned food and breakfast cereal.
- **Smart Shopping** Think of a pizza as a circle. Find the area of three different sizes of pizza. Then find the cost per square inch to see which size is the best buy for the amount of pizza you get.

Read More About It

Thompson, Julian. *The Taking of Mariasburg.*
Muller, Robert. *The Great Book of Math Teasers.*
Roth, Charlene Davis. *The Art of Making Puppets and Marionettes.*

496 **Chapter 12** Study Guide and Review

Chapter 12 Test

Using the Chapter Test

This page may be used as a chapter test or another chapter review.

Find the area of each shaded region to the nearest tenth.

1.
37.7 m²

2.
157.1 yd²

3.
150.8 in²

4. Draw two views of a rectangular prism whose dimensions are 4 units by 3 units by 5 units. **See Solutions Manual.**

Find the surface area of each solid to the nearest tenth.

5.
600 ft²

6.
72 cm²

7.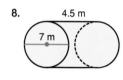
661.5 yd²

8.
175.9 m²

9. Draw a prism that has a pentagon as a base and is 3 units tall. **See Solutions Manual.**

Find the volume of each solid to the nearest tenth.

10.
532 mm³

11.
1,080 in³

12.
216 ft³

13.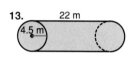
1,399.6 m³

14.
240 mm³

15.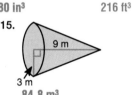
84.8 m³

16.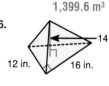
448 in³

17. How many significant digits are in 0.004? 1

18. Use significant digits to analyze 8.20 feet. accurate to 8.2 feet

19. A grain silo has a diameter of 20 feet and is 52 feet tall. Another grain silo has a diameter of 30 feet and is 38 feet tall. Which silo has a greater volume? the one measuring 30 ft × 38 ft

20. Phillipe counted six cyclists going past his house. His sister Rene counted 17 wheels. The cyclists rode bicycles and tricycles. Use a model to find how many of each Phillipe and Rene saw. 1 bicycle, 5 tricycles

Find the sum of the areas of the base and each triangular face.

Bonus How could you find the surface area of a pyramid?

Test and Review Generator software is provided in Apple, IBM, and Macintosh versions. You may use this software to create your own tests or worksheets, based on the needs of your students.

The **Performance Assessment Booklet** provides an alternate assessment for evaluating student progress. An assessment for this chapter can be found on pages 23–24.

Academic Skills Test

Directions: Choose the best answer. Write A, B, C, or D.

1. Bonnie is reading a 186-page book. She needs to read twice as many pages as she has already read. How many pages has she read?

   D

   A 372 pages   B 124 pages

   C 93 pages   D 62 pages

2. Max is 4 years younger than three times Carl's age. Carl is 14. Which equation can you solve to find Max's age?

   C

   A $3(m) - 4 = 14$

   B $m - 4 = 14$

   C $m + 4 = 3(14)$

   D $m - 4 = 3(14)$

3. Which figure has rotational symmetry?

   A

A   B

C   D

4. To the nearest tenth, what is the distance between points *A* and *B*?

   D

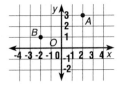

   A 2.2 units   B 2.3 units

   C 3.7 units   D 4.5 units

5. $0.3 =$

   D

   A 3%   B 0.3%

   C 0.03%   D none of these

6. Which is a solution set for the equation $y = 2x - 4$?

   A

   A $\{(-1, -6), (1, -2)\}$

   B $\{(-6, -1), (-2, 1)\}$

   C $\{(1, -2), (3, -2)\}$

   D $\{(-2, 1), (2, 3)\}$

7. A circular clock has a diameter of 14 inches. Which expression shows the area of the face of the clock?

   A

   A $\pi \cdot 7 \cdot 7$ B $\pi \cdot 28$

   C $\pi \cdot 14$ D $\pi \cdot 14 \cdot 14$

8. The bases of a triangular prism are right triangles with sides 3 cm, 4 cm, and 5 cm. The height is 10 cm. What is its surface area?

   D

   A 600 cm²   B 60 cm²

   C 150 cm²   D 132 cm²

9. To the nearest 10 cm², what is the area of the label on the can shown below?

   A

   A 380 cm²

   B 530 cm²

   C 830 cm²

   D 940 cm²

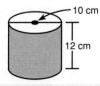

Directions: Write A if the quantity in Column A is greater. Write B if the quantity in Column B is greater. Write C if the quantities are equal. Write D if there is not enough information to decide.

	Column A	Column B
C **10.**	$5 + |\text{-}4|$	$|5| + |\text{-}4|$
A **11.**	the mean	the median
	Data: 12, 15, 19, 11, 20, 18, 16, 15, 14, 14	

12.
B

	volume of the prism	volume of the cylinder
B **13.**	$\dfrac{1}{5}$ of $\dfrac{1}{5}$	$\dfrac{1}{4}$ of $\dfrac{1}{6}$
C **14.**	the radius of a circle with circumference 4π	the diameter of a circle with circumference 2π
B **15.**	$\sqrt{100}$	$\sqrt{50} + \sqrt{50}$
C **16.**	$8c$	$3(12)$
	if $\dfrac{3}{8} = \dfrac{c}{12}$	
D **17.**	$\dfrac{1}{4}$ of x	0.25% of y

18.
B

8 cm, B, 4 cm, A, 7 cm, C

	tan A	tan B

Test-Taking Tip

In test questions like Exercises 10–23 treat the two expressions given as two sides of an inequality. Substitute values for any variables to get a sense of the correct answer. Be sure to use many types and combination of numbers. Do not make assumptions.

If the use of As and Bs in both the column names and answer choices is confusing, rename the columns with another pair of letters or numbers, such as X and Y or I and II.

	Column A	Column B
19. **C**	cost of $50 jeans, 20% off	cost of $50 jeans, $10 off
20. **B**	8% simple interest on $550 for 1 year	4.5% simple interest on $500 for 2 years
21. **A**	$f(5)$	10
	if $f(n) = 2x + 3$	
22. **A**	the LCM of 100 and 36	the LCM of 50 and 90
23. **B**	$\dfrac{3}{25}$	0.15

13 Discrete Math and Probability

Previewing the Chapter

In this chapter, students look at situations that are not certain but merely probable, and develop methods for expressing their probability of occurring. They study the Fundamental Principle of Counting, explore permutations, combinations, and compound events, and see how Pascal's Triangle can be applied to the study of probability. In the **problem-solving strategy** lesson, they learn to solve problems by acting them out. Students then apply the strategy to the calculation of experimental probabilities, using it with Punnett squares and random samples.

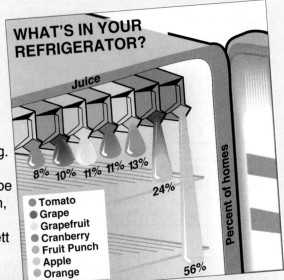

WHAT'S IN YOUR REFRIGERATOR?

Juice

8% 10% 11% 11% 13%

24%

56%

Percent of homes

- Tomato
- Grape
- Grapefruit
- Cranberry
- Fruit Punch
- Apple
- Orange

Lesson	Lesson Objectives	NCTM Standards	State/Local Objectives
13-1A	Discover how to determine whether a game is fair or unfair.	1–4, 11	
13-1	Count outcomes using a tree diagram or the Fundamental Principle of Counting.	1–4, 7, 11	
13-2	Find the number of permutations of objects.	1–4, 7, 11	
Decision Making	Analyze data and make a decision.	1–4, 7	
13-3	Find the number of combinations of objects.	1–4, 7, 11	
13-4	Identify patterns in Pascal's Triangle.	1–4, 7, 8, 11	
13-4B	Discover numerical and visual patterns in Pascal's Triangle.	1–5, 7, 8	
13-5	Find the probability of independent and dependent events.	1–4, 7, 11	
13-6	Solve problems by acting them out.	1–4, 7, 11	
13-7	Find experimental probability.	1–4, 7, 11	
13-8A	Discover how experimental probability is used in biology.	1–4, 11	
13-8	Predict actions of a larger group using a sample.	1–4, 7, 10	

Organizing the Chapter

A complete, 1-page lesson plan is provided for each lesson in the Lesson Plans Masters Booklet.

LESSON PLANNING GUIDE

Lesson	Materials/ Manipulatives	Extra Practice (Student Edition)	Blackline Masters Booklets										
			Study Guide	Practice	Enrichment	Evaluation	Technology	Lab Manual	Multicultural Activities	Application and Interdisciplinary Activities	Transparencies	Group Activity Cards
13-1A	counters							p. 76				
13-1		p. 614	p. 113	p. 113	p. 113					p. 13	13-1	13-1
13-2	4 different colored pencils or markers, calculator	p. 614	p. 114	p. 114	p. 114		p. 27				13-2	13-2
13-3	5 small index cards, calculator	p. 615	p. 115	p. 115	p. 115		p. 13	p. 13			13-3	13-3
13-4	calculator		p. 116	p. 116	p. 116	Quiz A, p. 115					13-4	13-4
13-4B	hexagonal grid, highlighter, calculator							p. 77				
13-5	counters, cup	p. 615	p. 117	p. 117	p. 117					p. 27	13-5	13-5
13-6	spinner, computer		p. 118	p. 118	p. 118						13-6	13-6
13-7	paper bag with 10 colored marbles, die, computer		p. 119	p. 119	p. 119						13-7	13-7
13-8A	counters, bags							p. 78				
13-8	calculator	p. 615	p. 120	p. 120	p. 120	Quiz B, p. 115					13-8	13-8
Study Guide and Review	coins	Multiple Choice Test, Forms 1A and 1B, pp. 109–112 Free Response Test, Forms 2A and 2B, pp. 113–114 Cumulative Review, p. 116 (free response)										
Test		Cumulative Test, p. 117 (multiple choice)										

Pacing Guide: Option II (Chapters 1–13) - 12 days; Option III (Chapters 1–14) - 11 days
You may wish to refer to the complete **Course Planning Guides** on page T25.

OTHER CHAPTER RESOURCES

Student Edition
Chapter Opener,
  pp. 500–501
Decision Making,
  pp. 510–511
Mid-Chapter Review,
  p. 518
Portfolio Suggestion, p. 530

 Manipulatives
Overhead Manipulative
  Resources
Middle School Mathematics
  Manipulative Kit

 Software/Technology
Interactive Mathematics
  Tools (Macintosh)
Test and Review Generator
  (IBM, Apple, Macintosh)
Teacher's Guide for
  Software Resources

Other Supplements
Transparency 13-0
Performance Assessment,
  pp. 25–26
Glencoe Mathematics
  Professional Series
Lesson Plans, pp. 142–152

INTERDISCIPLINARY BULLETIN BOARD

Meteorology Connection

Objective   Use weather records to predict future weather.

How To Use It   Have students choose an upcoming 7-day period and research weather records for the same period over the past several years. Have them use their data to predict the temperatures and weather for the upcoming seven days, recording their predictions in a chart. Then have them record the actual weather during those seven days and compare it to their predictions.

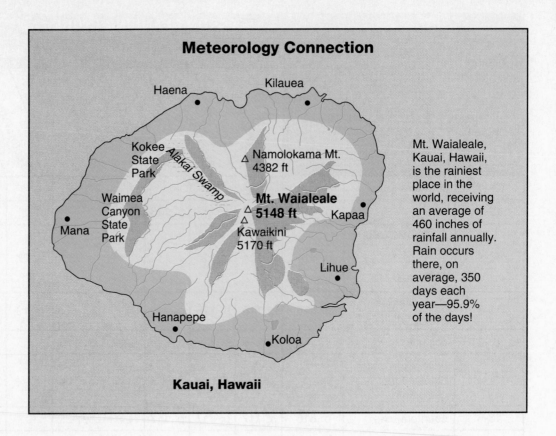

Meteorology Connection

Mt. Waialeale, Kauai, Hawaii, is the rainiest place in the world, receiving an average of 460 inches of rainfall annually. Rain occurs there, on average, 350 days each year—95.9% of the days!

Kauai, Hawaii

APPLICATIONS AND CONNECTIONS

Applications	Lesson	Example	Exercise
Business	13-1		19
Elections	13-2	1	
Sports	13-2	2	26
Music	13-2		27
Travel	13-3	2	
Business	13-3		28
Music	13-4		28
Business	13-4		29
Sports	13-4		30
Food	13-5	2	
Business	13-5		35
Economics	13-5		36
Entertainment	13-7		12
Retail Sales	13-8	X	
Military	13-8		22
Connections			
Algebra	13-1		20
Geometry	13-3		29
Algebra	13-4		26
Computer	13-6		16
Computer	13-7		13

TEAM ACTIVITIES

Multicultural Experiences

Outside Field Trips   Visit local stores and have students use the Fundamental Principle of Counting to determine the number of possible combinations of various items of clothing, furniture, food, and so on that are available.

Have students evaluate the number of different ways that various items in shop windows can be arranged.

In-Class Speakers   Invite a gardener or nursery operator to talk about crossing-pollenating hybrid plants and predicting the results.

A genetic counselor from a local hospital can discuss dominant and recessive genes and the transmission of genetically-determined diseases.

SUPPLEMENTARY BLACKLINE MASTER BOOKLETS

Some of the blackline masters for enhancing this chapter are shown below.

Application and Interdisciplinary Activity Masters, pp. 13, 27

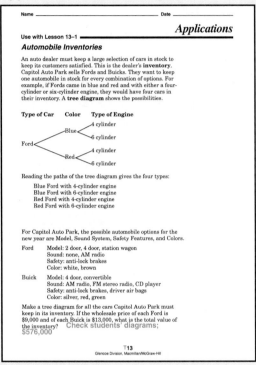

Name _____ Date _____

Applications

Use with Lesson 13–1

Automobile Inventories

An auto dealer must keep a large selection of cars in stock to keep its customers satisfied. This is the dealer's **inventory**. Capitol Auto Park sells Fords and Buicks. They want to keep one automobile in stock for every combination of options. For example, if Fords came in blue and red and with either a four-cylinder or six-cylinder engine, they would have four cars in their inventory. A **tree diagram** shows the possibilities.

Type of Car   Color   Type of Engine

Ford — Blue — 4 cylinder / 6 cylinder
     — Red — 4 cylinder / 6 cylinder

Reading the paths of the tree diagram gives the four types:

Blue Ford with 4-cylinder engine
Blue Ford with 6-cylinder engine
Red Ford with 4-cylinder engine
Red Ford with 6-cylinder engine

For Capitol Auto Park, the possible automobile options for the new year are Model, Sound System, Safety Features, and Colors.

Ford   Model: 2 door, 4 door, station wagon
        Sound: none, AM radio
        Safety: anti-lock brakes
        Color: white, brown

Buick   Model: 4 door, convertible
        Sound: AM radio, FM stereo radio, CD player
        Safety: anti-lock brakes, driver air bags
        Color: silver, red, green

Make a tree diagram for all the cars Capitol Auto Park must keep in its inventory. If the wholesale price of each Ford is $9,000 and of each Buick is $13,000, what is the total value of the inventory? Check students' diagrams; $576,000

T13
Glencoe Division, Macmillan/McGraw-Hill

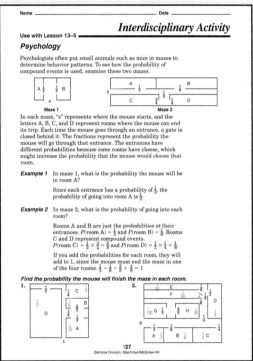

Name _____ Date _____

Interdisciplinary Activity

Use with Lesson 13–5

Psychology

Psychologists often put small animals such as mice in mazes to determine behavior patterns. To see how the probability of compound events is used, examine these two mazes.

In each maze, "s" represents where the mouse starts, and the letters A, B, C, and D represent rooms where the mouse can end its trip. Each time the mouse goes through an entrance, a gate is closed behind it. The fractions represent the probability the mouse will go through that entrance. The entrances have different probabilities because some rooms have cheese, which might increase the probability that the mouse would choose that room.

Example 1 In maze 1, what is the probability the mouse will be in room A?

Since each entrance has a probability of $\frac{1}{2}$, the probability of going into room A is $\frac{1}{2}$.

Example 2 In maze 2, what is the probability of going into each room?

Rooms A and B are just the probabilities at their entrances. $P(\text{room A}) = \frac{1}{3}$ and $P(\text{room B}) = \frac{1}{8}$. Rooms C and D represent compound events.
$P(\text{room C}) = \frac{1}{2} \times \frac{3}{4} = \frac{3}{8}$ and $P(\text{room D}) = \frac{1}{2} \times \frac{1}{4} = \frac{1}{8}$.

If you add the probabilities for each room, they will add to 1, since the mouse must end the maze in one of the four rooms. $\frac{1}{3} + \frac{1}{8} + \frac{3}{8} + \frac{1}{8} = 1$

Find the probability the mouse will finish the maze in each room.

1.   2.

T27
Glencoe Division, Macmillan/McGraw-Hill

Multicultural Activity Masters, p. 13

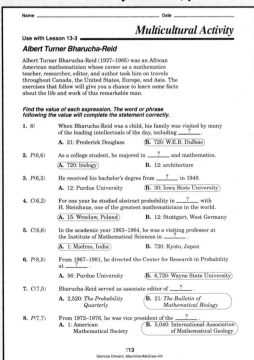

Name _____ Date _____

Multicultural Activity

Use with Lesson 13–3

Albert Turner Bharucha-Reid

Albert Turner Bharucha-Reid (1927–1985) was an African American mathematician whose career as a mathematics teacher, researcher, editor, and author took him on travels throughout Canada, the United States, Europe, and Asia. The exercises that follow will give you a chance to learn some facts about the life and work of this remarkable man.

Find the value of each expression. The word or phrase following the value will complete the statement correctly.

1. 6!   When Bharucha-Reid was a child, his family was visited by many of the leading intellectuals of the day, including ___?___.
   A. 21: Frederick Douglass   **B. 720: W.E.B. DuBois**

2. $P(6,6)$ As a college student, he majored in ___?___ and mathematics.
   A. 720: biology   B. 12: architecture

3. $P(6,2)$ He received his bachelor's degree from ___?___ in 1949.
   A. 12: Purdue University   **B. 30: Iowa State University**

4. $C(6,2)$ For one year he studied abstract probability in ___?___ with H. Steinhaus, one of the greatest mathematicians in the world.
   A. 15: Wroclaw, Poland   B. 12: Stuttgart, West Germany

5. $C(6,6)$ In the academic year 1963–1964, he was a visiting professor at the Institute of Mathematical Sciences in ___?___.
   A. 1: Madras, India   B. 720: Kyoto, Japan

6. $P(8,5)$ From 1967–1981, he directed the Center for Research in Probability at ___?___.
   A. 56: Purdue University   **B. 6,720: Wayne State University**

7. $C(7,5)$ Bharucha-Reid served as associate editor of ___?___.
   A. 2,520: *The Probability Quarterly*   **B. 21: *The Bulletin of Mathematical Biology***

8. $P(7,7)$ From 1972–1976, he was vice president of the ___?___.
   A. 1: American Mathematical Society   **B. 5,040: International Association of Mathematical Geology**

T13
Glencoe Division, Macmillan/McGraw-Hill

Technology Masters, p. 13

Name _____ Date _____

Calculator Activity

Use with Lesson 13-3

The Factorial Key

The factorial key [x!] provides a fast way to calculate factorials.

Example Find 8!.
ENTER: 8 [x!]
8! = 40,320

Example Find $C(6,3)$.
$C(6,3) = P(6,3) \div 3!$
ENTER: 6 [x] 5 [x] 4 [÷] 3 [x!] [=]
$C(6,3) = 20$

Find each value.

1. 0! 1	2. 9! 362,880	3. 7! 5,040
4. 5! 120	5. 8! 40,320	6. 2! 2
7. $C(9,7)$ 36	8. $C(7,4)$ 35	9. $C(12,11)$ 12
10. $C(8,6)$ 28	11. $C(6,5)$ 6	12. $C(6,4)$ 15
13. $C(1,1)$ 1	14. $C(10,10)$ 1	15. $C(10,7)$ 120

T13
Glencoe Division, Macmillan/McGraw-Hill

RECOMMENDED OUTSIDE RESOURCES

Books/Periodicals

Linn, Charles F., *Probability,* New York, NY: Thomas Y. Crowell Co., 1972.

Seattle Public Schools, *Multicultural Mathematics Posters and Activities,* Reston, VA: NCTM, 1984.

Films/Videotapes/Videodiscs

Probability, Wilmete, IL: Films Inc., 1970.

Situational Math, Level II, Niles, IL: United Learning, 1974.

Software

Probability Lab, (Apple II), MECC

For addresses of companies handling software, please refer to page T24.

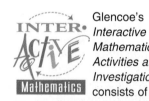
INTER·ACTIVE Mathematics

Glencoe's *Interactive Mathematics: Activities and Investigations* consists of 18 units that may be used as alternatives or supplemental material for *Mathematics: Applications and Connections.* The suggested units for this chapter are Unit 6, *The Road Not Taken,* Unit 10, *Against the Odds,* and Unit 17, *Infinite Windows.* See page T18 for more information.

This two-page introduction to the chapter provides a visual, relevant way to engage students in the mathematics of the chapter. Questions are included that help students see the need to learn the mathematics in the chapter. Data in charts and graphs provides statistical information that students can analyze and interpret at this point as well as later in the chapter. The Chapter Project provides an activity that applies the mathematics of the chapter.

MAKING MATHEMATICS RELEVANT

Spotlight on Food

Analysis of the body's nutritional needs is a complex subject requiring the use of considerable amounts of mathematics. Ask the following questions.

- *An active adult woman requires 22 calories per day for each pound of body weight. What is the one-day caloric requirement of a 125-pound woman?*
  2,750 calories

- *Apple juice is 12% carbohydrates. A quart container of apple juice contains 114 grams of carbohydrates. What is the weight of the juice?*
  950 grams

- *A skier uses 594 calories per hour. A bowler uses 264 calories per hour. How many more calories will a skier use in 4 hours than a bowler will?*   1,320 calories

Chapter

13

Discrete Math and Probability

Spotlight on Food

Have You Ever Wondered...

- What the shelf life of a bag of pretzels is?

- What kinds of juices are found in most refrigerators?

"Have You Ever Wondered?" Answers

- The shelf life of a bag of pretzels is 15 weeks.
- Orange and apple juice are found in the most refrigerators.

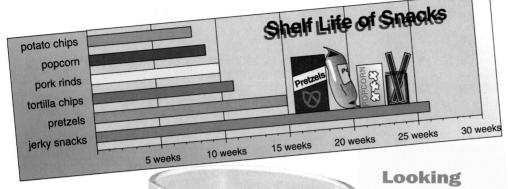

Shelf Life of Snacks

potato chips
popcorn
pork rinds
tortilla chips
pretzels
jerky snacks

5 weeks   10 weeks   15 weeks   20 weeks   25 weeks   30 weeks

Looking Ahead

In this chapter, you will see how mathematics can be used to answer questions about food. The major objectives of the chapter are to:

- count outcomes using a tree diagram or the Fundamental Principal of counting

- find the number of permutations or combinations of a group of objects

- identify patterns in Pascal's Triangle

- solve problems by acting them out or using a simulation

- use samples to predict actions in larger groups of data

Chapter Project

Food

Work in a group.

1. Take a survey of your classmates to find out their favorite kinds of fruit juice.

2. Find what percent of those you surveyed like each type of juice.

3. Estimate what results you would expect if you surveyed 12 adults about their favorite juice. Then take a survey of adults.

4. Make circle graphs to demonstrate your two sets of data. Compare the two graphs.

501

DATA ANALYSIS

Have students study the juice graph. Then ask the following questions.

- *Out of one million homes, how many would you expect have orange juice in the refrigerator?* about 560,000

- *A check of 258 homes found one type of juice in 64 of them. What type was it most likely to be?* apple juice

Data Search

A question related to these data is provided in Lesson 13-4, page 518, Exercise 31.

CHAPTER PROJECT

You may prefer to substitute a different food for juice as the project topic. Poll the class to determine student preferences so that students do not have to duplicate each other's efforts. Then have students poll other people outside of class. At the conclusion of the project, ask students to compare their overall results with those obtained in the class poll. Ask them to explain any similarities or differences that resulted.

Allow one week to complete the project.

Chapter Opener Transparency

Transparency 13-0 is available in the Transparency Package. It provides another full-color, motivating activity that you can use to capture students' interest.

NCTM Standards: 1–4, 11

Management Tips

For Students Pairs of students should be well separated from other pairs.

For the Overhead Projector
Overhead Manipulative Resources provides appropriate materials for teacher or student demonstration of the activities in this Mathematics Lab.

1 FOCUS

Introducing the Lab

Ask students to describe ways in which one player can gain an unfair advantage over another player in a game. Ask them to describe how the rules of a game might be changed to eliminate one player's unfair advantage.

Cooperative Learning

13-1A Fair and Unfair Games

A Preview of Lesson 13-1

Objective
Discover how to determine whether a game is fair or unfair.

Materials
3 counters
pencil

Many people enjoy playing games they believe are fair. A *fair game* is defined as one in which each player has an equal chance of winning. In an *unfair game*, players do *not* have an equal chance of winning.

Have you ever played *Scissors, Paper, Stone?* This ancient game, also known as *Hic, Haec, Hoc,* is played all over the world. On the count of three, two players simultaneously display one hand with either two fingers forming a V (scissors), an open hand (paper), or a fist (stone). The winner of the game is decided by the following rules.

a. scissors cut paper
b. paper wraps stone
c. stone breaks scissors

If both players pick the same object, the round is a draw.

Activity One

Work with a partner.

● Play 20 rounds of *Scissors, Paper, Stone* with your partner. Record the number of times each player wins in a table like the one below.

Player A	Player B	Winner

Possible Outcomes:
scissors, paper; scissors, stone; scissors, scissors; paper, scissors; paper, stone; paper, paper; stone, scissors; stone, paper; stone, stone

● Make a list of all possible outcomes.

What do you think?

1. How many different outcomes are possible? **9 different outcomes**
2. How many ways can player A win? **3 ways**
3. How many ways can player B win? **3 ways**
4. How many outcomes are a draw? **3 outcomes**
5. Is each outcome equally likely? **yes**
6. Is *Scissors, Paper, Stone* a fair game? Explain.
   Yes. Each player's chance of winning is $33\frac{1}{3}\%$.

Activity Two

- On one of three counters, write or tape an A on one side and a B on the other side. On the second counter, write or tape an A on one side and a C on the other. On the third counter, write or tape a B on one side and a C on the other. One player tosses all three counters. Player 1 wins if any two counters match. Player 2 wins if all three counters are different.

- Play 20 rounds of this game with your partner. Record the number of times each player wins. **Answers will vary.**

- Determine all the possible outcomes for this game.
  Possible Outcomes: AAB, AAC, ACB, ACC, BAB, BAC, BCB, BCC

What do you think?

7. How many different outcomes are possible? **8 different outcomes**
8. How many ways can Player 1 win? **6 ways**
9. How many ways can Player 2 win? **2 ways**
10. Is it possible to have a draw in this game? **no**
11. Is each outcome equally likely? **no**
12. Is this game fair or unfair? Explain. **Unfair. Player 1's chances of winning are 75%, and Player 2's chances of winning are 25%.**

Application

13. Four marbles are in a bag. Two are red and two are blue. Two marbles are drawn from the bag. Player X wins if the marbles are the same color. Player Y wins if the marbles are different colors. Is this game fair or unfair? Be prepared to defend your answer.
    Unfair. Player X has $\frac{1}{3}$ probability of choosing another like

Extension
    marble; Player Y has $\frac{2}{3}$ probability of choosing a different one.

14. Design and play a fair game similar to any of those you have played in this lab. **See students' work.**

Mathematics Lab 13-1A Fair and Unfair Games **503**

---

2 TEACH

Using Logical Reasoning
Although *Scissors, Paper, Stone* is a fair game, each player may not win exactly half of the 20 rounds. Point out that each player's winning percentage will approach 50% only after a great number of games.

3 PRACTICE/APPLY

Using Problem Solving To find the number of possible outcomes in each game, students should use the make-a-list strategy (see p. 219). Urge them to list the outcomes in a careful, logical order rather than randomly.

Close

Have students give examples of fair games and unfair games, and explain the meaning of each term.

OPTIONS

Lab Manual You may wish to make copies of the blackline master on p. 76 of the *Lab Manual* for students to use as a recording sheet.

Lab Manual, p. 76

Name _____ Date _____

Mathematics Lab Worksheet

Use with pages 502–503

Fair and Unfair Games

Try this!

Round	1	2	3	4	5	6	7	8	9	10	11	12	13	14	15	16	17	18	19	20
Winner																				

Player A	Player B	Winner
scissors	paper	A
scissors	stone	B
paper	scissors	B
paper	stone	A
stone	scissors	A
stone	paper	B

What do you think?

1. _____9_____ outcomes
2. _____3_____ ways
3. _____3_____ ways
4. _____3_____ draws
5. _____yes_____
6. Yes, each player has an

503

NCTM Standards: 1–4, 7, 11

Lesson Resources
- Study Guide Master 13-1
- Practice Master 13-1
- Enrichment Master 13-1
- Application Master, p. 13
- Group Activity Card 13-1

 Transparency 13-1 contains the 5-Minute Check and a teaching aid for this lesson.

⏱ 5-Minute Check
(Over Chapter 12)

1. Find the area of the circle. **113.10 in²**

   6 in.

2. Find the surface area and volume of the rectangular prism. **136 cm²; 96 cm³**

   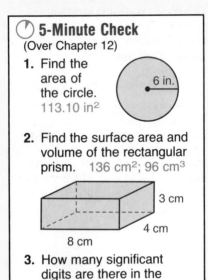

   3 cm
   4 cm
   8 cm

3. How many significant digits are there in the measurement 0.070 cm? **2**

1 FOCUS

Motivating the Lesson

Situational Problem Tell students they are the manager of a baseball team with four pitchers (Adams, Beck, Chi, and Dunn) and two catchers (Eck and Finn). Ask them to list all possible pitcher-catcher combinations.

2 TEACH

Using Models Use several shirts, slacks, and ties. Have students list all the possible three-piece outfits. Confirm the number using the Fundamental Principle of Counting.

504

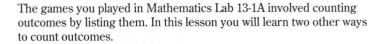

13-1 Counting Outcomes

Objective
Count outcomes using a tree diagram or the Fundamental Principle of Counting.

Words to Learn
outcome
tree diagram
Fundamental Principle of Counting

The games you played in Mathematics Lab 13-1A involved counting outcomes by listing them. In this lesson you will learn two other ways to count outcomes.

The Hopi Indians invented a game of chance called Totolospi. This game was played with three cane dice, a counting board inscribed on stone, and a counter for each player. Each cane die can land round side up (R) or flat side up (F). In Totolospi for two players, each player places a counter on the nearest circle. The moves of the game are determined by tossing the three cane dice.

- Advance 2 lines with three round sides up (RRR).
- Advance 1 line with three flat sides up (FFF).
- Lose a turn with any other combination.

The player reaching the opposite side first wins.

You can draw a diagram to find the number of possible combinations or **outcomes.**

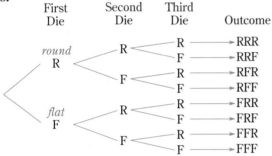

There are eight possible outcomes.

The diagram above is called a **tree diagram.** You can also find the total number of outcomes by multiplying. This principle is known as the **Fundamental Principle of Counting.**

Fundamental Principle of Counting	If event M can occur in *m* ways and is followed by event N that can occur in *n* ways, then the event M followed by the event N can occur in *m · n* ways.

The number of possible outcomes for the Totolospi game can be determined by using this principle.

number of ways first die can land	×	*number of ways second die can land*	×	*number of ways third die can land*	=	*number of possible outcomes*
2	×	2	×	2	=	8

504   **Chapter 13** Discrete Math and Probability

OPTIONS

Reteaching Activity

Using Charts When many choices present themselves, students may find an array, like the one below, more manageable than a tree diagram.

	1	2	3	4	5
A	A1	A2	A3	A4	A5
B	B1	B2	B3	B4	B5
C	C1	C2	C3	C4	C5

Study Guide Masters, p. 113

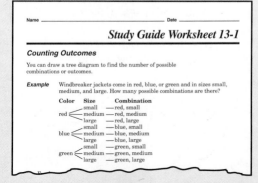

Name _____ Date _____

Study Guide Worksheet 13-1

Counting Outcomes

You can draw a tree diagram to find the number of possible combinations or outcomes.

Example Windbreaker jackets come in red, blue, or green and in sizes small, medium, and large. How many possible combinations are there?

Examples

1 Each spinner at the right is spun once. How many outcomes are possible?

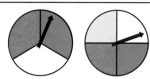

$$\begin{array}{ccccc} \textit{number of} & & \textit{number of} & & \\ \textit{outcomes for} & \times & \textit{outcomes for} & = & \textit{number of} \\ \textit{first spinner} & & \textit{second spinner} & & \textit{possible outcomes} \\ 3 & \times & 4 & = & 12 \end{array}$$

There are 12 possible outcomes.

2 The school store has small (S), medium (M), and large (L) sweatshirts in red (R), gray (G), or white (W). If the school store has one of every possible size and color sweatshirt, what is the probability of selecting a large red sweatshirt at random?

Use a tree diagram to find all the possible outcomes.

Size	Color	Outcome
S	R	SR
	G	SG
	W	SW
M	R	MR
	G	MG
	W	MW
L	R	LR
	G	LG
	W	LW

There are 9 possible outcomes.

$$P(\text{large red}) = \frac{1}{9}$$

The probability of selecting a large red sweatshirt is $\frac{1}{9}$

LOOK BACK

You can review probability on page 233.

Checking for Understanding

1. See Solutions Manual.

Communicating Mathematics

Read and study the lesson to answer each question.

1. **Draw** a tree diagram to list all the outcomes for Example 1.

2. **Write** a problem that corresponds to the tree diagram at the right.
   See students' work.
   See Solutions Manual.

3. **Tell** what advantage there is in using the Fundamental Principle of Counting rather than a tree diagram to count outcomes.

Tree diagram:
False	False	False
		True
	True	False
		True
True	False	False
		True
	True	False
		True

4. **Tell** if you think the possible outcomes in Totolospi, the Hopi Indian game, are equally likely. Explain. Yes they are, since the cane dice fall freely.

Lesson 13-1 Counting Outcomes   **505**

Bell Ringer

How many routes are there from A to D?   24

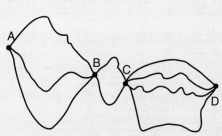

Interactive Mathematics Tools

This multimedia software provides an interactive lesson that is tied directly to Lesson 13-1. Students will generate data and explore probabilities.

Watch for students who fail to list all outcomes.

Prevent by reviewing the make-a-list strategy and by stressing the importance of a careful, logical approach to listing outcomes.

Close

Have students compare and contrast tree diagrams and the Fundamental Principle of Counting as methods for finding the number of outcomes of an event.

3 PRACTICE/APPLY

Assignment Guide
Maximum: 7–22
Minimum: 7–21

For **Extra Practice,** see p. 614.

Alternate Assessment

Speaking State the number of ways each of two events can occur. Have students state the number of ways the events can occur one after the other.

Enrichment Masters, p. 113

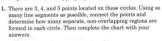

Name _____ Date _____

Enrichment Worksheet 13-1

Making Diagrams

There are two points on the circle at the right, and a line segment has been drawn connecting the points. Two points on a circle, when connected by a line segment, separate a circle into two separate, non-overlapping regions.

1. There are 3, 4, and 5 points located on these circles. Using as many line segments as possible, connect the points and determine how many separate, non-overlapping regions are formed in each circle. Then complete the chart with your answers.

Number of Points	Number of Regions
2	2
3	4
4	8
5	16

2. Based on the pattern formed in the chart, predict the number of regions formed for a circle with 6 points. **32**

3. This circle contains 6 points. Test your prediction. **There are 31 regions.**

4. Explain your results. **Predictions based on 3 or 4 examples must be tested; they may not be accurate for all cases.**

T 113
Glencoe Division, Macmillan/McGraw-Hill

506

Guided Practice

5. Two coins are tossed and a die is rolled.
   a. Draw a tree diagram that represents the situation. **See Solutions Manual.**
   b. How many outcomes are possible? **24 outcomes**
   c. How many outcomes show two heads? **6 outcomes**
   d. How many outcomes show a 6 on the die? **4 outcomes**
   e. How many outcomes show two tails and a 3 on the die? **1 outcome**
   f. What is the probability of one head and an even number on the die? $\frac{1}{4}$

6. A quiz has five true-false questions. How many outcomes for giving answers to the five questions are possible? **32 outcomes**

Exercises   For tree diagrams to Exercises 7–10, see Solutions Manual.

Independent Practice

Draw a tree diagram to find the number of possible outcomes for each situation.

7. A die is rolled. Then a coin is tossed.

7. 12 outcomes
8. 125 outcomes
9. 6 outcomes
10. 12 outcomes
11. 16 outcomes
12. 36 outcomes

8. The spinner at the right is spun three times.

9. A restaurant offers a choice of orange, tomato, or grape juice with a choice of bacon or ham.

10. Phones come in wall or desk models with straight or coiled cords. They come in three colors, black, almond, and green.

State the number of possible outcomes for each event.

11. Four coins are tossed.   12. Two dice are rolled.

13. Mark has three pairs of shorts, four shirts, and two pairs of athletic shoes. How many three-piece outfits are possible? **24 outfits**

14. Suppose there are only two colors of sweatshirts in Example 2. How many outcomes are possible? **6 outcomes**

15. A restaurant offers three types of pasta, three types of sauce, and three types of meat. How many combinations of one pasta, one sauce, and one meat are possible? **27 combinations**

Mixed Review

16. Solve $\frac{f}{2} + 10 = 14$. Check your solution. *(Lesson 2-7)* **8**

17. Solve $b = -3\frac{1}{3}(-6\frac{3}{5})$. Write your solution in simplest form. *(Lesson 7-3)* **22**

18. How many significant digits are in the measurement, 14.4 centimeters? *(Lesson 12-8)* **3 significant digits**

Problem Solving and Applications

For diagram, see Solutions Manual.

19. **Business** The Appliance Store found that customers preferred washers, dryers, and refrigerators in almond, black, and white. Use a tree diagram to find all the possibilities of appliances that are available. **9**

20. **Algebra** If x coins are tossed, write an algebraic expression for the number of possible outcomes. **2^x**

21. **Critical Thinking** When constructing a tree diagram, does it make a difference which event is listed first? Explain. **No. See Solutions Manual.**

22. **Journal Entry** Write one or two sentences explaining the Fundamental Principle of Counting. **See Solutions Manual.**

506   **Chapter 13** Discrete Math and Probability

OPTIONS

Extending the Lesson

Using Cooperative Groups Have students work in small groups to solve this problem: *29,160 outcomes are possible when spinning 4 spinners. Three of the spinners have 12, 15, and 9 possible outcomes, respectively. Find the number of possible outcomes on the fourth spinner.* **18**

Cooperative Learning Activity

Long-Distance Probability **13-1**

Use groups of 2.
Materials: Telephone book

Read the following.

Each region in the United States has its own area code. When you call someone in another region, you must dial the three-digit area code before you dial the person's seven-digit number. The first digit of an area code may not be 0 or 1. The second digit of an area code may be 0 or 1 only. The third digit of an area code may be any of the digits 1 through 9.

Answer the following questions.

1. How many area codes are possible?
2. What is the probability that a computer that dials telephone numbers at random will dial a telephone number in your area code? (Assume that the computer has been programmed to dial valid area codes only.)
3. What is the probability that the computer in the previous question will dial a telephone number in California?

Glencoe Mathematics: Applications and Connections, Course 3

13-2 Permutations

Objective
Find the number of permutations of objects.

Words to Learn
permutation
factorial

The track coach at Jay Neff Middle School is preparing the lineup for the 400-meter relay team. She must choose four runners from the six that have been practicing together. As she looks over the six names, she wonders how many possible arrangements there are.

She reasons that any of the 6 runners can start the race. Once that runner is chosen, there are 5 runners left who can run second. After the second runner is chosen, there are 4 runners left who can run third. Finally, there are 3 runners left who can run fourth. Using the Fundamental Principle of Counting, she finds there are $6 \times 5 \times 4 \times 3$, or 360, possible arrangements.

An arrangement or listing in which order is important is called a **permutation.** In the above example, the symbol $P(6, 4)$ represents the number of permutations of 6 runners taken 4 at a time.

Definition of P(n, r)	**In words**: $P(n, r)$ means the number of permutations of n things taken r at a time. **Arithmetic** $P(6, 4) = 6 \cdot 5 \cdot 4 \cdot 3$ **Algebra** $P(n, r) = n \cdot (n - 1) \cdot (n - 2) \cdot \ldots \cdot (n - r + 1)$

Mini-Lab

Work in groups of three or four.
Materials: 4 different colored pencils or markers

- On your notebook paper, draw four columns. Use the lines of the paper to complete a grid so that each row has four units.
- On the first row, color each unit a different color.
- On the next row, use the same four colors to color the units, but do not repeat the pattern you used in the first row.
- Continue coloring the units in each row until you have created all possible arrangements of the four colors.

Talk About It

a. How many rows did you color? **24 rows**
b. Is this an example of a permutation? Why? **Yes; order is important.**

Lesson 13-2 Permutations **507**

13-2 Lesson Notes

NCTM Standards: 1–4, 7, 11

Lesson Resources
- Study Guide Master 13-2
- Practice Master 13-2
- Enrichment Master 13-2
- Technology Master, p. 27
- Group Activity Card 13-2

Transparency 13-2 contains the 5-Minute Check and a teaching aid for this lesson.

5-Minute Check
(Over Lesson 13-1)

1. A fabric is available in 8 colors and 6 patterns. How many combinations of color and pattern are possible? 48

2. Draw a tree diagram to find the number of possible outcomes when both spinners are spun. 6

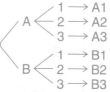

1 FOCUS

Motivating the Lesson

Activity Choose three students. Tell them they are standing in line at a movie theater. Have them arrange themselves in as many different orders as possible. 6

2 TEACH

Using the Mini-Lab Urge students to use a logical approach to coloring. One way is to leave the first color unchanged and find all possible arrangements of the last three colors. Then repeat using a different first color.

OPTIONS

Reteaching Activity

Using Models Have four students act out the number of different ways they can arrange themselves in four chairs. Then remove two chairs and have them act out the number of different ways two of the four can be seated.

Study Guide Masters, p. 114

Name _____ Date _____

Study Guide Worksheet 13-2

Permutations

An arrangement or listing in which order is important is called a permutation.

Example 5 people are running a race. How many arrangements of winner, second place, and third place are possible?

There are 5 choices for winner.
Then there are 4 choices for second place.
Finally there are 3 possible choices for third place.

$5 \times 4 \times 3 = 60$

There are 60 permutations.

For the example above, the permutation of 5 runners taken 3 at a time may be written: $P(5, 3) = 5 \times 4 \times 3$.

The product of ...

507

More Examples

For Example 1

Eight trained parakeets fly onto the stage but find there are only five perches. How many parakeet permutations are possible? 6,720

For Example 2

In how many different orders can six presidential candidates present their opening statements at a debate? 720

Checking for Understanding

Exercises 1-2 are designed to help you assess students' understanding through reading, writing, speaking, and modeling. You should work through these exercises with your students and then monitor their work on Guided Practice Exercises 3-10.

Close

Have students give an example of a permutation of objects in the classroom, explain why it is a permutation, and find the number of permutations of the objects.

Practice Masters, p. 114

Name _____ Date _____

Practice Worksheet 13-2

Permutations

Find each value.

1. $P(6, 2)$ 30
2. $P(8, 3)$ 336
3. 4!   24
4. 8!   40,320

5. 0!   1
6. $P(7, 4)$ 840
7. $P(4, 2)$ 12
8. 1!   1

9. 5!   120
10. $P(3, 2)$ 6
11. $P(9, 9)$ 362,880
12. 9!   362,880

How many different ways can the letters of each word be arranged?

13. BUY   6
14. BROUGHT   5,040
15. BREAK   120
16. PENCIL   720

17. How many odd four-digit numbers can be formed from the digits 1, 2, 3, and 4? Write the possible odd numbers.
12; 1243, 1423, 2341, 2431, 2143, 2413, 3241, 3421, 4123, 4213, 4231, 4321

18. How many even four-digit numbers can be formed from the digits 1, 2, 3 and 5? Write the possible even numbers.
6; 1352, 1532, 3152, 3512, 5132, 5312

19. In how many different ways can you arrange the letters in the word JOURNALISM if you take the letters six at a time?
a. Write the number of permutations in the form $P(n, r)$.
$P(10, 6)$
b. Write the number as a decimal numeral.
151,200

T 114
Glencoe Division, Macmillan/McGraw-Hill

The factorial key **x!** on your calculator provides a fast way to compute factorials. Find 7!.
7 **x!** 5040

The number of permutations in the Mini-Lab can be expressed as $P(4, 4)$. Notice that $P(4, 4)$ means the number of permutations of 4 things taken 4 at a time.

$$P(4, 4) = 4 \cdot 3 \cdot 2 \cdot 1$$

The mathematical notation 4! also means $4 \cdot 3 \cdot 2 \cdot 1$. The symbol 4! is read *four **factorial**. n!* means the product of all counting numbers beginning with *n* and counting backward to 1. We define 0! as 1.

Example 1 *Problem Solving*

Elections   Min, Karen, Linda, Juan, and Michael are running for student council governor. The student who receives the second highest number of votes will be lieutenant governor. How many ways can the students be elected to these 2 positions? Assume there are no ties.

There are 5 students running, but only 2 will be elected. The order of finish is important. So, you must find the number of permutations of 5 students taken 2 at a time.

$$P(5, 2) = 5 \cdot 4 \text{ or } 20$$

There are 20 different ways for the students to be elected.
You can draw a tree diagram to check the answer.

Example 2 *Problem Solving*

Sports   There are five members on the golf team. In how many different orders can they tee off?

You must find the number of permutations of 5 students taken 5 at a time.

$$\begin{aligned} P(5, 5) &= 5! \\ &= 5 \cdot 4 \cdot 3 \cdot 2 \cdot 1 \\ &= 120 \end{aligned}$$

They can tee off in 120 different orders.

Checking for Understanding

Communicating Mathematics   Read and study the lesson to answer each question.

1. **Draw** a tree diagram to show the number of different ways 3 books can be stacked 2 books at a time. See Solutions Manual; 6 ways.

2. **Tell** what 6! means. $6 \cdot 5 \cdot 4 \cdot 3 \cdot 2 \cdot 1$

Guided Practice   Find each value.

3. $P(4, 3)$ 24
4. $P(12, 4)$ 11,880
5. 3!   6
6. 7!   5,040

How many different ways can the letters of each word be arranged?

7. STUDY   120
8. MATH   24
9. EQUALS   720
10. FUN   6

508   **Chapter 13**   Discrete Math and Probability

OPTIONS

Gifted and Talented Needs

Have students research *circular permutations* in order to solve these problems.

1. How many ways can five card players be seated around a circular table? 24

2. How many ways can five keys be arranged on a circular ring if two are identical? 6

Exercises

Independent Practice

Find each value.

11. $P(6, 3)$ **120** **12.** $0!$ **1** **13.** $P(8, 4)$ **1,680** **14.** $9!$ **362,880**

15. $6!$ **720** **16.** $P(10, 5)$ **30,240** **17.** $5!$ **120** **18.** $P(8, 8)$ **40,320**

19. In how many different ways can you arrange the letters in the word *cards* if you take the letters 4 at a time? **120 ways**

20. How many 4-digit whole numbers can you write using the digits 2, 3, 5, and 8? In each number you write, use each digit only once. **24 numbers**

21. How many ways can 5 members of a family be seated in a theater if the father is seated on the aisle? **24 ways**

Mixed Review

22. Solve $r = \dfrac{352}{-11}$. *(Lesson 3-7)* **−32**

23. Find the GCF of 28, 126, and 56. *(Lesson 6-4)* **14**

24. What percent of 70 is 42? *(Lesson 10-6)* **60%**

25. A test has 5 multiple choice questions. Each question has three choices. How many outcomes for giving answers to the 5 questions are possible? *(Lesson 13-1)* **243 outcomes**

Problem Solving and Applications

26. Sports There are six runners in a race. Medals will be given to the first three runners who finish the race. How many ways can the medals be awarded? **120 ways**

27. Music Five band members play the trumpet. How many ways can these members be chosen for the first, second, and third chairs of the trumpet section? **60 ways**

28. Critical Thinking How many different arrangements can be made from the letters of the word *purchase* if each arrangement must begin with a consonant and end with a vowel? $5 \cdot (6 \cdot 5 \cdot 4 \cdot 3 \cdot 2 \cdot 1) \cdot 3 = 10,800$ **arrangements**

29. Make Up a Problem Write a problem where you would need to find the number of permutations of ten things taken three at a time. **See margin.**

30. Mathematics and Photography Read the following paragraph.

> The camera you use today is a great improvement over the first Kodak camera invented by George Eastman in 1888. To take a photo, you press the shutter of the camera, which lets light through the lens for a fraction of a second. The light forms a picture on the film inside the camera. The film is coated with chemicals that change slightly when light falls on them. To see the picture, the film has to be placed in other chemicals so that the picture develops. Edwin H. Land developed the Polaroid camera in 1947, which developed the black-and-white photos in the camera while you waited.

In how many orders can a photographer arrange nine cheerleaders in a line for a photo in a yearbook? **362,880 ways**

Lesson 13-2 Permutations **509**

Extending the Lesson

Mathematics and Photography
Remind students to use the counting principle to solve the problem, as the result is too large to make a tree diagram.

Cooperative Learning Activity

Puzzling Permutations 13-2

Use groups of 4.
Materials: Dictionaries

A popular puzzle found in many newspapers contains words whose letters have been scrambled. Sometimes you can unscramble the words in your head. Another strategy, especially for words you do not know, is to list all of the permutations of the letters. One of the permutations will be the unscrambled word.

→ Working in pairs, unscramble each of the words below. Since these words are not common, you may want to list all of the permutations and then look up the possibilities in a dictionary. Try to be the first pair to unscramble all three words.

o d m r k a g s

poit **hufic** **caxly**

Glencoe Mathematics: Applications and Connections, Course 3

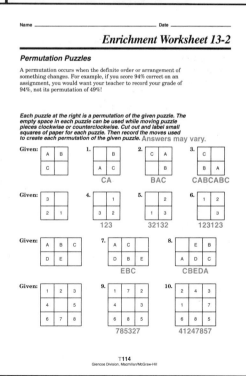
509

DECISION MAKING

DECISION MAKING

Ordering Inventory

Situation

Every spring your school sponsors a community-wide flea market. The school allows various school groups to have booths at the flea market to raise money for special projects. Your committee is in charge of the School Pride booth, which last year brought in $1,700, the best of any of the groups. You know how much inventory you had for last year's booth. What and how much of each item do you buy this year to guarantee another successful sale?

Hidden Data

Cost of returns: Are you allowed to return unsold items for credit?
Cost of credit: If you must buy on credit, will it be for more than 30 days? What percent of interest is charged after 30 days?
Taxes: By being a school group, are you exempt from paying taxes?
Cost of shipping: Do you know the cost of shipping your entire order?

NCTM Standards: 1–4, 7

Objective Analyze data and make a decision.

1 FOCUS

Introducing the Situation

Use the following questions to stimulate discussion:

- *Which of the items shown on page 511, printed with your school logo, would you be willing to purchase to help raise funds?*

- *Is the popularity of an item in the past always an indication of how well it will sell today? Why or why not?* No; tastes may change; people may be less willing to spend money today.

2 TEACH

Using Cooperative Groups

Have students find the individual cost of each item and decide on a selling price for each.

Analyzing the Data

After answering Question 1, have students consider whether making less than 100% profit and charging just $1 per bumper sticker would be better, so that customers could pay easily with a $1-bill rather than having to make change.

Answers

1. $1.05
2. 12

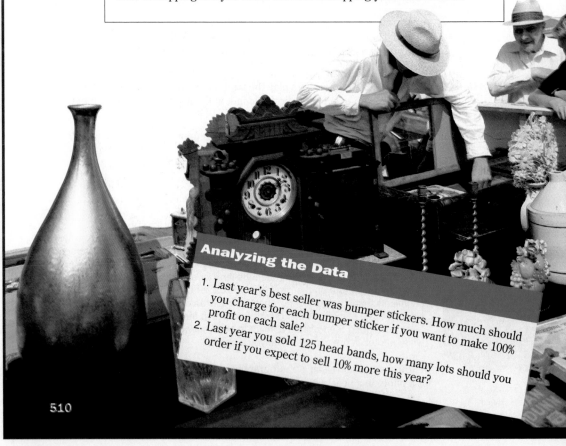

Analyzing the Data

1. Last year's best seller was bumper stickers. How much should you charge for each bumper sticker if you want to make 100% profit on each sale?
2. Last year you sold 125 head bands, how many lots should you order if you expect to sell 10% more this year?

510

Making a Decision

3. **Which colors** should you choose for your items with logos?
4. **Will you** accept checks for items purchased?
5. **Would it** be wise to take a survey of students to see if banners would be a good item to add to the inventory for the booth this year?

SCHOOL SPIRIT, Inc. CATALOG

Colors available: yellow, orange, red, green, blue
Logo colors: black or white

WARRIORS

Headbands
Heavy cotton with elastic thread. Plain or with logo.
Sold in lots of 12: one size fits all.

11⁹⁵ per lot

Specify color and school name (15 characters max.)

Pennants
Triangular felt on wooden stick. Plain or with logo. Sizes:
S is 4" X 12",
L is 6" X 18".
Sold in lots of 10.

S - 6⁹⁹
L - 9⁹⁹

Specify color and school name (15 characters max.)

Allow 1 week for delivery (3 weeks for printed orders). Order all you need – returns accepted (except on items with logos)

Bumper stickers
Peel-and-stick backing. Specify school name and background color (white letters only - 3 lines maximum, 15 characters/line).
Sold in lots of 20.

GREEN MACHINE
LOW THUNDER
GO WARRIORS

10⁵⁰ per lot

Banners
Suitable for indoor or outdoor use. Plain or with logo. Sizes:
S - 28" X 12".
L - 40" X 18".
Sold in lots of 4.

S - 9⁹⁹
L - 15⁹⁹

Need Credit? 30 day credit at rate of 10% of order total. Unpaid balances are charged 1.5% per month. Taxes collectible where applicable.

Making Decisions in the Real World

6. **Interview** some local merchants to see what factors they consider when ordering inventory.
7. **Investigate** other catalogs for ordering school pride items. Are there others that might offer better opportunities for your committee?

511

Checking for Understanding
Ask students to find the number of small pennants they can buy for the cost of a small banner.   3

3 PRACTICE/APPLY

Making a Decision
Each group should prepare a written report on its findings. The report should furnish answers to each question in the lesson, state the decisions made by the group concerning the number of items to order and the prices to charge, and outline the reasons behind the decision.

Making Decisions in the Real World
Have students talk to bankers, economists, or business owners to find out what a business plan is. Ask students to report on the factors a potential business owner must take into consideration before going into business.

511

Lesson Resources
- Study Guide Master 13-3
- Practice Master 13-3
- Enrichment Master 13-3
- Technology Master, p. 13
- Multicultural Activity, p. 13
- Group Activity Card 13-3

 Transparency 13-3 contains the 5-Minute Check and a teaching aid for this lesson.

🕐 5-Minute Check
(Over Lesson 13-2)

Find each value.
1. $P(6, 2)$ 30   **2.** 4! 24
3. $P(5, 3)$ 60   **4.** 6! 720

5. In how many different ways can a coach name the first three batters in a nine-batter softball lineup? 504

1 FOCUS

Motivating the Lesson

Questioning Ask students the following questions.

- *There are five digits in your ZIP code. Is the order of the digits important?* yes
- *There are five spectators on a bench at a ball game. Is the order of the spectators important?* no

2 TEACH

Using the Mini-Lab Students should search for distinct groups of three cards regardless of the order. To clarify this, point out that ABC, ACB, BAC, BCA, CAB, and CBA all count as a single group of cards, just as $\triangle ABC$, $\triangle ACB$, $\triangle BAC$, $\triangle BCA$, $\triangle CAB$, and $\triangle CBA$ all name the same triangle.

13-3 Combinations

Objective
Find the number of combinations of objects.

Words to Learn
combination

The Yogurt Oasis has a choice of 10 different toppings for their sundaes. How many different sundaes with 3 toppings can they serve?

In this problem, order is *not* important. That is, *raisins, peanuts, chocolate chips* is the same as *chocolate chips, raisins, peanuts. You will solve this problem in Example 1.*

Arrangements or listings, like these, where order is not important are called **combinations**.

Mini-Lab

Work with a partner to find the number of ways 5 cards can be selected 3 at a time.
Materials: 5 small index cards

- Mark five index cards with an A, B, C, D, and E. Select any three cards. Record your selections.
- Select another three cards, but not the same group you chose before. Record your selections.
- Continue selecting groups of three cards until all possible groups are recorded.

Talk About It
a. How many groups did you record? 10 groups   6 or 3!
b. In how many different orders can three letters be arranged?
c. Find $P(5, 3)$. 60   groups $= P(5, 3) \div 3!$
d. What is the relationship between the number of groups, the number of arrangements of three cards, and $P(5, 3)$?

A quick way to find the number of groupings, or combinations, of 5 cards taken 3 at a time, $C(5, 3)$, is to divide the number of permutations, $P(5, 3)$, by the number of orders 3 cards can be arranged, which is 3!.

$$C(5, 3) = \frac{P(5, 3)}{3!} \qquad \textit{Dividing by 3! eliminates the}$$
$$= \frac{5 \cdot 4 \cdot 3}{3 \cdot 2 \cdot 1} \qquad \textit{combinations that are the same.}$$
$$= \frac{60}{6} \text{ or } 10 \qquad \text{There are 10 groups.}$$

OPTIONS

Reteaching Activity

Using Cooperative Groups Have students work in groups of four or more. Have them count to find how many groups of three they can form from the members of their group. Have them confirm their results using the formula for combinations.

Study Guide Masters, p. 115

Name _____ Date _____

Study Guide Worksheet 13-3

Combinations

Arrangements or listings where order is not important are called combinations.

Example In how many ways can 3 representatives be chosen from a group of 12 people?

$C(12, 3)$ means the number of combinations of 12 things taken 3 at a time.

$C(12, 3) = \dfrac{12 \times 11 \times 10}{3 \times 2 \times 1}$ Find $P(12, 3)$. Divide by 3! to eliminate combinations that are the same.

$= \dfrac{1,320}{6}$ or 220

3 representatives can be chosen from a group of 12 people in

Definition of C(n, r)	In words:	$C(n, r)$ means the number of combinations of n things taken r at a time.

Arithmetic   **Algebra**

$$C(9, 3) = \frac{9 \cdot 8 \cdot 7}{3!} \text{ or } 84 \qquad C(n, r) = \frac{P(n, r)}{r!}$$

Example 1

Determine how many different sundaes with three toppings Yogurt Oasis can serve.

You need to find $C(10, 3)$.

$$C(10, 3) = \frac{P(10, 3)}{3!}$$
$$= \frac{10 \cdot 9 \cdot 8}{3 \cdot 2 \cdot 1}$$
$$= \frac{720}{6} \text{ or } 120$$

Yogurt Oasis can serve 120 different sundaes with three toppings.

Example 2 *Problem Solving*

Travel   Eight students are eligible to compete in the Mansfield University Writing Contest. Their sponsor, Miss Valentine, will take four of them in her car. Another parent will take the others. How many different groups of these students could she take?

Order does not matter, so you need to find the number of combinations of 8 things taken 4 at a time.

$$C(8, 4) = \frac{P(8, 4)}{4!} \text{ or } \frac{8 \cdot 7 \cdot 6 \cdot 5}{4!}$$

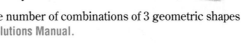 70

She can select from 70 different groups of 4 students.

Checking for Understanding   For answers to Exercises 1-3, see margin.

Communicating Mathematics

Read and study the lesson to answer each question.

1. **Tell** how you would find how many combinations of 5 cards there are in a standard deck of 52 cards.

2. **Write** an expression to represent the number of five-person committees that could be formed in your class.

3. **Tell,** without computing, which is greater, $P(3, 2)$ or $C(3, 2)$. Explain why.

4. **Draw** a model to show the number of combinations of 3 geometric shapes taken 2 at a time. See Solutions Manual.

Lesson 13-3 Combinations   **513**

Additional Answers

1. Find $P(52, 5)$ and divide by $5!$.
2. Sample answer:
   (class of 25 students)
   $$C(25, 5) = \frac{25 \cdot 24 \cdot 23 \cdot 22 \cdot 21}{5!}$$
3. $P(3, 2)$; To get $C(3, 2)$, you divide $P(3, 2)$ by $2!$.

Error Analysis

Watch for students who confuse permutations and combinations.

Prevent by having students decide whether order is important (permutations) or not (combinations).

Close

Have students write a few sentences explaining how to decide whether a problem involves permutations or combinations.

3 PRACTICE/APPLY

Assignment Guide

Maximum: 14–31

Minimum: 15–21 odd, 23–30

For **Extra Practice,** see p. 615.

Alternate Assessment

Modeling Have students use numbered cards to model combinations.

Enrichment Masters, p. 115

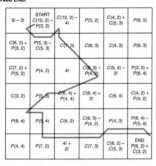

Guided Practice   Find each value.

5. $C(5, 2)$ 10   6. $C(4, 4)$ 1   7. $C(3, 2)$ 3   8. $C(12, 5)$ 792

Determine whether each situation is a permutation or a combination. **combination**

9. three books in a row **permutation**   10. a team of 5 players from 11

11. six CDs from a group of ten   12. arranging 9 model cars in a line
         combination   **permutation**

13. How many 3-letter combinations can be made from the letters in the word CARD? **4 combinations**

Exercises

Independent Practice   Find each value.

                                                2,042,975

14. $C(7, 2)$ 21   15. $C(6, 5)$ 6   16. $C(9, 4)$ 126   17. $C(25, 9)$

18. How many combinations of 3 flowers can you choose from one dozen different flowers? **220 combinations**

19. How many different 5-card hands is it possible to deal from a standard deck of 52 cards? **2,598,960**

20. How many different 3-digit numbers can you write using the digits 1, 2, 3, 5, and 8 only once in each number? **60 numbers**

21. How many ways can you choose 3 shirts from 8 shirts in a closet? **56 ways**

22. How many different volleyball teams of 6 players can be formed from a squad of 12 players? **924 different teams**

Mixed Review   23. How many liters are in 78 milliliters? *(Lesson 1-6)* **0.078 liters**

24. **Geometry**   Refer to the figure in Example 2 on page 178. Find m∠ 4. *(Lesson 5-1)* **80°**

25. The distance between two locations on a map is $2\frac{1}{4}$ inches. Find the actual distance, if the scale on the map is 1 inch:100 miles. *(Lesson 9-7)* **225 miles**

26. Find the value of $P(8, 3)$. *(Lesson 13-2)* **336**

Problem Solving and Applications   27. **Critical Thinking**   How many ways can a study group of 2 males and 3 females be formed from a class of 18 males and 12 females? **33,660 ways**

28. **Business**   A pizza shop has 12 different toppings from which to choose. This week, if you buy a 2-topping pizza, you get 2 more toppings free. How many different ways can the special pizza be ordered? **495 ways**

29. **Geometry**   Eight points are marked on a circle. How many different line segments can be drawn between pairs of points? **28 line segments**

30. **Critical Thinking**   Write a problem for which 792 combinations is the answer.   **See Solutions Manual.**

31. **Journal Entry**   Write one or two sentences explaining the difference between a permutation and a combination. **See Solutions Manual.**

514   Chapter 13   Discrete Math and Probability

OPTIONS

Extending the Lesson

Using Logical Reasoning   Have students simplify each of the following expressions:

a. $\frac{8!}{7!}$ 8   b. $\frac{5!}{4!}$ 5

c. $\frac{6!}{5!}$ 6   d. $\frac{10!}{9!}$ 10

e. Make a conjecture about the value of $\frac{247!}{246!}$.   247

Cooperative Learning Activity

A Winning Combination 13-3

Number of players: 3
Materials: Index cards

♦ Write each of the digits 1 through 7 on fifteen index cards. Shuffle the cards and divide them evenly. Decide which group member will go first.

➡ One group member places a card face up. In turn, beginning with the group member to the first group member's left, each of the other group members places face up a card that shows a different digit. The three digits on these cards show one three-digit combination of the seven digits you wrote on the cards. Taking turns again, continue to make three-digit combinations in the same way. Leave the cards showing combinations you have already formed face up so that you can refer to them. At any time, if you cannot play a card that makes a combination, the group member to your left gets a chance. If this group member cannot play a card either, the third group member gets a chance. Try to be the first to play all of your cards.

Glencoe Mathematics: Applications and Connections, Course 3

13-4 Pascal's Triangle

Objective
Identify patterns in Pascal's Triangle.

Words to Learn
Pascal's Triangle

The student council at Abington Junior High is having a pizza sale to raise money. They need to know how many toppings will be offered so they can advertise how many types of pizza will be available.

Their advisor prepared a table so they could begin working on their posters as soon as the number of toppings is determined.

The columns under *Number of Toppings Taken at a Time* lists how many combinations are possible for the number of toppings taken 0 at a time, 1 at a time, 2 at a time, 3 at a time, and 4 at a time. For example, the number of different 2-topping pizzas that can be made when 4 toppings are offered is 6. *C(4, 2) = 6*

Number of Toppings Offered	Number of Toppings Taken at a Time					Types of Pizza
	0	1	2	3	4	
0	1					1
1	1	1				2
2	1	2	1			4
3	1	3	3	1		8
4	1	4	6	4	1	16

4 toppings taken 2 at a time ⟶↑

Do you see a triangular pattern formed by the ones in the table? This pattern is known as a Chinese Triangle. When all the rows are centered over the bottom row, they form **Pascal's Triangle,** named after French mathematician Blaise Pascal who studied its patterns and applied it to the study of probability.

```
        1
      1   1
    1   2   1
  1   3   3   1
```

Pascal's Triangle

Mini-Lab

Work with a partner.

- Copy Pascal's Triangle and add another two rows on your copy. The top row is row 0.
- Then draw four tree diagrams to represent the possible outcomes for tossing 2, 3, 4, and 5 coins.

Talk About It   a. row 2; row 3; row 4; row 5
a. Which row of Pascal's Triangle matches the number of outcomes for tossing 2 coins? 3 coins? 4 coins? 5 coins?
b. When tossing 3 coins, how many ways can the outcome of 2 heads and 1 tail result? **3 ways**   row 3
c. Where is the answer to part b. located in Pascal's Triangle?

Lesson 13-4 Pascal's Triangle   **515**

13-4 Lesson Notes

NCTM Standards: 1–4, 7, 8, 11

Lesson Resources
- Study Guide Master 13-4
- Practice Master 13-4
- Enrichment Master 13-4
- Evaluation Master, Quiz A, p. 115
- Group Activity Card 13-4

 Transparency 13-4 contains the 5-Minute Check and a teaching aid for this lesson.

5-Minute Check
(Over Lesson 13-3)
Find each value.
1. $C(4, 3)$ 4
2. $C(5, 2)$ 10
3. $C(7, 4)$ 35

4. How many ways can you choose two ties from a rack of nine?   36
5. How many different basketball teams of 5 players can be formed from a squad of 10 players?   252

1 FOCUS

Motivating the Lesson

Activity   Sketch the figure below (without the numbers).

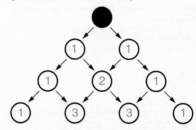

Have students find the number of ways to reach each circle, starting from the top circle and following the direction of the arrows.

2 TEACH

Using the Mini-Lab   Students can generate any number in Pascal's Triangle by adding the two numbers directly above.

516

Examples

Use Pascal's Triangle to answer each question.

1 How many combinations are possible for 5 things taken 3 at a time?

Since there are 5 things, you would use row 5.

Row 5	1	5	10	10	5	1
Number Taken at a Time	0	1	2	3	4	5

The fourth number in the fifth row of Pascal's Triangle is 10.

There are 10 combinations of 5 things taken 3 at a time.

Check: $C(5, 3) = \dfrac{P(5, 3)}{3!}$

$= \dfrac{5 \cdot 4 \cdot 3}{3 \cdot 2 \cdot 1}$ or 10 ✓

2 How many different committees of 4 students can be taken from a group of 6 students?

Since there are 6 students, you would use row 6.

Row 6	1	6	15	20	15	6	1
Number Taken at a Time	0	1	2	3	4	5	6

The fifth number in the sixth row of Pascal's Triangle is 15.

There are 15 different committees of 4 students that can be formed from a group of 6 students.

Check: $C(6, 4) = \dfrac{P(6, 4)}{4!}$

$= \dfrac{6 \cdot 5 \cdot 4 \cdot 3}{4!}$

 (6 × 5 × 4 × 3) ÷ 4 x! = 15 ✓

Checking for Understanding

Communicating Mathematics Read and study the lesson to answer each question.

1. **Tell** how the sum of the numbers in row 4 in Pascal's Triangle compares to the total number of outcomes possible for tossing 4 coins. Sum of each is 16.

2. **Show** how to find the third number in row 7 of Pascal's Triangle. See Solutions Manual

3. **Write** the seventh and eighth rows of Pascal's Triangle. See margin.

Guided Practice Use Pascal's Triangle to find each value.

4. *C*(5, 2) 10   5. *C*(7, 6) 7   6. *C*(8, 3) 56   7. *C*(4, 4) 1

516 **Chapter 13** Discrete Math and Probability

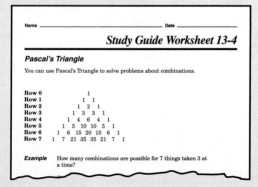

Use Pascal's Triangle to answer each question.

56 teams

8. How many different teams of 5 players can be taken from a squad of 8?

9. How many different 4-question quizzes can be formed from a test bank of 7 questions? **35 quizzes**

10. What is the second number in row 8? **8**

11. What is the second number in row 28? **28**

Exercises

Independent Practice

Use Pascal's Triangle to find each value.

12. $C(5, 3)$ **10**   13. $C(4, 1)$ **4**   14. $C(9, 5)$ **126**   15. $C(10, 4)$ **210**

Use Pascal's Triangle to answer each question.

16. How many varieties of pizza are possible if 4 toppings are offered? **16 varieties**

17. How many branches will there be in the last column of a tree diagram showing the outcomes of tossing 3 coins? **8 branches**

18. Six coins are tossed. What is the probability that all 6 will be heads? $\frac{1}{64}$

19. How many combinations are possible when 6 things are taken 5 at a time?
6 combinations

20. In which row will you find 20 other than the twentieth row? **sixth row**

21. What does the 6 in row 4 mean? **combination of 4 things taken 2 at a time**

Mixed Review

22. **Statistics**   Find the mean and median for the set {155, 154, 160, 152, 164, 158, 161}. Round to the nearest tenth. *(Lesson 4-5)* **157.7, 158**

23. Solve $t = 5\frac{1}{6} + 4\frac{2}{9}$. Write your solution in simplest form. *(Lesson 7-1)* $9\frac{7}{18}$

24. Find four solutions for $y = 3x + 10$. Write the solution set. *(Lesson 11-3)*
Sample answer: {(1, 13), (2,16), (3,19), (4,22)}

25. Find the value of $C(10, 3)$. *(Lesson 13-3)* **120**

Problem Solving and Applications

26. **Algebra**   Let n be the number of a row in Pascal's Triangle. Write an expression for the sum of the numbers in that row. 2^n

27. **Critical Thinking**   Ball bearings fall down a chute toward a tray. As they fall, they hit pegs. At each peg, there is an equal chance to go either left or right.

a. If 16 ball bearings go through the chute, how many will be in the tray for each branch? **1, 4, 6, 4, 1**

b. If 64 ball bearings go through the chute, how many will be in the tray for each branch? **4, 16, 24, 16, 4**

Lesson 13-4 Pascal's Triangle   **517**

Bell Ringer

For which values of n is the following statement true?

11^n = the number whose digits form row n of Pascal's Triangle

{0, 1, 2, 3, 4}   (The numbers are $11^0 = 1$, $11^1 = 11$, $11^2 = 121$, $11^3 = 1,331$, $11^4 = 14,641$.)

3 PRACTICE/APPLY

Assignment Guide
Maximum: 12–31
Minimum: 13–21 odd, 22–30
All: Mid-Chapter Review

Alternate Assessment

Speaking   Point to an entry in Pascal's Triangle. Have students state the number of items in a combination represented by the entry, and the number taken at a time.

Practice Masters, p. 116

Name _____   Date _____

Practice Worksheet 13-4

Pascal's Triangle

Use Pascal's Triangle to answer each question.

1. Use the Pascal's Triangle at the right. Write the next four rows.
See triangle.

2. a. What is the second number in row 3?
3

b. What is the second number in row 9?
9

c. What is the second number in row n?
n

```
            1
          1   1
        1   2   1
      1   3   3   1
    1   4   6   4   1
  1   5  10  10   5   1
1   6  15  20  15   6   1
1  7  21  35  35  21  7  1
1  8  28  56  70  56  28  8  1
1  9  36  84 126 126 84  36  9  1
```

3. How many different pizza varieties are possible:
a. if 5 toppings are offered?   b. if 7 toppings are offered?
32   128

4. If there are two true-false questions on a quiz, what does the "2" in row two mean?
Quiz answers are T, F or F, T.

5. If there are four true-false questions on a quiz, what do the ones in row four mean?
Quiz answers are four T or four F.

6. How many different ways can a quiz with eight true-false questions be answered?   256

7. Four coins are tossed.
a. What is the probability that all four will be heads? $\frac{1}{16}$

b. What is the probability that there will be two heads and two tails? $\frac{6}{16}$

c. What is the probability that at least one will be a head? $\frac{15}{16}$

Use Pascal's Triangle to find each value.

8. $C(3, 2)$ 3   9. $C(4, 3)$ 4   10. $C(4, 2)$ 6   11. $C(5, 3)$ 10

12. $C(6, 2)$ 15   13. $C(6, 3)$ 20   14. $C(7, 4)$ 35   15. $C(8, 5)$ 56

T116
Glencoe Division, Macmillan/McGraw-Hill

517

1. Sample answer:

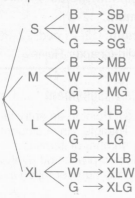

```
        B ──→ SB
  S ←── W ──→ SW
        G ──→ SG

        B ──→ MB
  M ←── W ──→ MW
        G ──→ MG

        B ──→ LB
  L ←── W ──→ LW
        G ──→ LG

        B ──→ XLB
 XL ←── W ──→ XLW
        G ──→ XLG
```

Enrichment Masters, p. 116

Name _____ Date _____

Enrichment Worksheet 13-4

Pinball Wizard

Sixty-four ball bearings will be dropped into this grid. Each
empty circle represents a post, and each ball bearing has an
equal chance to move left or right at each post. If the ball
bearings follow the theoretical probability of the grid, how many
ball bearings will be found in each tray at the bottom of the grid?

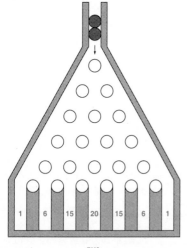

```
1   6   15   20   15   6   1
```

T116
Glencoe Division, Macmillan/McGraw-Hill

---

28. **Music** The Selingsgrove Middle School bell choir has 5 members who are each responsible for 2 bells. How many combinations are possible if 4 bells are rung at the same time? **210 combinations**

29. **Business** A shoe salesperson has 10 different styles of boots. Only five styles can be displayed in the counter window at any one time. How many different groupings of boots can be displayed? **252 groupings**

30. **Sports** The fastest two of eight runners will qualify for the final race. How many different combinations of two qualifiers are possible? **28 combinations**

31. **Data Search** Refer to pages 500 and 501. How many different combinations of juices are possible if there are three juices in the refrigerator? **35 combinations**

13

Assessment: Mid-Chapter Review

1. A new style of jeans is available in 3 colors (black, white, and gray), and in 4 sizes (small, medium, large, and extra large). Draw a tree diagram that illustrates the outcomes. *(Lesson 13-1)* **See margin.**

2. A salad bar offers 2 different kinds of lettuce, 4 different dressings, and 3 different toppings. How many different salads of 1 lettuce, 1 dressing, and 1 topping can be made? *(Lesson 13-1)* **24 salads**

3. How many ways can 6 people line up to buy concert tickets? *(Lesson 13-2)* **720 ways**

4. How many different ways can 2 student council members be elected from 5 candidates? *(Lesson 13-3)* **10 ways**

5. A committee of 3 students is to be chosen from a group of 6. Use Pascal's Triangle to determine how many different committees are possible. *(Lesson 13-4)* **20 committees**

OPTIONS

Extending the Lesson

Using Connections Have students use research materials to learn about Blaisé Pascal (1623–1662) and the many contributions he made to the development of mathematics.

Cooperative Learning Activity

Strategic Plan 13-4

Number of players: 2
Materials: index cards

- Make two sets of cards containing the numbers 1 through 15, one per card.

- Read the following instructions for a game. Devise a strategy for playing the game based on patterns in Pascal's Triangle. Then play the game to see if your strategy worked.

In each round of this game the first card placed face up represents the number of items to be combined, and the second card represents the number of items taken at a time. Take turns going first. In each round find the number of combinations for the number of items shown on the first card and the number of items taken at a time shown on the second card. When all of the cards have been played, find the sum of your combinations. The partner with more combinations wins.

Glencoe Mathematics: Applications and Connections, Course 3

Cooperative Learning

13-4B Patterns in Pascal's Triangle

A Follow-Up of Lesson 13-4

Objective
Discover numerical and visual patterns in Pascal's Triangle.

Materials
hexagonal grid
highlighter
calculator

You can review Fibonacci numbers on page 277.

A famous sequence of numbers is the Fibonacci sequence, 1, 1, 2, 3, 5, 8, ... The sequence begins with 1 and each number that follows is the sum of the previous two numbers.

The Fibonacci numbers and numerous other number patterns can be found in Pascal's Triangle.

Activity One

- Copy Pascal's Triangle and add another two rows to your copy.
- Draw diagonals beginning at each 1 along the left-hand side (passing under the 1 just above) and extend it to the far side of the triangle.
- Find the sum of the numbers each diagonal passes through.

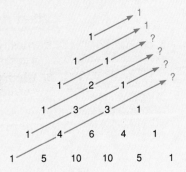

What do you think?

1. Do the sums form the Fibonacci sequence? **yes**
2. What should the sum along the next diagonal be? **13**

Activity Two

- Find the product of the shaded ring of numbers in the Pascal's Triangle at the right. **900**
- Find the product of any two other rings of the same shape and size in Pascal's Triangle. **See students' work.**

What do you think?

3. See students' work.

3. Determine the square root of the products of rings.
4. What conclusion can you make about the product of rings in Pascal's Triangle? **They are perfect squares.**

Mathematics Lab 13-4B Patterns in Pascal's Triangle   **519**

NCTM Standards: 1–5, 7, 8

Management Tips

For Students   Make copies of the grid triangle on page 520 and provide each group with a generous supply for use during Activity Three.

For the Overhead Projector
Overhead Manipulative Resources provides appropriate materials for teacher or student demonstration of the activities in this Mathematics Lab.

1 FOCUS

Introducing the Lab

Have students find the sum of the numbers in each of the first six rows of Pascal's Triangle. Ask them to describe the pattern. Each successive sum is twice the previous sum.

2 TEACH

Using Patterns   In Activity Two, have students write the prime factorizations of the numbers in each ring that they choose. Ask them to describe the unusual pattern of prime factors.   Each prime factor occurs an even number of times.

Using Patterns   Have students create an alteration of Pascal's Triangle by multiplying each entry times 2. Ask students whether the patterns discovered in the first two activities of this lab can also be found in the altered version of the triangle.   The sequence of sums from Activity One are not the Fibonacci numbers, but the sequence does follow the same rule; the products from Activity Two are all perfect squares.

Close

Have students describe three patterns that can be found in Pascal's Triangle.

Activity Three

Work in groups of four.

- Using a hexagonal grid triangle like the one shown below, one person in the group highlights all the numbers that are multiples of 2.
- On another triangle, another person in the group highlights all the numbers that are multiples of 3.
- On a third triangle, another person highlights all the numbers that are multiples of 4.
- On a fourth triangle, another person highlights all the numbers that are multiples of 7.
- Each person should highlight as many rows as necessary to determine a geometrical pattern.

What do you think?

5. Inverted triangles; yes, because when two numbers next to each other have the same factor, the number below them will also have the same factor.

5. What general visual pattern is common in all four triangles? Is this true for multiples of all numbers? Why?

6. Which multiples of the numbers 2, 3, 4, and 7 have patterns that are symmetrical at *each* of the three vertices of the triangle? **3**

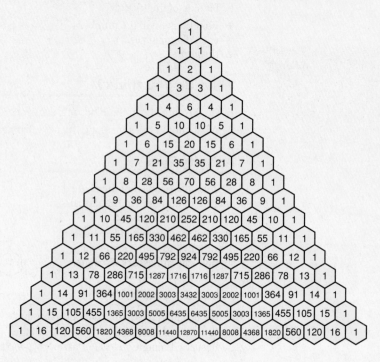

520   **Chapter 13** Discrete Math and Probability

OPTIONS

Lab Manual   You may wish to make copies of the blackline master on p. 77 of the *Lab Manual* for students to use as a recording sheet.

Lab Manual, p. 77

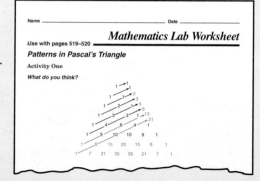

13-5 Probability of Compound Events

Objective
Find the probability of independent and dependent events.

Words to Learn
independent event
dependent event

You can review probability of simple events on page 233.

Do you have a pet? Human beings have always had pets. In Japan, children tame mice. In Australia, some children have pet kangaroos. In India, people make pets of mongooses.

Suppose you wanted to find if a household in the United States, chosen at random, had both pets and children. In the United States, $\frac{6}{10}$ of all households have some kind of pet. Also, approximately $\frac{1}{3}$ of all households have at least one child.

You can find the probability of pets and children in the same household by multiplying the probability of a household having a pet by the probability of a household with at least one child.

$$\begin{array}{l} \textit{number of ways it can occur} \\ \textit{total number of possible outcomes} \end{array} \quad\begin{array}{l}\rightarrow \\ \rightarrow\end{array}\quad \frac{6}{10} \cdot \frac{1}{3} = \frac{6}{30} \text{ or } \frac{1}{5}$$

The probability of a household having both pets and children is $\frac{1}{5}$.

Selecting a household with a pet does not depend on the selection of a household having a child. We call these **independent events.** The outcome of one event does not affect the outcome of the other event.

Probability of Two Independent Events	**In words:** The probability of two independent events can be found by multiplying the probability of the first event by the probability of the second event.
	In symbols: $P(A \text{ and } B) = P(A) \cdot P(B)$

Example 1

Two dice are rolled. Find the probability that an odd number is rolled on one die and a composite number is rolled on the other.

$P(\text{odd number}) = \frac{1}{2}$ $\qquad P(\text{composite number}) = \frac{2}{6}$ or $\frac{1}{3}$

$P(\text{odd number and composite number}) = \frac{1}{2} \cdot \frac{1}{3}$ or $\frac{1}{6}$

The probability that the two events will occur is $\frac{1}{6}$.

Lesson 13-5 Probability of Compound Events **521**

OPTIONS

Multicultural Education

David Blackwell is a professor of statistics at the University of California at Berkeley. He was the first African-American at Princeton's Institute for Advanced Study and the first elected to the National Academy of Sciences. He is widely noted for encouraging young African-American mathematicians.

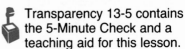
NCTM Standards: 1–4, 7, 11

Lesson Resources
• Study Guide Master 13-5
• Practice Master 13-5
• Enrichment Master 13-5
• Interdisciplinary Master, p. 27
• Group Activity Card 13-5

Transparency 13-5 contains the 5-Minute Check and a teaching aid for this lesson.

5-Minute Check
(Over Lesson 13-4)

1. Write the fourth and fifth rows of Pascal's Triangle.
   Row 4:   1 4 6 4 1
   Row 5:   1 5 10 10 5 1
2. Use Pascal's Triangle to find $C(5, 2)$.   10
3. How many combinations are possible when 4 things are taken 3 at a time?   4

1 FOCUS

Motivating the Lesson

Questioning   Ask students the following question: *Meg has flipped a coin 9 times and it landed heads each time. Are her chances of the coin landing heads on the tenth flip likely, unlikely, or even?*   About even; since one toss of a coin is unaffected by any previous tosses, the probability of landing heads this time is still $\frac{1}{2}$.

2 TEACH

More Examples

For Example 1

A coin is tossed and this spinner is spun. What is the probability of obtaining a head and a 5?
$\frac{1}{12}$

522

Using the Mini-Lab Ask students why the second column in the tree diagram shows only 2 red counters. One was drawn and not replaced, leaving two.

More Examples

For Example 2

	7th	8th	9th
Boys	12	8	10
Girls	15	15	6

The chart above shows the membership in the Middle School Student Council. What is the probability that a girl and a boy chosen randomly will both be seventh graders? $\frac{1}{6}$

For Example 3

A drawer contains 8 pairs of blue socks, 10 pairs of red socks, and 7 pairs of green socks. What is the probability that Kaitlin will randomly choose a pair of red socks followed by a pair of blue socks if the first pair is *not* replaced? $\frac{2}{15}$

Checking for Understanding

Exercises 1-3 are designed to help you assess students' understanding through reading, writing, speaking, and modeling. You should work through these exercises with your students and then monitor their work on Guided Practice Exercises 4-15.

Error Analysis

Watch for students who cannot distinguish between independent and dependent events.

Prevent by asking whether the results of the second event depend on the results of the first.

Example 2 *Problem Solving*

Food The chart below lists the number and types of muffins found in a bakery. An oat muffin is chosen at random. Then a bran muffin is chosen at random. Find the probability that the bran muffin has cranberries and the oat muffin has nuts.

Type of Muffin	Number of Muffins		
	with Nuts	with Cranberries	Plain
BRAN	4	6	5
OAT	4	3	2

$P(\text{bran with cranberries}) = \frac{6}{15} \text{ or } \frac{2}{5}$ $P(\text{oat with nuts}) = \frac{4}{9}$

$P(\text{bran with cranberries and oat with nuts}) = \frac{2}{5} \cdot \frac{4}{9} \text{ or } \frac{8}{45}$

The probability that the two events will occur is $\frac{8}{45}$.

Sometimes the outcome of one event affects the outcome of another.

Mini-Lab

Work with a partner.

Materials: 3 red counters, 2 blue counters, 1 cup

- Place all the counters in the cup. Without looking, draw one counter from the cup. Do *not* put the counter back into the cup. Without looking, draw another counter from the cup.
- Copy and complete the tree diagram for this activity.

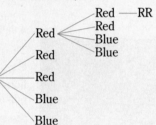

Talk About It

a. What is the probability of a red counter on the first draw? $\frac{3}{5}$

b. If you drew a red counter on the first draw, what is the probability of drawing a red counter on the second draw? $\frac{1}{2}$

c. How many equally likely outcomes are there?

d. How many outcomes show 2 red counters? 6 outcomes

e. Does not replacing the first counter affect the number of outcomes? If so, how?

c. 20 equally likely outcomes

e. Yes; there are 20 possible outcomes, rather than 25 if you replaced the counter.

If the outcome of one event affects the outcome of another event, the events are called **dependent events.** Like independent events, the probability of two dependent events is also found by multiplying the probability of the first event by the probability of the second event.

OPTIONS

Reteaching Activity

Using Models Provide 4 red and 4 blue counters. Have students find the probability of various 2-drawing situations, such as the following, by acting out each choice.

- Drawing 2 red counters when the first counter is replaced.
- Drawing 2 blue counters when the first is <u>not</u> replaced.

Study Guide Masters, p. 117

Name _____ Date _____

Study Guide Worksheet 13-5

Probability of Compound Events

If the outcome of one event does not affect the outcome of a second event, the two events are independent. The probability of two independent events can be found by multiplying the probability of the first event by the probability of the second event. $P(A \text{ and } B) = P(A) \times P(B)$

Example   A die is tossed and a coin is flipped. Find the probability of getting an odd number and a tail.

$P(\text{odd number}) = \frac{1}{2}$ $P(\text{tail}) = \frac{1}{2}$
$P(\text{odd number and tail}) = \frac{1}{2} \times \frac{1}{2} \text{ or } \frac{1}{4}$

The probability of getting an odd number and a tail is $\frac{1}{4}$.

If the outcome of one event affects the outcome of a second event, the two events are dependent. The probability of two dependent events can be found by multiplying: $P(A \text{ and } B) = P(A) \times P(B)$

Example 3

A paper bag contains 4 chocolate chip cookies, 5 oatmeal cookies, and 1 brownie. What is the probability that Julia pulls out an oatmeal cookie first, and then Joanne pulls out an oatmeal cookie too?

This is an example of dependent events because what Julia draws affects what Joanne draws.

First selection: $P(\text{oatmeal cookie}) = \dfrac{5}{10}$ or $\dfrac{1}{2}$

Second selection: $P(\text{oatmeal cookie}) = \dfrac{\text{number of oatmeal cookies left}}{\text{number of cookies left}}$

$$= \dfrac{4}{9}$$

$$P(\text{2 oatmeal cookies}) = \dfrac{1}{2} \cdot \dfrac{4}{9}$$
$$= \dfrac{4}{18} \text{ or } \dfrac{2}{9}$$

The probability that Joanne pulls out an oatmeal cookie after Julia pulls out an oatmeal cookie is $\dfrac{2}{9}$.

Checking for Understanding

Communicating Mathematics

Read and study the lesson to answer each question.

1. **Tell** what is meant by independent events. See margin.
2. **Write** an example of two dependent events. See margin.
3. **Tell** how to find the probability of two dependent events.
   Multiply the probability of the first times the probability of the second.

Guided Practice

A die is rolled and the spinner is spun. Find each probability.

4. $P(1 \text{ and B})$ $\dfrac{1}{30}$
5. $P(2 \text{ and C})$ $\dfrac{1}{30}$
6. $P(\text{prime and D})$ $\dfrac{1}{10}$
7. $P(7 \text{ and E})$ 0
8. $P(\text{an even number and a vowel})$ $\dfrac{1}{5}$
9. Do the probabilities in Exercises 4-8 represent dependent or independent events? Explain.
   Independent; one outcome does not affect the other.

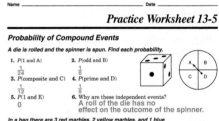

In a bag there are 5 red marbles, 2 yellow marbles, and 1 blue marble. Once a marble is selected, it is not replaced. Find the probability of each outcome.

10. a red marble and then a yellow marble $\dfrac{5}{28}$
11. a blue marble and then a yellow marble $\dfrac{1}{28}$
12. a red marble and then a blue marble $\dfrac{5}{56}$
13. any color marble except yellow and then a yellow marble $\dfrac{3}{14}$
14. a red marble three times in a row $\dfrac{5}{28}$
15. Do the probabilities in Exercises 10-14 represent dependent or independent events? Explain. Dependent; one outcome affects the other.

Lesson 13-5 Probability of Compound Events   **523**

Close

Have students explain the difference between independent and dependent events, giving an example of each.

3 PRACTICE/APPLY

Assignment Guide
Maximum: 16–37
Minimum: 17–29 odd, 30–36

For **Extra Practice,** see p. 615.

Alternate Assessment

Modeling   Have students use sets of different-colored counters to model independent and dependent events.

Additional Answers

1. Independent events: The outcome of one event does not affect the outcome of the other event.
2. Sample answer: Selecting one card from a deck of cards and then selecting another card without replacing the first.

Practice Masters, p. 117

Additional Answers

34. Bran with nuts and plain oat; they each have the lowest probability of occurring.

37. Sample answer: When events are dependent, the outcome of one event affects the outcome of the other. When events are independent, the outcome of one event does not affect the outcome of the other.

Exercises

Independent Practice

Two cards are drawn from a deck of nine cards numbered 2 through 10. Once a card is selected, it is not replaced. Find the probability of each outcome.

16. a 10 and then a 2 $\frac{1}{72}$

17. two odd numbers in a row $\frac{1}{6}$

18. two numbers greater than 7 $\frac{1}{12}$

19. three even numbers in a row $\frac{5}{42}$

20. an odd number and then an even number $\frac{5}{18}$

Each spinner is spun once. Find each probability.

21. a 3 and a D $\frac{1}{30}$

22. a 5 and a B $\frac{1}{30}$

23. a composite number and C $\frac{1}{15}$

24. an odd number and a consonant $\frac{3}{10}$

25. a 7 and a letter that is not a vowel 0

Suppose your favorite radio station is giving away one gift certificate prize each hour. At 8:00 A.M., the prize is selected at random from 3 CD certificates and 1 car wash certificate. At 9:00 A.M., the prize is selected at random from 2 pizza certificates and 3 certificates for a free game of miniature golf. For these two hours, find the probability of each outcome.

26. a car wash and a round of miniature golf $\frac{3}{20}$

27. a CD followed by a round of miniature golf $\frac{9}{20}$

28. a CD followed by a CD 0

29. a car wash and a pizza $\frac{1}{10}$

Mixed Review

30. Solve $4y = 196$. Check your solution. *(Lesson 2-4)* **49**

31. Order the set of numbers {226, –3, 18, –157, 2, –28} from least to greatest. *(Lesson 3-2)* **{–157, –28, –3, 2, 18, 226}**

32. **Geometry** Is every rectangle a square? Draw a figure to justify your answer. *(Lesson 5-4)* **No; see students' work.**

33. Use Pascal's Triangle to find $C(6, 2)$. *(Lesson 13-4)* **15**

Problem Solving and Applications

34. **Critical Thinking** In Example 2, suppose a bran muffin is selected at random followed by the selection of an oat muffin at random. Which combination of muffins is least likely to occur? Explain. **See margin.**

35. **Business** If 90% of a store's customers are women and 75% of the women have a credit card, what is the probability that a customer chosen at random is a woman who has a credit card? $67\frac{1}{2}$%

36. **Economics** A store is having a sale. The first 25 customers will randomly draw a card to determine a bonus discount. There are 9 cards for 10% off, 8 cards for 20% off, 5 cards for 35% off, and 3 cards for 50% off. The cards are not replaced after they are drawn. Find the probability of each outcome.

a. The first customer draws a 50% off card. $\frac{3}{25}$

b. The first customer draws a 10% off card and the next customer draws a 35% off card. $\frac{3}{40}$

37. **Journal Entry** Write a few sentences explaining the difference between independent and dependent events. **See margin.**

524 **Chapter 13** Discrete Math and Probability

OPTIONS

Extending the Lesson

Using Connections Have students use research materials or talk to a meteorologist to learn the meaning of probability in weather forecasting ("There is a 70% probability of rain today.") and how such probabilities are calculated.

Cooperative Learning Activity

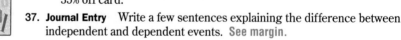

Number of players: 2
Materials: index cards, spinners
What Do You Expect? 13-5

Make one set of cards containing the numbers 1 through 20, one number per card. Shuffle the cards and divide them evenly. Label equal sections of two spinners with the following events: draw even number, draw odd number, draw prime number, draw multiple of 2, draw number less than 5, draw number greater than 10.

Each partner spins a spinner. Each partner then writes the probability that these two events will occur for the numbers on the cards in his or her hand *with* replacement of the first card before drawing the second. The partner with the greater probability wins the round. Continue in this way until you have played all of the cards in your hand. Then shuffle the cards together and play again. This time, write the probability that the two events will occur for the cards in your hand *without* replacement.

Glencoe Mathematics: Applications and Connections, Course 3

13-6 Act It Out

Objective
Solve problems by acting them out.

Word to Learn
simulation

There are three traffic lights along the route that Lori rides from school to her home. The three lights operate independently. The probability that any one of the lights is green is 0.4, and the probability that it is not green is 0.6. Estimate the probability that these lights will all be green on Lori's way home from school.

Explore *What do we know?*

$P(\text{green light}) = 0.4 \text{ or } \frac{2}{5}$

$P(\text{not green}) = 0.6 \text{ or } \frac{3}{5}$

What are we trying to find out?
The probability that all three lights will be green for Lori's trip.

Plan Model the situation by doing a **simulation.** That is, act it out. For example, construct a spinner with five equal sections like the one shown at the right. Spin the spinner and record the results for each light. Repeat the simulation ten times.

2 out of 5 or $\frac{2}{5}$ of spinner is green.

Solve

	First Light	Second Light	Third Light
Simulation 1	G	G	N
Simulation 2	N	G	G
Simulation 3	G	N	G
Simulation 4	G	N	N
Simulation 5	G	G	G
Simulation 6	N	G	N
Simulation 7	N	N	G
Simulation 8	N	N	N
Simulation 9	G	G	N
Simulation 10	G	N	G

Since one of the simulations results in 3 green lights, you can estimate the probability that all 3 lights will be green for Lori's trip is 0.1.

Lesson 13-6 Problem-Solving Strategy: Act It Out **525**

13-6 Lesson Notes

NCTM Standards: 1–4, 7, 11

Lesson Resources
• Study Guide Master 13-6
• Practice Master 13-6
• Enrichment Master 13-6
• Group Activity Card 13-6

Transparency 13-6 contains the 5-Minute Check and a teaching aid for this lesson.

⏱ 5-Minute Check
(Over Lesson 13-5)

1. The spinner is spun twice. Find the probability of spinning a 4 followed by an odd number. $\frac{1}{8}$

2. Four lions and four tigers escaped from a cage. Find the probability that the first two out the door were lions. $\frac{3}{14}$

1 FOCUS

Motivating the Lesson

Activity Ask students to devise an experiment to find the probability of obtaining two heads in two coin tosses. Then have them carry out their experiment.
Sample answer: Toss two coins ten times; $P(\text{HH}) = \frac{\text{number of successes}}{10}$.

2 TEACH

Using Discussion Explain that 0.064 in the Examine step on page 526 is the mathematical probability, but that experimental probabilities often differ from mathematical probabilities.

OPTIONS

Reteaching Activity

Using Charts Have students toss three coins 10 times and record the results in a table like the one shown on page 525. Have them estimate the probability of obtaining exactly two heads when tossing three coins.

Study Guide Masters, p. 118

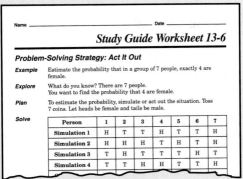

Study Guide Masters, p. 118

Name _____ Date _____

Study Guide Worksheet 13-6

Problem-Solving Strategy: Act It Out

Example Estimate the probability that in a group of 7 people, exactly 4 are female.

Explore What do you know? There are 7 people.
You want to find the probability that 4 are female.

Plan To estimate the probability, simulate or act out the situation. Toss 7 coins. Let heads be female and tails be male.

Solve

Person	1	2	3	4	5	6	7
Simulation 1	H	T	T	H	T	T	H
Simulation 2	H	H	H	T	H	T	H
Simulation 3	T	H	T	T	T	H	T
Simulation 4	T	T	H	H	T	T	H

526

Teaching Tip

After the Examine step, point out that the results of another set of simulations might be entirely different from the results recorded in the table.

Checking for Understanding

Exercises 1-3 are designed to help you assess students' understanding through reading, writing, speaking, and modeling. You should work through these exercises with your students and then monitor their work on Guided Practice Exercises 4-6.

Close

Have students compare and contrast mathematical probability with the probability found by conducting a simulation.

Additional Answers

1. Acting out a situation is a simulation.
2. Sample answer: Place 2 green slips of paper and 3 non-green slips of paper in a box. Without looking, draw a slip of paper. Record and replace it. Repeat the drawing 2 more times. Repeat the set of 3 drawings 10 times.

Practice Masters, p. 118

Examine | You can determine if your estimate is reasonable by finding the theoretical probability. Since the traffic lights operate independently, you can multiply the probability that each light is green.

$$0.4 \;\boxed{\times}\; 0.4 \;\boxed{\times}\; 0.4 \;\boxed{=}\; 0.064$$

The estimate is reasonable.

Checking for Understanding

Communicating Mathematics

Read and study the lesson to answer each question.

1. **Tell** what a simulation is. See margin.
2. **Write** another way to simulate the traffic light situation on page 525, using green and non-green slips of paper in a box. See margin.
3. **Tell** whether or not the results of a simulation will be exactly the same as computing the result. Explain your reasoning. See Solutions Manual.

Guided Practice

Solve by acting it out.

4. Carmen has a record of making one free throw out of every two tries, and she averages 6 free throw attempts per game. Act it out to find the number of free throws she will make in the next game. **Sample answer: 3 free throws**
5. Ed has 6 ties. On Thursday through Sunday, Ed works at the mall. He chooses a tie at random to wear at his job. Act it out to find the probability that Ed wears the same tie more than once in his four-day week. **Sample answer: $\frac{4}{10}$**
6. David has $1.15 made up of six United States coins. With the coins he has, he cannot make change for a dollar, a half dollar, a quarter, a dime, or a nickel. What are the six coins that David has? **1-50¢, 1-25¢, 4-10¢**

Problem Solving

Practice

Solve using any strategy.

7. Marlene is reading a 216-page book. She needs to read twice as many pages as she has already read to finish the book. How many pages has she read so far? **72 pages**

8. There are 16 tennis players in a single elimination tournament. How many tennis matches will be played during the tournament? **15 matches**
9. Dawn is running late for an appointment. Without turning on the lights, she reaches into her jewelry box and pulls out two earrings one at a time. The jewelry box contains pairs of blue, silver, red, pink, and gold earrings. The earrings are identical except for color. Act it out to find the probability that Dawn will select a pair of red earrings. **Sample answer: $\frac{1}{45}$**

526   **Chapter 13** Discrete Math and Probability

OPTIONS

Bell Ringer

Describe a simulation you could conduct to estimate the probability that from a group of four people, one will have been born on a Monday.

Sample answer: Spin a spinner with 7 numbers 4 times. Record each 1 as a success. Repeat many times.

$P(\text{Monday}) = \dfrac{\text{number of successes}}{\text{number of simulations}}$

Interactive Mathematics Tools

This multimedia software provides an interactive lesson that is tied directly to Lesson 13–6. Students will explore how to simulate situations to solve problems.

10. Sam bought a jacket and a shirt. The total cost, not including tax, was $62.50. The jacket cost four times as much as the shirt. How much did Sam spend on these additions to his wardrobe? **$12.50-shirt; $50-jacket**

11. **Math-Mrs. Gossell; Music-Ms. Alvarez; Social Studies-Mrs. Yamaguchi**

11. Mrs. Gossell, Ms. Alvarez, and Mrs. Yamaguchi teach at Watkins Middle School. One of the women is a mathematics teacher, one is a music teacher, and one is a social studies teacher. The music teacher, an only child, has taught the least number of years. Mrs. Yamaguchi who married Mrs. Gossell's brother, has taught more years than the math teacher. Name the subject each woman teaches.

12. Antonio places 10 pennies in a horizontal line on his desk. He adds enough pennies so that there are 5 pennies in a vertical line, 8 pennies in another vertical line, and 5 pennies in a diagonal line. What is the least number of pennies Antonio can use? **23 pennies**

13. A number is added to 8, and the result is multiplied by 20. The final answer is 100. Find the number. **−3**

14. **Data Search** Refer to page 666. What was the median U.S. home price in 1992? **about $141,100**

DATA SEARCH

15. In a recent survey of 120 students, 50 students said they play baseball and 60 students said they play soccer. If 20 students play both sports, how many students do not play either baseball or soccer? **30 students**

COMPUTER

16. **Computer Connection** You can use the RND function on a computer to simulate random events. The BASIC program below will generate 10 random numbers, greater than 0 and less than 1. A sample printout is also shown.

```
10  FOR X = 1 TO 10
20  PRINT RND(X)
30  NEXT X
```

```
0.08067539
0.17157252
0.96578311
0.71980542
0.61702572
0.19884118
0.24290394
0.43047297
0.91472936
0.86625558
```

Run each program below on a computer. Write a sentence that describes the output. Describe a simulation for which you might use each program.

b. The output is 20 lines listing a 1, a 2, a 3, a 4, or a 6. A simulation could be rolling a die 20 times.

a.
```
10  FOR X = 1 TO 20
20  PRINT INT(2 * RND(X))
30  NEXT X
```
a. The output is 20 lines listing a 0 or a 1. A simulation could be tossing a coin 20 times; 0 is heads and 1 is tails.

b.
```
10  FOR X = 1 TO 20
20  PRINT INT(6*RND(X) + 1)
30  NEXT X
```

Lesson 13-6 Problem-Solving Strategy: Act It Out **527**

Extending the Lesson

Using Models A cereal maker packs one of six photos of sports stars in each package. To model the purchase of three packages in hopes of obtaining a Michael Jordan photo, students should roll a number cube three times and see if a 1 turns up. Repeat 10 times and estimate the probability of getting one photo of Jordan in three packages.

Cooperative Learning Activity

Use groups of 2.

A Bright Idea 13-6

● A random number table contains the digits 0 through 9 in random order. In the random number table on the back of this card, the digits are arranged in groups of four.

➡ Read the following problem.

At a factory that makes light bulbs, the probability that a bulb will be defective is $\frac{1}{10}$. Estimate the probability that at least two of the bulbs in a four-pack are defective.

You know that you can estimate probability by doing a simulation. You can use the random number table on the back of this card to do a simulation. Since one bulb out of every ten is defective, you can have one of the ten digits in the random number table represent a defective bulb. The groups of four digits can represent four-packs of bulbs.

Work together to solve the problem.

Glencoe Mathematics: Applications and Connections, Course 3

527

NCTM Standards: 1–4, 7, 11

Lesson Resources
- Study Guide Master 13-7
- Practice Master 13-7
- Enrichment Master 13-7
- Group Activity Card 13-7

 Transparency 13-7 contains the 5-Minute Check and a teaching aid for this lesson.

🕐 5-Minute Check
(Over Lesson 13-6)

	1st Coin	2nd Coin
Simulation 1	T	H
Simulation 2	H	T
Simulation 3	H	T
Simulation 4	T	T
Simulation 5	H	T

Estimate each probability.
1. two tails $\frac{1}{5}$
2. exactly one head $\frac{4}{5}$

1 FOCUS

Motivating the Lesson

Questioning Ask students to give examples of theories that experiments later proved to be false. Sample answer: The Earth was once believed to be flat.

2 TEACH

Using the Mini-Lab Explain that as the number of times an experiment is conducted increases, the closer the experimental and theoretical probabilities become.

528

13-7 Experimental Probability

Objective
Find experimental probability.

Words to Learn
experimental probability
theoretical probability

Sometimes you can't tell what the probability of an event is until you conduct an experiment. For example, suppose you toss a thumbtack 50 times and count the number of times it lands point up. The results of this experiment allow you to estimate the probability of that thumbtack landing point up.

Probabilities that are based on frequencies obtained by conducting an experiment, or doing a simulation as you did in the previous lesson, are called **experimental probabilities.** Experimental probabilities may vary when an experiment is repeated.

Probabilities based on physical characteristics like 4 sections of a spinner or 6 sides of a die, are called **theoretical probabilities.** Theoretical probability tells you *approximately* what should happen in an experiment.

Technology Activity
You can use a graphing calculator to explore probability in Technology Activity 7 on page 664.

Mini-Lab

Work with a partner.
Materials: paper bag containing 10 colored marbles

- Draw one marble from the bag, record its color, and replace it in the bag. Repeat this 10 times.
- Find the experimental probability for each color of marble.

$$\text{experimental probability} = \frac{\text{number of times color was drawn}}{\text{total number of draws}}$$

- Repeat both steps described above for 20, 30, 40, and 50 draws.

Talk About It
a. Is it possible to have a certain color marble in the bag and never draw that color? yes
b. Open the bag and compute the theoretical probability of drawing each color of marble. See students' work.
c. Compare the experimental and theoretical probabilities.
   See students' work.

528   **Chapter 13** Discrete Math and Probability

OPTIONS

Reteaching Activity

Using Models Provide a sample of 100 pennies. Have students find the experimental probability that a penny:
a. was minted in 1989;
b. is more than 20 years old;
c. was minted in an even-numbered year.

Study Guide Masters, p. 119

Name _____ Date _____

Study Guide Worksheet 13-7

Experimental Probability

Probabilities determined by conducting an experiment are experimental probabilities.

Example Yolanda drew one card from a 52-card deck, tallied its suit, and returned the card to the deck. She performed the experiment 100 times. The chart shows the results.

	Heart	Club	Diamond	Spade
Tally	⅂⅂⅂⅂ ⅂⅂⅂⅂ ⅂⅂	⅂⅂⅂⅂ ⅂⅂ II	⅂⅂⅂⅂ ⅂⅂ II	⅂⅂⅂⅂ ⅂⅂ IIII
Total	32	22	17	29

Yolanda's experimental probability of drawing a heart is $\frac{32}{100}$ or $\frac{8}{25}$.

Example

Three pennies are tossed 40 times. The results are displayed in the circle graph.

a. In this trial, what was the experimental probability of no heads?

The outcome of *no heads* happened twice. The experimental probability was $\frac{2}{40}$ or 0.05.

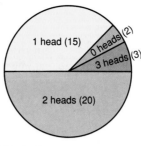

b. List the possible outcomes for tossing three coins.
HHH, HHT, HTH, HTT, THH, THT, TTH, TTT
Check your list by drawing a tree diagram.

c. What is the theoretical probability of no heads?

Since there are 8 outcomes when tossing three coins and only 1 outcome is no heads, the theoretical probability is $\frac{1}{8}$ or 0.125.

Checking for Understanding

Communicating Mathematics

Read and study the lesson to answer each question.

1. It is possible one of the outcomes doesn't turn up in an experiment.

1. **Tell** why the experimental probability and theoretical probability of an event are not always the same.

2. **Draw** a bar graph that shows the results of the trial in the Example. See students' work.

Guided Practice

Use the circle graph in the Example to answer Exercises 3 and 4.

3. Find the experimental probability of each outcome.
a. P(1 head) $\frac{3}{8}$
b. P(2 heads) $\frac{1}{2}$
c. P(3 heads) $\frac{3}{40}$

4. Find the theoretical probability of each outcome.
a. P(1 head) $\frac{3}{8}$
b. P(2 heads) $\frac{3}{8}$
c. P(3 heads) $\frac{1}{8}$

Exercises

Independent Practice

5. Ten students in Mr. Sopher's class believed that a coin is not fair. In other words, it appeared that the probability of getting heads was not $\frac{1}{2}$. To test this assumption, each student tossed the coin 40 times and recorded the results in the spreadsheet below.

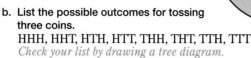

STUDENT	1	2	3	4	5	6	7	8	9	10
NUMBER OF HEADS	21	22	18	26	21	21	19	22	18	29
NUMBER OF TAILS	19	18	22	14	19	19	21	18	22	11

a. Find the P(heads) for each of the ten students. Then find P(heads) for all the students as a whole. See margin.

c. Do more experiments.

b. Based on this data, does the coin appear to be fair? yes

c. How could you get a better estimate of P(heads) for this coin?

Lesson 13-7 Experimental Probability **529**

More Examples

For the Example

The table below shows the results of rolling a number cube 30 times.

Number	Frequency
1	2
2	7
3	5
4	6
5	4
6	6

a. What is the experimental probability of rolling a 4? $\frac{1}{5}$

b. What is the theoretical probability of rolling a 4? $\frac{1}{6}$

Checking for Understanding

Exercises 1-2 are designed to help you assess students' understanding through reading, writing, speaking, and modeling. You shoud work through these exercises with your students and then monitor their work on Guided Practice Exercises 3-4.

Practice Masters, p. 119

Meeting Needs of Middle School Students

Nothing will inspire your students to greater achievement than sincere praise when it is warranted. A survey of men and women with Ph.D.'s in mathematics found this common thread: they all could remember the name of a teacher who praised their work.

Additional Answer

5a. $\frac{21}{40}, \frac{11}{20}, \frac{9}{20}, \frac{13}{20}, \frac{21}{40}, \frac{21}{40}, \frac{19}{40}, \frac{11}{20},$

$\frac{9}{20}, \frac{29}{40}, \frac{217}{400}$

Have students refer to the circle graph in the Example. Ask them to explain why the experimental probability of *no heads* is different from the experimental probability of *no tails*.

3 PRACTICE/APPLY

Assignment Guide
Maximum: 5–13
Minimum: 5–12

Alternate Assessment

Writing   Have students write a few sentences describing the difference between experimental probability and theoretical probability.

Enrichment Masters, p. 119

Name _____ Date _____

Enrichment Worksheet 13-7

Probability Regions

If a circular spinner is divided by a diameter into two equal regions, the theoretical probability of the pointer landing in any region is $\frac{1}{2}$.

If the circular spinner containing one diameter is divided by another diameter perpendicular to the first, the spinner is divided in 4 equal regions. The theoretical probability of the pointer landing in any region is $\frac{1}{4}$.

Read each description of a spinner. Using a ruler and protractor, divide each spinner into the indicated regions.
Diagrams may vary.
1. Divide this circular spinner into three regions so that the probability of landing in any region is $\frac{1}{3}$.

2. Divide this circular spinner into three regions so that the probability of landing in one region is $\frac{1}{2}$ and another region is $\frac{1}{4}$.

3. Divide this circular spinner into three regions so that the probability of landing in one region is $\frac{1}{4}$ and another region is $\frac{1}{8}$.

4. Divide this square spinner into three regions so that the probability of landing in one region is $\frac{3}{8}$ and another region is $\frac{5}{8}$.

5. This rectangular spinner must be divided into four regions of equal probability.
It has been divided in half along one diagonal.
It has been divided in half again along the other diagonal.
Is the spinner divided into four regions of equal probability? Explain your reasoning.
No. The area of each region is equal, but the central angles formed by the diagonals are not equal.

T119
Glencoe Division, Macmillan/McGraw-Hill

530

6. Roll a die 60 times. For answers to Exercises 6a–d, see students' work.
   a. Record the results.
   b. Based on your record, what is the probability of a 1?
   c. What is the probability of an even number? Explain.
   d. Are the probabilities in parts b and c examples of experimental or theoretical probabilities?

Mixed Review

7. Solve $p = -68 + 29$. *(Lesson 3-3)* **-39**

8. Find the GCF of 12 and 63. *(Lesson 6-4)* **3**

9. Two die are rolled. Find the probability that a prime number is rolled on one die and an odd number is rolled on the other die. *(Lesson 13-5)* $\frac{1}{4}$

Problem Solving and Applications

11. See students' work.

10. **Critical Thinking**   If you toss a fair coin 20 times, will the result always be 10 heads and 10 tails? Why? **No; experimental probabilities vary.**

11. **Portfolio Suggestion**   Select one of the assignments from this chapter that you found especially challenging. Place it in your portfolio.

12. **Entertainment**   The wheel on *Wheel of Fortune* is divided into 24 sections. If three of the sections have amounts higher than $1,000, what is the theoretical probability of the wheel stopping at one of these sections? $\frac{1}{8}$

C O M P U T E R
C O N N E C T I O N

13. **Computer Connection**   In the "bonus situation" in basketball, the shooter is awarded one free throw. If he or she makes the basket, a bonus of one more free throw is awarded. Therefore, there are three possibilities:
    A. Shooter misses first free throw.
    B. Shooter makes first free throw, misses the second.
    C. Shooter makes both free throws.

    Suppose the probability that a certain shooter makes any given free throw is 67%. The following computer program simulates the results of 10,000 trials and prints the experimental probability of each situation.

```
10   FOR X = 1 TO 10000
20   LET Y = RND(X)
30   IF Y > 0.67 THEN CA = CA + 1: GOTO 70
40   LET Y = RND(X)
50   IF Y > 0.67 THEN CB = CB + 1: GOTO 70
60   CC = CC + 1
70   NEXT X
80   PRINT "P(A) = ";CA/10000: PRINT "P(B) = ";
     CB/10000: PRINT "P(C) = ";CC/10000
```

13a. Sample answer: P(A) = 0.33, P(B) = 0.22, P(C) = 0.45

a. Run the program and list the probability of each outcome.

b. Modify the program if the probability that the shooter makes any given basket is 50%. **Replace 0.67 with 0.5 in lines 30 and 50.**

530   **Chapter 13** Discrete Math and Probability

OPTIONS

Extending the Lesson

Using Connections   Have students talk to people in the insurance industry to find out how companies determine the probabilities of accidents, illnesses, and so on, and how they use these figures to calculate the costs of insurance premiums.

Cooperative Learning Activity

The Name Game **13-7**

Use groups of 3.
Materials: Spinners

• Label equal sections of each of three spinners with the group members' first names. Find the theoretical probability that the same name will appear on each spinner when the spinners are spun at the same time.

➡ Each group member spins a spinner. Repeat this procedure fifty times. Then find the experimental probability that one name will appear on all three spinners at the same time. Find the experimental probability for seventy-five and one hundred spins of all three spinners. Write a description of your results. What happens to the experimental probability as the number of spins increases?

Cooperative Learning

13-8A Punnett Squares

A Preview of Lesson 13-8

Objective

Discover how experimental probability is used in biology.

Materials

40 yellow counters
40 red counters
2 paper bags

DID YOU KNOW

Around 1865, an Austrian monk named Gregor Mendel explained what dominant and recessive traits were.

In the early 1900s, Reginald Punnett developed a model to show the possible ways genes can combine at fertilization. In a **Punnett square,** *dominant* genes are shown with capital letters. *Recessive* genes are shown with the lowercase of the same letter. Letters representing the parent's genes are placed on the outer sides of the Punnett square. Letters inside the boxes of the square show the possible gene combinations for their offspring.

Let **T** represent the dominant gene for tallness. Let **t** represent the recessive gene for shortness. A pea plant with **TT** genes is pure dominant and is tall. A pea plant with **tt** genes is recessive and is short. A pea plant with **Tt** genes is hybrid and is tall because it has a dominant gene. Notice that the capital letter goes first in hybrid genes.

The Punnett square at the right represents a cross between two hybrid tall pea plants.

You can use a Punnett square to do a simulation that demonstrates how random fertilization works.

	T	t
T	T T	T t
t	T t	t t

Try this!

Work in groups of four to simulate the birth of 40 offspring.

- Place 20 yellow counters and 20 red counters into a paper bag. Label the bag *female parent*. This represents a parent with one dominant gene and one recessive gene.

- Place 20 yellow counters and 20 red counters into a second paper bag. Label this bag *male parent*. This represents a parent with one dominant gene and one recessive gene.

- Make a Punnett square to show the expected offspring of these parents. Use **R** for the dominant gene, red. Use **r** for the recessive gene, yellow.

Mathematics Lab 13-8A Punnett Squares **531**

NCTM Standards: 1–4, 11

Management Tips

For Students In each group, two students should draw counters and two should record the results. After completing half the experiment, have students switch roles.

For the Overhead Projector
Overhead Manipulative Resources provides appropriate materials for teacher or student demonstration of the activities in this Mathematics Lab.

1 FOCUS

Introducing the Lab

Ask students to give examples of genetic traits that appear to run in their families. Ask them to give examples of character traits that are acquired (after birth) rather than inherited.

2 TEACH

Using Connections Explain that a dominant gene will always dominate a recessive gene. Thus, all hybrid pea plants with Tt genes will be tall. Only pea plants with pure recessive tt genes will be short.

3 PRACTICE/APPLY

Using Logical Reasoning
Students should expect each gene combination in a Punnett square to have an equal probability of occurring. In a 2 × 2 square, each combination will occur about one-fourth of the time.

Classroom Vignette

"This lesson is a great opportunity to team teach with a science teacher. In science class they can discuss how Punnett squares are used in biology, and then the connection can be made to the Math Lab Activity. It can be a very interesting lesson."

William Collins
Author

Have students complete the Punnett square below. Have them state the percent of offspring that can be expected to be red.   100%

	R	w
R	RR	Rw
R	RR	Rw

R = red
w = white

Additional Answers

6.

	F	F
F	FF	FF
f	Ff	Ff

$P(FF) = \frac{1}{2}$; $P(Ff) = \frac{1}{2}$

7.

	F	F
F	FF	FF
F	FF	FF

$P(FF) = 1$

8.

	f	f
f	ff	ff
f	ff	ff

$P(ff) = 1$

9.

	F	f
f	Ff	ff
f	Ff	ff

$P(Ff) = \frac{1}{2}$; $P(ff) = \frac{1}{2}$

Trial	Male Parent		Female Parent		Gene Pairs
	Red Counters	Yellow Counters	Red Counters	Yellow Counters	
1					
2					
3					
4					
40					

- Copy the table at the left.
- Shake the bags. Reach into each bag and, without looking, remove one counter. Record the colors of the counters in your table next to trial 1. Put the counters back into the bags from which they came.
- Repeat the previous steps 39 more times.

What do you think?

1. Out of 40 offspring, how many did you expect to be pure dominant (**RR**)? hybrid (**Rr**)? pure recessive (**rr**)? 10, 20, 10

2. Which of the three gene combinations did you expect to occur most often? Rr

3. What is the theoretical probability of an offspring having pure dominant genes? hybrid genes? pure recessive genes? $\frac{1}{4}, \frac{1}{2}, \frac{1}{4}$

4. Find the experimental probability. Describe how it compares to the theoretical probability. See students' work.

5. What determines how offspring will look?
the combination of genes that come together in the offspring

Application

In humans, free earlobes is a dominant trait over attached earlobes. Let F represent free earlobes and f represent attached earlobes. Draw a Punnett square for each parent combination below. Find the theoretical probability for the offspring. For answers to Exercises 6-9, see margin.

6. FF, Ff   7. FF, FF   8. ff, ff   9. Ff, ff

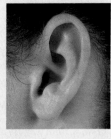
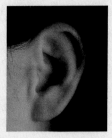

Extension

10. How does the prediction of 1 pure dominant, 2 hybrid, and 1 recessive offspring relate to Pascal's Triangle? Row two of Pascal's Triangle is 1, 2, 1.

OPTIONS

Lab Manual   You may wish to make copies of the blackline master on p. 78 of the *Lab Manual* for students to use as a recording sheet.

Lab Manual, p. 78

Name _____   Date _____

Mathematics Lab Worksheet

Use with pages 531–532

Punnett Squares

Try this!

	R	r
RR	RR	Rr
r	Rr	rr

What do you think?

1. Out of 40 offspring, I expect ____10____ to be pure dominant, ____20____ to be hybrid, and ____10____ to be pure recessive.

2. I expect the hybrid or Rr

13-8 Using Experiments to Predict

Objective
Predict actions of a larger group using a sample.

Words to Learn
sample
population
random

In the 1990 census, it was estimated that more than 1.6% of the people living in the United States were not counted. This may sound like a small error, but it means over 4 million people were missed!

One of the main reasons for the inaccurate count was that many Americans did not return their census forms. Since it would take too much time and require too many workers to contact each of these people individually, the Census Bureau decided to have field-workers survey a smaller group of people called a **sample.** A sample is representative of a larger group called the **population.**

In the 1990 census, over 300,000 field workers were sent to one hundred geographical areas that were selected at **random.** In a random sample everything in the population has an equal chance of being selected. The results of the field workers were to be used to correct the undercount.

Example *Problem Solving*

Retail Sales The student council at Euclid Middle School plans to sell school jackets. They need to know how many of each size to order. They surveyed a sample of the school population. The sample consisted of one homeroom from each grade level. The results of the survey are shown in the frequency table at the right.

Size	Tally	Frequency
Small	꒐꒐꒐ IIII	19
Medium	꒐꒐ II	12
Large	꒐꒐꒐꒐ II	27
Extra Large	꒐꒐꒐ II	17

Problem-Solving Hint
• • • • • • • • • •
Notice that this is an example of the problem-solving strategy, *solve a simpler problem.*

a. How many students were surveyed for this sample?

$19 + 12 + 27 + 17 = 75$ *The sum of the frequencies is the sample size.*

75 students were surveyed.

b. What percent of the sample wear a large or medium jacket?

12 + 27 or 39 students wear a large or medium jacket.
Compare 39 to the total (75).

39 [÷] 75 [=] 0.52

52% of the sample wear a large or medium jacket.

Lesson 13-8 Statistics Connection: Using Experiments to Predict   **533**

13-8 Lesson Notes

NCTM Standards: 1–4, 7, 10

Lesson Resources
• Study Guide Master 13-8
• Practice Master 13-8
• Enrichment Master 13-8
• Evaluation Master, Quiz B, p. 115
• Group Activity Card 13-8

 Transparency 13-8 contains the 5-Minute Check and a teaching aid for this lesson.

🕐 5-Minute Check
(Over Lesson 13-7)

The table below lists the results of tossing two coins 50 times.

Result	Number
0 heads	8
1 head	28
2 heads	14

1. What is the experimental probability of 2 heads?
$\frac{7}{25}$ or 0.28

2. List the possible outcomes for tossing 2 coins.
HH, HT, TH, TT

3. What is the theoretical probability of 2 heads?
$\frac{1}{4}$ or 0.25

1 FOCUS

Motivating the Lesson

Questioning Ask students to describe a "typical" student, one who could be used to represent the entire class. Point out that this student is a *sample* representing the class *population.*

2 TEACH

Using Connections Point out that sampling involves finding a proportion in a small random group (the sample), assuming that it applies to a large group (the population), and then applying the proportion to that large group.

OPTIONS

Reteaching Activity

Using Connections Use simple fractions and percents in questions like the following to clarify sampling. *One-tenth of a sample of people were left-handed. How many of one million people would you expect to be left-handed?* 100,000

Study Guide Masters, p. 120

Name _____ Date _____

Study Guide Worksheet 13-8

Using Experiments to Predict

Data gathered from a representative sample can be used to make predictions about a population.

Example In a county survey of companies with between 500 and 1,000 employees, 82 said the number of employees had grown over the past year, 180 said the number of employees had remained the same, and 38 said the number of employees had decreased. If there are 12,000 companies with between 500 and 1,000 employees in the county, for how many might you expect that the number of employees grew over the past year?

Number of companies surveyed = 82 + 180 + 38 = 300

Solve a proportion to find the number of companies in the county that grew over the past year.

Sample companies that grew = 82 ← Companies in the county that grew

c. If 300 jackets are to be ordered, how many of them should be small jackets?

LOOKBACK

You can review proportions on page 344.

Set up a proportion and solve.

small jackets in sample → $\frac{19}{75} = \frac{x}{300}$ ← small jackets to order
total jackets in sample →   ← total jackets to order

19 ☒ 300 ÷ 75 ☰ 76

76 small jackets should be ordered.

d. Would the student council have a representative sample if all seventy-five students were in the eighth grade?

No, because eighth graders will wear larger sizes, on average.

Checking for Understanding

Communicating Mathematics

Read and study the lesson to answer each question.

1. **Tell** how a sample group survey can be used to predict the actions of a whole population. **by setting up and solving a proportion**

2. **Tell** what is the most important thing a surveyor needs to consider when a sample is used. **whether the people in the sample are chosen at random and are representative of the population**

Guided Practice

Use the survey on favorite radio stations to answer each question.

3. What is the size of the sample? 400
4. What fraction chose WXGT? $\frac{9}{20}$
5. For the 158,800 people in the listening range of these stations, how many would you expect to listen to WFRM? 15,880 people

Favorite Radio Station	
WFRM	40
WKIK	110
WXGT	180
WMOO	70

The Sunshine Orange Juice Company conducts a taste test. Out of 600 people that compare Sunshine Juice to Brand X, 327 prefer Sunshine Juice. Which statements below are true? Write *true* or *false*. Explain your answer.

6. "Consumers prefer Sunshine Juice 2 to 1." false; 327:273 < 2:1
7. "Over 50% of the people surveyed prefer Sunshine Juice."
8. "More people always choose Sunshine Juice over Brand X."

8. False; this cannot be determined from the survey. 7. true; $\frac{327}{600} = 54.5\%$

Use the survey on favorite soft drinks to answer each question.

9. What is the size of the sample? 72
10. What is the mode? cola
11. What fraction chose fruit juice? $\frac{1}{6}$
12. If 7,200 people are expected to order drinks at the football playoff game, how many colas should the Band Boosters order? 2,500 colas

Favorite Soft Drink	
Lemon-Lime	17
Cola	25
Root Beer	10
Fruit Juice	12
Ginger Ale	8

534 **Chapter 13** Discrete Math and Probability

534

Exercises

Independent Practice

The bookstore sells 3-ring binders. All incoming sixth-grade students will need a binder. The binders come in 4 colors: red, green, blue, or yellow. The students who run the store decide to survey 50 sixth graders to find out their favorite color. Using this information, they will order binders to sell to the 450 students who will start the sixth grade in the fall.

13. From an alphabetical list, the students survey every fifth student. Is this a good sample? Why or why not? **yes; randomly taken**

14. Of the students surveyed, 25 chose red, 10 chose green, and 2 chose yellow. How many chose blue? **13 students**

15. For the 450 students, how many of each color should be ordered?
    225 red, 90 green, 18 yellow, 117 blue

Use the sample data on school jacket price ranges to answer each question.

16. What is the size of the sample? **180**

17. If the price was less than $29, about how many would buy a school jacket? **92**

Amount Willing to Pay for School Jacket	
no more than $25	8
no more than $27	80
no more than $29	82
no more than $31	10

18. If there are 400 students in the eighth grade, about how many would buy a school jacket that cost $26?
    about 382 students

Mixed Review

19. Express $8\frac{9}{25}$ as a decimal. *(Lesson 6-6)* **8.36**

20. **Algebra** Find the solution for the system $y = 2x - 7$ and $y = -2x + 9$.
    (Lesson 11-5) **(4, 1)**

21. Refer to the graph in the Example on page 529. Find $P(2$ heads$)$.
    (Lesson 13-7) $P(2 \text{ heads}) = \frac{1}{2}$

Problem Solving and Applications

22. **Military** The graph at the right shows the sizes of camouflage tops worn by one platoon of soldiers.

    a. How many soldiers are in the platoon? **45 soldiers**

    b. If the supply sergeant needed to order a new pattern of camouflage tops for 720 soldiers, how many of each size should be ordered?
       80 extra small, 128 small, 320 medium, 144 large, 48 extra large

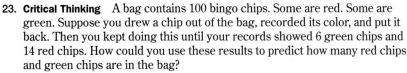

Sizing Up the Military

23. Solve $\frac{6}{20} = \frac{g}{100}$ to predict the number of green chips. Solve $\frac{14}{20} = \frac{r}{100}$ to predict the number of red chips.

23. **Critical Thinking** A bag contains 100 bingo chips. Some are red. Some are green. Suppose you drew a chip out of the bag, recorded its color, and put it back. Then you kept doing this until your records showed 6 green chips and 14 red chips. How could you use these results to predict how many red chips and green chips are in the bag?

Lesson 13-8 Statistics Connection: Using Experiments to Predict   **535**

Extending the Lesson

Using Cooperative Groups Have students work in small groups to conduct an opinion poll on a subject of interest. Have groups describe the population, tell how they chose their sample, and state the number in the population they believe to hold each of the views sampled in the survey.

Cooperative Learning Activity

Riddled Grid 13-8

Use groups of 2.
Materials: Grid paper

▸ Use grid paper to make two game boards like the one shown at the right. Each partner then takes a game board and secretly shades at least ten squares.

➡ One partner names ten squares on the other partner's game board by giving coordinates such as A7 or B2. The other partner tells how many of these ten squares are shaded. Trade roles and repeat the procedure. Then use the number of shaded squares out of ten to predict the total number of squares your partner shaded. Trade papers to see how close your prediction was.

Glencoe Mathematics: Applications and Connections, Course 3

Chapter

13 Study Guide and Review

Communicating Mathematics

Choose the letter that best matches each phrase.

1. an arrangement or listing in which order is important f
2. an arrangement or listing in which order is not important e
3. the product of all counting numbers from n to 1 h
4. a diagram used to find the total number of outcomes of an event g
5. a smaller group representative of a larger group d
6. probabilities based on frequencies obtained in an experiment a
7. probabilities based on physical characteristics b

   See students' work.

8. Write the definition of the Fundamental Principle of Counting.
9. Explain how to find row 6 of Pascal's Triangle. **See margin.**
10. Tell what $C(8, 2)$ means. **the number of combinations of 8 things taken 2 at a time**

a. experimental probabilities
b. theoretical probabilities
c. population
d. sample
e. combination
f. permutation
g. tree diagram
h. $n!$
i. $P(n, r)$

Self Assessment

Objectives and Examples
Upon completing this chapter, you should be able to:

Review Exercises
Use these exercises to review and prepare for the chapter test.

● count outcomes using a tree diagram or the Fundamental Principle of Counting *(Lesson 13-1)*

Two coins are tossed. How many outcomes are possible?

1st Coin	2nd Coin	Outcome
H	H	H H
	T	H T
T	H	T H
	T	T T

There are 4 outcomes.

State the number of possible outcomes for each event.

11. A diner offers three types of soft drinks, with or without ice. **6 outcomes**
12. A car comes in 2 models and 4 colors. There is a choice of a standard or automatic transmission. **16 outcomes**

● find the number of permutations of objects *(Lesson 13-2)*

The symbol $P(n, r)$ represents the number of permutations of n things taken r at a time.

$P(n, r) =$
$n \cdot (n-1) \cdot (n-2) \cdot \ldots \cdot (n - r + 1)$

Solve.   **720 ways**

13. How many different ways can 6 different books be arranged on a shelf?
14. How many different ways can you arrange the letters in the word OBJECTS if you take the letters 3 at a time? **210 ways**

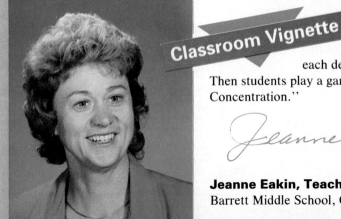

Objectives and Examples

- find the number of combinations of objects *(Lesson 13-3)*

  The symbol $C(n, r)$ represents the number of combinations of n things taken r at a time.

  $$C(n, r) = \frac{P(n, r)}{r!}$$

- identify patterns in Pascal's Triangle *(Lesson 13-4)*

  How many different groups of 3 people can be taken from a group of 5 people?

Row 5	1	5	10	10	5	1
number taken at a time	0	1	2	3 ↑	4	5

  There are 10 different groups.

- find the probability of independent and dependent events *(Lesson 13-5)*

  The probability of two events can be found by multiplying the probability of the first event by the probability of the second event.

- find experimental probability *(Lesson 13-7)*

  Experimental probabilities are probabilities based on frequencies obtained by conducting an experiment.

- predict actions of a larger group using a sample *(Lesson 13-8)*

  If 18 out of a sample of 54 students prefer plain milk over chocolate milk, how many cartons of plain milk does the cafeteria need for 750 students?

  plain milk ⟶ $\frac{18}{54} = \frac{p}{750}$ ⟵ *plain milk*
  sample   *order*
  total sample ⟶   ⟵ *total order*

  18 ☒ 750 ÷ 54 ⊟ 250

  The cafeteria needs to order 250 cartons of plain milk.

Review Exercises

Solve.

15. How many different pairs of kittens can be selected from a litter of six? **15 pairs**

16. How many different groups of 4 marbles can be chosen from a box containing 20 marbles? **4,845 groups**

Use Pascal's Triangle to answer each question.
35 combinations

17. How many combinations are possible when 7 objects are chosen 4 at a time?

18. How many different kinds of 3-topping pizzas can be made when 6 toppings are offered? **20 pizzas**

19. Find the value of $C(9, 3)$. **84**

Two dice are rolled. Find each probability.

20. an even number and an odd number $\frac{1}{4}$

21. a prime number and a composite number $\frac{1}{6}$

22. 2 and a number divisible by 3 $\frac{1}{18}$

23. Toss two coins 40 times.
    a. Record the results. **See students' work.**
    b. What is the experimental probability of no heads? Of one head and one tail? **See students' work.**
    c. What are the theoretical probabilities for part b? $\frac{1}{4}, \frac{1}{2}$

The Goody Hot Dog Company conducted a survey. Participants in the survey were asked to choose one brand of hot dog they would buy. Of those surveyed, 96 said they would buy Goody brand, 68 said they would buy brand X, and 36 said they would buy brand Y.

24. What is the size of the sample? **200**

25. What fraction chose brand Y? $\frac{9}{50}$

26. For 8,000 people, how many would buy a Goody brand hot dog? **3,840 people**

You may wish to use a Chapter Test from the Evaluation Masters booklet as an additional chapter review. The two free-response forms are shown below. One of the two multiple-choice forms is shown on the next page.

Evaluation Masters, pp. 113–114

Form 2A   *Chapter 13 Test*

The school store has small, medium, and large shirts in blue, white, and gray. They come with lettering and without.

1. Draw a tree diagram to show the possible outcomes.
2. If a shirt is chosen at random, what is the probability of selecting a large blue shirt with lettering?
3. How many outcomes show lettering?

Find each value.

4. $P(6, 3)$ 5. $C(6, 3)$
6. How many groups of 3 players can be chosen from 15?
7. In how many ways can 4 people be lined up in a row?
8. Raul has 5 paintings. How many ways can he hang 3 of them in a row?

Use Pascal's Triangle to answer each question.

9. How many combinations of 2 football cards can be chosen from 6 football cards?
10. What is the middle number in row 7?

In a bag there are 4 blue marbles, 2 red marbles, and 6 green marbles. Once a marble is selected, it is not replaced. Find the probability of each outcome.

11. a green marble and then a blue marble
12. any color marble except blue and then a blue marble

Two coins are tossed 20 times. Four times zero heads were tossed, ten times one head was tossed, and six times two heads were tossed.

13. List the possible outcomes for tossing two coins.
14. What is the experimental probability of two heads?
15. What is the theoretical probability of two heads?

Use the survey at the right.

Favorite Sandwich	
hamburger	14
cheeseburger	12
fish	10
vegetarian	4

16. What is the size of this sample?
17. What percent chose fish?
18. What percent of the sample chose a cheeseburger or vegetarian sandwich?
19. The ecology club plans to sell sandwiches to raise money for recycling containers. How many hamburgers should they make if they plan to sell 200 sandwiches?
20. Conrad averages three foul shots out of every five tries and averages 10 foul shots a game. What is the probable number of foul shots he makes in the next game?

BONUS How many straight lines can be drawn through 7 points if no 3 of the points lie on any straight line?

1. See students' diagrams.
2. $\frac{1}{18}$
3. 9
4. 120
5. 20
6. 455
7. 24
8. 60
9. 15
10. 35
11. $\frac{2}{11}$
12. $\frac{8}{33}$
13. HH,TT,HT,TH
14. 0.3
15. 0.25
16. 40
17. 25%
18. 40%
19. 70
20. 6
    21

113
Glencoe Division, Macmillan/McGraw-Hill

Name _____ Date _____

Form 2B   *Chapter 13 Test*

Use the chart. An outfit consists of pants, a shirt, and a sweater.

Pants	Shirts	Sweaters
blue	blue	white
white	white	red
	gray	

1. Draw a tree diagram to find the possible outfits.
2. If an outfit is chosen at random, what is the probability of selecting an all-white outfit?
3. How many outfits are blue pants and a white shirt?
4. Find the value of $P(7, 2)$.   5. Find the value of $C(5, 4)$.
6. In how many ways can a committee of 5 students be selected from a group of 10 students?
7. Five people decided to go to a concert. How many different ways could they stand in line to buy tickets?
8. There are 14 teams in a basketball conference. In how many ways can they be paired for games?

Use Pascal's Triangle to answer each question.

9. Find the value of $C(8, 4)$.
10. What are the numbers in row 7?

In a bag there are 5 blue marbles, 4 red marbles, and 6 white marbles. Once a marble is selected, it is not replaced. Find the probability of each outcome.

11. a blue marble and then a red marble
12. any color marble except white and then a white marble

Two coins are tossed 40 times. Eight times zero heads were tossed, 21 times one head was tossed, and 11 times two heads were tossed.

13. How many possible outcomes are there?
14. What is the experimental probability of zero heads?
15. What is the theoretical probability of zero heads?

Use the survey at the right.

Television Shows	
Comedy	30
Sports	20
Drama	15
Music	35

16. What is the size of this sample?
17. What percent chose sports?
18. What percent chose music or drama?
19. If 250 people were asked their favorite type of television show, how many would choose comedy?
20. Rita averages 1 hit out of every 3 times at bat. She averages 6 times at bat per game. What is the probable number of hits she will make in the next game?

BONUS In how many orders can 4 men and 4 women be seated at a round table if the men and women alternate?

1. See students' diagrams.
2. $\frac{1}{12}$
3. 2
4. 42
5. 5
6. 252
7. 120
8. 91
9. 70
10. 1, 7, 21, 35, 35, 21, 7, 1
11. $\frac{2}{21}$
12. $\frac{9}{35}$
13. 4
14. 0.2
15. 0.25
16. 100
17. 20%
18. 50%
19. 75
20. 2
    144

114
Glencoe Division, Macmillan/McGraw-Hill

538

Applications and Problem Solving

27. **Sports** There are nine players on a baseball team that bat. How many different batting orders are possible? *(Lesson 13-2)* **362,880 batting orders**

28. **Business** Orange Crate Records is having a sale on CDs. They are offering 3 CDs for $32. If there are 40 CDs to choose from, how many combinations of 3 CDs can be chosen? *(Lesson 13-3)* **9,880 combinations**

29. **Food** Frank's Restaurant has a Tuesday dinner special that offers a choice of soup or salad for an appetizer, a choice of steak, fish, or chicken for the main dish, and a choice of pudding or ice cream for dessert. Draw a tree diagram to find the number of possible outcomes for a complete meal. *(Lesson 13-1)* **See Solutions Manual.**

30. Jay jogs past four benches in the park. Based on his observation, he estimates that any one bench is occupied 0.3 of the time. Act it out to find the probability that all four benches will be occupied as Jay jogs past. *(Lesson 13-7)* **Sample answer: 0.0081**

Curriculum Connection Projects

- **Zoology** Survey your classmates to learn how many prefer dogs or cats as pets. Predict how many students in the school prefer each. Display the results in a creative way.

- **Health** List at least three of your favorite breakfast cereals and at least two of your favorite fruits to have on cereal. Find how many mornings you could have a different cereal-fruit combination.

- **Food** Find how many different three-item lunches you can assemble from the selections on today's lunch menu.

Read More About It

Asher, Herbert. *Polling and the Public: What Every Citizen Should Know.*
Blackwood, Gary. *The Dying Sun.*
Burns, Marilyn. *The I Hate Mathematics Book.*
McCauley, David. *Pyramid.*

538   **Chapter 13** Study Guide and Review

13 Test

Televisions come in three sizes, a 13-, 19-, or 27-inch screen, and with one or two speakers. They come with or without remote control.

1. Draw a tree diagram to find the number of possible outcomes. **See Solutions Manual.**

2. If a television is chosen at random, what is the probability of selecting a 19-inch, two speaker television with remote control? $\frac{1}{12}$

3. How many outcomes show a one-speaker television? **6 outcomes**

Find each value.

4. $P(8, 3)$ **336**   5. $C(15, 5)$ **3,003**

6. Michelle has 7 tennis trophies. How many ways can she arrange 4 of them in a row? **840 ways**

7. How many teams of 6 players can be chosen from 18 players? **18,564 teams**

8. In how many ways can 5 students stand in a line? **120 ways**

Use Pascal's Triangle to answer each question.   **10 combinations**

9. How many combinations of 3 baseball cards can be chosen from 5 baseball cards?

10. What does the 20 in row 6 mean? **the number of combinations of 6 things taken 3 at a time**

In a bag there are 5 blue marbles, 3 red marbles, and 2 green marbles. Once a marble is selected, it is not replaced. Find the probability of each outcome.

11. a red marble and then a blue marble $\frac{1}{6}$ 12. two green marbles $\frac{1}{45}$

13. Does the probability in Problem 11 represent dependent or independent events? **dependent**

Two coins are tossed 20 times. No heads were tossed five times, one head was tossed eleven times, and two heads were tossed four times.

14. What is the experimental probability of two heads? $\frac{1}{5}$

15. What is the theoretical probability of two heads? $\frac{1}{4}$

16. Why is the experimental probability and theoretical probability of two heads different? **See Solutions Manual.**

Use the survey on favorite chocolate bars to answer each question.

Favorite Chocolate Bar	
milk chocolate	13
with almonds	18
with crisps	11
with caramel	8

17. What is the size of this sample? **50**

18. What percent of the sample chose a chocolate bar with almonds? **36%**

19. The school choir plans on selling chocolate bars to raise money for new uniforms. How many chocolate bars with almonds should they order if they plan on selling 800 chocolate bars? **288 chocolate bars with almonds**

20. Olivia reaches into a bag containing 3 apples, 2 pears, and 2 tangerines. Act it out to find the probability that she picks out 2 tangerines. **Sample answer:** $\frac{1}{21}$

Bonus In how many ways can 2 boys and 2 girls stand in a line, if boys and girls are to alternate in line? **8 ways**

Chapter 13 Test   **539**

Using the Chapter Test

This page may be used as a chapter test or another chapter review.

Evaluation Masters, pp. 109–110

Name _____ Date _____

Form 1A _____   *Chapter 13 Test*

Use a tree diagram to find the number of possible outcomes for each situation in Exercises 1–3.

1. A die is rolled three times.
   A. 36   B. 18   C. 72   D. 216   1. ___D___

2. Choosing an outfit from 3 skirts, 4 blouses, 2 sweaters, and 2 pairs of shoes.
   A. 11   B. 48   C. 28   D. 96   2. ___B___

3. A die is rolled and then a coin is tossed.
   A. 8   B. 36   C. 12   D. 24   3. ___C___

4. Find the value of $P(8, 2)$.
   A. 4   B. 16   C. 14   D. 56   4. ___D___

5. How many ways can 6 people stand in a line?
   A. 720   B. 5,040   C. 120   D. 40,320   5. ___A___

6. How many 3-digit numbers can you write using the digits 1, 2, 3, 4, and 5? In each number you write, use each digit only once.
   A. 36   B. 24   C. 72   D. 60   6. ___D___

7. Find the value of $C(6, 5)$.
   A. 5,040   B. 120   C. 6   D. 720   7. ___C___

8. How many committees of 3 students each can be selected from 8 students?
   A. 24   B. 336   C. 56   D. 120   8. ___C___

9. Pete's Pizza has a choice of 7 toppings for their pizzas. They are having a special on pizzas with 4 toppings. How many different pizzas with 4 toppings can they serve?
   A. 840   B. 35   C. 120   D. 720   9. ___B___

Use Pascal's Triangle for Exercises 10 and 11.

10. How many combinations are possible for 6 things taken 4 at a time?
    A. 15   B. 45   C. 30   D. 360   10. ___A___

11. What is the middle number in row 8?
    A. 20   B. 35   C. 50   D. 70   11. ___D___

In a bag, there are 3 red marbles and 7 blue marbles. Once a marble is selected, it is not replaced. Find the probability of each outcome in Exercises 12–14.

12. a red marble and then a red marble
    A. $\frac{1}{15}$ B. $\frac{1}{6}$ C. $\frac{2}{15}$ D. $\frac{1}{3}$ 12. ___A___

109
Glencoe Division, Macmillan/McGraw-Hill

Name _____ Date _____

Chapter 13 Test, Form 1A (continued)

13. a blue marble and then a red marble
    A. $\frac{7}{15}$ B. $\frac{1}{15}$ C. $\frac{7}{30}$ D. $\frac{2}{15}$ 13. ___C___

14. they are different colors
    A. $\frac{4}{15}$ B. $\frac{8}{15}$ C. $\frac{7}{30}$ D. $\frac{7}{15}$ 14. ___D___

Three coins are tossed 20 times. The results are displayed in the chart at the right. Use this information for Exercises 15 and 16.

zero tails	1
one tail	8
two tails	10
three tails	1

15. What is the experimental probability of one tail?
    A. 0.25   B. 0.3   C. 0.5   D. 0.4   15. ___D___

16. What is the theoretical probability of one tail?
    A. 0.375   B. 0.625   C. 0.875   D. 0.125   16. ___A___

Use the survey on favorite flavors of yogurt to answer the questions for Exercises 17–19.

Favorite Flavors of Yogurt	
vanilla	22
coffee	10
chocolate	16
lemon	7
strawberry	5

17. What is the size of the sample?
    A. 100   B. 60   C. 75   D. 50   17. ___B___

18. What fraction chose chocolate yogurt?
    A. $\frac{4}{15}$ B. $\frac{7}{15}$ C. $\frac{11}{15}$ D. $\frac{1}{6}$ 18. ___A___

19. For 150 people, how many would you expect to choose chocolate yogurt?
    A. 60   B. 50   C. 70   D. 40   19. ___D___

20. Use the data in the simulation chart at the right to find the probability of at least three heads in the tossing of six coins.

simulation 1	H	T	H	H	T	H
simulation 2	T	T	H	H	H	T
simulation 3	H	H	H	T	T	H
simulation 4	T	T	H	T	T	T
simulation 5	T	H	H	T	H	H

    A. 0.8   B. 0.6   C. 0.4   D. 0.7   20. ___A___

BONUS In how many ways can a baseball team be arranged if the catcher and pitcher never change positions?
A. 40,320   B. 5,040   C. 120   D. 720   ___B___

110
Glencoe Division, Macmillan/McGraw-Hill

Test and Review Generator software is provided in Apple, IBM, and Macintosh versions. You may use this software to create your own tests or worksheets, based on the needs of your students.

The **Performance Assessment Booklet** provides an alternate assessment for evaluating student progress. An assessment for this chapter can be found on pages 25–26.

14 Algebra: Investigations with Polynomials

Previewing the Chapter

This chapter on polynomials, heavily discovery-oriented, provides an ideal introduction to middle-level algebra. Students use area tiles to discover methods of operating on polynomials. Only then are methods generalized and algorithms stated. Students learn to simplify, add, subtract, multiply, and factor polynomials. Models and the distributive property are used to introduce methods of multiplying a polynomial by a monomial and multiplying two binomials. The **problem-solving strategy** lesson teaches students to solve problems by using logical reasoning.

Lesson	Lesson Objectives	NCTM Standards	State/Local Objectives
14-1A	Make area models for algebraic expressions.	1–4, 9, 12	
14-1	Represent polynomials with area models.	1–4, 7, 9	
14-2	Simplify polynomials using area models.	1–4, 7, 9	
14-3	Add polynomials using area models.	1–4, 7, 9	
14-4	Subtract polynomials using area models.	1–4, 7, 9	
14-5A	Model products with area tiles.	1–4, 7, 9	
14-5	Multiply a polynomial by a monomial and factor polynomials using models.	1–4, 7, 9	
14-6	Multiply binomials using area models.	1–4, 7, 9	
14-6B	Factor polynomials using area models.	1–4, 7, 9	
14-7	Solve problems by using logical reasoning.	1–4	

Organizing the Chapter

A complete, 1-page lesson plan is provided for each lesson in the Lesson Plans Masters Booklet.

LESSON PLANNING GUIDE

Lesson	Materials/ Manipulatives	Extra Practice (Student Edition)	Blackline Masters Booklets											
			Study Guide	Practice	Enrichment	Evaluation	Technology	Lab Manual	Multicultural Activities	Application and Interdisciplinary Activities	Transparencies	Group Activity Cards
14-1A	yellow and red construction paper, scissors							p. 79				
14-1	area tiles	p. 616	p. 121	p. 121	p. 121						14-1	14-1
14-2	area tiles	p. 616	p. 122	p. 122	p. 122		p. 14				14-2	14-2
14-3	area tiles	p. 616	p. 123	p. 123	p. 123						14-3	14-3
14-4	area tiles	p. 617	p. 124	p. 124	p. 124	Quiz A, p. 124				p. 28	14-4	14-4
14-5A	area tiles, product mat							p. 80				
14-5	area tiles	p. 617	p. 125	p. 125	p. 125					p. 14	14-5	14-5
14-6	area tiles, product mat	p. 617	p. 126	p. 126	p. 126		p. 28				14-6	14-6
14-6B	area tiles, product mat							p. 81				
14-7			p. 127	p. 127	p. 127	Quiz B, p. 124				p. 14	14-7	14-7
Study Guide and Review	area tiles		Multiple Choice Test, Forms 1A and 1B, pp. 118–121 Free Response Test, Forms 2A and 2B, pp. 122–123 Cumulative Review, p. 125 (free response)									
Test	area tiles		Cumulative Test, p. 126 (multiple choice)									

Pacing Guide: Option III (Chapters 1–14) - 9 days

You may wish to refer to the complete **Course Planning Guides** on page T25.

OTHER CHAPTER RESOURCES

Student Edition
Chapter Opener, pp. 540–541
Save Planet Earth, p. 549
Mid-Chapter Review, p. 555
Portfolio Suggestion, p. 566
Academic Skills Test, pp. 570–571

 Manipulatives
Overhead Manipulative Resources
Middle School Mathematics Manipulative Kit

 Software/Technology
Interactive Mathematics Tools (Macintosh)
Test and Review Generator (IBM, Apple, Macintosh)
Teacher's Guide for Software Resources

Other Supplements
Transparency 14-0
Performance Assessment, pp. 27–28
Glencoe Mathematics Professional Series
Lesson Plans, pp. 153–162

INTERDISCIPLINARY BULLETIN BOARD

Sports Connection

Objective Write polynomials representing sports scoring systems.

How To Use It Have students research and write explanations of scoring systems used in sports other than basketball. For each sport, students should write a polynomial like the one given for basketball and give an example of how it can be used.

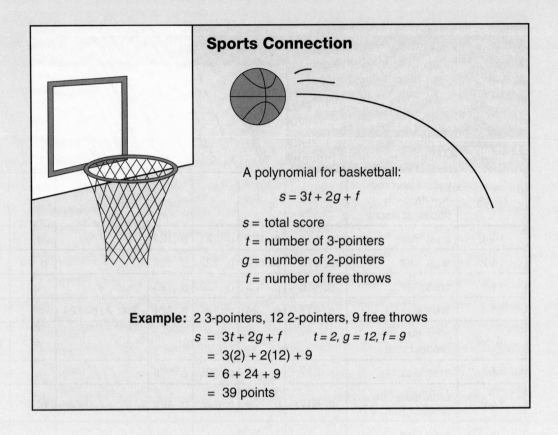

Sports Connection

A polynomial for basketball:

$$s = 3t + 2g + f$$

$s =$ total score
$t =$ number of 3-pointers
$g =$ number of 2-pointers
$f =$ number of free throws

Example: 2 3-pointers, 12 2-pointers, 9 free throws

$$
\begin{aligned}
s &= 3t + 2g + f \qquad t = 2,\, g = 12,\, f = 9 \\
&= 3(2) + 2(12) + 9 \\
&= 6 + 24 + 9 \\
&= 39 \text{ points}
\end{aligned}
$$

APPLICATIONS AND CONNECTIONS

Applications	Lesson	Example	Exercise
Business	14-1		28
Money	14-2		30
Construction	14-3		26
Gardening	14-5		31
Connections			
Algebra	14-3	2	
Geometry	14-3		27
Geometry	14-4		28
Geometry	14-6		24, 26

TEAM ACTIVITIES

Multicultural Experiences

Outside Field Trips Visit a rental store and have students write polynomials representing the rental costs of items as functions of the amount of time for which they are rented. For example, for a rototiller renting for $12 plus $5 per hour, the polynomial 12 + 5h expresses the rental fee.

In-Class Speakers Invite a guest, such as a lawyer, a private investigator, or a public health worker, to explain how they use logical reasoning in their work.

The school librarian can discuss examples of deductive reasoning in the Sherlock Holmes mysteries.

SUPPLEMENTARY BLACKLINE MASTER BOOKLETS

Some of the blackline masters for enhancing this chapter are shown below.

Application and Interdisciplinary Activity Masters, pp. 14, 28

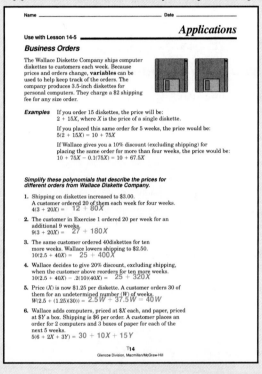

Name _____ Date _____

Applications

Use with Lesson 14-5

Business Orders

The Wallace Diskette Company ships computer diskettes to customers each week. Because prices and orders change, **variables** can be used to help keep track of the orders. The company produces 3.5-inch diskettes for personal computers. They charge a $2 shipping fee for any size order.

Examples If you order 15 diskettes, the price will be:
$2 + 15X$, where X is the price of a single diskette.

If you placed this same order for 5 weeks, the price would be:
$5(2 + 15X) = 10 + 75X$

If Wallace gives a 10% discount (excluding shipping) for placing the same order for more than four weeks, the price would be:
$10 + 75X - 0.1(75X) = 10 + 67.5X$

Simplify these polynomials that describe the prices for different orders from Wallace Diskette Company.

1. Shipping on diskettes increased to $3.00. A customer ordered 20 of them each week for four weeks.
$4(3 + 20X) = \quad 12 + 80X$

2. The customer in Exercise 1 ordered 20 per week for an additional 9 weeks.
$9(3 + 20X) = \quad 27 + 180X$

3. The same customer ordered 40 diskettes for ten more weeks. Wallace lowers shipping to $2.50.
$10(2.5 + 40X) = \quad 25 + 400X$

4. Wallace decides to give 20% discount, excluding shipping, when the customer above reorders for ten more weeks.
$10(2.5 + 40X) - .2(10)(40X) = \quad 25 + 320X$

5. Price (X) is now $1.25 per diskette. A customer orders 30 of them for an undetermined number (W) of weeks.
$W(2.5 + (1.25)(30)) = \quad 2.5W + 37.5W = 40W$

6. Wallace adds computers, priced at $X each, and paper, priced at $Y a box. Shipping is $6 per order. A customer places an order for 2 computers and 3 boxes of paper for each of the next 5 weeks.
$5(6 + 2X + 3Y) = \quad 30 + 10X + 15Y$

T14
Glencoe Division, Macmillan/McGraw-Hill

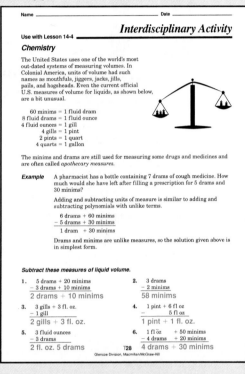

Name _____ Date _____

Interdisciplinary Activity

Use with Lesson 14-4

Chemistry

The United States uses one of the world's most out-dated systems of measuring volumes. In Colonial America, units of volume had such names as mouthfuls, jiggers, jacks, jills, pails, and hogsheads. Even the current official U.S. measures of volume for liquids, as shown below, are a bit unusual.

60 minims = 1 fluid dram
8 fluid drams = 1 fluid ounce
4 fluid ounces = 1 gill
4 gills = 1 pint
2 pints = 1 quart
4 quarts = 1 gallon

The minims and drams are still used for measuring some drugs and medicines and are often called *apothecary* measures.

Example A pharmacist has a bottle containing 7 drams of cough medicine. How much would she have left after filling a prescription for 5 drams and 30 minims?

Adding and subtracting units of measure is similar to adding and subtracting polynomials with unlike terms.

6 drams + 60 minims
− 5 drams + 30 minims
1 dram + 30 minims

Drams and minims are unlike measures, so the solution given above is in simplest form.

Subtract these measures of liquid volume.

1. 5 drams + 20 minims
− 3 drams + 10 minims
2 drams + 10 minims

2. 3 drams
− 2 minims
58 minims

3. 3 gills + 3 fl. oz.
− 1 gill
2 gills + 3 fl. oz.

4. 1 pint + 6 fl oz
− 5 fl oz
1 pint + 1 fl. oz.

5. 3 fluid ounces
− 3 drams
2 fl. oz. 5 drams

6. 1 fl oz + 50 minims
− 4 drams + 20 minims
4 drams + 30 minims

T28
Glencoe Division, Macmillan/McGraw-Hill

Multicultural Activity Masters, p. 14

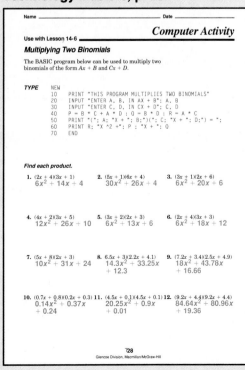

Name _____ Date _____

Multicultural Activity

Use with Lesson 14-7

Hispanic Scientists and Engineers

Helicopters became widely used in the early 1950s. However, did you know that a similar aircraft, the *autogiro*, was developed in Spain nearly thirty years earlier? The inventor was Juan de la Cierva (1895–1936), and for many years his aircraft were used in rescue work. The modern helicopter is faster and more versatile, but it retains many features of Cierva's autogiro.

Hispanics have made many contributions to the sciences and engineering. In the following puzzle, you will learn about the contributions of five Hispanic Americans.

Luis Alvarez, Franklin Chang-Diaz, Margarita Colmenares, Antonia Novello, and Severo Ochoa are an astronaut, biochemist, engineer, physician, and physicist, but not necessarily in that order. The following are some facts about them. Use the facts to find who is the engineer.

1. Alvarez was the winner of the Nobel Prize for Physics in 1968.

2. Ochoa won the Nobel Prize for Physiology or Medicine in 1959, but he is not the physician.

3. The engineer is the first woman president of the Society of Hispanic Professional Engineers.

4. The physician is the first woman surgeon general of the United States.

5. In 1986, the astronaut became the first Hispanic American to travel in space. He was a mission specialist aboard the space shuttle *Columbia*.

6. Colmenares is not the physician.

7. Ochoa was born 45 years before the astronaut.

Who is the engineer? _Margarita Colmenares_

	astronaut	biochemist	engineer	physician	physicist
Alvarez	✗	✗	✗	✗	✓
Chang-Diaz	✓	✗	✗	✗	✗
Colmenares	✗	✗	✓	✗	✗
Novello	✗	✗	✗	✓	✗
Ochoa	✗	✓	✗	✗	✗

T14
Glencoe Division, Macmillan/McGraw-Hill

Technology Masters, p. 28

Name _____ Date _____

Computer Activity

Use with Lesson 14-6

Multiplying Two Binomials

The BASIC program below can be used to multiply two binomials of the form $Ax + B$ and $Cx + D$.

```
TYPE    NEW
        10  PRINT "THIS PROGRAM MULTIPLIES TWO BINOMIALS"
        20  INPUT "ENTER A, B, IN AX + B"; A, B
        30  INPUT "ENTER C, D, IN CX + D"; C, D
        40  P = B * C + A * D: Q = B * D: R = A * C
        50  PRINT "("; A; "X + "; B;")("; C; "X + "; D;") = ";
        60  PRINT R; "X ^2 +"; P; "X + "; Q
        70  END
```

Find each product.

1. $(2x + 4)(3x + 1)$
$6x^2 + 14x + 4$

2. $(5x + 1)(6x + 4)$
$30x^2 + 26x + 4$

3. $(3x + 1)(2x + 6)$
$6x^2 + 20x + 6$

4. $(4x + 2)(3x + 5)$
$12x^2 + 26x + 10$

5. $(3x + 2)(2x + 3)$
$6x^2 + 13x + 6$

6. $(2x + 4)(3x + 3)$
$6x^2 + 18x + 12$

7. $(5x + 8)(2x + 3)$
$10x^2 + 31x + 24$

8. $(6.5x + 3)(2.2x + 4.1)$
$14.3x^2 + 33.25x + 12.3$

9. $(7.2x + 3.4)(2.5x + 4.9)$
$18x^2 + 43.78x + 16.66$

10. $(0.7x + 0.8)(0.2x + 0.3)$
$0.14x^2 + 0.37x + 0.24$

11. $(4.5x + 0.1)(4.5x + 0.1)$
$20.25x^2 + 0.9x + 0.01$

12. $(9.2x + 4.4)(9.2x + 4.4)$
$84.64x^2 + 80.96x + 19.36$

T28
Glencoe Division, Macmillan/McGraw-Hill

RECOMMENDED OUTSIDE RESOURCES

Books/Periodicals

Grouws, Douglas A., Thomas J. Cooney, and Douglas Jones, *Effective Mathematics Teaching,* Reston, VA: NCTM, 1988.

Harnadek, Anita, *Algebra Word Problems,* Pacific Grove, CA: Midwest Publications, 1989.

Films/Videotapes/Videodiscs

Equations in Algebra, Chicago, IL: International Film Bureau, Inc., 1963.

The View from the People Wall, Chicago, IL: Encyclopedia Britannica Films, 1973.

Software

Algebra Concepts, (Apple II, IBM/Tandy, Macintosh), Ventura Educational Systems

For addresses of companies handling software, please refer to page T24.

Glencoe's *Interactive Mathamatics: Activities and Investigations* consists of 18 units that may be used as alternatives or supplemental material for *Mathematics: Applications and Connections.* The suggested units for this chapter are Unit 5, *Get a Clue,* and Unit 16, *Growing Pains.* See page T18 for more information.

This two-page introduction to the chapter provides a visual, relevant way to engage students in the mathematics of the chapter. Questions are included that help students see the need to learn the mathematics in the chapter. Data in charts and graphs provide statistical information that students can analyze and interpret at this point as well as later in the chapter. The Chapter Project provides an activity that applies the mathematics of the chapter.

MAKING MATHEMATICS RELEVANT

Spotlight on Transportation

Ask the following questions as examples of the costs involved in transportation.

- A truck driver pays a highway tax of $0.035 per mile. What is the cost of driving 500 miles per day 250 days per year? $4,375

- Marcus drove 486 miles and spent $19.44 for gas. If gas sold for $1.08 per gallon, what was Marcus's mileage rate (miles per gallon)? 27 mi/gal

- By buying her plane ticket seven days in advance, Maria saved 25% of the regular price. If her ticket cost $222, what was the regular price? $296

- A taxi costs $2.50 for the first mile plus $0.35 for each additional $\frac{1}{4}$ mile. If the fare for a certain cab ride was $5.65, how far did the cab travel? $3\frac{1}{4}$ miles

Chapter

14

Algebra: Investigations with Polynomials

Spotlight on Transportation

Have You Ever Wondered...

- How much subway fares have increased over the years?

- If the price of a rental car depends on the city in which it is rented?

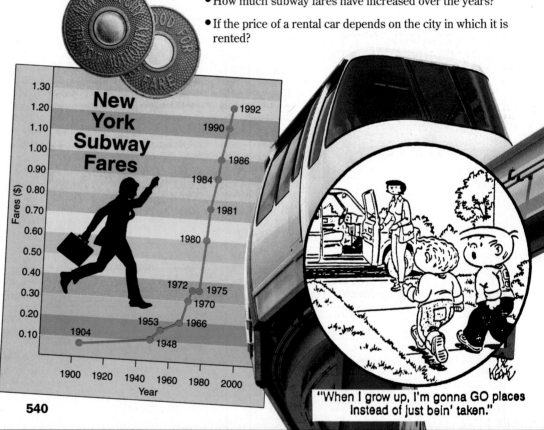

540

"Have You Ever Wondered?" Answers

- Students can see from the subway-fare chart that the fare has increased from 8¢ to $1.25.

- Students can see from the rental chart that the charge does depend on the city in which the car is rented.

Chapter Project

Transportation
Work in a group.

1. Choose a place you would like to visit.

2. Determine how much it would cost to get there by different means of transportation, such as by car, by plane, by train, by bus, or by boat.

3. Make a poster of your information. Include the advantages and disadvantages of each type of transportation and which one you would most likely choose.

Looking Ahead

In this chapter, you will see how mathematics can be used to answer questions about transportation. The major objectives of the chapter are to:

- represent polynomials with area models

- use area models to simplify algebraic expression, and add, subtract, multiply, and divide polynomials.

- solve problems using logical reasoning

RENTING A CAR			
City	Compact	Midsize	Full-size
Atlanta			
Avis	$41.00	$45.00	$46.00
Budget	$34.99	$36.99	$38.99
Hertz	$45.99	$49.99	$53.99
National	$26.90	$29.90	$33.90
Chicago			
Avis	$58.00	$60.00	$65.00
Budget	$53.00	$55.50	$61.00
Hertz	$56.99	$58.99	$63.99
National	$22.90	$22.90	$31.90
Dallas			
Avis	$43.00	$46.00	$47.00
Budget	$48.99	$52.99	$53.99
Hertz	$22.99	$25.99	$27.99
National	$35.90	$40.90	$41.90

City	Compact	Midsize	Full-size
Los Angeles			
Avis	$35.00	$39.00	$42.00
Budget	$22.89	$23.89	$28.99
Hertz	$46.99	$48.99	$51.99
National	$33.90	$34.90	$40.90
New York			
Avis	$56.98	$64.98	$67.98
Budget	$53.00	$59.00	$67.50
Hertz	$54.99	$57.99	$63.99
National	$45.90	$47.90	$55.90
St. Louis			
Avis	$37.00	$41.00	$43.00
Budget	$36.99	$37.99	$43.99
Hertz	$39.99	$45.99	$47.99
National	$25.00	$27.00	$30.00

541

DATA ANALYSIS

Have students study the subway-fare graph and car-rental chart. Then ask the following questions.

- *Which decade showed the greatest increase in subway fares?* the 1980's

- *How much greater was the fare increase during the 22-year period after 1970 compared to the 22-year period before 1970?* $0.75

- *Which company offers the lowest car-rental rates in the most cities?* National

Data Search
A question related to these data is provided in Lesson 14-2, page 549, Exercise 33.

CHAPTER PROJECT

Students can find transportation and lodging rates from newspaper ads, automobile club literature, or conversations with travel agents. Encourage students to be thorough in estimating expenses. The costs of many incidental items (for example, tips, sun tan lotion) can easily be overlooked. Encourage students to display their findings in a creative manner.

Allow two weeks to complete the project.

Chapter Opener Transparency

Transparency 14-0 is available in the Transparency Package. It provides another full-color, motivating activity that you can use to capture students' interest.

NCTM Standards: 1–4, 9, 12

Management Tips

For Students   Instead of using a ruler to measure their tiles, students should choose arbitrary measures of 1 unit and x units. Have students save the area tiles made in the Extension for use throughout this chapter.

For the Overhead Projector
Overhead Manipulative Resources provides appropriate materials for teacher or student demonstration of the activities in this Mathematics Lab.

1 FOCUS

Introducing the Lab

Ask students to find the areas of the figures below.   36 cm²; mn units²

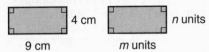

2 TEACH

Using Problem Solving   Ask students how they could find the area of the larger square if they knew the value of x.   area: x^2

3 PRACTICE/APPLY

Using Problem Solving   Ask students to write an expression for the difference in area between the large and small squares. $x^2 - 1$

Close

Have students state the relationship between the length, width, and area of a rectangle.
area = length × width

Cooperative Learning
14-1A   Area Models
A Preview of Lesson 14-1

Objective
Make area models for algebraic expressions.

Materials
yellow and red
  construction paper
scissors

Throughout this text, you have used rectangles to show multiplication problems. For example, the figure at the right shows the multiplication problem 4×5 as a rectangle that is 4 units wide and 5 units long. Its area is 20 square units.

In this lab, you will show algebraic expressions using models called area tiles.

Try this!

Work with a partner.

● From yellow construction paper, cut out a square that is 1 unit long and 1 unit wide.

● Draw a line segment that is longer than 1 unit. Since the line segment can be any length, we will say that it is x units long. From yellow construction paper, cut out a rectangle that is 1 unit wide and x units long.

● Using the same measure for x, cut out a square that is x units long and x units wide from yellow construction paper.

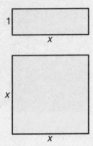

What do you think?

1. Find the area of each shape and write the area on each tile.   1, x, x^2
2. For each tile, write a sentence that tells the relationship between the length, width, and area.   The area is the product of the length and width.

Extension

3. From yellow construction paper, cut out four more sets of tiles. Label each with its area.   See students' work.
4. From red construction paper, cut out five sets of tiles with the same dimensions as the yellow tiles. Label the areas -1, -x, and -x^2.
   See students' work.

OPTIONS

Lab Manual   You may wish to make copies of the blackline master on p. 79 of the *Lab Manual* for students to use as a recording sheet.

Lab Manual, p. 79

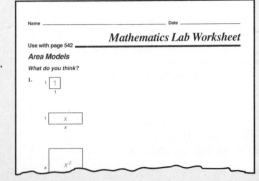

14-1 Area Models of Polynomials

Objective
Represent polynomials with area models.

Words to Learn
monomial
polynomial

When an engineer designs a new sports car, he or she often makes a model of the car. The model helps the engineer visualize the car and determine characteristics like structural strength and fuel efficiency. In mathematics we also use models to help us visualize concepts.

In the previous mathematics lab, you made area tiles.

The expressions 1, x, and x^2 are called **monomials.** A monomial is a number, a variable, or a product of a number and one or more variables. You can model any monomial using area tiles.

Examples

Model each monomial using area tiles or drawings.

1 $2x^2$

To model this expression, you need 2 yellow x^2-tiles.

2 $-3x$

Use red tiles to model negative values. To model this expression, you need 3 red x-tiles.

3 4

To model this expression, you need 4 yellow 1-tiles.

Sometimes, algebraic expressions contain more than one monomial. These expressions are called **polynomials.** A polynomial is the sum or difference of two or more monomials. You can also model polynomials with area tiles.

Lesson 14-1 Area Models of Polynomials **543**

OPTIONS

Reteaching Activity

Using Models Have students model a monomial using any number of x^2-tiles only, then a second monomial using only x-tiles, and finally a third monomial using only 1-tiles. Then have them place the tiles together and name the polynomial modeled by the tiles.

Study Guide Masters, p. 121

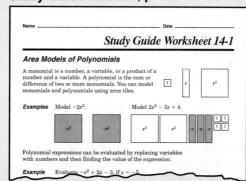

14-1 Lesson Notes

NCTM Standards: 1–4, 7, 9

Lesson Resources
• Study Guide Master 14-1
• Practice Master 14-1
• Enrichment Master 14-1
• Group Activity Card 14-1

Transparency 14-1 contains the 5-Minute Check and a teaching aid for this lesson.

5-Minute Check
(Over Chapter 13)

1. Cakes are sold in 5 flavors, 4 shapes, and 3 frostings. How many types are sold?   60
2. In how many orders can 5 people stand in line?   120
3. Find $C(7, 2)$.   21
4. Two coins are tossed. Find P(two heads). $\frac{1}{4}$

1 FOCUS

Motivating the Lesson

Activity Display a counter and say that it represents 1 unit. Then ask the following questions.

- *How could you represent 8 units?*   Use 8 counters.
- *If the counter represents x units, how can you represent 5x units?*   Use 5 counters.

2 TEACH

Using Connections Students may think that $x + x = x^2$. Use the distributive property to show that the sum is $2x$:

$$x + x = 1x + 1x$$
$$= (1 + 1)x$$
$$= 2x$$

543

More Examples

Model each monomial or polynomial using area tiles or drawings.

For Example 1

$-2x^2$

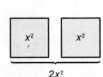

For Example 2

$5x$

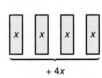

For Example 3

-2

For Example 4

$-x^2 + x + 6$

For Example 5

$2x^2 - x - 1$

For Example 6

Evaluate $-x^2 + x + 3$ if $x = 3$. -3

Practice Masters, p. 121

Name _____ Date _____

Practice Worksheet 14-1

Area Models of Polynomials

Write a monomial or polynomial for each model.

1.
$x^2 + 2x + 3$

2.
$-x^2 + x - 2$

3.
$2x^2 - 2$

4.
$-3x^2$

Model each monomial or polynomial using area tiles or drawings.

5. $x^2 - 3x$

6. $-2x^2 + 3x$

7. $4x + 1$

8. -6

Evaluate each expression.

9. $3x - 8$, if $x = 10$
22

10. $x^2 + 4x$, if $x = -4$
0

11. $x^2 + x + 3$, if $x = -2$
5

12. $3x^2 - 12$, if $x = 8$
180

T121
Glencoe Division, Macmillan/McGraw-Hill

544

Examples

Model each polynomial using area tiles or drawings.

4 $2x^2 + 4x + 9$

$2x^2$ $+ 4x$ $+ 9$

5 $x^2 - 2x - 3$

x^2 $-2x$ -3

Polynomial expressions can be evaluated by replacing variables with numbers and then finding the value of the numerical expression.

Example 6 *Connection*

LOOK BACK

You can review order of operations on page 44.

Algebra   Evaluate $3x^2 - 5x + 2$ if $x = -2$.

$$\begin{aligned}3x^2 - 5x + 2 &= 3(-2)^2 - 5(-2) + 2 \\ &= 3(4) - 5(-2) + 2 \\ &= 12 - (-10) + 2 \\ &= 24\end{aligned}$$

Replace x with -2.
Use the order of operations.

Checking for Understanding

Communicating Mathematics

Read and study the lesson to answer each question.

1. **Write** two expressions that are monomials and two that are polynomials.
Sample answers: a, $4y^3$; $a^2 + 2ab$, $6g^3 + 14g + 8$

2. **Tell** how to model a monomial like $-2x$. Use 2 red x-tiles.

3. **Write** the polynomial represented by the model at the right.

4. **Draw** a model of $-3x^2 + 2x - 5$.
See Solutions Manual.

Guided Practice

Write a monomial or polynomial for each model.

$2x^2 - x + 6$

5.
$-x^2 + 3x - 4$

6.
$-4x + 2$

544   **Chapter 14**   Algebra: Investigations with Polynomials

---

OPTIONS

Team Teaching

Models of theories have been developed in many disciplines, so that they can be studied. Ask the other teachers on your team to discuss possible examples with their students. Suggestions for curriculum integration are:

Science: atomic model of matter
Social Studies: Malthus' model of population growth

Additional Answer

29.

Model each monomial or polynomial using area tiles or drawings. See Solutions Manual.

7. $3x^2$ 8. $2x - 1$ 9. $-x^2 + 5x - 6$

10. Evaluate $x^2 - 3x - 4$ if $x = 5$. 6

Exercises

Write a monomial or polynomial for each model.

11.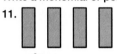

$-4x$

12.

$x^2 + 4x$

13.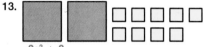

$-2x^2 + 9$

14.

$4x - 7$

Model each monomial or polynomial using area tiles or drawings. See Solutions Manual.

15. $-2x^2$ 16. $5x + 3$ 17. $3x^2 + 2x + 6$

18. $4x^2 - 3$ 19. $-x^2 - 2x - 1$ 20. $x^2 - 8$

Evaluate each expression.

21. $2x - 5$, if $x = 8$ 11   22. $x^2 + 3x$, if $x = -2$ -2

23. $x^2 - 10x + 25$, if $x = 5$ 0   24. $-x^2 + 4x$, if $x = -1$ -5

Mixed Review

25. **Geometry** Find the circumference of a circle with a radius of 8.2 millimeters. *(Lesson 7-8)* 51.52 mm

26. Thirty is 60% of what number? *(Lesson 10-1)* 50

27. **Statistics** Refer to the favorite soft drink survey at the right. For 6,300 people, how much ginger ale should the Band Boosters order? *(Lesson 13–8)* 700 ginger ales

Favorite Soft Drink	
Flavor	Number of Responses
Lemon-Lime	17
Cola	25
Root Beer	10
Fruit	12
Ginger Ale	8

Problem Solving and Applications

28. **Business** Carla volunteers to get lunch for members of the Ecology Club. She represents their lunch order of 13 burgers, 7 shakes, and 10 orders of french fries as the polynomial expression $13b + 7s + 10f$. Determine the cost of the order if burgers are $1.99 each, shakes are $1.49 each, and fries are $0.99 each. $46.20

29. See margin.

29. **Critical Thinking** The model x 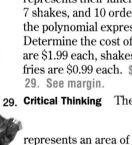 represents an area of x. Suppose y represents an area of y. Draw a model that represents an area of xy.

30. **Journal Entry** Make up a polynomial and use a drawing to represent it. See students' work.

Lesson 14-1 Area Models of Polynomials   **545**

Extending the Lesson

Using Drawings Ask students to make a drawing of the polynomial $x^3 + x^2 + x + 1$.

Cooperative Learning Activity

Number of players: 2
Materials: Index cards, spinner, counters

What's Your Evaluation? **14-1**

● Copy onto cards the expressions shown on the back of this card, one per card. Shuffle the cards and place them face down in a pile. Label equal sections of a spinner "1," "2," "3." On a large sheet of paper (or several smaller sheets taped together) copy the game board shown below. Make sure that a counter will fit in each square.

➡ Each partner places a counter on the "Start" square. One partner spins the spinner. Then, in turn, each partner selects a card and evaluates it for the value of x on the spinner. Continue in this way, taking turns at the spinner. Shuffle and reuse cards if necessary. The first partner to reach the "Win" square wins. A partner who lands on or goes past the "Lose" square automatically loses. Play several rounds, reshuffling the cards each time.

Lose   Start   Win

Glencoe Mathematics: Applications and Connections, Course 3

NCTM Standards: 1–4, 7, 9

Lesson Resources
- Study Guide Master 14-2
- Practice Master 14-2
- Enrichment Master 14-2
- Technology Master, p. 14
- Group Activity Card 14-2

 Transparency 14-2 contains the 5-Minute Check and a teaching aid for this lesson.

🕐 5-Minute Check
(Over Lesson 14-1)

1. Write a polynomial for this model. $x^2 - 2x + 4$

2. Draw a model of the polynomial $-x^2 + 4x$.

3. Evaluate $x^2 + 3x - 5$, if $x = 2$. 5

1 FOCUS

Motivating the Lesson

Questioning Ask students to find two methods for solving this problem: *Midori bought 6 dozen eggs at one store and 5 dozen at another. How many eggs did she buy altogether?* Sample answer: Method 1: $6 \cdot 12 + 5 \cdot 12 = 72 + 60$ or 132; Method 2: $6 + 5 = 11$, $11 \cdot 12 = 132$

14-2 Simplifying Polynomials

Objective
Simplify polynomials using area models.

Words to Learn
term
like term
simplest form

TEEN SCENE

Scouting is an organization that teaches young people to be good citizens and to develop their interests. Nearly 7 million young men and women belong to either the Boy Scouts or the Girl Scouts.

The members of Boy Scout Troop 92 were buying supplies for their spring camping trip. The Hawk Patrol bought one bag of apples, six boxes of granola bars, and two packages of recyclable paper plates. The Falcon Patrol bought two bags of apples, eight boxes of granola bars, and twelve packages of pre-sweetened drink mix.

The quantity bought can be described using polynomials. If x represents the number of granola bars in one box, $6x + 8x$ represents the total number of granola bars bought. We can model this situation with area tiles.

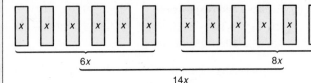

The polynomial $6x + 8x$ contains two monomials. Each monomial in the polynomial is called a **term.** The monomials $6x$ and $8x$ are called **like terms** because they have the same variable to the same power. When you use area tiles, you can recognize like terms because they have the same size and shape.

The model shown above suggests that you can simplify polynomials that have like terms. An expression that has no like terms is in **simplest form.** In simplest form, $6x + 8x$ is $14x$.

Example 1

Simplify $2x^2 + 3x^2 + 2x$.

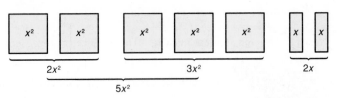

$$2x^2 + 3x^2 + 2x = 5x^2 + 2x$$

Classroom Vignette

''I often encourage my students to learn word roots to better understand math terms. I pointed out that *mono* means 'one' and refers to one term, and that *poly* means 'more than one' and refers to many terms. Then I have my students find examples of other words having these roots.''

Arthur C. Howard
Author

What do you suppose happens when you have both positive and negative terms in a polynomial? Let's use area tiles to find out.

Mini-Lab

Work with a partner to simplify $3x + 2 - 5x + 1$.

Materials: area tiles

- Model the polynomial.

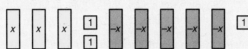

- Rearrange the tiles so that like terms are next to each other.

LOOK BACK

You can review zero pairs on page 92.

- When a positive tile is paired with a negative tile of the same size and shape, the result is called a *zero pair*. You can add or remove a zero pair without changing the value of the set. Remove all zero pairs.

- Write the polynomial for the tiles that remain.

Talk About It

a. How many zero pairs did you remove? **3**

b. What kinds of tiles remained at the end? **-x-tiles, 1-tiles**

c. What is the simplest form of the polynomial? **-2x + 3**

So far, we have used the variable x when dealing with polynomials. Other variables are possible.

Examples

Simplify each polynomial.

2 $y^2 + 2y^2$

These are like terms because they have the same variable to the same power.

$y^2 + 2y^2 = 3y^2$

3 $3x + 2y$

These are not like terms because the variables are different.

$3x + 2y$ is in simplest form.

Lesson 14-2   Simplifying Polynomials   **547**

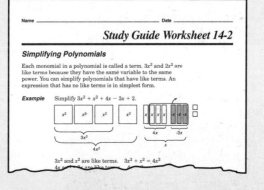
547

3 PRACTICE/APPLY

Assignment Guide
Maximum: 11–33
Minimum: 11–25 odd, 27–32

For **Extra Practice**, see p. 616.

Alternate Assessment

Modeling   Have students use tiles to show how zero pairs can be used to simplify polynomials with positive and negative terms.

Additional Answer

1. Like terms have the same variable(s) to the same power. Their models have the same size and shape.

Practice Masters, p. 122

Name _____ Date _____

Practice Worksheet 14-2

Simplifying Polynomials

Name the like terms in each list of terms.

1. $3x$, $2x$, $4x^2$, x
   $3x$, $2x$, x; $4x^2$

2. $2a$, $2b$, $3a$, $3b$
   $2a$, $3a$; $2b$, $3b$

3. 5, $2x$, $5y$, 2
   5, 2; $2x$; $5y$

4. $-3x^2$, $2x^2$, $3x$, 4
   $-3x^2$, $2x^2$; $3x$; 4

5. 2, x, y, $2x$, $2y$, 8, x^2
   2, 8; x, $2x$; y, $2y$; x^2

6. $3x^2$, $3x$, 3
   $3x^2$; $3x$; 3

Simplify each polynomial using the model.

7. $2a^2 - a - a^2 + 3a$

   $a^2 + 2a$

8. $3x - 2y + x - 2y + 2x + y$

   $6x - 3y$

Simplify each polynomial. Use area tiles or drawings if necessary.

9. $4x + 3 + 2x + 4$
   $6x + 7$

10. $-2x^2 + 3x - x^2 - x^2$
   $-4x^2 + 3x$

11. $6 + 3y^2 - 2 - y^2 + 5y$
   $2y^2 + 5y + 4$

12. $x^2 - x^2 - x^2 - x^2 - x$
   $-2x^2 - x$

13. $3x + 3y$
   $3x + 3y$

14. $2y + 1 - 2y + 1$
   2

Simplify each expression. Then evaluate if $a = 3$ and $b = -2$.

15. $4a + 3b - a + 3b$
   $3a + 6b$; -3

16. $a - b - b - a$
   $-2b$; 4

17. $b^2 - 4a - 2b^2$
   $-b^2 - 4a$; -16

18. $3x^2 + 2x - x^2 - 2x - 2x^2$
   0

T122
Glencoe Division, Macmillan/McGraw-Hill

548

Checking for Understanding

Communicating Mathematics

Read and study the lesson to answer each question.

1. **Tell** how you can recognize like terms in a polynomial. **See margin.**

2. **Write** a polynomial containing three or more monomials to represent the model at the right.

2. Sample answer: $x^2 - x + 3$

3. **Draw** a model of $2x^2 + 3x - x^2 - 5x + 3$.

3. See Solutions Manual

4. **Tell** whether $3a$ and $3b$ are like terms. Explain why or why not.
   No; the variables are not the same.

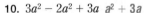

Guided Practice

Name the like terms in each list of terms.

5. $3x^2$, $4x$, $10x$, $-2x^2$ $3x^2$, $-2x^2$; $4x$, $10x$

6. $4y$, 8, 9, $-2y$, $-3y$ $4y$, $-2y$, $-3y$; 8, 9

7. $10x$, $13y$, $15z$ none

8. $-a^2$, $4a^2$, $-2x^2$ $-a^2$, $4a^2$

Simplify each polynomial using the model.

9. $2x + 3 - x + x^2 - 4$ $x^2 + x - 1$

10. $3a^2 - 2a^2 + 3a$ $a^2 + 3a$

Exercises

Independent Practice

Name the like terms in each list of terms.

11. $6y$, $-4y^2$, $-11y$ $6y$, $-11y$

12. 4, $3m^2$, -5, $2m$ 4, -5

13. $15y^2$, $2y$, 8 none

14. $7a$, $6b$, $10a$, $14b$ $7a$, $10a$; $6b$, $14b$

Simplify each polynomial using the model.

15. $-x^2 + 4x + 2x + x^2$ $6x$

16. $2x + 3y - 4x - y$ $-2x + 2y$

548   **Chapter 14**   Algebra: Investigations with Polynomials

---

OPTIONS

Meeting Needs of Middle School Students

This chapter provides a lead-in to high school algebra. Point out the real-world connections when possible, but also encourage students to appreciate abstraction. Characterize the study of polynomials as a tribute to your students' mathematical maturity.

Simplify each polynomial. Use area tiles or drawings, if necessary.

17. $3x + 1 + 2x + 4$ **$5x + 5$**

18. $5y + 2 - 3y$ **$2y + 2$**

19. $2x^2 + 3 + 4x - 7$ **$2x^2 + 4x - 4$**

20. $-3y^2 - 2y^2 - 4y + 3$ **$-5y^2 - 4y + 3$**

21. $a^2 - 5a - a^2 - 2a$ **$-7a$**

22. $10x + 3y - 8x + 5y$ **$2x + 8y$**

Simplify each expression. Then evaluate if $a = -2$ and $b = 7$.

23. $2a + 5b + 7a + 9b$ **$9a + 14b; 80$**

24. $3a + 9b + 14a + 2b$ **$17a + 11b; 43$**

25. $4b + 3a - 2a + 5b$ **$a + 9b; 61$**

26. $7a + 10b - 7b$ **$-4a$ $3a + 3b; 15$**

Mixed Review

27. **Statistics** Explain how to find the interquartile range from a box-and-whisker plot. *(Lesson 4-7)* **Subtract the lower quartile from the upper quartile.**

28. Express *$9.60 for 8 feet* as a unit rate. *(Lesson 9-1)* **$1.20/foot**

29. Graph $y = -2.5x + 3.5$ *(Lesson 11-4)* **See Solutions Manual.**

30. Evaluate $2x^2 - 3x + 5$ if $x = -2$. *(Lesson 14-1)* **19**

Problem Solving and Applications

31. $4q + 8d + 5n;$ $2.05

31. **Money** On her way home from school, Karen stops in a convenience store to buy a large drink. In her backpack she finds three quarters, five dimes, and two nickels. In her pocket she had one quarter, three dimes and three nickels. Using q for quarters, d for dimes, and n for nickels, represent all the coins Karen had as a polynomial expression in simplest form. Then evaluate the simplified expression to determine how much money Karen has.

32. **Critical Thinking** Simplify $4x^3 + 2x^2 - x^3 + 4x^2 - 5x + 3$. **$3x^3 + 6x^2 - 5x + 3$**

DATA SEARCH

33. **Data Search** Refer to pages 540 and 541.
Determine the lowest total cost for renting a compact car in Atlanta for three days, and then a midsize car in Los Angeles for four days. **$176.26**

SAVE THE PLANET • SAVE THE PLANET •

Save Planet Earth

Conservation of Trees About 10,000 years ago, more than 15 billion acres worldwide were covered with forest. Today, barely 10 billion acres of the world are forested. Why should you care about the world's forests? The relationship between trees and life on Earth is simple: we need oxygen and we produce carbon dioxide; trees require carbon dioxide and they produce oxygen. The loss of a tree not only reduces carbon dioxide consumption, it also releases the carbon dioxide stored in the tree.

How You Can Help

Plant a tree. Each tree that you plant will provide benefits for years to come.

Extending the Lesson

Save Planet Earth Ask students to make a list of the items they use on a daily basis that contain or are made of wood. Ask them to discuss ways that they can reduce the use of wood and wood by-products.

Cooperative Learning Activity

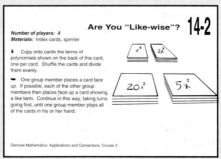

Are You "Like-wise"? **14-2**

Number of players: 4
Materials: Index cards, spinner

● Copy onto cards the terms of polynomials shown on the back of this card, one per card. Shuffle the cards and divide them evenly.

➞ One group member places a card face up. If possible, each of the other group members then places face up a card showing a like term. Continue in this way, taking turns going first, until one group member plays all of the cards in his or her hand.

Glencoe Mathematics: Applications and Connections, Course 3

Enrichment Masters, p. 122

Name _____ Date _____

Enrichment Worksheet 14-2

Making a Line Design

Connect each pair of equivalent expressions with a straight line segment. Although you will draw only straight lines, the finished design will appeared curved!

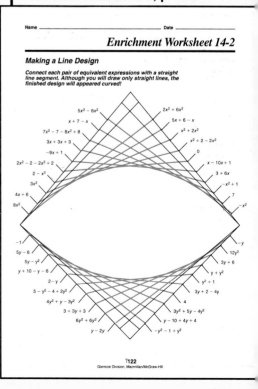

T122
Glencoe Division, Macmillan/McGraw-Hill

NCTM Standards: 1–4, 7, 9

Lesson Resources
- Study Guide Master 14-3
- Practice Master 14-3
- Enrichment Master 14-3
- Group Activity Card 14-3

 Transparency 14-3 contains the 5-Minute Check and a teaching aid for this lesson.

🕐 5-Minute Check
(Over Lesson 14-2)

Simplify each polynomial. Use area tiles or drawings if necessary.

1. $6x + 2 + 5 + 3x$
   $9x + 7$

2. $n^2 + 8n - 5n - n^2$
   $3n$

3. $4a + 7b - 5b + a$
   $5a + 2b$

4. Simplify $5x - 3y + 5y - 3x$. Then evaluate if $x = 3$ and $y = -3$.
   $2x + 2y; 0$

1 FOCUS

Motivating the Lesson

Questioning Ask students to solve this problem: *Find the sum of 8 h 5 min 9 sec and 3 h 6 min 2 sec.* 11 h 11 min 11 sec

2 TEACH

Using the Mini-Lab Ask students to tell how the following problem is like the problem in the *Motivating the Lesson* paragraph above. The x^2-, x-, and 1-tiles are like yards, feet, and inches, respectively, in the problem above. Only like measurements can be combined, just as only like terms can be combined when adding the polynomials.

14-3 Adding Polynomials

Objective
Add polynomials using area models.

People in the United States use the English system of measurement for most everyday weight measurement. It is customary to express many weights in combinations of pounds and ounces.

 **DID YOU KNOW**

Twins occur about once in every 89 births. Triplets occur about once in 7,900 births.

Suppose twin baby boys were born today. One weighed 6 pounds 5 ounces and the other weighed 5 pounds 10 ounces. What was their combined weight?

$$\begin{array}{r} 6 \text{ lb} + 5 \text{ oz} \\ + 5 \text{ lb} + 10 \text{ oz} \\ \hline 11 \text{ lb} + 15 \text{ oz} \end{array}$$

Their combined weight was 11 pounds 15 ounces.

To find the combined weight, "like terms" are added. In this case, the like terms are pounds and ounces. Two or more polynomials can be added in a similar way.

Mini-Lab

Problem Solving Hint
• • • • • • • • • •
It may be convenient to arrange like terms in columns before removing zero pairs.

Work with a partner to find $(x^2 - 2x + 4) + (2x^2 + 5x - 5)$.

Materials: area tiles

- Model each polynomial.

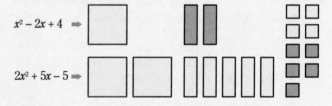

$x^2 - 2x + 4 \Rightarrow$

$2x^2 + 5x - 5 \Rightarrow$

- Combine like terms and remove all zero pairs.
- Write the polynomial for the tiles that remain.

Talk About It
a. How is this method like the method you used when simplifying polynomials? It is the same.
b. What is $(x^2 - 2x + 4) + (2x^2 + 5x - 5)$? $3x^2 + 3x - 1$

550 **Chapter 14** Algebra: Investigations with Polynomials

OPTIONS

Reteaching Activity

Using Cooperative Groups Write a polynomial on each of 12 index cards and shuffle the cards. The first of two players draws two cards and writes the sum. The second player draws a card and adds the polynomial to the first player's sum. Play continues, with each player adding to the previous sum.

Study Guide Masters, p. 123

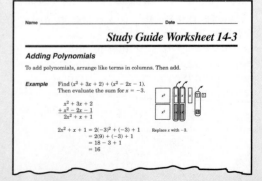

Name _____ Date _____

Study Guide Worksheet 14-3

Adding Polynomials

To add polynomials, arrange like terms in columns. Then add.

Example Find $(x^2 + 3x + 2) + (x^2 - 2x - 1)$.
Then evaluate the sum for $x = -3$.

$$\begin{array}{r} x^2 + 3x + 2 \\ + x^2 - 2x - 1 \\ \hline 2x^2 + x + 1 \end{array}$$

$\begin{aligned} 2x^2 + x + 1 &= 2(-3)^2 + (-3) + 1 \quad \text{Replace } x \text{ with } -3. \\ &= 2(9) + (-3) + 1 \\ &= 18 - 3 + 1 \\ &= 16 \end{aligned}$

Example 1

Write the two polynomials represented below. Then find their sum.

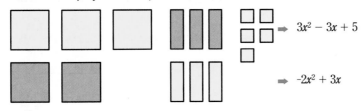

$\Rightarrow 3x^2 - 3x + 5$

$\Rightarrow -2x^2 + 3x$

$(3x^2 - 3x + 5) + (-2x^2 + 3x) = x^2 + 5$

Example 2 *Connection*

Algebra Find $(x^2 + 2x + 1) + (x^2 - 3x - 2)$. Then evaluate the sum for $x = -2$.

$$\begin{array}{l} x^2 + 2x + 1 \\ + \; x^2 - 3x - 2 \\ \hline 2x^2 - 1x - 1 \end{array} \quad \textit{Arrange like terms in columns. Then add.}$$

Now evaluate for $x = -2$.

$2x^2 - 1x - 1 = 2(-2)^2 - 1(-2) - 1$ *Replace x with -2.*
$= 2(4) - (-2) - 1$
$= 8 + 2 - 1$ or 9

Checking for Understanding

Communicating Mathematics

Read and study the lesson to answer each question.

1. **Write** the two polynomials represented below. Then find their sum.

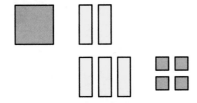

$-x^2 + 2x, 3x - 4, -x^2 + 5x - 4$

2. **Show** how to find the sum of $3x^2 - 3x + 5$ and $x^2 + 2x - 7$ using area tiles or drawings. See Solutions Manual.

Guided Practice

Find each sum using area tiles or drawings.

3. $(2x + 5) + (-3x + 1)$ $-x + 6$ 4. $(a^2 - 4a) + (2a^2 - 6a)$ $3a^2 - 10a$
5. $(-2x^2 + 4x - 6) + (-5x^2 - 3x + 7)$ $-7x^2 + x + 1$

6. Find the sum of $-3y^2 + 4y$ and $-1y^2 - 3y$. Then evaluate the sum for $y = 1$.
   $-4y^2 + y; -3$

Lesson 14-3   Adding Polynomials   **551**

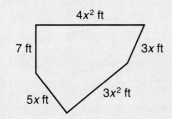

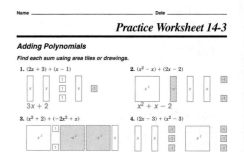
551

Error Analysis

Watch for students who add exponents when adding like terms.

Prevent by drawing a parallel between adding like terms and adding real objects:
2 pears + 3 pears = 5 pears, not 5 pears^2
$2x + 3x = 5x$, not $5x^2$

Close

Have students find the sum of two polynomials using area tiles and using the column format.

3 PRACTICE/APPLY

Assignment Guide
Maximum: 7–28
Minimum: 7–21 odd, 22–28

For **Extra Practice,** see p. 616.

Alternate Assessment

Writing Have students evaluate the sum of the polynomials $-x^2 + 3x - 2$ and $2x^2 - 3x + 5$ for $x = 3$.   12

Enrichment Masters, p. 123

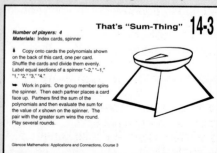

Name _____ Date _____

Enrichment Worksheet 14-3

A Cross-Number Puzzle

Use the clues at the bottom of the page to complete the puzzle.
You are to write one digit in each box.

Across	Down
A $x^2 - 4$ for $x = 5$	A $(6x^2 - 1) + (4x^2 - 3)$ for $x = 5$
B $3xy^2$ for $x = 4$ and $y = -1$	B $7y + 8y - 2$ for $y = 1$
C $(2x + 50) + (x - 15)$ for $x = 0$	D $x + x^2y^2$ for $x = 7$ and $y = 1$
E $x^2 - 4x - y^2$ for $x = 10$ and $y = 5$	F $5(7w + 3w)$ for $w = 10$
G x^2y for $x = 3$ and $y = 7$	H $(z^2 + 2z + 1) + (z^2 - 2z - 2)$ for $z = 4$
I $10w + 5y$ for $w = 6$ and $y = 1$	J $6xy^2 - xy + 60$ for $x = 10$ and $y = 10$
K $3x^2 + 5x + 8$ for $x = -10$	K $w^2 - w - 3$ for $w = 6$
L $(y - 8) + (10 - 4y)$ for $y = -6$	L $(3y - 20) + (45 - 3y)$ for $y = 16$
M $23x - 16x$ for $x = 11$	M $11x^2 - 8x^2$ for $x = -5$
O $7x + 100y$ for $x = 5$ and $y = 6$	N $x^2 - 2x + y^2$ for $x = 10$ and $y = 8$
Q $(6x^2 - 2) + (4x^2 - 3)$ for $x = -7$	P $(2x + 52) + (x - 11)$ for $x = -3$
T $(x^2 - x + 7) + (x^2 - 2)$ for $x = 3$	R $2x^2 - 5x - 140$ for $x = 12$
U x^2y for $x = -2$ and $y = 8$	S $(y - 75) + (120 + 4y)$ for $y = -6$
V $7y - 12y - 2$ for $y = -10$	
W $w^2 - w - 7$ for $w = 9$	

T123
Glencoe Division, Macmillan/McGraw-Hill

552

Exercises

Independent Practice

Find each sum. Use area tiles or drawings if necessary.

7. $5x^2 - 2x + 5$
    $+\ x^2 + 4x - 3$
    _____
    $6x^2 + 2x + 2$

8. $-4r^2 + 3r - 2$
    $+ 6r^2 - 5r - 7$
    _____
    $2r^2 - 2r - 9$

9. $2y^2 +\ y + 4$
    $+ 3y^2 + 2y + 1$
    _____
    $5y^2 + 3y + 5$

10. $4a - 7b - 6c$
    $+ 3a + 5b + 2c$
    _____
    $7a - 2b - 4c$

11. $(3x + 7y) + (9x + 5y)$ $12x + 12y$

12. $(5m + 3n) + (4m + 2n)$ $9m + 5n$

13. $(8s - 3t) + (s + 5t)$ $9s + 2t$

14. $(5r - 7s) + (3r + 8s)$ $8r + s$

15. $(3a^2 + 2a) + (7a^2 - 3)$ $10a^2 + 2a - 3$

16. $(3x^2 - 5x + 7) + (-x^2 + 2x - 3)$
    $2x^2 - 3x + 4$

17. Find the sum of $-3x + 4$ and $5x^2$. $5x^2 - 3x + 4$

Find each sum. Then evaluate for $c = 8$ and $d = 5$.   19. $7c - d + 1$; 52

18. $(2c + 5d) + (6c - 3d)$ $8c + 2d$; 74

19. $(4c + 3d + 2) + (3c - 4d - 1)$

20. $(-2c + 7d) + (8c - 8d)$ $6c - d$; 43

21. $(15c + 2d - 1) + (c - 3d + 2)$
    $16c - d + 1$; 124

Mixed Review

22. Evaluate $[3(18 - 2)] - 4^2$. *(Lesson 2-1)* 32

23. Solve $b^2 = 1.69$. *(Lesson 8-3)* 1.3, -1.3

24. **Geometry** Find the volume of a cone with a radius of 2 meters and a height of 12 meters. *(Lesson 12-7)* 50.27 m^3

25. Simplify $6x - 2x + 3x^2 + x^2$. *(Lesson 14-2)* $4x^2 + 4x$

Problem Solving and Applications

26. **Construction** A standard measurement for a window is *united inch*. You can find the united inches of a window by adding the length of the window to the width. If the length of a window is represented by the polynomial $x^2 + 2x - 3$, and the width is represented by $x + 3$, what is the size of the window in united inches? $x^2 + 3x$

28. Answers will vary; For 25 students, the probability is about 55%.

27. **Geometry** Write and simplify an expression for the perimeter of each figure.

a.
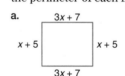
$3x + 7$
$x + 5$ $x + 5$
$3x + 7$
$8x + 24$

b.
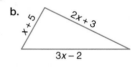
$x + 5$ $2x + 3$
$3x - 2$
$6x + 6$

c.
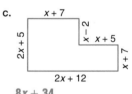
$x + 7$
$2x + 5$ $x - 2$ $x + 5$
$2x + 12$ $x + 7$
$8x + 34$

DATA SEARCH

28. **Data Search** Refer to page 668. What is the theoretical probability that two people in your math class share the same birthday?

29. **Critical Thinking** If $(5x - 13y) + (8x + 4y) = 13x - 9y$, what is $(13x - 9y) - (5x - 13y)$? $8x + 4y$

552   **Chapter 14**   Algebra: Investigations with Polynomials

---

OPTIONS

Extending the Lesson

Using Connections Provide students with the box scores of a basketball game. Have them write each team's score as a polynomial sum of 3-point field goals (t), 2-point field goals (g), and 1-point free throws (f). Then have them add the polynomials and evaluate the sum for $t = 3$, $g = 2$, and $f = 1$.

Cooperative Learning Activity

That's "Sum-Thing" **14-3**

Number of players: 4
Materials: Index cards, spinner

♦ Copy onto cards the polynomials shown on the back of this card, one per card. Shuffle the cards and divide them evenly. Label equal sections of a spinner "-2," "-1," "1," "2," "3," "4."

♦ Work in pairs. One group member spins the spinner. Then each partner places a card face up. Partners find the sum of the polynomials and then evaluate the sum for the value of x shown on the spinner. The pair with the greater sum wins the round. Play several rounds.

Glencoe Mathematics: Applications and Connections, Course 3

14-4 Subtracting Polynomials

Objective
Subtract polynomials using area models.

When you learned to subtract integers, you may have used counters. The figure at the right shows $-8 - (-2)$. You start with 8 negative counters on the mat and remove 2 negative counters. Six negative counters remain. Therefore, $-8 - (-2) = -6$.

In a similar manner, you can subtract polynomials using area models. Consider the problem $(5x^2 + 6x + 7) - (3x^2 + 2x + 1)$. Model $(5x^2 + 6x + 7)$ using area tiles. Then remove 3 x^2-tiles, 2 x-tiles, and 1 1-tile.

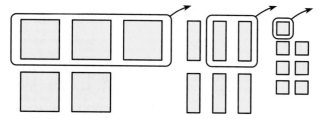

There are 2 x^2-tiles, 4 x-tiles, and 6 1-tiles remaining: $(5x^2 + 6x + 7) - (3x^2 + 2x + 1) = (2x^2 + 4x + 6)$.

Mini-Lab

Work with a partner to find $(2x + 5) - (-1x + 2)$.
Materials: area tiles

- Model the polynomial $2x + 5$.

- Now remove 1 negative x-tile and 2 1-tiles. You can remove the 1-tiles, but there are no negative x-tiles, so you can't remove $-1x$. Add a zero pair, then remove the negative x-tile.

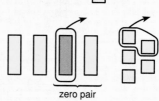

zero pair

Talk About It

a. What kinds of tiles remain? **3 x-tiles and 3 1-tiles**

b. What is $(2x + 5) - (-1x + 2)$? **$3x + 3$**

c. Why can you add or remove a zero pair? **It doesn't change the value.**

Lesson 14-4   Subtracting Polynomials   **553**

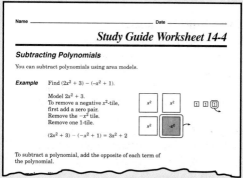
NCTM Standards: 1–4, 7, 9

Lesson Resources
- Study Guide Master 14-4
- Practice Master 14-4
- Enrichment Master 14-4
- Evaluation Master, Quiz A, p. 124
- Interdisciplinary Master, p. 28
- Group Activity Card 14-4

Transparency 14-4 contains the 5-Minute Check and a teaching aid for this lesson.

5-Minute Check
(Over Lesson 14-3)

Find each sum. Use area tiles or drawings if necessary.

1. $4x^2 + 5x - 7$
    $+ \ x^2 - 3x + 5$
    _____
    $5x^2 + 2x - 2$

2. $(-2n^2 + 5n) + (n^2 - 2)$
    $-n^2 + 5n - 2$

3. Find the sum of $2x - 4y$ and $-5x + 2y$. Then evaluate for $x = 2$ and $y = 3$. $-3x - 2y; -12$

1 FOCUS

Motivating the Lesson

Activity   Model $4x$ using area tiles. Ask the following questions.

- *How could you subtract $2x$?*
  Remove two x-tiles.

- *What would you add to the model of $4x$ so that you could take out $-3x$?*   Add three zero pairs.

2 TEACH

Using the Mini-Lab   Ask students to explain why they must add a zero pair to solve the problem.   Adding a zero pair provides one negative x-tile, which can then be removed.

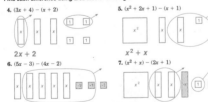
554

To subtract an integer, you add its opposite. For example, $5 - 7 = 5 + (-7)$. In a similar manner, to subtract a polynomial, add the opposite of each term of the polynomial.

Examples

Find each difference.

1 $\quad \begin{array}{r} 5x + 3 \\ -(2x + 1) \end{array} \rightarrow \left\{ \begin{array}{l} \text{The opposite of } 2x \text{ is } -2x. \\ \text{The opposite of } 1 \text{ is } -1. \end{array} \right\} \rightarrow \begin{array}{r} 5x + 3 \\ +(-2x - 1) \\ \hline 3x + 2 \end{array}$

2 $\quad (2x^2 - 5x + 3) - (4x^2 + 2x - 1)$

$\begin{array}{r} 2x^2 - 5x + 3) \\ -(4x^2 + 2x - 1) \end{array} \rightarrow \begin{array}{r} 2x^2 - 5x + 3 \\ +(-4x^2 - 2x + 1) \\ \hline -2x^2 - 7x + 4 \end{array}$

Checking for Understanding

Read and study the lesson to answer each question.

1. **Tell** the opposite of $5x$. $-5x$

2. **Write** the subtraction problem shown in the figure at the right.

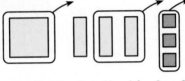

2. $(x^2 + 3x - 3) - (x^2 + 2x - 3)$

3. **Show** how to find the difference of $2x^2 + 5x$ and $3x^2 - 2x$ using area tiles or drawings.
See Solutions Manual.

State the opposite of each term of the polynomial.

4. x $-x$

5. $-5x^2$ $5x^2$

6. 4 -4

7. $10x^2 + 3x$
$-10x^2; -3x$

Find each difference using area tiles or drawings.

8. $(5x + 3) - (2x + 1)$ $3x + 2$

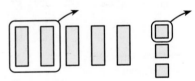

9. $(x^2 + 2x) - (2x^2 + x)$ $-x^2 + x$

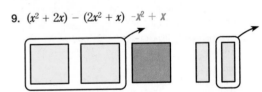

10. $(7x + 5) - (3x + 4)$ $4x + 1$

11. $(5x^2 - 3x + 2) - (3x^2 - 3)$
$2x^2 - 3x + 5$

12. $(2x^2 - 5x - 1) - (x^2 - x - 1)$
$x^2 - 4x$

13. $(-3x^2 + 2x + 1) - (x^2 + 3x - 1)$
$-4x^2 - x + 2$

OPTIONS

Bell Ringer

Find a polynomial which, when added to $-2x^2 + 4x - 3$, gives the sum of $x^2 - 3x - 7$. $3x^2 - 7x - 4$

Exercises

Find each difference. Use area tiles or drawings if necessary.

14.
$$3x + 7$$
$$\underline{- (2x + 5)}$$
$$x + 2$$

15.
$$4a^2 - 3a - 2$$
$$\underline{- (2a^2 + 2a + 7)}$$
$$2a^2 - 5a - 9$$

16. $(9s - 1) - (7s + 2)$ $2s - 3$

17. $(-4a + 5) - (a - 1)$ $-5a + 6$

18. $(5x^2 + 9) - (4x^2 + 9)$ x^2

19. $(10m - 2n) - (6m + 3n)$ $4m - 5n$

20. $(6x^2 + 2x + 9) - (3x^2 + 5x + 9)$
$3x^2 - 3x$

21. $(4p^2 - 3p + 1) - (2p^2 - 2p)$
$2p^2 - p + 1$

22. Find $(3r^2 - 3rt + t^2)$ minus $(2r^2 + 5rt - 3t^2)$. $r^2 - 8rt + 4t^2$

23. What is $(7a^2 + ab - 2b^2)$ decreased by $(-a^2 - ab + b^2)$? $8a^2 + 2ab - 3b^2$

Mixed Review

24. Solve $j = -7(15)(-10)$ *(Lesson 3-6)* 1,050

25. Find the prime factorization of 48. *(Lesson 6-2)* $2^4 \cdot 3$

26. Find $P(8, 3)$. *(Lesson 13-2)* 336

27. Find $(-3m^2 + 6m - 2) + (-m^2 + 4m + 11)$. *(Lesson 14-3)* $-4m^2 + 10m + 9$

Problem Solving and Applications

28. **Geometry** Find the length of the third side of the triangle shown at the right. The perimeter of the triangle is $7x + 2y$ units. $2x + 6y$

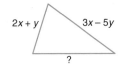

$2x + y$ $3x - 5y$

?

29. **Critical Thinking** The sum of two polynomials is $x^2 - 2x - 3$. The difference is $3x^2 - 4x + 5$. Find the polynomials. $2x^2 - 3x + 1; -x^2 + x - 4$

30. **Journal Entry** Does using area tiles help you subtract polynomials? How do you remember which terms to combine without using the tiles? See students' work.

14

Assessment: Mid-Chapter Review

Model each polynomial using area tiles or drawings. *(Lesson 14-1)* See Solutions Manual.

1. $3x^2 - 2x + 7$

2. $-x^2 + 5x - 2$

Simplify each polynomial. Use area tiles or drawings, if necessary. *(Lesson 14-2)*

3. $3x^2 - 5 + 5x^2 - 2$ $8x^2 - 7$

4. $7a + 2b + 3c$ $7a + 2b + 3c$

Find each sum or difference. Use area tiles or drawings, if necessary.
(Lessons 14-3, 14-4)

5. $(4x^2 - 5x) + (3x^2 + x)$ $7x^2 - 4x$

6. $(a^2 - 6) - (3a^2 + 1)$ $-2a^2 - 7$

7. $(3n + 6) - (n - 1)$ $2n + 7$

8. $(4x + 3y) + (-7x + 3y)$ $-3x + 6y$

Lesson 14-4 Subtracting Polynomials **555**

Extending the Lesson

Using Cooperative Groups Have small groups solve this problem: *By how much does the perimeter of the quadrilateral exceed that of the triangle?* x + 7

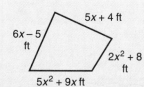

5x + 4 ft

$6x - 5$ ft

$2x^2 + 8$ ft

$5x^2 + 9x$ ft

$4x^2 + 5x$ ft

8x ft

$3x^2 + 6x$ ft

Cooperative Learning Activity

Process of Elimination 14-4

Number of players: 2
Materials: Index cards

↓ Make one set of cards containing the polynomials shown on the back of this card. Shuffle the cards and divide them evenly. Then, make a set of cards containing the terms shown on the back of this card. Shuffle the cards and divide them evenly.

➤ One partner places a polynomial card face up. The other partner selects from his or her hand cards showing like terms for the terms in the polynomial on the first partner's card. This partner then uses these terms to write a polynomial that will be subtracted from the polynomial on the first partner's card. The object is to eliminate terms in the difference. Award yourself 1 point for each term you eliminate through subtraction of the two polynomials. Continue in this way, taking turns going first, until both partners run out of cards. The partner with more points wins.

Error Analysis

Watch for students who find the additive inverse for only the first term of a polynomial when subtracting.

Prevent by reviewing the distributive property.

Close

Have students explain how a subtraction problem involving polynomials can be rewritten as an addition problem.

3 PRACTICE/APPLY

Assignment Guide

Maximum: 14–30
Minimum: 14–29
All: Mid-Chapter Review

For **Extra Practice,** see p. 617.

Alternate Assessment

Writing Write two polynomials on the chalkboard. Have students write a paragraph detailing the steps to use in subtracting the polynomials.

Enrichment Masters, p. 124

Name _____ Date _____

Enrichment Worksheet 14-4

Polynomials With Fractional Coefficients

Polynomials may have fractional coefficients in some or all of the terms. Computation with these types of polynomials is done in the same way as with whole-number coefficients.

Add or subtract. Write all coefficients as fractions.

1. Add $\frac{3}{4}x^2 + \frac{2}{3}y^2$ and $\frac{1}{3}x^2 - \frac{4}{5}y^2$. $\frac{11}{12}x^2 - \frac{14}{15}y^2$

2. From $\frac{1}{2}x^2 - \frac{1}{3}xy + \frac{1}{4}y^2$, take $\frac{1}{3}x^2 - \frac{1}{2}xy + \frac{5}{6}y^2$. $\frac{1}{6}x^2 + \frac{1}{6}xy - \frac{7}{12}y^2$

3. Add $\frac{3}{8}x - \frac{4}{7}y$, $-\frac{7}{8}x - \frac{6}{7}y$, and $y - \frac{1}{4}x$. $\frac{3}{8}x - \frac{25}{21}y$

4. Subtract $\frac{1}{3}x^2 + \frac{1}{8}x - \frac{1}{4}$ from $\frac{3}{4}x^2 + \frac{5}{8}x + \frac{1}{2}$. $\frac{1}{2}x^2 + \frac{1}{2}x + \frac{3}{4}$

5. Add $\frac{1}{3}xy + \frac{11}{12}y^2$ to $\frac{7}{12}xy - \frac{1}{6}y^2$. $\frac{7}{12}xy + \frac{3}{4}y^2$

6. Add $\frac{1}{3}x^2 - \frac{3}{8}x - \frac{1}{3}$ and $\frac{3}{16}x^2 + \frac{7}{8}x + \frac{1}{9}$. $\frac{1}{2}x^2 + \frac{1}{2}x - \frac{2}{9}$

7. From $\frac{1}{2} + \frac{2}{3}y + \frac{3}{4}y^2$, take $\frac{1}{8} + \frac{1}{2}y - \frac{5}{6}y^2$. $\frac{3}{8} + \frac{1}{2}y + \frac{19}{12}y^2$

8. Subtract $\frac{7}{12}x - \frac{1}{4}$ from $\frac{3}{4}x - \frac{1}{3}$. $\frac{1}{6}x - \frac{1}{12}$

9. Add $\frac{3}{8}x^2 - \frac{1}{3}xy + \frac{2}{9}y^2$ and $\frac{1}{2}x^2 - \frac{1}{2}xy - \frac{1}{3}y^2$. $\frac{7}{8}x^2 - \frac{5}{6}xy + \frac{2}{9}y^2$

10. Subtract $\frac{3}{4}y^2 + \frac{1}{2}y$ from $\frac{1}{3}y^2 + \frac{7}{8}y$. $-\frac{7}{12}y^2 + \frac{3}{8}y$

T124
Glencoe Division, Macmillan/McGraw-Hill

NCTM Standards: 1–4, 7, 9

Management Tips

For Students
Students can use frame corners to keep their tiles aligned.

For the Overhead Projector
Overhead Manipulative Resources provides appropriate materials for teacher or student demonstration of the activities in this Mathematics Lab.

1 FOCUS

Introducing the Lab

Ask students to explain how they can use the distributive property to find the product $9 \cdot 32$ mentally.

$$9 \cdot 32 = 9(30 + 2)$$
$$= 9 \cdot 30 + 9 \cdot 2$$
$$= 270 + 18$$
$$= 288$$

2 TEACH

Using Logical Reasoning Ask students how they would change the first step in the *Try this!* part of the lab in order to find $4(x + 2)$.
Use a length of $x + 1 + 1$ and a width of $1 + 1 + 1 + 1$.

3 PRACTICE/APPLY

Using Logical Reasoning
Students should be sure to use a width of x in Exercise 2, and then again in Exercise 4.

Close

Have students state the product represented by this drawing.

x	1
x	1
x	1

$3(x + 1) = 3x + 3$

Objective
Model products with area tiles.

Materials
area tiles
product mat

The area tiles that you have been using are based on the fact that the area of a rectangle is the product of the width and length.

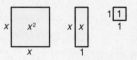

In this lab, you will use these area tiles to build more complex rectangles. These rectangles will help you understand how to find the product of simple polynomials. The width and length each represent a polynomial being multiplied; the area of the rectangle represents their product.

Try this!

Work with a partner to find $2(x + 1)$.

- You will make a rectangle with a width of 2 units and a length of $x + 1$ units. Use your area tiles to mark off the dimensions on a product mat.

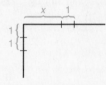

- Using the marks as a guide, fill in the rectangle with area tiles.

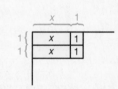

- The area of the rectangle is $x + x + 1 + 1$. In simplest form, the area is $2x + 2$. Therefore, $2(x + 1) = 2x + 2$.

Application

Find each product using area tiles.

1. $3(x + 3)$ $3x + 9$
2. $x(x + 2)$ $x^2 + 2x$
3. $2(2x + 1)$ $4x + 2$

Extension   See Solutions Manual

Make possible rectangles for each area. Then find each length and width.

4. $x^2 + 3x$
5. $4x + 8$
6. $6x + 6$

556   **Chapter 14**   Algebra: Investigations with Polynomials

---

OPTIONS

Lab Manual You may wish to make copies of the blackline master on p. 80 of the *Lab Manual* for students to use as a recording sheet.

Lab Manual, p. 80

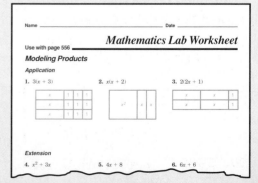

14-5 Multiplying a Polynomial by a Monomial

Objectives

Multiply a polynomial by a monomial and factor polynomials using area models.

Words to Learn

factoring

A carpenter was working with a piece of plywood that was 3 feet longer than it was wide.

To find the area of the plywood, you multiply the length by the width. Let x represent the width. Then $x + 3$ represents the length.

This diagram of the plywood shows that the area is $x(x + 3)$ square feet.

This diagram of the plywood shows that the area is $x^2 + 3x$ square feet.

x | $A = x(x + 3)$
$x + 3$

x | $A = x^2$
x

x | $A = 3x$
3

LOOKBACK

You can review factors on page 35 and the distributive property on page 9.

Since the areas are equal, $x(x + 3) = x^2 + 3x$. The expressions x and $(x + 3)$ are *factors* of the product $x^2 + 3x$.

The situation above shows how the distributive property can be used to multiply a polynomial by a monomial. Recall that the distributive property allows you to multiply the factor *outside* the parentheses by each term *inside* the parentheses.

Examples

Find each product.

1 $3(n + 4)$

$3(n + 4) = 3 \cdot n + 3 \cdot 4$
$= 3n + 12$

| $n + 4$ |
| n | 1 1 1 1 |
3 | n | 1 1 1 1 |
| n | 1 1 1 1 |

2 $x(x - 4)$

$x(x - 4) = x \cdot x - x \cdot 4$
$= x^2 - 4x$

Lesson 14-5 Multiplying a Polynomial by a Monomial **557**

14-5 Lesson Notes

NCTM Standards: 1–4, 7, 9

Lesson Resources
- Study Guide Master 14-5
- Practice Master 14-5
- Enrichment Master 14-5
- Application Master, p. 14
- Group Activity Card 14-5

Transparency 14-5 contains the 5-Minute Check and a teaching aid for this lesson.

🕐 5-Minute Check
(Over Lesson 14-4)

Find each difference. Use area tiles or drawings if necessary.

1. $6x + 7$
   $\underline{- (4x + 2)}$ $2x + 5$

2. $3n^2 - 5n + 6$
   $\underline{- (n^2 - 4n + 7)}$
   $2n^2 - n - 1$

3. $(-x^2 + 3x) - (2x^2 + 1)$
   $-3x^2 + 3x - 1$

1 FOCUS

Motivating the Lesson

Questioning Ask students the following questions.

- *What is the prime factorization of 35?* 5×7
- *What is a factor of a product? Give an example.* A number that divides the product evenly; 5 and 7 are factors of 35.

2 TEACH

More Examples

Find each product.

For Example 1

$2(p + 3)$ $2p + 6$

For Example 2

$n(5 - n)$ $5n - n^2$

OPTIONS

Reteaching Activity

Using Connections Show how to factor a polynomial using the GCF of the terms.

Example: Factor $21m + 7$.
Step 1 GCF($21m, 7$) = 7
Step 2 Divide terms by the GCF.

$\frac{21m}{7} = 3m; \frac{7}{7} = 1$

Step 3 $21m + 7 = 7(3m + 1)$
GCF

Study Guide Masters, p. 125

Name _____ Date _____

Study Guide Worksheet 14-5

Multiplying a Polynomial by a Monomial

You can use the distributive property to multiply a polynomial by a monomial.

Example Find the product $n(n - 4)$.

Multiply each term inside the parentheses by n.
$n(n - 4) = n \times n - n \times 4$
$= n^2 - 4n$

You can factor to find the monomial and polynomial if you are given their product.

Example Factor $2r + 6$.

557

Sometimes you know the product of a polynomial and monomial and are asked to find the factors. This is called **factoring.** Using the area tiles, this means that you know the area of a rectangle and are asked to find the length and width.

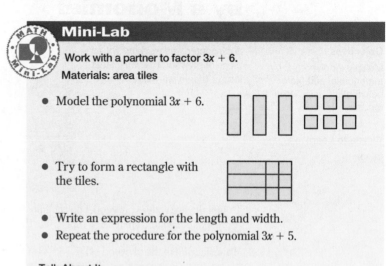

Mini-Lab

Work with a partner to factor $3x + 6$.

Materials: area tiles

- Model the polynomial $3x + 6$.

- Try to form a rectangle with the tiles.

- Write an expression for the length and width.
- Repeat the procedure for the polynomial $3x + 5$.

Talk About It

a. What are the factors of $3x + 6$? **3 and $x + 2$**

b. What are the factors of $3x + 5$? **1 and $3x + 5$**

c. Explain how to factor $x^2 + 8x$. **Build a rectangle with an area of $x^2 + 8x$.**

d. Name a polynomial that cannot be factored. **Sample answer: $x^2 + 7x + 5$**

Checking for Understanding

Communicating Mathematics

Read and study the lesson to answer each question. **1. Distributive property.**

1. **Tell** what property you use to find the product of a monomial and a polynomial.

2. **Tell** the product of $2x$ and $3x + 1$ using the rectangle at the right. **$6x^2 + 2x$**

3. **Draw** a rectangle to model $x(x + 1)$ and another to model $(x + 1)x$. Explain how they are the same and how they are different. **See Solutions Manual.**

4. **Show** how to factor the polynomial represented by the model shown below. **The factors are $x + 2$ and x.**

OPTIONS

Multicultural Education

In addition to making numerous contributions to mathematics, Pythagoras also recognized women and men as equals in mathematics. Students at his school in Italy (500 B.C.) included many women, his wife Theano among them. After his death, Theano started several schools of her own.

Guided Practice Find each product.

5. $2(x + 5)$ $2x + 10$

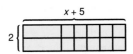
x + 5

6. $x(x + 3)$ $x^2 + 3x$

x + 3

7. $5(y + 9)$ $5y + 45$

8. $y(y + 2)$ $y^2 + 2y$

9. $a(a + 2)$ $a^2 + 2a$

Factor.

10. $4z + 4$ $4(z + 1)$

z	1
z	1
z	1
z	1

11. $y^2 + 5y$ $y(y + 5)$

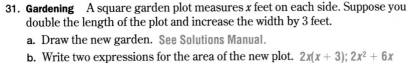

Exercises

Independent Practice Find each product. Use area tiles or drawings if necessary.

12. $6(n + 10)$ $6n + 60$ **13.** $4(b + 3)$ $4b + 12$ **14.** $3(2 + y)$ $6 + 3y$

15. $d(d + 15)$ $d^2 + 15d$ **16.** $3(2c + 4)$ $6c + 12$ **17.** $2x(2x + 1)$ $4x^2 + 2x$

Factor. Use area tiles or drawings if necessary.

18. $5x + 10$ $5(x + 2)$ **19.** $6x^2 + 3x$ $3x(2x + 1)$ **20.** $2x + 5$ $1(2x + 5)$

21. $8a^2 + 8$ $8(a^2 + 1)$ **22.** $12m + 6$ $6(2m + 1)$ **23.** $4 + 20x$ $4(1 + 5x)$

24. Find the product of $2y$ and $4y + 1$. $8y^2 + 2y$

25. Factor $2y + 8$. $2(y + 4)$ **26.** Multiply $x + 2$ by $3x$. $3x^2 + 6x$

Mixed Review **27.** Solve $156 = y + 73$. *(Lesson 2-3)* 83

28. 28% increase   **28.** Find the percent of change if last month's electric bill was $52.50 and this month's bill is $67.20. *(Lesson 10-8)*

29. Graph $y = -3x^2 + 1$. *(Lesson 11-7)* See Solutions Manual.

30. Find $(8x - 1) - (5x + 3)$. *(Lesson 14-4)* $3x - 4$

Problem Solving and Applications **31. Gardening** A square garden plot measures x feet on each side. Suppose you double the length of the plot and increase the width by 3 feet.

a. Draw the new garden. See Solutions Manual.

b. Write two expressions for the area of the new plot. $2x(x + 3); 2x^2 + 6x$

c. If the original plot was 10 feet on a side, what is the area of the new plot? 260 ft²

32. Critical Thinking A trapezoid has an area of 19.5 cm² and a height of 3 cm. Base 2 is 1 centimeter longer than twice the length of base 1. Find the length of base 1.
Use $A = \frac{1}{2}h(b_1 + b_2)$. 4 cm

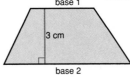
base 1
3 cm
base 2

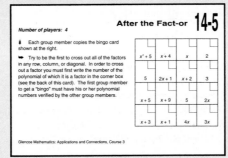

Lesson 14-5 Multiplying a Polynomial by a Monomial   **559**

Extending the Lesson

Using Connections Have students solve the following equation. $x = 4$
$8(x + 5) - 6(x + 3) = 5(x + 2)$

Cooperative Learning Activity

Number of players: 4

After the Fact-or **14-5**

Each group member copies the bingo card shown at the right.

Try to be the first to cross out all of the factors in any row, column, or diagonal. In order to cross out a factor you must first write the number of the polynomial of which it is a factor in the corner box (see the back of this card). The first group member to get a "bingo" must have his or her polynomial numbers verified by the other group members.

$x^2 + 5$	$x + 4$	x	2
5	$2x + 1$	$x + 2$	3
$x + 5$	$x + 9$	5	$2x$
$x + 3$	$x + 1$	$4x$	$3x$

Glencoe Mathematics: Applications and Connections, Course 3

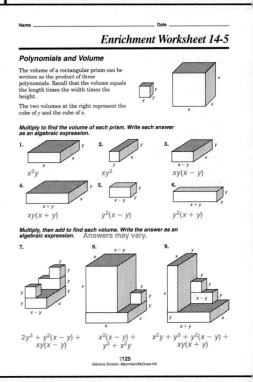

NCTM Standards: 1–4, 7, 9

Lesson Resources
- Study Guide Master 14-6
- Practice Master 14-6
- Enrichment Master 14-6
- Technology Master, p. 28
- Group Activity Card 14-6

 Transparency 14-6 contains the 5-Minute Check and a teaching aid for this lesson.

⏱ 5-Minute Check
(Over Lesson 14-5)

Find each product. Use area tiles or drawings if necessary.

1. $3(x + 5)$ $3x + 15$
2. $n(n - 4)$ $n^2 - 4n$

Factor. Use area tiles or drawings if necessary.

3. $3k + 6$ $3(k + 2)$
4. $m^2 + 7m$ $m(m + 7)$
5. Find the product of $2y$ and $4y - 7$. $8y^2 - 14y$

1 FOCUS

Motivating the Lesson

Activity   On the chalkboard, show how 43 and 12 are multiplied. That is, stress that each digit in the first number is multiplied by each digit in the second.

2 TEACH

Using the Mini-Lab   At the end of the mini-lab, ask students to use the rectangle showing $(x + 1)(x + 2)$ and find the polynomial product $(x + 1)^2$.
$x^2 + 2x + 1$

14-6   Multiplying Binomials

Objective
Multiply binomials using area models.

Words to Learn
binomial

What do the words bicycle, bicuspid, biped, and binomial have in common? They all begin with the prefix *bi-,* meaning two. A bicycle is a cycle with two wheels, a bicuspid is a tooth with two points, a biped is an animal with two feet, and a **binomial** is a polynomial with two terms. Some examples of binomials are $x + 3$, $2y - 1$, and $a + b$. You can find the product of simple binomials by using area tiles.

Mini-Lab

Work with a partner to find $(x + 2)(x + 1)$.

Materials: area tiles, product mat

- Make a rectangle with a width of $x + 2$ and a length of $x + 1$. Use your area tiles to mark off the dimensions on a product mat.

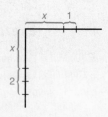

- Using the marks as a guide, fill in the rectangle with area tiles.

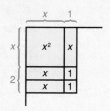

Talk About It

a. How is this method like the method you used when multiplying a monomial by a polynomial?   It is the same.

b. What is $(x + 2)(x + 1)$? $x^2 + 3x + 2$

You can also use the distributive property to find the product of two binomials. The figure at the right shows the rectangle from the Mini-Lab, separated into four parts. Notice that each term from the first parentheses $(x + 2)$ is multiplied by each term from the second parentheses $(x + 1)$.

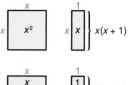

OPTIONS

Reteaching Activity

Using Cooperative Groups   Write a binomial on each of 12 index cards. Have students work in pairs. One student draws two cards and models the product using area tiles. The second student finds the product using the distributive property. Students then compare answers.

Study Guide Masters, p. 126

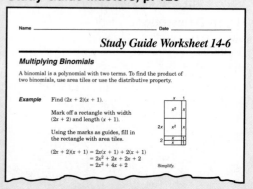

Find each product.

1 $(2x + 1)(x + 3)$

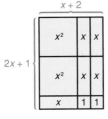

$$(2x + 1)(x + 3) = 2x(x + 3) + 1(x + 3)$$
$$= 2x^2 + 6x + 1x + 3$$
$$= 2x^2 + 7x + 3 \quad \textit{Simplify.}$$

2 $(y + 4)(y + 1)$
$$(y + 4)(y + 1) = y(y + 1) + 4(y + 1)$$
$$= y^2 + 1y + 4y + 4$$
$$= y^2 + 5y + 4 \quad \textit{Simplify.}$$

Checking for Understanding

Communicating Mathematics

1. A binomial is a polynomial with two terms.

Read and study the lesson to answer each question.

1. **Tell** the definition of *binomial*.

2. **Draw** a rectangle with a width of $(x + 3)$ and a length of $(2x + 2)$. **See Solutions Manual.**

3. **Write** the product shown at the right. $2x^2 + 5x + 2$

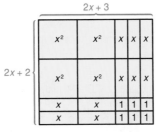

Guided Practice

Find each product.

4. $(x + 1)(x + 2)$ $x^2 + 3x + 2$

5. $(2x + 2)(2x + 3)$ $4x^2 + 10x + 6$

6. $(m + 4)(m + 3)$ $m^2 + 7m + 12$

7. $(3a + 1)(2a + 3)$ $6a^2 + 11a + 3$

8. $(x + 1)(2x + 3)$ $2x^2 + 5x + 3$

9. $(3z + 1)(4z + 5)$ $12z^2 + 19z + 5$

Gifted and Talented Needs

Have students find this product:
$(x + A)(x + B)$.
$x^2 + (A + B)x + AB$

Have them use this result to devise a method for factoring polynomials of the form $x^2 + Mx + N$. Find two integers, h and k, whose sum is M and whose product is N. Then, $x^2 + Mx + N = (x + h)(x + k)$.

More Examples

Find each product.

For Example 1

$(3x + 2)(x + 1)$
$3x^2 + 5x + 2$

For Example 2

$(n + 6)(n + 3)$
$n^2 + 9n + 18$

Checking for Understanding

Exercises 1-3 are designed to help you assess students' understanding through reading, writing, speaking, and modeling. You should work through these exercises with your students and then monitor their work on Guided Practice Exercises 4-9.

Close

Have students write problems involving the multiplication of two binomials, exchange with another student, and solve.

Practice Masters, p. 126

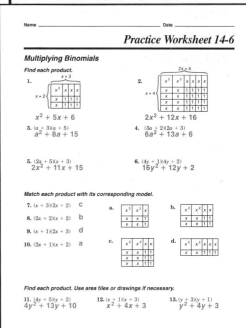

Name _____ Date _____

Practice Worksheet 14-6

Multiplying Binomials

Find each product.

1. $x^2 + 5x + 6$

2. $2x^2 + 12x + 16$

3. $(a + 3)(a + 5)$ $a^2 + 8a + 15$

4. $(3a + 2)(2a + 3)$ $6a^2 + 13a + 6$

5. $(2x + 5)(x + 3)$ $2x^2 + 11x + 15$

6. $(4y + 1)(4y + 2)$ $16y^2 + 12y + 2$

Match each product with its corresponding model.

7. $(x + 3)(2x + 2)$ c

8. $(2x + 2)(x + 2)$ b

9. $(x + 1)(2x + 3)$ d

10. $(2x + 1)(x + 2)$ a

Find each product. Use area tiles or drawings if necessary.

11. $(4y + 5)(y + 2)$ $4y^2 + 13y + 10$

12. $(x + 1)(x + 3)$ $x^2 + 4x + 3$

13. $(y + 3)(y + 1)$ $y^2 + 4y + 3$

14. $(3x + 2)(x + 4)$ $3x^2 + 14x + 8$

15. $(3x + 2)(3x + 2)$ $9x^2 + 12x + 4$

16. $(4x + 1)(2x + 2)$ $8x^2 + 10x + 2$

T126
Glencoe Division, Macmillan/McGraw-Hill

561

Assignment Guide
Maximum: 10–27
Minimum: 10–26

For **Extra Practice,** see p. 617.

Alternate Assessment

Speaking Have students identify the product represented below.

$$(2x + 1)(x + 3) = 2x^2 + 7x + 3$$

Enrichment Masters, p. 126

Name _____ Date _____

Enrichment Worksheet 14-6

Patterns in Pascal's Triangle

The triangular arrangement of numbers at the right is called Pascal's Triangle. The rows in the triangle can be used to write powers of binomials.

Complete this chart to show four of the powers of the binomial $(x + y)$. Look for patterns in the coefficients and the exponents.

	Power	Binomial Expansion	Coefficients of the Terms
1.	$(x + y)^2$	$x^2 + 2xy + y^2$	1, 2, 1
2.	$(x + y)^3$	$x^3 + 3x^2y + 3xy^2 + y^3$	1, 3, 3, 1
3.	$(x + y)^4$	$x^4 + 4x^3y + 6x^2y^2 + 4xy^3 + y^4$	1, 4, 6, 4, 1
4.	$(x + y)^5$	$x^5 + 5x^4y + 10x^3y^2 + 10x^2y^3 + 5xy^4 + y^5$	1, 5, 10, 10, 5, 1

Many other interesting patterns can be found in Pascal's Triangle. Here are two of them. You will need to extend the triangle until it has 13 rows.

Fill in each triangle and find the pattern.

5. Shade all numbers divisible by 2. Predict the pattern before you start.

6. Shade all numbers divisible by 5. Predict the pattern before you start.

T126
Glencoe Division, Macmillan/McGraw-Hill

562

Exercises

Independent Practice

Match each product with its corresponding model.

10. $(x + 5)(2x + 3)$ c

11. $(2x + 3)(x + 4)$ d

12. $(x + 3)(3x + 2)$ b

13. $(x + 3)(x + 3)$ a

a.

b.

c.

d.

Find each product. Use area tiles or drawings if necessary.

14. $x^2 + 4x + 3$
15. $x^2 + 5x + 4$
16. $2x^2 + 11x + 5$

14. $(x + 3)(x + 1)$
15. $(x + 1)(x + 4)$
16. $(2x + 1)(x + 5)$
17. $(x + 2)(2x + 1)$ $2x^2 + 5x + 2$
18. $(2x + 2)(2x + 3)$ $4x^2 + 10x + 6$
19. $(x + 1)(x + 1)$ $x^2 + 2x + 1$
20. Find the product of $(2x + 5)$ and $(x + 1)$. $2x^2 + 7x + 5$

Mixed Review

21. Find $\sqrt{\dfrac{9}{16}}$. *(Lesson 8-1)* $\dfrac{3}{4}$

22. Aiko borrowed $2,400 and paid back $116 a month for 24 months. Find the annual rate of simple interest. *(Lesson 10-10)* 8%

23. Find the product of x and $(2x + 3)$. *(Lesson 14-5)* $2x^2 + 3x$

Problem Solving and Applications

24. **Geometry** A square has dimensions of x feet $\times$ x feet. A rectangle is 4 feet longer and 3 feet wider than the square. Find the area of the rectangle.

24. $x^2 + 7x + 12$
25. $(x + 2)(x - 1)$; $x^2 + x - 2$

25. **Critical Thinking** Write the multiplication problem shown in the figure at the right. Name the product.

26. **Geometry** The model at the right represents the square of a binomial.

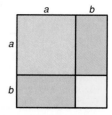

a. What product of binomials does this model represent? $(a + b)(a + b)$

b. What is the area of each small square and rectangle? a^2, ab, b^2

c. Write the area of the square as a polynomial. $a^2 + 2ab + b^2$

27. **Journal Entry** What concept in this chapter have you found most challenging? What do you think made it more difficult for you?

See students' work.

562 **Chapter 14** Algebra: Investigations with Polynomials

OPTIONS

Extending the Lesson

Using Cooperative Groups Have students work in small groups to find the volume of this rectangular prism.

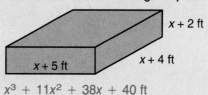

$x + 2$ ft
$x + 5$ ft
$x + 4$ ft

$x^3 + 11x^2 + 38x + 40$ ft

Cooperative Learning Activity

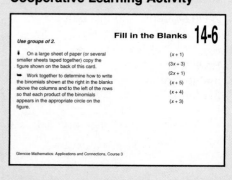

Fill in the Blanks 14-6

Use groups of 2.

On a large sheet of paper (or several smaller sheets taped together) copy the figure shown on the back of this card.

Work together to determine how to write the binomials shown at the right in the blanks above the columns and to the left of the rows so that each product of the binomials appears in the appropriate circle on the figure.

$(x + 1)$
$(3x + 3)$
$(2x + 1)$
$(x + 5)$
$(x + 4)$
$(x + 3)$

Glencoe Mathematics: Applications and Connections, Course 3

Cooperative Learning

14-6B Factoring Polynomials

A Follow-Up of Lesson 14-6

Objective
Factor polynomials using area models.

Materials
area tiles
product mat

From the previous lesson, you know that $(x + 1)(x + 2) = x^2 + 3x + 2$. The binomials $(x + 1)$ and $(x + 2)$ are the factors of $x^2 + 3x + 2$.

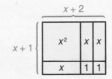

In this lab, you will use area tiles to find the factors of several polynomials. The polynomial can be factored if the tiles can be arranged into a rectangle.

Try this!

Work with a partner to factor $x^2 + 5x + 6$.

- Model the polynomial.

- Try to form a rectangle with the tiles. Use a product mat.

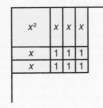

- Write an expression for the length and width of the rectangle.

- Repeat the procedure for the polynomial $x^2 + x + 1$.

What do you think?

1. What are the factors of $x^2 + 5x + 6$? $(x + 3), (x + 2)$
2. What are the factors of $x^2 + x + 1$? not factorable

Application

If possible, factor each polynomial using tiles or drawings.
3. $x^2 + 7x + 6$ $(x + 6)(x + 1)$ 4. $x^2 + 6x + 9$ $(x + 3)(x + 3)$
5. $2x^2 + 7x + 6$ $(2x + 3)(x + 2)$ 6. $x^2 + 4x + 5$ not factorable

Mathematics Lab 14-6B Factoring Polynomials **563**

NCTM Standards: 1–4, 7, 9

Management Tips

For Students Encourage students to keep an orderly arrangement of tiles. This will permit them to find the proper rectangle more easily.

For the Overhead Projector
Overhead Manipulative Resources provides appropriate materials for teacher or student demonstration of the activities in this Mathematics Lab.

1 FOCUS

Introducing the Lab

Review common factors from Lesson 6-4. Then assist students in factoring the following polynomials, looking for the common factor of the terms.

a. $4x + 12$ $4(x + 3)$
b. $x^2 + 5x$ $x(x + 5)$

2 TEACH

Using Logical Reasoning

Have students suggest methods for forming the rectangle logically rather than by trial-and-error.

3 PRACTICE/APPLY

Using Connections Draw a parallel between the polynomial $x^2 + 5x + 6$ and composite numbers, both of which can be factored. Ask students to name the type of number to which the polynomial $x^2 + x + 1$ is similarly related.   prime number

Close

Have students name the polynomial modeled below, and its factors. $x^2 + 2x + 1$;
$(x + 1)(x + 1)$

OPTIONS

Lab Manual You may wish to make copies of the blackline master on p. 81 of the *Lab Manual* for students to use as a recording sheet.

Lab Manual, p. 81

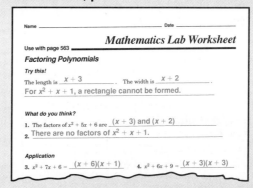

Name _____ Date _____

Mathematics Lab Worksheet

Use with page 563 ____

Factoring Polynomials

Try this!

The length is ___ $x + 3$ ___.   The width is ___ $x + 2$ ___.

For $x^2 + x + 1$, a rectangle cannot be formed.

What do you think?

1. The factors of $x^2 + 5x + 6$ are ___ $(x + 3)$ and $(x + 2)$ ___
2. There are no factors of $x^2 + x + 1$.

Application

3. $x^2 + 7x + 6 =$ ___ $(x + 6)(x + 1)$ ___   4. $x^2 + 6x + 9 =$ ___ $(x + 3)(x + 3)$ ___

563

NCTM Standards: 1–4

Lesson Resources
- Study Guide Master 14-7
- Practice Master 14-7
- Enrichment Master 14-7
- Evaluation Master, Quiz B, p. 124
- Multicultural Activity, p. 14
- Group Activity Card 14-7

 Transparency 14-7 contains the 5-Minute Check and a teaching aid for this lesson.

⏱ 5-Minute Check

(Over Lesson 14-6)

Find each product. Use area tiles or drawings if necessary.

1. $(x + 2)(x + 3)$
   $x^2 + 5x + 6$

2. $(x + 2)(x + 6)$
   $x^2 + 8x + 12$

3. $(x + 3)(2x + 3)$
   $2x^2 + 9x + 9$

4. $(2x + 1)(3x + 2)$
   $6x^2 + 7x + 2$

Practice Masters, p. 127

Name _____ Date _____

Practice Worksheet 14-7

Problem-Solving Strategy: Use Logical Reasoning

Solve using logical reasoning.

1. It takes five minutes to hard-boil one egg. How long does it take to hard-boil three eggs?
   5 minutes

2. Professor Ufo knows that only the pictures of space creatures **A, E,** and **G** are authentic, because they follow the rule. What is the rule? **Space creatures have curly hair and square mouths.**

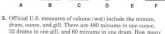

3. Official U.S. measures of volume (wet) include the minum, dram, ounce, and gill. There are 480 minums in one ounce, 32 drams in one gill, and 60 minums in one dram. How many ounces are in one gill? **4 ounces.**

4. How many cubic feet of dirt are in a hole 3 feet wide, 2 feet long and 4 feet deep? **There is no dirt in a hole.**

Solve using any strategy.

5. A = 622,521   B = 714,025   C = 412,168   D = 243,049   E = 306,916

   Without computing, choose the number which is *not* a perfect square. Explain your answer.
   C, because a perfect square cannot end with an "8."

6. Chue and Lew have to take tablets to fight an infection. Chue takes 2 tablets every 90 minutes, and Lew takes 5 tablets every 3½ hours. If they both swallow their first tablets at exactly noon on Monday, when will they have swallowed the same number of pills?
   At noon on Monday, after swallowing the first pill

T127
Glencoe Division, Macmillan/McGraw-Hill.

564

Objective
Solve problems by using logical reasoning.

Throughout this text, you have learned many different problem-solving strategies. One of the most important strategies for problem solving is to use logical reasoning. You can apply this strategy in every situation, especially when you play games or solve puzzles.

Example

Allan, Kevin, Eduardo, and Bob are friends. Each of them is on one of the following school teams: football, soccer, cross country, or golf. Allan is shorter than the boy who plays soccer. Eduardo only likes to play games with round balls. Bob has a problem with his knee and cannot run. Kevin practices kicking a ball as part of his training. Who plays each sport?

Explore   There are four boys and four sports. You must match each boy with the sport he plays.

Plan   Make a chart to organize the information. Use the clues to rule out possibilities.

Solve   Put an X to show that Allan does not play soccer. Put two X's to show that Eduardo does not play football or run cross country. Put three X's to show that Bob does not play football, soccer, or cross country. Since only one student plays golf, put X's in the rest of the boxes in that row.

Now you can see that Eduardo plays soccer. Place an X to show that Kevin does not run cross country, which means he plays football. Therefore, Allan's sport is cross country.

	Allan	Kevin	Eduardo	Bob
football	✗	✔	✗	✗
soccer	✗	✗	✔	✗
cross country	✔	✗	✗	✗
golf	✗	✗	✗	✔

Examine   Check the answer in the words of the problem. Allan runs cross country, Kevin plays football, Eduardo plays soccer, and Bob plays golf.

❝When am I ever going to use this?❞

A computer programmer writes a detailed plan or procedure for solving a problem in an ordered sequence of instructions.

Programming requires a degree in computer science with a working knowledge of computer languages and mathematics.

For more information, contact:
Association for Computing Machinery,
11 W. 42nd St.
3rd Floor
New York, NY 10036

OPTIONS

Reteaching Activity

Using Logical Reasoning Have three students each secretly choose a profession and inform you of their choice. Write the professions on the chalkboard. Have the remaining students attempt to match these students and the professions by asking yes-or-no questions and eliminating possibilities.

Study Guide Masters, p. 127

Name _____ Date _____

Study Guide Worksheet 14-7

Problem-Solving Strategy: Use Logical Reasoning

Example   Mr. Guzman drove the 30 miles from his home to work in 45 minutes. For 15 minutes, he was in road construction and traveled at 20 miles per hour. What was his average speed for the remainder of his trip?

Explore   What do you know?
Mr. Guzman drove 30 miles in 45 minutes.
For 15 minutes, he drove at 20 miles per hour.
You want to find his average speed for the remainder of the trip.

Plan   Multiply to find how far Mr. Guzman drove in 15 minutes.
Subtract to find how far he traveled in the remaining 30 minutes.
Use a ratio to find his average speed.

Solve   15 minutes is $\frac{1}{4}$ hour. In $\frac{1}{4}$ hour traveling at 20 miles per hour, Mr. Guzman traveled $\frac{1}{4} \times 20$ or 5 miles. He drove 45 or 30

Checking for Understanding

Communicating Mathematics

Read and study the lesson to answer each question.

1. **Tell** why you can put X's in the remaining boxes of a row after you have matched one of the boys with his sport. **See margin.**

2. **Tell** about a situation in your life in which you use logical reasoning. **Answers will vary.**

Guided Practice

Solve using logical reasoning.

3. On average, it takes three minutes to saw through a log. How long will it take to saw a log into four pieces? **9 minutes**

4. The Science and History Clubs are going on a research trip to the Museum of Natural History. There are 22 students in the Science Club and 26 students in the History Club. Five teachers will also make the trip. How many mini-buses will be needed if each bus holds 16 passengers? **4 mini-buses**

Problem Solving

Practice

Solve using any strategy.

5. Without computing, choose the number that is the cube of 123. Explain your reasoning. **See margin.**

   a. 1,815,848
   b. 1,860,867
   c. 1,953,125
   d. 1,906,624

6. Brenda has four cats named Beanie, Tiger, Flower, and Snowball. One cat is white with brown markings, one is all white and one is all black. The fourth cat is calico. Snowball was all white as a kitten, but now has spots. Tiger and the black cat are brother and sister. Beanie does not get along with the black cat. Tiger has orange markings. What color is each cat? **Beanie: all white, Tiger: calico, Flower: all black, Snowball: white with brown markings**

7. **Mathematics and Architecture** Read the following paragraph.

Louis Henry Sullivan (1856–1924) was an American architect who, with his partner Dankmer Adler, designed over 100 buildings between 1881 and 1895. They are known for adapting modern methods to building design.

A section of a building is being redesigned into new offices. The current design has square-shaped offices on the perimeter of the floor. When the renovation is complete, each office will be 2 feet wider and 4 feet longer. Find the area of each new office in terms of the original length and width. $x^2 + 6x + 8$

8. **Portfolio Suggestion** Review the items in your portfolio. Make a table of contents of the items, noting why each item was chosen. Replace any items that are no longer appropriate. **See students' work.**

Extending the Lesson

Mathematics and Architecture
Ask students to represent the new length and width, $(x + 2)$ and $(x + 4)$. Then ask them to find the original area of each square-shaped office in terms of x.

Cooperative Learning Activity

Get a Clue **14-7**

Number of players: 4
Materials: Index cards

- Copy onto cards the names, locations, and types of clothing shown on the back of this card, one per card. For each category, shuffle the cards and then remove one card. Place these three cards aside, face down. Shuffle the remaining cards together and divide them evenly.

➡ You will use your cards and the answers other group members give to determine what will be on the cover of the next J. Tweedies catalog. The three cards that remain face down tell what *will* be on the cover, so the cards that were selected tell what *won't* be.

One player asks the player to his or her left a question in this form: "Is it (model) on the (location) wearing the (clothing type)?" If the player being asked has a card that will eliminate one of these possibilities, he or she must show it to the player asking the question. Continue in the same way, taking turns asking questions and writing "yes" and "no" in the chart to confirm or eliminate possibilities. If you think you know the cover, you may guess and look at the cards on your turn. If you are wrong, you may not guess again, but you may continue to be asked questions by the other players.

Glencoe Mathematics: Applications and Connections, Course 3

---

1 FOCUS

Motivating the Lesson

Situational Problem *Harry, Diane, and Carlos played a game. Carlos scored highest. Diane did not score lowest. Who had the lowest score?*

2 TEACH

More Examples

For the Example

Jake, Flora, and Mimi are a farmer, a grocer, and a mechanic, though not necessarily in that order. Flora lives in the city. Neither she nor Jake is the grocer. Match each person with their profession. Jake, farmer; Flora, mechanic; Mimi, grocer

3 PRACTICE/APPLY

Assignment Guide
Maximum: 5–7
Minimum: 5–6

Enrichment Masters, p. 127

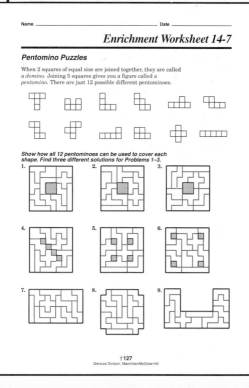

Name _____ Date _____

Enrichment Worksheet 14-7

Pentomino Puzzles

When 2 squares of equal size are joined together, they are called a *domino*. Joining 5 squares gives you a figure called a *pentomino*. There are just 12 possible different pentominoes.

Show how all 12 pentominoes can be used to cover each shape. Find three different solutions for Problems 1–3.

1. 2. 3.

4. 5. 6.

7. 8. 9.

T127
Glencoe Division, Macmillan/McGraw-Hill

The Chapter Study Guide and Review begins with a section on Communicating Mathematics. This includes questions that review the new terms and concepts that were introduced in the chapter.

Then, the Skills and Concepts presented in the chapter are reviewed using a side-by-side format. Encourage students to refer to the Objectives and Examples on the left as they complete the Review Exercises on the right.

The Chapter Study Guide and Review ends with problems that review Applications and Problem Solving.

Additional Answer

7. Sample answer: A monomial is a number, a variable, or a product of a number and one or more variables.

Chapter

14 Study Guide and Review

Communicating Mathematics

State whether each sentence is *true* or *false*. If false, replace the underlined word or number to make a true sentence.

1. The expression $b^2 - 3b$ is an example of a <u>monomial</u>. false; binomial
2. A polynomial is the sum or <u>difference</u> of two or more monomials. true
3. The <u>additive</u> inverse of $9y^2 - 5y + 2$ is $-9y^2 + 5y - 2$. true
4. A polynomial with two unlike terms is called a <u>*binomial*</u>. true
5. The product of $2m$ and $m^2 + 8m$ will have <u>three</u> terms. false; two

6. Draw and label a rectangle with an area of $6x^2 + 2x$. See Solutions Manual.
7. Write the definition of a monomial in your own words. See margin.
8. Explain how to factor $x^2 + 7x + 6$ using area tiles or drawings. Model the polynomial. Then form a rectangle with the tiles. The factors are the dimensions of the rectangle.

Self Assessment

Objectives and Examples	Review Exercises
Upon completing this chapter, you should be able to:	*Use these exercises to review and prepare for the chapter test.*

● represent polynomials with area models *(Lesson 14-1)*

Model $x^2 + 2x + 5$.

$x^2 + 2x + 5$ ➡

Model each polynomial using area tiles or drawings. For answers to Exercises 9-12, see Solutions Manual.

9. $4x - 6$
10. $2x^2 - 3$
11. $-3x^2 + 4x - 8$
12. $x^2 - 5$

● simplify polynomials using area models *(Lesson 14-2)*

Simplify $2b^2 + 7 + b^2$.

$2b^2 \ + \ 7 \ + \ b^2 \ = \ 3b^2 \ + \ 7$

Simplify each polynomial. Use area tiles or drawings if necessary.

13. $4m^2 + 6m + 11m^2 + 2m$ $15m^2 + 8m$
14. $9p - 4p - 15$ $5p - 15$
15. $14x - 3x^2 - 8x + 5x^2$ $2x^2 + 6x$
16. $3a + 9b - a - 6b$ $2a + 3b$
17. $17m^2 - 2m + 4m - 3m^2$ $14m^2 + 2m$

Objectives and Examples

- **add polynomials using area models** *(Lesson 14-3)*

  Find $(2b^2 + 8b) + (4b^2 - 3b)$.

  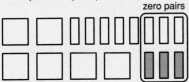

  zero pairs

  $2b^2 + 8b + 4b^2 - 3b = 6b^2 + 5b$

- **subtract polynomials using area models** *(Lesson 14-4)*

  Find $(8t^2 + 4) - (5t^2 - 2)$.

  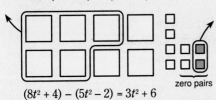

  zero pairs

  $(8t^2 + 4) - (5t^2 - 2) = 3t^2 + 6$

- **multiply a polynomial by a monomial using area models** *(Lesson 14-5)*

  Find $7x(3x + 5)$

  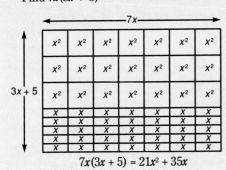

  $7x(3x + 5) = 21x^2 + 35x$

- **multiply binomials using area models** *(Lesson 14-6)*

  Name the two binomials being multiplied and give their product.

  $\Rightarrow (x + 2)(x + 3) =$
  $x^2 + 5x + 6$

Review Exercises

Find each sum. Use area tiles or drawings if necessary. 21. $4b^2 - 3b - 4$

18. $(11m^2 - 2m) + (4m^2 + 5m)$ $15m^2 + 3m$

19. $(5d + 1) + (9d + 7)$ $14d + 8$

20. $(2a^2 + 5a) + (2a^2 - 4a)$ $4a^2 + a$

21. $(b^2 - 4b + 2) + (3b^2 + b - 6)$

22. $(3x^2 - 8x) + (x^2 + 9x)$ $4x^2 + x$

Find each difference. Use area tiles or drawings if necessary.

23. $(9g + 3) - (6g + 1)$ $3g + 2$

24. $(2m - 8) - (-2m + 3)$ $4m - 11$

25. $(4s^2 + 9) - (s^2 + 4)$ $3s^2 + 5$

26. $(7k^2 - 2) - (2k^2 - 6k - 1)$ $5k^2 + 6k - 1$

27. $(8p^2 + 4p - 7) - (6p^2 + 9p - 3)$
    $2p^2 - 5p - 4$

Find each product. Use area tiles or drawings if necessary.

28. $5(2y + 4)$ $10y + 20$

29. $4z(z + 3)$ $4z^2 + 12z$

30. $c(3c + 1)$ $3c^2 + c$

31. $3t(t + 6)$ $3t^2 + 18t$

Find each product. Use area tiles or drawings if necessary.

32. $(x + 4)(x + 2)$ $x^2 + 6x + 8$

33. $(x + 3)(2x + 2)$ $2x^2 + 8x + 6$

34. $(2x + 2)(2x + 5)$ $4x^2 + 14x + 10$

35. $(x + 5)(x + 2)$ $x^2 + 7x + 10$

36. $(3x + 1)(x + 2)$ $3x^2 + 7x + 2$

Chapter 14   Study Guide and Review   **567**

You may wish to use a Chapter Test from the Evaluation Masters booklet as an additional chapter review. The two free-response forms are shown below. One of the two multiple-choice forms is shown on the next page.

Evaluation Masters, pp. 122–123

Name _____ Date _____

Form 2A _____ *Chapter 14 Test*

State whether each expression is a polynomial.

1. $6x^3 + 3xy^2 + 1$ 2. $\frac{m}{3}$
3. $\frac{5}{r}$ 4. $\sqrt{z} - 1$

Evaluate each polynomial if r = 2, s = -3, and t = 5.

5. $s + tr^3$ 6. $r^3 - 2t - 4s$ 7. $s^3 - st^2r$

8. Write a polynomial for the model at the right.

Simplify each polynomial. Use area tiles or drawings if necessary.

9. $4a^2 - 13ab^2 + 3a^2 + 15ab^2$
10. $3x^2 + 5xy - 4x^2 + y^2$
11. $7c^2 - 5c - 3c^2 - 8c$ 12. $15m^2 + n^2 - 8m^2 + 3n^2$

Find each sum or difference. Use area tiles or drawings if necessary.

13. $x^2 + 3x + (5x - 2x^2)$ 14. $(16s^2 + 3s - 2) - (5s^2 + 6)$
15. $(n^2 + 2n - 5) + (n^2 + 3n)$
16. $(9w^2 + w - 2) - (w^2 + 3w)$
17. $9b^2 - 3b + 7$
    $+ b^2 - b - 3$
18. $2y^2 + 8y + 7$
    $-(6y^2 + 5y - 1)$

Match each product with its corresponding model.

19. $(x + 2)(x + 3)$ a.   b.
20. $(x + 2)(2x + 4)$
21. $(x + 2)(x + 2)$ c.   d.
22. $(2x + 1)(x + 3)$

Find each product. Use area tiles or drawings if necessary.

23. $6a(4a + 2)$
24. $(3x + 2)(2x + 1)$
25. Marsha, Sean, Nate, and Jenny attend different schools. The names of the schools are Jennison, Sampson, Nason, and Marshfield. Marsha goes to the Sampson School. None goes to the school that has the same letter as his or her name. Neither Nate or Jenny has ever been to the Marshfield School. Which school does Sean attend?

BONUS Make a model that shows the product $3x^2 + 8x + 4$.

1.	polynomial
2.	polynomial
3.	not a polynomial
4.	not a polynomial
5.	37
6.	10
7.	123
8.	$4x^2 + 3x + 5$
9.	$7a^2 + 2ab^2$
10.	$x^2 + 5xy + y^2$
11.	$4c^2 - 13c$
12.	$7m^2 + 4n^2$
13.	$-x^2 + 8x$
14.	$11s^2 + 3s - 8$
15.	$5n - 5$
16.	$8w^2 - 2w - 2$
17.	$10b^2 - 4b + 4$
18.	$-4y^2 + 3y + 8$
19.	d
20.	a
21.	b
22.	c
23.	$24a^2 + 12a$
24.	$6x^2 + 7x + 2$
25.	Marshfield

122
Glencoe Division, Macmillan/McGraw-Hill

Name _____ Date _____

Form 2B _____ *Chapter 14 Test*

State whether each expression is a polynomial.

1. $x + 8$ 2. $3 - 2xy + 2x^3$
3. $\frac{r}{2x - 1}$ 4. -21

Evaluate each polynomial if r = -2, s = 2, and t = 3.

5. $s - r^3t$ 6. $t + s^3 - 2r$ 7. $r^2s^2t - 4s$

8. Write a polynomial for the model at the right.

Simplify each polynomial. Use area tiles or drawings if necessary.

9. $a^2 + 3a^2b + 2a^2 + 6a^2b$ 10. $2m^2 + 3mn - 5m^2 + n^2$
11. $6e^2 - 7e - 2e^2 - e$ 12. $11u^2 + v^2 - 9u^2 + 5v^2$

Find each sum or difference. Use area tiles or drawings if necessary.

13. $(15i^2 - 3i + 2) + (-9i^2 + 6i - 2)$
14. $(t^2 + 3t) - (t^2 + t + 1)$
15. $(c^2 - 5) + (6c + 8)$ 16. $(7l^2 + 2l - 3) - (2l^2 + 5l)$
17. $8x^2 + 5x - 3$
    $+ 3x^2 - x - 3$
18. $7n^2 - 2n + 8$
    $-(3n^2 - 3n - 3)$

Match each product with its corresponding model.

19. $(x + 4)(x + 2)$ a.   b.
20. $(x + 4)(x + 3)$
21. $(2x + 2)(x + 2)$ c.   d.
22. $(3x + 2)(x + 1)$

Find each product. Use area tiles or drawings if necessary.

23. $3s(2s + 2)$
24. $(3x + 1)(2x + 3)$
25. Albert, Betsy, and Courtney each belong to one school club. The clubs are debate, chess, and ecology. Albert dislikes board games. Courtney walks home with the debater. Betsy is in the chess player's music class and she is a faster swimmer than the ecologist. Who belongs to the ecology club?

BONUS Express $(5x + 1)(x + 3) - (x + 4)(2x + 1)$ in simplest form.

1.	polynomial
2.	polynomial
3.	not a polynomial
4.	polynomial
5.	26
6.	15
7.	40
8.	$2x^2 + 5x + 6$
9.	$3a^2 + 9a^2b$
10.	$3m^2 + 3mn + n^2$
11.	$4e^2 - 8e$
12.	$2u^2 + 6v^2$
13.	$6i^2 + 3i$
14.	$2t - 1$
15.	$c^2 + 6c + 3$
16.	$5l^2 - 3l - 3$
17.	$11x^2 + 4x - 6$
18.	$4n^2 + n + 11$
19.	d
20.	c
21.	a
22.	b
23.	$6s^2 + 6s$
24.	$6x^2 + 11x + 3$
25.	Albert

$3x^2 + 7x - 1$

123
Glencoe Division, Macmillan/McGraw-Hill

Applications and Problem Solving

37. **Interior Design**   The amount of carpeting needed for the Glasers' living room is $2x^2 + x$ square meters. Find the dimensions of the living room. *(Lesson 14-5)* **$(2x + 1)$ meters by x meters**

38. **Gardening**   Mrs. Keyser has a rectangular flower bed. The length is $3x - 1$ feet, and the width is $2x + 3$ feet. Find the perimeter of the flower bed. *(Lesson 14-3)* **$10x + 4$ feet**

39. **Exercise**   Tami rode her bicycle around a square city block. The measure of each side of the block is $3x + 8$ yards. What is the total distance that Tami rode her bicycle? *(Lesson 14-5)* **$12x + 32$ yards**

40. **Geometry**   The measures of two angles of a triangle are $-2x^2 - 3x + 9$ and $-3x^2 - x + 7$. Find the measure of the third angle. *(Lesson 14–4)* **$5x^2 + 4x + 164$ degrees**

41. This statement is true: All rhombuses are parallelograms. Decide which of the following statements are also true. *(Lesson 14-7)* **c**

    a. All parallelograms are rhombuses.

    b. If a quadrilateral is a parallelogram, then it is a rhombus.

    c. If a quadrilateral is not a parallelogram, then it is not a rhombus.

    d. If a quadrilateral is not a rhombus, then it is not a parallelogram.

Curriculum Connection Projects

- **Zoology**   You decide to raise rabbits. Your first rabbit has a litter of x bunnies. Each of her offspring has identical size litters. Use a tree diagram to represent the three generations. Then write a polynomial representing the number of rabbits you have. **See students' work.**

- **Design**   Draw a floor plan of a one-story house. Use the scale 1 cm = 1 m. Let $x = 1$ cm, $y = 3$ cm, and $z = 5$ cm. Make the dimensions multiples of x, y, and z. Write a polynomial for the area of your house. **See students' work.**

Read More About It

Duane, Diane. *High Wizardry.*
Sarnoff, Jane and Ruffins, Reynold. *The Chess Book.*
Weiss, Harvey. *Model Buildings and How to Make Them.*

568   **Chapter 14**   Study Guide and Review

14 Test

Model each monomial or polynomial using area tiles or drawings. For answers to Exercises 1-4, see Solutions Manual.

1. $6x^2 + 3x$ 2. $-5x^2 - 2x + 8$ 3. $4x^2 + 7x - 2$ 4. $x^2 - x$

Evaluate each polynomial if $r = -1$, $s = 2$, and $t = 4$.

5. $r^3t - s$ -6   6. $s^3 - 3s + t$ 6   7. $r^2st^2 - 3t$ 20

8. Identify the polynomial represented by the model at the right. $3x^2 + x + 4$

Simplify each polynomial. Use area tiles or drawings if necessary.

9. $3x^2 + 5x + 4x^2 + 7x$ $7x^2 + 12x$ 10. $5c^2 + 2c - 2c^2 + c$ $3c^2 + 3c$
11. $4x^2 + y - 6x^2 + y$ $-2x^2 + 2y$ 12. $2a^2 + 8a - 3a^2 + 4a - 1$ $-a^2 + 12a - 1$

Find each sum or difference. Use area tiles or drawings if necessary.

13. $(8z^2 - 2z) - (4z^2 + 9z)$ $4z^2 - 11z$ 14. $(5c^2 + 3c) + (-3c^2 + c)$ $2c^2 + 4c$
15. $(6n^2 - 5n + 1) - (3n - 4)$ $6n^2 - 8n + 5$ 16. $(-x^2 + 3x - 4) + (x^2 - 7x)$ $-4x - 4$
17.
$$\begin{aligned}6r^2 - 5r + 4 \\ + \ r^2 - 4r - 8 \\ \hline 7r^2 - 9r - 4\end{aligned}$$
18.
$$\begin{aligned}9y^2 + 5y - 8 \\ - \ (6y^2 + 8y - 9) \\ \hline 3y^2 - 3y + 1\end{aligned}$$

Match each product with its corresponding model. Then state the product.

19. $(x + 3)(x + 4)$ a; $x^2 + 7x + 12$
20. $(x + 1)^2$ d; $x^2 + 2x + 1$
21. $(2x + 1)(x + 2)$ b; $2x^2 + 5x + 2$
22. $(x + 1)(3x + 2)$ c; $3x^2 + 5x + 2$

Find each product. Use area tiles or drawings if necessary.

23. $4d(2d + 5)$ $8d^2 + 20d$
24. $x(5x + 3)$ $5x^2 + 3x$

25. Jacob, Amerette, Susan, and Lonny have after-school jobs. One works at the local Chicken Flicken, one is a stock person at the 24-hour grocery, one delivers fliers door-to-door, and one babysits. Amerette has nothing to do with food. Jacob and the babysitter are brothers. Jacob and the stock person do not know each other. What is each student's job? Jacob, Chicken Flicken; Amerette, fliers; Susan, stock person; Lonny, babysitter.

Bonus Write a formula for finding the product of $ax + b$ and $cx + d$, where a, b, c, and d are whole numbers. $(ax + b)(cx + d) = acx^2 + (ad + bc)x + bd$

Using the Chapter Test

This page may be used as a chapter test or another chapter review.

Evaluation Masters, pp. 118–119

Name _____ Date _____

Form 1A _____ *Chapter 14 Test*

Identify the monomial or polynomial for each model.

1. A. $x^2 - 3x + 7$ B. $2x^2 + 7x + 3$
   C. $x^2 + 3x + 7$ D. $x^2 + 3x - 7$ 1. C

2. A. $x^2 + 2x + 3$ B. $2x^2 + x + 3$
   C. $x^2 - x + 3$ D. $2x^2 + 4x$ 2. B

3. A. $3x^2 + 5x + 5$ B. $3x^2 + 6x + 5$
   C. $3x^2 + 5x + 6$ D. $3x^2 + 6x - 5$ 3. A

4. Evaluate $x^2 - 6x + 9$, if $x = -2$.
   A. 10 B. -1 C. 25 D. 19   4. C

5. Name the like terms in $6x$, $7y$, $11x$, and $13z$.
   A. $11x$, $13z$ B. $6x$, $7y$ C. $7y$, $13z$ D. $6x$, $11x$ 5. D

Simplify the polynomial using the model.

6. A. $x^2 + 10x + 1$ B. $x^2 + 9x + 1$
   C. $2x^2 + 7x + 1$ D. $x^2 + 8x + 1$ 6. C

7. A. $x^2 - x + 1$ B. $x^2 - x - 1$
   C. $x^2 + x - 1$ D. $-x^2 + x + 1$ 7. A

8. A. $2x^2 + 3x + y - 1$
   B. $-2x^2 + 3x + 3y + 4$
   C. $-2x^2 + x^3y^3 + 3$
   D. $-2x^2 + x + y + 2$ 8. D

Find each sum. Use area tiles or drawings if necessary.

9. $\begin{aligned}4x^2 - 3x + 6 \\ + \ x^2 + 5x - 4\end{aligned}$
   A. $3x^2 - 8x + 10$ B. $-5x^2 - 2x + 2$
   C. $5x^2 + 2x + 2$ D. $-5x^2 + 2x + 2$ 9. C

10. $(7s - 2t) + (s + t)$
    A. $8s - t$ B. $t - 8s$ C. $-13st$ D. $5st$ 10. A

11. $(2m + 6m^2) + (8m^2 - 4m)$
    A. $12m^2$ B. $12m^3$ C. $14m^2 + 2m$ D. $14m^2 - 2m$ 11. D

12. Find the sum of $-3a^2 + 2a - 1$ and $5a^2 - 4a - 6$.
    A. $2a^2 - 2a + 7$ B. $2a^2 - 2a - 7$
    C. $2a^2 - 2a - 5$ D. $2a^2 + 2a - 7$ 12. B

Find each difference. Use area tiles or drawings if necessary.

13. $\begin{aligned}5x^2 - 4x - 3 \\ - \ (3x^2 + 3x + 6)\end{aligned}$
    A. $2x^2 - x + 3$ B. $8x^2 - x + 3$
    C. $-8x^2 + x - 3$ D. $2x^2 - 7x - 9$ 13. D

14. $(12c - 4d) - (8c - 3d)$
    A. $4c - 7d$ B. $4c + 7d$ C. $4c + d$ D. $4c - d$ 14. D

Name _____ Date _____

Chapter 14 Test, Form 1A (continued)

15. $(-5t + 3) - (t - 2)$
    A. $-6t + 5$ B. $-4t + 1$ C. $-4t - 1$ D. $-6t + 1$ 15. A

16. $(7x^2 + 3x + 5) - (3x^2 + 5x + 5)$
    A. $4x^2 + 2x$ B. $-4x^2 - 2x$ C. $4x^2 - 2x$ D. $4x^2 + 2x + 10$ 16. C

17. Multiply $3(2x - 1)$. Use area tiles or drawings if necessary.
    A. $6x - 3$ B. $6x - 1$ C. $5x - 1$ D. $5x - 3$ 17. A

18. Find the product of $3c$ and $c + 5$. Use area tiles or drawings if necessary.
    A. $3c + 15$ B. $3c^2 + 5$ C. $4c + 5$ D. $3c^2 + 15c$ 18. D

19. Factor $6y + 18$. Use area tiles or drawings if necessary.
    A. $6(y + 18)$ B. $6(y + 3)$ C. $3(2y + 6)$ D. $6(y + 12)$ 19. B

20. Factor $8p^2 + 2p$. Use area tiles or drawings if necessary.
    A. $p(8p + 2)$ B. $2(4p^2 + p)$ C. $2p(4p + 2)$ D. $2p(4p + 1)$ 20. D

Find each product. Use area tiles or drawings if necessary.

21. $(x + 1)(x + 3)$
    A. $x^2 + 4x + 3$ B. $x^2 + 4x + 4$
    C. $x^2 + 2x + 3$ D. $x^2 + 3x + 3$ 21. A

22. $(x + 1)(2x + 3)$
    A. $2x^2 + 6x + 3$ B. $2x^2 + 5x + 4$
    C. $2x^2 + 5x + 3$ D. $2x^2 + 6x + 4$ 22. C

23. $(2x + 1)(2x + 3)$
    A. $4x^2 + 7x + 3$ B. $4x^2 + 8x + 3$
    C. $4x^2 + 7x + 4$ D. $4x^2 + 8x + 4$ 23. B

24. Find the product of $(x + 4)$ and $(2x + 1)$.
    A. $2x^2 + 7x + 5$ B. $2x^2 + 9x + 5$
    C. $2x^2 + 9x + 4$ D. $2x^2 + 8x + 4$ 24. C

25. Four students have birthdays in January, February, June, and October. Becky's birthday is in the summer. Anne was not born in the winter. Linda's birthday is the month before Jane's. In what month was Jane born?
    A. January B. February
    C. June D. October   25. B

BONUS Find the area of the shaded region in simplest form.
    A. $4x^2$ B. $4x^2 + 8x + 4$
    C. $8x + 4$ D. $8x^2 + 4x$ C

Chapter Test

Test and Review Generator software is provided in Apple, IBM, and Macintosh versions. You may use this software to create your own tests or worksheets, based on the needs of your students.

The **Performance Assessment Booklet** provides an alternate assessment for evaluating student progress. An assessment for this chapter can be found on pages 27–28.

The Academic Skills Test may be used to help students prepare for standardized tests. The test items are written in the same style as those in state proficiency tests. The test items cover skills and concepts covered up to this point in the text.

These pages can be used as an overnight assignment. After students have completed the pages, discuss how each problem can be solved, or provide copies of the solutions from the *Solutions Manual*.

Chapter

14 Academic Skills Test

Standard Format, Chapters 1-14

Academic Skills Test

Directions: Choose the best answer. Write A, B, C, or D.

1. If $2c - 5 = -3$, what is the value of c? **C**

   A -4   B -1

   C 1   D 4

2. What is $0.\overline{39}$ written as a fraction? **C**

   A $\frac{1}{3}$ B $\frac{4}{10}$

   C $\frac{13}{33}$ D $\frac{39}{100}$

3. If $0.3x = 5.28$, what is the value of x? **A**

   A 17.6   B 15.84

   C 1.76   D 1.584

4. Each spinner is spun once. What is the probability of spinning a prime number and a vowel? **A**

   A $\frac{1}{5}$ B $\frac{3}{7}$

   C $\frac{4}{15}$ D $\frac{9}{10}$

5. What is the value of x in the square shown below? **C**

   A 2 units

   B $\sqrt{10}$ units

   C 10 units

   D none of these

6. In a scale drawing of a room, 1 unit = 6 in. What are the scale dimensions of a 40 in. by 60 in. table? **B**

   A 4 by 6   B $6\frac{2}{3} \times 10$

   C 8 by 12   D 24×36

7. 36.5% = **C**

   A 36.5   B 3.65

   C 0.365   D 0.0365

8. What percent of 30 is 2.5? **A**

   A $8\frac{1}{3}$ %   B 12%

   C 75%   D $83\frac{1}{3}$ %

9. Which is the graph of $y = 3x - 3$? **D**

   A   B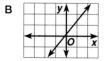

   C   D

10. What are the coordinates of rectangle *MATH* translated by $(2, -1)$ if $M(-3, 1)$, $A(2, 6)$, $T(6, 2)$, and $H(1, -3)$? **B**

    A $(-3, -1), (2, -6), (6, -2), (1, 3)$

    B $(-1, 0), (4, 5), (8, 1), (3, -4)$

    C $(3, 1), (-2, 6), (-6, 2), (-1, -3)$

    D $(5, 1), (4, 7), (8, 3), (3, 4)$

11. Alison owns a tent in the shape of a pyramid. The base of the tent is 8' by 10'. The tent is 7' tall at the center. How can you find the volume of the air inside the tent? **A**

   A Find $8 \times 10 \times 7$ and divide by 3.
   B Add $2\left(\frac{1}{2} \cdot 7 \cdot 8\right)$ and $2\left(\frac{1}{2} \cdot 7 \cdot 10\right)$.
   C Find $7 \cdot 8 \cdot 10$.
   D None of these

12. How many significant digits are there in 0.0250 cm? **C**

   A 5   B 4
   C 3   D 2

13. Luis is redecorating his room. He has a choice of 4 colors of paint, 3 colors of carpet, and 2 colors of curtains. How many combinations of paint, carpet, and curtain colors can he use? **D**

   A 8   B 9
   C 12   D 24

14. In how many ways can all four of the shapes be arranged in a row? **C**

   A 4   B 12
   C 24   D 36

15. How many combinations of 4 flowers can you choose from one dozen flowers? **B**

   A 11,880   B 495
   C 48   D 24

16. $3x + 6x - 5x =$ **B**

   A $9x - 5$ B $4x$
   C $4x^3$ D $14x$

17. In a random sample of 150 students, 60 ride the bus to school, 54 ride in car pools, and 36 walk. If there are to be 800 students next year, about how many will need bus transportation? **A**

   A 320   B 160
   C 80   D 60

18. $(3a + 1) + (2a + 5) =$ **B**

   A $4a + 7a$ B $5a + 6$
   C $5a^2 + 5$ D $6a + 5$

19. $4(3x - 2) =$ **C**
   A $12x^2 - 8$ B $12x - 2$
   C $12x - 8$ D $12x + 8$

20. A triangle has an area of $6x^2 + x - 1$ square centimeters. Find the altitude and the base of the triangle if $x = 2$ centimeters. **C**
   A $4x + 2$ cm,   B 10 cm, 5 cm
      $3x - 1$ cm
   C A and B   D none of these

Chapter 14   Academic Skills Test   **571**

EXTENDED PROJECTS HANDBOOK

PURPOSE

The projects students will undertake are similar to those people may face in the real world in the course of doing their jobs or in dealing with issues in their lives. The projects involve gathering, organizing, interpreting, and presenting data. They require students to use questioning techniques, and debate real-life issues.

In working through these projects, students will work in groups. Knowing how to work cooperatively with others is an important life-long skill. As part of the problem-solving process, students must learn how to communicate effectively with others, which includes working on their abilities to listen, share, and be supportive.

The projects take place over time and may include out-of-class as well as in-class time. You will need to set aside some class time for groups to share and discuss the results of their work.

In the course of completing the projects, students will need to do research. This research may involve using library resources or it may involve designing and conducting a survey or an experiment to find out what their classmates are thinking.

The goals of these long-term projects are for students to become better at working together to gather, interpret, and use information. They are learning about a real-world process, not merely short answers to short-answer questions. These are not meant to be short-term projects.

In each project, students will need to organize the information they gather in order to use it. One group member can be responsible for this task, but all group members can make suggestions and contributions.

To The Student

One of the goals of *Mathematics: Applications and Connections* is to give you the opportunity to work with the mathematics that you will likely encounter outside the classroom. This includes the mathematics demanded by many of the courses you will take in high school and by most jobs as well as the mathematics that will be required of a good citizen of the United States.

Equally important, the authors want you to approach the mathematics you will encounter in your life with curiosity, enjoyment, and confidence.

Hopefully, the **Extended Projects Handbook** reflects these goals.

Three of the most important "big" ideas you are working with throughout *Mathematics: Applications and Connections* are the following. The **Extended Projects** include these "big" ideas.

1. Proportional Reasoning

You probably have a great deal of experience with proportional reasoning. One example is a straight line in which the "rise" is proportional to the "run" and their ratio is the slope of the line. Other topics include ratio, rate, percent, similarity, scale drawings, and probability.

You have made connections among the various applications of proportional reasoning and in this way have seen that the various items listed above are all part of a very big idea — proportions.

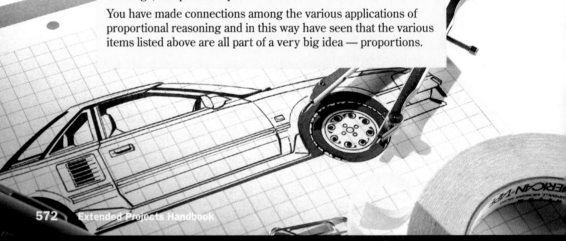

572 Extended Projects Handbook

2. Multiple Representations

Mathematics provides you with many ways to present information and relationships. These include sketches, perspective drawings, tables, charts, graphs, physical models, verbalizing, and writing. You can use a computer to make graphs, data bases, spreadsheets, and simulations.

You have represented information and relationships in many different ways to completely describe various kinds of situations using mathematics.

3. Patterns and Generalizations

Mathematics has been called the science of patterns. You have experience recognizing and describing simple number and geometric patterns. You will be asked to make, test, and then use generalizations about given information in order to help you solve problems.

You may have used an algebraic expression to generalize a number pattern or the idea of similarity to make a scale drawing.

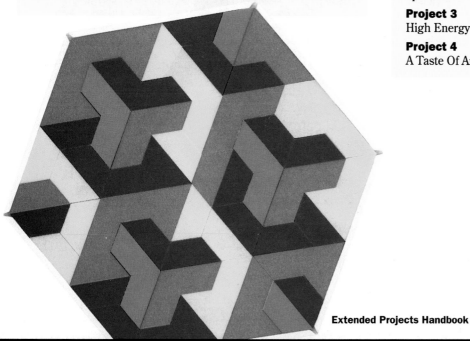

In each project, students will need to work together to formulate a plan to attack a problem. It is important that the groups spend enough time on this step in the problem-solving process to develop an effective strategy. Students may find it necessary to revise their plan as they gather new information. Encourage groups to look back at their plan and talk about what worked well, what didn't work as well, and how they would do it differently the next time.

MANAGING COOPERATIVE GROUPS

For successful cooperative learning experiences, research (Johnson and Johnson) indicates that the teacher's responsibilities include:

1. Deciding on the size of the groups.
2. Assigning students to the groups.
3. Arranging the room.
4. Describing the objectives.
5. Planning teaching materials.
6. Assigning roles to students.
7. Explaining the tasks involved.
8. Describing group responsibilities.
9. Establishing individual accountability.
10. Explaining the criteria for success.
11. Specifying desired student behaviors.
12. Monitoring students' behavior.
13. Providing task assistance.
14. Intervening to teach cooperative learning skills.
15. Providing closure to the lesson.
16. Evaluating the quality of learning.
17. Assessing group function.

(See general information about cooperative learning in the Teacher's Handbook, pp. T4–T5.)

Project 1

OVERVIEW

Objective State hypotheses, construct experiments, and analyze the results about the angle at which an object on a ramp begins to slide.

Summary

In this project, students will work in groups to plan and construct a series of experiments. In the first experiment, students test whether an object's weight affects its slippage on a ramp. In the second experiment, students test whether the texture of the object affects its slippage. Students will be able to understand that the angle at which slippage between two flat surfaces begins depends only on the material composition of the two surfaces.

Suggested Group Size

3–4 students

Time Required

If used as a complete unit:
5 days
If interspersed with other lessons:
2 weeks

Materials Needed

Smooth hardwood boards are available at many hardware stores, but are somewhat expensive. Foam craft board is an inexpensive alternative. You will need ramps that are about 50 cm long and 20 cm wide. Other materials include:
small covered boxes
small stones, aquarium gravel, or sand to add weight to the boxes
rulers or protractors
sandpaper

Key Terms

friction
independent variable
dependent variable

Project 1 **Slip Sliding Away**

Everyone seems to like sliding down hills. You can see people trying it in cold weather with skis and sleds. Some people, like Tommy Moe and Picabo Street, take it to extremes. They won medals in the downhill skiing events in the 1994 Winter Olympics at Lillehammer, Norway.

In hot weather, people also take part in sliding activities. From sliding boards to water slides, people of all ages enjoy the thrill of this kind of motion.

Have you ever watched people on a water slide? What are some factors that affect sliding?

In this project, you will pose questions, state hypotheses (or theories), and analyze the results of experiments.

Getting Started

Think what will happen if you put some boxes on a ramp and then begin to raise one end of the ramp. Will all the boxes start to slip at the same time? Will a lightweight box slip before a heavier one? Will a rough box slip less than a smooth one?

An object's weight and surface texture seem to be important factors in determining if it slips on a raised ramp. Write a hypothesis or guess about how you think the steepness of a ramp at which a box just begins to slip down the ramp is related to the box's weight.

- What variable is the independent variable in your hypothesis?
- How will you measure it? How will you change it?
- What variable is the dependent variable in your hypothesis?
- How will you measure it?
- What variables must you control?

After thinking about the answers to these questions, write a procedure to test your hypothesis. Also, design a table for the data you will collect. Perform your experiment.

Now, write a hypothesis about how you think the steepness of the ramp at which a box just begins to slide is related to the box's surface texture.
- Answer the questions posed above for your new hypothesis.

Write a procedure to test your hypothesis and perform your experiment.

Analyze the results of your experiments. Share the results with your classmates.
- Did the results of your experiments support your hypotheses?
- Were there any surprises? Explain.
- Did you and your classmates have the same hypotheses?
- Did you and your classmates get the same results?
- What is the important factor in predicting how easily an object will begin sliding down a ramp?
- How does this factor relate to snow skiing and water slides?

Extension:
Rolling Along

One way to reduce the surface texture of an object on a ramp is to put the object on wheels. Using a toy car, design an experiment to find the relationship between the height of the ramp and the distance a toy car will travel.

OVERVIEW

Objective   Collect information and present it in a book.

Summary

Students will begin this activity by gathering information on an endangered species of their choice. They will research causes of the species' decline, detail current efforts to rescue it from extinction, and propose further protective measures that might be taken. They will present their findings in a hardcover book.

Suggested Group Size

3 students

Time Required

If used as a complete unit:
5 days
If interspersed with other lessons:
4 weeks

Materials Needed

cardboard
decorative paper
glue
plastic tape
resource materials on
    endangered species
ruler
scissors

Key Terms

conservation
endangered species
extinction
habitat
predator

Project

2 Endangered Species

Wolves, whooping cranes, and grizzly bears are just three endangered species in North America. Many large zoos around the country work directly for conservation of animals by establishing captive breeding programs for endangered species. For example, the Minnesota Zoo has been successfully breeding snow leopards from the mountains of southern Asia.

Although this is an important first step, its value is lessened if some of the offspring cannot be successfully returned to the wild. The introduction and survival of captive-raised animals in their native habitat is much more difficult than you might expect.

In this project, you will research the controversies and issues surrounding the extinction of an animal.

Getting Started

Use resource materials to find out more about animals facing extinction. Gather background information about each animal and answer the following questions.

- What is the animal's natural habitat?
- What factors have caused endangerment of the animal?
- What efforts have been made to save the animal from extinction?
- What is the extended outlook for the survival of this animal?

576   Project 2

Many people see little wildlife except when they visit a zoo. What problems do you think might arise when establishing a breeding population in a zoo? Do you think breeding in zoos will help or hurt the species in the long run? Consider the following difficulties:

- Under zoo conditions, captive animals cannot search for food and protect themselves from predators in their natural habitat. What do you think will happen to an animal who is returned to the wild after having been born and raised in a zoo?
- Under zoo conditions, captive animals lose their fear of man. Why is this disastrous for animals that may be hunted?
- How is an animal's behavior in a cage at the zoo different from his behavior in the wild?

Use your information to make a book about an endangered species, what is being done to protect this animal, and how you propose to help. You can include photos, interviews with a local zookeeper, background information about the history of the animal, and any attempts that have been made to breed the animal in captivity.

To make your own hardcover book, follow these steps.

- Handwrite or word process your story on an $8\frac{1}{2}$ by 11-inch sheet of paper. Staple the pages together using two staples along the side about $\frac{1}{4}$ inch from the left edge.
- To form the front and back cover, cut out two rectangles of cardboard that are $8\frac{3}{4}$ inches by $11\frac{1}{4}$ inches.
- Cut larger rectangles of paper to cover and decorate each piece of cardboard. You might use contact paper, old wallpaper, or construction paper. You could also use plain paper and then draw a design on the cover.

- Place the completed back cover on the table with the decorated side down. Place a thin line of glue on the left edge of the top side. Place your stapled story face-up onto the cover. Place a thin line of glue along the left edge of your stapled story. Then place the other cover, decorated side up, on top of the story. Be sure to align the two covers.
- You might want to use colored plastic tape to add a binding edge along the left side of your book.

Extension: Show Time

You can trade your books with other classmates and learn about different endangered species. You can also use the information from your book as a reference and share your information with younger students.

Create animal puppets and put on an informative puppet show for younger children. The more people know, understand, and enjoy animals, the more they will care about preserving them.

Project 2 577

Before students begin their research, ask them to list threats faced by animals in the wild today. (Sample answers: destruction of habitat; poisons; hunting) Point out that while extinction of species has always gone on, it is accelerating at an alarming rate today. The Nature Conservancy estimates that three species become extinct each day. By the year 2000, 20% of Earth's species may be extinct.

Encourage students to see endangerment as a symptom of more widespread environmental distress. Ask them to describe possible consequences of the extinction of species to humans.

Be sure groups do not choose the same species to study.

EXTENSION

After students have studied each others' book, have them list things that individiuals, communities, and nations can do to reduce the rate of species extinction.

OVERVIEW

Objective State hypotheses, conduct experiments searching for patterns and proportional relationships, and generalize results.

Summary

In this activity, students will conduct experiments to analyze the behavior of bouncing balls. Before beginning each experiment, students will propose a hypothesis. They will test their hypotheses by measuring the height of the drops and bounces of several balls. Students will then analyze their results and state their conclusions.

Suggested Group Size

4 students

Time Required

If used as a complete unit:
4 days
If interspersed with other lessons:
2 weeks

Materials Needed

balls
carpet square
meter stick, tape measure, or yardstick
tape

Key Terms

energy
hypothesis
kinetic
physics
potential

High Energy

In physics, energy is the capacity for doing work. It may exist as *potential* energy or *kinetic* energy. Potential energy is energy of position. That is, because of its state, an object may have the ability to perform work. Examples of objects with potential energy are a lawn mower filled with gasoline or a baseball player waiting on-deck to bat.

Kinetic energy is energy in motion. The lawn mower cutting the grass displays kinetic energy. A ball player swinging a bat also shows kinetic energy.

In this project, you will pose questions, state hypotheses (or theories), and analyze the results of physics experiments.

Getting Started

Work in groups and have each member of the group bring in different kinds of balls, such as a tennis ball, a baseball, a Ping Pong ball, a styrofoam ball, a sponge ball, a croquet ball, a golf ball, and so on.

In the experiment, you will measure the energy of different balls under different conditions. In addition to the various balls, you will need a tape measure or yardstick taped to the wall and a piece of carpet. Each ball will be dropped and the height of the first bounce of the ball will be recorded. First you will drop the ball onto the bare floor, and then you will drop it onto the carpet.

Which ball will bounce the highest? Write a hypothesis, or guess, before you begin the experiment.

- Hold the ball at the top of the yardstick or tape measure. *This is potential energy.*
- Release the ball. *The falling ball is kinetic energy.*
- Observe the bounce. Record the height of the first bounce.
- Repeat these steps for each ball.

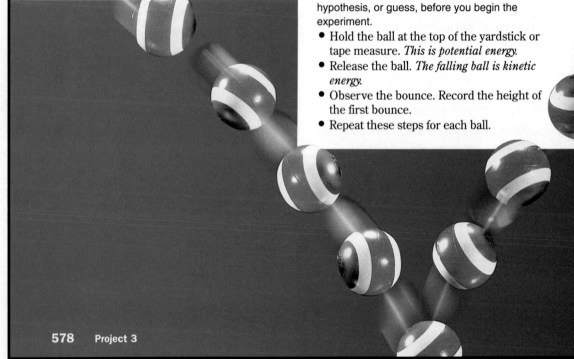

Will a ball bounce higher on carpet or the bare floor? Write a hypothesis.

- Repeat the steps above, but drop each ball onto the carpet square instead of the bare floor.
- Record the height of the first bounce.

Analyze the results of the experiment.

- When the ball hits the floor, what happens to the energy of the falling ball?
- Does the shape of the ball change as it is being bounced?
- How does the carpet affect the amount of "squish" in this ball?

Without conducting an experiment, discuss the following issues with your group. Write a plan how you would prove your hypotheses.

- Does a new tennis ball or an old one have a higher bounce?
- Does the drop height make a difference in the bounce height? Determine the ratio between the drop height and the bounce height. Does this ratio stay the same when a ball is dropped from different heights?

- Why do balls with a hard exterior such as golf balls and baseballs bounce? They are not "squishable" and would appear not to be able to spring back and bounce. Nevertheless, they can still bounce. How can you explain this?
- Does the weight of the ball affect the height of the bounce?

Extension: Wind It Up

Have you ever wondered what makes a wind-up toy move? What happens inside the toy to make it move?

Buy an inexpensive wind-up toy and take it apart. Inside you will find gears and a spiral spring. Energy is stored in the spring. Explain how it transfers stored energy to the toy to make it move.

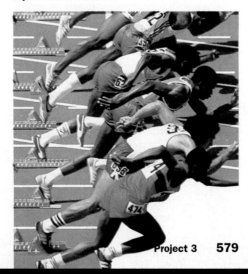

Project 3   **579**

TEACHING NOTES

In the past, some scientists thought that heavy objects fall faster than light ones. Aristotle (384–322 B.C.) theorized that the heavier a stone, the faster it falls. Galileo (1564–1642) was forced to resign from University of Pisa when he disputed this theory. Experiments showed heavy and light objects fall at the same rate. Discuss with students whether scientists should change a theory, conduct further experiments, or falsify the experimental results to support a theory.

Encourage students to spend some time developing a method for measuring bounce-height accurately. They may wish to take the average of several measurements.

Groups should prepare reports describing their experiments and detailing their conclusions.

EXTENSION

Have students list other everyday examples of potential energy being converted to kinetic energy.

OVERVIEW

Objective Use random samples and proportions to make a prediction.

Summary

In this activity, students will conduct a poll to assess the relative popularities of various ethnic foods. They will use their results to predict the type of restaurant most likely to succeed in the polling area. Finally, they will collect, analyze, and display additional data relevant to the question of whether to open an ethnic restaurant or not.

Suggested Group Size

3–4 students

Time Required

If used as a complete unit:
5 days
If interspersed with other lessons:
4 weeks

Materials Needed

calculator
resource materials on local
    community
survey materials

Key Terms

ethnic
poll
probability
random sample
survey

Project 4

A Taste of America

The many kinds of foods available in major cities in this country are one reflection of the many different cultures that make up America's population. For example, in Boston, people can choose from many kinds of restaurants including Chinese, Thai, Indian, Ethiopian, Italian, Middle Eastern, French, Indonesian, Spanish, Hungarian, Brazilian, German, Caribbean, Japanese, French, Russian, Vietnamese, and Mexican.

In this project, you will use random samples to predict which kind of restaurant would be profitable to open in your community.

Discuss with your group the kinds of ethnic food you like to eat. Did any two people suggest the same type of food?

Since people's tastes vary, it may be difficult to decide on which type of restaurant to open with just the opinions of your group members. Therefore, you will need to conduct a survey for a random sample of people.

The number of people you poll will vary depending on the size of your community. You will want to question people in a neutral, public place, such as a library or grocery store. Ask them, "If a new restaurant were to open in this area in the near future, what kind of food would you like it to serve?" Have a list of types from which they may choose.

Record your data in a chart. Use your random samples to predict which kind of restaurant most people would like to see in the neighborhood.

Example:

$$P(\text{Italian}) = \frac{50 \leftarrow \text{number of people who chose Italian}}{100 \leftarrow \text{total number of people surveyed}}$$

$P(\text{Italian}) \times$ number of people in community = expected number of people who prefer this kind of restaurant

After you have calculated the probability for each type of response, analyze your data and examine your results. Was there enough information from the responses to assist you in determining what kind of restaurant you would open? How many people did you poll? Do you think this was a fair sample?

Getting Started

Opening a new restaurant involves making many decisions. Make a list of the factors you should consider if you hope to have a successful business.

Examples:
- How large is the community where your restaurant will be located?
- What other kinds of food establishments are located in your neighborhood?
- How important is location?
- What kind of customers are you hoping to attract (families, business people, teenagers)?
- What would make people want to go to your restaurant?

Decide on a location and make a map of the surrounding area. Label the map with all of the restaurants in the vicinity of your planned site. If the area already has too many restaurants, you may want to modify your plans.

Once you have addressed these issues, you should try to locate some data about the size of your community, how often people go out to eat, and how much money they spend on a meal. Some possible sources are: a local Chamber of Commerce, a restaurant association, or local restaurant owners. Record your data in a chart.

Extension:

Create a menu from appetizers to desserts for your new restaurant. Be sure to include prices and descriptions of the kind of food you will be serving. You may need to research this information thoroughly before you begin writing. Make your menus as attractive as possible by using pictures from cooking magazines.

Discuss the possibilities of having a Multicultural Food Day and have each group prepare a food from your menus and share it with the class.

Project 4   **581**

Trigonometric Ratios

Angle	sin	cos	tan	Angle	sin	cos	tan
0°	0.0000	1.0000	0.0000	45°	0.7071	0.7071	1.0000
1°	0.0175	0.9998	0.0175	46°	0.7193	0.6947	1.0355
2°	0.0349	0.9994	0.0349	47°	0.7314	0.6820	1.0724
3°	0.0523	0.9986	0.0524	48°	0.7431	0.6691	1.1106
4°	0.0698	0.9976	0.0699	49°	0.7547	0.6561	1.1504
5°	0.0872	0.9962	0.0875	50°	0.7660	0.6428	1.1918
6°	0.1045	0.9945	0.1051	51°	0.7771	0.6293	1.2349
7°	0.1219	0.9925	0.1228	52°	0.7880	0.6157	1.2799
8°	0.1392	0.9903	0.1405	53°	0.7986	0.6018	1.3270
9°	0.1564	0.9877	0.1584	54°	0.8090	0.5878	1.3764
10°	0.1736	0.9848	0.1763	55°	0.8192	0.5736	1.4281
11°	0.1908	0.9816	0.1944	56°	0.8290	0.5592	1.4826
12°	0.2079	0.9781	0.2126	57°	0.8387	0.5446	1.5399
13°	0.2250	0.9744	0.2309	58°	0.8480	0.5299	1.6003
14°	0.2419	0.9703	0.2493	59°	0.8572	0.5150	1.6643
15°	0.2588	0.9659	0.2679	60°	0.8660	0.5000	1.7321
16°	0.2756	0.9613	0.2867	61°	0.8746	0.4848	1.8040
17°	0.2924	0.9563	0.3057	62°	0.8829	0.4695	1.8807
18°	0.3090	0.9511	0.3249	63°	0.8910	0.4540	1.9626
19°	0.3256	0.9455	0.3443	64°	0.8988	0.4384	2.0503
20°	0.3420	0.9397	0.3640	65°	0.9063	0.4226	2.1445
21°	0.3584	0.9336	0.3839	66°	0.9135	0.4067	2.2460
22°	0.3746	0.9272	0.4040	67°	0.9205	0.3907	2.3559
23°	0.3907	0.9205	0.4245	68°	0.9272	0.3746	2.4751
24°	0.4067	0.9135	0.4452	69°	0.9336	0.3584	2.6051
25°	0.4226	0.9063	0.4663	70°	0.9397	0.3420	2.7475
26°	0.4384	0.8988	0.4877	71°	0.9455	0.3256	2.9042
27°	0.4540	0.8910	0.5095	72°	0.9511	0.3090	3.0777
28°	0.4695	0.8829	0.5317	73°	0.9563	0.2924	3.2709
29°	0.4848	0.8746	0.5543	74°	0.9613	0.2756	3.4874
30°	0.5000	0.8660	0.5774	75°	0.9659	0.2588	3.7321
31°	0.5150	0.8572	0.6009	76°	0.9703	0.2419	4.0108
32°	0.5299	0.8480	0.6249	77°	0.9744	0.2250	4.3315
33°	0.5446	0.8387	0.6494	78°	0.9781	0.2079	4.7046
34°	0.5592	0.8290	0.6745	79°	0.9816	0.1908	5.1446
35°	0.5736	0.8192	0.7002	80°	0.9848	0.1736	5.6713
36°	0.5878	0.8090	0.7265	81°	0.9877	0.1564	6.3138
37°	0.6018	0.7986	0.7536	82°	0.9903	0.1392	7.1154
38°	0.6157	0.7880	0.7813	83°	0.9925	0.1219	8.1443
39°	0.6293	0.7771	0.8098	84°	0.9945	0.1045	9.5144
40°	0.6428	0.7660	0.8391	85°	0.9962	0.0872	11.4301
41°	0.6561	0.7547	0.8693	86°	0.9976	0.0698	14.3007
42°	0.6691	0.7431	0.9004	87°	0.9986	0.0523	19.0811
43°	0.6820	0.7314	0.9325	88°	0.9994	0.0349	28.6363
44°	0.6947	0.7193	0.9657	89°	0.9998	0.0175	57.2900
45°	0.7071	0.7071	1.0000	90°	1.0000	0.0000	∞

Extra Practice

Lesson 1-2   Use mental math to find each answer.

1. $2 + (24 \div 6)$ 6
2. $24 \div (10 + 2)$ 2
3. $4 \cdot (25 \cdot 9)$ 900
4. $500 - 468$ 32
5. $(7 \cdot 20) \cdot 5$ 700
6. $462 + 195$ 657
7. 5×25 125
8. $26 + 41 + 14$ 81
9. $\$1.99 \times 3$ $5.97
10. $5 \cdot (10 + 7)$ 85
11. 6×35 210
12. $2 \cdot 84 \cdot 50$ 8,400
13. $6 + 27 + 14$ 47
14. $200 - 95$ 105
15. $7 \cdot 19$ 133
16. $1,762 + 124$ 1,886
17. $5 \times 6 \times 2$ 60
18. 12×25 300

Lesson 1-3   Estimate. Use an appropriate strategy.   Sample answers are given.

1. $216 + 492$ 700
2. $1,235 + 5,645$ 6,800
3. $6,478 - 2,345$ 4,000
4. $601 \div 6$ 100
5. $298 + 109$ 400
6. $8,710 - 610$ 8,000
7. $364 \div 6$ 60
8. $410 \div 7$ 60
9. $0.245 + 0.256$ 0.5
10. $17.985 - 9.001$ 9
11. $11.75 \div 3$ 4
12. $1,616 + 2,439$ 4,000
13. $601 - 295$ 300
14. $8.52 + 9.410$ 17.9
15. $149 \div 5$ 30
16. $39 + 41 + 40 + 38 + 39$ 200
17. $1.12 + 0.9865 + 1.023 + 0.99 + 0.98$ 5

Lesson 1-6   Complete each sentence.

1. $1 \text{ kg} = \underline{\quad} \text{ g}$ 1,000
2. $632 \text{ mg} = \underline{\quad} \text{ g}$ 0.632
3. $2.9 \text{ kL} = \underline{\quad} \text{ L}$ 2,900
4. $400 \text{ mm} = \underline{\quad} \text{ cm}$ 40
5. $30 \text{ g} = \underline{\quad} \text{ kg}$ 0.030
6. $13.5 \text{ L} = \underline{\quad} \text{ kL}$ 0.0135
7. $0.3 \text{ km} = \underline{\quad} \text{ m}$ 300
8. $38.6 \text{ kg} = \underline{\quad} \text{ g}$ 38,600
9. $3.5 \text{ kL} = \underline{\quad} \text{ L}$ 3,500
10. $4.8 \text{ cm} = \underline{\quad} \text{ mm}$ 48
11. $9.5 \text{ mg} = \underline{\quad} \text{ g}$ 0.0095
12. $16 \text{ L} = \underline{\quad} \text{ mL}$ 16,000
13. $12.6 \text{ g} = \underline{\quad} \text{ mg}$ 12,600
14. $16.35 \text{ kL} = \underline{\quad} \text{ L}$ 16,350
15. $415 \text{ m} = \underline{\quad} \text{ cm}$ 41,500
16. $21 \text{ g} = \underline{\quad} \text{ mg}$ 21,000
17. $63 \text{ L} = \underline{\quad} \text{ mL}$ 63,000
18. $1.7 \text{ m} = \underline{\quad} \text{ cm}$ 170
19. $1.02 \text{ kg} = \underline{\quad} \text{ g}$ 1,020
20. $6.53 \text{ kL} = \underline{\quad} \text{ L}$ 6,530
21. $45 \text{ cm} = \underline{\quad} \text{ mm}$ 450

Lesson 1-7   Complete each sentence.

1. 7 ft = _____ in. **84**
2. 5 T = _____ lb **10,000**
3. 2 lb = _____ oz **32**
4. 5 mi = _____ yd **8,800**
5. $\frac{1}{4}$ lb = _____ oz **4**
6. 31,680 ft = _____ mi **6**
7. $\frac{1}{4}$ mi = _____ ft **1,320**
8. 24 fl oz = _____ c **3**
9. 8 pt = _____ c **16**
10. 10 pt = _____ qt **5**
11. 9 ft = _____ in. **108**
12. 24 in. = _____ ft **2**
13. 4 gal = _____ qt **16**
14. 4 qt = _____ fl oz **128**
15. 12 pt = _____ c **24**
16. 5 yd = _____ ft **15**
17. 15 qt = _____ gal **$3\frac{3}{4}$**
18. 4 pt = _____ c **8**
19. 2 mi = _____ ft **10,560**
20. 3 T = _____ lb **6,000**
21. 6 lb = _____ oz **96**

Lesson 1-9   Write each product using exponents.

1. $4 \cdot 4 \cdot 4 \cdot 4$ **4^4**
2. $3 \cdot 3$ **3^2**
3. $7 \cdot 7 \cdot 7 \cdot 7 \cdot 7 \cdot 7$ **7^6**

Evaluate each expression.

4. 4^3 **64**
5. 6^2 **36**
6. 2^6 **64**
7. $5^2 \times 6^2$ **900**
8. 3×2^4 **48**
9. $10^4 \times 3^2$ **90,000**
10. $5^3 \times 1^9$ **125**
11. $2^2 \times 2^4$ **64**
12. $2 \times 3^2 \times 4^2$ **288**
13. 7^3 **343**
14. $9^2 + 3^2$ **90**
15. 0.5^2 **0.25**

Lesson 2-1   Evaluate each expression.

1. $15 - 5 + 9 - 2$ **17**
2. $6 \times 6 + 3.6$ **39.6**
3. $12 + 20 \div 4 - 5$ **12**
4. $6 \times 3 \div 9 - 1$ **1**
5. $(4^2 + 2^3) \times 5$ **120**
6. $24 \div 8 - 2$ **1**
7. $3 \times (4 + 5) - 7$ **20**
8. $4.3 + 24 \div 6$ **8.3**
9. $(5^2 + 2) \div 3$ **9**
10. $27 \div 3^2 \times 2$ **6**
11. $4 \times 4^2 \times 2 - 8$ **120**
12. $12 \div 3 - 2^2 + 6$ **6**
13. $3^3 \times 2 - 5 \times 3$ **39**
14. $10 \times 2 + 7 \times 3$ **41**
15. $7 - 2 \times 8 \div 4$ **3**
16. $17 - 2^3 + 5$ **14**
17. $5 \times 6 \div 10 + 1$ **4**
18. $18 + 4 \div 2$ **20**
19. $(7 + 5 \times 4) \div 9$ **3**
20. $100 \div (28 + 9 \times 8)$ **1**
21. $6 \times 4 - 8 \times 3$ **0**

Lesson 2-2 Solve each equation.

1. $19 + 4 = y$ 23
2. $5 \cdot 6 = n$ 30
3. $q - 7 = 7$ 14
4. $7 + a = 10$ 3
5. $x - 3 = 12$ 15
6. $2m = 8$ 4
7. $4y = 24$ 6
8. $36 = 6z$ 6
9. $19 + j = 29$ 10
10. $13 = 9 + c$ 4
11. $p \div 4 = 4$ 16
12. $6 = t \div 5$ 30
13. $42 = 6n$ 7
14. $\frac{m}{7} = 5$ 35
15. $45 = 9d$ 5
16. $24 = 14 + k$ 10
17. $2a = 18$ 9
18. $c \div 8 = 2$ 16
19. $12 + f = 15$ 3
20. $17 = g - 37$ 54
21. $25 = 5x$ 5

Lesson 2-3 Solve each equation. Check your solution.

1. $g - 3 = 10$ 13
2. $b + 7 = 12$ 5
3. $a + 3 = 15$ 12
4. $r - 3 = 4$ 7
5. $t + 3 = 21$ 18
6. $s + 10 = 23$ 13
7. $9 + n = 13$ 4
8. $13 + v = 31$ 18
9. $s - 0.4 = 6$ 6.4
10. $x - 1.3 = 12$ 13.3
11. $18 = y + 3.4$ 14.6
12. $7 + g = 91$ 84
13. $63 + f = 71$ 8
14. $0.32 = w - 0.1$ 0.42
15. $c - 18 = 13$ 31
16. $23 = n - 5$ 28
17. $j - 3 = 7$ 10
18. $18 = p + 3$ 15
19. $12 + p = 16$ 4
20. $25 = y - 50$ 75
21. $x + 2 = 4$ 2

Lesson 2-4 Solve each equation. Check your solution.

1. $4x = 36$ 9
2. $39 = 3y$ 13
3. $4z = 16$ 4
4. $t \div 5 = 6$ 30
5. $100 = 20b$ 5
6. $8 = w \div 8$ 64
7. $10a = 40$ 4
8. $s \div 9 = 8$ 72
9. $420 = 5s$ 84
10. $8k = 72$ 9
11. $2m = 18$ 9
12. $\frac{m}{8} = 5$ 40
13. $0.12 = 3h$ 0.04
14. $\frac{w}{7} = 8$ 56
15. $18q = 36$ 2
16. $9w = 54$ 6
17. $4 = p \div 4$ 16
18. $14 = 2p$ 7
19. $12 = 3t$ 4
20. $\frac{m}{4} = 12$ 48
21. $6h = 12$ 2

Lesson 2-6   Write each phrase or sentence as an algebraic expression.

1. 12 more than a number $12 + n$
2. 3 less than a number $n - 3$
3. a number divided by 4 $\frac{n}{4}$ or $n \div 4$
4. a number increased by 7 $n + 7$
5. a number decreased by 12 $n - 12$
6. 8 times a number $8n$
7. 28 multiplied by m $28m$
8. 15 divided by a number $\frac{15}{n}$ or $15 \div n$
9. 54 divided by n $\frac{54}{n}$ or $54 \div n$
10. 18 increased by y $18 + y$
11. q decreased by 20 $q - 20$
12. n times 41 $41n$

Lesson 2-7   Solve each equation. Check your solution.

1. $2x + 4 = 14$ 5
2. $5p - 10 = 0$ 2
3. $5 + 6a = 41$ 6
4. $\frac{x}{3} - 7 = 2$ 27
5. $18 = 6(q - 4)$ 7
6. $18 = 4m - 6$ 6
7. $3(r - 1) = 9$ 4
8. $2x + 3 = 5$ 1
9. $0 = 4x - 28$ 7
10. $3x - 1 = 5$ 2
11. $3z + 5 = 14$ 3
12. $3(x - 5) = 12$ 9
13. $9a - 8 = 73$ 9
14. $2x - 3 = 7$ 5
15. $3t + 6 = 9$ 1
16. $2y + 10 = 22$ 6
17. $15 = 2y - 5$ 10
18. $3c - 4 = 2$ 2
19. $6 + 2p = 16$ 5
20. $8 = 2 + 3x$ 2
21. $4(b + 6) = 24$ 0

Lesson 2-9   Find the perimeter and area of each figure.

1.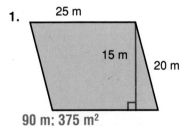
25 m
15 m
20 m
90 m; 375 m²

2.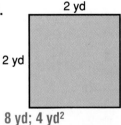
2 yd
2 yd
8 yd; 4 yd²

3.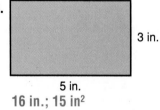
3 in.
5 in.
16 in.; 15 in²

4.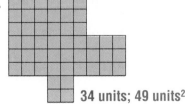
34 units; 49 units²

5.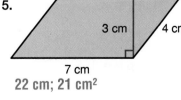
3 cm   4 cm
7 cm
22 cm; 21 cm²

6.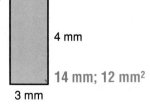
4 mm
3 mm
14 mm; 12 mm²

Lesson 2-10 Solve each inequality. Show the solution on a number line.

1. $y + 3 > 7$ $y > 4$

2. $c - 9 < 5$ $c < 14$

3. $x + 4 > 9$ $x > 5$

4. $y - 3 < 15$ $y < 18$

5. $t - 13 > 5$ $t > 18$

6. $5p < 25$ $p < 5$

7. $4x < 12$ $x < 3$

8. $15 < 3m$ $m > 5$

9. $\frac{d}{3} > 15$ $d > 45$

10. $8 < r \div 7$ $r > 56$

11. $2y + 5 > 15$ $y > 5$

12. $16 < 5d + 6$
$d > 2$

13. $3x + 2 > 11$ $x > 3$

14. $\frac{a}{3} - 2 > 1$ $a > 9$

15. $9g < 27$ $g < 3$

16. $14 < 2x + 4$ $x > 5$

17. $\frac{x}{2} - 6 > 0$ $x > 12$

18. $k + 5 < 6$ $k < 1$

19. $15 > c - 2$ $c < 17$

20. $4p > 24$ $p > 6$

21. $24 < 14 + k$
$k > 10$

For graphs to Exercises 1–21, see Solutions Manual.

Lesson 3-1 Graph each set of numbers on a number line.

1. {–8, –9, –6, –10}

2. {–3, 2, 0, –1}

3. {5, 6, 8, 7, 9}

For graphs to Exercises 1–3, see Solutions Manual.

Find each absolute value.

4. $|-1|$ 1

5. $|-92|$ 92

6. $|3|$ 3

7. $|160 + 32|$ 192

8. $|80 - 100|$ 20

9. $|0|$ 0

10. $|7 - 3|$ 4

11. $|3 - 7|$ 4

12. $|-161|$ 161

13. $|150|$ 150

14. $|2 - 102|$ 100

15. $|-116|$ 116

Lesson 3-2 Replace each ● with >, <, or = .

1. -3 ● 0 <

2. -1 ● -2 >

3. -5 ● -4 <

4. 6 ● -7 >

5. 8 ● 10 <

6. -6 ● 6 <

7. -11 ● -20 >

8. -8 ● 2 <

9. -13 ● -12 <

10. 5 ● 2 >

11. 9 ● -8 >

12. 19 ● -19 >

13. $|-2|$ ● $|5|$ <

14. $|13|$ ● $|-19|$ <

15. $|-6|$ ● $|2|$ >

16. $|14|$ ● $|-14|$ =

17. $|0|$ ● $|-4|$ <

18. $|23|$ ● $|-20|$ >

19. $|-75|$ ● $|75|$ =

20. -71 ● 72 <

21. -15 ● -35 >

Lesson 3-3   Solve each equation.

1. $-7 + (-7) = h$ -14
2. $k = -36 + 40$ 4
3. $m = 18 + (-32)$ -14
4. $47 + 12 = y$ 59
5. $y = -69 + (-32)$ -101
6. $-120 + (-2) = c$ -122
7. $x = -56 + (-4)$ -60
8. $14 + 16 = k$ 30
9. $-18 + 11 = d$ -7
10. $-42 + 29 = r$ -13
11. $h = -13 + (-11)$ -24
12. $x = 95 + (-5)$ 90
13. $-120 + 2 = b$ -118
14. $w = 25 + (-25)$ 0
15. $a = -4 + 8$ 4
16. $g = -9 + (-6)$ -15
17. $42 + (-18) = f$ 24
18. $-33 + (-12) = w$ -45
19. $-96 + (-18) = g$ -114
20. $-100 + 98 = a$ -2
21. $5 + (-7) = y$ -2

Lesson 3-4   Solve each equation. Check by solving another way.

1. $a = 7 + (-13) + 6 + (-7)$ -7
2. $x = -6 + 12 + (-20)$ -14
3. $4 + 9 + (-14) = k$ -1
4. $c = -20 + 0 + (-9) + 25$ -4
5. $b = 5 + 9 + 3 + (-17)$ 0
6. $-36 + 40 + (-10) = y$ -6
7. $(-2) + 2 + (-2) + 2 = m$ 0
8. $6 + (-4) + 9 + (-2) = d$ 9
9. $9 + (-7) + 2 = n$ 4
10. $b = 100 + (-75) + (-20)$ 5
11. $x = -12 + 24 + (-12) + 2$ 2
12. $9 + (-18) + 6 + (-3) = c$ -6
13. $(-10) + 4 + 6 = k$ 0
14. $c = 4 + (-8) + 12$ 8

Lesson 3-5   Solve each equation.

1. $3 - 7 = y$ -4
2. $-5 - 4 = w$ -9
3. $a = -6 - 2$ -8
4. $12 - 9 = x$ 3
5. $a = 0 - (-14)$ 14
6. $a = 58 - (-10)$ 68
7. $n = -41 - 15$ -56
8. $c = -81 - 21$ -102
9. $26 - (-14) = y$ 40
10. $6 - (-4) = b$ 10
11. $z = 63 - 78$ -15
12. $-5 - (-9) = h$ 4
13. $m = 72 - (-19)$ 91
14. $-51 - 47 = x$ -98
15. $-99 - 1 = p$ -100
16. $r = 8 - 13$ -5
17. $-2 - 23 = c$ -25
18. $-20 - 0 = d$ -20
19. $55 - 33 = k$ 22
20. $84 - (-61) = a$ 145
21. $z = -4 - (-4)$ 0

Lesson 3-6   Solve each equation.

1. $5(-2) = d$ -10
2. $-11(-5) = c$ 55
3. $-5(-5) = z$ 25
4. $x = -12(6)$ -72
5. $b = 2(-2)$ -4
6. $-3(2)(-4) = j$ 24
7. $a = (-4)(-4)$ 16
8. $4(21) = y$ 84
9. $a = -50(0)$ 0
10. $b = 3(-13)$ -39
11. $a = 2(2)$ 4
12. $d = -2(-2)$ 4
13. $x = 5(-12)$ -60
14. $2(2)(-2) = b$ -8
15. $a = 6(-4)$ -24
16. $x = -6(5)$ -30
17. $-4(8) = a$ -32
18. $3(-16) = y$ -48
19. $c = -2(2)$ -4
20. $6(3)(-2) = k$ -36
21. $y = -3(12)$ -36

Lesson 3-7   Solve each equation.

1. $a = 4 \div (-2)$ -2
2. $16 \div (-8) = x$ -2
3. $-14 \div (-2) = c$ 7
4. $h = -18 \div 3$ -6
5. $-25 \div 5 = k$ -5
6. $n = -56 \div (-8)$ 7
7. $x = 81 \div 9$ 9
8. $-55 \div 11 = c$ -5
9. $-42 \div (-7) = y$ 6
10. $g = 18 \div (-3)$ -6
11. $t = 0 \div (-1)$ 0
12. $-32 \div 8 = m$ -4
13. $81 \div (-9) = w$ -9
14. $18 \div (-2) = a$ -9
15. $x = -21 \div 3$ -7
16. $d = 32 \div 8$ 4
17. $8 \div (-8) = y$ -1
18. $c = -14 \div (-7)$ 2
19. $-81 \div 9 = y$ -9
20. $q = -81 \div (-9)$ 9
21. $-49 \div (-7) = y$ 7

Lesson 3-9   Solve each equation. Check your solution.

1. $-4 + b = 12$ 16
2. $z - 10 = -8$ 2
3. $-7 = x + 12$ -19
4. $a + 6 = -9$ -15
5. $r \div 7 = -8$ -56
6. $-2a = -8$ 4
7. $r - (-8) = 14$ 6
8. $0 = 6r$ 0
9. $\frac{y}{12} = -6$ -72
10. $m + (-2) = 6$ 8
11. $3m = -15$ -5
12. $c \div (-4) = 10$ -40
13. $5 + q = 12$ 7
14. $\frac{16}{x} = -4$ -4
15. $-6f = -36$ 6
16. $81 = -9w$ -9
17. $t + 12 = 6$ -6
18. $8 + p = 0$ -8
19. $0.12 = -3h$ -0.04
20. $12 - x = 8$ 4
21. $14 + t = 10$ -4

Lesson 3-10

Name the ordered pair for the coordinates of each point graphed on the coordinate plane below.

1. A (3, 1)
2. B (-2, -1)
3. C (2, -2)

4. D (0, -1)
5. E (-3, 2)
6. F (4, -1)

7. G (-5, 0)
8. H (-2, 1)
9. I (-4, -2)

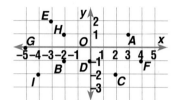

Graph each point on the same coordinate plane. See Solutions Manual.

10. (3, -2)
11. (2, 4)
12. (-1, 6)
13. (0, 5)
14. (-2, -3)

15. (-4, 0)
16. (4, -4)
17. (0, 0)
18. (3, 1)
19. (-4, -1)

Lesson 4-2

Use the histogram below to answer each question.

1. How large is each interval? **10 feet**

2. Which interval has the most buildings? **31-40**

3. Which interval has the least buildings? **81-90**

4. Compared to the total, how would you describe the number of buildings over 70 feet tall? **About $\frac{1}{4}$ are over 70 feet tall.**

5. How does the number of buildings between 61 and 80 feet tall compare to the number of buildings between 31 and 50 feet tall? **There are 2 more buildings between 31 and 50 feet tall.**

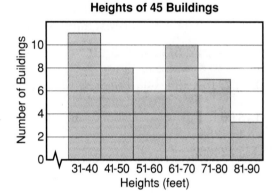

Lesson 4-3

Make a line plot for each set of data. See Solutions Manual.

1. 8, 12, 10, 15, 11, 9, 12, 7, 14, 13, 8, 15, 17, 14, 11, 9, 8, 12, 15

2. 32, 41, 46, 38, 34, 51, 55, 49, 37, 42, 55, 46, 39, 58, 40, 35, 34, 52, 46

3. 161, 158, 163, 162, 165, 157, 159, 160, 163, 162, 158, 164, 161, 157, 166, 164

4. 78, 82, 83, 90, 58, 67, 95, 87, 97, 88, 75, 82, 78, 89, 86, 88, 79, 80, 91, 77

5. 49¢, 55¢, 77¢, 65¢, 51¢, 74¢, 68¢, 56¢, 49¢, 73¢, 62¢, 71¢, 54¢, 50¢, 70¢, 65¢

6. 2, 4, 12, 10, 2, 5, 7, 11, 7, 6, 3, 9, 12, 7, 5, 3, 7, 11, 2, 8, 7, 10, 8, 3, 7

7. 303, 298, 289, 309, 300, 294, 299, 301, 296, 308, 302, 289, 306, 308, 298, 299

8. 67, 73, 78, 61, 63, 77, 66, 75, 79, 66, 72, 69, 70, 74, 61, 63, 76, 64, 65, 78, 66

Lesson 4-4   Make a stem-and-leaf plot for each set of data.   See Solutions Manual.

1. 5.5, 6.2, 6.8, 5.9, 7.3, 8.6, 5.4, 6.3, 8.2, 7.5, 7.1, 5.7, 8.4, 5.9, 6.1, 8.8

2. 115, 153, 145, 119, 136, 154, 142, 137, 125, 121, 112, 156, 129, 133, 140, 123, 155

3. 55, 58, 45, 60, 47, 52, 53, 63, 47, 55, 49, 65, 56, 61

4. 71.3, 72.4, 74.8, 71.8, 73.5, 74.2, 71.9, 73.6, 73.9, 72.3, 73.7, 72.2

5. 415, 427, 412, 398, 407, 395, 422, 401, 393, 412, 427, 419, 424, 405, 391, 413

6. 11, 23, 27, 46, 36, 32, 17, 22, 49, 36, 19, 41, 26, 33, 15, 32, 35, 21

7. Make a back-to-back stem-and-leaf plot for the data in the table below.

| Quiz 2 Scores | 42 37 32 45 34 29 46 33 45 44 37 43 42 39 38 41 36 |
| Quiz 3 Scores | 48 49 40 50 44 39 45 49 37 47 49 41 46 48 50 42 45 |

Lesson 4-5   Find the mean, median, and mode for each set of data. Round to the nearest tenth.

1. 2, 7, 9, 12, 5, 14, 4, 8, 3, 10
    7.4, 7.5, no mode
3. 122, 134, 129, 140, 125, 134, 137
    131.6, 134, 134

2. 58, 52, 49, 60, 61, 56, 50, 61
    55.9, 57, 61
4. 25.5, 26.7, 20.9, 23.4, 26.8, 24.0, 25.7
    24.7, 25.5, no mode

5. 3 | 6
      4 | 1358
      5 | 24667
      6 | 045
      5 | 2 means 52
      52.1, 54, 56

6.

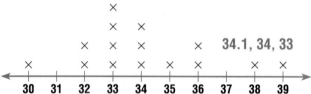

34.1, 34, 33

Lesson 4-6   Find the range of each set of data.

1. 15, 12, 21, 18, 25, 11, 17, 19, 20 **14**

3. 189, 149, 155, 190, 141, 152 **49**

2. 2, 10, 6, 13, 8, 6, 11, 4 **11**

4. 451, 501, 388, 428, 510, 480, 390 **122**

Find the median and upper and lower quartiles of each set of data.

5. 22, 18, 9, 26, 14, 15, 6, 19, 28
    18, 24, 11.5
7. 46, 45, 50, 40, 49, 42, 52
    46, 50, 42
9. 8, 3, 2, 6, 4, 12, 10, 2, 6, 11
    6, 10, 3
11. 378, 410, 370, 336, 361, 394, 345, 328, 388, 339   **365.5, 388, 339**

6. 245, 238, 251, 255, 248, 241, 250
    248, 251, 241
8. 128, 148, 130, 142, 164, 120, 152, 168
    145, 158, 129
10. 88, 84, 92, 93, 90, 96, 87, 97
    91, 94.5, 87.5

Lesson 4-7   Draw a box-and-whisker plot for each set of data. **See Solutions Manual.**

1. 79, 70, 84, 66, 72, 64, 75, 82

2. 307, 313, 304, 306, 312, 301, 310

3. 7, 4, 10, 3, 2, 9, 6, 3, 7

4. 32, 39, 27, 40, 45, 30, 22, 36, 24, 48

5. 61, 67, 53, 56, 51, 66, 58, 63, 52

6. $32, $26, $39, $23, $18, $30, $21, $34

7.
```
5 | 2459
6 | 1336
7 | 48
8 | 013457
9 | 1278
```
8 | 3 means 83

8.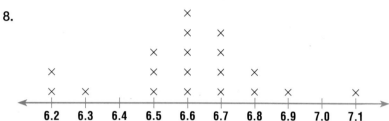

Lesson 4-8   Determine whether a scatter plot of the data below would show a positive, negative, or no relationship.

1. height and hair color **no relationship**

2. hours spent studying and test scores **positive**

3. income and month of birth **no relationship**

4. price of oranges and number available
   negative

5. size of roof and number of shingles
   positive

6. number of clouds and number of stars seen
   negative

7.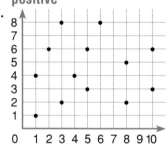

no relationship

8.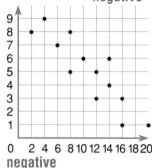

negative

9.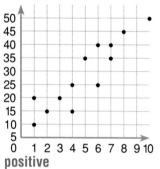

positive

Lesson 5-1   Name the parallel segments, if any, in each figure.

1.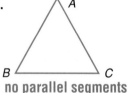

no parallel segments

2.

$\overline{MT}, \overline{KH}; \overline{MK}, \overline{TH}$

3.

$\overline{WX}, \overline{ZY}; \overline{WZ}, \overline{XY}$

Use the figure at the right for Exercises 4–7.

4. Find $m\angle 6$, if $m\angle 3 = 42°$. **42°**

5. Find $m\angle 4$, if $m\angle 7 = 71°$. **109°**

6. Find $m\angle 1$, if $m\angle 8 = 128°$. **128°**

7. Find $m\angle 7$, if $m\angle 2 = 83°$. **83°**

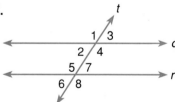

Lesson 5-3   Classify each triangle by its sides and by its angles.

1.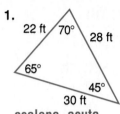
22 ft 70° 28 ft
65°
45°
30 ft
scalene, acute

2.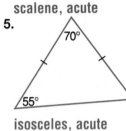
60°
7 in. 7 in.
60° 60°
7 in.
equilateral, acute

3.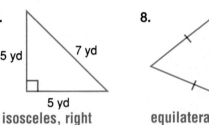
scalene, right

4. 3 cm 130° 3 cm
25° 25°
isosceles, obtuse

5.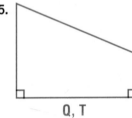
70°
55°
isosceles, acute

6.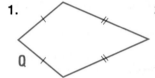
10 m
120° 39°
16 m
21°
23 m
scalene, obtuse

7.
5 yd 7 yd
5 yd
isosceles, right

8.
equilateral, acute

Lesson 5-4   Let Q = quadrilateral, P = parallelogram, R = rectangle, S = square, RH = rhombus, and T = trapezoid. Write all letters that describe each figure.

1.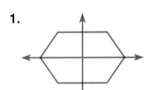
Q

2.
Q, T

3.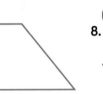
Q, P, RH

4.
Q, P, R

5.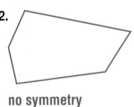
Q, T

6.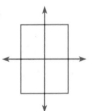
Q, P, RH

7.
Q, T

8.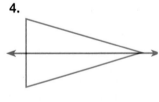
Q, P, R, S, RH

Lesson 5-5   Trace each figure. Determine if the figure has line symmetry. If so, draw the lines of reflection.

1.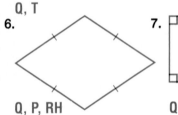

2.
no symmetry

3.

4.

Determine if each figure has rotational symmetry.

5.
yes

6.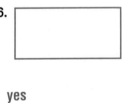
yes

7.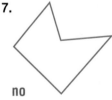
no

8.
yes

Lesson 5-6

Tell if each pair of figures is *congruent*, *similar*, or *neither*.
Justify your answer. For justifications, see Solutions Manual.

1.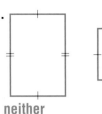

neither

2.

congruent

3.

similar

Find the value of x in each pair of figures.

4. $\triangle ABC \cong \triangle JKI$ 10

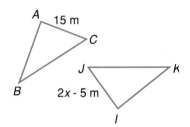

A 15 m
C
J
k
B 2x - 5 m
I

5. $\triangle LFR \sim \triangle GPC$ 13

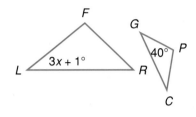

F
G
3x + 1°
40° P
L
R
C

6. $\square XTDH \cong \square PEBL$ 6

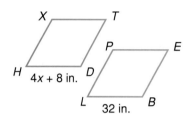

X
T
P
E
H 4x + 8 in. D
L 32 in. B

Lesson 6-1

Using divisibility rules, determine whether each number is divisible by 2, 3, 4, 5, 6, 8, 9, or 10.

1. 210 2, 3, 5, 6, 10
2. 614 2
3. 985 5
4. 756 2, 3, 4, 6, 9

5. 432 2, 3, 4, 6, 8, 9
6. 96 2, 3, 4, 6, 8
7. 87 3
8. 113 none

Use divisibility rules to determine if the first number is divisible by the second number. Write *yes* or *no*.

9. 936; 6 yes
10. 752; 6 no
11. 1,249; 8 no
12. 208; 4 yes

13. 216; 9 yes
14. 1,346; 2 yes
15. 1,687; 3 no
16. 448; 8 yes

Lesson 6-2

Determine whether each number is *prime*, *composite*, or *neither*.

1. 17 prime
2. 1,258 composite
3. 37 prime
4. 483 composite
5. 97 prime
6. 0 neither
7. 25 composite
8. 61 prime
9. -45 composite
10. 419 prime

Find the prime factorization of each number.

11. 20 $2^2 \times 5$
12. 65 5×13
13. 52 $2^2 \times 13$
14. 30 $2 \times 3 \times 5$

15. 28 $2^2 \times 7$
16. 72 $2^3 \times 3^2$
17. 155 5×31
18. 50 2×5^2

19. 96 $2^5 \times 3$
20. 201 3×67
21. 1,250 2×5^4
22. 2,648 $2^3 \times 331$

Lesson 6-4 Find the GCF for each set of numbers.

1. 8, 18 **2**
2. 6, 9 **3**
3. 4, 12 **4**
4. 18, 24 **6**

5. 8, 24 **8**
6. 17, 51 **17**
7. 65, 95 **5**
8. 42, 48 **6**

9. 64, 32 **32**
10. 72, 144 **72**
11. 54, 72 **18**
12. 60, 75 **15**

13. 16, 24 **8**
14. 12, 27 **3**
15. 25, 30 **5**
16. 48, 60 **12**

17. 16, 20, 36 **4**
18. 12, 18, 42 **6**
19. 30, 45, 15 **15**

20. 20, 30, 40 **10**
21. 81, 27, 108 **27**
22. 9, 18, 12 **3**

Lesson 6-5 Write each fraction in simplest form.

1. $\frac{12}{16}$ $\frac{3}{4}$
2. $\frac{28}{32}$ $\frac{7}{8}$
3. $\frac{75}{100}$ $\frac{3}{4}$
4. $\frac{8}{16}$ $\frac{1}{2}$
5. $\frac{6}{18}$ $\frac{1}{3}$

6. $\frac{27}{36}$ $\frac{3}{4}$
7. $\frac{16}{64}$ $\frac{1}{4}$
8. $\frac{8}{16}$ $\frac{1}{2}$
9. $\frac{50}{100}$ $\frac{1}{2}$
10. $\frac{24}{40}$ $\frac{3}{5}$

11. $\frac{32}{80}$ $\frac{2}{5}$
12. $\frac{8}{24}$ $\frac{1}{3}$
13. $\frac{20}{25}$ $\frac{4}{5}$
14. $\frac{4}{10}$ $\frac{2}{5}$
15. $\frac{3}{5}$ $\frac{3}{5}$

16. $\frac{14}{19}$ $\frac{14}{19}$
17. $\frac{9}{12}$ $\frac{3}{4}$
18. $\frac{6}{8}$ $\frac{3}{4}$
19. $\frac{15}{18}$ $\frac{5}{6}$
20. $\frac{9}{20}$ $\frac{9}{20}$

21. $\frac{8}{21}$ $\frac{8}{21}$
22. $\frac{10}{15}$ $\frac{2}{3}$
23. $\frac{9}{24}$ $\frac{3}{8}$
24. $\frac{6}{31}$ $\frac{6}{31}$
25. $\frac{18}{32}$ $\frac{9}{16}$

Lesson 6-6 Express each fraction as a decimal.

1. $\frac{2}{5}$ **0.4**
2. $\frac{3}{8}$ **0.375**
3. $-\frac{3}{4}$ **-0.75**
4. $\frac{5}{16}$ **0.3125**
5. $\frac{3}{4}$ **0.75**

6. $-\frac{7}{8}$ **-0.875**
7. $\frac{17}{20}$ **0.85**
8. $\frac{14}{25}$ **0.56**
9. $\frac{7}{10}$ **0.7**
10. $\frac{7}{20}$ **0.35**

Express each decimal as a fraction or mixed number in simplest form.

11. 0.5 $\frac{1}{2}$
12. 0.8 $\frac{4}{5}$
13. 0.32 $\frac{8}{25}$
14. -0.75 $-\frac{3}{4}$
15. 1.54 $1\frac{27}{50}$

16. 0.38 $\frac{19}{50}$
17. -0.486 $-\frac{243}{500}$
18. 20.08 $20\frac{2}{25}$
19. -9.36 $-9\frac{9}{25}$
20. 10.18 $10\frac{9}{50}$

21. 0.06 $\frac{3}{50}$
22. 1.75 $1\frac{3}{4}$
23. -0.375 $-\frac{3}{8}$
24. 0.79 $\frac{79}{100}$
25. 1.9 $1\frac{9}{10}$

Lesson 6-7   Write the first ten decimal places of each decimal.

1. $0.\overline{09}$
   0.0909090909
2. $0.\overline{076923}$
   0.0769230769
3. $0.8\overline{4563}$
   0.8456345634
4. $0.98\overline{745}$
   0.9874545454

5. $0.\overline{254}$
   0.2542542542
6. $0.\overline{1470}$
   0.1470147014
7. $0.12\overline{7}$
   0.1277777777
8. $0.\overline{3}$
   0.3333333333

Express each decimal using bar notation.

9. $0.161616\ldots$
   $0.\overline{16}$
10. $0.12351235\ldots$
    $0.\overline{1235}$
11. $0.6666\ldots$
    $0.\overline{6}$
12. $0.15151\ldots$
    $0.\overline{15}$

13. $0.125656\ldots$
    $0.12\overline{56}$
14. $0.1254777\ldots$
    $0.1254\overline{7}$
15. $85.0124124\ldots$
    $85.0\overline{124}$
16. $0.214111\ldots$
    $0.214\overline{1}$

Express each repeating decimal as a fraction.

17. $0.\overline{3}$ $\frac{1}{3}$
18. $0.\overline{4}$ $\frac{4}{9}$
19. $0.\overline{27}$ $\frac{3}{11}$
20. $0.8\overline{3}$ $\frac{5}{6}$

21. $0.\overline{24}$ $\frac{8}{33}$
22. $0.58\overline{3}$ $\frac{7}{12}$
23. $0.7\overline{3}$ $\frac{11}{15}$
24. $0.\overline{8}$ $\frac{8}{9}$

Lesson 6-8   A date is chosen at random from the month of November. Find the probability of choosing each date.

1. The date is the thirteenth. $\frac{1}{30}$

2. The date is Friday. $\frac{2}{15}$

3. It is after the twenty-fifth. $\frac{1}{6}$

4. It is before the seventh. $\frac{1}{5}$

5. It is an odd-numbered date. $\frac{1}{2}$

6. The date is divisible by 3. $\frac{1}{3}$

November						
S	M	T	W	T	F	S
		1	2	3	4	5
6	7	8	9	10	11	12
13	14	15	16	17	18	19
20	21	22	23	24	25	26
27	28	29	30			

Lesson 6-9   Find the LCM for each set of numbers.

1. 5, 6   30
2. 9, 27   27
3. 12, 15   60
4. 8, 12   24

5. 5, 15   15
6. 13, 39   39
7. 16, 24   48
8. 18, 20   180

9. 21, 14   42
10. 25, 30   150
11. 28, 42   84
12. 7, 13   91

13. 6, 30   30
14. 12, 42   84
15. 8, 10   40
16. 30, 10   30

17. 12, 18, 6   36
18. 15, 75, 25   75
19. 6, 10, 15   30

20. 3, 6, 9   18
21. 21, 14, 6   42
22. 12, 35, 10   420

Lesson 6-10   Replace each ● with a <, >, or = to make a true sentence.

1. -5.6 ● 4.2 <

2. 4.256 ● 4.25 >

3. 0.233 ● $0.\overline{23}$ >

4. $\dfrac{5}{7}$ ● $\dfrac{2}{5}$ >

5. $\dfrac{6}{7}$ ● $\dfrac{7}{9}$ >

6. $\dfrac{2}{3}$ ● $\dfrac{2}{5}$ >

7. $\dfrac{3}{8}$ ● 0.375 =

8. $-\dfrac{1}{2}$ ● 0.5 <

9. 12.56 ● $12\dfrac{3}{8}$ >

Order each set of numbers from least to greatest.

10. 0.24, 0.2, 0.245, 2.24, 0.25
    0.2, 0.24, 0.245, 0.25, 2.24

11. $0.\overline{3}$, 0.3, $0.3\overline{4}$, $0.\overline{34}$, 0.33
    0.3, 0.33, $0.\overline{3}$, $0.3\overline{4}$, $0.\overline{34}$

12. $\dfrac{2}{5}, \dfrac{2}{3}, \dfrac{2}{7}, \dfrac{2}{9}, \dfrac{2}{1}$ $\dfrac{2}{9}, \dfrac{2}{7}, \dfrac{2}{5}, \dfrac{2}{3}, \dfrac{2}{1}$

13. $\dfrac{1}{2}, \dfrac{5}{7}, \dfrac{2}{9}, \dfrac{8}{9}, \dfrac{6}{6}$ $\dfrac{2}{9}, \dfrac{1}{2}, \dfrac{5}{7}, \dfrac{8}{9}, \dfrac{6}{6}$

Lesson 6-11   Express each number in standard form.

1. 4.5×10^3 4,500

2. 2×10^4 20,000

3. 1.725896×10^6 1,725,896

4. 9.61×10^2 961

5. 1×10^7 10,000,000

6. 8.256×10^8 825,600,000

7. 5.26×10^4 52,600

8. 3.25×10^2 325

9. 6.79×10^5 679,000

Express each number in scientific notation.

10. 720
    7.2×10^2

11. 7,560
    7.56×10^3

12. 892
    8.92×10^2

13. 1,400
    1.4×10^3

14. 91,256
    9.1256×10^4

15. 51,000
    5.1×10^4

16. 145,600
    1.456×10^5

17. 90,100
    9.01×10^4

18. 123,568,000,000
    1.23568×10^{11}

Lesson 7-1   Solve each equation. Write each solution in simplest form.

1. $\dfrac{17}{21} + \left(-\dfrac{13}{21}\right) = m$ $\dfrac{4}{21}$

2. $t = \dfrac{5}{11} + \dfrac{6}{11}$ 1

3. $k = -\dfrac{8}{13} + \left(-\dfrac{11}{13}\right)$ $-1\dfrac{6}{13}$

4. $-\dfrac{7}{12} + \dfrac{5}{12} = a$ $-\dfrac{1}{6}$

5. $\dfrac{13}{28} - \dfrac{9}{28} = g$ $\dfrac{1}{7}$

6. $b = -1\dfrac{2}{9} - \dfrac{7}{9}$ -2

7. $r = \dfrac{15}{16} + \dfrac{13}{16}$ $1\dfrac{3}{4}$

8. $2\dfrac{1}{3} - \dfrac{2}{3} = n$ $1\dfrac{2}{3}$

9. $-\dfrac{4}{35} - \left(-\dfrac{17}{35}\right) = c$ $\dfrac{13}{35}$

10. $\dfrac{3}{8} + \left(-\dfrac{5}{8}\right) = w$ $-\dfrac{1}{4}$

11. $s = \dfrac{8}{15} - \dfrac{2}{15}$ $\dfrac{2}{5}$

12. $d = -2\dfrac{4}{7} - \dfrac{3}{7}$ -3

13. $-\dfrac{29}{9} - \left(-\dfrac{26}{9}\right) = y$ $-\dfrac{1}{3}$

14. $2\dfrac{3}{5} + 7\dfrac{3}{5} = i$ $10\dfrac{1}{5}$

15. $x = \dfrac{5}{18} - \dfrac{13}{18}$ $-\dfrac{4}{9}$

16. $j = -2\dfrac{2}{7} + \left(-1\dfrac{6}{7}\right)$ $-4\dfrac{1}{7}$

17. $p = -\dfrac{3}{10} + \dfrac{7}{10}$ $\dfrac{2}{5}$

18. $\dfrac{4}{11} + \dfrac{9}{11} = e$ $1\dfrac{2}{11}$

Lesson 7-2   Solve each equation. Write each solution in simplest form.

1. $r = \dfrac{7}{12} + \dfrac{7}{24}$ $\dfrac{7}{8}$

2. $-\dfrac{3}{4} + \dfrac{7}{8} = z$ $\dfrac{1}{8}$

3. $\dfrac{2}{5} + \left(-\dfrac{2}{7}\right) = q$ $\dfrac{4}{35}$

4. $d = -\dfrac{3}{5} - \left(-\dfrac{5}{6}\right)$ $\dfrac{7}{30}$

5. $\dfrac{5}{24} - \dfrac{3}{8} = j$ $-\dfrac{1}{6}$

6. $g = -\dfrac{7}{12} + \dfrac{3}{4}$ $\dfrac{1}{6}$

7. $-\dfrac{3}{8} + \left(-\dfrac{4}{5}\right) = x$ $-1\dfrac{7}{40}$

8. $t = \dfrac{2}{15} + \left(-\dfrac{3}{10}\right)$ $-\dfrac{1}{6}$

9. $r = -\dfrac{2}{9} - \left(-\dfrac{2}{3}\right)$ $\dfrac{4}{9}$

10. $a = -\dfrac{7}{15} - \dfrac{5}{12}$ $-\dfrac{53}{60}$

11. $\dfrac{3}{8} + \dfrac{7}{12} = s$ $\dfrac{23}{24}$

12. $-2\dfrac{1}{4} + \left(-1\dfrac{1}{3}\right) = m$ $-3\dfrac{7}{12}$

13. $3\dfrac{2}{5} - 3\dfrac{1}{4} = v$ $\dfrac{3}{20}$

14. $b = \dfrac{3}{4} + \left(-\dfrac{4}{15}\right)$ $\dfrac{29}{60}$

15. $f = -1\dfrac{2}{3} + 4\dfrac{3}{4}$ $3\dfrac{1}{12}$

16. $-\dfrac{1}{8} - 2\dfrac{1}{2} = n$ $-2\dfrac{5}{8}$

17. $p = 3\dfrac{2}{5} - 1\dfrac{1}{3}$ $2\dfrac{1}{15}$

18. $y = 5\dfrac{1}{3} + \left(-8\dfrac{3}{7}\right)$ $-3\dfrac{2}{21}$

Lesson 7-3   Solve each equation. Write each solution in simplest form.

1. $\dfrac{2}{11} \cdot \dfrac{3}{4} = m$ $\dfrac{3}{22}$

2. $4\left(-\dfrac{7}{8}\right) = r$ $-3\dfrac{1}{2}$

3. $d = -\dfrac{4}{7} \cdot \dfrac{3}{5}$ $-\dfrac{12}{35}$

4. $g = \dfrac{6}{7}\left(-\dfrac{7}{12}\right)$ $-\dfrac{1}{2}$

5. $b = \dfrac{7}{8} \cdot \dfrac{1}{3}$ $\dfrac{7}{24}$

6. $\dfrac{3}{4} \cdot \dfrac{4}{5} = t$ $\dfrac{3}{5}$

7. $-1\dfrac{1}{2} \cdot \dfrac{2}{3} = k$ -1

8. $x = \dfrac{5}{6} \cdot \dfrac{6}{7}$ $\dfrac{5}{7}$

9. $c = 8\left(-2\dfrac{1}{4}\right)$ -18

10. $-3\dfrac{3}{4} \cdot \dfrac{8}{9} = q$ $-3\dfrac{1}{3}$

11. $\dfrac{10}{21} \cdot -\dfrac{7}{8} = n$ $-\dfrac{5}{12}$

12. $w = -1\dfrac{4}{5}\left(-\dfrac{5}{6}\right)$ $1\dfrac{1}{2}$

13. $a = 5\dfrac{1}{4} \cdot 6\dfrac{2}{3}$ 35

14. $-8\dfrac{3}{4} \cdot 4\dfrac{2}{5} = p$ $-38\dfrac{1}{2}$

15. $y = 6 \cdot 8\dfrac{2}{3}$ 52

16. $i = \left(\dfrac{3}{5}\right)^2$ $\dfrac{9}{25}$

17. $-4\dfrac{1}{5}\left(-3\dfrac{1}{3}\right) = h$ 14

18. $-8 \cdot \left(\dfrac{3}{4}\right)^2 = v$ $-4\dfrac{1}{2}$

Lesson 7-4   Name the multiplicative inverse of each of the following.

1. $3\dfrac{1}{3}$

2. -5 $-\dfrac{1}{5}$

3. $\dfrac{2}{3}$ $\dfrac{3}{2}$

4. $2\dfrac{1}{8}$ $\dfrac{8}{17}$

5. $\dfrac{a}{b}$ $\dfrac{b}{a}$

6. -8 $-\dfrac{1}{8}$

7. $\dfrac{1}{15}$ 15

8. 0.75 $\dfrac{4}{3}$

9. c $\dfrac{1}{c}$

10. $-\dfrac{3}{5}$ $-\dfrac{5}{3}$

11. $1\dfrac{1}{3}$ $\dfrac{3}{4}$

12. 0.5 2

13. $-2\dfrac{3}{7}$ $-\dfrac{7}{17}$

14. $-\dfrac{1}{11}$ -11

15. 12 $\dfrac{1}{12}$

16. $\dfrac{7}{9}$ $\dfrac{9}{7}$

17. $\dfrac{x}{y}$ $\dfrac{y}{x}$

18. $-1\dfrac{3}{7}$ $-\dfrac{7}{10}$

19. $\dfrac{21}{5}$ $\dfrac{5}{21}$

20. $\dfrac{4}{5}$ $\dfrac{5}{4}$

21. 0.8 $\dfrac{5}{4}$

22. $-\dfrac{8}{15}$ $-\dfrac{15}{8}$

23. $\dfrac{1}{m}$ m

24. $-6\dfrac{5}{11}$ $-\dfrac{11}{71}$

25. $\dfrac{3}{11}$ $\dfrac{11}{3}$

26. $3\dfrac{1}{4}$ $\dfrac{4}{13}$

27. $-5\dfrac{3}{5}$ $-\dfrac{5}{28}$

28. $\dfrac{24}{9}$ $\dfrac{9}{24}$

29. $-\dfrac{1}{b}$ $-b$

30. $4\dfrac{5}{8}$ $\dfrac{8}{37}$

Lesson 7-6

State whether each sequence is *arithmetic, geometric,* or *neither.* Then write the next three terms of each sequence. See Solutions Manual.

1. 1, 5, 9, 13, …
2. 2, 6, 18, 54, …
3. 1, 4, 9, 16, 25, …
4. 729, 243, 81, …
5. 2, –3, –8, –13, …
6. 5, –5, 5, –5, …
7. 810, –270, 90, –30, …
8. 11, 14, 17, 20, 23, …
9. 33, 27, 21, …
10. 21, 15, 9, 3, …
11. $\frac{1}{8}, -\frac{1}{4}, \frac{1}{2}, -1, \ldots$
12. $\frac{1}{81}, \frac{1}{27}, \frac{1}{9}, \frac{1}{3}, \ldots$
13. $\frac{3}{4}, 1\frac{1}{2}, 3, \ldots$
14. 2, 5, 9, 14, …
15. $-1\frac{1}{4}, -1\frac{3}{4}, -2\frac{1}{4}, -2\frac{3}{4}, \ldots$
16. 9.9, 13.7, 17.5, …
17. $\frac{1}{2}, 1\frac{1}{2}, 2\frac{1}{2}, 3\frac{1}{2}, \ldots$
18. 2, 12, 32, 62, …
19. 3, –6, 12, –24, …
20. 5, 7, 9, 11, 13, …
21. –0.06, 2.24, 4.54, …
22. 7, 14, 28, …
23. –5.4, –1.4, 2.6, …
24. –96, 48, –24, 12, …
25. 4, 12, 36, …
26. 20, 19, 18, 17, …
27. 768, 192, 48, …

Lesson 7-7

Find the area of each figure described below.

1. triangle: base, $2\frac{1}{2}$ in.; height, 7 in. $8\frac{3}{4}$ in²
2. triangle: base, 12 cm; height, 3.2 cm 19.2 cm²
3. trapezoid: bases, 5 ft and 7 ft; height, 11 ft 66 ft²
4. trapezoid: bases, $4\frac{1}{4}$ yd and $3\frac{1}{2}$ yd; height, 5 yd $19\frac{3}{8}$ yd²

State the measures of the base(s) and the height of each triangle or trapezoid. Then find the area.

5.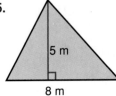
6.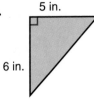
7.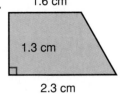
8.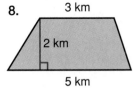

$b = 8$ m, $h = 5$ m,
$A = 20$ m²

$b = 5$ in., $h = 6$ in.
$A = 15$ in²

$a = 1.6$ cm, $b = 2.3$ cm,
$h = 1.3$ cm, $A = 2.535$ cm²

$a = 3$ km, $b = 5$ km,
$h = 2$ km, $A = 8$ km²

Lesson 7-8

Find the circumference of each circle described below. Round answers to the nearest tenth.

1. 14 mm, diameter
   44.0 mm
2. 18 cm, diameter
   56.5 cm
3. 24 in., radius
   150.8 in.
4. 42 m, diameter
   131.9 m

5.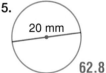
   62.8 mm
6. 3.5 m
   22.0 m
7. 6 yd
   37.7 yd
8. 4 in.
   25.1 in.

9. 16 ft
   50.3 ft
10. 2.4 cm
    15.1 cm
11. 56 mm
    175.9 mm
12. 35 in.
    110.0 in.

Lesson 7-9   Solve each equation. Write each solution in simplest form.

1. $x = \frac{2}{3} \div \frac{3}{4}$ $\frac{8}{9}$

2. $-\frac{4}{9} \div \frac{5}{6} = c$ $-\frac{8}{15}$

3. $\frac{7}{12} \div \frac{3}{8} = q$ $1\frac{5}{9}$

4. $m = \frac{5}{18} \div \frac{2}{9}$ $1\frac{1}{4}$

5. $a = \frac{1}{3} \div 4$ $\frac{1}{12}$

6. $5\frac{1}{4} \div \left(-2\frac{1}{2}\right) = g$ $-2\frac{1}{10}$

7. $-6 \div \left(-\frac{4}{7}\right) = d$ $10\frac{1}{2}$

8. $n = -6\frac{3}{8} \div \frac{1}{4}$ $-25\frac{1}{2}$

9. $p = \frac{6}{7} \div \frac{3}{5}$ $1\frac{3}{7}$

10. $e = 3\frac{1}{3} \div (-4)$ $-\frac{5}{6}$

11. $2\frac{5}{12} \div 7\frac{1}{3} = r$ $\frac{29}{88}$

12. $v = \frac{5}{6} \div 1\frac{1}{9}$ $\frac{3}{4}$

13. $\frac{3}{8} \div (-6) = b$ $-\frac{1}{16}$

14. $i = \frac{5}{8} \div \frac{1}{6}$ $3\frac{3}{4}$

15. $4\frac{1}{4} \div 6\frac{3}{4} = w$ $\frac{17}{27}$

16. $f = 4\frac{1}{6} \div 3\frac{1}{8}$ $1\frac{1}{3}$

17. $t = 8 \div \left(-1\frac{4}{5}\right)$ $-4\frac{4}{9}$

18. $j = -5 \div \frac{2}{7}$ $-17\frac{1}{2}$

19. $\frac{3}{5} \div \frac{6}{7} = y$ $\frac{7}{10}$

20. $4\frac{8}{9} \div \left(-2\frac{2}{3}\right) = h$ $-1\frac{5}{6}$

21. $f = 8\frac{1}{6} \div 3$ $2\frac{13}{18}$

22. $k = -\frac{3}{4} \div 9$ $-\frac{1}{12}$

23. $s = 1\frac{11}{14} \div 2\frac{1}{2}$ $\frac{5}{7}$

24. $-2\frac{1}{4} \div \frac{4}{5} = z$ $-2\frac{13}{16}$

Lesson 7-10   Solve each equation. Check your solution.

1. $434 = -31y$ -14

2. $6x = -4.2$ -0.7

3. $\frac{3}{4}a = -12$ -16

4. $-10 = \frac{b}{-7}$ 70

5. $7.2 = \frac{3}{4}c$ 9.6

6. $2r + 4 = 14$ 5

7. $-2.4i = 7.2$ -3

8. $7 = \frac{1}{2}d - 3$ 20

9. $3.2n - 0.64 = -5.44$ -1.5

10. $\frac{t}{3} - 7 = 2$ 27

11. $\frac{3}{8} = \frac{1}{2}x$ $\frac{3}{4}$

12. $\frac{1}{2}h - 3 = -14$ -22

13. $-0.46k - 1.18 = 1.58$ -6

14. $4\frac{1}{2}s = -30$ $-6\frac{2}{3}$

15. $\frac{2}{3}f = \frac{8}{15}$ $\frac{4}{5}$

16. $\frac{2}{3}m + 10 = 22$ 18

17. $\frac{2}{3}g + 4 = 4\frac{5}{6}$ $1\frac{1}{4}$

18. $7 = \frac{1}{2}v + 3$ 8

19. $\frac{g}{1.2} = -6$ -7.2

20. $\frac{4}{7}z - 4\frac{5}{8} = 15\frac{3}{8}$ 35

21. $-12 = \frac{1}{5}j$ -60

Lesson 8-1   Find each square root.

1. $\sqrt{9}$ 3

2. $\sqrt{0.16}$ 0.4

3. $\sqrt{81}$ 9

4. $\sqrt{0.04}$ 0.2

5. $-\sqrt{625}$ -25

6. $\sqrt{36}$ 6

7. $-\sqrt{169}$ -13

8. $\sqrt{144}$ 12

9. $\sqrt{2.25}$ 1.5

10. $\sqrt{961}$ 31

11. $\sqrt{25}$ 5

12. $\sqrt{225}$ 15

13. $\sqrt{0.01}$ 0.1

14. $-\sqrt{4}$ -2

15. $-\sqrt{0.09}$ -0.3

16. $\sqrt{529}$ 23

17. $-\sqrt{484}$ -22

18. $\sqrt{196}$ 14

19. $\sqrt{0.49}$ 0.7

20. $\sqrt{1.69}$ 1.3

21. $\sqrt{729}$ 27

22. $\sqrt{0.36}$ 0.6

23. $\sqrt{289}$ 17

24. $-\sqrt{16}$ -4

25. $\sqrt{1,024}$ 32

26. $\sqrt{\frac{289}{10,000}}$ $\frac{17}{100}$

27. $\sqrt{\frac{169}{121}}$ $\frac{13}{11}$

28. $-\sqrt{\frac{4}{9}}$ $-\frac{2}{3}$

29. $-\sqrt{\frac{81}{64}}$ $-\frac{9}{8}$

30. $\sqrt{\frac{25}{81}}$ $\frac{5}{9}$

Lesson 8-2   Estimate to the nearest whole number.

1. $\sqrt{229}$ 15
2. $\sqrt{63}$ 8
3. $\sqrt{290}$ 17
4. $\sqrt{27}$ 5
5. $\sqrt{1.30}$ 1

6. $\sqrt{8.4}$ 3
7. $\sqrt{96}$ 10
8. $\sqrt{19}$ 4
9. $\sqrt{200}$ 14
10. $\sqrt{76}$ 9

11. $\sqrt{17}$ 4
12. $\sqrt{34}$ 6
13. $\sqrt{137}$ 12
14. $\sqrt{540}$ 23
15. $\sqrt{165}$ 13

16. $\sqrt{326}$ 18
17. $\sqrt{52}$ 7
18. $\sqrt{37}$ 6
19. $\sqrt{79}$ 9
20. $\sqrt{18.35}$ 4

21. $\sqrt{71}$ 8
22. $\sqrt{117}$ 11
23. $\sqrt{410}$ 20
24. $\sqrt{25.70}$ 5
25. $\sqrt{333}$ 18

26. $\sqrt{23}$ 5
27. $\sqrt{89}$ 9
28. $\sqrt{47}$ 7
29. $\sqrt{62}$ 8
30. $\sqrt{742}$ 27

Lesson 8-3   Name the set or sets of numbers to which each real number belongs.

1. 6.5 rational
2. $\sqrt{25}$ natural, whole, integer, rational
3. $\sqrt{3}$ irrational
4. –7.2 rational
5. $-0.\overline{61}$ rational

Find an approximation for each square root. Then graph the square root on the number line.

6. $-\sqrt{12}$ –3.5
7. $\sqrt{23}$ 4.8
8. $\sqrt{2}$ 1.4
9. $\sqrt{10}$ 3.2
10. $-\sqrt{30}$ –5.5

For graphs to Exercises 6-10, see Solutions Manual.

Solve each equation. Round decimal answers to the nearest tenth.

11. $y^2 = 49$ 7, –7
12. $x^2 = 225$ 15, –15
13. $x^2 = 64$ 8, –8
14. $y^2 = 79$ 8.9, –8.9

15. $x^2 = 16$ 4, –4
16. $y^2 = 24$ 4.9, –4.9
17. $y^2 = 625$ 25, –25
18. $x^2 = 81$ 9, –9

Lesson 8-5   Find the missing measure for each right triangle. Round decimal answers to the nearest tenth.

1. a, 6 cm; b, 5 cm
   7.8 cm
2. a, 12 ft; b, 12 ft
   17 ft
3. a, 8 in.; b, 6 in.
   10 in.
4. a, 20 m; c, 25 m
   15 m
5. a, 9 mm; c, 14 mm
   10.7 mm
6. b, 15 m; c, 20 m
   13.2 m
7. a, 5 ft; b, 50 ft
   50.2 ft
8. a, 4.5 yd; c, 8.5 yd
   7.2 yd

Write an equation to solve for x. Then solve. Round decimal answers to the nearest tenth.

9.
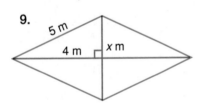

10.
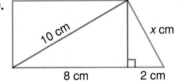

11.
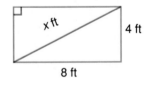

$x^2 + 16 = 25;\ x = 3$

$x^2 = 36 + 4;\ x \approx 6.3$

$x^2 = 64 + 16;\ x \approx 8.9$

Determine whether each triangle with sides of a given length is a right triangle.

12. 15 m, 8 m, 17 m yes
13. 7 yd, 5 yd, 9 yd no
14. 5 in., 12 in., 13 in. yes

Lesson 8-7

Find the distance between each pair of points whose coordinates are given. Round answers to the nearest tenth.

1.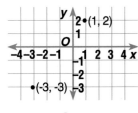

6.4

2.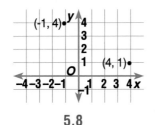

5.8

3.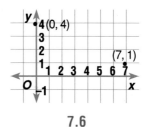

7.6

Graph each pair of ordered pairs. Then find the distance between the points. Round answers to the nearest tenth. **For graphs, see Solutions Manual.**

4. (-4, 2); (4, 17) **17**   **5.** (5, -1); (11, 7) **10**   **6.** (-3, 5); (2, 7) **5.4**   **7.** (7, -9); (4, 3) **12.4**

8. (5, 4); (-3, 8) **8.9**   **9.** (-8, -4); (-3, 8) **13**   **10.** (2, 7); (10, -4) **13.6** **11.** (9, -2); (3, 6) **10**

Lesson 8-8

Find the lengths of the missing sides. Round answers to the nearest tenth.

1.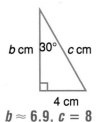

4 cm

$b \approx 6.9, c = 8$

2.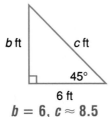

6 ft

$b = 6, c \approx 8.5$

3.

14 mm a mm b mm   30°

$a = 7, b \approx 12.1$

4.

c in.   10 in.   45° a in.

$a = 10, c \approx 14.1$

5.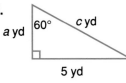

60° c yd a yd   5 yd

$a \approx 2.9, c \approx 5.8$

6.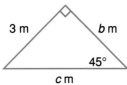

3 m b m   45° c m

$b = 3, c \approx 4.2$

7.

12 m c m   30° b m

$b \approx 20.8, c = 24$

8.

45° c ft b ft   17 ft

$b = 17, c \approx 24.0$

Lesson 9-1

Express each ratio or rate as a fraction in simplest form.

1. 27 to 9 $\frac{3}{1}$

2. 4 inches per foot $\frac{1}{3}$

3. 16 out of 48 $\frac{1}{3}$

4. 10 : 50 $\frac{1}{5}$

5. 40 min. per hour $\frac{2}{3}$

6. 35 is to 15 $\frac{7}{3}$

7. 16 wins, 16 losses $\frac{1}{1}$

8. 7 out of 13 $\frac{7}{13}$

9. 5 out of 50 $\frac{1}{10}$

Express each as a unit rate.

10. $24 per dozen **$2 each**

11. 600 students to 30 teachers $\frac{20 \text{ students}}{1 \text{ teacher}}$

12. 6 pounds gained in 12 weeks $\frac{0.5 \text{ lb}}{\text{week}}$

13. $800 for 40 tickets $\frac{\$20}{1 \text{ ticket}}$

14. $6.50 for 5 pounds $\frac{\$1.30}{1 \text{ lb}}$

15. 6 inches of rain in 3 weeks $\frac{2 \text{ in.}}{1 \text{ week}}$

Lesson 9-2 Tell whether each pair of ratios form a proportion.

1. $\frac{3}{5}, \frac{5}{10}$ no

2. $\frac{8}{4}, \frac{6}{3}$ yes

3. $\frac{10}{15}, \frac{5}{3}$ no

4. $\frac{2}{8}, \frac{1}{4}$ yes

5. $\frac{6}{18}, \frac{3}{9}$ yes

6. $\frac{14}{21}, \frac{12}{18}$ yes

7. $\frac{4}{20}, \frac{5}{25}$ yes

8. $\frac{9}{27}, \frac{1}{3}$ yes

Solve each proportion.

9. $\frac{2}{3} = \frac{a}{12}$ 8

10. $\frac{7}{8} = \frac{c}{16}$ 14

11. $\frac{3}{7} = \frac{21}{d}$ 49

12. $\frac{2}{5} = \frac{18}{x}$ 45

13. $\frac{3}{5} = \frac{n}{21}$ $12\frac{3}{5}$

14. $\frac{5}{12} = \frac{b}{5}$ $2\frac{1}{12}$

15. $\frac{4}{36} = \frac{2}{y}$ 18

16. $\frac{3}{10} = \frac{z}{36}$ $10\frac{4}{5}$

17. $\frac{2}{3} = \frac{t}{4}$ $2\frac{2}{3}$

18. $\frac{9}{10} = \frac{r}{25}$ $22\frac{1}{2}$

19. $\frac{16}{8} = \frac{y}{12}$ 24

20. $\frac{7}{8} = \frac{a}{12}$ $10\frac{1}{2}$

Lesson 9-3 Use a proportion to solve each problem.

1. On a radar screen the distance between two planes is $3\frac{1}{2}$ inches. If the scale is 1 inch on the screen to 2 miles in the air, what is the actual distance between the two planes. **7 miles**

2. A car travels 144 miles on 4 gallons of gasoline. At this rate, how many gallons are needed to drive 450 miles? **12.5 gallons**

3. A park ranger stocks a pond with 4 sunfish for every three perch. Suppose 296 sunfish are put in the pond. How many perch should be stocked? **222 perch**

4. A furniture store bought 8 identical sofas for $4,000. How much did each sofa cost? **$500**

Lesson 9-5 Tell whether each pair of polygons are similar.

1.
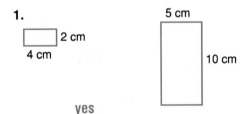

yes

2.
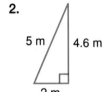 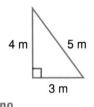

no

3.
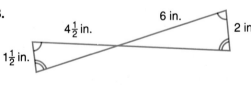

yes

4.
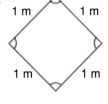

yes

Lesson 9-6

Write a proportion to find the value of *x*. Assume the triangles are similar.

1.

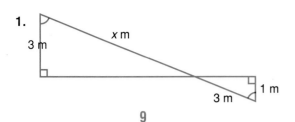

9

2.

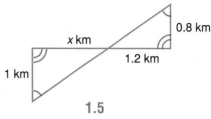

4.5

3.

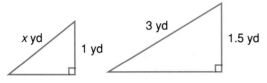

2

4.

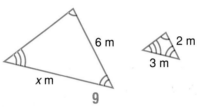

1.5

5.

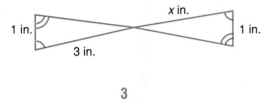

3

6.

9

Lesson 9-7

The distance on a map is given. Find the actual distance, if the scale on the map is 1 cm : 50 miles.

1. 2 cm **100 miles**	**2.** 0.5 cm **25 miles**	**3.** 1 cm **50 miles**	**4.** 5 cm **250 miles**
5. 1.5 cm **75 miles**	**6.** 2.8 cm **140 miles**	**7.** 3.2 cm **160 miles**	**8.** 10 cm **500 miles**
9. 0.2 cm **10 miles**	**10.** 4.5 cm **225 miles**	**11.** 3 cm **150 miles**	**12.** 6.4 cm **320 miles**
13. 7 cm **350 miles**	**14.** 0.6 cm **30 miles**	**15.** 8 cm **400 miles**	**16.** 45 cm **2,250 miles**

Lesson 9-8   See Solutions Manual.

1. Graph segment *PQ* with *P*(4, 4) and *Q*(2, 0). Then graph its image for a dilation with a scale factor of 4.

2. Graph segment *AB* with *A*(3, 6) and *B*(0, -1). Then graph its image for a dilation with a scale factor of $\frac{1}{2}$.

3. Graph segment *XY* with *X*(-2 ,-4) and *Y*(1, 3). Then graph its image for a dilation with a scale factor of 3.

Triangle *ABC* has vertices *A*(2, 2), *B*(-1, 4), and *C*(-3, -5). Find the coordinates of its image for a dilation with each given scale factor. Graph the original triangle and its dilation.

4. 1   **5.** 0.5   **6.** 2   **7.** 3   **8.** $\frac{1}{4}$

Lesson 9-9 Use the figures below. Write the ratios in simplest form. Find angle measures to the nearest degree.

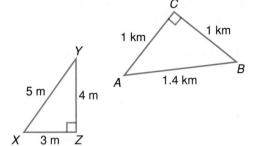

1. Find tan X. $\frac{4}{3}$

2. Find tan Y. $\frac{3}{4}$

3. Find tan A. 1

4. Find tan B. 1

5. Find m∠X. 53°

6. Find m∠Y. 37°

7. Find m∠A. 45°

8. Find m∠B. 45°

Lesson 9-10 Use the figures below. Write the ratios in simplest form. Find angle measures to the nearest degree.

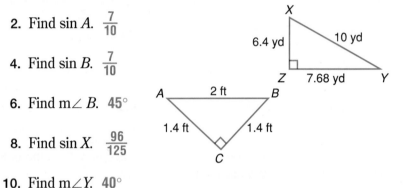

1. Find cos A. $\frac{7}{10}$

2. Find sin A. $\frac{7}{10}$

3. Find m∠A. 45°

4. Find sin B. $\frac{7}{10}$

5. Find cos B. $\frac{7}{10}$

6. Find m∠B. 45°

7. Find cos Y. $\frac{96}{125}$

8. Find sin X. $\frac{96}{125}$

9. Find m∠X. 50°

10. Find m∠Y. 40°

Lesson 10-1 Express each fraction as a percent.

1. $\frac{2}{100}$ 2%

2. $\frac{3}{25}$ 12%

3. $\frac{20}{25}$ 80%

4. $\frac{10}{16}$ 62.5%

5. $\frac{4}{6}$ $66\frac{2}{3}$%

6. $\frac{1}{4}$ 25%

7. $\frac{26}{100}$ 26%

8. $\frac{3}{10}$ 30%

9. $\frac{21}{50}$ 42%

10. $\frac{7}{8}$ 87.5%

11. $\frac{1}{3}$ $33\frac{1}{3}$%

12. $\frac{2}{3}$ $66\frac{2}{3}$%

13. $\frac{2}{5}$ 40%

14. $\frac{2}{50}$ 4%

15. $\frac{8}{10}$ 80%

16. $\frac{5}{12}$ $41\frac{2}{3}$%

17. $\frac{7}{10}$ 70%

18. $\frac{9}{20}$ 45%

19. $\frac{1}{2}$ 50%

20. $\frac{3}{20}$ 15%

21. $\frac{10}{25}$ 40%

22. $\frac{3}{8}$ 37.5%

23. $\frac{4}{20}$ 20%

24. $\frac{19}{25}$ 76%

Write a percent proportion to solve each problem. Round answers to the nearest tenth.

25. 39 is 5% of what number? $\frac{39}{n} = \frac{5}{100}$; 780

26. What is 19% of 200? $\frac{19}{100} = \frac{n}{200}$; 38

27. 28 is what percent of 7? $\frac{28}{7} = \frac{n}{100}$; 400%

28. 24 is what percent of 72? $\frac{24}{72} = \frac{n}{100}$; 33.3%

29. 9 is $33\frac{1}{3}$% of what number? $\frac{33\frac{1}{3}}{100} = \frac{9}{n}$; 27

30. Find 55% of 134. $\frac{55}{100} = \frac{n}{134}$; 73.7

Lesson 10-2

Express each decimal as a percent.

1. 0.35 **35%** 2. 14.23 **1,423%** 3. 0.9 **90%** 4. 0.13 **13%** 5. 6.21 **621%**

6. 0.23 **23%** 7. 0.08 **8%** 8. 0.036 **3.6%** 9. 2.34 **234%** 10. 0.39 **39%**

Express each percent as a fraction in simplest form.

11. 40% $\frac{2}{5}$ 12. 24.5% $\frac{49}{200}$ 13. 42% $\frac{21}{50}$ 14. $33\frac{1}{3}$% $\frac{1}{3}$ 15. 81% $\frac{81}{100}$

16. 8% $\frac{2}{25}$ 17. 55% $\frac{11}{20}$ 18. 4.5% $\frac{9}{200}$ 19. 16.5% $\frac{33}{200}$ 20. 2% $\frac{1}{50}$

Express each percent as a decimal.

21. 2% **0.02** 22. 25% **0.25** 23. 29% **0.29** 24. 6.2% **0.062** 25. 16.8% **0.168**

26. 14% **0.14** 27. 23.7% **0.237** 28. 42% **0.42** 29. 25.4% **0.254** 30. 98% **0.98**

Lesson 10-3

Express each percent as a fraction or mixed number in simplest form.

1. 540% $5\frac{2}{5}$ 2. $\frac{25}{50}$% $\frac{1}{200}$ 3. 0.02% $\frac{1}{5,000}$ 4. 620% $6\frac{1}{5}$ 5. 0.7% $\frac{7}{1,000}$

6. 111.5% $1\frac{23}{200}$ 7. $\frac{7}{35}$% $\frac{1}{500}$ 8. 0.72% $\frac{9}{1,250}$ 9. 0.004% $\frac{1}{25,000}$ 10. 364% $3\frac{16}{25}$

11. 0.15% $\frac{3}{2,000}$ 12. 1,250% $12\frac{1}{2}$ 13. $\frac{9}{10}$% $\frac{9}{1,000}$ 14. 730% $7\frac{3}{10}$ 15. 100.01% $1\frac{1}{10,000}$

Express each percent as a decimal.

16. 0.07% **0.0007** 17. $5\frac{2}{3}$% **0.056̄** 18. 310% **3.1** 19. 6.05% **0.0605** 20. 7,652% **76.52**

21. $\frac{12}{50}$% **0.0024** 22. 0.93% **0.0093** 23. 200% **2** 24. 197.6% **1.976** 25. 10.75% **0.1075**

26. 0.66% **0.0066** 27. 417% **4.17** 28. 7.76% **0.0776** 29. 390% **3.9** 30. $10\frac{7}{10}$% **0.107**

Lesson 10-5

Estimate. **Sample answers given.**

1. 33% of 12 **4** 2. 24% of 84 **20** 3. 39% of 50 **20** 4. 1.5% of 135 **2**

Estimate the percent of each area shaded.

5.
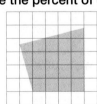
40%

6.

40%

7.
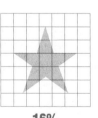
16%

Estimate the percent. **Sample answers given.**

8. 11 out of 99 **10%** 9. 28 out of 89 $33\frac{1}{3}$% 10. 9 out of 20 **50%** 11. 25 out of 270 **10%**

12. 6 out of 25 **25%** 13. 17 out of 65 $33\frac{1}{3}$% 14. 72 out of 280 **25%** 15. 120 out of 181 $66\frac{2}{3}$%

Extra Practice   **607**

Lesson 10-6   Solve.

1. Find 5% of $73. **$3.65**
2. What is 15% of 15? **2.25**
3. Find 80% of $12. **$9.60**
4. What is 7.3% of 500? **36.5**
5. Find 21% of $720. **$151.20**
6. What is 12% of $62.50? **$7.50**
7. Find 0.3% of 155. **0.465**
8. What is 75% of $450 **$337.50**
9. Find 7.2% of 10. **0.72**
10. What is 10.1% of $60? **$6.06**
11. Find 23% of 47. **10.81**
12. What is 89% of 654? **582.06**
13. $20 is what percent of $64? **31.25%**
14. Sixty-nine is what percent of 200? **34.5%**
15. Seventy is what percent of 150? **$46\frac{2}{3}$%**
16. 26 is 30% of what number? **$86\frac{2}{3}$**
17. 7 is 14% of what number? **50**
18. $35.50 is what percent of $150? **$23\frac{2}{3}$%**
19. $17 is what percent of $25? **68%**
20. 152 is 2% of what number? **7,600**

Lesson 10-7   Make a circle graph for each set of data. See Solutions Manual.

1.

Sporting Goods Sales	
Shoes	44%
Apparel	30%
Equipment	26%

2.

Energy Use in Home	
Heating/cooling	51%
Appliances	28%
Lights	21%

3.

Household Income	
Primary job	82%
Secondary job	9%
Investments	5%
Other	4%

4.

Students in North High School	
White	30%
Black	28%
Hispanic	24%
Asian	18%

Lesson 10-8   Estimate the percent of change. Sample answers given.   30% decrease

1. old: $97 **50%**
   new: $149 increase
2. old: $54 **20%**
   new: $64 increase
3. old: $0.39 **200%**
   new: $1.20 increase
4. old: $450
   new: $325

5. old: $0.48 **100%**
   new: $1.02 increase
6. old: $2.39 **10%**
   new: $2.59 increase
7. old: $46.50 **20%**
   new: $37.99 decrease
8. old: 50¢
   new: 95¢
   100% increase

Find the percent of change. Round to the nearest whole percent.   **40% increase**

9. old: $35 **17%**
   new: $29 decrease
10. old: $550 **23%**
    new: $425 decrease
11. old: $72 **22%**
    new: $88 increase
12. old: $25
    new: $35

13. old: $28 **32%**
    new: $19 decrease
14. old: $46 **20%**
    new: $55 increase
15. old: $78 **44%**
    new: $44 decrease
16. old: $120
    new: $75
    38% decrease

Lesson 10-9 Find the amount of discount and the sale price of each item.

1. $4,220 piano, 35% off
   $1,477, $2,743
2. $14 scissors, 10% off
   $1.40, $12.60
3. $29 book, 40% off
   $11.60, $17.40
4. $38 sweater, 25% off
   $9.50, $28.50
5. $45 pants, 50% off
   $22.50, $22.50
6. $280 VCR, 25% off
   $70, $210
7. $3,540 motorcycle, 30% off
   $1,062, $2,478
8. $15.95 compact disc, 20% off
   $3.19, $12.76

Find the percent of discount.

9. regular price: $250
   discount: $35 14%
10. regular price: $15.50
    discount: $2.48 16%
11. regular price: $27.50
    discount: $11 40%

Lesson 10-10 Find the simple interest to the nearest cent.

1. $500 at 7% for 2 years $70
2. $2,500 at 6.5% for 36 months $487.50
3. $8,000 at 6% for 1 year $480
4. $1,890 at 9% for 42 months $595.35

Find the total amount in each account.

5. $300 at 10% after 3 years $390
6. $3,200 at 8% after 6 months $3,328
7. $20,000 at 14% after 20 years $76,000
8. $4,000 at 12.5% after 4 years $6,000

Find the annual rate of simple interest.

9. principal: $4,500; interest: $526.50; time: 3 years 3.9%

10. principal: $7,400; interest: $878.75; time: 30 months 4.75%

Lesson 11-1 Complete each function table.

1. $f(n) = -4n$

n	-4n	f(n)
-2	-4(-2)	8
-1	-4(-1)	4
0	-4(0)	0
1	-4(1)	-4
2	-4(2)	-8

2. $f(n) = n + 6$

n	n + 6	f(n)
-6	-6+6	0
-4	-4+6	2
-2	-2+6	4
0	0+6	6
2	2+6	8

3. $f(n) = 3n + 2$

n	3n + 2	f(n)
-3.5	3(-3.5)+2	-8.5
-2.5	3(-2.5)+2	-5.5
-1.5	3(-1.5)+2	-2.5
0	3(0)+2	2
1.5	3(1.5)+2	6.5

4. $f(n) = 2n - 6$

n	2n - 6	f(n)
$-2\frac{1}{2}$	$2(-2\frac{1}{2})-6$	-11
-1	2(-1)-6	-8
$-\frac{1}{4}$	$2(-\frac{1}{4})-6$	$-6\frac{1}{2}$
0	2(0)-6	-6
$\frac{1}{2}$	$2(\frac{1}{2})-6$	-5

5. $f(n) = -\frac{1}{2}n + 4$

n	$-\frac{1}{2}n + 4$	f(n)
-4	$-\frac{1}{2}(-4)+4$	6
-2	$-\frac{1}{2}(-2)+4$	5
0	$-\frac{1}{2}(0)+4$	4
2.5	$-\frac{1}{2}(2.5)+4$	2.75
6	$-\frac{1}{2}(6)+4$	1

6. $f(n) = -5n + 1$

n	-5n + 1	f(n)
-4	-5(-4)+1	21
-2	-5(-2)+1	11
0	-5(0)+1	1
1	-5(1)+1	-4
4	-5(4)+1	-19

Lesson 11-2   Write the ordered pairs for each function. Then graph the function.

1. $f(n) = 6n + 2$

n	f(n)	(n, f(n))
-3	-16	(-3, -16)
-1	-4	(-1, -4)
1	8	(1, 8)
$\frac{7}{3}$	16	$(\frac{7}{3}, 16)$

2. $f(n) = -2n + 3$

n	f(n)	(n, f(n))
-2	7	(-2, 7)
-1	5	(-1, 5)
0	3	(0, 3)
1	1	(1, 1)
2	-1	(2, -1)

3. $f(n) = 4.5n$

n	f(n)	(n, f(n))
-4	-18	(-4, -18)
-2	-9	(-2, -9)
0	0	(0, 0)
1	4.5	(1, 4.5)
6	27	(6, 27)

Make a function table for each function. Then graph each function. **See Solutions Manual.**

4. $f(n) = \dfrac{8}{n}$

5. $f(n) = \dfrac{2}{3}n + 1$

6. $f(n) = n^2 - 1$

7. $f(n) = 3.5n$

8. $f(n) = 4n - 1$

9. $f(n) = \dfrac{3}{5}n + \left(-\dfrac{1}{5}\right)$

Lesson 11-3   Copy and complete the table for each equation.

1. $y = 3x - 1$

x	y
-5	-16
-3	-10
-1	-4
0	-1
1	2

2. $y = \dfrac{x}{4} + 2$

x	y
-8	0
-4	1
0	2
4	3

3. $y = -1.5x - 3$

x	y
-4	3
-2	0
2	-6
6	-12
10	-18

4. $y = 4x - 3$

x	y
-2	-11
$\frac{1}{2}$	-1
0	-3
$2\frac{1}{4}$	6

Find four solutions for each equation. Write the solution set. **See Solutions Manual.**

5. $y = -3x + 5$

6. $y = 2x - 1$

7. $y = \dfrac{2}{3}x + 4$

8. $y = -0.4x$

9. $y = 12x - 8$

10. $y = \dfrac{3}{4}x + 2$

11. $y = -2.4x - 3$

12. $y = 5x + 7$

Lesson 11-4   Graph each function. **See Solutions Manual.**

1. $y = -5x$

2. $y = 10x - 2$

3. $y = -2.5x - 1.5$

4. $y = 7x + 3$

5. $y = \dfrac{x}{4} - 8$

6. $y = 3x + 1$

7. $y = 25 - 2x$

8. $y = \dfrac{x}{6}$

9. $y = -2x + 11$

10. $y = 7x - 3$

11. $y = \dfrac{x}{2} + 5$

12. $y = 4 - 6x$

13. $y = -3.5x - 1$

14. $y = 4x + 10$

15. $y = 8x$

16. $y = -5x + \dfrac{1}{2}$

17. $y = \dfrac{x}{3} + 9$

18. $y = -7x + 15$

19. $y = 10x - 2$

20. $y = 1.5x - 7.5$

Lesson 11-5

Solve each system of equations by graphing. For graphs, see Solutions Manual.

1. $y = x$
   $y = -x + 4$ (2, 2)

2. $y = -x + 8$
   $y = x - 2$ (5, 3)

3. $y = -3x$
   $y = -4x + 2$ (2, -6)

4. $y = x - 1$
   $y = -x + 11$
   (6, 5)

5. $y = -x$
   $y = 2x$ (0, 0)

6. $y = -x + 3$
   $y = x + 3$ (0, 3)

7. $y = x - 3$
   $y = 2x + 8$
   (-11, -14)

8. $y = -x + 6$
   $y = x + 2$
   (2, 4)

9. $y = -x + 1$
   $y = x - 4$ $(2\frac{1}{2}, -1\frac{1}{2})$

10. $y = -3x + 6$
    $y = x - 2$ (2, 0)

11. $y = 3x - 4$
    $y = -3x - 4$ (0, -4)

12. $y = 2x + 4$
    $y = 3x - 9$
    (13, 30)

13. $y = -x + 4$
    $y = x - 10$ (7, -3)

14. $y = -x + 6$
    $y = 2x$ (2, 4)

15. $y = x - 4$
    $y = -2x + 5$ (3, -1)

16. $y = 2x$
    $y = -x + 3$
    (1, 2)

Lesson 11-7

Graph each quadratic function. See Solutions Manual.

1. $y = x^2 - 1$

2. $y = 1.5x^2 + 3$

3. $f(n) = n^2 - n$

4. $y = 2x^2$

5. $y = x^2 + 3$

6. $y = -3x^2 + 4$

7. $y = -x^2 + 7$

8. $f(n) = 3n^2$

9. $f(n) = 3n^2 + 9n$

10. $y = -x^2$

11. $y = \frac{1}{2}x^2 + 1$

12. $y = 5x^2 - 4$

13. $y = -x^2 + 3x$

14. $f(n) = 2.5n^2$

15. $y = -2x^2$

16. $y = 8x^2 + 3$

17. $y = -x^2 + \frac{1}{2}x$

18. $y = -4x^2 + 4$

19. $f(n) = 4n^2 + 3$

20. $y = -4x^2 + 1$

21. $y = 2x^2 + 1$

22. $y = x^2 - 4x$

23. $y = 3x^2 + 5$

24. $f(n) = 0.5n^2$

25. $f(n) = 2n^2 - 5n$

26. $y = \frac{3}{2}x^2 - 2$

27. $y = 6x^2 + 2$

28. $f(n) = 5n^2 + 6n$

Lesson 11-8

For graphs, see Solutions Manual.
Find the coordinates of the vertices of each figure after the translation described. Then graph the figure and its translation.

1. $\triangle ABC$ with vertices $A(-6, -2)$, $B(-1, 1)$, and $C(2, -2)$, translated by (4, 3)
   $A'(-2, 1)$, $B'(3, 4)$, $C'(6, 1)$

2. $\triangle XYZ$ with vertices $X(-4, 3)$, $Y(0, 3)$, and $Z(-2, -1)$, translated by (5, -2)
   $X'(1, 1)$, $Y'(5, 1)$, $Z'(3, -3)$

3. rectangle $HIJK$ with vertices $H(1, 3)$, $I(4, 0)$, $J(2, -2)$, and $K(-1, 1)$, translated by (-4, -6)
   $H'(-3, -3)$, $I'(0, -6)$, $J'(-2, -8)$, $K'(-5, -5)$

4. rectangle $PQRS$ with vertices $P(-7, 6)$, $Q(-5, 6)$, $R(-5, 2)$, and $S(-7, 2)$, translated by (9, -1)
   $P'(2, 5)$, $Q'(4, 5)$, $R'(4, 1)$, $S'(2, 1)$

5. pentagon $DGLMR$ with vertices $D(1, 3)$, $G(2, 4)$, $L(4, 4)$, $M(5, 3)$, and $R(3, 1)$, translated by (-5, -7)
   $D'(-4, -4)$, $G'(-3, -3)$, $L'(-1, -3)$, $M'(0, -4)$, $R'(-2, -6)$

Lesson 11-9 Graph △*CAT* with vertices *C*(2, 3), *A*(8, 2), and *T*(4, –3). See Solutions Manual.

1. Find the coordinates of the vertices after a reflection over the *y*-axis.
2. Graph △*C′A′T′*. See Solutions Manual. *C′*(–2, 3), *A′*(–8, 2), *T′*(–4, –3)

Graph trapezoid *TRAP* with vertices *T*(–2, 5), *R*(1, 5), *A*(4, 2), and *P*(–5, 2). See Solutions Manual.

3. Find the coordinates of the vertices after a reflection over the *x*-axis. *T′*(–2, –5), *R′*(1, –5), *A′*(4, –2), *P′*(–5, –2)
4. Graph trapezoid *T′R′A′P′* See Solutions Manual.

Graph rectangle *ABCD* with vertices *A*(4, –1), *B*(7, –4), *C*(4, –7), and *D*(1, –4). See Solutions Manual.

5. Find the coordinates of the vertices after a reflection over the *y*-axis. *A′*(–4, –1), *B′*(–7, –4), *C′*(–4, –7), *D′*(–1, –4)
6. Graph rectangle *A′B′C′D′*. See Solutions Manual.

Lesson 11-10 Triangle *ABC* has vertices *A*(–2, –1), *B*(0, 1), and *C*(1, –1).

1. Graph △*ABC*. See Solutions Manual.
2. Find the coordinates of the vertices after a 90° counterclockwise rotation.
3. Graph △*A′B′C′*. See Solutions Manual. *A′*(1, –2), *B′*(–1, 0), *C′*(1, 1)

Rectangle *WXYZ* has vertices *W*(1, 1), *X*(1, 3), *Y*(6, 3), and *Z*(6, 1).

4. Graph rectangle *WXYZ*. See Solutions Manual.
5. Find the coordinates of the vertices after a rotation of 180°. *W′*(–1, –1), *X′*(–1, –3), *Y′*(–6, –3), *Z′*(–6, –1)
6. Graph rectangle *W′X′Y′Z′*. See Solutions Manual.

Lesson 12-1 Find the area of each circle whose radius or diameter is given. Round answers to the nearest tenth.

1. radius, 4 m
   50.3 m²
2. diameter, 6 in.
   28.3 in²
3. radius, 12 in.
   452.4 in²
4. diameter, 16 yd
   201.1 yd²
5. diameter, 11 ft
   95.0 ft²
6. radius, 5 in.
   78.5 in²
7. radius, 19 cm
   1,134.1 cm²
8. diameter, 29 mm
   660.5 mm²

9.
227 mm²

10.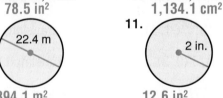
394.1 m²

11.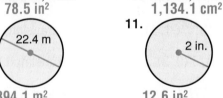
12.6 in²

12.
254.5 ft²

13.
314.2 yd²

14.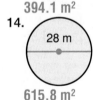
615.8 m²

15.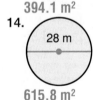
1,520.5 cm²

16.
38.5 in²

Lesson 12-4   Find the surface area of each prism.

1. length = 2 in.
   width = 1 in.
   height = 10 in. **64 in²**

2. length = 18 m
   width = 7 m
   height = 14 m **952 m²**

3. length = 2.5 cm
   width = 1 cm
   height = 4.5 cm **36.5 cm²**

4. length = 6 m
   width = 4 m
   height = 10 m **248 m²**

5. length = 14 ft
   width = 7 ft
   height = 14 ft **784 ft²**

6. length = 10 cm
   width = 10 cm
   height = 10 cm **600 cm²**

7. length = 4.5 yd
   width = 3.6 yd
   height = 10.6 yd **204.12 yd²**

8. length = 18 in.
   width = 12 in.
   height = 11 in. **1,092 in²**

9. length = 12.6 mm
   width = 6.8 mm
   height = 10.4 mm
   574.88 mm²

Lesson 12-5   Find the surface area of each cylinder. Round answers to the nearest tenth.

1. 14 cm / 3 cm
   320.4 cm²

2. 8 in. / 6 in.
   251.3 in²

3. 14 mm / 8 mm
   659.7 mm²

4. 3 m / 19 m
   414.7 m²

5. 8.2 in. / 22 in.
   1,556.0 in²

6. 3.6 yd / 14.2 yd
   402.6 yd²

7. radius = 4.2 cm
   height = 12.4 cm
   438.1 cm²

8. radius = 5 in.
   height = 10 in.
   471.2 in²

9. radius = 6.3 ft
   height = 4.6 ft
   431.5 ft²

Lesson 12-6   Find the volume of each solid. Round answers to the nearest tenth.

1. 3 m / 3 m / 3 m
   27 m³

2. 5 in. / 10 in. / 5 in.
   250 in³

3. 6 yd / 11 yd
   1,244.1 yd³

4. 26 cm / 8 cm
   4,247.4 cm³

5. 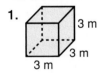 7 mm / 9 mm / 8 mm
   504 mm³

6. 7 ft / 30 ft
   4,618.1 ft³

7. 4 in. / 12 in. / 18 in.
   864 in³

8. 10 m / 2 m
   125.7 m³

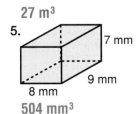

Lesson 12-7   Find the volume of each solid. Round answers to the nearest tenth.

1.

5 cm

3 cm   4 cm

20 cm³

2.

60 in.

60 in.

60 in.

72,000 in³

3.

12 yd

7 yd

615.8 yd³

4.

3 cm

4 cm

2 cm

8 cm³

5.

15 ft

11 ft

1,900.7 ft³

6.

6 mm

18 mm

4 mm

144 mm³

7.

14 in.

7 in.   7 in.

228.7 in³

8.

9 m

20 m

1,696.5 m³

Lesson 13-1   Draw a tree diagram to find the number of possible outcomes for each situation. For diagrams, see Solutions Manual.

1. A choice of yellow, white, chocolate, or marble cake with a choice of chocolate or vanilla frosting. **8 outcomes**

2. A particular car comes in white, black, or red with standard or automatic transmission and with a 4-cylinder or 6-cylinder engine. **12 outcomes**

3. A choice of roses or carnations in red, yellow, pink, or white. **8 outcomes**

4. A choice of a queen or king size bed with a firm or super firm mattress. **4 outcomes**

5. A pizza can be ordered with a regular or deep dish crust and with a choice of one topping, two toppings, or three toppings. **6 outcomes**

6. A choice of red, white, blue, or black women's shoes with a choice of high, medium, or low heels. **12 outcomes**

Lesson 13-2   Find each value.

1. 8! **40,320**   2. 10! **3,628,800**   3. 0! **1**   4. 7! **5,040**   5. 6! **720**

6. 5! **120**   7. 2! **2**   8. 11! **39,916,800**   9. 9! **362,880**   10. 4! **24**

11. $P(5, 4)$ **120**   12. $P(3, 3)$ **6**   13. $P(12, 5)$ **95,040**   14. $P(8, 6)$ **20,160**

15. $P(10, 2)$ **90**   16. $P(6, 4)$ **360**   17. $P(7, 6)$ **5,040**   18. $P(9, 9)$ **362,880**

19. How many ways can a family of four be seated in a car if the father is driving? **6 ways**

20. In how many different ways can you arrange the letters in the word *orange* if you take the letters five at a time? **720 ways**

21. How many ways can you arrange five different colored marbles in a row if the blue one is always in the center? **24 ways**

22. In how many different ways can Kevin listen to each of his ten CDs once if he always saves a certain CD for last? **362,880 ways**

Lesson 13-3   Find each value.

1. $C(8, 4)$ 70
2. $C(30, 8)$ 5,852,925
3. $C(10, 9)$ 10
4. $C(7, 3)$ 35
5. $C(12, 5)$ 792
6. $C(17, 16)$ 17
7. $C(24, 17)$ 346,104
8. $C(9, 7)$ 36

9. How many ways can you choose five compact discs from a collection of 17? **6,188 ways**

10. How many combinations of three flavors of ice cream can you choose from 25 different flavors of ice cream? **2,300 combinations**

11. How many ways can you choose three books to read out of a selection of ten books?
    120 ways

12. How many ways can you choose seven apples out of a bag of two dozen apples?
    346,104 ways

13. How many ways can you choose two movies to rent out of ten possible movies? **45 ways**

Lesson 13-5   Two socks are drawn from a drawer which contains one red sock, three blue socks, two black socks, and two green socks. Once a sock is selected, it is not replaced. Find the probability of each outcome.

1. a black sock and then a green sock $\frac{1}{14}$
2. a red sock and then a green sock $\frac{1}{28}$
3. a blue sock two times in a row $\frac{3}{28}$
4. a green sock two times in a row $\frac{1}{28}$

There are three quarters, five dimes, and twelve pennies in a bag. Once a coin is drawn from the bag, it is not replaced. If two coins are drawn, find the probability of each outcome.

5. a quarter and then a penny $\frac{9}{95}$
6. a nickel and then a dime 0
7. a dime and then a penny $\frac{3}{19}$
8. a dime two times in a row $\frac{1}{19}$

Lesson 13-8   Use the survey on favorite type of music to answer each question.

1. What is the size of the sample? **250**

2. What is the mode? **light rock**

3. What fraction prefers country music? $\frac{36}{125}$

4. What fraction prefers rap music? $\frac{9}{50}$

Favorite Type of Music	
Country	72
Heavy Metal	41
Rap	45
Light Rock	92

Use the survey on favorite fruit to answer each question.

5. What is the size of the sample? **600**

6. If 7,950 people were to choose one of these three fruits, how many would you expect to choose an orange? **3,975 people**

Favorite Fruit	
Apple	155
Orange	300
Banana	145

Lesson 14-1   Write a monomial or polynomial for each model.

1.

$x^2 - 2x + 1$

2.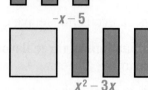

$-x - 5$

3.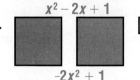

$-2x^2 + 1$

4.

$x^2 - 3x$

Model each monomial or polynomial using area tiles or drawings. **See Solutions Manual.**

5. $-x^2 + 7$
6. $3x + 3$
7. $3x^2 - 2x + 1$
8. $-5x + 1$

9. $x + 2$
10. $-2x^2 + 3x$
11. $-x - 4$
12. $x^2 + 2x + 3$

13. $2x^2 - 2$
14. $2x - 5$
15. $-x^2 + 7x$
16. $2x^2 - 3x$

Lesson 14-2   Name the like terms in each list of terms.   2. $-a, -3a; 2b^2, b^2$

1. $10x, 6y, y^2, 3x$ $10x, 3x$
2. $-a, 2b^2, -3a, b^2$
3. $2m, n, -m, n$ $2m, -m; n, n$

4. $9, 2, 7m, -m^2$ $9, 2$
5. $3y, 6, 5, y^2$ $6, 5$
6. $4x, 6, 2x, x^2$ $4x, 2x$

Write a polynomial in simplest form for each model.

7.

$-x^2 + 3x - 1$

8.

$3x^2 + 2$

9. $x^2 + 3y + 3$
10. $4m^2 + m + n$

Simplify each polynomial. If necessary, use area tiles or drawings.   **11.** $a^2 + 3b^2 + 3$

9. $-2y + 3 + x^2 + 5y$
10. $m + m^2 + n + 3m^2$
11. $a^2 + b^2 + 3 + 2b^2$

12. $1 + a + b + 6$
   $a + b + 7$
13. $x + x^2 + 5x - 3x^2$
   $-2x^2 + 6x$
14. $-2y + 3 + y - 2$
   $-y + 1$

Lesson 14-3   Find each sum. Use area tiles or drawings, if necessary.

1. $2x^2 - 5x + 7$
   $\underline{x^2 - x + 11}$
   $3x^2 - 6x + 18$

2. $2m^2 + m + 1$
   $\underline{-m^2 + 2m + 3}$
   $m^2 + 3m + 4$

3. $2a - b + 6c$
   $\underline{3a - 7b + 2c}$
   $5a - 8b + 8c$

4. $5a + 3a^2 - 2$
   $\underline{2a + 8a^2 + 4}$
   $7a + 11a^2 + 2$

5. $3c + b + a$
   $\underline{-c + b - a}$
   $2c + 2b$

6. $-z^2 + x^2 + 2y^2$
   $\underline{3z^2 + x^2 + y^2}$
   $2z^2 + 2x^2 + 3y^2$

7. $(5x + 6y) + (2x + 8y)$ $7x + 14y$
8. $(4a + 6b) + (2a + 3b)$ $6a + 9b$

9. $(7r + 11m) + (4m + 2r)$ $15m + 9r$
10. $(-z + z^2) + (-2z + z^2)$ $2z^2 - 3z$

11. $(3x - 7y) + (3y + 4x + 1)$ $7x - 4y + 1$
12. $(5m + 3n - 3) + (8m + 6)$ $13m + 3n + 3$

13. $(a + a^2) + (3a - 2a^2)$ $-a^2 + 4a$
14. $(3s - 5t) + (8t + 2s)$ $5s + 3t$

Lesson 14-4   Find each difference. Use area tiles or drawings, if necessary.

1. $(5a - 6m) - (2a + 5m)$ $3a - 11m$
2. $(2a - 7) - (8a - 11)$ $-6a + 4$
3. $(3 + 2a + a^2) - (5 + 8a)$ $a^2 - 6a - 2$
4. $(9r^2 - 3) - (11r^2 + 12)$ $-2r^2 - 15$
5. $(7y + 9x) - (6x + 5y)$ $3x + 2y$
6. $(5 - 2x) - (7 + 8x)$ $-10x - 2$
7. $(9x + 3y) - (9y + x)$ $8x - 6y$
8. $(3x^2 + 2x - 1) - (2x + 2)$ $3x^2 - 3$
9. $(a^2 + 6a + 3) - (5a^2 + 5)$ $-4a^2 + 6a - 2$
10. $(5a + 2) - (3a^2 + a + 8)$ $-3a^2 + 4a - 6$
11. $(3x^2 - 7x) - (8x - 6)$ $3x^2 - 15x + 6$
12. $(3m + 3n) - (m + 2n)$ $2m + n$
13. $(3m - 2) - (2m + 1)$ $m - 3$
14. $(x^2 - 2) - (x + 3)$ $x^2 - x - 5$
15. $(5x^2 - 4) - (3x^2 + 8x + 4)$ $2x^2 - 8x - 8$
16. $(7z^2 + 1) - (3z^2 + 2z - 6)$ $4z^2 - 2z + 7$

Lesson 14-5   Find each product. Use area tiles or drawings, if necessary.

1. $m(m + 2)$ $m^2 + 2m$
2. $x(x - 1)$ $x^2 - x$
3. $y(y - 2)$ $y^2 - 2y$
4. $a(a - 3)$ $a^2 - 3a$
5. $6(a + 3)$ $6a + 18$
6. $m(m - 7)$ $m^2 - 7m$
7. $z(z + 3)$ $z^2 + 3z$
8. $x(x + 10)$ $x^2 + 10x$
9. $y(y - 5)$ $y^2 - 5y$
10. $-2(x + 1)$ $-2x - 2$
11. $m(m - 2)$ $m^2 - 2m$
12. $3(y + 6)$ $3y + 18$
13. $3(m + 1)$ $3m + 3$
14. $z(z + 5)$ $z^2 + 5z$
15. $b(b + 1)$ $b^2 + b$
16. $-3(a + 2)$ $-3a - 6$

Factor. Use area tiles or drawings, if necessary.

17. $3m + 3$ $3(m + 1)$
18. $-2x - 2$ $-2(x + 1)$
19. $-4b - 4$ $-4(b + 1)$
20. $2z + 2$ $2(z + 1)$
21. $z^2 - 5z$ $z(z - 5)$
22. $c^2 + 2c$ $c(c + 2)$
23. $z^2 + 3z$ $z(z + 3)$
24. $-6a - 6$ $-6(a + 1)$
25. $a^2 + 3a$ $a(a + 3)$
26. $2m^2 + m$ $m(2m + 1)$
27. $y^2 - 2y$ $y(y - 2)$
28. $n^2 + 4n$ $n(n + 4)$
29. $6b + 6$ $6(b + 1)$
30. $x^2 + 6x$ $x(x + 6)$
31. $5x + 5$ $5(x + 1)$
32. $7y - 7$ $7(y - 1)$

Lesson 14-6   Name the two binomials being multiplied and give their product.

1.
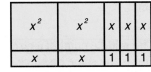

2.
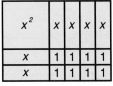

$(2x + 3)(x + 1) = 2x^2 + 5x + 3$ $(x + 4)(x + 2) = x^2 + 6x + 8$

Find each product. Use area tiles or drawings, if necessary.

8. $a^2 + 10a + 21$ 11. $2z^2 + 17z + 8$
5. $3x^2 + 10x + 7$

3. $(r + 3)(r + 4)$ $r^2 + 7r + 12$
4. $(z + 5)(z + 2)$ $z^2 + 7z + 10$
5. $(3x + 7)(x + 1)$
6. $(x + 5)(2x + 3)$ $2x^2 + 13x + 15$
7. $(c + 1)(c + 1)$ $c^2 + 2c + 1$
8. $(a + 3)(a + 7)$
9. $(b + 3)(b + 1)$ $b^2 + 4b + 3$
10. $(2y + 1)(y + 3)$ $2y^2 + 7y + 3$
11. $(z + 8)(2z + 1)$
12. $(2m + 4)(m + 5)$
13. $(x + 3)(x + 2)$ $x^2 + 5x + 6$
14. $(c + 2)(c + 8)$
15. $(r + 4)(r + 4)$ $r^2 + 8r + 16$
16. $(2x + 4)(x + 4)$ $2x^2 + 12x + 16$
17. $(6y + 1)(y + 3)$
12. $2m^2 + 14m + 20$
14. $c^2 + 10c + 16$
17. $6y^2 + 19y + 3$

Glossary

A **absolute value** (87)   The number of units a number is from zero on the number line.

acute angle (183)   Any angle that measures between 0° and 90°.

addition property of equality (51)   If you add the same number to each side of an equation, the two sides remain equal. If $a = b$, then $a + c = b + c$.

additive inverse (99)   Two integers that are opposites of each other are called additive inverses. The sum of any number and its additive inverse is zero, $a + (-a) = 0$.

algebraic expression (45)   A combination of variables, numbers, and at least one operation.

alternate exterior angles (176)   In the figure, transversal t intersects lines ℓ and m. $\angle 1$ and $\angle 7$, and $\angle 2$ and $\angle 8$ are alternate exterior angles. If lines ℓ and m are parallel these angles are congruent.

alternate interior angles (176)   In the figure, transversal t intersects lines ℓ and m. $\angle 3$ and $\angle 5$, and $\angle 4$ and $\angle 6$ are alternate interior angles. If lines ℓ and m are parallel these angles are congruent.

altitude (75, 278)   A segment in a quadrilateral that is perpendicular to both bases, with endpoints on the base lines.

altitude (487)   The segment that goes from the vertex of a pyramid to its base and is perpendicular to the base.

area (73)   The number of square units needed to cover a surface.

arithmetic sequence (272)   A sequence of numbers in which you can find the next term by adding the same number to the previous term.

associative property of addition (9)   For any numbers a, b, and c, $(a + b) + c = a + (b + c)$.

associative property of multiplication (9)   For any numbers a, b, and c, $(a \cdot b) \cdot c = a \cdot (b \cdot c)$.

B **back-to-back stem-and-leaf plot** (141)   Used to compare two sets of data. The leaves of one set of data are on one side of the stem and the leaves for the other set are on the other side of the stem.

bar notation (230)   In repeating decimals, the line or bar placed over the digits that repeat. Another way to write 2.636363 is $2.\overline{63}$.

base (35)   The number used as a factor. In 10^3, 10 is the base.

base (75)   Any side of a parallelogram.

base (278)   The parallel sides of a trapezoid.

base (381)   In a percent proportion, the number to which the percentage is compared.

base (471)   The bases of a prism are the two parallel, congruent sides.

binomial (560)   A polynomial with two terms.

box-and-whisker plot (155)   A diagram that summarizes data using the median, the upper and lower quartiles, and the extreme values. A box is drawn around the quartile value and the whiskers extend from each quartile to the extreme data points.

C **center** (284)   The middle point of a circle or sphere. The center is the same distance from all points on the circle or sphere.

circle (284)   The set of all points in a plane that are the same distance from a given point called the center.

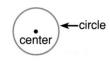

circle graph (403)   A type of statistical graph used to compare parts of a whole.

circular cone (488)   A shape in space that has a circular base and one vertex.

circular cylinder (478)   A cylinder with two bases that are parallel, congruent circular regions.

circumference (284)   The distance around a circle.

clustering (11)   A method used to estimate decimal sums and differences by rounding a group of closely related numbers to the same whole number.

combination (512)   Arrangements or listings where order is not important.

common difference (272)   The difference between any two consecutive terms in an arithmetic sequence.

common ratio (273)   The constant factor used to multiply consecutive terms in a geometric sequence.

commutative property of addition (8)   For any numbers a and b, $a + b = b + a$.

commutative property of multiplication (8)   For any numbers a and b, $a \cdot b = b \cdot a$.

compatible numbers (11)   Two numbers that are easy to divide mentally. They are often members of fact families and can be used as an estimation strategy.

compensation (8)   A math strategy in which you simplify a problem by making equivalent adjustments to each part.
$$397 + 3 \rightarrow 400$$
$$+ 103 - 3 \rightarrow \underline{100}$$
$$500$$

composite number (215)   Any whole number greater than one that has more than two factors.

congruent figures (197)   Figures that are exactly the same size and shape.

converse (321)   The converse of the Pythagorean Theorem can be used to test whether a triangle is a right triangle. If the sides of the triangle have lengths a, b, and c, such that $c^2 = a^2 + b^2$, then the triangle is a right triangle.

coordinate (86)   A number associated with a point on a number line.

coordinate system (117)   Two perpendicular number lines that intersect at their zero points form a coordinate system.

corresponding angles (177)   Angles that hold the same position on two different parallel lines cut by a transversal.

cosine (368)   If $\triangle ABC$ is a right triangle and A is an acute angle,
$$\cos A = \frac{\text{measure of the leg adjacent to } \angle A}{\text{measure of the hypotenuse}}.$$

cross product (344) If the cross products in a ratio are equal then the ratio forms a proportion. In the proportion $\frac{2}{3} = \frac{8}{12}$, the cross products are 2×12 and 3×8.

customary system (26)   A system of weights and measures frequently used in the United States. The basic unit of weight is the pound, and the basic unit of capacity is the quart.

D   data analysis (130)   To study data and draw conclusions from the numbers observed.

dependent event (522)   Two or more events in which the outcome of one event does affect the outcome of the other event or events.

diameter (284)   The distance across a circle through its center.

dilation (361)   The process of reducing or enlarging an image in mathematics.

discount (409)   The amount by which the regular price is reduced.

distributive property (8)   The sum of two addends multiplied by a number is the sum of the product of each addend and the number.
$$a \cdot (b + c) = a \cdot b + a \cdot c.$$

divisible (212)   A number is divisible by another if the quotient is a whole number and the remainder is zero.

division property of equality (55)   If each side of an equation is divided by the same nonzero number, then the two sides remain equal.
If $a = b$, then $\frac{a}{c} = \frac{b}{c}$, $c \neq 0$.

domain (423)   The set of input values in a function.

E **edge** (471)   The intersection of faces of three-dimensional figures.

equation (48)   A mathematical sentence that contains an equals sign, =.

equilateral triangle (183)   A triangle that has three congruent sides.

evaluate (35, 44)   To find the value of an expression by replacing variables with numerals.

event (233)   A specific outcome or type of outcome.

experimental probability (528)   An estimated probability based on the relative frequency of positive outcomes occurring during an experiment.

exponent (35)   The number of times the base is used as a factor. In 10^3, the exponent is 3.

F **face** (471)   Any surface that forms a side or a base of a prism.

factor (35)   When two or more numbers are multiplied, each number is a factor of the product.

factorial (507)   The expression $n!$ is the product of all counting numbers beginning with n and counting backwards to 1.

factoring (558)   Finding the factors of a product.

factor tree (215)   A diagram used to illustrate the factorization of a number.

frequency table (130)   A table for organizing a set of data that shows the number of times each item or number appears.

front-end-estimation (11)   A method used to estimate decimal sums and differences by adding or subtracting the front-end digits, then adjusting by estimating the sum or difference of the remaining digits, then adding the two values.

function (422)   A relationship in which the output value depends upon the input according to a specified rule. For example, with a function $f(x) = 2x$, if the input is 5, the output is 10.

Fundamental Principle of Counting (504)   If event M can occur in m ways and is followed by event N that can occur in n ways, then the event M followed by event N can occur in $m \times n$ ways.

G **geometric sequence** (273)   When consecutive terms of a sequence are formed by multiplying by a constant factor, the sequence is called a geometric sequence.

gram (23)   The basic unit of mass in the metric system.

graph (86)   A dot marking a point that represents a number on a number line or an ordered pair on a coordinate plane.

greatest common factor (GCF) (221)   The greatest of the common factors of two or more numbers. The greatest common factor of 18 and 24 is 6.

H **height** (73, 278)   The length of the altitude of a quadrilateral.

histogram (133)   A special kind of bar graph that displays the frequency of data that has been organized into equal intervals. The intervals cover all possible values of data, therefore there are no spaces between the bars of the graph.

hypotenuse (319)   In a right triangle, the side opposite the right angle is called the hypotenuse.

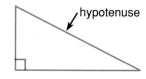
hypotenuse

I **independent event** (521)   Two or more events in which the outcome of one event does not affect the outcome of the other event or events.

indirect measurement (356)   A technique using proportions to find a measurement.

inequality (77)   Any sentence that contains $>$, $<$, $\neq$, $\leq$, $\geq$.

integers (86)   The whole numbers and their opposites. . . . , -3, -2, -1, 0, 1, 2, 3, . . .

interest (412)   The amount charged or paid for the use of money.

interquartile range (151)   The range of the middle half of data.

inverse operation (52)   Pairs of operations that undo each other. Addition and subtraction are inverse operations. Multiplication and division are inverse operations.

irrational number (310)   Numbers that cannot be expressed as $\frac{a}{b}$, where a and b are integers and $b \neq 0$.

isosceles triangle (183)   A triangle that has two congruent sides.

leaf (141)   The second greatest place value of data in a stem-and-leaf plot.

least common denominator (LCD) (241)   The least common multiple of the denominators of two or more fractions.

least common multiple (LCM) (236)   The least of the common multiples of two or more numbers, other than zero. The least common multiple of 2 and 3 is 6.

leg (319)   Either of the two sides of a right triangle that form the right angle.

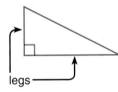

like terms (546)   Expressions that contain the same variables, such as $3ab$ and $7ab$.

linear function (433)   An equation in which the graphs of the solutions form a line.

line plot (136)   A graph that uses an X above a number on a number line each time that number occurs in a set of data.

line symmetry (192)
Figures that match exactly when folded in half have line symmetry.

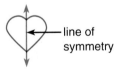

line of symmetry (451)   A fold line on a figure that shows symmetry. Some figures can be folded in more than one way to show symmetry.

liter (23)   The basic unit of capacity in the metric system. A liter is a little more than a quart.

lower quartile (152)   The median of the lower half of data in an interquartile range.

mean (145)   The sum of the numbers in a set of data divided by the number of pieces of data; the arithmetic average.

median (146)   The number in the middle when the data are arranged in order. When there are two middle numbers, the median is their mean.

meter (23)   The basic unit of length in the metric system.

metric system (23)   A system of weights and measures based on tens. The meter is the basic unit of length, the kilogram is the basic unit of weight, and the liter is the basic unit of capacity.

mixed number (256)   A number that shows the sum of a whole number and a fraction. $6\frac{2}{3}$ and $9\frac{1}{2}$ are mixed numbers.

mode (145)   The number or item that appears most often in a set of data.

monomial (543)   A number, a variable, or a product of a number and one or more variables.

multiple (236)   The product of a number and any whole number.

multiplication property of equality (55)   If each side of an equation is multiplied by the same number, then the two sides remain equal. If $a = b$, then $ac = bc$.

multiplicative inverse (265)   A number times its multiplicative inverse is equal to 1. The multiplicative inverse of $\frac{2}{3}$ is $\frac{3}{2}$.

numerical expression (44)   A mathematical expression that has a combination of numbers and at least one operation. $4 + 2$ is a numerical expression.

obtuse (183)   Any angle that measures between 90° and 180°.

open sentence (48)   An equation that contains a variable.

opposite (99)   Two integers are opposites if they are represented on the number line by points that are the same distance from zero, but on opposite sides of zero. The sum of opposites is zero.

order of operations (44)   The rules to follow when more than one operation is used. 1. Do all operations within grouping symbols first; start with the innermost grouping symbols. 2. Do all powers before other operations. 3. Do multiplication and division in order from left to right. 4. Do all addition and subtraction in order from left to right.

ordered pair (117)   A pair of numbers where order is important. An ordered pair that is graphed on a coordinate plane is written in this form: (x-coordinate, y-coordinate).

origin (117)   The point of intersection of the x-axis and y-axis in a coordinate system.

outcome (233, 504)   One possible result of a probability event. 4 is an outcome when a die is rolled.

outliers (155)   Data that are more than 1.5 times the interquartile range from the upper or lower quartiles.

P parallel (176)   Lines that are in the same plane but do not intersect.

parallelogram (73)   A quadrilateral that has both pairs of opposite sides parallel.

Pascal's Triangle (515)   A triangular arrangement of numbers in which each number is the sum of the two numbers to the right and to the left of it in the row above.

pentagon (353)   A polygon having five sides.

percent (380) A ratio that compares a number to 100.

percent proportion (381)
$$\frac{\text{Percentage}}{\text{Base}} = \text{Rate or } \frac{P}{B} = \frac{r}{100}.$$

percentage (381)   In a percent proportion, a number (P) that is compared to another number called the base (B).

perfect square (304)   Squares of whole numbers.

perimeter (73)   The distance around a geometric figure.

permutation (507)   An arrangement, or listing, of objects in which order is important.

perpendicular lines (183)   Two lines or line segments that intersect to form right angles.

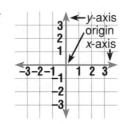

polygon (353)   A simple closed figure in a plane formed by three or more line segments.

polynomial (543)   The sum or difference of two or more monomials.

population (533)   The entire group of items or individuals from which the samples under consideration are taken.

power (35)   A number expressed using an exponent. The power 7^3 is read *seven to the third power,* or *seven cubed.*

precision (491)   The precision of a measurement depends on the unit of measure. The smaller the unit the more precise the measurement is.

prime factorization (215)   A composite number that is expressed as the product of prime numbers. The prime factorization of 12 is $2 \times 2 \times 3.$

prime number (215)   A number that has exactly two factors, 1 and the number itself.

principal (412)   The amount of an investment or a debt.

principal square root (304)   A nonnegative square root.

prism (471)   A three-dimensional figure that has two parallel and congruent bases in the shape of polygons.

probability (233)   The ratio of the number of ways an event can occur to the number of possible outcomes; how likely it is that an event will occur.

proportion (344)   A proportion is an equation that shows that two ratios are equivalent; $\frac{a}{b} = \frac{c}{d}, b \neq 0, d \neq 0$.

pyramid (487)   A figure in space with three or more triangular faces and a base in the shape of a polygon.

Pythogorean Theorem (319)   In a right triangle, the square of the hypotenuse is equal to the sum of the squares of the legs. $c^2 = a^2 + b^2$.

Pythagorean triple (323)   A set of three integers that satisfy the Pythagorean Theorem.

Q **quadrant** (117)   One of the four regions into which two perpendicular number lines separate a plane.

quadratic function (442)   A function in which the greatest power is 2.

quadrilateral (187)   Any four-sided figure.

quartile (151)   Values that divide data into four equal parts.

R **radical sign** (304)   The symbol used to represent a nonnegative square root is $\sqrt{}$.

radius (284)   The distance from the center of a circle to any point on the circle.

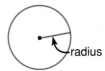

random (233)   Outcomes occur at random if each outcome is equally likely to occur.

random (533)   Making selections unsystematically where everything has an equal chance of being selected.

range (151)   The difference between the greatest number and the least number in a set of data.

range (423)   The set of output values in a function.

rate (338)   A ratio of two quantities with different units.

rate (381)   In a percent proportion, the ratio of a number to 100.

rate (412)   The percent charged or paid for the use of money.

ratio (338)   A comparison of two numbers by division. The ratio comparing 2 to 3 can be stated as 2 out of 3, 2 to 3, 2:3, or $\frac{2}{3}$.

rational number (224)   Any number that can be expressed in the form $\frac{a}{b}$, where a and b are integers and $b \neq 0$.

real number (311)   Irrational numbers together with rational numbers form the set of real numbers.

reciprocal (265)   Another name for a multiplicative inverse.

rectangle (73)   A parallelogram with all angles congruent.

rectangular prism (475)   A prism with rectangles as bases.

reflection (192, 451)   A mirror image of a figure across a line of symmetry.

repeating decimal (230)   A decimal whose digits repeat in groups of one or more. Examples are $0.181818\ldots$ and $0.83333\ldots$ Using bar notation, these examples are written $0.\overline{18}$ and $0.8\overline{3}$.

replacement set (49)   A set of numbers from which to choose the value of a variable for an equation.

rhombus (187)   A parallelogram that has four congruent sides.

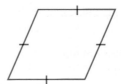

right angle (183)   An angle that measures exactly 90°.

rotation (202, 454)   Transformations of tessellations that involve a turn about the vertices of the base figure.

rotational symmetry (193)   A figure has rotational symmetry if it can be turned less than 360° about its center and still looks like the original.

rounding (11)   A method used to estimate by changing numbers to the nearest tens, hundreds, thousands, and so on. 387 in round numbers would be 390 to the nearest tens or 400 to the nearest hundreds.

S **sale price** (409)   The price after the discount has been subtracted.

sample (165, 533)   A randomly selected group chosen for the purpose of collecting data.

scale factor (361)   The ratio of a dilated image to the original image.

scalene triangle (183)   A triangle with no congruent sides.

scatter plot (159)   A graph that shows the general relationship between two sets of data.

scientific notation (245)   A way of expressing numbers as the product of a number that is at least 1, but less than 10, and a power of 10. In scientific notation 5,500 is 5.5×10^3.

sequence (272)   A list of numbers in a specific order.

significant digits (491)   All of the digits of a measurement that are known to be accurate plus one estimated digit.

similar figures (198) Figures that have the same shape but may differ in size are similar.

similar polygons (353)   Two polygons are similar if their corresponding angles are congruent and their corresponding sides are in proportion. They have the same shape but may not have the same size.

simplest form (224)   The form of a fraction where the GCF of the numerator and denominator is 1.

simplest form (546)   An expression that has no like terms in it. In simplest form $6x + 8x$ is $14x$.

simulation (525)   The process of acting out a problem.

sine (368)   If $\triangle ABC$ is a right triangle and A is an acute angle,
$$\sin A = \frac{\text{measure of the leg opposite } \angle A}{\text{measure of the hypotenuse}}.$$

solid (471)   Three-dimensional figures.

solution (48)   The value for a variable that makes an equation true. The solution for $10 + y = 25$ is 15.

square (73)   A parallelogram with all sides congruent and all angles congruent.

square root (304)   One of the two equal factors of a number. If $a^2 = b$, then a is the square root of b. The square root of 144 is 12 because $12^2 = 144$.

statistics (130)   The branch of mathematics that deals with collecting, organizing, and analyzing data.

stem (141)   The greatest place value of data in a stem-and-leaf plot.

stem-and-leaf plot (141)   A system used to condense a set of data where the greatest place value of the data forms the stem and the next greatest place values forms the leaves.

subtraction property of equality (51)   If you subtract the same number from each side of an equation, then the two sides remain equal. If $a = b$, then $a - c = b - c$.

substitute (44)   To replace a variable in an algebraic expression with a number, creating a numerical expression.

surface area (475)   The sum of the area of all the faces of a three-dimensional figure.

symmetric (451)   Figures that can be folded into two identical parts.

system of equations (436)   A common solution for two or more equations.

T **tangent** (365)   If $\triangle ABC$ is a right triangle and A is an acute angle,
$$\tan A = \frac{\text{measure of the leg opposite } \angle A}{\text{measure of the leg adjacent to } \angle A}.$$

term (546)   A number, a variable, or a product of numbers and variables.

term of the sequence (272)   A number in a sequence.

terminating decimal (227)   A quotient in which the division ends with a remainder of zero. 0.25 and 0.125 are terminating decimals.

tessellation (202)   A repetitive pattern of polygons that fit together with no holes or gaps.

theoretical probability (528)   The long-term probability of an outcome based on mathematical principles.

time (412)   When used to calculate interest, time is given in years.

transformation (202)   Movements of geometric figures to modify tessellations.

translation (202)   A method used to make changes in the polygons of tessellations by sliding a pattern to create the same change on opposite sides.

translation (447)   To translate a point as described by an ordered pair, add the coordinates of the ordered pair to the coordinates of the point. (x, y) moved (a, b) becomes $(x = a, y = b)$.

transversal (176)   A line that intersects two other lines to form eight angles.

trapezoid (187, 278)   A quadrilateral with exactly two parallel sides.

tree diagram (504)   A diagram used to show the total number of possible outcomes in a probability experiment.

triangular prism (476)   A prism with triangles as bases.

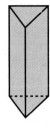

trigonometry (368)   The study of triangle measurement.

unit rate (338)   A rate that has a denominator of 1. This type of rate is frequently used when comparing statistics.

upper quartile (152)   The median of the upper half of data in an interquartile range.

variable (45)   A symbol, usually a letter, used to represent a number in mathematical expressions or sentences.

variation (151)   The spread in the values in a set of data.

Venn diagram (181)   A diagram using circles and rectangles to represent various types of mathematical sets and to show the relationship between them.

vertex (471)   A vertex of a polygon is any point of intersection of the sides of a polygon.

vertex (487)   The vertex of a pyramid is the point where all the faces except the base intersect.

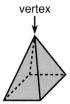

vertex

volume (482)   The number of cubic units required to fill a space.

x-axis (117)   The horizontal line of the two number lines in a coordinate plane.

x-coordinate (117)   The first number of an ordered pair.

y-axis (117)   The vertical line of the two perpendicular number lines in a coordinate plane.

y-coordinate (117)   The second number of an ordered pair.

Selected Answers

1 Tools for Problem Solving

Pages 6-7   Lesson 1-1
4. 12:30 A.M.   5.a. beaker + sodium chloride = 84.8 grams; beaker = 63.3 grams   b. subtract the two masses   c. 21.5 grams   d. yes
7. 3,000 ft   9. $0.50   11. 2,000 ft   13. 4 by 4 by 4

Pages 9-10   Lesson 1-2
4. 67   5. 145   6. 677   7. 320   8. 148
9. 93,000   10. 245   11. 4,300   12. 169
13. 153   15. 135   17. 5,300   19. 827
21. 100   23. 1,400   25. 79   27. 1,123
29. 300   31. $2.65   32. 3 hours
33. 28 cards

Pages 13-14   Lesson 1-3
4. 5,000   5. 700   6. 0.09   7. front-end estimation, 1,590   8. rounding, 1,000
9. rounding, 1,000   10. rounding, $9
11. rounding, 6   12. clustering, 10   13. 9,000, 8,900   15. 0.3, 0.25   17. 60
19. 20,000   21. 200   23. 60   25. 198   27. 42 pounds   28. 96 pounds   29. 315   30. 622
31. about 200,000 sheets of paper   33.a. about 2,500 ft of fence

Pages 15-16   Lesson 1-4
3. No 45,000 ÷ 1,500 = 30, not 300   4. 200 crates
5. $10.00   7. They are equal.   9. 50 sit-ups
11. 23¢ for each ounce over 1 ounce; more

Pages 18-19   Lesson 1-5
3. b   4. c   5. b   7. 3981 or 1101   9. 10
11. a

Page 19   Mid-Chapter Review
1. $55.02   3. $7.97   5. 28   7. 1,000   9. 37

Pages 24-25   Lesson 1-6
4. centimeter   5. milliliter   6. kilogram
7. kilometer   8. kiloliter   9. millimeter
10. × by 1,000 = 10,000 mg   11. × by 1,000 = 1,000,000 m   12. ÷ by 1,000 = 0.00439 L
13. ÷ by 1,000 = 0.0015 L   14. ÷ by 1,000 =

0.0593 kg   15. ÷ by 1,000 = 0.00789 km
17. 0.525   19. 1,370   21. 9,240   23. 92.4
25. 0.0723 mm   27. 947 mL   28. 4 goldfish
29. 378, distributive property   30. 4,000
31. 6

Pages 27-28   Lesson 1-7
4. × by 16 = 48   5. ÷ by 2,000 = 3   6. ÷ by 4 = 6   7. × by 36 = 90   8. ÷ by 5,280 ≈ 1.52
9. × by 8 = 80   11. 26,400   13. 56   15. 3.5
17. 42   19. $\frac{1}{4}$ gallon   21. 144 in.
23. Subtract 5 from both numbers and subtract the new numbers; 251.   24. 1,400   25. 279 cm
26. 32 coffee mugs   29. 105 feet   31. about 45 feet   33. 9.72 s faster

Page 34   Lesson 1-8
4. 7   5. 14   6. 100   7. all but 0   8. 3
9. 5 years old   11. $20.30

Pages 36-37   Lesson 1-9
5. 5^3 6. 10^4 7. 8^5 8. 125   9. 49
10. 144   11. 1,080,000   13. $6^3 \cdot 7^2$ 15. 625
17. 32   19. 196   21. 1,000,000   23. 32
25. 342   26. $40   27. 5.734 kg   28. 3 pints
29. 2.5 lb for $2.70   33. 2,048
35.a. 2,870,000,000   b. 10^7 and 10^8

Pages 38-40   Study Guide and Review
7. 27   9. 145   11. 517   13. $7.56
15. 84   17. 149   19. 3,400   21. 40
23. 20,000   25. 0.0034   27. 0.620
29. 0.00862   31. 4.5   33. 5   35. 64
37. $3^2 \cdot 8^3$ 39. 16   41. 1,250,000
43. 2.25 min   45. 80 yd

2 An Introduction to Algebra

Pages 46-47   Lesson 2-1
5. multiplication; 39   6. multiplication; 17
7. division; 1   8. addition in parentheses; 5
9. power in parentheses; 75   10. subtraction in parentheses; 6   11. 39   12. 8   13. 78   14.
42   15. 36   16. 144   17. 53   19. 10   21. 22
23. 2   25. 101   27. 0   29. 72 ÷ (6 + 3) = 8

31. $7 + 4^2 \div (2 + 6) = 9$ **33.** $4 + 8 - (7 - 5)$ $= 10$ **34.** 3 **35.** 1,500 **36.** 1,725 meters **37.** 4,000 pounds **38.** 288 **39.** 68 grams of protein **41.** $(4 \cdot 7 - 3)\ (6 - 5 + 2 + 1)$

Pages 49-50   Lesson 2-2
4. 52 **5.** $0.80 **6.** 16 **7.** 99 **8.** 20 **9.** 50 **10.** $1.74 **11.** 15 **13.** $2.67 **15.** $6.06 **17.** 7 **19.** 31 **21.** 7 **23.** 7,800 **24.** 3,500 **25.** $5^2 \cdot 8^3$ **26.** 3 **27.** 10,800 ft^2 **29.** $99 **31.** less than 150 pounds

Pages 52-53   Lesson 2-3
5. 6 **6.** 30 **7.** 224 **8.** 123 **9.** 33 **10.** 25 **11.** 29 **12.** 0.3 **13.** 6 **15.** 90 **17.** 20.1 **19.** 254 **21.** 2.22 **23.** 9.8 **25.** 2.89 **26.** 444 **27.** 4,280 mg **28.** $2\frac{1}{2}$ gallons **29.** 52 **31.** 60°

Pages 55-56   Lesson 2-4
4. 3 **5.** 4 **6.** 8 **7.** 126 **8.** 92 **9.** 540 **10.** 92 **11.** 2.16 **12.** 40.5 **13.** 61 **15.** 350 **17.** 2.3 **19.** 200 **21.** $16 **23.** about 90 **24.** 28 **25.** 93 **27.** 350 items

Pages 58-59   Lesson 2-5
4. 1 **5.** 100 **6.** 198 **7.** $136.50 **9.** $52.80 **11.** $8,100

Page 59   Mid-Chapter Review
1. 40 **3.** 19 **5.** 9 m **7.** 19.1 **9.** 150

Pages 63-64   Lesson 2-6
4. $p + 17$ **5.** $\frac{x}{3}$ **6.** $6r$ **7.** $m - 4$ **8.** $2t + 3$ **9.** $6 - m = 25$ **10.** $8 - \frac{a}{4} = 19$ **11.** $5x + 2 = 37$ **13.** $18 - n$ **15.** $24 - 2x$ **17.** $s + 200 **19.** $\frac{24}{x} - 2 = 2$ **21.** $2p + 6$ **23.** $3c - 14 = 46$ **25.** 98 **26.** 0.0347 liters **27.** 56 ounces **28.** 32 **29.** 7

Pages 68-69   Lesson 2-7
4. subtract 3; 2 **5.** subtract 8; 3 **6.** add 5.3; 1 **7.** subtract 0.8; 4.5 **8.** add 3; 28 **9.** subtract 7; 2 **11.** 4 **13.** 2 **15.** 192 **17.** 0.5 **19.** 0.15 **21.** 0.5 **23.** $\frac{x}{6} - 7 = 12; 114$

25. about 12 **26.** 432 **27.** 112 **28.** $4x - 8$ **29.a.** $\frac{x}{625} = 24$ **b.** 15,000 cans **31.** $10 + 6x = 40; 5$

Pages 71-72   Lesson 2-8
4. $0.68 **5.** 5 **6.** 126 adult, 252 student **7.** 31.25 days **9.** 12 **11.** about 2 **13.** West-$29,900 more; midwest $27,300 less; northeast-$15,400 more; south-$36,600 less **15.a.** 39.8 grams **b.** 16-karat gold

Pages 75-76   Lesson 2-9
4. 26 m; 42.25 m^2 **5.** 22 yd; 30 yd^2 **6.** 36 ft; 66 ft^2 **7.** 18.4 in.; 18.6 in^2 **9.** 20 units; 24 units^2 **11.** 16 m; 12.4 m^2 **13.** 48 cm **15.** 13,000 lb **16.** 100 **17.** 12 **21.a.** the third one **b.** when the darkened squares are not squares of the same color on a checkerboard.

Pages 78-79   Lesson 2-10
5. $t > 5$ **6.** $a > 7$ **7.** $d < 9$ **8.** $y < 15$ **9.** $m > 5$ **10.** $p < 9$ **11.** $x < 17$ **13.** $b > 15$ **15.** $g < 9$ **17.** $a > 7$ **19.** $c > 3$ **21.** $a > 4$ **23.** $5x > 60; x > 12$ **25.** $4x + 15 > 13; x > 2$ **26.** 1,169 **27.** $\frac{x}{3} + 20 = 25$ **28.** 28 **29.** $P = 14$ cm; $A = 10$ cm^2 **33.b.** 2,4; 3; 0,1

Pages 80-82   Study Guide and Review
9. 30 **11.** 20 **13.** 56 **15.** 30 **17.** 113 **19.** 42 **21.** 5 **23.** 2.48 **25.** 6 **27.** $8 - y$ $= 31$ **29.** $8 + 6u$ **31.** 55 **33.** 208 **35.** 7 **37.** 24 m, 28 m^2 **39.** $g > 6$ **41.** $a > 3$ **43.** $8, $12 **45.** 5 necklaces

3 Integers

Page 88   Lesson 3-1
5. A, -6; B, -1; C, 2; D, 5 **6.** 4 **7.** 3 **8.** 23 **9.** 129 **10.** 0

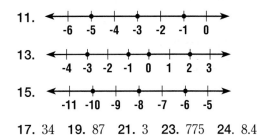

11. $\begin{array}{|c c c c c c c|} \hline \text{-6} & \text{-5} & \text{-4} & \text{-3} & \text{-2} & \text{-1} & 0 \\ \hline \end{array}$

13. $\begin{array}{|c c c c c c c c|} \hline \text{-4} & \text{-3} & \text{-2} & \text{-1} & 0 & 1 & 2 & 3 \\ \hline \end{array}$

15. $\begin{array}{|c c c c c c c|} \hline \text{-11} & \text{-10} & \text{-9} & \text{-8} & \text{-7} & \text{-6} & \text{-5} \\ \hline \end{array}$

17. 34 **19.** 87 **21.** 3 **23.** 775 **24.** 8.4

25. $b > 6$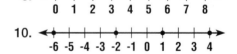
(number line showing open circle at 6, marked 0 1 2 3 4 5 6 7 8 9 10 11)

Page 90   Lesson 3-2
4. > **5.** > **6.** < **7.** < **8.** > **9.** <
10. {-99, -7, -1, 0, 8, 34, 123} **11.** {129, 78, 65,
34, 1, -6, -99, -665} **13.** < **15.** < **17.** >
19. < **21.** {-56, -33, -9, -7, 0, 34, 99} **23.** 21
24. 24 **25.** 16

Pages 93-94   Lesson 3-3
5. − **6.** − **7.** + **9.** 0 **10.** − **11.** 20
12. -7 **13.** 41 **14.** -59 **15.** 0 **16.** 108
17. -33 **19.** 72 **21.** -130 **23.** -56 **25.** 54
27. 718 **29.** 50 **31.** -8 **33.** -5
35. 6 pounds **36.** $4^2 \cdot 6^3$ **37.** 7 **38.** $4x$
39. < **41.** They will lose $6.99 because they
are selling the shoes for less than they bought
them for. **43.a.** about 1,200 **b.** No one could
afford telephone service during the depression.

Pages 96-97   Lesson 3-4
4. 18 **5.** 14 **6.** -3 **7.** 22 **8.** 0 **9.** -3
10. 19 **11.** 15 **12.** 14 **13.** -4 **15.** 17
17. 20 **19.** 3 **21.** 12 **23.** 54 **25.** -36
27. -11 **29.** 2 **31.** 22 **32.** 36 oz **33.** 32
34. $s < 9$ **35.** 38 **39.a.** gained 3 yards
b. lost 8 yards

Pages 100-101   Lesson 3-5
5. -10 **6.** 9 **7.** -30 **8.** 29 **9.** $4 + 7 = y$; 11
10. $n = -43 + (-99)$; -142 **11.** $p = -23 + 2$; -21
12. $53 + (-78) = z$; -25 **13.** $y = 14 + (-14)$; 0
14. $11 + 19 = p$; 30 **15.** $x = 17 + 26$; 43
16. $123 + 33 = n$; 156 **17.** $b = -345 + 67$; -412
19. 93 **21.** 1,313 **23.** -131 **25.** -8 **27.** 78
29. -735 **31.** 143 **33.** 52 **35.** 13 **37.** -3
39. -6 **41.** 125 **42.** 20 **43.** 64 cm²
44. {128, 52, 15, 4, 0, -3, -22, -78} **45.** 47
47.a. Asia: 9,247 m; S. America: 6,999 m;
N. America: 6,280 m; Europe: 5,661 m; Africa:
6,050 m. **b.** -115 meters

Page 101   Mid-Chapter Review
1. 64 **3.** 4 **5.** {-7, -3, -2, 0, 5, 6, 8} **7.** 0
9. 0 **11.** -114

Pages 104-105   Lesson 3-6
6. − **7.** − **8.** + **9.** 0 **10.** -27 **11.** -150

12. -99 **13.** 21 **14.** 24 **15.** 96 **16.** -108
17. 120 **18.** -18 **19.** 64 **20.** 70 **21.** 35
23. -63 **25.** -81 **27.** 78 **29.** 504 **31.** 805
33. 441 **35.** -72 **37.** 54 **39.** -108 **41.** $55
42. 0.0394 km **43.** 41
44.
(number line marked -4 -3 -2 -1 0 1 2 3 with points at -3, -1, 1)
45. 83 **47.** Alaska; Hawaii

Pages 107-108   Lesson 3-7
4. − **5.** − **6.** + **7.** − **8.** -4 **9.** -73
10. 3 **11.** -49 **12.** -7 **13.** -2 **14.** 9
15. 28 **16.** 7 **17.** -31 **19.** -188 **21.** 59
23. -98 **25.** 33 **27.** -80 **29.** 5 **31.** -38
33. -31 **35.** 150 **37.** 186 **38.** 18
39. 32 inches **40.** 11 **41.** 960 **43.** about
$5,150

Pages 109-110   Lesson 3-8
3. not enough information **4.** too much
information; 143°F **5.** too much information;
about 2,500 feet **7.** not enough information
9. 125 **11.** $560

Pages 115-116   Lesson 3-9
4. -45 **5.** -80 **6.** -448 **7.** -275 **8.** 6
9. -20 **10.** -48 **11.** -9 **13.** -318 **15.** 35
17. -600 **19.** 72 **21.** -72 **23.** 15
25. $-7x = 35$; -5 **27.** 8,000 **28.** 171 **29.** 60
30. -133 **31.** -8 **33.** averaged a 5 yard loss
on each play **35.a.** -$10 **b.** There was a loss.

Pages 118-119   Lesson 3-10
5. (-3, 5) **6.** (3, 4) **7.** (5, 0) **8.** (3, -4)
9. (-3, -3) **10.** (-5, 2) **17.** (-2, 3) **19.** (-3, -1)
21. (-3, -3) **23.** (3, -2) **25.** (3, 3) **34.** 6
35. $4x < 20$; $x < 5$ **36.** 217 **37.** -9 **38.** -20
41. (1, 5)

Pages 120-122   Study Guide and Review
8.
(number line marked 0 1 2 3 4 5 6 7 8 with points at 2, 4, 6)
10.
(number line marked -6 -5 -4 -3 -2 -1 0 1 2 3 4 with points at -6, -3, 1, 4)
13. = **15.** < **17.** -282 **19.** 32 **21.** 81
23. 108 **25.** 10 **27.** -96 **29.** 80 **31.** -11
33. 32 **35.** 18 **37.** -122 **43.a.** Niko 6;
Chuck -2; Rachel -4; Trenna 2; Amanda 0
45. 15 points **47.** -33

4 Statistics and Data Analysis

Pages 131-132   Lesson 4-1

3.

Talking on Phone Time (hr)	Tally	Frequency
0–1	₩ I	6
2–3	₩ IIII	9
4–5	IIII	4
6–7	I	1

5.

Video Game Prices	Tally	Frequency
0–10.99	I	1
11–20.99	III	3
21–30.99	III	3
31–40.99	₩ I	6
41–50.99	IIII	4
51–60.99	I	1

5.a. 18   **b.** $40

7.

Subscriptions Sold	Tally	Frequency
10–19	II	2
20–29	II	2
30–39	III	3
40–49	III	3
50–59	II	2
60–69	I	1
70–79	₩ I	6
80–89	I	1

9.

Points Scored	Tally	Frequency
61–75	III	3
76–90	₩ I	6
91–105	₩ II	7
106–120	III	3
121–135	I	1

Pages 134-135   Lesson 4-2

6. 10 scores   **7.** 61-70 and 81-90   **8.** Intervals from 1-41 have been omitted.

9.

Science Test Scores	
Scores	Frequency
41–50	1
51–60	2
61–70	5
71–80	4
81–90	5
91–100	3

11.

Amount of Change		
¢	Tally	Frequency
61–70	IIII	4
71–80	₩ III	8
81–90	₩ I	6
91–100	II	2

12. 105   **13.** 14 units

Pages 137-138   Lesson 4-3

4.

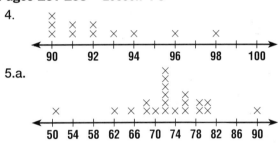

5.a.

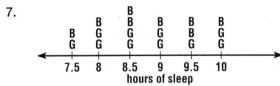

b. Most weigh 72 pounds.

7.

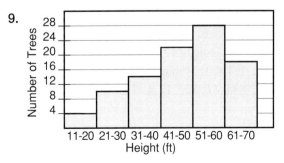

8. -241

9.

Pages 142-144   Lesson 4-4

4. 55 inches   **5.** 72 inches

6.a.
```
5 | G G G B
6 | B B B B B B G G B G G G G
7 | G B B
```

b. You can see where most girls' and boys' heights fall.

c. You lose individual amounts

7.a. 0, 1, 2, 3, 4, 5, 6

b.
```
0 | 7 8 9
1 | 1 2 3 4 4 6 7 8 8 9
2 | 2 2 4 5
3 | 0 2 2 3 4 5
4 | 1 3 5 6
5 | 1 6            6 | 1 means 61.
6 | 1
```

c. 7, 61   **d.** teens

9. 0, 1, 2, 3, 4, 5
```
0 | 9
1 | 1 2 4
2 | 4
3 | 3
4 |
5 | 1        3 | 2 means 32.
```

11. 5, 6, 7, 8
```
5 | 49
6 | 3
7 | 15
8 | 6            5 | 4 means 5.4.
```

13.a. Bender Co.   **b.** Sample answer: calculating expenses for health care benefits

14. 20   **15.** -16

16.

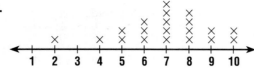

Pages 147-148   Lesson 4-5

5. 6, 7, 7   **6.** 27, 25, 25   **7.** $50; $50; $49, $50, $52   **8.** 10.4, 10.17, no mode   **9.** 6.9; 6; 5, 6, 13
11. 157.8, 155, no mode   **13.** 2.5, 2.5, 1.8
15. 68.2, 70, 75   **17.a.** 3.92, 3.6, 3.7   **b.** Only mean would change. It would increase.
c. Mean increases slightly; same mode; median increases slightly.   **18.** 2.98   **19.** 152

20.
```
1 | 5 6 8
2 | 1 2 3 4 6 9
3 | 2 4 5 6 7
4 | 2 3 5 8
5 | 2 6            2 | 3 means 23.
```

Page 148   Mid-Chapter Review

1.

25-pt. History Test	
Score	**Frequency**
11–13	2
14–16	6
17–19	6
20–22	4
23–25	6

3. 14–16, 17–19, 23–25   **5.** Mode; because it is most representative of the central values.

Pages 153-154   Lesson 4-6

5. 7   **6.** 11   **7.** 63   **8.** 7, 8, 4   **9.** 17, 20.5, 14
10. 156, 177, 135.5   **11.** 41.5   **13.** 26   **15.** 7.5
17. 57   **19.** 33   **21.** 38, 29   **23.** 73   **24.** 960
25. 8.5, 8.5, 12 and 6

Pages 157-158   Lesson 4-7

5. same median, same lower extreme   **6.** The top set of data is more widely dispersed than the lower one.   **7.** Top plot; the box is longer.

8.

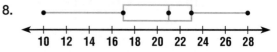

9. 21   **10.** 23   **11.** 17   **12.** 10   **13.** 6
14. no   **15.** 8 and 32   **17.** 63   **19.** 67.5
21. 7.5   **23.** 48.75 and 78.75; no   **25.** 10

27.

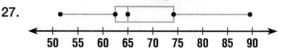

28. 3.5 gallons   **29.** 35   **30.** {120, 18, 3, -24, -52, -186, -219}   **31.** 184, 194, 172

35.

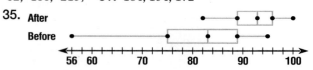

Pages 160-161   Lesson 4-8

3. negative   **4.** positive   **5.** negative
6. positive   **7.** no relationship   **8.** positive
9. no relationship   **10.** negative   **11.** positive

13. no relationship **15.** positive
17. negative **19.** 194 **20.** $x < 2$ **21.** -37
22.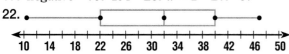

23.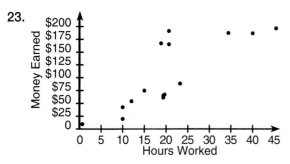

a. (hours worked, money earned) **b.** yes; positive

Pages 165-167   Lesson 4-9
4.a. increased by 2,000 **b.** relatively small change in numbers but the picture of the house changed; wider and taller **c.** yes
5. The mode, 88, because it's the highest.
7. mean **9.** no **11.** no **13.** 180 **14.** 32
15. No relationship; fishing is mostly chance.
19.a. No, samples should be more random.
b. Sample answer: What is the past history of the product or is it a new product?

Pages 168-170   Study Guide and Review
11.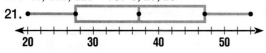

13. 7.7, 7.8, no mode **15.** 154.2, 157, no mode
17. 46, 150, 129 **19.** 8, 29, 23
21.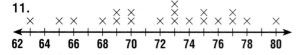

23. negative
25.a.

Cost of Air Fare	Tally	Frequency
$200–399	JHT IIII	9
$400–599	II	2
$600–799	JHT	5
$800–999	II	2

b.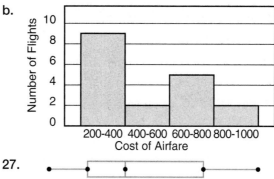

27.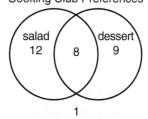

5 Investigations in Geometry

Pages 178-179   Lesson 5-1
6. $\overline{PQ} \parallel \overline{SR}, \overline{PS} \parallel \overline{QR}$ **7.** $\overline{WX} \parallel \overline{ZY}, \overline{WZ} \parallel \overline{XY}$
8. $\overline{AB} \parallel \overline{ED}, \overline{BC} \parallel \overline{EF}, \overline{CD} \parallel \overline{FA}$ **9.a.** 60
b. 120 **c.** 120 **d.** 60 **e.** 60 **f.** 120 **g.** 120
11. none **13.** 35 **15.** 122 **17.** 4 **19.** 60
20. $2.51 **21.** 10 **22.** mean **23.a.** They are parallel. **b.** They are parallel. **c.** 90

Page 182   Lesson 5-2
3.a. 13 states **b.** 1 state
4.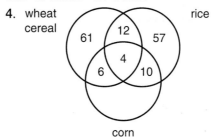

5.a.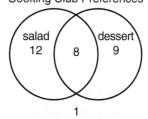
Cooking Club Preferences

5.b. 12 people **c.** 1 person **7.** 35

Pages 184-186   Lesson 5-3
6. scalene, right **7.** scalene, acute
8. isosceles, acute **9.** equilateral, acute
10. scalene, obtuse **11.** isosceles, right
13. isosceles, right **15.** scalene, right
17. equilateral, acute **19.** true **21.** false

23. true **25.** 40 **26.** 92 **27.** -384

28. $\frac{3}{4}$ of the days

29. $\overline{HI} \parallel \overline{KJ}$ **31.b.** Triangles will not collapse as easily as other figures.

Pages 188-190 Lesson 5-4

5. Q, P, R, S, RH **6.** Q, T **7.** Q **8.** 60°

9. Q, P **11.** Q, P, R, S, RH **13.** Q

15. parallelogram, rectangle, square, rhombus

17. square, rhombus **19.** false **21.** 70

23. 17 cm, 16.5 cm² **24.** IV **25.** 12

29.a. **b.** Yes, height would only be 176 feet instead of 2,648 feet.

2,648 ft

100 ft

Page 190 Mid-Chapter Review

1. $\overline{AB} \parallel \overline{CD}$ **3.** scalene, acute **5.** square

Pages 194-195 Lesson 5-5

4. **6.**

7. all of them **9.** no line symmetry **11.** yes

13. yes **15.** parallelogram, rectangle, square, rhombus **17.** -229 **18.** positive **19.** 30

21. A, B, C, D, E, H, I, K, M, O, T, U, V, W, X, Y

Pages 199-200 Lesson 5-6

6. similar **7.** congruent **8.** neither

9. similar **11.** congruent **13.** similar

15. 18 **16.** 8,000; 8,700 **17.** 27 **18.** yes

19.a. $28.50 **b.** Family Show

Pages 204-205 Lesson 5-7

7. 4: translation; 5: rotation; 6: translation

14. 90 **16.** congruent

Pages 206-208 Study Guide and Review

11. $\overline{WX} \parallel \overline{ZY}, \overline{ZW} \parallel \overline{YX}$ **13.** scalene, right

15. Q, P, RH

17.

19. yes **21.** similar **25.** 4 pairs

27. Cape May (C)

6 Patterns and Number Sense

Pages 213-214 Lesson 6-1

5. 2 **6.** 3, 9 **7.** 2, 3, 5, 6, 10 **8.** none

9. 3, 5 **10.** yes **11.** no **12.** no **13.** yes

14. Sample answer: $2 \cdot 63, 3 \cdot 42$ **15.** Sample answer: 6, 12 **17.** yes **19.** no **21.** yes

23. no **25.** Sample answers: $2 \cdot 21,605$; $5 \cdot 8,642$ **27.** 486 **29.** 26, 378 **30.** $1.89

31. -829 **32.** Probably no relationship

Page 217 Lesson 6-2

4. composite **5.** prime **6.** prime

7. composite **8.** $3 \cdot 19$ **9.** $2^2 \cdot 3^2$

10. $2 \cdot 3^2 \cdot 5$ **11.** $2^2 \cdot 3^2 \cdot 5$ **13.** composite

15. composite **17.** composite **19.** prime

21. 3^4 **23.** 2^6 **25.** $2^4 \cdot 5^2$ **27.** $-1 \cdot 2^2 \cdot 3^3 \cdot 5^2$

29. $m < 6$ **31.** no symmetry **32.** yes

33.a. 3, 5; 5, 7; 11, 13; 17, 19; 41, 43; 71, 73

b. 4, 6, 12, 18; Even numbers; yes; twin primes are both odd, therefore, the number in the middle is even. **35.** prime **37.** 41

Page 220 Lesson 6-3

3. 2 factors: 53; 3 factors: 49; 4 factors: 51, 5 factors: 81 **4.** 6; 123, 132, 231, 213, 312, 321

5. 81, 625, 2,401; n^4, where n is prime **7.** 12 teams **9.** 900 mL **11.** 20, 10, 5, 4, 2

Pages 222-223 Lesson 6-4

5. 4 **6.** 5 **7.** 14 **8.** 15 **9.** 3 **10.** 15

11. 9 **12.** 1 **13.** 2 **15.** 8 **17.** 25 **19.** 12

21. 5 **23.** 30 **25.** if the units digit is 0 or 5

27. 0.864 L **28.** 21 **29.** scalene, obtuse

30. $2^3 \cdot 7$ **31.a.** 6 in. × 6 in. tile **b.** 20 tiles

33. Sample answer: 7, 14, 21

Pages 225-226   Lesson 6-5

5. R 6. R 7. R 8. W, I, R 9. $-\frac{7}{8}$

10. simplest form 11. $\frac{1}{2}$ 12. $\frac{1}{4}$ 13. simplest

form 15. R 17. W, I, R 19. $-\frac{1}{4}$ 21. $\frac{4}{9}$

23. $\frac{1}{17}$ 25. $-\frac{5}{8}$ 27. $\frac{7}{33}$ 29. 35 30. -12

31. 27 32. 36 33. yes; 2.5 or $2\frac{1}{2}$ 35. $\frac{16}{25}$

Pages 228-229   Lesson 6-6

5. 0.4 6. -0.875 7. 3.25 8. -0.35 9. 3.56

10. $-\frac{2}{5}$ 11. $\frac{3}{4}$ 12. $\frac{17}{100}$ 13. $3\frac{3}{25}$ 14. $-5\frac{3}{8}$

15. -0.8 17. -0.28 19. -5.375 21. 7.25

23. -0.28125 25. $\frac{1}{20}$ 27. $\frac{16}{25}$ 29. $3\frac{17}{20}$

31. $-\frac{3}{40}$ 33. terminating 35. $\frac{y}{3} - 15$

36. $>$ 37. 9, 10, 11, 12 38. I, R

Page 229   Mid-Chapter Review

1. yes 3. yes 5. $2^2 \cdot 3^2$ 7. 2^7 9. $30°$F

11. 16 13. $\frac{1}{4}$ 15. $\frac{1}{5}$ 17. $-\frac{4}{5}$ 19. -0.625

Pages 231-232   Lesson 6-7

5. 0.2642642642 6. 0.9222222222

7. 0.5082508250 8. 0.5082082082

9. 0.2161616161 10. 100 11. 10 12. 10

13. 100 15. $29.\overline{27}$ 17. $-2.\overline{45}$ 19. $-7.0\overline{74}$

21. 8.32 23. $-1\frac{7}{9}$ 25. $\frac{6}{11}$ 27. $2\frac{5}{9}$

29. $\frac{8}{33}$ 31. $\frac{115}{333}$ 32. $4^3 \cdot 5^2$ 33. 15 34. 25

36. $8\frac{17}{25}$ 37. $\frac{17}{57} \approx 0.298245614$

Pages 234-235   Lesson 6-8

6. $\frac{1}{2}, 0.5$ 7. 0 8. $\frac{1}{3}, 0.\overline{3}$ 9. $\frac{1}{7}, 0.\overline{142857}$

10. 1 11. 0 12. $\frac{3}{10}$ 13. $\frac{7}{20}$ 14. $\frac{4}{5}$ 15. 1

16. $\frac{4}{5}$ 17. $\frac{2}{11}$ 19. 0 21. $\frac{3}{11}$ 23. $\frac{24}{29}$

25. 1 27. $\frac{4}{49}$ 29. 0 30. $P = 36$ in.,

$A = 60$ in^2 31. -13 32. neither 33. $8\frac{8}{11}$

35.a. 150 cards b. 2,000 cards c. 400 cards
d. 7,450 cards 37. No; the number of ways
something can occur cannot be negative.

Pages 237-238   Lesson 6-9

5. 0, 5, 10, 15, 20, 25 6. 0, 18, 36, 54, 72, 90

7. 0, 20, 40, 60, 80, 100 8. 0, n, $2n$, $3n$, $4n$, $5n$

9. 15 10. 105 11. 180 12. 840

13. 48 14. 60 15. 1,225 16. 72 17. 60

19. 420 21. 100 23. 24 25. 24 27. 8,449

29. no 30. 559 31. 28 32. 608 33. no

34. true 35. $\frac{1}{2}$ 37. when one number is a

factor of the other 39. $24n^2$

Pages 243-244   Lesson 6-10

3. 6 4. 40 5. 18 6. 100 7. $<$ 8. $=$

9. $<$ 10. $<$ 11. $>$ 12. $=$ 13. $=$

14. -12, -5, -1, 2, 5 15. 0, $\frac{2}{5}, \frac{1}{2}, \frac{4}{5}$

16. 0.367, $\frac{3}{8}$, 0.376, $\frac{2}{5}$ 17. $<$ 19. $<$

21. $<$ 23. $<$ 25. $<$ 27. 200 29. $-\frac{1}{3}, -\frac{1}{4}$,

$\frac{1}{10}, \frac{1}{9}$ 31. $0.\overline{18}$, 0.182, $0.18\overline{2}$, $0.182\overline{5}$

32. 14 quarts 33. -11 34. 7, 7, 3 35. 120

39.a. 2.7 b. Asheville, NC

Page 247   Lesson 6-11

4. 34,500,000 5. 0.000089 6. 37,770

7. 1.23×10^7 8. 1.23×10^6 9. 1.23×10^{-4}

10. 1.23×10^1 11. 5.6789×10^{-3}

12. 8.29×10^2 13. 7.0×10^{-6} 14. 1.0×10^{-6}

15. -0.0000000999 17. 0.0000042 19. 0.096

21. 93,000,000 23. 8.542×10^7

25. 5.6×10^{-5} 27. 4.0×10^{-8} 29. 7.2×10^{-8}

30. 29.2 31. $c > 8$ 32. -221 33. 24

35.a. Jupiter b. 4.83×10^8 miles c. $3.901 \times$
10^8 miles

Pages 248-250   Study Guide and Review

7. no 9. yes 11. yes 13. $2^4 \cdot 3$

15. $5^2 \cdot 7$ 17. $3 \cdot 11$ 19. 18 21. 7 23. 40

25. $\frac{3}{4}$ 27. $-\frac{2}{3}$ 29. $0.\overline{18}$ 31. $6.\overline{6}$

33. $-\frac{7}{250}$ 34. $-11\frac{3}{8}$ 37. $-5\frac{28}{99}$ 39. $6\frac{70}{111}$

41. $-\frac{1}{33}$ 43. $\frac{3}{4}$ 45. 60 47. 216 49. 870

51. $<$ 53. $>$ 55. 7.35×10^{-5} 57. 6.8×10^{-4}

59. 4th week

7 Rational Numbers

Pages 257-258   Lesson 7-1

4. $\frac{1}{2}$ 5. $\frac{1}{5}$ 6. $1\frac{1}{3}$ 7. $1\frac{1}{8}$ 8. $-\frac{1}{5}$ 9. $\frac{4}{7}$

11. $1\frac{7}{9}$ 13. $-\frac{1}{3}$ 15. $-3\frac{1}{2}$ 17. $-3\frac{1}{9}$

Selected Answers   **633**

19. $\frac{2}{3}$ **21.** $\frac{1}{2}$ **23.** -3 **25.** 3 **27.** -3
29. n **31.** $3\frac{1}{2}$ tons **32.** 3
33. yes **34.** 5.238×10^7 **35.** 6 min **37.a.** $\frac{1}{3}$
b. $\frac{2}{3}$ **c.** 1

Pages 260-261 Lesson 7-2

3. 7 **4.** 5 **5.** 17 **6.** 11 **7.** $-\frac{1}{12}$ **8.** $1\frac{1}{6}$
9. $-\frac{3}{8}$ **10.** $1\frac{5}{18}$ **11.** $1\frac{2}{3}$ **12.** $6\frac{5}{6}$ **13.** $1\frac{3}{10}$
15. $-1\frac{1}{12}$ **17.** $-9\frac{3}{8}$ **19.** $8\frac{7}{8}$ **21.** $-10\frac{13}{18}$
23. $-10\frac{7}{10}$ **25.** $3\frac{71}{72}$ **27.** $3\frac{13}{36}$ **28.** 27
29. 132, 143, 124 **30.** $\frac{3}{4}$ **31.** $-2\frac{1}{3}$

Pages 263-264 Lesson 7-3

4. $\frac{3}{8}$ **5.** $\frac{8}{27}$ **6.** $\frac{8}{9}$ **7.** 3 **8.** $2\frac{2}{9}$ **9.** $-\frac{3}{4}$
10. $3\frac{3}{8}$ **11.** $-1\frac{1}{2}$ **12.** $4\frac{1}{5}$ **13.** $-\frac{3}{4}$
15. $-\frac{10}{27}$ **17.** $2\frac{13}{16}$ **19.** $-13\frac{1}{2}$ **21.** $27\frac{1}{2}$
23. $\frac{4}{9}$ **25.** $3\frac{1}{5}$ **27.** $-7\frac{1}{2}$ **29.** $\frac{15}{16}$
30. 20 cm, 25 cm² **31.** 38
32. $-\frac{1}{5}, -\frac{1}{10}, \frac{1}{8}, \frac{1}{3}, \frac{1}{2}$ **33.** $-4\frac{19}{24}$

Pages 266-267 Lesson 7-4

5. yes **6.** no **7.** no **8.** yes **9.** $\frac{1}{5}$
10. $-\frac{3}{2}$ **11.** 5 **12.** $\frac{5}{14}$ **13.** $-\frac{1}{12}$ **14.** $6\frac{2}{5}$
15. 22 **17.** $-\frac{5}{3}$ **19.** $\frac{9}{26}$ **21.** -1 **23.** $-\frac{1}{x}$
25. yes; $\frac{3}{10} \cdot \frac{10}{3} = 1$ **27.** $-4\frac{1}{2}$ **29.** $1\frac{5}{8}$
31. 0 **33.** $-2\frac{1}{12}$ **34.** 2,750 mm **35.** 30
36. 8 **37.** $-\frac{7}{36}$

Page 271 Lesson 7-5

3. 21 **4.** 14 **5.** 50 **7.** 36 exercises **9.** 6

Pages 274-275 Lesson 7-6

5. N; 25, 36, 49 **6.** G; $-\frac{1}{125}, \frac{1}{625}, -\frac{1}{3,125}$
7. G; 32, 64, 128 **8.** A; 97.4, 97, 96.6
9. A; -15, -21, -27 **10.** A; 36, 40, 44
11. A; 55, 44, 33 **12.** G; 81, -243, 724
13. A; 7.5, 9, 10.5 **14.** A and G; 89, 89, 89
15. A; 2, 4, 6 **16.** G; 32, -16, 8 **17.** 64, 55, 46
19. -3, -6, -9 **21.** -157, 78.5, -39.25
23. 11, 12.5, 14 **25.** 26, 37, 50

27. $\frac{1}{108}, \frac{1}{324}, \frac{1}{972}$ **29.** 55 **31.** 22, 20, 18, 16
33. 335 **34.** 46

35.

36. -0.625 **37.** $2\frac{6}{7}$ **39.** $6,246.40

Page 275 Mid-Chapter Review

1. $-\frac{1}{2}$ **3.** $6\frac{3}{11}$ **5.** $-10\frac{5}{24}$ **7.** -28
9. $12\left(3 + \frac{3}{4}\right) = 12 \cdot 3 + 12 \cdot \frac{3}{4}$
11. A; 32, 35, 38

Pages 280-281 Lesson 7-7

5. $2\frac{2}{3}$ ft, $3\frac{3}{4}$ ft, 5 ft² **6.** 5.8 cm, 2.2 cm, 3.6 cm,
14.4 cm² **7.** $4\frac{1}{2}$ in., $5\frac{1}{3}$ in., 6 in., $29\frac{1}{2}$ in²
8. $8\frac{7}{16}$ ft² **9.** 11.7 cm² **10.** 35 in² **11.** 90 m²
12. 0.08 km² **13.** $9\frac{3}{4}$ yd² **15.** $3\frac{1}{2}$ ft, $5\frac{1}{2}$ ft,
$2\frac{2}{3}$ ft, 12 ft² **17.** 30 cm, 12 cm, 180 cm²
19. 3 ft, 4 ft, 6 ft² **21.** 297 yd² **23.** $4\frac{31}{64}$ in²
25. 112 mm² **27.** 255 ft² **29.** 68.88 km²
31. 0.204 m² **32.** $2c + 3 = 15$ **33.** -500
34. 31.75, 33, 40 **35.** similar **36.** 64, 60, 56
37. 570 ft² **39.a.** $A \approx \frac{1}{2}(273)(219)$ **b.** about
29,894 mi²

Pages 286-287 Lesson 7-8

4. 56.55 in. **5.** 8.17 m **6.** 15.7 cm
7. 43.98 in. **8.** 42.73 m **9.** 16.5 in or 16.49 in.
10. 21.99 km **11.** 3.14 ft **13.** 27.49 in. or
$27\frac{1}{2}$ in. **15.** 42.6 m **17.** 50.27 ft **19.** 27.65 m
21. $28\frac{2}{7}$ yd or 28.27 yd **22.** 64

23.a.

5	8
6	2 5 7
7	1 1 2 3 5 6 9
8	2 3 4 5 8
9	1 3 4 7

7 | 1 means 71.

b. 70–79
24. 15 yd, 20 yd, 10 yd, 175 yd² **25.** rectangle;
7.5 cm × 28.6 cm **27.** ≈ 235,933.6 miles
29.a. 56.55 **b.** about 4.2 inches

Pages 289-290   Lesson 7-9

6. $\frac{4}{5}$ 7. $\frac{5}{12}$ 8. $-3\frac{3}{4}$ 9. $\frac{2}{27}$ 10. $3\frac{5}{9}$

11. $\frac{3}{5}$ 12. $5\frac{1}{2}$ 13. $-\frac{17}{18}$ 14. $\frac{9}{25}$ 15. 4

17. -5 19. 6 21. 6 23. $\frac{2}{3}$ 25. $\frac{3}{14}$

27. $2\frac{3}{4}$ or 2.75

28. $b > -8$

29. 16 30. $15.\overline{36}$ 31. 31.4 mm
33. 128 slices

Pages 292-293   Lesson 7-10

3. -5.5   4. $-\frac{52}{75}$ 5. 3.24 6. $4\frac{1}{2}$ 7. $2\frac{3}{10}$

8. $-2\frac{1}{2}$ 9. 22.8 10. 84 11. $0.2\overline{27}$ 13. -18

15. -15.2 17. 1.8875 19. -0.12 21. $-1\frac{1}{9}$

23. $-1\frac{4}{5}$ 25. 1,200 26. positive 27. 6

28. 90 29. $\frac{5}{8}$ 31.a 35 mph b. 55 mph

c. 25 mph

Pages 294-296   Study Guide and Review

11. $-\frac{3}{4}$ 13. $-\frac{4}{15}$ 15. $-11\frac{5}{12}$ 17. $-10\frac{1}{2}$

19. $2\frac{1}{3}$ 21. $-\frac{3}{19}$ 23. $2\frac{4}{5}$ 25. $G; \frac{1}{3}, \frac{1}{9}, \frac{1}{27}$

27. A; 44, 40, 36 29. 51 cm^2 31. 15.08 m

33. 17.28 in. 35. $\frac{3}{5}$ 37. $\frac{5}{24}$ 39. -17.34

41. 4.1 43. 18.85 cm

8 Real Numbers

Pages 301-302   Lesson 8-1

4. 7 5. 9 6. 11 7. -8 9. 20 11. -3

13. 25 15. -10 17. 0.4 19. $\frac{8}{10}$

21. 1.3 meters 22. 7.5 yards 24. 3 25. $-\frac{1}{3}$

27. $23.80

Page 305   Lesson 8-2

3. 7 4. 12 5. 5 6. 3 7. 5 9. 7 11. 7

13. 13 15. 20 17. 31 19. 6 20. $-1\frac{7}{12}$

21. 30 23. about 36.6 miles

Pages 308-309   Lesson 8-3

5. irrational 6. rational 7. integer, rational
8. rational 9. 2.6 10. 2.8 11. 4.5

12. -1.4 13. 12, -12 14. 30, -30 15. 7.1,
-7.1 17. irrational 19. rational 21. rational
23. 2.4 25. 5.2 27. 8, -8 29. 19.0, -19.0
31. 1.2, -1.2 33. 12 34. -336 35. 59, 59, no
mode 36. $2\frac{1}{8}$ 37. 17 39. 36

Pages 311-312   Lesson 8-4

3. 135 miles   4. -$2,005   5. 65 miles per hour
7. 720 ft^2 9.a. 4 miles b. about 20 seconds

Page 312   Mid-Chapter Review

1. 6 3. -5 5. 9 7. 5 9. natural, whole,
integer, rational 11. rational 13. 7, -7
15. 120 feet per second

Pages 317-318   Lesson 8-5

4. $c^2 = 144 + 81$, 15 5. $c^2 = 144 + 25$, 13
6. $1,681 = 81 + b^2$, 40 7. no 8. yes
9. 7.9 ft 11. 7.4 m 13. 18.4 cm 15. 9 in.
17. $x^2 = 100 + 100$, 14.1 19. $x^2 = 1 + 2$, 1.7
21. yes 23. yes 25. yes 26. 1,250 grams
27. 32, 33, 34, 35 28. -0.0000347 29. 12, -12
31. 17 yards

Pages 321-322   Lesson 8-6

3. 20.1 ft, 15 ft   4. 21.4 miles   5. 14.7 ft
7. Sample answer: 16–30–34, 40–75–85
9. Sample answer: 18–80–82, 45–200–205
11. 8 12. no 13. about 13.2 m
15. about 70 ft

Pages 326-327   Lesson 8-7

4. 5 units 5. 10 units 6. 5 units
7. 4.1 units 9. 5.1 units 11. 7.6 units
13. 10.3 units 15. 4.2 units 16. 42 17. -80
18. about 31.5 ft 19.b. 34.6 units 21. 9.4
miles

Pages 330-331   Lesson 8-8

4. 8.7 cm, 10 cm 5. 8 ft, 11.3 ft 6. 6 in.,
10.4 in. 7. 15 cm 8. 6 in. 9. 34.6 ft, 40 ft
11. 9.5 in., 16.5 in. 13. 3.75 in. 14. 60, 64, 50
15. $\frac{2}{3}$ 16. 10 units 17. 12 feet

Pages 332-334   Study Guide and Review

11. -1.5 13. $\frac{7}{10}$ 15. 2.3 17. 7 19. 19
21. 16 23. integer, rational 25. rational
numbers 27. 8.6 cm 29. 4 in. 31. 36 in.

33. 3.6 units **34.** 7.8 units **37.** 14 in., 24.2 in.
39. 15 mm, 21.2 mm **41.** 1.25 m per second

9 Applications with Proportion

Pages 340-341   Lesson 9-1
4. $\frac{5}{7}$ **5.** $\frac{1}{8}$ **6.** $\frac{4}{5}$ **7.** $\frac{7}{11}$
8. 3 brown-eyed/2 blue-eyed **9.** $\frac{1}{3}$
10. 25 miles/1 hour; unit rate
11. 3 pounds/1 week; unit rate
12. 2 inches/15 days; not a unit rate
13. 34 passengers/3 minivans; not a unit rate
15. $\frac{7}{11}$ **17.** 1 win/1 loss **19.** $\frac{13}{21}$ **21.** $\frac{4}{1}$
23. $\frac{3}{2}$ **25.** $\frac{1}{4}$ **27.** $\frac{1}{3}$ **29.** $2.50/disk
31. $28/ticket **33.** $0.08/egg **35.** 10
36. Mean is the arithmetic average. Median is the middle number when data are ordered from least to greatest. Mode is the most frequent data.
37. 1 out of 10 chances of winning a prize
38. $7\frac{2}{7}$, 7.35, $\frac{37}{5}$ **39.** 15 **40.** natural numbers, whole numbers, integers, rational numbers, real numbers **43.** Eisenhower Middle School
45. 0.320

Pages 345-346   Lesson 9-2
3. yes **4.** no **5.** yes **6.** no **7.** 6 **8.** 0.2
9. 300 **10.** 4.9 **11.** yes **13.** yes **15.** yes
17. no **19.** 15 **21.** 85 **23.** 10.5 **25.** 3.5
27. -12 **28.** 40° **29.** 16 **30.** 40 shrimp/1 pound

Pages 348-349   Lesson 9-3
3. $26.88 **4.** 14 pounds **5.** 3 cups
7. 262.5 min **9.** 18 cans **10.** 9.6 **11.** -8
12. 12 **13.** 21 pounds **15.** Alvarez 75,000; Cruz 90,000; Hoffman 55,000; Newton 30,000

Pages 351-352   Lesson 9-4
3. 49 seats **4.** 4 games **5.** -19
7. 28 handshakes **9.** 9 meters

Page 352   Mid-Chapter Review
1. $\frac{3}{4}$ **3.** $0.80/dozen **5.** 10 **7.** 1,050 bushels

Pages 354-355   Lesson 9-5
4. no **5.** yes **6.** 12 **7.** 18 **8.** They would be half the original lengths. **9.** yes
11. $\angle EAD \cong \angle CAB$, $\angle AED \cong \angle ACB$, $\angle ADE \cong \angle ABC$ **13.** 12 **15.** $4^3 \cdot 8^2$
16. 51, 23, 0, -8, -16, -30, -51 **17.** $\frac{7}{9}$
18. 10 tablespoons **21.** 2.3 inches

Pages 357-358   Lesson 9-6
5. 35 feet **6.** 20 feet **7.** 12.5 km **9.** 45 miles
10. 45 **11.** 240 **12.** $\frac{AC}{DF}$, $\frac{AB}{DE}$, $\frac{BC}{EF}$
13. 169.25 feet **15.** 985.92 ft

Page 360   Lesson 9-7
4. 120 ft, 16 ft **5.** 180 miles **6.** 135 miles
7. 247.5 miles **8.** 37.5 miles **9.** 24 ft
11. 10 ft **13.** 6 **14.** 1,250 feet **15.** 384 cm

Pages 362-363   Lesson 9-8
4. (6, 8) **5.** (15, 20) **6.** 3 **7.** 25 **13.** 4
15. 712.5 mi **17.a.** rectangle **b.** 42 units, 108 units^2 **d.** 126 units, 972 units^2 **e.** $\frac{3}{1}$ **f.** $\frac{9}{1}$

Pages 366-367   Lesson 9-9
4. $\frac{3}{5}$ **5.** $\frac{5}{3}$ **6.** $\frac{9}{5}$ **7.** $\frac{5}{9}$ **8.** 31° **9.** 59°
10. 61° **11.** 29° **12.** 3.0 inches **13.** 5 ft
15. $\frac{12}{5}$, $\frac{5}{12}$, 67°, 23° **17.** 6.9 in. **19.** 3.6 km
22. $4\frac{13}{16}$ **25.** about 48 feet

Pages 370-371   Lesson 9-10
4. $\frac{3}{5}$ **5.** $\frac{4}{5}$ **6.** 53° **7.** $\frac{3}{5}$ **8.** $\frac{4}{5}$ **9.** 37°
10. $\frac{5}{13}$ **11.** $\frac{5}{13}$ **12.** 23° **13.** 67°
15. $\frac{4}{5}$, $\frac{3}{5}$, $\frac{3}{5}$, $\frac{4}{5}$, 53°, 37° **17.** 12.0 **19.** 45°
21. -180 **22.** 0.00092 **23.** $\frac{3}{4}$
25. about 39.2 feet **27.** 66 ft

Pages 372-374   Study Guide and Review
9. $\frac{1}{2}$ **11.** $\frac{36}{5}$ **13.** 15 **15.** 40.5 **17.** $175
19. 25 pages **21.** similar **23.** 105 km
25. 56 km **27.** 147 km **31.** 0.4167
33. 0.8824 **34.** 0.4706 **37.** $\frac{7}{16}$

10 Applications with Percent

Pages 382-383 Lesson 10-1
4. 68% 5. 35% 6. 87.5% 7. 90% 8. 5%
9. b 10. a 11. c 12. 101.1 13. 11
14. 60% 15. 9% 17. 70% 19. 46%
21. $66\frac{2}{3}$% 23. 80% 25. 80.5 27. 12.5%
29. 190 31. 112 33. 64% 34. $67.20
35. 21; 23; 17 36. 80° 37. $\frac{5}{9}$ 38. 14.8
39. 23°

Pages 386-387 Lesson 10-2
4. 70% 5. 60.5% 6. 26% 7. 2% 8. $\frac{13}{20}$
9. $\frac{13}{200}$ 10. $\frac{1}{8}$ 11. $\frac{24}{25}$ 12. 0.78 13. 0.09
14. 0.123 15. 0.084 17. 0.3 19. 18%
21. 70.4% 23. 55.3% 25. $\frac{29}{50}$ 27. $\frac{89}{200}$
29. $\frac{73}{400}$ 31. 0.28 33. 0.8425 35. 0.384
37. 0.2, 20%, $\frac{1}{5}$ 38. -21 39. $-2 \cdot 3^4$ 40. -7.2
41. They will have the same shape. 42. 70

Pages 389-390 Lesson 10-3
5. $\frac{1}{5,000}$ 6. $\frac{1}{1,000}$ 7. $1\frac{3}{4}$ 8. $\frac{1}{500}$
9. 1.78 10. 2.012 11. 0.006 12. 0.0005
13. > 14. < 15. $\frac{3}{1,000}$ 17. $7\frac{3}{5}$
19. $2\frac{43}{100}$ 21. $\frac{1}{625}$ 23. 2.12 25. 0.0003
27. 0.007 29. 0.00008 31. $\frac{3}{8}$%, 67%, 0.8, 7
32. 6 33. 8.4×10^{-5} 34. 14.5 feet 35. $\frac{1}{27}$
36. $0.385 = \frac{77}{200}$ 37. 0.0985
39. Yes, the purchase price of the camera is 100% + 5.5% tax = 105.5%.

Page 392 Lesson 10-4
3. 105 4. 20,100 5. 63 6. 18 7. 6.5%
9. 50 calories 11. 128,000 people 13. $\frac{1}{4}$

Pages 394-396 Lesson 10-5
4. a 5. b 6. b 7. a 8. 30 9. 10 10. 54
11. 50% 12. $66\frac{2}{3}$% 13. 150% 14. 28%
15. 20% 17. 9 19. 22 21. 5 23. 30% and 150 25. 64% 27. 40% 29. 20% 31. 25%

33. 58.5 ft² 34. $\frac{1}{6}$ 35. $0.32/ounce 36. $\frac{1}{250}$
39. 17,600; 8,800; 7,200; 8,800; 880; 440

Page 396 Mid-Chapter Review
1. 24 3. 44% 5. 62.5% 7. 0.80, $\frac{4}{5}$
9. 0.375, $\frac{3}{8}$ 11. 0.004, $\frac{1}{250}$ 13. 0.00875, $\frac{7}{800}$
15. 6 cheerleaders 17. b 19. c

Pages 401-402 Lesson 10-6
4. 24.44 5. 44.8 6. 48.1% 7. 0.06% 8. $160
9. 82.1% 10. $23\frac{1}{3}$% 11. 9.9 12. 16,666.67
13. 9.072 15. 500 17. 2.96 19. 325
21. 120% 23. $50 25. 24 27. $6,540 29. 40
30. -a 31. 11, -11 32. 18 33. $48,700
37. $242.64 39. 7%

Pages 404-405 Lesson 10-7
5. 100% 6. 360° 11. 28 12. 306
13. 37.5%

Pages 407-408 Lesson 10-8
4. 50% 5. 10% 6. $16\frac{2}{3}$% 7. 33% 8. 11%
9. 13% 11. 25% 13. 17% 15. 36% 17. 11%
19. 7% 20. 4.5 pints 21. 9.2 ft

Pages 410-411 Lesson 10-9
3. $9.80 4. $100 5. $3.44 6. $5.78
7. $809.10 8. $199.50 9. $28.46 10. $28
11. 38.5% 12. 12.5% 13. $7.49; $22.46
15. $2.18; $12.32 17. $39.83; $79.67 19. 25%
21. 50% 23. $3.41 25. 20% 27. 20
28. $19\frac{1}{32}$ 29. 7.2 30. 3.5% 31.a. $4.56
b. $2.94 c. 60%

Pages 413-415 Lesson 10-10
4. $10.78 5. $90 6. $195.84 7. $2.57
8. $643.70 9. $142.95 10. $128.28
11. $256.95 12. 6% 13. 12.75% 15. $75
17. $674.56 19. $945 21. $210.13
23. $240.41 25. $10,650 27. 9%
29. Number of people who watch 0–5 hours is greater than the number of people who watch 15–17 hours. 30. $\frac{5}{54}$ 31. 55 miles
32. $26.70; $62.30 33. $1,064 37.a. to change the percent to a decimal b. 2330

c. A10: 4000; B10: $\frac{B2}{100}$; C10: C2; D10: A10 *
B10 * C10; E10: A10 + D10

Pages 416-418   Study Guide and Review

11. 112   **13.** 82   **15.** 80   **17.** $\frac{2}{25}$ **19.** $\frac{7}{40}$
21. $\frac{1}{125}$ **23.** $\frac{3}{700}$ **25.** 20   **27.** 9   **29.** 28
31. 18.75%   **33.** 150   **35.** 20% increase
37. 25% increase   **39.** $9, $51   **41.** $21, $63
43. $74.52   **45.** $22.50   **47.** $29.99
49. 10% increase

11 Algebra: Functions and Graphs

Pages 423-424   Lesson 11-1

5.

n	-5n	f(n)
-4	-5(-4)	20
-2	-5(-2)	10
0	-5(0)	0
2.5	-5(2.5)	-12.5

6.

n	2n + (-6)	f(n)
-2	2(-2) + (-6)	-10
-1	2(-1) + (-6)	-8
0	2(0) + (-6)	-6
$\frac{1}{2}$	$2\left(\frac{1}{2}\right)$ + (-6)	-5

7. 2   **8.** 14   **9.** 25

11.

n	3n	f(n)
-1	3(-1)	-3
0	3(0)	0
$\frac{2}{3}$	$3\left(\frac{2}{3}\right)$	2
1	3(1)	3

13.

n	-0.5n + 1	f(n)
-4	-0.5(-4) + 1	3
-2	-0.5(-2) + 1	2
0	-0.5(0) + 1	1
2.5	-0.5(2.5) + 1	-0.25
8	-0.5(8) + 1	-3

15. -8   **17.** 18.12

18. Sample answer:

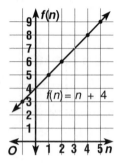

19. 6 cm   **20.** $304

Pages 426-427   Lesson 11-2

5.

n	f(n)	(n, f(n))
-1	3	(-1, 3)
1	5	(1, 5)
2	6	(2, 6)
4	8	(4, 8)
5	9	(5, 9)

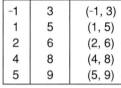

6.

n	f(n)	(n, f(n))
$\frac{1}{2}$	16	$\left(\frac{1}{2}, 16\right)$
2	4	(2, 4)
4	2	(4, 2)
8	1	(8, 1)
16	$\frac{1}{2}$	$\left(16, \frac{1}{2}\right)$

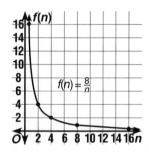

7.

n	f(n)	(n, f(n))
0	1	(0, 1)
1	4	(1, 4)
2	7	(2, 7)
3	10	(3, 10)

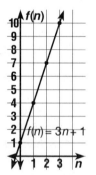

9.

n	f(n)	(n, f(n))
8	2	(8, 2)
2	8	(2, 8)
4	4	(4, 4)
$\frac{8}{3}$	6	$\left(\frac{8}{3}, 6\right)$

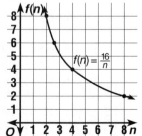

11.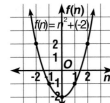

12. 16.96 mm

13. -7

6.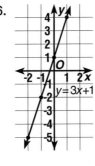

9.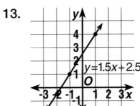

15.a.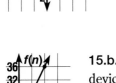

15.b. No, there is a safety device that only lets it rise so far; yes.

13.

17. $A + 6$

18.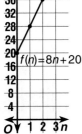

19. 4.375 in² **20.** Sample answer: $\{(0, 8), (3, 9), (-3, 7), (-6, 6)\}$

21.a. $(0, 32)$, $(100, 212)$ **c.** Find the coordinates of other points on the line.

Pages 429-430   Lesson 11-3

4. -2, 0, 2, 3 **5.** 2, -1, 0, -3 **6.** $-6, 8, \frac{1}{3}$

7. Sample answers: $(-4, -1)$, $(-1, 2)$, $(0, 3)$, $(5, 8)$

9. $3, 5, 6, 6\frac{2}{3}$ **11.** Sample answer: $\{(-2, -3),$ $(-1, -1), (0, 1), (1, 3)\}$ **13.** Sample answer: $\{(-4, 1), (-2, 2), (0, 3), (2, 4)\}$

15. Sample answer: $\{(-2, 7), (-1, 5), (0, 3), (2, -1)\}$

17. $\{(6, 2), (3, 5), (-45, 53)\}$ **18.** 280 **19.** $2\frac{4}{9}$

20.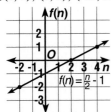

22.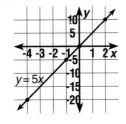

21.a. $y = x + 9$; $(-10, -1)$, $(0, 9)$, $(1, 10)$

b. $y = 2x + 3$; $(0, 3)$, $(1, 5)$, $(-2, -1)$

c. $x + y = 0$; $(1, -1)$, $(-2, 2)$, $(0, 0)$

23. 52, 63, 71, 87, 90

Pages 433-434   Lesson 11-4

4.

x	y	(x, y)
-4	-20	(-4, -20)
-1	-5	(-1, -5)
0	0	(0, 0)
2	10	(2, 10)

Pages 437-438   Lesson 11-5

6. $(6, 2)$ **7.** $(-4, -4)$ **8.** $(1, -1)$ **9.** $(0, 4)$

10. $(-3, 5)$ **11.** $(-1, 2)$ **12.** $(-2, 1)$

13. no solution **15.** $(2, 2)$ **17.** $(6, 9)$

19. $(5, -6)$ **21.** $(2, 1)$ **22.** positive **23.** $>$

24. about 8

25.

27.b. (2, 9)   **27.c.** perpendicular lines

Page 438   Mid-Chapter Review

1. Sample answer:

n	f(n)	(n, f(n))
0	5	(0, 5)
1	3	(1, 3)
4	-3	(4, -3)

3. {(0, 4), (3, 5), (-3, 3), (-6, 2)}

5. (3, 2)

Pages 440-441   Lesson 11-6

3. about $660 billion   **4.** from March to April
5. decrease in business loans and increase in government securities   **7.** 15   **9.** 1955-1960
11. Foreign cars are taking over the majority of motor vehicle production.

Pages 444-445   Lesson 11-7

4.

x	f(x)	(x, f(x))
-2	4	(-2, 4)
-1	1	(-1, 1)
0	0	(0, 0)
1	1	(1, 1)
2	4	(2, 4)

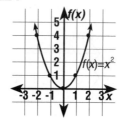

6.

x	f(x)	(x, f(x))
-2	9	(-2, 9)
-1.5	5.5	(-1.5, 5.5)
0	1	(0, 1)
3	19	(3, 19)
4	33	(4, 33)

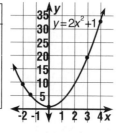

9. 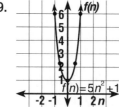   **13.**

17. {(-2, 8), (0, -4), (1, -1)}   **19.** 97   **20.** -31
21. $3\frac{7}{20}$ **22.** (3, 2)
25.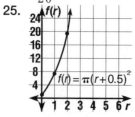

Pages 448-449   Lesson 11-8

4. (4, 5)   **5.** (10, -5)   **6.** P'(-6, 3), Q'(-9, -1), R'(-5, 6)   **7.** W'(1, 4), X'(3, 6), Y'(1, 8), Z'(-1, 6)   **9.** P'(-5, 5), Q'(1, 8), R'(2, 6), S'(-4, 3)   **11.** (5, 2)   **13.** yes

14.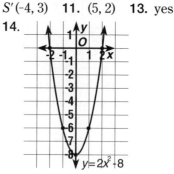

15.a. 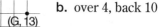   **b.** over 4, back 10

Pages 452-453   Lesson 11-9

4. y-axis   **5.** x-axis   **6.** x-axis   **7.a.** C'(3, -3), O'(0, 0), W'(6, 1)   **7.b.** C'(-3, 3), O'(0, 0), W'(-6, -1)   **9.a.** M'(1, -2), O'(0, 0), N'(-5, 0), Y'(-4, -2)   **11.** 28   **12.** A'(-1, 1), B'(1, 4), C'(4, 2)

Pages 456-457   Lesson 11-10

4. yes   **5.** yes   **6.** no   **7.a.** H'(-4, -3), A'(-4, -5), I'(2, -5), R'(2, -3)   **b.** H'(3, -4), A'(5, -4), I'(5, 2), R'(3, 2)   **8.** Sample answers: square, regular hexagon   **9.b.** R'(3, -1), S'(9, -6), T'(5, -8)   **11.** (-4, 1), (-1, 4), (-5, -8)   **13.** 105
14. 12   **15.a.** T'(1, 1), R'(3, 1), A'(3, 3), B'(1, 3)
b. T'(-1, -1), R'(-3, -1), A'(-3, -3), B'(-1, -3)
17. 2, 4, 10, Jack, Queen, King of hearts; 2, 4, 10, Jack, Queen, King of clubs; 2, 3, 4, 5, 6, 8, 9, 10, Jack, Queen, King, Ace of diamonds; 2, 4, 10, Jack, Queen, King of spades

11.

n	f(n)	(n, f(n))
-1	-3	(-1, -3)
-0.5	-1	(-0.5, -1)
0	1	(0, 1)
0.5	3	(0.5, 3)
1	5	(1, 5)

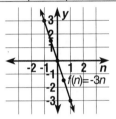

$f(n) = 4n + 1$

13.

n	f(n)	(n, f(n))
-1	3	(-1, 3)
-0.5	1.5	(-0.5, 1.5)
0	0	(0, 0)
0.5	-1.5	(0.5, -1.5)
1	-3	(1, -3)

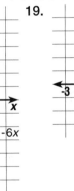

$f(n) = -3n$

15. Sample answer: {(-2, 2), (-1, 3), (0, 4), (1, 5)}

17.

$y = -6x$

19.

$y = -3.5x + 1.5$

21. (1, 6)

23.

$y = \frac{1}{2}x^2 + 3$

25.

$f(n) = 4 - n^2$

27. $R'(-1, 5)$, $S'(1, 5)$, $T'(1, 3)$, $U'(-1, 3)$

29. $A'(2, -5)$, $B'(6, -5)$, $C'(6, -3)$, $D'(2, -3)$

31. $L'(-4, 1)$, $A'(-7, 4)$, $T'(-4, 7)$, $E'(-1, 4)$

33. It will never occur since the graphs of their profit equations never meet.

12 Area and Volume

Pages 466-467   Lesson 12-1

5. 153.9 ft^2 **6.** 32.2 km^2 **7.** 95.0 yd^2 **8.** $\frac{1}{100}$

9. 19.6 cm^2 **11.** 63.6 cm^2 **13.** 78.5 m^2

15. 7.7 m^2 **17.** 25.1 in^2 **18.** 12   **19.** 8.2 units

21.a. 28.3 in^2, 84.8 in^2, 141.4 in^2 **b.** $\frac{1}{3}$

23.a. 201.06 in^2, 226.19 in^2

b. L = \$0.0447126, M = \$0.0441645   **c.** L = \$0.04, M = \$0.04; same price per square inch

Page 469   Lesson 12-2

3. 12 cubes   **5.** \$75   **7.** c

Pages 472-473   Lesson 12-3

4. $2 \times 3 \times 5$ units   **5.**

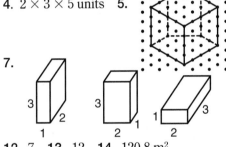

7.

12. 7   **13.** 12   **14.** 120.8 m^2

Pages 476-477   Lesson 12-4

4. rectangular prism, 108 ft^2 **5.** triangular prism, 97.84 m^2 **6.** rectangular prism, 468 in^2

7. 528 yd^2 **9.** 527.4 cm^2 **11.** 64.5 m^2

13. 122 cm^2 **15.** 384 ft^2 **16.** 1,024   **17.** No, the last 2 digits are not divisible by 4.

19. Monica's cube—it has the greatest surface area   **21.** 8,100 in^2

Pages 479-481   Lesson 12-5

5. 251.3 m^2 **6.** 1,407.4 cm^2 **7.** 32.99 in^2

9. 280.8 cm^2 **11.** 150.8 in^2 **13.** 397.2 m^2

14. $b < 2$

15. $17\frac{1}{2}$ **16.** 0.352   **17.** 62 in^2

21. about 55 in^2

Page 481   Mid-Chapter Review

1. about 113.1 cm² 5. 1,885 m² 7. 1,188 in²

Pages 484-485   Lesson 12-6

6. 120 m³ 7. 314.2 ft³ 8. 60 yd³ 9. 141.4 cm³
10. 18 in³ 11. 1,125.7 cm³ 13. 1,032.2 cm³
15. 1.728 cm³ 17. 5,513.5 mm³ 19. 300 ft³
22. -9 23. 326.73 cm²

Pages 488-489   Lesson 12-7

4. 40 in³ 5. 20.9 m³ 6. 56 yd³ 7. 339.3 m³
9. 100.4 m³ 11. 80 yd³ 13. 45 m³ 15. 27,
33, 39, 45 16. D' (6, 12), E' (20, 16), F' (18, 6)
17. 502.65 feet³ 19. about 229 cm³

Pages 492-493   Lesson 12-8

4.a. 3 b. closer to 5.5 ft than 5.51 ft
5. 20.3, accurate to meter, 3 tenths is estimate;
4,200 accurate to thousands, 200 is estimate;
0.00251, accurate to 0.0025, 1 hundred
thousandth is estimate; 0.0580, accurate to 0.058,
0 ten thousandths is an estimate. 6. 34.3 oz;
tenths of an ounce is a more precise unit than an
ounce or a pound 7. Accurate to $212 billion, 9
hundred million is estimate; it is closer to $212.9
billion than to $212.8 or $213.0 billion. 15. 305
feet 18. 0.000094 19. 153.94 m³
21. nearest tenth of a second 23. accurate to
next to last digit of input

Pages 494-496   Study Guide and Review

11. 50.3 m² 17. 54 cm² 19. 4,523.89 yd²
21. 378 m³ 23. 6 mm³ 25. 3 27. 4
29. accurate to 5.0 miles, 2 hundredths is
estimate 31. 55 cubes

13 Discrete Math and Probability

Pages 505-506   Lesson 13-1

5.b. 24 c. 6 d. 4 e. 1 f. $\frac{1}{4}$ 6. 32
7. 12 9. 6 11. 16 13. 24 15. 27 16. 8
17. 22 18. 3 19. 9

Pages 508-509   Lesson 13-2

3. 24 4. 11,880 5. 6 6. 5,040 7. 120
8. 24 9. 720 10. 6 11. 120 13. 1,680
15. 720 17. 120 19. 120 21. 24 22. -32
23. 14 24. 60% 25. 243 27. 60

Pages 513-514   Lesson 13-3

5. 10 6. 1 7. 3 8. 792 9. permutation
10. combination 11. combination
12. permutation 13. 4 15. 6 17. 2,042,975
19. 2,598,960 21. 56 23. 0.078 liters
24. 80° 25. 225 miles 26. 336 29. 28

Pages 517-518   Lesson 13-4

4. 10 5. 7 6. 56 7. 1 8. 56 9. 35
10. 8 11. 28 13. 4 15. 210 17. 8 19. 6
21. combination of 4 things taken two at a time
22. 157.7, 158 23. $9\frac{7}{18}$ 24. Sample answer:
{(1, 13), (2, 16), (3, 19), (4, 22)} 25. 120
29. 252 31. 35

Page 518   Mid-Chapter Review

1. 12 outcomes 3. 720 5. 20

Pages 523-524   Lesson 13-5

4. $\frac{1}{30}$ 5. $\frac{1}{30}$ 6. $\frac{1}{10}$ 7. 0 8. $\frac{1}{5}$
9. Independent; one outcome does not affect the
other. 10. $\frac{5}{28}$ 11. $\frac{1}{28}$ 12. $\frac{5}{56}$ 13. $\frac{3}{14}$
14. $\frac{5}{28}$ 15. Dependent; one outcome affects
the other. 17. $\frac{1}{6}$ 19. $\frac{5}{42}$ 21. $\frac{1}{30}$ 23. $\frac{1}{15}$
25. 0 27. $\frac{9}{20}$ 29. $\frac{1}{10}$ 30. 49 31. {-157,
-28, -3, 2, 18, 226} 32. no 33. 15 35. 67.5%

Pages 526-527   Lesson 13-6

4. Sample answer: 3 5. Sample answer: $\frac{4}{10}$
6. 1 half dollar, 1 quarter, 4 dimes 7. 72 pages
9. Sample answer: $\frac{1}{45}$ 11. Math—Mrs.
Gossell; Music—Ms. Alvarez; Social Studies—
Mrs. Yamaguchi 13. -3 15. 30 students

Pages 529-530   Lesson 13-7

3.a. $\frac{3}{8}$ b. $\frac{1}{2}$ c. $\frac{3}{40}$ 4.a. $\frac{3}{8}$ b. $\frac{3}{8}$ c. $\frac{1}{8}$
5.a. $\frac{217}{400}$ or 0.5425 b. yes c. conduct more
experiments 7. -39 8. 3 9. $\frac{1}{4}$
13.a. Sample answer: $P(A) = 0.33$, $P(B) = 0.22$,
$P(C) = 0.45$ b. Replace 0.67 with 0.5 in lines
30 and 50.

Pages 534-535   Lesson 13-8

3. 400 4. $\frac{9}{20}$ 5. 15,880 people 6. false;

$327{:}273 < 2{:}1$ **7.** true; $\frac{327}{600} = 54.5\%$

8. False; this cannot be determined from this survey.   **9.** 72   **10.** cola   **11.** $\frac{1}{6}$ **12.** 2,500 colas   **13.** yes; randomly taken   **15.** 225 red, 90 green, 18 yellow, 117 blue   **17.** 92   **19.** 8.36   **20.** (4, 1)   **21.** $\frac{1}{2}$

Pages 536-538   Study Guide and Review

11. 6 outcomes   **13.** 720 ways   **15.** 15 pairs   **17.** 35 combinations   **19.** 84   **21.** $\frac{1}{6}$ **23.c.** $\frac{1}{4}, \frac{1}{2}$ **25.** $\frac{9}{50}$ **27.** 362,880 orders   **29.**

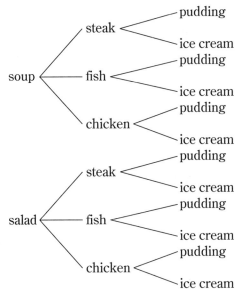

12 outcomes

14 Algebra: Investigations Polynomials

Pages 544-545   Lesson 14-1

5. $-x^2 + 3x - 4$ **6.** $-4x + 2$ **10.** 6   **11.** $-4x$ **13.** $-2x^2 + 9$ **21.** 11   **23.** 0   **25.** 51.52 mm   **26.** 50   **27.** 700 ginger ales

Pages 548-549   Lesson 14-2

5. $3x^2, -2x^2; 4x, 10x$ **6.** $4y, -2y, -3y; 8, 9$ **7.** none   **8.** $-a^2, 4a^2$ **9.** $x^2 + x - 1$ **10.** $a^2 + 3a$ **11.** $6y, -11y$ **13.** none   **15.** $6x$ **17.** $5x + 5$ **19.** $2x^2 + 4x - 4$ **21.** $-7a$ **23.** $9a + 14b; 80$ **25.** $a + 9b; 61$

27. Subtract the lower quartile from the upper quartile.   **28.** \$1.20/foot   **30.** 19   **31.a.** $4q + 8d + 5n; \$2.05$ **33.** \$176.26

Pages 551-552   Lesson 14-3

3. $-x + 6$ **4.** $3a^2 - 10a$ **5.** $-7x^2 + x + 1$ **6.** $-4y^2 + y; -3$ **7.** $6x^2 + 2x + 2$ **9.** $5y^2 + 3y + 5$ **11.** $12x + 12y$ **13.** $9s + 2t$ **15.** $10a^2 + 2a - 3$ **17.** $5x^2 - 3x + 4$ **19.** $7c - d + 1; 52$ **21.** $16c - d + 1; 124$ **22.** 32   **23.** 1.3, -1.3   **24.** 50.27 m³   **25.** $4x^2 + 4x$ **27.a.** $8x + 24$ **b.** $6x + 6$ **c.** $8x + 34$

Pages 554-555   Lesson 14-4

4. $-x$ **5.** $5x^2$ **6.** -4 **7.** $-10x^2; -3x$ **8.** $3x + 2$ **9.** $-x^2 + x$ **10.** $4x + 1$ **11.** $2x^2 - 3x + 5$ **12.** $x^2 - 4x$ **13.** $-4x^2 - x + 2$ **15.** $2a^2 - 5a - 9$ **17.** $-5a + 6$ **19.** $4m - 5n$ **21.** $2p^2 - p + 1$ **23.** $8a^2 + 2ab - 3b^2$ **24.** 1,050   **25.** $2^4 \cdot 3$ **26.** 336   **27.** $-4m^2 + 10m + 9$

Page 555   Mid-Chapter Review

3. $8x^2 - 7$ **5.** $7x^2 - 4x$ **7.** $2n + 7$

Pages 558-559   Lesson 14-5

5. $2x + 10$ **6.** $x^2 + 3x$ **7.** $5y + 45$ **8.** $y^2 + 2y$ **9.** $a^2 + 2a$ **10.** $4(z + 1)$ **11.** $y(y + 5)$ **13.** $4b + 12$ **15.** $d^2 + 15d$ **17.** $4x^2 + 2x$ **19.** $3x(2x + 1)$ **21.** $8(a^2 + 1)$ **23.** $4(1 + 5x)$ **25.** $2(y + 4)$ **27.** 83   **28.** 28% increase   **29.**

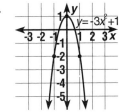

30. $3x - 4$ **31.b.** $2x(x + 3); 2x^2 + 6x$ **c.** 260 ft²

Pages 561-562   Lesson 14-6

4. $x^2 + 3x + 2$ **5.** $4x^2 + 10x + 6$ **6.** $m^2 + 7m + 12$ **7.** $6a^2 + 11a + 3$ **8.** $2x^2 + 5x + 3$ **9.** $12z^2 + 19z + 5$ **11.** d   **13.** a   **15.** $x^2 + 5x + 4$ **17.** $2x^2 + 5x + 2$ **19.** $x^2 + 2x + 1$ **21.** $\frac{3}{4}$ **22.** 8%   **23.** $2x^2 + 3x$

Page 565   Lesson 14-7

3. 9 minutes   **4.** 4 mini-buses   **5.** b; 3 cubed is 27 so 123 cubed will have seven in the ones place.   **7.** $x^2 + 6x + 8$

Pages 566-568   Study Guide and Review

13. $15m^2 + 8m$ **15.** $2x^2 + 6x$ **17.** $14m^2 + 2m$
19. $14d + 8$ **21.** $4b^2 - 3b - 4$ **23.** $3g + 2$
25. $3s^2 + 5$ **27.** $2p^2 - 5p - 4$ **29.** $4z^2 + 12z$
31. $3t^2 + 18t$ **33.** $2x^2 + 8x + 6$
35. $x^2 + 7x + 10$ **37.** $(2x + 1)$ meters by x meters   **39.** $12x + 32$ yards   **41.** c

Index

Index **645**

Greatest common factors (GCF), 218, 221–223, 225, 248, 262, 338
Greatest integer function, 90
Grouping symbols, 44–47, 658
Guess and check, 32–34, 48–49, 78

H

Height, 75–76, 278–281
Hints
  calculator, 36, 45, 96, 145, 216, 230, 237, 301, 345, 366, 435, 443, 483, 507
  computer, 282
  estimation, 12, 55, 114, 183, 308, 316, 354, 388, 394, 400, 406, 407, 409, 433, 465
  mental math, 24, 52, 95, 146, 156, 198, 212, 227, 242, 245, 246, 320, 356, 384, 385, 455, 466
  problem solving, 27, 236, 326, 339, 394, 426, 533, 543, 550
  test-taking, 125, 253, 377, 499, 571
Histograms, 133–135, 168
Hypotenuse, 315–317, 326, 328, 333, 364, 368–369

I

Identify properties, 265
Improper fractions, 224–225
Inches, 26–28
Independent events, 521–526, 537
Inequalities, 77–79
  solving, 77–79, 81
Input, 65–66, 422, 428
Integers, 84–123, 224–226, 306
  absolute values of, 87–88, 91–93
  adding, 91–97, 99, 120–121
  additive inverses, 99–100, 113–114
  comparing, 89–90, 120
  dividing, 106–108, 121
  multiplying, 102–106, 121
  order of, 89–90
  subtracting, 98–101, 121
Interest, 412–415, 418
Interior angles, 177
International system, 23
Interquartile ranges, 151–154, 156–157
Inverse operations, 52, 54, 554
Inverse property of multiplication, 265–266

Inverses
  additive, 99–100, 113–114
  multiplicative, 265–267, 288, 389
Irrational numbers, 307–308
  graphing, 323–324
Isosceles trapezoids, 188
  diagonals of, 190
Isosceles triangles, 183–185, 206

J

Journal entries, 7, 10, 37, 56, 64, 76, 105, 108, 116, 138, 148, 158, 179, 186, 200, 220, 232, 238, 258, 261, 281, 302, 309, 331, 358, 360, 371, 390, 396, 408, 427, 434, 457, 473, 477, 485, 506, 514, 524, 538, 545, 555, 562

L

Labs, *See* Mathematics Labs *and* Mini-Labs.
Least common denominators (LCD), 241, 259
Least common multiples (LCM), 236–238, 241, 249, 259–260
Leaves, 141–143
Legs, 315–317, 329, 364–366, 368–370
Leonardo, 276
LET statements, 47
Like terms, 546–549, 550
Linear functions, 432–438, 450, 459, 663
  slopes of, 450
Line graphs, 439–441
Line plots, 136–138, 146–148, 151, 168
Lines
  best-fit, 431
  graphs of, 425, 431–438, 450, 458, 663
  number, 77–79, 86–89, 91, 117, 120, 242, 307–308, 323–324, 380
  parallel, 176–180
  of reflections, 191
  slopes of, 450
  of symmetry, 192–193, 207, 451–453
  transversals, 176–178
Line symmetry, 192–195, 207, 451–453

Liters, 23–25
Logical reasoning, 564–565
LOGO, 205
Lower quartiles, 152–158, 169

M

Mathematics Labs *See also* Mini-Labs.
  area and Pick's Theorem, 282–283
  area models, 542
  basketball math, 218
  constructing congruent triangles, 201
  constructing parallel lines, 180
  customary measures, 29
  data base, 128–129
  density property, 239–240
  dilations, 196
  estimating square roots, 303
  exploring spheres, 490
  factoring polynomials, 563
  fair and unfair games, 502–503
  Fibonacci Sequence, 276–277
  function input and output, 65–66
  golden ratio, 342–343
  graphing irrational numbers, 323–324
  graphing linear functions, 431
  making predictions, 149–150
  maps and statistics, 139–140
  measurement in geometry, 174–175
  modeling products, 556
  nets, 474
  patterns in Pascal's Triangle, 519–520
  percent scavenger hunt, 397
  Punnett squares, 531–532
  Pythagorean Theorem, 313–314
  reflections, 191
  right triangles, 364
  solving equations, 111–112
  spreadsheets, 30–31
  surface area and volume, 486
  using nonstandard units, 22
  writing expressions and equations, 60–61
Means
  geometric, 309
  of sets of data, 145–148, 165, 169, 239–240, 659

Photo Credits

Rossotto/The Stock Market; **290,** MAK-I; **291,** Doug Martin; **293,** Jack Sullivan/Photo Researchers, Inc.; **296,** (t) David Brownell, (b) Will & Deni McIntyre/Photo Researchers, Inc.; **298,** (t) ©Angabe A. Schmidecker/FPG International, Inc., (l) Dr. E.R. Degginger, (bm) Animals Animals/Ted Levin, (br) Robert Mullenix; **299,** (ml) DR. E.R. Degginger/Animals Animals/Earthscenes, (mr) E.Delaney/Profiles West, (b) Bob Winsett/Profiles West; **300,** Luis Villota/The Stock Market; **301,** Derek Berwin/The Image Bank; **302,** (t) Lisl Dennis/The Image Bank, (b) Ken Frick; **303,** Pictures Unlimited; **304,** MAK-I; **305,** ©Joe Baker/FPG International, Inc.; **309,** Comstock, Inc.; **310,** Ken Cooper/The Image Bank; **311,** Comstock, Inc.; **312,** Keith Kent/Science Photo Library/Photo Researchers, Inc.; **315,** ©FPG International, Inc.; **318,** Andreqa Pistolesi/The Image Bank; **319,** History of Mathematics, Vol.1 by David Eugene Smith, © 1951 by Eva May Luse Smith, Dover Publications, Inc., New York, New York; **322,** Matchncer; **323,** Historical Pictures Service; **328,** Duomo/Daniel Forster; **331,** MAK-I; **334,** Duomo/David Madison; **336,** (l) Viesti Associates,Inc./Joe Viesti, (r) Comstock, Inc; **337,** (t) Reprinted with special permission of North American Syndicate, (m) Tomas del Amo/Profiles West, (b) Brian Vikander; **338,** Duomo/Bryan Yablonsky; **339,** file photo; **341,** H. Armstrong Roberts; **343,** (t) Pictures Unlimited, (l) F. Grehan/Photo Researchers, Inc., (m) SYGMA , (r) Archivi Alinari/Art Resource, New York; **344,** Gregory Heisler/The Image Bank; **345,** Doug Martin; **347,** Pictures Unlimited; **348,** MAK-I; **349,** Comstock, Inc.; **350-351,** MAK-I; **353,** ©Peter Gridley/FPG International, Inc.; **355-356,** MAK-I; **358,** Brent Petersen/The Stock Market; **359,** Ken Frick; **360,** Alvin E. Staffan; **361,** Kay Chernush/The Image Bank; **363,** Photo by: Albert Chong, courtesy Bernice Steinbaum Gallery, New York; **364,** MAK-I; **365,** Ken Frick; **368,** Gian Berto Vanni/Art Resource, New York; **371,** ©Chris Michaels/FPG International, Inc.; **374,** Pictures Unlimited; **378,** (m) GARFIELD reprinted by permission of United Features Syndicate, Inc., (b) Larry Lefever/Grant Heilman Photography Inc.; **379,** (t) J.Chenet/Woodfin Camp, (b) Mark Gibson; **380-381, 383,** Pictures Unlimited; **384** Ken Frick; **387,** file photo; **388,** The Bettmann Archive; **390,** First Image; **391,** Blair Seitz/Photo Researchers, Inc.; **392,** MAK-I; **393,** BLT Production; **393,** Doug Martin; **395, 397,** MAK-I; **398,** Robert Mullenix; **399,** (t) KS Studios, (b) Robert Mullenix; **401,** Doug Martin; **402,** MAK-I; **403,** ©Travelpix/FPG International, Inc.; **405,** MAK-I; **407,** Pictures Unlimited; **408,** Pictures Unlimited; **409,** Comstock, Inc.; **411,** Ken Frick; **412-413,** Pictures Unlimited; **415,** Doug Martin; **418,** ©Chris Michaels/FPG International, Inc.; **420,** (t) Charles Seaborn/Woodfin Camp, (m) Australia Picture Library/Westlight, (bl) The Bettmann Archive, (br) Robert Mullenix; **421,** Sygma; **422,** MAK-I; **425,** Tim Courlas; **427,** Randy Scheiber; **428,** Doug Martin; **430,** Comstock, Inc./Jack K. Clark; **432,** Pictures Unlimited; **434,** Comstock, Inc.; **435,** Pictures Unlimited; **438,** Doug Martin; **441,** (t) MAK-I, (b) Tim Courlas; **442,** ©S.M. Estvanik/FPG International, Inc.; **445,** Jeff Adamo/The Stock Market; **446,** JPH Images/The Image Bank; **449,** Ken Frick; **451,** The Stock Market; **454,** Comstock, Inc.; **457,460,** MAK-I; **462,** (bl) reprinted by permission of Tribune Media Services, (b) Dr.E.R.Degginger; **463,** KS Studios; **464,** Werner Bokelberg/The Image Bank; **466,** Pictures Unlimited; **468,** Robert Mullenix; **469,** Pictures Unlimited; **470,** National Museum of American Art/Art Resource, New York; **473,** (t) Robert Mullenix, (b) The Bettmann Archive; **476,** Ellen Schuster/The Image Bank; **478,** Ken Frick; **480,482,** Robert Mullenix; **486,** Comstock, Inc.; **487,** Steve Krongard/The Image Bank; **491,** Duomo/David Madison; **493,** Jean Miele/The Stock Market; **496,** Pictures Unlimited; **500,** (t) Robert Mullenix, (b) GARFIELD reprinted by permission of United Features Syndicate, Inc.; **501,** Robert Mullenix; **502,** MAK-I; **503,** Pictures Unlimited; **506,** Elaine Shay; **507,** Pictures Unlimited; **508,** MAK-I; **509,** (t) The Bettmann Archive, (b) ©FPG International, Inc.; **510,** Rafael Macia/Photo Researchers Inc.; **511,** K.L.Giese/Profiles West; **512,** ©R. Pleasant/FPG International, Inc.; **513,** Pictures Unlimited; **514,** MAK-I; **515,** Robert Mullenix; **516,** Bud Fowle; **518,** MAK-I; **521,** (l) ©Gveracy Cubitt/FPG International, Inc., (r) ©T. Quing/FPG International, Inc.; **523,** Pictures Unlimited; **524,** ©Gerard Fritz/FPG International, Inc.; **525,** Gref Davis/The Stock Market; **526,** Duomo/Steven E. Sutton; **527,** ©William D. Adams/FPG International, Inc.; **528,** Pictures Unlimited; **532,** (l) First Image, (r) file photo; **533,** David Frazier/Tony Stone Worldwide; **534,** Doug Martin; **538,** Ivor Sharp/The Image Bank; **540,** (l) Robert Mullenix, (bl) Mike Dobel/Masterfile, (br) Reprinted with special permission of King Features Syndicate; **541,** (t) Porterfield/Chickering/Photo Researchers Inc., (b) Allen Russell/Profiles West; **543,** Tim Davis/Science Source/Photo Researchers, Inc.; **545-546,** Robert Mullenix; **549,** Gary Cralle/The Image Bank; **550,** ©Michael Krasowitz/FPG International, Inc.; **552,** Naideau/The Stock Market; **557,** Robert Mullenix; **559,** Pictures Unlimited; **561,** ©Lee Kuhn/FPG International, Inc.; **562,564,** Pictures Unlimited; **565,** ©FPG International, Inc.; **568,** Studiohio; **572,** KS Studio; **573,** Ken Frick; **574,** Allsport USA/Vandystadt/Zoom; **575,** Mark Burnett; **576,** (l) Roy Morsch/The Stock Market, (r) Animals Animals/Patricia Caulfield; **577,** Allen Russell/Profiles West; **578,** Globus Brothers/The Stock Market; **579,** (t) Jon Feingersh/The Stock Market, (m) Ed Bock/The Stock Market, (b) Tony Duffy/Allsport; **580,** Philip Kretchmar/The Image Bank; **581,** (l) Jan Cobb/The Image Bank, (r) Claudia Parks/The Stock Market; **658, 660, 663, 664, 665,** Elaine Shay; **666,** David W. Hamilton/Image Bank; **667,** William R. Sallaz/Duomo; **668,** Elaine Shay.

TECHNOLOGY ACTIVITIES & DATA BANK

Time Required

1 day

TEACHING NOTES

- Use the Activity after completing Example 4 in Lesson 2–1.
- Allow students plenty of time to explore the various keys of their calculators. It may be beneficial to have students work in pairs to assist each other in the exploration and discovery process.
- Stress that the order of operations will be followed by the calculator. Have students test the calculator by entering the expression $3 + 2 \times 2$. A calculator that does not use the order of operations will give $(3 + 2) \times 2$ or 10 as a solution. A calculator that uses the order of operations will give $3 + (2 \times 2)$ or 7 as a solution.

TECHNOLOGY ACTIVITY 1:

Evaluating Expressions with a Graphing Calculator

Use with Lesson 2-1, pages 44-47

Graphing calculators observe the order of operations when an expression is evaluated. So there is no need to perform each operation in the expression separately. You can enter the expression just as it is written to evaluate it. The calculators also have parentheses that you key into the calculator in the same way as parentheses are written in an expression. You can also use parentheses to indicate multiplication. For example, 3(2) or (3)(2) can be entered for 3×2.

The expression appears as you enter it in a graphing calculator. On TI calculators, the multiplication and division signs do not appear on the screen as they do on the keys. Instead, the calculator displays symbols used in computer language. That is, * means multiplication, and / means division.

Example

Evaluate $3(x - 6) \div 2 + (x^2 - 15)$ if $x = 8$.

The $\boxed{x^2}$ key is located above the $\boxed{\sqrt{}}$ key on the Casio fx-7700. Press $\boxed{SHIFT}$ $\boxed{\sqrt{}}$ to access the x^2 function.

TI: 3 $\boxed{(}$ 8 $\boxed{-}$ 6 $\boxed{)}$ $\boxed{\div}$ 2 $\boxed{+}$ $\boxed{(}$ 8 $\boxed{x^2}$ $\boxed{-}$ 15 $\boxed{)}$
$\boxed{ENTER}$

Casio: 3 $\boxed{(}$ 8 $\boxed{-}$ 6 $\boxed{)}$ $\boxed{\div}$ 2 $\boxed{+}$ $\boxed{(}$ 8 $\boxed{x^2}$ $\boxed{-}$ 15 $\boxed{)}$
$\boxed{EXE}$

$3(x - 6) \div 2 + (x^2 - 15) = 52$ if $x = 8$.

If you get an error message or discover that you entered the expression incorrectly, you can use the REPLAY feature to correct your error and reevaluate without reentering your expression. Follow the steps below to use the REPLAY feature.

TI: On the TI-81, press $\boxed{\blacktriangle}$. On the TI-82, press $\boxed{2nd}$ $\boxed{ENTRY}$. Use the arrow keys to move to the location of the correction. Then type over, use $\boxed{INS}$, or use $\boxed{DEL}$ to make the correction. Then press $\boxed{ENTER}$ to evaluate. You don't have to move the cursor to the end.

Casio: Press $\boxed{\Rightarrow}$ or $\boxed{\Leftarrow}$. The answer disappears and the cursor goes to the beginning or end of the expression. Make changes and then press $\boxed{EXE}$ to evaluate.

Exercises

Use a graphing calculator to evaluate each expression if $x = 4$, $y = 7$, and $z = 9$.

1. $17 - z$ 8
2. $x^2 + 9$ 25
3. xy^2 196
4. $\dfrac{2(z - x)}{(y - 2)^2}$ $\dfrac{2}{5}$
5. $\dfrac{3xz}{2} - 12$ 42
6. $x(y + z) - 7$ 57

TECHNOLOGY ACTIVITY 2:

Finding a Mean with a Spreadsheet

Use with Lesson 4-5, pages 145-148

Mrs. Roberts uses tests, quizzes, homework, and class participation to determine the final grades in her U.S. History course. In order to determine the test portion of the grade, she will find the mean of each student's four test scores. A portion of the spreadsheet she set up to find the grades is shown below.

	A	B	C	D	E	F
1	Student	Test 1	Test 2	Test 3	Test 4	Mean
2	Kenneth	78	76	81	83	(B2+C2+D2+E2)/4
3	Rena	84	82	85	88	(B3+C3+D3+E3)/4
4	Kelly	72	83	85	83	(B4+C4+D4+E4)/4
5	Anthony	88	92	90	91	(B5+C5+D5+E5)/4
6	Umeko	90	88	87	92	(B6+C6+D6+E6)/4

The formulas in the cells in column F find the mean of the scores that are entered in the cells in columns B, C, D, and E. The formula first finds the sum of the scores, then divides the sum by 4 to find the average. The printout below shows the results when the calculations are complete.

	A	B	C	D	E	F
1	Student	Test 1	Test 2	Test 3	Test 4	Mean
2	Kenneth	78	76	81	83	79.5
3	Rena	84	82	85	88	84.75
4	Kelly	72	83	85	83	80.75
5	Anthony	88	92	90	91	90.25
6	Umeko	90	88	87	92	89.25

Exercises

Use the spreadsheet above to answer each question.

1. Suppose Theo's test grades are 92, 84, 89, and 95. What is his test average? 90

2. How would you alter the spreadsheet to find the mean of seven quiz scores? See margin.

Objective Use a spreadsheet to find a mean of a set of values.

Time Required

30 minutes

TEACHING NOTES

- Use the Activity after discussing the mean in Lesson 4-5.
- Each spreadsheet program has a different way of entering formulas and text into the cells. Consult the User's Guide to learn how to enter information into your specific program.
- You may wish to have students work in pairs to enter the spreadsheet program into the computer. Have one student read the program while the other enters the lines into the computer.

Additional Answers

2. Make columns F, G, and H for the three additional scores. The cells in column 1 would be the formulas for the mean. The formulas for the mean should find the sum of the seven scores and divide the sum by 7.

TECHNOLOGY ACTIVITY 3:
Distance Between Two Points on a Graphing Calculator

A graphing calculator can be used to write and run programs just like larger computers. The program below will find the distance between two points in the coordinate plane. In order to use the program, you must first enter the program into the calculator's memory. You may want to refer to the User's Guide for your graphing calculator. To access the TI-81 program memory, use the following keystrokes.

Enter: [PRGM] [▶] 1

Enter the program exactly as it is shown. Consult the User's Guide for the locations of commands in the menus.

Example

Find the distance between the points (-3, 5) and (9, 1) on a graphing calculator. Round your answer to the nearest tenth.

Run the program.

Enter the coordinates of the points as the program asks for them.

Enter: [(−)] 3 [ENTER]

5 [ENTER] 9

[ENTER] 1

[ENTER]

The calculator automatically rounds the distance to the nearest tenth of a unit. The distance between (-3, 5) and (9, 1) is approximately 12.6 units.

```
Prgm 1: DISTANCE
:Fix 1
:Disp "ENTER THE X-
  COORDINATE OF POINT 1"
:Input A
:Disp "ENTER THE Y-
  COORDINATE OF POINT 1"
:Input B
:Disp "ENTER THE X-
  COORDINATE OF POINT 2"
:INPUT C
:DISP "ENTER THE Y-
  COORDINATE OF POINT 2"
:Input D
: √ ((A-C)^2+(B-D)^2) → E
:Disp "THE DISTANCE IS"
:Disp E
```

The program is written for use on a TI-81 graphing calculator. If you have a different type of programmable calculator, consult your User's Guide to adapt the program for use on your calculator.

Exercises
Use the program to find the distance between each pair of points to the nearest tenth.
1. (9, 1), (-2, 1) 11.0
2. (3, 3), (-7, -1) 10.8
3. (-12, 1), (15, -5) 27.7
4. (-3, -2), (-19, -9)
5. (-8, 3), (-2, -4) 9.2
6. (2.4, 6.1), (0.2, 0.3) 6.5
7. (0, 3), (8, -4) 10.6
8. (-47, 21), (125, 72)

4. 17.5
8. 179.4

TECHNOLOGY ACTIVITY 4:

Proportions with a Spreadsheet

Use with Lesson 9-3, pages 347-349

The Elegant Eatery is catering the annual fall festival picnic. Their chili dip recipe is shown on the card at the right.

There are 120 people expected at the picnic. In order to determine how much of each ingredient to use, Rosa set up the spreadsheet below.

Chili Dip

1 c. cottage cheese	$\frac{1}{4}$ c. chili sauce
$\frac{1}{4}$ t. onion powder	$\frac{1}{4}$ c. skim milk
3 T. grated Parmesan cheese	

Mix all ingredients in blender until smooth. Chill. Serves 20.

CHILI DIP RECIPE

	A	B	C
1	People To Serve =	B1	
2	Batches needed =	B1/20	
3	INGREDIENT	NUMBER	
4	cottage cheese	B2	cups
5	chili sauce	B2/4	cups
6	onion powder	B2/4	t.
7	skim milk	B2/4	cups
8	parmesan cheese	B2 * 3	T.

In order to use the spreadsheet, Rosa entered the number of people expected at the picnic, 120, in cell B1. The spreadsheet told her to use 6 cups of cottage cheese, $1\frac{1}{2}$ cups of chili sauce, $1\frac{1}{2}$ teaspoons of onion powder, $1\frac{1}{2}$ cups of skim milk, and 18 tablespoons of parmesan cheese.

The spreadsheet uses proportions to determine the amount of each ingredient that should be used in order to make enough chili dip for a group. Solving the proportion

$$\frac{number\ of\ people\ expected}{number\ of\ servings\ per\ batch} = \frac{number\ of\ batches\ needed}{1\ batch}$$

will give the number of batches needed. Since B1 is the number of people and the number of servings per batch is 20, we can rewrite the proportion as $\frac{B1}{20} = \frac{x}{1}$. Thus, the number of batches is $\frac{B1}{20}$. The formula in cell B2 uses B1 ÷ 20 to find the number of batches that need to be made.

Exercises 1-2. See margin.

1. Use the spreadsheet to find the amount of each ingredient need to make enough chili dip for 180 people.

2. How could you alter the spreadsheet if one batch of chili dip served 12 people?

3. Kevin wants to add $\frac{1}{8}$ teaspoon of Tabasco sauce to each batch of chili dip. Write the formula to enter in a cell to find the number of teaspoons of Tabasco sauce to add to a batch for a group of people. B1/8

Proportions with a Spreadsheet   661

Objective   Use a spreadsheet to solve proportions.

Time Required

30 minutes

TEACHING NOTES

- Use the Activity after discussing Example 2 in Lesson 9–3.
- Have students solve the proportion for the number of batches that Rosa will need to make. Then verify the amounts of the ingredients that will be required.
- You may wish to have students write a spreadsheet program to solve other proportions such as determining gas mileage or sales tax.

Answers

1. 9 cups of cottage cheese,
   $2\frac{1}{4}$ cups of chili sauce,
   $2\frac{1}{4}$ teaspoons of onion powder,
   $2\frac{1}{4}$ cups of skim milk, and
   27 tablespoons of parmesan cheese.
2. Change the formula in cell B2 to B1/12.

Objective Find the sale price of an item with a spreadsheet.

Time Required
30 minutes

TEACHING NOTES

- Use the Activity after discussing the example in Lesson 10–9.
- Have students consult the User's Guide to determine how to enter formulas and text in your spreadsheet program.
- Have students write a spreadsheet program for finding the amount of savings on each item in the spreadsheet.

TECHNOLOGY ACTIVITY 5:
Discounts with a Spreadsheet
Use with Lesson 10-9, pages 409-411

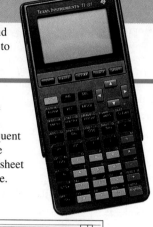

The sale price of an item can be found by multiplying the percent paid by the original price. A spreadsheet like the one below can be used to generate a table of sale prices for various original prices.

Suppose you are the manager of the casual clothes department of a local department store. The store has frequent sales when many items are the same percentage off. You have the spreadsheet below to generate signs for each sale.

	A	B	C
1	Discount Rate =	B1	
2	Item	Original Price	Sale Price
3	Cotton Sweaters	29.99	(100-B1)/100 * B3
4	Denim Jackets	36.29	(100-B1)/100 * B4
5	Team Sweatshirts	24.89	(100-B1)/100 * B5
6	Sport Socks 3-Pack	6.59	(100-B1)/100 * B6
7	T-Shirts	7.99	(100-B1)/100 * B7

Exercises
Use the spreadsheet to answer each question.
1. At the Midnight Madness Sale, all items were 25% off. What was the sale price of a denim jacket? $27.22
2. What is the sale price of a cotton sweater if the discount rate is 33%? $20.09
3. What is the discount on a T-shirt if the discount rate is 40%? $3.20
4. Suppose you wanted to add a new row to the spreadsheet for a $99.59 suede jacket. List each of the cell entries (A8, B8, and C8) that you would enter.

The discount rate is entered into cell B1. Then the formulas in the cells in column C determine the sale prices. The formulas find the percent paid by subtracting the percentage off from 100, then dividing by 100. Then the percentage paid is multiplied by the price of each item.

4. A8 = "Suede Jacket"; B8 = 99.59; C8 = (100-B1)/100 * B8

TECHNOLOGY ACTIVITY 6:

Linear Equations on a Graphing Calculator

Use with Lesson 11-4, pages 432-434

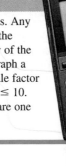

A graphing calculator is a powerful tool for studying functions. Any of the graphing calculators will graph linear functions, but the procedure for graphing is slightly different for each one. On any of the calculators, you must set an appropriate range before you can graph a function. A viewing window of [-10, 10] by [-10, 10] with a scale factor of 1 on both axes denotes the values $-10 \leq x \leq 10$ and $-10 \leq y \leq 10$. The scale factor of 1 indicates that the tick marks on both axes are one unit apart. This is called the **standard viewing window**.

Example

Graph $y = 2x - 4$ in the standard viewing window.

Be sure that your calculator is in the correct mode for graphing functions.

Casio fx-7000: MODE +

Casio fx-7700: MODE +   MODE   MODE   +

TI: Press the MODE key. If "Function" and "Rect" are not highlighted, use the arrow and ENTER keys to highlight them.

Press 2nd   QUIT to return to the home screen.
Now graph the function.

Casio fx-7000: Graph 2
   ALPHA   X
   − 4 EXE

Casio fx-7700: Graph 2
   X,θ,T   −
   4 EXE

On the TI-82, x is entered using the X,T,θ key.

TI: Y= 2 XT   − 4 GRAPH

Exercises

Graph each function on a graphing calculator. Then sketch the graph on a piece of paper. See students' work.
1. $y = 5 - x$
2. $y = 4x - 2$
3. $y = 3$
4. $y = \frac{1}{2}x - 1$
5. $y = -2x + 3$
6. $y = -0.5x + 2$

You will need to clear the graphics screen before you can graph a second function. To clear the screen on a Casio, press SHIFT   Cls   EXE . Changing the range before entering a new function to be graphed on a Casio calculator will also clear the graphics screen. To clear the graphics screen on a TI, press Y= and use the arrow and CLEAR keys to clear the Y= list.

Objective   Graph linear equations on a graphing calculator.

Time Required
30 minutes

TEACHING NOTES

- Use the Activity after discussing the Example in Lesson 11–4.
- You may wish to have students use the graphing calculator as a check to their own graphs. Have students graph an equation. Then graph on the graphing calculator and compare.
- If students have had little experience with graphing calculators, you may wish to have them work in pairs. Have one student read the instructions while the other operates the calculator. Then have them switch roles.

Objective Use a graphing calculator to simulate probability experiments.

Time Required

1 day

TEACHING NOTES

- Use the Activity after discussing the Example in Lesson 13–7.
- If students have had little experience with graphing calculators, they will need help in entering the program into the memory. Explain that many of the TI-81 programming commands are found in the menus. Consult the User's Guide for the locations of specific commands.
- You may wish to have students who are new to graphing calculators work in pairs. Have one student read the instructions while the other operates the calculator. Then have them switch roles.

TECHNOLOGY ACTIVITY 7:

Probability on a Graphing Calculators

Use with Lesson 13-7, pages 528-530

The graphing calculator program below will generate random numbers. You can use the program to simulate real events like rolling a number cube or tossing a coin. To use the program, you must first enter the program into the calculator's memory. You may want to refer to the User's Guide for your graphing calculator. To access the TI-81 program memory, use the following keystrokes.

Enter: PRGM ▶ 1

Example

Use the graphing calculator program to simulate rolling a number cube fifty times. Make a table to show the results.

Run the program.

The program will generate integers between two numbers that you enter. Since the numbers on a number cube are 1 through 6, enter 1 as the least integer and 6 as the greatest integer.

Enter: 1 ENTER 6 ENTER

You want the calculator to generate fifty numbers.

Enter: 50 ENTER

The calculator will display the number generated and wait for you to press ENTER before it continues.

```
Prgm 1: RAND.NUM
:ClrHome
:Disp "LEAST INTEGER"
:Input S
:Disp "GREATEST
 INTEGER"
:Input L
:Disp "NUMBER OF
 VALUES TO GENERATE"
:Input A
: 0 → B
:Lbl 1
:B + 1 → B
:Int ((L − S + 1)Rand + S)
 → R
:Disp R
:Pause
:If A ≠ B
:Goto 1
```

The program is written for use on a TI-81 graphing calculator. If you have a different type of programmable calculator, consult your User's Gude to adapt the program for use on your calculator.

Exercises

Use the table of results from your graphing calculator experiment to answer each question.

1. Do you think that each number on a number cube has an equal chance of occurring when you throw the cube?

2. How could you use the graphing calculator program to simulate spinning a game spinner that had seven equal-sized regions 15 times?

1. Answers may vary.
2. Enter 1-7 as least to greatest integers and 15 as the number of numbers to generate.

D A T A B A N K

POSTAGE RATES AND PLANETS

First Class Postage Rates (1994)

Weight not exceeding (ounces)	First Class Cost
1	$0.29
2	0.52
3	0.75
4	0.98
5	1.21
6	1.44

Minimum Size:

All pieces must be at least 0.007 inch thick. Pieces that are $\frac{1}{4}$ inch or less thick must

be: (1) rectangular in shape, (2) at least $3\frac{1}{2}$ inches high, and (3) at least 5 inches long.

Planets of our Solar System

Planets	Diameter	Average Distance from Sun	Number of Moons	1 Rotation*	Orbit*
Mercury	3,100 miles (4,987.0 km)	36 million miles (75.9 million km)	0	59 days	88 days
Venus	7,500 miles (12,067.5 km)	67 million miles (107.8 million km)	0	243 days	225 days
Earth	7,926 miles (12,752.0 km)	93 million miles (149.6 million km)	1	24 hours	365 days
Mars	4,218 miles (6,786.8 km)	14.2 million miles (228.5 million km)	2	24.4 hours	687 days
Jupiter	89,400 miles (143,844.6 km)	483 million miles (777.1 million km)	16	10 hours	11.86 years
Saturn	75,000 miles (120,675 km)	886 million miles (14,235.6 km)	20	10.4 hours	29.46 years
Uranus	32,300 miles (51,970.7 km)	1.8 billion miles (2.9 billion km)	15	17 hours	84 years
Neptune	30,000 miles (48,270 km)	2.8 billion miles (4.5 billion km)	3	18-22 hours	165 years
Pluto	1900 miles (3057.1 km)	3.7 billion miles (5.95 billion km)	1	6.4 days	248 years

*Hours, days, and years are Earth Time.

Data Bank 665

The Data Bank provides students with up-to-date statistical information. Students must refer to the Data Bank to answer questions that appear throughout the text. The following table lists the lessons in which the questions appear.

Data Bank Page	Lesson and Page
p. 665	1–4, p. 16 6–4, p. 223
p. 666	2–8, p. 72 9–1, p. 341 10–4, p. 392 11–3, p. 430 13–6, p. 527
p. 667	3–6, p. 105 4–6, p. 154 5–5, p. 195 7–5, p. 271 8–5, p. 318
p. 668	12–8, p. 493 14–3, p. 552

HOME BUYING AND MILEAGE

Home prices in the U.S.

The median U.S. home price in 1993 was $141,900, up 0.6% from 1992. The breakdown by region is shown below:

Northeast $157,300

Midwest $114,600

West $171,800

South $105,300

Source: Chicago Title & Trust

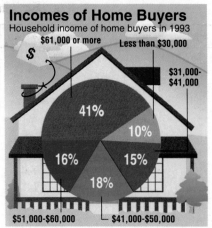

Incomes of Home Buyers

Household income of home buyers in 1993

$61,000 or more

Less than $30,000

$31,000-$41,000

41%

10%

16%

15%

18%

$51,000-$60,000

$41,000-$50,000

Source: Chicago Title & Trust

Mileage Chart From:	To:	Atlanta	Birmingham	Charlotte	Columbia	Jackson	Jacksonville	Memphis	Miami	Nashville	Orlando
Atlanta, GA			150	240	214	399	313	382	663	246	426
Birmingham, AL		150		391	362	245	463	255	754	194	526
Charlotte, NC		240	391		94	632	393	630	740	421	534
Columbia, SC		214	362	94		602	296	616	643	437	437
Jackson, MS		399	245	632	602		609	213	912	414	700
Jacksonville, FL		313	463	393	296	609		694	353	563	140
Memphis, TN		382	255	630	616	213	694		997	209	776
Miami, FL		663	754	740	643	912	353	997		910	229
Nashville, TN		246	194	421	437	414	563	209	910		688
Orlando, FL		426	546	534	437	700	140	776	229	688	

HOME BUYING AND MILEAGE

Home prices in the U.S.

The median U.S. home price in 1993 was $141,900, up 0.6% from 1992. The breakdown by region is shown below:

Northeast **$157,300**

Midwest **$114,600**

West **$171,800**

South **$105,300**

Source: Chicago Title & Trust

Incomes of Home Buyers
Household income of home buyers in 1993

$61,000 or more

Less than $30,000

$31,000-$41,000

41%

10%

16%

15%

18%

$51,000-$60,000

$41,000-$50,000

Source: Chicago Title & Trust

Mileage Chart From:	To:	Atlanta	Birmingham	Charlotte	Columbia	Jackson	Jacksonville	Memphis	Miami	Nashville	Orlando
Atlanta, GA			150	240	214	399	313	382	663	246	426
Birmingham, AL		150		391	362	245	463	255	754	194	526
Charlotte, NC		240	391		94	632	393	630	740	421	534
Columbia, SC		214	362	94		602	296	616	643	437	437
Jackson, MS		399	245	632	602		609	213	912	414	700
Jacksonville, FL		313	463	393	296	609		694	353	563	140
Memphis, TN		382	255	630	616	213	694		997	209	776
Miami, FL		663	754	740	643	912	353	997		910	229
Nashville, TN		246	194	421	437	414	563	209	910		688
Orlando, FL		426	546	534	437	700	140	776	229	688	

POSTAGE RATES AND PLANETS

First Class Postage Rates (1994)

Weight not exceeding (ounces)	First Class Cost
1	$0.29
2	0.52
3	0.75
4	0.98
5	1.21
6	1.44

Minimum Size:

All pieces must be at least 0.007 inch thick. Pieces that are $\frac{1}{4}$ inch or less thick must

be: (1) rectangular in shape, (2) at least $3\frac{1}{2}$ inches high, and (3) at least 5 inches long.

Planets of our Solar System

Planets	Diameter	Average Distance from Sun	Number of Moons	1 Rotation*	Orbit*
Mercury	3,100 miles (4,987.0 km)	36 million miles (75.9 million km)	0	59 days	88 days
Venus	7,500 miles (12,067.5 km)	67 million miles (107.8 million km)	0	243 days	225 days
Earth	7,926 miles (12,752.0 km)	93 million miles (149.6 million km)	1	24 hours	365 days
Mars	4,218 miles (6,786.8 km)	14.2 million miles (228.5 million km)	2	24.4 hours	687 days
Jupiter	89,400 miles (143,844.6 km)	483 million miles (777.1 million km)	16	10 hours	11.86 years
Saturn	75,000 miles (120,675 km)	886 million miles (14,235.6 km)	20	10.4 hours	29.46 years
Uranus	32,300 miles (51,970.7 km)	1.8 billion miles (2.9 billion km)	15	17 hours	84 years
Neptune	30,000 miles (48,270 km)	2.8 billion miles (4.5 billion km)	3	18-22 hours	165 years
Pluto	1900 miles (3057.1 km)	3.7 billion miles (5.95 billion km)	1	6.4 days	248 years

Hours, days, and years are Earth Time.

Data Bank 665

The Data Bank provides students with up-to-date statistical information. Students must refer to the Data Bank to answer questions that appear throughout the text. The following table lists the lessons in which the questions appear.

Data Bank Page	Lesson and Page
p. 665	1–4, p. 16 6–4, p. 223
p. 666	2–8, p. 72 9–1, p. 341 10–4, p. 392 11–3, p. 430 13–6, p. 527
p. 667	3–6, p. 105 4–6, p. 154 5–5, p. 195 7–5, p. 271 8–5, p. 318
p. 668	12–8, p. 493 14–3, p. 552

TEMPERATURES, PLAYING FIELDS, AND HELVETICA FONT

Record High and Low Temperatures

State	Low	High	State	Low	High	State	Low	High
AL	-27	112	LA	-16	114	OH	-39	113
AK	-80	100	ME	-48	105	OK	-27	120
AZ	-40	127	MD	-40	109	OR	-54	119
AR	-29	120	MA	-35	107	PA	-42	111
CA	-45	134	MI	-51	112	RI	-23	104
CO	-61	118	MN	-59	114	SC	-19	111
CT	-32	105	MS	-19	115	SD	-58	120
DE	-17	110	MO	-40	118	TN	-32	113
FL	-2	109	MT	-70	117	TX	-23	120
GA	-17	112	NE	-47	118	UT	-69	117
HI	12	100	NV	-50	122	VT	-50	105
ID	-60	118	NH	-46	106	VA	-30	110
IL	-35	117	NJ	-34	110	WA	-48	118
IN	-35	116	NM	-50	116	WV	-37	112
IA	-47	118	NY	-52	108	WI	-54	114
KS	-40	121	NC	-34	110	WY	-63	114
KY	-34	114	ND	-60	121			

Playing Field Dimensions

Sport	Dimensions
Baseball	90 x 90 feet (diamond)
Basketball	26 x 15 meters
Football	360 x 160 feet
Olympic Swimming	50 x 21 meters
Soccer	100 x 73 meters
Tennis	78 x 36 feet (doubles)
Volleyball	18 x 9 meters

Helvetica Font

A B C D E F G H I J K L M N

O P Q R S T U V W X Y Z

OLYMPIC RACES AND BIRTHDAYS

Olympic 1,500 Meter Race Winners

Women's 1,500-Meter Race		
Year	Winner, Country	Time
1972	Lyudmila Bragina, USSR	4 m 1.4 s
1976	Tatyana Kazankina, USSR	4 m 5.5 s
1980	Tatyana Kazankina, USSR	3 m 56.6 s
1984	Gabriella Dorio, Italy	4 m 3.3 s
1988	Paula Ivan, Romania	3 m 54.0 s
1992	Hassiba Boulmerka, Algeria	3 m 55.3 s

Men's 1,500-Meter Race		
Year	Winner, Country	Time
1972	Pekka Vasala, Finland	3 m 36.3 s
1976	John Walker, New Zealand	3 m 39.2 s
1980	Sebastian Coe, Great Britain	3 m 38.4 s
1984	Sebastian Coe, Great Britain	3 m 32.5 s
1988	Peter Rono, Kenya	3 m 36.0 s
1992	Fermin Cacho Ruiz, Spain	3 m 40.1 s

Likelihood of Sharing a Birthday

This graph shows the probability of two people in a group sharing the same birthday. For example, if there are 20 people in a group, there is a 40% probability that two of them have the same birthday.

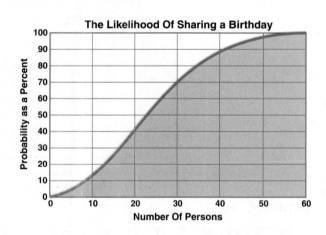

The Likelihood Of Sharing a Birthday